PEARSON ALWAYS LEARNING

Jeffrey Bennett • William Briggs

Mathematical Tools for the Real World Using and Understanding Mathematics

A Quantitative Reasoning Approach FDMAT 108

A Fourth Custom Edition for Brigham Young University-Idaho

Taken from:
Using and Understanding Mathematics: A Quantitative Reasoning Approach, Fifth Edition
by Jeffrey Bennett and William Briggs

Cover Art: Courtesy of Stockbyte/Getty Images, Photodisc/Getty Images, and Shane Goodwin.

Taken from:

Using and Understanding Mathematics: A Quantitative Reasoning Approach, Fifth Edition
by Jeffrey Bennett and William Briggs

Published by Addison-Wesley
Boston, Massachusetts 02116

Pearson Learning Solutions, 501 Boylston Street, Suite 900, Boston, MA 02116
A Pearson Education Company
www.pearsoned.com

Printed in the United States of America

7 8 9 10 V064 17 16 15 14 13

000200010271676745

CT

PEARSON

ISBN 10: 1-256-79004-4
ISBN 13: 978-1-256-79004-4

Understand It. Use It.

We use math constantly in our day-to-day lives, even when we don't realize it. The goal of this course, and this book, is to increase your mathematical literacy because when we *understand* the math, we *use* it more effectively. From the real-world context to the study tools in each chapter, this text is designed to help you succeed in the course and to make better decisions outside of class.

MATH FOR THE REAL WORLD

This book keeps you interested and engaged by focusing on the math you need for your daily life.

A hands-on activity begins each chapter, helping you get into the material from page one. Activities guide you through applications of the math and prepare you to use math in practical ways.

ACTIVITY Student Loans

Use this activity to gain a sense of the kinds of problems this chapter will enable you to study. Try working through it before you begin the chapter, then return to it after you've learned the chapter material.

If you are like most college students in the United States, you probably have received money through at least one student loan, and you are likely to need more student loans in the future. Even if you don't personally have a student loan, many of your friends probably do. But student loans don't always have the same cost. For example, two students who each borrow $10,000 won't necessarily owe the same amounts at graduation, and they may not have the same interest rate or monthly payments once they take a job. Moreover, rules, fees, and penalties also differ for student loans. Because they are such an important part of most students' lives, let's use student loans to begin thinking about the financial topics that will be covered in this chapter.

1. Do you have a student loan? If you do, did you really need the loan in order to attend college, or did you have other options for paying for your college education? If you don't have a student loan, how have you managed to avoid having one, and do you think you will need one in the future?
2. If you have one or more student loans, look up their terms. What are the interest rates? When will you have to start paying back the loans? How long will you have to make payments, and what will your monthly payments be? If you don't have a student loan, answer these questions for a loan that you could in principle take out.
3. Suppose that you need to borrow $10,000 to pay for your next year of college. Use resources available through your college or the Web to investigate your options for a new $10,000 student loan. Which option seems the best, and why?
4. Whether or not you have student loans, college is expensive. What makes you think that it is worth its cost? How do you expect to benefit from your college education?

page 198

Using Technology boxes show you how to use a graphing calculator, Excel,® or other software when applying math concepts.

USING TECHNOLOGY

The Compound Interest Formula for Interest Paid More than Once a Year

Standard Calculators The procedure with interest paid more than once a year is essentially the same as that for the basic compound interest formula (see Using Technology, p. 213), except you'll need to enter APR/n instead of just APR and nY instead of just Y. Let's apply the procedure to Example 5, in which we have $P = \$5000$, APR $= 0.03$, $n = 12$, and $Y = 5$ years.

General Procedure	Our Example	Calculator Steps*	Output
$A = P \times \left(1 + \frac{\text{APR}}{n}\right)^{(nY)}$ (1. parentheses; 2. exponent; 3. multiply)	$A = 5000 \times \left(1 + \frac{0.03}{12}\right)^{(12\times5)}$ (1. parentheses; 2. exponent; 3. multiply)	Step 1: 1 (+) 0.03 (÷) 12 (=)	1.0025
		Step 2: (^) (() 12 (×) 5 ()) (=)	1.1616...
		Step 3: (×) $5000 (=)	5808.08

*If your calculator does not have parentheses keys, then you will need to do the exponent ($nY = 12 \times 5$) before you start and keep track of it either on paper or in the calculator's memory.

Excel We use the built-in function FV, just as we did for the basic compound interest formula (p. 213), *except*

- because *rate* is the interest rate *for each compounding period*, in this case it is the monthly interest rate APR/n = 0.03/12.
- because *nper* is the total number of compounding periods, in this case it is $nY = 12 \times 5$. (Note that Excel uses an asterisk * for multiplication.)

The following screen shot shows the direct entry of the FV function for our example.

	A	B	C
1	=FV(0.03/12,12*5,0,5000)		
2	FV(rate, nper, pmt, [pv], [type])		
3			

Again, it's best to show your work by referencing clearly labeled cells. In this case, we start with and Y, because these are the variables used in the compound interest formula in this book. Thes enced to create the inputs for the FV function. You should create your own Excel worksheet to con the result from Example 5 (A = $5808.08).

	A	B
1	APR	0.03
2	n (monthly compounding)	12
3	Y (number of years)	5
4	**rate** for each compounding period = APR/n	=B1/B2
5	**nper** (total number of compounding periods = *nY*)	=B2*B3
6	**pmt** (no monthly payment in this case)	0
7	**pv** (present value = starting principal P)	5000
8	**FV** (future value = accumulated balance A)	=FV(B4,B5,B6,

page 217

Practical Matters focus on common-sense applications and daily occurrences when math is applied, such as avoiding credit card trouble and spotting a bad cell phone deal.

PRACTICAL MATTERS

Building a Portfolio

Before you bought a new television for a few hundred dollars, you'd probably do a fair amount of research to make sure that you were getting a good buy. You should be even more diligent when making investments that may determine your entire financial future.

The best way to plan your savings is to learn about investments by reading financial pages of newspapers and some of the many books and magazines devoted to finance. You may also want to consult a professional financial planner. With this background, you will be prepared to create a personal financial *portfolio* (set of investments) that meets your needs.

Most financial advisors recommend that you create a *diversified* portfolio—that is, a portfolio with a mixture of low-risk and high-risk investments. No single mixture is right for everyone. Your portfolio should balance risk and return in a way that is appropriate for your situation. For example, if you are young and retirement is far in the future, you may be willing to have a relatively risky portfolio that offers the hope of high returns. In contrast, if you are already retired, you may want a low-risk portfolio that promises a safe and steady stream of income.

However you structure your portfolio, the most important step in meeting your financial goals is making sure that you save enough money. You can use the tools in this unit to help you determine what is "enough." Make a reasonable estimate of the annual return you can expect from your overall portfolio. Use this annual return as the interest rate in the savings plan formula, and calculate how much you must invest each month or each year to meet your goals (see Examples 3 and 4). Then make sure you actually put this money in your investment plan. If you need further motivation, consider this: Every $100 you spend today is gone, but even at a fairly low (by historical standards) annual return of 4%, every $100 you invest today will be worth $148 in 10 years, $219 in 20 years, and $711 in 50 years.

page 238

STUDY AND REVIEW

Features like these appear in every chapter and are designed to help you understand the material.

page 223

Time Out to Think

Aside from long-term government bonds, it is extremely difficult to find investments with a constant interest rate for 18 years. Nevertheless, financial planners often make such assumptions when exploring investment options. Explain why such calculations can be useful, despite the fact that you can't be sure of a steady interest rate.

Time Out to Think questions appear throughout the book and pose short conceptual questions designed to help you reflect on important new ideas.

Example 4 Credit Card Debt

You have a credit card balance of \$2300 with an annual interest rate of 21%. You decide to pay off your balance over 1 year. How much will you need to pay each month? Assume you make no further credit card purchases.

Solution Your starting loan principal is $P = \$2300$, the interest rate is APR = 0.21, and monthly payments mean $n = 12$. Because you want to pay off the loan in 1 year, we set $Y = 1$. The required payments are

$$\text{PMT} = \frac{P \times \left(\frac{\text{APR}}{n}\right)}{\left[1 - \left(1 + \frac{\text{APR}}{n}\right)^{(-nY)}\right]} = \frac{\$2300 \times \left(\frac{0.21}{12}\right)}{\left[1 - \left(1 + \frac{0.21}{12}\right)^{(-12\times1)}\right]} = \$214.16$$

You must pay \$214.16 per month to pay off the balance in 1 year.

Now try Exercises 29–32.

page 254

Now Try references appear at the end of every example, and direct you to exercises that test your comprehension of the concept covered in the example.

EXERCISES

A wide range of exercises and problem types keeps homework interesting and gives you the practice you need to master the concepts.

Quick Quizzes appear before the problem sets, offering ten questions to briefly check your understanding of the concepts before starting the homework.

page 204

QUICK QUIZ

Choose the best answer to each of the following questions. Explain your reasoning with one or more complete sentences.

1. By evaluating your monthly budget, you can learn how to
   a. keep your personal spending under control.
   b. make better investments.
   c. earn more money.
2. The two things you must keep track of in order to understand your budget are
   a. your income and your spending.
   b. your wages and your bank interest.
   c. your wages and your credit card debt.
3. A *negative* monthly cash flow means that
   a. your investments are losing value.
   ...more money than you are taking in.
   ...more money than you are spending.
4. When you are making your monthly budget, what should you do with your once-a-year expenses for December holiday gifts?
   a. Ignore them.
   b. Include them only in your calculation for December's budget.
   c. Divide them by 12 and include them as a monthly expense.
5. For the average person, the single biggest category of expense is
   a. food.
   b. housing.
   c. entertainment.
6. According to Figure 4.1, which of ... tends to increase the most as a per...
   a. housing
   b. transportation
   c. health care

page 208

IN YOUR WORLD

61. Personal Bankruptcies. The rate of personal bankruptcies has been increasing for several years. Find at least three news articles on the subject, document the increase in bankruptcies, and explain the primary reasons for the increase.
62. Consumer Debt. Find data on the increase in consumer (credit card) debt in the United States. Based on your reading, do you think consumer debt is (a) a crisis, (b) a significant occurrence but nothing to worry about, or (c) a good thing? Justify your conclusion.
63. U.S. Savings Rate. When it comes to saving disposable income, Americans have a remarkably low savings rate. Find sources that compare the savings rates of Asian and European countries to that of the United States. Discuss your observations and put your own savings habits on the scale.

DOES IT MAKE SENSE?

Decide whether each of the following statements makes sense (or is clearly true) or does not make sense (or is clearly false). Explain your reasoning.

7. When I figured out my monthly budget, I included only my rent and my spending on gasoline, because nothing else could possibly add up to much.
8. My monthly cash flow was −\$150, which explained why my credit card debt kept rising.
9. My vacation travel cost a total of \$1800, which I entered into my monthly budget as \$150 per month.
10. Emma and Emily are good friends who do everything together, spending the same amounts on eating out, entertainment, and other leisure activities. Yet Emma has a negative monthly cash flow while Emily's is positive, because Emily has more income.
11. Brandon discovered that his daily routine of buying a slice of pizza and a soda at lunch was costing him more than \$15,000 per year.

page 205

Does It Make Sense? questions test your conceptual understanding by asking whether a statement is sensible, and then asking you to explain why or why not in your own words.

In Your World exercises challenge you to find examples of unit concepts in the news or in your everyday life.

What Is Quantitative Reasoning? or Why Am I in This Course?

The ability to interpret and reason with quantitative information—information that involves numbers or mathematical ideas—is a crucial aspect of literacy. This so-called quantitative reasoning is essential to making important decisions and understanding issues that appear in the news every day.

The topics covered in this text will help you work with quantitative information and make critical decisions. For example:

- You should possess strong skills in critical and logical thinking so that you can make wise personal decisions, navigate the media, and be an informed citizen. For example, should you accept a deal in which you take a 10% pay cut now but are promised an 11% pay raise later? This particular question is covered in Unit 3A, but throughout the book you'll learn how to evaluate quantitative questions on topics ranging from personal decisions to major global issues.
- You should have a strong number sense and be proficient at estimation so that you can put numbers from the news into a context that makes them understandable. For example, do you know how to make sense of the more than $12 trillion federal debt? Unit 3B discusses how you can put such huge numbers in perspective, and Unit 4F discusses how the federal debt grew so large.
- You should possess the mathematical tools needed to make basic financial decisions. For example, do you enjoy a latte every morning before class? Sometimes two? New Unit 4A explores how such a seemingly harmless habit can drain more than $2400 from your wallet every year.
- You should be able to read news reports of statistical studies in a way that will allow you to evaluate them critically and decide whether and how they should affect your personal beliefs. For example, how should you decide whether a new opinion poll accurately reflects the views of Americans? Chapter 5 covers the basic concepts that lie behind the statistical studies and graphics you'll see in the news, and discusses how you can decide for yourself whether you should believe a statistical study.
- You should be familiar with basic ideas of probability and risk and be aware of how they affect your life. For example, would you pay $20,000 for a product that, over 20 years, will kill as many people as live in San Francisco? In Unit 7D, you'll see that the answer is very likely yes—just one of many surprises that you'll encounter as you study probability in Chapter 7.
- You should understand how mathematics helps us study important social issues, such as global warming, the growth of populations, the depletion of resources, and methods of voting. For example, Unit 12D discusses the nature of redistricting and how gerrymandering has made congressional elections less competitive than they might otherwise be.

In sum, this course will focus on understanding and interpreting mathematical topics to help you develop the quantitative reasoning skills you will need for college, career, and life.

PEARSON Education

Customer Technical Support

Pearson Customer Technical Support is committed to providing the highest standard of support and service to instructors and students.

Instructor Support

In addition to the Help resources that accompany your product, our Technical Support website offers assistance, 24/7.

Go to **http://247pearsoned.custhelp.com**

- **Self-help:** Access our extensive self-help knowledgebase 24/7.
- **Call toll-free**: 1-800-677-6337 Monday – Friday 8 AM – 8 PM ET / Sunday 5 PM – 11:59 PM ET.
- **Chat online with a representative:** Monday – Thursday 8 AM – 11 PM ET / Friday – 8 AM – 8 PM ET / Sunday 5 PM – 11:59 PM ET.
- **Email your questions:** Support representatives are available to answer, 24/7!

Student Support

In addition to the online Help resources on your course website, our Technical Support website offers student assistance, 24/7.

Go to **http://247pearsoned.custhelp.com**

- **Self-help:** Access our extensive self-help knowledgebase 24/7.
- **Chat online with a representative:** Monday – Thursday 8 AM – 11 PM ET / Friday – 8 AM – 8 PM ET / Sunday 5 PM – 11:59 PM ET.
- **Email your questions:** Support representatives are available to answer, 24/7!

What customers are saying about Pearson 24/7…

"My agent was patient, kind, and understanding with my dilemma. He stayed with me on the phone until we were assured that I was able to access the account on the computer. BRAVO!"

"Thanks for your continued support. Concerns are dealt with in an expedient fashion. The staff is most accommodating."

"The specialist didn't treat me like an idiot. He treated me like I was 'telling him the truth!' But, the most important thing was that he continued to seek a resolution while I was at work, e-mailed me with an option, and stayed with it until I was back up-and-running! He was very professional, courteous, diligent and thorough. Good work ethics are obvious and impossible to fake."

"I could not/would not use the program without your excellent support."

"Thank goodness you have a great support team. My problem was promptly addressed and resolved. Thanks so much."

"Thank you for the assistance. As a first-time user and computer novice, you resolved the problem in terms even I understood!"

"This is the only help desk I don't mind calling. I always get just the help I need. Thank you for making my job easier."

Access all of these helpful resources at 247pearsoned.custhelp.com

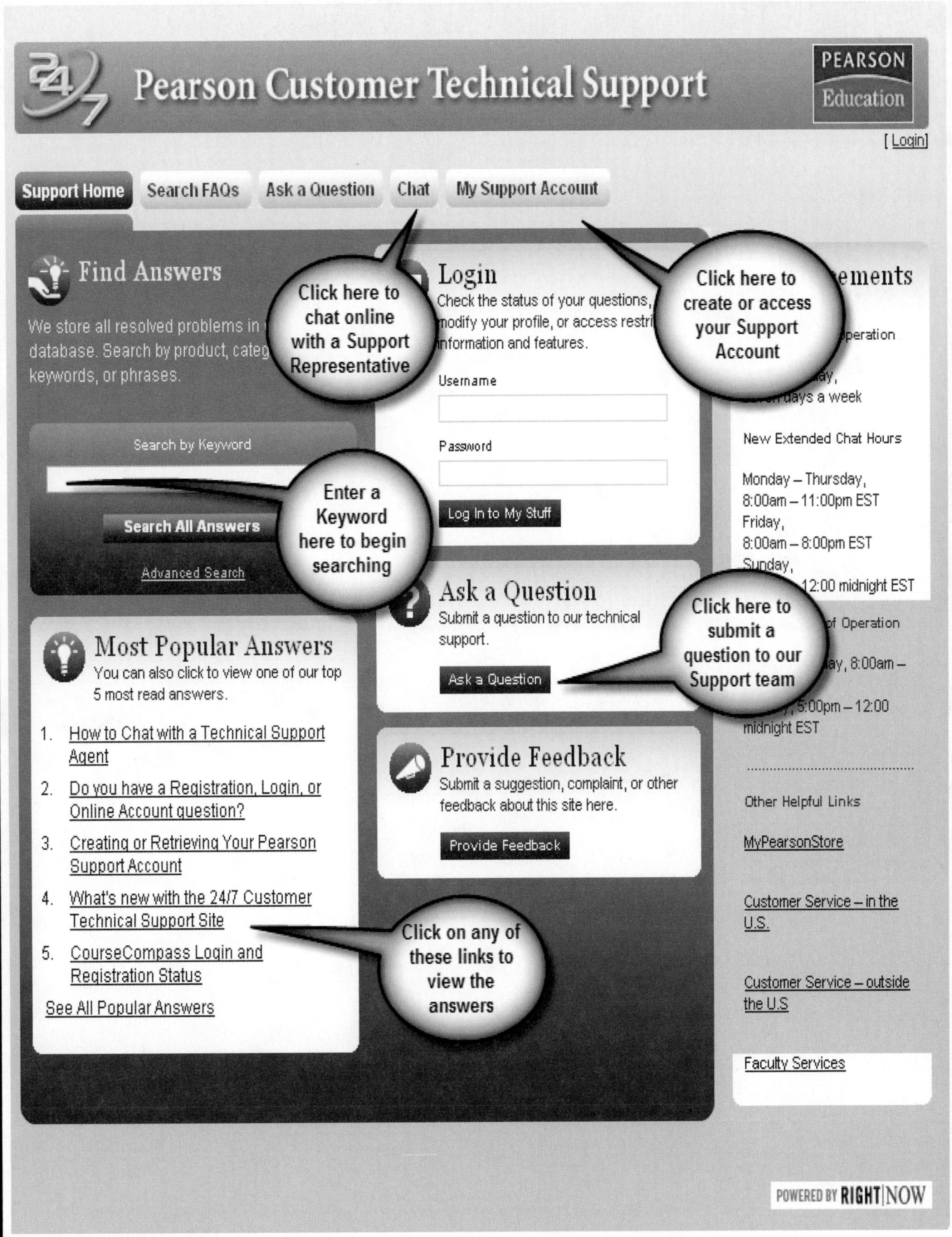

USING & UNDERSTANDING

MATHEMATICS

This book is dedicated to everyone who wants a better understanding of our world, and especially to those who have struggled with mathematics in the past. We hope this book will help you achieve your goals.

And it is dedicated to those who make our own lives brighter, especially Lisa, Julie, Katie, Grant, and Brooke.

CONTENTS

PREFACE

Human history becomes more and more a race between education and catastrophe.

—H. G. Wells, *The Outline of History,* 1920

To the Student

There is no escaping the importance of mathematics in the modern world. However, for most people, the importance of mathematics lies not in its abstract ideas, but in its application to personal and social issues. This book is designed with such practical considerations in mind. In particular, we've designed this book with three specfic purposes:

- To prepare you for the mathematics you will encounter in other **college** courses, particularly core courses in social and natural sciences.
- To develop your ability to reason with quantitative information in a way that will help you achieve success in your **career**.
- To provide you with the critical thinking and quantitative reasoning skills needed to understand major issues in **life**.

We hope this book will be useful to everyone, but it is designed primarily for those who are *not* planning to major in a field that requires advanced mathematical skills. In particular, if you've ever felt any fear or anxiety about mathematics, we've written this book with you in mind. Perhaps you will discover that mathematics is much more important and relevant to your life than you had guessed and not as difficult as previously imagined.

Wherever your interests lie—social sciences, environmental issues, politics, business and economics, art and music, or any of many other topics—you will find many relevant and up-to-date examples in this book. But the most important idea to take away from this book is that mathematics can help you understand a variety of topics and issues, making you more aware and a better educated participant in society. Once you have completed your study of this book, you should be prepared to understand most quantitative issues that you will encounter.

To the Instructor

Whether you've taught this course many times or are teaching it for the first time, you are undoubtedly aware that mathematics courses for nonmajors present challenges that differ from those presented by more traditional courses. First and foremost, there isn't even a clear consensus on what exactly should be taught in these courses. While there's little debate about what mathematical content is necessary for science, technology, engineering, and mathematics (STEM) students—for example, these students all need to learn calculus—there's great debate about what we should teach to the non-STEM students, especially the large majority who will *not* make use of formal mathematics in their careers or daily lives.

As a result of this debate, core mathematics courses for non-STEM students fall into a broad and diverse range. Some schools require these students to take a traditional, calculus-track course, such as college algebra. Others have instituted courses that teach students about the ways in which contemporary mathematics contributes to society, focusing on interesting and esoteric ideas that students are unlikely to encounter elsewhere. These approaches have their merits, and they can certainly be made interesting and relevant, but we believe they are less than optimal because they neglect an important fact: The vast majority (typically 95%) of non-STEM students will *never* take another college mathematics course after completing their core requirements.

Given this fact, we believe it is essential to teach these students the mathematical ideas that they will *need* for their remaining college course work, their careers, and their daily lives. In other words, while there are many topics that might be new and interesting, we must emphasize those topics that are truly important to the future success of these students. The focus of this approach is less on formal calculation—though some is certainly required—and more on teaching students how to think critically with numerical or mathematical information. In the terminology adopted by MAA, AMATYC, and other mathematical organizations, students need to learn *quantitative reasoning* and to become *quantitatively literate*. This book is designed to help you succeed in teaching quantitative reasoning to your students.

The Key to Success: A Context-Driven Approach

Broadly speaking, approaches to teaching mathematics can be divided into two categories:

- A *content-driven* approach is organized by mathematical ideas. After each mathematical topic is presented, examples of its applications are shown.
- A *context-driven* approach is organized by practical contexts. Applications drive the course, and mathematical ideas are presented as needed to support the applications.

The same content can be covered through either approach, but the context-driven approach has an enormous advantage for students: It shows them directly how mathematics is important to them. In contrast, the content-driven approach tends to come across as "learn this content because it's good for you," causing many students to tune out before you ever reach the practical applications. For more details, see our article "General Education Mathematics: New Approaches for a New Millennium" (*AMATYC Review,* Fall 1999); you can also find a PowerPoint presentation on this topic on the lead author's Web site: www.jeffreybennett.com.

The Challenge: Winning Over Your Students

Perhaps the greatest challenge in teaching mathematics to students lies in winning them over—that is, convincing them that you have something useful to teach them. This challenge arises because, by the time they reach college, many students dislike or fear mathematics. Indeed, the vast majority of students in general education mathematics courses are there not by choice, but because such courses are required for graduation. Reaching your students therefore requires that you teach with enthusiasm and convince them that mathematics is useful and enjoyable.

We've built this book around two important strategies that are designed to help you win students over:

- Confront negative attitudes about mathematics head on, showing students that their fear or loathing is ungrounded and that mathematics actually is relevant to their lives. This strategy is embodied in the Prologue of this book (pages 1–12), which we urge you to emphasize in class. It continues implicitly throughout the rest of the text.
- Focus on goals that are meaningful to students—namely, on the goals of learning mathematics for *college*, *career*, and *life*. Your students will then learn mathematics because they will see how it affects their lives. This strategy forms the backbone of this book, as we have tried to build every unit around topics relevant to college, career, and life.

Modular Structure of the Book

We'd all love to have a year or more to teach mathematics to general education students. Unfortunately, most schools have only a one-quarter or one-semester mathematics requirement, so we can cover only a fraction of the material we'd cover in an ideal course. This book is therefore organized with a modular structure that allows you to create a course to meet your particular concerns and constraints. The 12 chapters are organized broadly by contextual areas. Each chapter, in turn, is divided into a set of self-contained *units* that focus on particular concepts or applications. In most cases, you can cover chapters in any order; and while the units within each chapter build sequentially in terms of sophistication, in many cases you can skip certain units, particularly those toward the end of the chapter.

Prerequisite Mathematical Background

Because of its modular structure, this book can be used by students with a wide range of mathematical backgrounds. Many of the units require nothing more than arithmetic and a willingness to think about quantitative issues in new ways. Other units use techniques of algebra or geometry, which are reviewed as they arise. This book should therefore be accessible to any student who has completed two or more years of high school mathematics. Note, however, that this book is *not* remedial; while much of the book relies on mathematical techniques from secondary school, the techniques always arise in applications that require students to demonstrate a high level of critical thinking.

Changes in the Fifth Edition

We've been pleased by the positive responses of so many users to the fourth edition of this text. Nevertheless, a book that relies heavily on facts and data always requires a major updating effort to keep it current, and you'll see numerous changes throughout the book that ensure the topics and data are up to date and relevant. Other changes that prior edition users will notice are the following:

Hands-on Activities A hands-on activity now begins each chapter, encouraging students to engage with math as a preview to what they will learn in that chapter. These chapter-opening activities can be used for either individual or group work.

Complete Activity Manual A complete Activity Manual, with more than 20 additional activities, is now available online in MyMathLab for those who wish to do more activities in the course. The contents of the Activity Manual are correlated to the textbook, making it easy to see where individual activities can be used. Instructor notes are also available, providing background, materials needed, and discussion ideas.

Using Technology A new Using Technology feature appears throughout the book, giving students guidance in how they can do some of the calculations described in this book with a calculator, spreadsheet, or online tools.

Stepped-out Examples Select examples are now displayed in two columns, so that multistep problems can be stepped out for students in a more visual way that helps them learn how to solve the problems.

Updates Related to Recent Financial and Political Events As a result of recent financial and political events, we've made especially significant updates to our material on finance and politics, including our discussions of stocks, mortgages, taxes, and the federal budget in Chapter 4 and our discussion of Congressional redistricting in Chapter 12.

Quick Quizzes A Quick Quiz now ends each unit, to test students' conceptual understanding before they begin the exercises. Answers are included at the back of the text so that students can check their solutions.

Revised Exercise Sets We have thoroughly revised the exercise sets, changing or replacing more than 500 exercises and adding new sets of Using Technology exercises, where warranted, to encourage students' further exploration of technology.

Improved Art Program We have continued to improve the art program, with new figures and additional use of annotations on figures as a tool for learning.

Pedagogical Features

Besides the main narrative of the text, this book includes the following features, each designed with a specific pedagogical purpose in mind.

Chapter Overview Appearing at the beginning of each chapter, this feature offers a unit-by-unit overview of the chapter. It is designed both to show students how the chapter is organized and to help instructors decide which units to cover in class.

Chapter Opening Activity After the overview, the chapter opens with an activity designed to spur student discussion of some interesting facet of the topics covered in the chapter. The activities may be done either individually or in small groups. Note: Additional activities are available online in MyMathLab.

Time Out to Think Appearing throughout the book, the "Time Out to Think" features pose short conceptual questions designed to help students reflect on important new ideas. They also serve as excellent starting points for classroom discussions and/or clicker questions.

Summary Boxes Flowing right along with the narrative are boxes that summarize key ideas, definitions, and formulas.

Examples and Case Studies Numbered examples are designed to build understanding and to offer practice with the types of questions that appear in the exercises. Each example is accompanied by a "Now Try" tag that relates the example to specific similar exercises. Occasional case studies go into more depth than the numbered examples.

Margin Features This book includes a wide margin so that students have room to make notes while studying. The margin also contains material that should spur student interest but is peripheral to the main discussion. This material comes in three basic forms:

- *By the Way* features contain interesting notes and asides relevant to the topic at hand.
- *Historical Note* remarks give historical context to the ideas presented in the chapter.
- *Take Note* boxes contain details that are important mathematically, but generally do not affect students' understanding of the material.

Using Technology Appearing within the margin or in text, these features give students clear instructions in the use of various technologies for computation, including scientific calculators, Microsoft Excel, and online technologies such as those built in to Google. Note: Instructions for computations with a graphing calculator, such as the TI-83 and TI-84, are available online in MyMathLab.

A Brief Review This feature reviews key mathematical skills that students should have learned previously but in which many students still need review and practice. They appear in the book wherever a particular skill is first needed, and exercises based on the review boxes can be found at the end of the unit.

Practical Matters These focus on topics of particularly high practical importance, such as how to understand jewelry purchases and how to invest money in a sensible way.

Thinking About This feature builds upon ideas in the main narrative but goes somewhat beyond the level of other material in the book. Examples include boxes on the proof of the Pythagorean theorem, on Zeno's paradox, and on derivations of the financial formulas used for savings plans and mortgage loans.

Chapter Summary Appearing at the end of each chapter, the Chapter Summary offers a detailed outline of the chapter that students can use as a study guide.

Assessment Opportunities

Quick Quiz This 10-question quiz, which appears at the end of each unit, allows students to check whether they understand key concepts before starting the exercise set. Note that students are asked not only to choose the correct multiple-choice answer but also to write a brief explanation of the reasoning behind their choice. Answers are included in the back of the text so that students can check their solutions.

Review Questions Designed primarily for self-study, these questions ask students to summarize the important ideas covered in the unit and generally can be answered simply by reviewing the text.

Does It Make Sense? These qualitative questions test conceptual understanding by asking students to decide whether the given statements are sensible and to explain why or why not.

Basic Skills & Concepts These questions offer practice with the concepts covered in the unit. They can be used for homework assignments or for self-study (answers to most odd-numbered exercises appear in the back of the book).

Further Applications Through additional applications, these exercises extend the ideas and techniques covered in the text.

Web Projects The Web Projects require searching for data or other information on the Web. They can be used for extended projects, discussion, group activities, or essays.

In Your World These questions ask students to find examples from the news or from daily life of the ideas presented in the unit. These questions may be assigned as homework or used for class discussions.

Using Technology These exercises, which appear at the end of units in which there are Using Technology features, give students an opportunity to practice with the technologies introduced for computation.

Supplements

Student Supplements

Student's Study Guide and Solutions Manual

(ISBN 0-321-65297-5 / 978-0-321-65297-3)

James Lapp

- Includes detailed, worked-out solutions to the odd-numbered unit exercises
- More than just a solutions manual, this supplement provides study tips and additional guidance.

Video Resources on DVD

(ISBN 0-321-65299-1 / 978-0-321-65299-7)

- In unit-specific videos, engaging lecturers provide comprehensive lessons on each objective in the textbook, using consistent methodology and terminology throughout.
- Affordable and portable, this complete set of digitized videos for student use at home or on campus is ideal for distance learning and supplemental instruction.
- Includes optional English and Spanish subtitles

Instructor Supplements

Instructor's Edition

(ISBN 0-321-65294-0 / 978-0-321-65294-2)

- Answers to all of the exercises are included in the back of the book.

NEW! Insider's Guide

(ISBN 0-321-66417-5 / 978-0-321-66417-4)

- Developed by instructors, for instructors
- The guide includes sample syllabi, teaching tips for each unit, project ideas, and more!
- This guide will prove to be an invaluable resource for both new and experienced instructors.

Online Activity Manual

Shane Goodwin, *Brigham Young University–Idaho*, and Suzanne Topp, *Salt Lake Community College*

- More than 20 new activities correlated to the textbook for those who wish to incorporate a more hands-on approach
- Can be completed by students individually or in a group
- Includes instructor notes with background information and discussion points
- Available within MyMathLab

Instructor's Solutions Manual

(ISBN 0-321-65293-2 / 978-0-321-65293-5)

James Lapp

- Includes detailed, worked-out solutions to all of the exercises in the text

Instructor's Testing Manual

Alicia Gordon, *Meredith College*

- Provides four alternative tests per chapter, including answer keys
- Available within MyMathLab or at *www.pearsonhighered.com/irc*

TestGen®

- Enables instructors to build, edit, print, and administer tests, using a computerized bank of questions developed to cover all the objectives of the text
- Algorithmically based, allowing instructors to create multiple but equivalent versions of the same question or test with the click of a button
- Tests can be printed or administered online.
- Available as part of MyMathLab or at *www.pearsonhighered.com/irc*

PowerPoint® Lecture Presentation

- Classroom presentation slides are geared specifically to the sequence and philosophy of this textbook.
- Includes lecture content and key graphics from the book
- Available within MyMathLab or at *www.pearsonhighered.com/irc*

Media Supplements

MyMathLab® Online Course (access code required)

MyMathLab is a series of text-specific, easily customizable online courses for Pearson Education's textbooks in mathematics and statistics. For students, MyMathLab provides a personalized interactive learning environment that adapts to each student's learning style and gives students immediate feedback and help. Because MyMathLab is delivered over the Internet, students can learn at their own pace and work whenever they want. MyMathLab provides instructors with a rich and flexible set of text-specific resources, including course management tools, to support online, hybrid, or traditional courses. MyMathLab is available to qualified adopters. For more information, visit www.mymathlab.com or contact your Pearson representative.

New to the MyMathLab course:

- A new problem type presents an excerpt from a current news article or video clip and asks students to apply math concepts to a real-world situation.
- Live RSS feeds from news sources such as ABC News are available in MyMathLab so that instructors and students have access to regular news updates. These articles can be used in class discussions and projects, as appropriate.
- Increased exercise coverage in MathXL and MyMathLab gives students more problems with which to practice the skills.
- The Image Library contains all art from the text, for instructors to use in their own presentations and handouts.
- New activities correlated to the textbook can be completed by students individually or in a group. Instructor notes with background information and discussion points are included.

MathXL® Online Course (access code required)

MathXL is a powerful online homework, tutorial, and assessment system that accompanies Pearson Education's textbooks in mathematics and statistics. With MathXL, instructors can do the following:

- Create, edit, and assign online homework and tests using algorithmically generated exercises correlated at the objective level to the textbook.
- Create and assign their own online exercises and import TestGen tests for added flexibility.
- Maintain records of all student work tracked in MathXL's online gradebook.

With MathXL, students can do the following:

- Take chapter tests in MathXL and receive personalized study plans based on their test results.
- Use the study plan to link directly to tutorial exercises for the objectives they need to study and retest.
- Access supplemental animations and video clips directly from selected exercises.

MathXL is available to qualified adopters. For more information, visit our Web site at www.mathxl.com, or contact your Pearson sales representative.

ACKNOWLEDGMENTS

A textbook may carry author names, but it is the result of hard work by hundreds of committed individuals. This book has been under development for more than 20 years, and even its beginnings were a group effort, as one of the authors was a member of a committee at the University of Colorado that worked to establish one of the nation's first courses in quantitative reasoning. Since that beginning, the book has benefited from input and feedback from many faculty members and students.

First and foremost we extend our thanks to Bill Poole and Elka Block, whose faith in this project allowed it to grow from class notes into a true textbook. We'd also like to thank the other members of our outstanding publishing team, including Greg Tobin, Sheila Spinney, Roxanne McCarley, Beth Paquin, Rachel S. Reeve, Sandi Goldstein, Elle Driska, and Carl Cottrell. Special thanks go to our editor, Marnie Greenhut, and production manager, Sally Lifland. We also thank Lauri Semarne and Kelly Carey for an excellent job on accuracy checking.

We'd like to thank the following people for their help with one or more editions of this book. Those who assisted with this fifth edition are marked with an asterisk.

Lou Barnes, *Boulder West Financial Services*
Carol Bellisio, *Monmouth University*
Bob Bernhardt, *East Carolina University*
Terence R. Blows, *Northern Arizona University*
W. Wayne Bosché, Jr., *Dalton College*
Kristina Bowers, *University of South Florida*
Michael Bradshaw, *Caldwell Community College and Technical Institute*
W. E. Briggs, *University of Colorado, Boulder*
Annette Burden, *Youngstown State University*
Ovidiu Calin, *Eastern Michigan University*
Susan Carr, *Oral Roberts University*
Margaret Cibes, *Trinity College*
Walter Czarnec, *Framingham State College*
Adrian Daigle, *University of Colorado, Boulder*
Andrew J. Dane, *Angelo State University*
Greg Dietrich, *Florida Community College at Jacksonville*
Marsha J. Driskill, *Aims Community College*
John Emert, *Ball State University*
Kathy Eppler, *Salt Lake Community College*
Kellie Evans, *York College of Pennsylvania*
Fred Feldon, *Coastline Community College*
David E. Flesner, *Gettysburg College*
Pat Foard, *South Plains College*
*Shane Goodwin, *Brigham Young University–Idaho*
Barbara Grover, *Salt Lake Community College*
Louise Hainline, *Brooklyn College*
Ward Heilman, *Bridgewater State University*
Peg Hovde, *Grossmont College*
Andrew Hugine, *South Carolina State University*
Lynn R. Hun, *Dixie College*
Hal Huntsman, *University of Colorado, Boulder*
Joel Irish, *University of Southern Maine*
David Jabon, *DePaul University*
Melvin F. Janowitz, *University of Massachusetts, Amherst*
Craig Johnson, *Brigham Young University–Idaho*
Vijay S. Joshi, *Virginia Intermont College*
Anton Kaul, *University of South Florida*
Bonnie Kelly, *University of South Carolina*
William Kiley, *George Mason University*
Jim Koehler, *University of Colorado, Denver*
Robert Kuenzi, *University of Wisconsin, Oshkosh*
*Erin Lee, *Central Washington University*
Deann Leoni, *Edmonds Community College*
Linda Lester, *Wright State University*
Paul Lorczak, *MathSoft, Inc.*
Jay Malmstrom, *Oklahoma City Community College*
Erich McAlister, *University of Colorado, Boulder*
*Judith McKnew, *Clemson University*
Patricia McNicholas, *Robert Morris College*
Elaine Spendlove Merrill, *Brigham Young University–Hawaii*
Carrie Muir, *University of Colorado, Boulder*
Colm Mulcahy, *Spelman College*
*Stephen Nicoloff, *Paradise Valley Community College*
Paul O'Heron, *Broome Community College*
L. Taylor Ollmann, *Austin Community College*
A. Dean Palmer, *Pima Community College*
Mary K. Patton, *University of Illinois at Springfield*
Frank Pecchioni, *Jefferson Community College*

Jonathan Prewett, *University of Wyoming*
*Evelyn Pupplo-Cody, *Marshall University*
Scott Reed, *College of Lake County*
Frederick A. Reese, *Borough of Manhattan Community College*
*Nancy Rivers, *Wake Technical Community College*
Anne Roberts, *University of Utah*
*Sylvester Roebuck, Jr., *Olive Harvey College*
Lori Rosenthal, *Austin Community College*
Hugo Rossi, *University of Utah*
*Doris Schraeder, *McLennan Community College*
Dee Dee Shaulis, *University of Colorado, Boulder*
Judith Silver, *Marshall University*
*Laura Smallwood, *Chandler-Gilbert Community College*
Sybil Smith-Darlington, *Middlesex County College*
Alu Srinivasan, *Temple University*
John Supra, *University of Colorado, Boulder*
Scott Surgent, *Arizona State University*
Timothy C. Swyter, *Frederick Community College*
Louis A. Talman, *Metropolitan State College of Denver*
David Theobald, *University of Colorado, Boulder*
*Robert Thompson, *Hunter College (CUNY)*
Terry Tolle, *Southwestern Community College*
*Kathy Turrisi, *Centenary College*
Christina Vertullo, *Marist College*
Pam Wahl, *Middlesex Community College*
Thomas Wangler, *Benedictine University*
Richard Watkins, *Tidewater Community College*
Emily Whaley, *DeKalb College*
David Wilson, *University of Colorado, Boulder*
Robert Woods, *Broome Community College*
Fred Worth, *Henderson State University*
Margaret Yoder, *Eastern Kentucky University*
Marwan Zabdawi, *Gordon College*
Fredric Zerla, *University of South Florida*
Donald J. Zielke, *Concordia Lutheran College*

Prologue

Literacy for the Modern World

Mathematics is the key to opportunity. No longer just the language of science, mathematics now contributes in direct and fundamental ways to business, finance, health, and defense. For students, it opens doors to careers. For citizens, it enables informed decisions. For nations, it provides knowledge to compete in a technological economy. To participate fully in the world of the future, America must tap the power of mathematics.

—From *Everybody Counts*

ACTIVITY Job Satisfaction

Each chapter in this book will begin with an activity, which you may do individually or in groups. For this Prologue, we begin with an activity that will help you examine the role of mathematics in careers.

Top 20 Jobs for Job Satisfaction

1. Mathematician
2. Actuary (works with insurance statistics)
3. Statistician
4. Biologist
5. Software Engineer
6. Computer Systems Analyst
7. Historian
8. Sociologist
9. Industrial Designer
10. Accountant
11. Economist
12. Philosopher
13. Physicist
14. Parole Officer
15. Meteorologist
16. Medical Laboratory Technician
17. Paralegal Assistant
18. Computer Programmer
19. Motion Picture Editor
20. Astronomer

Source: JobsRated.com, 2009 survey.

Everyone wants to find a career path that will bring lifelong job satisfaction, but what careers are most likely to do that? A recent survey by JobsRated.com evaluated 200 different jobs according to five criteria: salary, long-term employment outlook, work environment, physical demands, and stress. The table to the left shows the top 20 jobs according to this survey. Notice that most of the top 20 jobs require mathematical skills, and all of them require an ability to reason with quantitative information.

You and your classmates can conduct your own smaller study of job satisfaction. There are many ways you might do this, but here is one procedure you might try:

1. Each of you should identify at least three people with full-time jobs to interview briefly. You may choose parents, friends, acquaintances, or just someone whose job interests you.
2. Identify an appropriate job category for each interviewee (similar to the categories in the table to the left). Ask each interviewee to rate his or her job on a scale of 1 (worst) to 5 (best) on each of the five criteria: salary, long-term employment outlook, work environment, physical demands, and stress. You can then add the ratings for the five criteria to come up with a total "job satisfaction" rating for each job.
3. Working together as a class, compile the data to rank all the jobs. Show the final results in a table that ranks the jobs in order of job satisfaction.
4. Discuss the results. Are they consistent with the JobsRated.com results? Do they surprise you in any way? Will they have any effect on your own career plans?
5. Bonus: Look up the methodology used in the JobsRated.com survey. How does it compare to your methodology? Do you think it is valid? Have there been any follow-up surveys since the 2009 data reported here?

Calvin and Hobbes **by Bill Watterson**

Calvin and Hobbes © 1990 Watterson. Reprinted with permission of Universal Press Syndicate.

What Is Quantitative Literacy?

Literacy is the ability to read and write, and it comes in varying degrees. Some people can recognize only a few words and write only their names; others read and write in many languages. A primary goal of our educational system is to provide citizens with a level of literacy sufficient to read and write about the important issues of our time.

Today, the abilities to interpret and reason with **quantitative information**—information that involves mathematical ideas or numbers—are crucial aspects of literacy. This so-called **quantitative literacy** is essential to understanding issues that appear in the news every day. The process of interpreting and reasoning with quantitative information is called **quantitative reasoning**. The purpose of this book is to help you gain skills in quantitative reasoning as it applies to issues you will encounter in

- your subsequent course work,
- your career, and
- your daily life.

Quantitative Reasoning and Culture

Quantitative reasoning enriches the appreciation of both ancient and modern culture. The historical record shows that all great cultures devoted substantial energy to mathematics and to science (or to observational studies that predated modern science). Without a sense of how quantitative concepts are used in art, architecture, and science, you cannot fully appreciate the incredible achievements of the Mayans in Central America, the builders of the great city of Zimbabwe in Africa, the ancient Egyptians and Greeks, the early Polynesian sailors, and countless others.

Similarly, quantitative concepts can help you understand and appreciate the great works of the modern artists. You can more fully appreciate the excerpt here from a Maya Angelou poem if you know that dinosaurs have been extinct for 65 million years and are able to put this amount of time into perspective. The ties between mathematics and music can be found in modern and classical music, as well as in the digital production of music. Indeed, it is hard to find popular works of art, film, or literature that do not make at least some indirect reference to mathematics.

A Rock, A River, A Tree
Hosts to species long since departed
Marked the mastodon,
The dinosaur, who left dry tokens
Of their sojourn here
On our planet floor,
Any broad alarm of their hastening doom
Is lost in the gloom of dust and ages.

—Maya Angelou,
On the Pulse of the Morning

Quantitative Reasoning in the Work Force

Quantitative reasoning is important in the work force. A lack of quantitative skills puts out of reach many of the most challenging and highest paying jobs. Table 1 defines skill levels in language and mathematics on a scale of 1 to 6, and Table 2 shows the typical levels needed in many jobs.

Note that the occupations requiring high skill levels are generally the most prestigious and highest paying. Note also that most of these occupations call for high skill levels in *both* language and math, refuting the myth that if you're good at language you don't have to be good at mathematics, and vice versa.

TABLE 1 Skill Levels

Level	Language Skills	Math Skills
1	Recognizes 2500 two- or three-syllable words. Reads at a rate of 95–120 words per minute. Writes and speaks simple sentences.	Adds and subtracts two-digit numbers. Does simple calculations with money, volume, length, and weight.
2	Recognizes 5000–6000 words. Reads 190–215 words per minute. Reads adventure stories and comic books, as well as instructions for assembling model cars. Writes compound and complex sentences with proper grammar and punctuation.	Adds, subtracts, multiplies, and divides all units of measure. Computes ratio, rate, and percentage. Draws and interprets bar graphs.
3	Reads novels and magazines, as well as safety rules and equipment instructions. Writes reports with proper format and punctuation. Speaks well before an audience.	Understands basic geometry and algebra. Calculates discount, interest, profit and loss, markup, and commissions.
4	Reads novels, poems, newspapers, and manuals. Prepares business letters, summaries, and reports. Participates in panel discussions and debates. Speaks extemporaneously on a variety of subjects.	Has true quantitative reasoning abilities. Understands logic, problem solving, ideas of statistics and probability, and modeling.
5	Reads literature, book and play reviews, scientific and technical journals, financial reports, and legal documents. Can write editorials, speeches, and critiques.	Knows calculus and statistics. Is able to deal with econometrics.
6	Same types of skills as level 5, but more advanced.	Works with advanced calculus, modern algebra, and statistics.

Source: Data from the *Wall Street Journal.*

TABLE 2 Skill-Level Requirements

Occupation	Language Level	Math Level	Occupation	Language Level	Math Level
Biochemist	6	6	Web page designer	5	4
Computer engineer	6	6	Corporate executive	5	5
Mathematician	6	6	Computer sales agent	4	4
Cardiologist	6	5	Athlete's agent	4	4
Social psychologist	6	5	Management trainee	4	4
Lawyer	6	4	Insurance sales agent	4	4
Tax attorney	6	4	Retail store manager	4	4
Newspaper editor	6	4	Cement mason	3	3
Accountant	5	5	Poultry farmer	3	3
Personnel manager	5	4	Tile setter	3	3
Corporate president	5	5	Travel agent	3	3
Weather forecaster	5	5	Janitor	3	2
Secondary teacher	5	5	Short-order cook	3	2
Elementary teacher	5	4	Assembly-line worker	2	2
Financial analyst	5	5	Toll collector	2	2
Journalist	5	4	Laundry worker	1	1

Source: Data from the *Wall Street Journal.*

Misconceptions About Mathematics

Do you consider yourself to have "math phobia" (fear of mathematics) or "math loathing" (dislike of mathematics)? We hope not; but if you do, you aren't alone. Many adults harbor fear or loathing of mathematics, and, unfortunately, these attitudes are often reinforced by classes that present mathematics as an obscure and sterile subject.

In reality, mathematics is not nearly so dry as it sometimes seems in school. Indeed, attitudes toward mathematics often are directed not at what mathematics really is but at some common misconceptions about mathematics. Let's investigate a few of these misconceptions and the reality behind them.

In a sense, we are all mathematicians—and superb ones. It makes no difference what you do. Your real forte lies in navigating the complexities of social networks, weighing passions against histories, calculating reactions, and generally managing a system of information that, when all laid out, would boggle a computer.

—A. K. Dewdney, *200% of Nothing*

Misconception One: Math Requires a Special Brain

One of the most pervasive misconceptions is that some people just aren't good at mathematics because learning mathematics requires special or rare abilities. The reality is that nearly everyone can do mathematics. All it takes is self-confidence and hard

Thinking About...

People Who Studied Mathematics

The critical thinking skills developed through the study of mathematics are valuable in many careers. The following is only a small sample of people who studied mathematics but became famous for work in other fields. Most of the names come from "Famous Nonmathematicians," a list compiled by Steven G. Buyske, Rutgers University.

Ralph Abernathy, civil rights leader, BS in mathematics, Alabama State University

Corazon Aquino, former president of the Philippines, a mathematics minor

Harry Blackmun, former Supreme Court justice, summa cum laude in mathematics, Harvard University

Lewis Carroll (Charles Dodgson), author of *Alice in Wonderland,* a mathematician

David Dinkins, former mayor of New York City, BA in mathematics, Howard University

Alberto Fujimori, former president of Peru, MS in mathematics, University of Wisconsin

Art Garfunkel, musician, MA in mathematics, Columbia University

Grace Hopper, computer pioneer and first woman Rear Admiral in the U.S. Navy, Ph.D. in mathematics, Yale

Mae Jemison, first African-American woman in space, studied mathematics as part of her degree in chemical engineering from Stanford University

John Maynard Keynes, economist, MA in mathematics, Cambridge University

Lee Hsien Loong, politician in Singapore, BA in mathematics, Cambridge University

Danica McKellar, actress, BA with highest honors in mathematics, UCLA, and co-discoverer of the Chayes-McKellar-Winn theorem

Edwin Moses, three-time Olympic champion in the 400-meter hurdles, studied mathematics as part of his degree in physics from Morehouse College

Florence Nightingale, pioneer in nursing, studied mathematics and applied it to her work

Sally Ride, first American woman in space, studied mathematics as part of her Ph.D. in physics from Stanford University

David Robinson, basketball star, bachelor's degree in mathematics, U.S. Naval Academy

Alexander Solzhenitsyn, Nobel prize winning Russian author, degrees in mathematics and physics from the University of Rostov

Bram Stoker, author of *Dracula,* studied mathematics at Trinity University, Dublin

Laurence Tribe, Harvard law professor, summa cum laude in mathematics, Harvard University

Virginia Wade, Wimbledon champion, bachelor's degree in mathematics, Sussex University

Math phobic's nightmare

work—the same qualities needed to learn to read, to master a musical instrument, or to become skilled at a sport. Indeed, the belief that mathematics requires special talent found in a few elite people is peculiar to the United States. In other countries, particularly in Europe and Asia, *all* students are expected to become proficient in mathematics.

Of course, different people learn mathematics at different rates and in different ways. For example, some people learn by concentrating on concrete problems, others by thinking visually, and still others by thinking abstractly. No matter what type of thinking style you prefer, you can succeed in mathematics.

Misconception Two: The Math in Modern Issues Is Too Complex

> Equity for all requires excellence for all; both thrive when expectations are high.
>
> —from *Everybody Counts*

Some people claim that the advanced mathematical concepts underlying many modern issues are too complex for the average person to understand. It is true that only a few people receive the training needed to work with or discover advanced mathematical concepts. However, most people are capable of understanding enough about the mathematical basis of important issues to develop informed and reasoned opinions.

The situation is similar in other fields. For example, years of study and practice are required to become a proficient professional writer, but most people can read a book. It takes hard work and a law degree to become a lawyer, but most people can understand how the law affects them. And though few have the musical talent of Mozart, anyone can learn to appreciate his music. Mathematics is no different. If you've made it this far in school, you can understand enough mathematics to succeed as an individual and a concerned citizen. Don't let anyone tell you otherwise!

Misconception Three: Math Makes You Less Sensitive

Some people believe that learning mathematics will somehow make them less sensitive to the romantic and aesthetic aspects of life. In fact, understanding the mathematics that explains the colors of a sunset or the geometric beauty in a work of art can only enhance aesthetic appreciation. Furthermore, many people find beauty and elegance in mathematics itself. It's no accident that people trained in mathematics have made important contributions to art, music, and many other fields.

Misconception Four: Math Makes No Allowance for Creativity

The "turn the crank" nature of the problems in many textbooks may give the impression that mathematics stifles creativity. Some of the facts, formalisms, and skills required for mathematical proficiency are fairly cut and dried, but *using* these mathematical tools takes creativity. Consider designing and building a home. The task demands specific skills to lay the foundation, frame in the structure, install plumbing and wiring, and paint walls. But building the home involves much more: Creativity is needed to develop the architectural design, respond to on-the-spot problems during construction, and factor in constraints based on budgets and building codes. The mathematical skills you've learned in school are like the skills of carpentry or plumbing. Applying mathematics is like the creative process of building a home.

Skills are to mathematics what scales are to music or spelling is to writing. The objective of learning is to write, to play music, or to solve problems—not just to master skills.

—from *Everybody Counts*

Misconception Five: Math Provides Exact Answers

A mathematical formula will yield a specific result, and in school that result may be marked right or wrong. But when you use mathematics in real-life situations, answers are never so clear-cut. For example:

> *A bank offers simple interest of 5%, paid at the end of one year (that is, after one year the bank pays you 5% of your account balance). If you deposit $1000 today and make no further deposits or withdrawals, how much will you have in your account after one year?*

A straight mathematical calculation seems simple enough: 5% of $1000 is $50; so you should have $1050 at the end of a year. But will you? How will your balance be affected by service charges or taxes on interest earned? What if the bank fails? What if the bank is located in a country in which the currency collapses during the year? Choosing a bank in which to invest your money is a *real* mathematics problem that doesn't necessarily have a simple or definitive solution.

Probably the most harmful misconception is that mathematics is essentially a matter of computation. Believing this is roughly equivalent to believing that writing essays is the same as typing them.

—John Allen Paulos

Misconception Six: Math Is Irrelevant to My Life

No matter what your path in college, career, and life, you will find mathematics involved in many ways. A major goal of this text is to show you hundreds of examples in which mathematics applies to everyone's life. We hope you will find that mathematics is not only relevant but also interesting and enjoyable.

What *Is* Mathematics?

In discussing misconceptions, we identified what mathematics is *not*. Now let's look at what mathematics *is*. The word *mathematics* is derived from the Greek word *mathematikos,* which means "inclined to learn." Literally speaking, to be mathematical is to be curious, open-minded, and interested in always learning more! Today, we tend to look at mathematics in three different ways: as the sum of its branches, as a way to model the world, and as a language.

Mathematics as the Sum of Its Branches

As you progressed through school, you undoubtedly learned to associate mathematics with some of its branches. Among the better known branches of mathematics are these:

- **logic**—the study of principles of reasoning;
- **arithmetic**—methods for operating on numbers;
- **algebra**—methods for working with unknown quantities;
- **geometry**—the study of size and shape;
- **trigonometry**—the study of triangles and their uses;
- **probability**—the study of chance;
- **statistics**—methods for analyzing data; and
- **calculus**—the study of quantities that change.

One can view mathematics as the sum of its branches. Indeed, most "traditional" mathematics books focus on one branch of mathematics at a time. In this book, we emphasize the connections between the branches rather than their differences. Nevertheless, familiarity with the various branches of mathematics is helpful, even if only to know when you are using them.

Mathematics as a Way to Model the World

Mathematics also may be viewed as a tool for creating models, or representations of real phenomena. Modeling is not unique to mathematics. For example, a road map is a model that represents the roads in some region.

Mathematical models can be as simple as a single equation that predicts how the money in your bank account will grow or as complex as a set of thousands of interrelated equations and parameters used to represent the global climate. By studying models, we gain insight into otherwise unmanageable problems. A global climate model, for example, can help us understand weather systems and ask "what if" questions about how human activity may affect the climate. When a model is used to make a prediction that does *not* come true, it points out areas where further research is needed. Today, mathematical modeling is used in nearly every field of study. Figure 1 indicates some of the many disciplines that use mathematical modeling to solve problems.

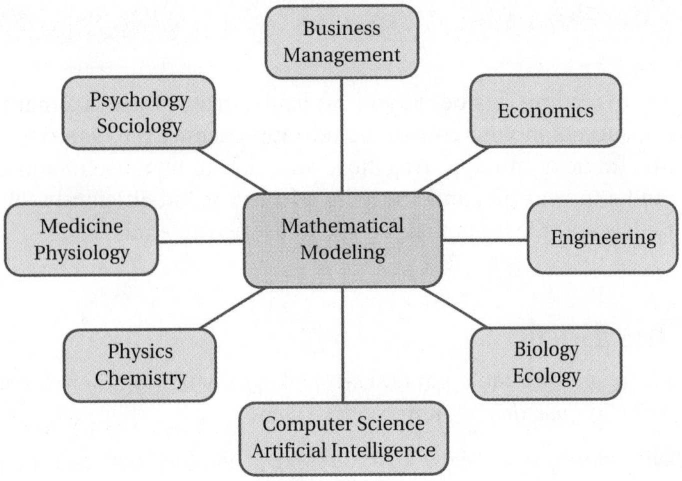

FIGURE 1

Mathematics as a Language

A third way to look at mathematics is as a language with its own vocabulary and grammar. Indeed, mathematics often is called "the language of nature" because it is so useful for modeling the natural world. As in any language, different degrees of fluency are possible. From this point of view, quantitative literacy is the level of fluency required for success in today's world.

The idea of mathematics as a language also is useful in thinking about how to *learn* mathematics. Table 3 compares learning mathematics to learning a language and learning art.

> Mathematics is a way of thinking that can help make muddy relationships clear. It is a language that allows us to translate the complexity of the world into manageable patterns.
>
> —K. C. Cole, *The Universe and the Teacup*

TABLE 3 Learning Mathematics: An Analogy to Language and Art

Learning a Language	Learning the Language of Art	Learning the Language of Mathematics
Become familiar with many styles of speaking and writing, such as essays, poetry, and drama.	Become familiar with many styles of art, such as classical, renaissance, impressionist, and modern.	Become familiar with techniques from many branches of mathematics, such as arithmetic, algebra, and geometry.
Place literature in context by studying its history and the social conditions under which it was created.	Place art in context by studying its history and the social conditions under which it was created.	Place mathematics in context by studying its history, purposes, and applications.
Learn the elements of language—such as words, parts of speech (nouns, verbs, etc.), and rules of grammar—and practice their proper use.	Learn the elements of visual form—such as lines, shapes, colors, and textures—and practice using them in your own art work.	Learn the elements of mathematics—such as numbers, variables, and operations—and practice using them to solve simple problems.
Develop the ability to analyze the language in complex forms critically—novels, short stories, essays, poems, speeches, debates, and similar works.	Develop the ability to analyze works of art critically—painting, sculpture, architecture, photography, and similar works.	Develop the ability to analyze quantitative information critically—mathematical models, statistical studies, economic forecasts, investment strategies, and similar works.
Use language creatively for your own purposes, such as writing a term paper or story or engaging in debate.	Use your sense of art creatively, such as in designing your house, taking a photograph, or making a sculpture.	Use mathematics creatively to solve problems you encounter and to help you understand important issues in the world around you.

How to Succeed in Mathematics

If you are reading this book, you probably are enrolled in a mathematics course. The keys to success in your course include approaching the material with an open and optimistic frame of mind, paying close attention to how useful and enjoyable mathematics can be in *your* life, and studying effectively and efficiently. The following sections offer a few specific hints that may be of use as you study.

Using This Book

Before we get into more general strategies for studying, here are a few guidelines that will help you use *this* book most effectively.

- Before doing any assigned exercises, read assigned material *twice:*
  - On the first pass, read quickly to gain a "feel" for the material and concepts presented.
  - On the second pass, read the material in more depth and work through the examples carefully.
- During the second reading, take notes that will help you when you go back to study later. In particular:
  - Use the margins! The wide margins in this textbook are designed to give you plenty of room for making notes as you study.
  - Don't highlight—underline! Using a pen or pencil to underline material requires greater care than highlighting and therefore helps to keep you alert as you study.
- After you complete the reading, and again when studying for exams, make sure you can answer the Quick Quiz and Review Questions at the end of each unit.
- You'll learn best by *doing,* so do plenty of the end-of-unit exercises. In particular, try some of the exercises that have answers in the back of the book, in addition to those assigned by your instructor.

Budgeting Your Time

The single most important key to success in any college course is to spend enough time studying. A general rule of thumb for college classes is that you should expect to study about 2 to 3 hours per week *outside* class for each unit of credit. For example, a student taking 15 credit hours should spend 30 to 45 hours each week studying outside of class. Combined with time in class, this works out to a total of 45 to 60 hours per week—not much more than the time required of a typical job, and you get to choose your own hours. Of course, if you are working or taking care of a family while you attend school, you will need to budget your time carefully.

The following table gives some rough guidelines for how you might divide your studying time in your mathematics course. If you are spending fewer hours than these guidelines suggest, you could probably improve your grade by studying more. If you are spending more hours than these guidelines suggest, you may be studying inefficiently; in that case, you should talk to your instructor about how to study more effectively.

If Your Course Is	Time for Reading the Assigned Text (per Week)	Time for Homework Assignments (per Week)	Time for Review and Test Preparation (Average per Week)	Total Study Time (per Week)
3 credits	1 to 2 hours	3 to 5 hours	2 hours	6 to 9 hours
4 credits	2 to 3 hours	3 to 6 hours	3 hours	8 to 12 hours
5 credits	2 to 4 hours	4 to 7 hours	4 hours	10 to 15 hours

General Strategies for Studying

- Don't miss class. Listening to lectures and participating in discussions is much more effective than reading someone else's notes. Active participation will help you retain what you are learning.
- Budget your time effectively. An hour or two each day is more effective, and far less painful, than studying all night before homework is due or before exams. It's also good to study shortly after class, while the lessons are still fresh in your mind.
- If a concept gives you trouble, do additional reading or problem solving beyond what has been assigned. If you still have trouble, ask for help. You surely can find friends, colleagues, or teachers who will be glad to help you learn.
- Working together with friends can be valuable, as you will solidify and enhance your own understanding when discussing concepts with others. However, be sure that you learn *with* your friends and do not become dependent on them.
- Be sure that all your work is of collegiate quality: neat and easy to read, well organized, and demonstrating mastery of the subject matter. Although it takes extra effort to create work of this quality, it will help you solidify your learning and is good practice for meeting the expectations that future professors and employers will have.

Preparing for Exams

- Rework exercises and other assignments. Try additional exercises to be sure you understand the concepts. Study your performance on assignments, quizzes, or exams from earlier in the semester.
- Study your notes from lectures and discussions. Pay attention to what your instructor expects you to know for an exam.
- Reread the relevant sections in the textbook, paying special attention to notes you have made in the margins.
- Study individually before joining a study group with friends. Study groups are effective only if *every* individual comes prepared to contribute.
- Don't stay up too late before an exam. Don't eat a big meal within an hour of the exam (thinking is more difficult when blood is going to the digestive system).
- Try to relax before and during the exam. If you have studied effectively, you are capable of doing well. Staying relaxed will help you think clearly.

PROLOGUE DISCUSSION QUESTIONS

1. **Mathematics in Modern Issues.** Describe at least one way that mathematics is involved in each issue below.

   Example: The spread of AIDS: Mathematics is used to study the probability of contracting AIDS.

   a. The long-term viability of the Social Security system

   b. The appropriate level for the federal gasoline tax

   c. The fairness of medical insurance rates

   d. Job discrimination against women or ethnic minorities

   e. Effects of population growth (or decline) on your community

   f. Possible bias in standardized tests (e.g., the SAT)

   g. The degree of risk posed by carbon dioxide emissions

   h. Immigration policy of the United States

   i. Violence in public schools

   j. An issue of your choice from today's newspaper

2. **Quantitative Concepts in the News.** Identify the major unresolved issue discussed on the front page of today's newspaper. List at least three areas in which quantitative concepts play a role in the policy considerations of this issue.

3. **Mathematics and the Arts.** Choose a well-known historical figure in a field of art in which you have a personal interest (e.g., a painter, sculptor, musician, or architect). Briefly describe how mathematics played a role in or influenced that person's work.

4. **Quantitative Literature.** Choose a favorite work of literature (poem, play, short story, or novel). Describe one or more instances in which quantitative reasoning is helpful in understanding the subtleties intended by the author.

5. **Your Quantitative Major.** Identify ways in which quantitative reasoning is important within your major field of study. (If you haven't yet chosen a major, pick a field that you are considering for your major.)

6. **Career Preparation.** Realizing that most Americans change careers several times during their lives, identify at least three occupations in Table 2 that interest you. Do you have the necessary skills for them at this time? If not, how can you acquire these skills?

7. **Attitudes Toward Mathematics.** Most children have a natural affinity for mathematics; they take pride in their counting skills and enjoy puzzles, building blocks, and computers. Unfortunately, this natural interest seems to be snuffed out in most people by the time they reach adulthood. What is your attitude toward mathematics? If you have a negative attitude, can you identify when in your childhood that attitude developed? If you have a positive attitude, can you explain why? How might you encourage someone with a negative attitude to become more positive?

Civilized life depends upon the success of reason in social intercourse, the prevalence of logic over violence in interpersonal conflict.

—Juliana Geran Pilon

Thinking Critically

The primary goal of this book is to help you develop the quantitative reasoning skills that you will need to succeed in other college courses, in your career, and in your life as a citizen in an increasingly complex world. Quantitative reasoning combines basic mathematical skills—most of which you already have—with the ability to approach problems in a critical and analytical way. For this reason, we devote this first chapter to studying ideas of logic that will develop your ability to think critically.

UNIT 1A

Recognizing Fallacies: We begin our study of critical thinking by looking at deceptive arguments, or fallacies.

UNIT 1B

Propositions and Truth Values: We define and study basic components of logic, including propositions, truth values, and truth tables. We also consider the logical connectors *and, or,* and *if . . . then.*

UNIT 1C

Sets and Venn Diagrams: We explore the way in which propositions can express relationships between sets, or categories, and use Venn diagrams to help visualize these relationships.

UNIT 1D

Analyzing Arguments: We study the basic differences between inductive and deductive arguments and discuss ways of evaluating each type.

UNIT 1E

Critical Thinking in Everyday Life: We put the experience gained in earlier units to work in studying critical thinking situations of the type we regularly encounter in everyday life.

ACTIVITY Bursting Bubble

Use this activity to gain a sense of the kinds of problems this chapter will enable you to study. Try working through it before you begin the chapter, then return to it after you've learned the chapter material.

The deep global recession that began in 2007 was spurred in large part by a collapse in housing prices, which led many homeowners to default on their home mortgages, which in turn created a crisis for banks and other institutions that bought, sold, or insured home mortgages. If we hope to avoid similar crises in the future, a key question is whether there were early warning signs that might have allowed both individuals and policy makers to make decisions that could have prevented the problems before they occurred.

The graph below shows how average (median) home prices have compared to average income over the past four decades. A ratio of 3, for example, means that the average home price is three times the average annual household income of Americans; that is, if you had a household income of $50,000 per year and bought an average house, the price of your house would be $150,000. Notice that the ratio remained below about 3.5 until 2001, when it suddenly started shooting up, which is why the period from 2001 to about 2006 has become known as the *housing bubble*.

Median Home Price/Median Household Income Ratio (1968–2008)

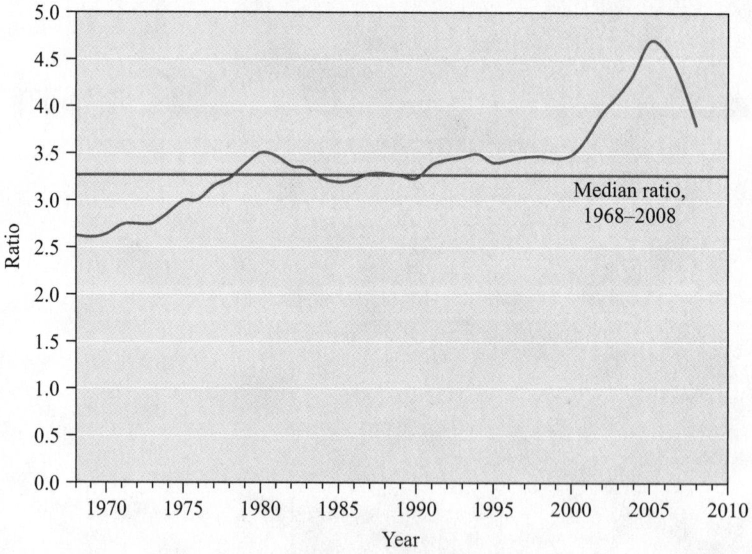

Source: Data from *The State of the Nation's Housing 2009*, used with permission from the Joint Center for Housing Studies of Harvard University. All rights reserved.

Was the change in the home price to income ratio a warning sign that should have been heeded? Use your powers of logic—the topic of this chapter—to discuss the following questions.

1. Consider a family with an annual income of $50,000. If they bought an average home, how much would they have spent in 2000, when the home price to income ratio was 3.5? How much would they have spent in 2005, when the ratio was 4.7?
2. In percentage terms, a rise in the ratio from 3.5 to 4.7 is an increase of nearly 35%. Because the ratio was *below* 3.5 for decades before 2001, we can conclude that the average home was at least 35% more expensive relative to income in 2005 than it

had been historically. What can you conclude about how the percentage of income that a family spent on housing changed during the housing bubble? (Note: Ignore changes in mortgage interest rates; although these changes affect affordability, other factors played greater roles during this period.)

3. In general, a family can increase the percentage of their income that they spend on housing only if some combination of the following three things happens: (1) their income increases, so they can afford to spend more of it on housing; (2) they cut expenses in other areas; or (3) they borrow more money. Based on your understanding of the housing crisis, what happened in most cases during the housing bubble?
4. Overall, do you think it was inevitable that the bubble would burst? Why or why not?
5. How could you use the data on the home price to income ratio to help *you* make a decision about how much to spend when you are looking to buy a home?
6. ***Bonus:*** As home prices rose during the bubble, the optimists claimed that the higher prices could be sustained. Do a bit of Web research to learn how they justified this belief. Do you think their arguments sounded reasonable at the time? Do they still sound reasonable with hindsight?
7. ***Additional Research:*** The data shown here reflect a nationwide average, but the home price to income ratio varies considerably in different cities and regions. Find data for a few different cities or regions, and discuss the differences.

UNIT 1A Recognizing Fallacies

We often try to persuade other people of our views. These discussions take many different forms, some of which are more useful than others. Consider the following "argument" between two classmates.

Mike: *The death penalty is immoral.*

Erica: *No it isn't.*

Mike: *Yes it is! Judges who give the death penalty should be impeached.*

Erica: *You don't even know how the death penalty is decided.*

Mike: *I know a lot more than you know!*

Erica: *I can't talk to you; you're an idiot!*

> People generally quarrel because they cannot argue.
>
> —G. K. Chesterton (1874–1936), English author

This type of heated conversation is fairly common, but it accomplishes little. Rather than helping Mike or Erica sway the other, it is likely to leave both of them upset and angry. Fortunately, there is a better way to argue. We can use skills of **logic**—the study of the methods and principles of reasoning. Arguing logically may not change Mike's or Erica's position, but it can help them understand each other.

In this book, the term **argument** refers to reasoned or thoughtful processes. Specifically, an argument uses a set of facts or assumptions, called **premises**, to support a **conclusion.** Some arguments provide strong support for their conclusions, but others do not. An argument that fails to make a compelling case for its conclusion may contain some error in reasoning, or **fallacy** (from the Latin for "deceit" or "trick"). In other words, a fallacious argument tries to persuade in a way that doesn't really make sense when analyzed carefully.

DEFINITIONS

Logic is the study of the methods and principles of reasoning.

An **argument** uses a set of facts or assumptions, called **premises**, to support a **conclusion.**

A **fallacy** is a deceptive argument—an argument in which the conclusion is not well supported by the premises.

BY THE WAY

It is estimated that U.S. businesses spend more than $300 billion per year on advertising and that the average American sees more than 1 million advertisements by age 18.

You might expect fallacies to be rare, but they are not. If you study advertisements, political campaigns, or editorial commentaries, you'll find that many of them are filled with fallacies. Moreover, fallacies are not always easy to recognize, in part because public relations specialists have spent billions of dollars researching how subtle fallacies can be used to persuade us to buy products, vote for candidates, or support particular policies.

Because fallacies are so common, it is important to be able to recognize them. We therefore begin our study of critical thinking with examples of a few of the most common fallacies. The fallacy in each example has a fancy name, but learning the names is far less important than learning to recognize the faulty reasoning. The experience you gain by analyzing fallacies will provide a foundation upon which to build additional critical thinking skills.

Example 1 Appeal to Popularity

"Ford makes the best pickup trucks in the world. After all, more people drive Ford pickups than any other light truck."

Analysis The first step in dealing with any argument is recognizing which statements are premises and which are conclusions. This argument tries to make the case that *Ford makes the best pickup trucks in the world,* so this statement is its conclusion. The only evidence it offers to support this conclusion is the statement *more people drive Ford pickups than any other light truck.* This is the argument's one and only premise. Overall, this argument has the form

Premise: More people drive Ford pickups than any other light truck.

Conclusion: Ford makes the best pickup trucks in the world.

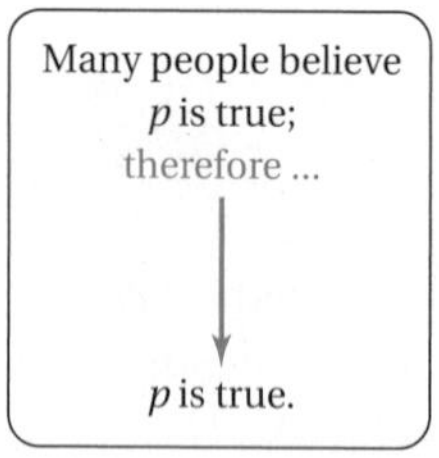

FIGURE 1.1 The fallacy of appeal to popularity. The letters p and q (used in later diagrams) represent statements.

Note that the original written argument states the conclusion before the premise. Such "backward" structures are common in everyday speech and are perfectly legitimate as long as the argument is well reasoned. In this case, however, the reasoning is faulty. The fact that more people drive Ford pickups does not necessarily mean that they are the best trucks.

This argument suffers from the fallacy of *appeal to popularity* (or *appeal to majority*), in which the fact that large numbers of people believe or act some way is used inappropriately as evidence that the belief or action is correct. We can represent the general form of this fallacy with a diagram in which the letter p stands for a particular statement (Figure 1.1). In this case, p stands for the statement *Ford makes the best pickup trucks in the world.*

Now try Exercise 11.

Example 2 False Cause

"I placed the quartz crystal on my forehead, and in five minutes my headache was gone. The crystal made my headache go away."

Analysis We identify the premises and conclusion of this argument as follows:

Premise: I placed the quartz crystal on my forehead.

Premise: Five minutes later my headache was gone.

Conclusion: The crystal made my headache go away.

The premises tell us that one thing (crystal on forehead) happened before another (headache went away), but they don't prove any connection between them. That is, we cannot conclude that the crystal *caused* the headache to go away.

This argument suffers from the fallacy of *false cause*, in which the fact that one event came before another is incorrectly taken as evidence that the first event *caused* the second event. We can represent this fallacy with a diagram in which *A* and *B* represent two different events (Figure 1.2). In this case, *A* is the event of putting the crystal on the forehead and *B* is the event of the headache going away. (We'll discuss how cause *can* be established in Chapter 5.) **Now try Exercise 12.**

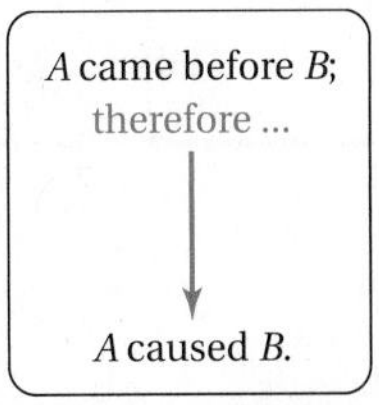

FIGURE 1.2 The fallacy of false cause. The letters *A* and *B* represent events.

Example 3 Appeal to Ignorance

"Scientists have not found any concrete evidence of aliens visiting Earth. Therefore, anyone who claims to have seen a UFO must be hallucinating."

Analysis If we strip the argument to its core, it says this:

Premise: There's no proof that aliens have visited Earth.
Conclusion: Aliens have not visited Earth.

The fallacy should be clear: A *lack* of proof of alien visits does not mean that visits have not occurred. This fallacy is called *appeal to ignorance* because it uses ignorance (lack of knowledge) about the truth of a proposition to conclude the opposite (Figure 1.3). We sometimes sum up this fallacy with the statement "An absence of evidence is not evidence of absence." **Now try Exercise 13.**

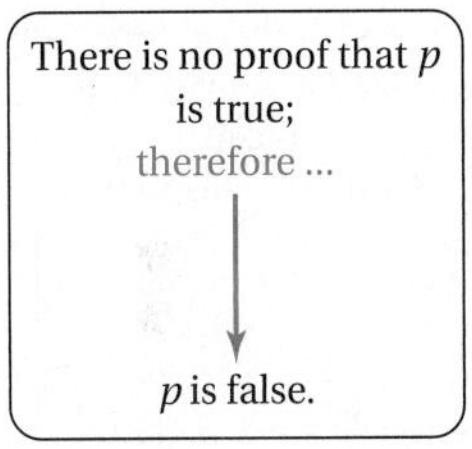

FIGURE 1.3 The fallacy of appeal to ignorance.

Time Out to Think

Suppose a person is tried for a crime and found *not* guilty. Can you conclude that the person is innocent? Why or why not? Why do you think our legal system demands that prosecutors prove guilt, rather than demanding that defendants (suspects) prove innocence? How is this idea related to the fallacy of appeal to ignorance?

Example 4 Hasty Generalization

"Two cases of childhood leukemia have occurred along the street where the high-voltage power lines run. The power lines must be the cause of these illnesses."

Analysis The premise of this argument cites two cases in which leukemia occurred on the street with the power lines. But two cases are not enough to establish a pattern, let alone to conclude that the power lines are the cause of the illnesses.

This argument illustrates the fallacy of *hasty generalization*, in which a conclusion is drawn from an inadequate number of cases or cases that have not been sufficiently analyzed. If any connection between power lines and leukemia exists, it will have to be established with far more evidence than is provided in this argument (decades of research have found no clear connection). We can represent this fallacy with a diagram in which *A* and *B* represent two linked events (Figure 1.4). **Now try Exercise 14.**

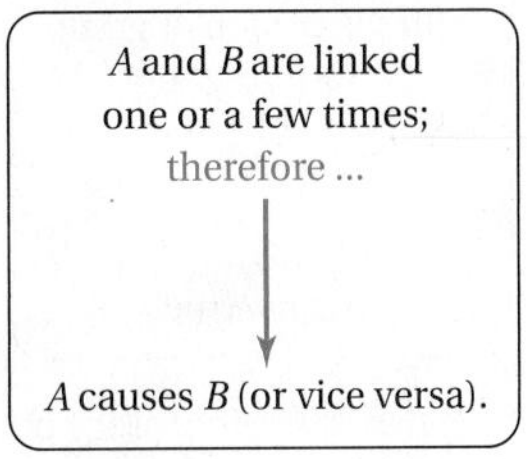

FIGURE 1.4 The fallacy of hasty generalization.

Example 5 Limited Choice

"You don't support the President, so you are not a patriotic American."

Analysis This argument has the form

Premise: You don't support the President.
Conclusion: You are not a patriotic American.

The argument suggests that there are only two types of Americans: patriotic ones who support the President and unpatriotic ones who don't. But there are many other possibilities, such as being patriotic while disliking a particular president.

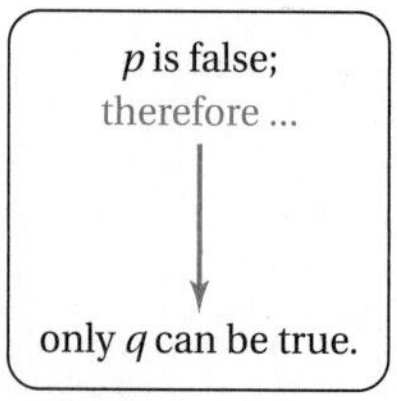

FIGURE 1.5 The fallacy of limited choice.

This fallacy is called *limited choice* (or *false dilemma*) because it artificially precludes choices that ought to be considered. Figure 1.5 shows one common form of this fallacy. Limited choice also arises with questions such as "Have you stopped smoking?" Because both *yes* and *no* answers imply that you smoked in the past, the question precludes the possibility that you never smoked. (In legal proceedings, questions of this type are disallowed because they attempt to "lead the witness.") Another simple and common form of this fallacy is "You're wrong, so I must be right." **Now try Exercise 15.**

Example 6 Appeal to Emotion

In a commercial for Michelin tires, a picture of a baby is shown with the words "because so much is riding on your tires."

Analysis If we can consider this an argument at all, it has the form

Premise: You love your baby.

Conclusion: You should buy Michelin tires.

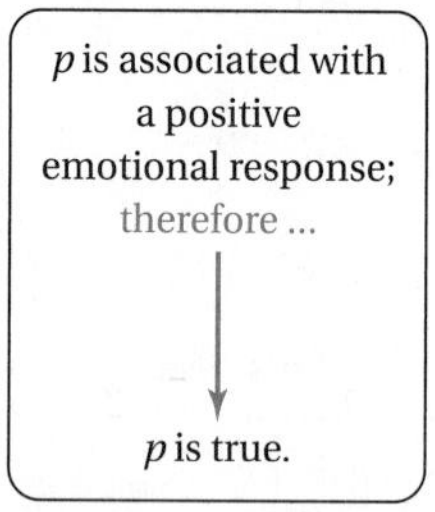

FIGURE 1.6 The fallacy of appeal to emotion.

The argument makes no appeal to logic. Instead, the advertisers hope that the love you feel for a baby will make you want to buy their tires. This attempt to evoke an emotional response as a tool of persuasion represents the fallacy of *appeal to emotion*. Figure 1.6 shows its form when the emotional response is positive. Sometimes the appeal is to negative emotions. For example, the statement *if my opponent is elected, your tax burden will rise* tries to convince you that electing the other candidate will lead to consequences you won't like. (In this negative form, the fallacy is sometimes called *appeal to force*.) **Now try Exercise 16.**

Example 7 Personal Attack

Gwen: You should stop drinking because it's hurting your grades, endangering people when you drink and drive, and destroying your relationship with your family.

Merle: I've seen you drink a few too many on occasion yourself!

Analysis Gwen's argument is well reasoned, with premises offering strong support for her conclusion that Merle should stop drinking. Merle rejects this argument by noting that Gwen sometimes drinks too much herself. Even if Merle's claim is true, it is irrelevant to Gwen's point. Merle has resorted to attacking Gwen personally rather than arguing logically, so we call this fallacy *personal attack* (Figure 1.7). (It is also called *ad hominem*, Latin for "to the person.")

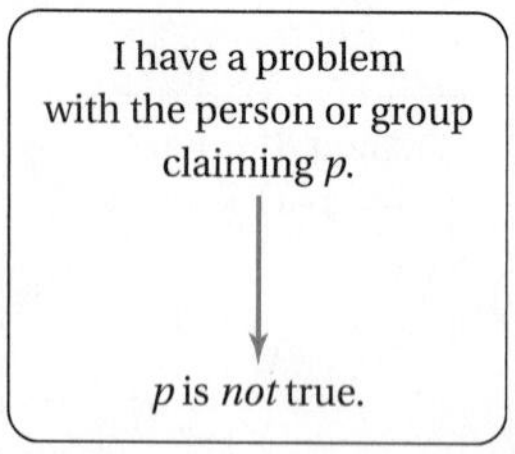

FIGURE 1.7 The fallacy of personal attack.

The fallacy of personal attack can also apply to groups. For example, you might hear someone say, "This new bill will be an environmental disaster because its sponsors received large campaign contributions from heavy industrial polluters." This argument is fallacious because it doesn't challenge the provisions of the bill. Instead, it questions the motives of the sponsors. **Now try Exercise 17.**

Time Out to Think

A person's (or group's) character, circumstances, and motives occasionally *are* logically relevant to an argument. That is why, for example, witnesses in criminal cases often are asked questions about their personal lives. If you were a judge, how would you decide when to allow such questions?

Example 8 Circular Reasoning

"Society has an obligation to shelter the homeless because the needy have a right to the resources of the community."

Analysis This argument states the conclusion (*society has an obligation to shelter the homeless*) before the premise (*the needy have a right to the resources of the community*). But if you read them carefully, you'll see that the premise and the conclusion both say essentially the same thing. After all, society has an obligation to provide shelter only if the needy have a right to societal resources. This argument suffers from *circular reasoning* (Figure 1.8). **Now try Exercise 18.**

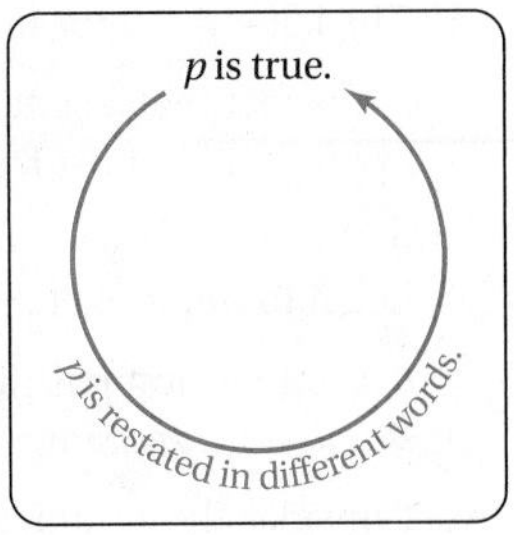

FIGURE 1.8 The fallacy of circular reasoning.

Example 9 Diversion (Red Herring)

"We should not continue to fund cloning research because there are so many ethical issues involved. Ethics is at the heart of our society, and we cannot afford to have too many ethical loose ends."

Analysis The argument begins with its conclusion—*we should not continue to fund cloning research*. However, the discussion is all about ethics. This argument represents the fallacy of *diversion* (Figure 1.9) because it attempts to divert attention from the real issue (funding for cloning research) by focusing on another issue (ethics). The issue to which attention is diverted is sometimes called a *red herring*. (A herring is a fish that turns red when rotten. Use of the term *red herring* to mean a diversion can be traced back to the 19th century, when British fugitives discovered that they could divert bloodhounds from their pursuit by rubbing a red herring across their trail.) Note that personal attacks (see Example 7) are often used as diversions. **Now try Exercise 19.**

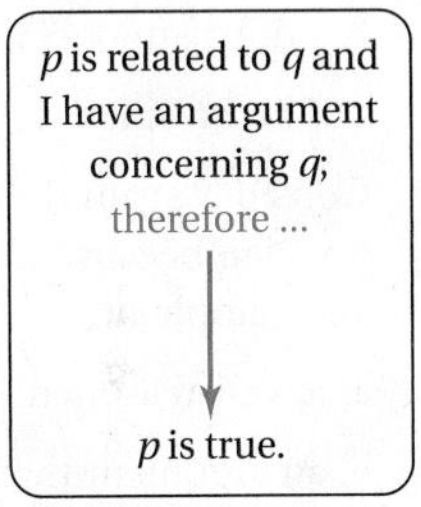

FIGURE 1.9 The fallacy of diversion.

Example 10 Straw Man

The mayor of a large city has proposed decriminalizing drug possession in order to reduce overcrowding in jails. His challenger in the upcoming election says, "The mayor doesn't think there's anything wrong with drug use, but I do."

Analysis The mayor did not say that drug use is acceptable. His proposal for decriminalization is designed to solve another problem—overcrowding of jails—and tells us nothing about his general views on drug use. Thus, the speaker has distorted the mayor's views. Any argument based on a distortion of someone's words or beliefs is called a *straw man* (Figure 1.10). The term comes from the idea that the speaker has used a poor representation of a person's beliefs in the same way that a straw man is a poor representation of a real man. A straw man is similar to a diversion. The primary difference is that a diversion argues against an unrelated issue, while the straw man argues against a distorted version of the real issue. **Now try Exercise 20.**

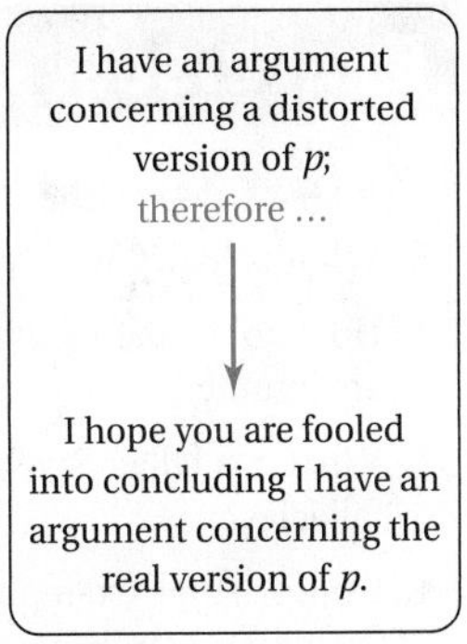

FIGURE 1.10 The straw man fallacy.

QUICK QUIZ

Choose the best answer to each of the following questions. Explain your reasoning with one or more complete sentences.

1. A logical argument always includes
   a. at least one premise and one conclusion.
   b. at least one premise and one fallacy.
   c. at least one fallacy and one conclusion.
2. A fallacy is
   a. a statement that is untrue.
   b. a heated argument.
   c. a deceptive argument.
3. Which of the following could *not* qualify as a logical argument?
   a. a series of statements in which the conclusion comes before the premises
   b. a list of premises that do not lead to a conclusion
   c. a series of statements that generate heated debate
4. An argument in which the conclusion essentially restates the premise is an example of
   a. circular reasoning.
   b. limited choice.
   c. logic.

5. The fallacy of appeal to ignorance occurs when

   a. the fact that a statement p is true is taken to imply that the opposite of p must be false.

   b. the fact that we cannot prove a statement p to be true is taken to imply that p is false.

   c. a conclusion p is disregarded because the person who stated it is ignorant.

6. Consider the argument "I don't support the President's tax plan because I don't trust his motives." What is the conclusion of this argument?

   a. I don't trust his motives.

   b. I don't support the President's tax plan.

   c. The President is not trustworthy.

7. Consider again the argument "I don't support the President's tax plan because I don't trust his motives." This argument is an example of

   a. a well-reasoned, logical argument.

   b. an argument that uses the fallacy of personal attack.

   c. an argument that uses the fallacy of appeal to emotion.

8. Consider the argument "Your lack of enthusiasm for soccer proves that you are not a sports fan." This argument is an example of

   a. a well-reasoned, logical argument.

   b. an argument that uses the fallacy of diversion.

   c. an argument that uses the fallacy of limited choice.

9. Suppose that the fact that an event A occurs before event B is used to conclude that A caused B. This is an example of

   a. a well-reasoned, logical argument.

   b. an argument that uses the fallacy of false cause.

   c. hasty generalization.

10. When we speak of a *straw man* in an argument, we mean

    a. a misrepresentation of someone else's idea or belief.

    b. a person who has not used good logic.

    c. an argument so weak that it is as if it were made of straw.

Exercises 1A

REVIEW QUESTIONS

1. What is logic? Briefly explain how logic can be useful.
2. How do we define *argument*? What is the basic structure of an argument?
3. What is a fallacy? Why is it important to be able to recognize fallacies?
4. Choose three examples of fallacies from this unit and, in your own words, describe how the given argument is deceptive.

DOES IT MAKE SENSE?

Decide whether each of the following statements makes sense (or is clearly true) or does not make sense (or is clearly false). Explain your reasoning.

5. Mike and Erica couldn't have had an argument, because they weren't shouting at each other.
6. I persuaded my father that I was right with a carefully constructed argument that contained no premises at all.
7. I didn't believe the premises on which he based his argument, so he clearly didn't convince me of his conclusion.
8. She convinced me she was right, even though she stated her conclusion before supporting it with any premises.
9. I disagree with your conclusion, so your argument must contain a fallacy.
10. Even though your argument contains a fallacy, your conclusion is believable.

BASIC SKILLS & CONCEPTS

11–20: Analyzing Fallacies. Consider the following examples of fallacies.

a. Identity the premise(s) and conclusion of the argument.

b. Briefly describe how the stated fallacy occurs in the argument.

c. Make up another argument that exhibits the same fallacy.

11. (Appeal to popularity) Apple's iPhone outsells all other smart phones, so it must be the best smart phone on the market.
12. (False cause) Tax cuts must cause recessions, because the current recession began just a few years after large tax cuts.
13. (Appeal to ignorance) Fifty years of searching has not revealed life on other planets, so life in the universe must be confined to Earth.
14. (Hasty generalization) Since 1982, federal deficits have increased under Republican presidents and decreased under Democratic presidents. Clearly, only Democrats can balance the federal budget.
15. (Limited choice) He refused to testify by invoking his Fifth Amendment rights, so he must be guilty.
16. (Appeal to emotion) Thousands of unarmed people, many of them children, are killed by firearms every year. It's time we ban the sale of all guns.
17. (Personal attack) If the Senator doesn't have any religious affiliation, then he can't have the personal values required to represent me.

18. (Circular reasoning) Illegal immigration is against the law, so illegal immigrants are criminals.
19. (Diversion) Good grades are needed to get into college, and a college diploma is necessary for a good career. Therefore, attendance should count in high school grades.
20. (Straw man) The mayor wants to raise taxes to fund social programs, so she must not believe in the value of hard work.

FURTHER APPLICATIONS

21–36: Recognizing Fallacies. In the following arguments, identify the premise(s) and conclusion, explain why the argument is deceptive, and, if possible, identify the type of fallacy it represents.

21. Obesity among Americans has increased steadily for the last decade, as has the sale of video games. It follows that video games are compromising the health of Americans.
22. The polls show the Republican candidate leading by a 2 to 1 margin. So you should vote for the Republican.
23. All the mayors of my home town have been men, which shows that men are better qualified for high office than women.
24. My father tells me that I should exercise daily. But he never exercised when he was young, so I see no need to follow his advice.
25. My baby was vaccinated and later developed autism, which is why I believe that vaccines cause autism.
26. The state has no right to take a life, so the death penalty should be abolished.
27. Everyone loves Shakespeare, because his plays have been read for many centuries.
28. All of those studies about the risks of driving without seat belts are flawed. It's certainly not a good idea to have your seat belt on if your car is on fire or underwater.
29. I will not give money to the tsunami relief organization. After I last gave to a charity, an audit showed that most of the money was used to pay its administrators in the front office.
30. It's not surprising that the President's budget contains spending increases. Democrats don't care about taxpayers' money.
31. The Congressperson is a member of the National Rifle Association, so I'm sure she will not support a ban on assault rifles.
32. My three friends who drink wine have never had heart attacks. My two friends who have had heart attacks are non-drinkers. Drinking wine is clearly a good therapy.
33. Responding to Republicans who want to end the estate tax, which falls most heavily on the wealthy, a Democrat says, "The Republicans think that rich people aren't rich enough."
34. The Wyoming toad has not been seen outside of captivity since 2002, so it must be extinct in the wild.
35. My little boy loves dolls and my little girl loves trucks, so there's no truth to the claim that boys are more interested in mechanical toys while girls prefer maternal toys.

36. Responding to Democrats who want to raise the fuel efficiency standards for new cars and trucks, a Republican says, "Democrats think that government is the solution to all our problems . . . ."

37–40: Additional Fallacies. Consider the following fallacies (which are not discussed in the text). Explain why the fallacy applies to the example and create your own argument that displays the same fallacy.

37. The *fallacy of division* has this form:

Premise:	*X* has some property.
Conclusion:	All things or people that belong to *X* must have the same property.
Example:	Americans use more gasoline than Europeans, so Jake, who is an American, must use more gasoline than Europeans.

38. The *gambler's fallacy* has this form:

Premise:	*X* has been happening more than it should.
Conclusion:	*X* will come to an end soon.
Example:	It has rained for 10 days, which is unusual around here. Tomorrow will be sunny.

39. The *slippery slope fallacy* has this form:

Premise:	*X* has occurred and is related to *Y*.
Conclusion:	*Y* will inevitably occur.
Example:	America has sent troops to three countries recently. Before you know it, we will have troops everywhere.

40. The *middle ground fallacy* has this form:

Premise:	*X* and *Y* are two extreme positions on a question.
Conclusion:	*Z*, which lies between *X* and *Y*, must be correct.
Example:	Senator Peters supports a large tax cut, and Senator Willis supports no tax cut. That means a small tax cut must be best.

WEB PROJECTS

41. **Campaign Site.** Find the Web site for a candidate or initiative (for or against) in an upcoming or recent election. Study the arguments given on the site, looking for examples of fallacies. Write a brief summary of the fallacies. Overall, does the site make a strong or weak case for its candidate or position? Explain.
42. **Gun Control Debate.** One of the most contentious debates in American politics concerns the question of whether the United States should enact stricter gun control laws. Visit one or more of the many Web sites for each side in the gun control debate. Identify at least two fallacies given by each side. Without stating which side you support, give your opinion of the logical quality of the arguments on the Web sites for the two sides—that is, do the arguments on one side involve more fallacies than those on the other side? Explain.
43. **Death Penalty Debate.** The death penalty is another contentious issue in American politics. Visit one or more of the many Web sites for each side in the death penalty debate. Identify at least two fallacies given by each side. Without stating which side you support, give your opinion of the logical quality of the arguments on the Web sites for the two sides—that is, do the arguments on one side involve more fallacies than those on the other side? Explain.
44. **Health Care Debate.** Choose some aspect of the health care debate in the United States, such as whether there should be coverage for prescription drugs or national insurance for all citizens. Find a Web site for each side of the debate. Without stating which side you support, give your opinion of the logical quality of the arguments on the Web sites for the two sides—that is, do the arguments on one side involve more fallacies than those on the other side? Explain.
45. **Fallacy Web Sites.** There are many Web sites devoted to the study of fallacies. Visit one and choose a fallacy of a type not covered in this unit. Explain the fallacy and give an example of it.

IN YOUR WORLD

46. **Editorial Fallacies.** Examine editorials and letters to the editor in your local newspaper. Find at least three examples of fallacies. In each case, describe how the argument is deceptive. If the fallacy represents one or more of the common types described in this unit, state the type.
47. **Fallacies in Advertising.** Pick a single night and a single commercial television channel and analyze the advertisements shown over a 1-hour period. Describe how each advertisement tries to persuade the viewer, and discuss whether the argument is fallacious. What fraction of the advertisements involve fallacies? Are any fallacy types more common than others?
48. **Fallacies in Politics.** Discuss the tactics used by both sides in a current or recent political campaign. How much of the campaign is/was based on fallacies? Describe some of the fallacies. Overall, do you believe that fallacies influenced (or will influence) the outcome of the vote?
49. **Personal Fallacies.** Describe an instance in which you were persuaded of something that you later decided was untrue. Explain how you were persuaded and why you later changed your mind. Did you fall victim to any fallacies? If so, how might you prevent the same thing from happening in the future?

UNIT 1B Propositions and Truth Values

"Contrariwise," continued Tweedledee, "if it was so, it might be; and if it were so, it would be; but as it isn't, it ain't. That's logic."

—Lewis Carroll, *Through the Looking Glass*

Having discussed fallacies in Unit 1A, we now study proper arguments. The building blocks of arguments are called **propositions**—statements that make (propose) a claim that may be either true or false. A proposition must have the structure of a complete sentence and must make a distinct assertion or denial. For example:

- *Joan is sitting in the chair* is a proposition because it is a complete sentence that makes an assertion.
- *I did not take the pen* is a proposition because it is a complete sentence that makes a denial.
- *Are you going to the store?* is not a proposition because it is a question. It does not assert or deny anything.
- *three miles south of here* is not a proposition because it does not make any claim and it is not a complete sentence.
- $7 + 9 = 2$ is a proposition, even though it is false. It can be read as a complete sentence and it makes a distinct claim. **Now try Exercises 13–18.**

> **DEFINITION**
>
> A **proposition** makes a claim (either an assertion or a denial) that may be either true or false. It must have the structure of a complete sentence.

Negation (Opposites)

The opposite of a proposition is called its **negation.** For example, the negation of *Joan is sitting in the chair* is *Joan is not sitting in the chair,* and the negation of $7 + 9 = 2$ is $7 + 9 \neq 2$. If we represent a proposition with a letter such as p, then its negation is *not* p (sometimes written $\sim p$). Note that negations are also propositions, since they have the structure of a complete sentence and may be either true or false.

A proposition has a **truth value** of either true (T) or false (F). If a proposition is true, its negation must be false, and vice versa. We can represent these facts with a simple **truth table**—a table that has a row for each possible set of truth values. The following truth table shows the possible truth values for a proposition p and its negation *not p*. It has two rows because there are only two possibilities.

p	*not* p	
T	F	← This row shows that if p is true (T), *not* p is false (F).
F	T	← This row shows that if p is false (F), *not* p is true (T).

DEFINITIONS

Any proposition has two possible **truth values:** T = true or F = false.

The **negation** of a proposition p is another proposition that makes the opposite claim of p. It is written *not p* (or $\sim p$) and has the opposite truth value of p.

A **truth table** is a table with a row for each possible set of truth values for the propositions being considered.

Historical Note

The Greek philosopher Aristotle (384–322 B.C.E.) made the first known attempt to put logic on a rigorous foundation. He believed that truth could be established from three basic laws: (1) A thing is itself. (2) A statement is either true or false. (3) No statement is both true and false. Aristotle's laws were used by Euclid (c. 325–270 B.C.E.) to establish the foundations of geometry, and logic remains an important part of mathematics.

Example 1 Negation

Consider the proposition *Betsy is the fastest runner on the team.* Write its negation. If the negation is false, is Betsy really the fastest runner on the team?

Solution The negation of the given proposition is *Betsy is not the fastest runner on the team.* If the negation is false, the original statement must be true, meaning that Betsy is the fastest runner on the team.

Now try Exercises 19–22.

Double Negation

The Groucho Marx quotation in the margin may be an extreme example, but many everyday statements contain double (or multiple) negations. We've already seen that the negation *not p* has the opposite truth value of the original proposition p. The double negation *not not p* must therefore have the same truth value as the original proposition p. We can show this fact with a truth table. The first column contains the two possible truth values for p. Two additional columns show the corresponding truth values for *not p* and *not not p*.

p	*not p*	*not not p*
T	F	T
F	T	F

In ordinary language, double negations rarely involve phrases like "not not," so we must analyze wording carefully to recognize them.

I cannot say that I do not disagree with you.

—Groucho Marx

If people don't want to come out to the baseball park, then nobody's going to stop them.

—Yogi Berra

Example 2 Radiation and Health

After reviewing data showing an association between low-level radiation and cancer among older workers at the Oak Ridge National Laboratory, a health scientist from the University of North Carolina (Chapel Hill) was asked about the possibility of a similar association among younger workers at another national laboratory. He was quoted as saying (*Boulder Daily Camera*):

> *My opinion is that it's unlikely that there is no association.*

Does the scientist think there is an association between low-level radiation and cancer?

Solution Because of the words "unlikely" and "no association," the scientist's statement contains a double negation. To see the effects of these words clearly, let's start with a simpler proposition:

p = *it's likely that there is an association (between low-level radiation and cancer).*

The word "unlikely" gives us the statement *it's unlikely that there is an association,* which we identify as *not p*. The words "no association" transform this last statement into the original statement, *it's unlikely that there is no association,* which we recognize as *not not p*. Because the double negation has the same truth value as the original proposition, we conclude that the scientist believes it likely that there *is* an association between low-level radiation and cancer. **Now try Exercises 23–24.**

BY THE WAY

Ernesto Miranda confessed to and was convicted of a 1963 rape and kidnapping. His lawyer argued that the confession should not have been admitted as evidence because Miranda had not been told of his right to remain silent. The Supreme Court agreed and overturned his conviction. He was then retried, and again convicted (on the basis of evidence besides the confession). Miranda was stabbed to death during a bar fight after his release from prison. A suspect in his killing chose to remain silent upon arrest, and police never filed charges.

Example 3 The 2000 Miranda Ruling

In a June 2000 decision (*Dickerson v. United States*), the U.S. Supreme Court voted 7–2 to uphold the basic requirements of the 1966 Miranda decision (*Miranda v. State of Arizona*). That decision required that suspects taken into custody be informed of their constitutional rights, such as the right to remain silent and the right to legal counsel. In his majority opinion, Chief Justice William Rehnquist wrote:

> . . . *[legal] principles weigh heavily against overruling [Miranda] now.*

According to this statement, did the Chief Justice feel that legal principles support or oppose the original Miranda decision?

Solution Analyzed carefully, the Chief Justice's statement contains a double negation. The first negation comes from the term "overruling," which alone would imply opposition to the original decision. But the statement argued *against* overruling, and therefore implies that legal principles support the original Miranda decision. **Now try Exercises 25–28.**

Logical Connectors

Propositions are often joined together with *logical connectors*—words such as *and, or,* and *if . . . then.* For example, consider the following two propositions:

p = *The test was hard.*
q = *I got an A.*

If we join the two propositions with *and,* we get a new proposition that reads *the test was hard and I got an A.* If we join them with *or,* we get the statement *the test was hard or I got an A.* Although such statements are familiar from everyday speech, we must analyze them carefully.

And Statements (Conjunctions)

An *and* statement is called a **conjunction.** According to the rules of logic, the conjunction *p and q* is true only if *p* and *q* are *both* true. For example, the statement *the test was hard and I got an A* is true only if it *was* a hard test and you *did* get an A.

THE LOGIC OF *AND*

Given two propositions *p* and *q*, the statement *p and q* is called their **conjunction**. It is true only if *p* and *q* are *both* true.

To make a truth table for the conjunction *p and q*, we analyze all possible combinations of the truth values of the individual propositions *p* and *q*. Because *p* and *q* each have two possible truth values (true or false), there are $2 \times 2 = 4$ cases to consider. The four cases become the four rows of the truth table.

BY THE WAY

In symbolic logic, the connector *and* is denoted by $\wedge$. Thus, the conjunction *p and q* is written $p \wedge q$.

Truth Table for Conjunction *p and q*

p	*q*	*p and q*	
T	T	T	← case 1: *p*, *q* both true
T	F	F	← case 2: *p* true, *q* false
F	T	F	← case 3: *p* false, *q* true
F	F	F	← case 4: *p*, *q* both false

Now try Exercises 29–30.

Note that the *and* statement is true only in the first case shown in the table, where both individual propositions are true.

Example 4 *And* Statements

Evaluate the truth value of the following two statements.

a. The capital of France is Paris and Antarctica is cold.
b. The capital of France is Paris and the capital of America is Madrid.

Solution

a. The statement contains two distinct propositions: *The capital of France is Paris* and *Antarctica is cold.* Because both propositions are true, their conjunction is also true.
b. The statement contains two distinct propositions: *The capital of France is Paris* and *the capital of America is Madrid.* Although the first proposition is true, the second is false. Therefore, their conjunction is false. **Now try Exercises 31–36.**

BY THE WAY

Logical rules lie at the heart of modern computer science. Computers generally use electric current to represent only two numbers: 0 and 1. A 1 means a circuit carries current and a 0 means a circuit carries no current. Computer scientists think of 1 as true and 0 as false and use logical connectors to design circuits. For example, an *and* circuit allows current to pass (its value is 1 = true) only if both incoming circuits carry current.

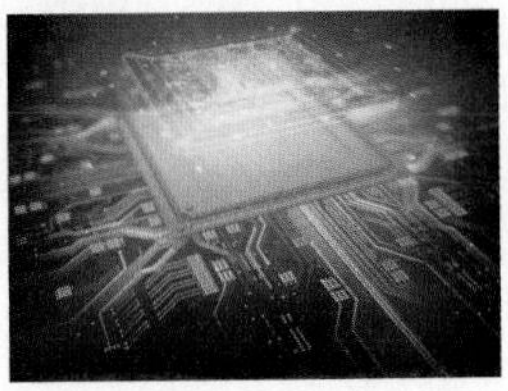

Example 5 Triple Conjunction

Suppose you are given three individual propositions *p*, *q*, and *r*. Make a truth table for the conjunction *p and q and r*. Under what circumstances is the conjunction true?

Solution When we considered the statement *p and q*, we saw that there were four possible cases for truth values. For each of these four cases, proposition *r* can be either true or false. Thus, the statement *p and q and r* has $4 \times 2 = 8$ possible cases for truth values. The following truth table contains a row for each of the eight cases. Note that the four cases for *p and q* each appear twice, once with *r* true and once with *r* false.

p	*q*	*r*	*p and q and r*
T	T	T	T
T	T	F	F
T	F	T	F
T	F	F	F
F	T	T	F
F	T	F	F
F	F	T	F
F	F	F	F

The conjunction *p and q and r* is true only if all three statements are true, as shown in the first row. You can see why if you remember that the conjunction of two statements is true only if both statements are true. Because we can think of *p and q* as a single statement (which is true only when *p* and *q* are both true), the conjunction of this statement with *r* can be true only if *r* is also true. **Now try Exercises 37–38.**

Time Out to Think

Given four propositions *p*, *q*, *r*, and *s*, how many rows are required for a truth table of the conjunction *p and q and r and s*? When is the conjunction true?

Understanding *Or*

The connector *or* can have two different meanings. If a health insurance policy says that it covers hospitalization in cases of illness *or* injury, it probably means that it covers either illness or injury *or both*. This is an example of the **inclusive *or*** that means "either or both." In contrast, when a restaurant offers a choice of soup *or* salad, you probably are not supposed to choose both. This is an example of the **exclusive *or*** that means "one or the other."

TWO TYPES OF *OR*

The word *or* can be interpreted in two distinct ways:

- An **inclusive *or*** means "either or both."
- An **exclusive *or*** means "one or the other, but not both."

In everyday life, we determine whether an *or* statement is inclusive or exclusive by its context. But in logic, we assume that *or* is inclusive unless told otherwise.

Example 6 Inclusive or Exclusive?

Kevin's insurance policy states that his house is insured for earthquakes, fire, *or* robbery. Imagine that a major earthquake levels much of his house, the rest burns in a fire, and his remaining valuables are looted in the aftermath. Would Kevin prefer that the *or* in his insurance policy be inclusive or exclusive? Why?

Solution He would prefer an inclusive *or* so that his losses from all three events (earthquake, fire, looting) would be covered. If the *or* were exclusive, the insurance would cover only one set of losses. **Now try Exercises 39–44.**

Or Statements (Disjunctions)

A compound statement made with *or* is called a **disjunction.** We assume that the *or* is inclusive, so the disjunction *p or q* is true if either or both propositions are true. A disjunction *p or q* is false only if both individual propositions are false.

BY THE WAY

In symbolic logic, the connector *or* is denoted by $\vee$. Thus, the disjunction *p or q* is written $p \vee q$.

THE LOGIC OF *OR*

Given two propositions *p* and *q*, the statement *p or q* is called their **disjunction.** In logic, we assume that *or* is *inclusive*, so the disjunction is true if either or both propositions are true, and false only if *both* propositions are false.

These rules lead to the following truth table.

Truth Table for Disjunction *p or q*

p	*q*	*p or q*
T	T	T
T	F	T
F	T	T
F	F	F

Now try Exercises 45–50.

Example 7 Smart Cows?

Consider the statement *airplanes can fly or cows can read.* Is it true?

Solution The statement is a disjunction of two propositions: *airplanes can fly* and *cows can read.* The first proposition is clearly true, while the second is clearly false. As shown in the second row of the truth table for the disjunction, *p or q* is true in this case. Thus, the statement *airplanes can fly or cows can read* is true.

Now try Exercises 51–56.

Example 8 Key Word Search

You are doing a research report for which you need to find articles about the federal debt that appeared in either *Time* or *Newsweek* between 2008 and 2010. You have access to a database that allows you to search on date, magazine, and title. How should you structure the search?

Solution In general, using OR widens the search whereas using AND narrows the search. For the date, the key word search

2008 OR *2009* OR *2010*

will generate a list with articles published in any of the three years (because *or* is assumed to be inclusive). Similarly, for the magazine, you would search on

Time OR *Newsweek*

to ensure that both magazines are included on the list.

The title requires a bit more thought. Searching on *federal* OR *debt* would lead to a list with many articles unrelated to the federal debt, such as articles on federal crimes or corporate debt. Searching on *federal* AND *debt* would limit the search to articles containing both words in the title, but might miss relevant articles with different key words in their titles. For example, it would miss an article with the title "the United States budget debt." One way to solve this problem is to use a more complex set of search criteria, such as

(*federal* OR *United States* OR *government*) AND (*debt* OR *budget*)

This search would find articles with any of the following word combinations in their titles: *federal debt, United States debt, government debt, federal budget, United States budget,* or *government budget.*

Now try Exercises 57–60.

BY THE WAY

Most search engines automatically connect words in the search box with the logical connector AND. For example, a search on *television entertainment* is really a search on *television* AND *entertainment,* and it will return any Web page that has both words, regardless of whether the words come together. If you want the exact phrase *"television entertainment,"* you must put the phrase in quotes.

If . . . Then Statements (Conditionals)

Another common way to connect propositions is with the words "if . . . then," as in the statement "If all politicians are liars, then Representative Smith is a liar." Statements of this type are called **conditional propositions** (or *implications*) because they propose something to be true (the *then* part of the statement) on the *condition* that something else is true (the *if* part of the statement).

BY THE WAY

In symbolic logic, a right arrow ($\Rightarrow$) is used to represent a conditional; $p \Rightarrow q$ is read "p implies q."

We can represent a conditional proposition as *if p, then q*, Proposition p is called the **hypothesis** (or *antecedent*) and proposition q is called the **conclusion** (or *consequent*).

Let's use an example to examine the truth table for a conditional proposition. Suppose that while running for Congress, candidate Jones claimed:

If I am elected, then the minimum wage will increase.

This proposition has the standard form *if p, then q*, where p = *I am elected* and q = *the minimum wage will increase.* Because each individual proposition can be either true or false, we must consider four possible cases for the truth value of *if p, then q:*

1. **p and q both true.** In this case, Jones *was* elected (p true) and the minimum wage increased (q true). Jones kept her campaign promise, so her claim, *if I am elected, then the minimum wage will increase,* was true.
2. **p true and q false.** In this case, Jones was elected, but the minimum wage did not increase. Because things did not turn out as she promised, her claim was false.
3. **p false and q true.** This is the case in which Jones was *not* elected, yet the minimum wage still increased. The conditional statement only makes a claim about what should happen in the event that Jones is elected. Because she was not elected, she surely did not break any campaign promise, regardless of whether or not the minimum wage increased. According to the rules of logic, Jones's original statement was true.
4. **p and q both false.** Now we have the case in which Jones was not elected and the minimum wage did not increase. Again, because she was not elected, she surely did not violate her campaign promise, even though the minimum wage did not increase. The rules of logic dictate that the original statement was true.

In summary, the statement *if p, then q* is true in all cases except when the hypothesis p is true and the conclusion q is false. Here is the truth table.

Truth Table for Conditional *if p, then q*

p	q	*if p, then q*
T	T	T
T	F	F
F	T	T
F	F	T

Now try Exercises 61–62.

THE LOGIC OF *IF . . . THEN*

A statement of the form *if p, then q* is called a **conditional proposition** (or *implication*). Proposition p is called the **hypothesis** and proposition q is called the **conclusion**. The conditional *if p, then q* is true in all cases except the case in which p is true and q is false.

Time Out to Think

Suppose candidate Jones had made the following campaign promise: *If I am elected, I will personally eliminate all poverty on Earth.* According to the rules of logic for cases (3) and (4) above, we consider this statement to be true in the event that Jones is *not* elected. Is this logical definition of truth the same one that you would use if you heard her make this promise? Explain.

Example 9 Conditional Truths

Evaluate the truth of the statement *if* $2 + 2 = 5$, *then* $3 + 3 = 4$.

Solution The statement has the form *if p, then q*, where p is $2 + 2 = 5$ and q is $3 + 3 = 4$. Both p and q are clearly false. However, according to the rules of logic, the conditional *if p, then q* is true any time p is false, regardless of what q says. Thus, the statement *if* $2 + 2 = 5$, *then* $3 + 3 = 4$ is true. **Now try Exercises 63–70.**

> **Historical Note**
>
> The system of logic presented in this chapter was first developed by the ancient Greeks and is called *binary logic* because a proposition is either true or false, but not both and certainly nothing in between. Recently, mathematicians have developed systems of logic in which other truth values are possible. One form, called *fuzzy logic*, allows for a continuous range of values between absolutely true and absolutely false. Fuzzy logic is used in many new technologies.

Alternative Phrasings of Conditionals

In ordinary language, conditional statements don't always appear in the standard form *if p, then q*. In such cases, it can be useful to rephrase the statements in the standard form. For example, the claim *I'm not coming back if I leave* has the same meaning as *if I leave, then I'm not coming back*. Similarly, the statement *more rain will lead to a flood* can be recast as *if there is more rain, then there will be a flood.*

Two particularly important ways of phrasing conditionals use the words *necessary* and *sufficient*, respectively. The statement *if p, then q* means that p cannot be true unless q is true. Therefore, the statement *if p, then q* is equivalent to the statement *q is necessary for p*. For example, the statement *breathing is necessary for living* can be rephrased as *if you are living, then you must breathe*. This does not mean that breathing is the only necessity for living. It is one of many necessities (such as eating, breathing, and having a heartbeat).

The statement *if p, then q* also means that q will be true if p is true. Therefore, the statement *if p, then q* is equivalent to the statement *p is sufficient for q*. For example, the statement *being in Denver is sufficient for being in Colorado* can be rephrased as *if you are in Denver, then you are in Colorado*. This does not mean that being in Denver is necessary for being in Colorado, because many other places are also in Colorado.

> **ALTERNATIVE PHRASINGS OF CONDITIONALS**
>
> The following are common alternative ways of stating *if p, then q*:
>
> | | | |
> |---|---|---|
> | *p is sufficient for q* | *p will lead to q* | *p implies q* |
> | *q is necessary for p* | *q if p* | *q whenever p* |

Example 10 Rephrasing Conditional Propositions

Recast each of the following statements in the form *if p, then q*. Discuss whether the statement is true or false.

a. A rise in sea level will devastate Florida.
b. A red tag on an item is sufficient to mean it's on sale.
c. Being male is necessary for being president of the United States.

Solution

a. This statement is equivalent to *if sea level rises, then Florida will be devastated*. The truth of the statement depends on how much sea level rises. A few inches might have only limited effects, while a few feet could flood most of the state.
b. This statement can be written as *if an item is marked with a red tag, then it is on sale*. This statement is true only if all red tag items really are on sale.
c. This statement can be expressed as *if a person is president, then the person is male*. While it is true that all American presidents to date have been male, many other nations have had female presidents and the United States may have a female president in the future. Therefore, the statement is false. **Now try Exercises 71–76.**

Converse, Inverse, and Contrapositive

The order of the propositions does not matter in a conjunction or disjunction. For example, *p and q* has the same meaning as *q and p*, and *p or q* has the same meaning as *q or p*. However, when we switch the order of the propositions in a conditional, we create a different proposition called the **converse**. The following box summarizes definitions for the converse and two other variations on a conditional proposition *if p, then q*.

Take Note

The contrapositive is sometimes said to be the "inverse of the converse." You can see why by starting with the converse of *if p, then q*, which is *if q, then p*. Now, making the inverse of this converse gives us the statement *if not q, then not p*, which is the contrapositive of the original conditional *if p, then q*.

VARIATIONS ON THE CONDITIONAL

Name	Form	Example
Conditional	*if p, then q*	If you are sleeping, then you are breathing.
Converse	*if q, then p*	If you are breathing, then you are sleeping.
Inverse	*if not p, then not q*	If you are not sleeping, then you are not breathing.
Contrapositive	*if not q, then not p*	If you are not breathing, then you are not sleeping.

We can determine the truth values for the converse, inverse, and contrapositive with a truth table. Because all the statements use the same two propositions (*p*, *q*), the table has four rows. The first two columns show the truth values for *p* and *q*, respectively. The next two columns show the truth values for the negations *not p* and *not q*, which are needed for the inverse and contrapositive. The fifth column shows the truth values found previously for the conditional proposition *if p, then q*. We then find the truth values for the converse, inverse, and contrapositive by applying the rule that a conditional is false only when the hypothesis is true and the conclusion is false.

(*if p, then q* and *if not q, then not p*: logically equivalent)

p	*q*	*not p*	*not q*	*if p, then q*	*if q, then p* (converse)	*if not p, then not q* (inverse)	*if not q, then not p* (contrapositive)
T	T	F	F	T	T	T	T
T	F	F	T	F	T	T	F
F	T	T	F	T	F	F	T
F	F	T	T	T	T	T	T

(converse and inverse: logically equivalent)

Note that the truth values for the conditional *if p, then q* are the same as those for its contrapositive. We therefore say that a conditional and its contrapositive are **logically equivalent**: If one is true, so is the other, and vice versa. The table also shows that the converse and inverse are logically equivalent.

DEFINITION

Two statements are **logically equivalent** if they share the same truth values: If one is true, so is the other, and if one is false, so is the other.

Example 11 Logical Equivalence

Consider the statement *if a creature is a whale, then it is a mammal*. Write its converse, inverse, and contrapositive. Evaluate the truth of each statement. Which statements are logically equivalent?

Solution The statement has the form *if p, then q*, where *p* = *a creature is a whale* and *q* = *a creature is a mammal*. Therefore, we find

converse (*if q, then p*): *if a creature is a mammal, then it is a whale.* This statement is false, because most mammals are not whales.

inverse (*if not p, then not q*): *if a creature is not a whale, then it is not a mammal.* This statement is also false; for example, dogs are not whales, but they are mammals.

contrapositive (*if not q, then not p*): *if a creature is not a mammal, then it is not a whale.* This statement is true, because all whales are mammals.

Note that the original proposition and its contrapositive have the same truth value and are logically equivalent. Similarly, the converse and inverse have the same truth value and are logically equivalent. **Now try Exercises 77–82.**

QUICK QUIZ

Choose the best answer to each of the following questions. Explain your reasoning with one or more complete sentences.

1. The statement "Mathematics is fun" is
   a. an argument. b. a fallacy. c. a proposition.
2. Suppose you know the truth value of a proposition *p*. Then you also know the truth value of this proposition's
   a. negation. b. truth table. c. conjunction.
3. Which of the following has the form of a *conditional* statement?
   a. *x or y* b. *x and y* c. *if x, then y*
4. Suppose you want to make a truth table for the statement *x or y or z*. How many rows will the table require?
   a. 2 b. 4 c. 8
5. Suppose the statement *p or q* is true. Then you can be certain that
   a. *p* is true.
   b. *q* is true.
   c. one or both of the statements are true.
6. Suppose the statement *p* is false and the statement *q* is true. Which of the following statements would be false?
   a. *p and q* b. *p or q* c. *if p, then q*
7. You want to search for articles containing the word *Calcutta* OR *Bombay*. Using an advanced search in Google, you should enter the two words with instructions to find results
   a. with all of the words.
   b. with the exact phrase.
   c. with at least one of the words.
8. You want to search for articles containing the words *Calcutta* AND *Bombay*. Using an advanced search in Google, you should enter the two words with instructions to find results
   a. with all of the words.
   b. with the exact phrase.
   c. with at least one of the words.
9. Two statements are logically equivalent if
   a. they mean the same thing.
   b. they have the same truth values.
   c. they are both true.
10. Consider the statement "You've got to play if you want to win." If you put this statement in the form *if p, then q*, then *q* would be
    a. "You've got to play."
    b. "You want to win."
    c. "You've got to play if you want to win."

Exercises 1B

REVIEW QUESTIONS

1. What is a proposition? Give a few examples, and explain why each is a proposition.
2. What do we mean by the *negation* of a proposition? Make up your own example of a proposition and its negation.
3. Define *conjunction, disjunction,* and *conditional,* and give an example of each in words.
4. What is the difference between an inclusive *or* and an exclusive *or*? Give an example of each.
5. Make a truth table for each of the following: *p and q*; *p or q*; *if p, then q*. Explain all the truth values in the tables.
6. Describe how to make the converse, inverse, and contrapositive of a conditional proposition. Make a truth table for each. Which statement is logically equivalent to the original conditional?

DOES IT MAKE SENSE?

Decide whether each of the following statements makes sense (or is clearly true) or does not make sense (or is clearly false). Explain your reasoning.

7. My logical proposition is a question that you must answer.
8. The professor opposes the ban on torture, so he must be a compassionate person.
9. We intend to catch him, dead or alive.
10. When Sally is depressed, she listens to her iPod. I saw her today listening to her iPod, so she must have been depressed.
11. Now that I've studied logic, I can always determine the truth of any statement by making a truth table for it.
12. Your statement is the converse of mine, so if mine is true then yours must be false.

BASIC SKILLS & CONCEPTS

13–18: A Proposition? Determine whether the following statements are propositions and give an explanation.

13. The world is a stage.
14. Change we can believe in.
15. Back to the future.
16. All reprobates are nefarious.
17. What were you thinking?
18. The former king was a superb cook.

19–22: Negation. Write the negation of the given proposition. Then state the truth value of the original proposition and its negation.

19. Asia is in the northern hemisphere.
20. Spain is in North America.
21. The Beatles were not a German band.
22. Brad Pitt is not an American actor.

23–28: Multiple Negations. Explain the meaning of the given statement, which contains a multiple negation. Then answer the question that follows.

23. Sarah did not decline the offer to go to dinner. Did Sarah go to dinner?
24. The Senator opposes the ban on anti-war demonstrations. Does the Senator approve of the demonstrations?
25. The Congressman voted against the anti-discrimination bill. Did the Congressman vote in favor of discrimination?
26. The House failed to overturn the veto on a bill that would stop logging. Based on this vote, will logging continue?
27. Paul denies that he opposes the plan to build a new dorm. Does Paul support building a new dorm?
28. The mayor failed to gain enough support to strike down the law prohibiting cell phones in public meetings. Does the mayor oppose the use of cell phones in public meetings?

29–30: Truth Tables. Make a truth table for the given statement. The letters p, q, r, and s represent propositions

29. *q and r*
30. *p and s*

31–36: *And* Statements. The following propositions have the form *p and q*. State p and q, and give their truth values. Then determine whether the entire proposition is true or false, and explain why.

31. Cucumbers are vegetables and apples are fruit.
32. $12 + 6 = 18$ and $3 \times 5 = 8$.
33. The Mississippi River flows through Louisiana and the Colorado River flows through Arizona.
34. Bach was a composer and U2's Bono is a violinist.
35. Some people are happy and some people are short.
36. Not all dogs are black and not all cats are white.

37–38: Truth Tables. Make a truth table for the given statement. Assume that p, q, r, and s represent propositions.

37. *q and r and s*
38. *p and q and r and s*

39–44: Interpreting *or*. State whether *or* is used in the inclusive or exclusive sense in the following propositions.

39. I will dress in red or blue.
40. Before the entrée, you have a choice of soup or salad.
41. My next vacation will be in Mexico or Costa Rica.
42. The oil change is good for 5000 miles or three months.
43. While in New York, I would be thrilled to attend concerts or theater.
44. The insurance policy covers fire or theft.

45–50: Truth Tables. Make a truth table for the given statement. Assume that p, q, r, and s represent propositions.

45. *r or s*
46. *p or r*
47. *p and (not p)*
48. *q or (not q)*
49. *p or q or r*
50. *p or (not p) or q*

51–56: ***Or* Statements.** The following propositions have the form *p or q*. State *p* and *q*, and give their truth value. Then determine whether the entire proposition is true or false, and explain why.

51. Oranges are vegetables or oranges are fruit.
52. $3 \times 5 = 15$ or $3 + 5 = 8$.
53. The Nile River is in Africa or China is in Europe.
54. Bachelors are married or bachelors are single.
55. Trees walk or rocks run.
56. France is a country or Paris is a continent.

57–60: **Keyword Searches.** The advanced search on Google allows you to search (a) on exactly the following phrase, (b) on all of the following words, (c) on at least one of the following words, or (d) excluding the following words. Describe how you would conduct an advanced search for information on the following topics.

57. Economic depressions in America
58. Natural disasters in Japan
59. Ohio or Indiana politicians named Jones
60. Symphonies written by 17th- or 18th-century German composers

61–62: **Truth Tables.** Make a truth table for the given statement. Assume that *p*, *q*, *r*, and *s* represent propositions.

61. *if p, then r*
62. *if q, then s*

63–70: ***If . . . then* Statements.** Identify the hypothesis and conclusion in the following propositions, and state their truth values. Then determine whether the entire proposition is true or false.

63. If eagles can fly, then eagles are birds.
64. If London is in England, then Chicago is in America.
65. If London is in England, then Chicago is in Bolivia.
66. If London is in Mongolia, then Chicago is in America.
67. If pigs can fly, then fish can brush their teeth.
68. If $2 \times 3 = 6$, then $2 + 3 = 6$
69. If butterflies can fly, then butterflies are birds.
70. If butterflies are birds, then butterflies can fly.

71–76: **Rephrasing Conditional Statements.** Express the following statements in the form *if p, then q*. Identify *p* and *q* clearly.

71. All monkeys are mammals.
72. A resident of Tel Aviv is a resident of Israel.
73. Eating is a sufficient condition for being alive.
74. Eating is necessary for being alive.
75. Being bald is sufficient for being male.
76. She is educated if she is an art historian.

77–82: **Converse, Inverse, and Contrapositive.** Write the converse, inverse, and contrapositive of the following propositions. Of these four propositions, state which pairs are equivalent.

77. If José owns a computer, then he owns a Mac.
78. If the patient is alive, then the patient is breathing.
79. If Teresa works in Boston, then she works in Massachusetts.
80. If I am using electricity, then the lights are on.
81. If the sun is shining, then it is warm outside.
82. If the polar ice caps melt, then the oceans will rise.

FURTHER APPLICATIONS

83–86: **Famous Quotes.** Rephrase the following quotations using one or more conditional statements (*if p, then q*). Defend your opinion about whether the statement is true or false.

83. Only the good die young. —Billy Joel (most recently)
84. If a man hasn't discovered something that he will die for, he isn't fit to live. —Martin Luther King, Jr.
85. If a free society cannot help the many who are poor, it cannot save the few who are rich. —John F. Kennedy
86. The man who reads nothing at all is better educated than the man who reads nothing but newspapers. —Thomas Jefferson

87–90: **Writing Conditional Propositions.** Create your own example of a proposition that has the given property.

87. A true conditional proposition whose converse is false
88. A true conditional proposition whose converse is true
89. A true conditional proposition whose contrapositive is true
90. A false conditional proposition whose inverse is true
91. Suppose you want to find the book *Grapes of Wrath* by John Steinbeck in a searchable database. State whether the book would be on the search list for each of the following key word combinations. Explain.
    a. *Steinbeck* OR *grapes*
    b. *Grapes of Wrath*
    c. *grapes* AND *Steinbeck*
    d. *Hemingway* OR *Steinbeck*
    e. *Hemingway* AND *grapes*
    f. (*Steinbeck* OR *Hemingway*) AND *grapes*
92. **Alimony Tax Laws.** The federal tax policy on alimony payments is as follows:
    (1) Alimony you receive after you remarry is taxable if the payer did not know you had remarried.
    (2) Alimony you receive after you remarry is not taxable if the payer did know you had remarried.
    (3) Alimony you pay is never deductible by the payer.

    Rephrase these three statements as conditional propositions.

93–96: **Necessary and Sufficient.** Write the following conditional statements in the form (a) *p* is sufficient for *q* and (b) *q* is necessary for *p*.

93. If you believe, then you can achieve. —Tupak Shakur
94. If it's true that our species is alone in the universe, then I'd have to say that the universe aimed rather low. —George Carlin
95. If I love until it hurts, then there is no hurt, but only more love. —Mother Teresa

96. If you need both of your hands for whatever it is you're doing, then your brain should probably be in on it too. —Ellen DeGeneres

97–102: **Logical Equivalence.** Consider the following pairs of statements in which *p*, *q*, *r*, and *s* represent propositions. Make a truth table for each statement of the pair and determine whether the two statements are logically equivalent.

97. *not (p and q); (not p) or (not q)*
98. *not (p or q); (not p) and (not q)*
99. *not (p and q); (not p) and (not q)*
100. *not (p or q); (not p) or (not q)*
101. *(p and q) or r; (p or r) and (p or q)*
102. *(p or q) and r; (p and r) or (q and r)*

WEB PROJECT

103. **Web Searches.** Investigate rules for key word searches on several Web sites or search engines. Are the rules consistent with the laws of logic described in this chapter? Of the sites you checked, which offers the most "user-friendly" search? Explain why you like it.

IN YOUR WORLD

104. **Logical Or.** Find a news article or advertisement in which the connector *or* is used. Is it used in an inclusive or exclusive sense? Explain its meaning in the given context.
105. **Multiple Negation.** Find a news article or advertisement in which a double (or multiple) negation is used. Explain the meaning of the sentence in which it occurs.
106. **Conditional News.** Find a news article or editorial in which a conditional statement is used. If necessary, rephrase the statement in standard *if p, then q* form. Comment on the truth of the individual propositions *p* and *q*, and of the conditional proposition *if p, then q*.

UNIT 1C Sets and Venn Diagrams

We've seen that propositions come in many forms. The only general requirement is that a proposition must make a clear claim (assertion or denial). In this unit, we focus on propositions that claim a relationship between two categories of things. For example, the proposition *all whales are mammals* makes the claim that the category *whales* is entirely contained within the category *mammals.*

Propositions of this type are most easily studied with the aid of two key ideas. The first is the idea of a *set,* which is really just another word for a collection. The second is the idea of a *Venn diagram,* which is a simple visual way of illustrating relationships between sets. Both ideas are very useful for organizing information and hence are important tools of critical thinking.

Relationships Among Sets

A **set** is a collection of objects, living or nonliving. The **members** of a set are the specific objects within it. For example:

- The members of the set *days of the week* are the individual days Sunday, Monday, Tuesday, Wednesday, Thursday, Friday, and Saturday.
- The members of the set *American military services* are the Army, Navy, Air Force, and Marine Corps.
- The members of the set *Academy Award winning actresses* are the individual actresses who have won Academy Awards.

BY THE WAY

The four military services are organized under the United States Department of Defense. The United States Coast Guard is often grouped with these services, but it is administered by the Department of Homeland Security.

Set Notation

Sets are often described by listing all their individual members within a pair of braces, { }. For example, the set *American military services* can be written as

{Army, Navy, Air Force, Marine Corps}

Every member of the set is listed within the braces, with each member separated from the next by a comma.

Some sets have so many members that it would be difficult or impossible to list all of them. In that case, we can use three dots, . . . , to indicate that the list continues in the same basic manner. (The three dots are called an *ellipsis,* but most people just say "dot-dot-dot" when reading them.) If the dots come at the end of a list, they indicate that the list continues indefinitely. For example, we can write the set of *dog breeds* as

{Rottweiler, German Shepherd, Poodle, . . . }

The three dots indicate that the list continues as you would expect—in this case, with the names of all other dog breeds. It does not matter how many members you list, as long as the pattern is clear. Listing three members, as in the dog breed list, is usually enough to make the point.

In other cases, the dots may come in the middle of the list, representing members that were not explicitly written. For example, the set

{A, B, C, . . . , Z}

represents the entire alphabet in capital letters. The dots are simply a convenience, saving us from having to write every letter.

Although it is less common, the three dots can also come at the beginning of a list. For example, the set

$\{\ldots, -3, -2, -1\}$

represents all negative integers. Here, the dots indicate that the list continues to the left, to ever smaller (more negative) numbers.

The whole is more than the sum of its parts.

—Aristotle, *Metaphysica*

DEFINITIONS

A **set** is a collection of objects; the individual objects are the **members** of the set. We write sets by listing their members within a pair of braces, { }. If there are too many members to list, we use three dots, . . . , to indicate a continuing pattern.

Time Out to Think

How would you use braces notation to describe the set of students in your mathematics class? How about the set of countries you have visited? Describe one more example of a set that affects you personally, and write it with braces notation.

Example 1 Set Notation

Use braces to write the contents of each of the following sets:

a. the set of *countries larger in land area than the United States*
b. the set of *years of the Cold War,* generally taken to have started in 1945 and ended in 1991
c. the set of *natural numbers greater than 5*

Solution

a. The set of *countries larger in land area than the United States* is {Russia, Canada}.
b. The set of *years of the Cold War* is {1945, 1946, 1947, . . . , 1991}; the dots indicate that the list includes all the years between 1947 and 1991, even though they are not listed explicitly.
c. The set of *natural numbers greater than 5* is {6, 7, 8, . . . }; the dots indicate that the list continues to ever-higher numbers. **Now try Exercises 29–36.**

Illustrating Relationships with Venn Diagrams

The English logician John Venn (1834–1923) invented a simple visual way of describing relationships between sets. His diagrams, now called **Venn diagrams**, use

A Brief Review Sets of Numbers

In mathematics, we commonly work with the following important sets of numbers.

The set of **natural numbers** (or *counting numbers*) is

$$\{1, 2, 3, \dots\}$$

We can represent the natural numbers on a *number line* with equally spaced dots beginning at 1 and continuing to the right forever.

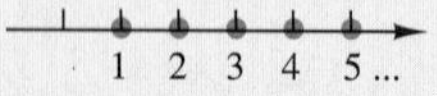

The set of **whole numbers** is the same as the set of natural numbers except it includes zero. Thus, its members are

$$\{0, 1, 2, 3, \dots\}$$

We can represent the whole numbers on a number line with equally spaced dots beginning at 0 and continuing to the right forever.

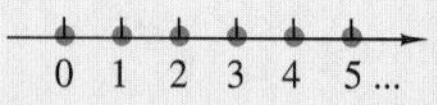

The set of **integers** includes the whole numbers and their negatives. Thus, its members are

$$\{\dots, -3, -2, -1, 0, 1, 2, 3, \dots\}$$

On the number line, the integers extend forever both to the left and to the right.

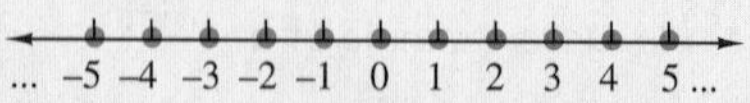

The set of **rational numbers** includes the integers and the fractions that can be made by dividing one integer by another, as long as we don't divide by zero. (The word *rational* refers to a *ratio* of integers.) In other words, rational numbers can be expressed in the form

$$\frac{x}{y}, \text{ where } x \text{ and } y \text{ are integers and } y \neq 0$$

(Recall that the symbol $\neq$ means "is not equal to.")

When expressed in decimal form, rational numbers are either terminating decimals with a finite number of digits (such as 0.25, which is $\frac{1}{4}$) or repeating decimals in which a pattern repeats over and over (such as 0.333 . . . , which is $\frac{1}{3}$).

Irrational numbers are numbers that *cannot* be expressed in the form x/y. When written as decimals, irrational numbers neither terminate nor have a repeating pattern. For example, the number $\sqrt{2}$ is irrational because it cannot be expressed exactly in a form x/y; as a decimal, we can write it as 1.414213562 . . . , where the dots mean that the digits continue forever with no pattern. The number π is also an irrational number, which as a decimal is written 3.14159265. . . .

The set of **real numbers** consists of both rational and irrational numbers; hence it is represented by the entire number line. Each point on the number line has a corresponding real number, and each real number has a corresponding point on the number line. In other words, the real numbers are the integers and "everything in between." A few selected real numbers are shown on the number line below.

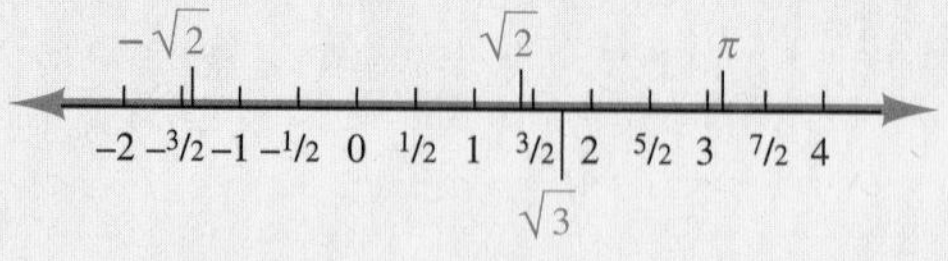

Examples:

- The number 25 is a natural number, which means it is also a whole number, an integer, a rational number, and a real number.
- The number −6 is an integer, which means it is also a rational number and a real number.
- The number $\frac{2}{3}$ is a rational number, which means it is also a real number.
- The number 7.98418 . . . is an irrational number; the dots indicate that the digits continue forever with no particular pattern. It is also a real number.

Now try Exercises 13–28.

circles to represent sets. Venn diagrams are fairly intuitive and best learned through examples.

Consider the sets *whales* and *mammals*. Because every member of the set *whales* is also a member of the set *mammals*, we say that the set *whales* is a **subset** of the set *mammals*. We represent this relationship in a Venn diagram by drawing the circle for whales *inside* the circle for mammals (Figure 1.11). Notice that the diagram illustrates only the relationship between the sets. The sizes of the circles do not matter.

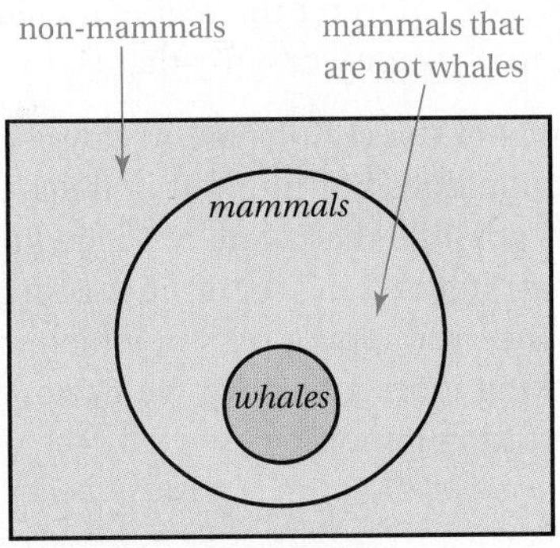

FIGURE 1.11 The set *whales* is a subset of the set *mammals*.

The circles are enclosed by a rectangle, so this diagram has three regions:

- The inside of the *whales* circle represents all whales.
- The region outside the *whales* circle but inside the *mammals* circle represents mammals that are not whales (such as cows, bears, and people).
- The region outside the *mammals* circle represents non-mammals; from the context, we interpret this region to represent animals (or living things) that are not mammals, such as birds, fish, and insects.

Next, consider the sets *dogs* and *cats*. A pet can be either a dog or a cat, but not both. We draw the Venn diagram with separated circles that do not touch, and we say that *dogs* and *cats* are **disjoint sets** (Figure 1.12). Again, we enclose the circles in a rectangle. This time, the context suggests that the region outside both circles represents pets that are neither dogs nor cats, such as birds and hamsters.

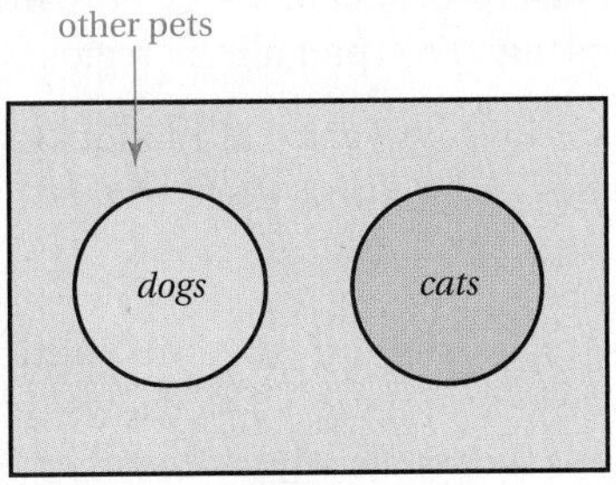

FIGURE 1.12 The set *dogs* is disjoint from the set *cats*.

For our last general case, consider the sets *nurses* and *women*. As shown in Figure 1.13, these are **overlapping sets** because it is possible for a person to be

Historical Note

John Venn was an ordained priest who wrote books on logic, statistics, and probability. He also wrote a history of Cambridge University, where he was both a student and a teacher. Though well respected for many of his contributions to logic, he is best known for the diagrams that bear his name.

Take Note

Some logicians distinguish between Venn diagrams and Euler (pronounced "oiler," after Leonhard Euler) diagrams, depending on the precise way the circles are used. In this book, we use the term *Venn diagrams* for all circle diagrams.

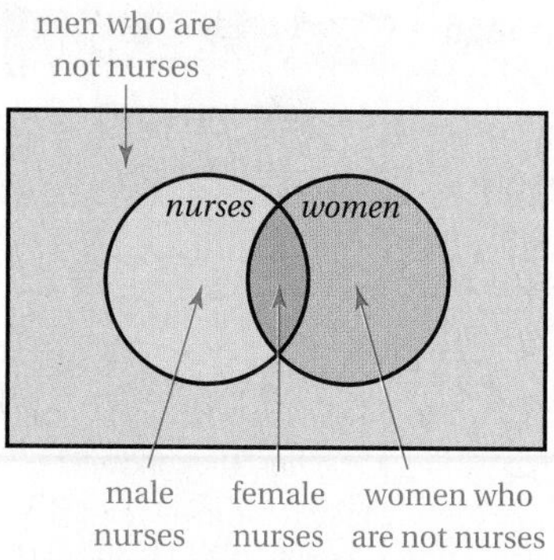

FIGURE 1.13 The sets *nurses* and *women* are overlapping.

both a woman and a nurse. Because of the overlapping region, this diagram has four regions:

- The overlapping region represents people who are both women and nurses—that is, female nurses.
- The non-overlapping region of the *nurses* circle represents nurses who are not women—that is, male nurses.
- The non-overlapping region of the *women* circle represents women who are not nurses.
- From the context, we interpret the region outside both circles to represent people who are neither nurses nor women—that is, men who are not nurses.

Note that the sizes of the regions are not important. For example, the small size of the overlapping region does not imply that female nurses are less common than male nurses. In fact, it is possible that some of the regions might have *no* members. For example, imagine that Figure 1.13 represents a single clinic where all four nurses are male. In that case, the overlapping region, which represents female nurses, would have no members. Speaking more generally, we use overlapping circles whenever two sets *might* have members in common.

Take Note

Mathematically, there is a fourth way that two sets can be related: They can be *equal,* meaning that they have precisely the same members.

SET RELATIONSHIPS AND VENN DIAGRAMS

Two sets *A* and *B* may be related in three basic ways:

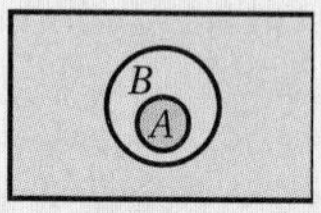

- *A* may be a **subset** of *B* (or vice versa), meaning that all members of *A* are also members of *B*. The Venn diagram for this case shows the circle for *A* inside the circle for *B*.

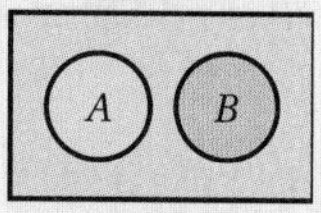

- *A* may be **disjoint** from *B*, meaning that the two sets have no members in common. The Venn diagram for this case consists of separated circles that do not touch.

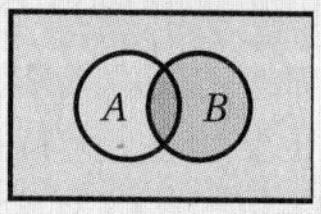

- *A* and *B* may be **overlapping** sets, meaning that the two sets share some of the same members. The Venn diagram for this case consists of two overlapping circles. We also use overlapping circles for cases in which the two sets might share common members.

Example 2 Venn Diagrams

Describe the relationship between the given pairs of sets and draw a Venn diagram showing this relationship. Interpret all the regions of the Venn diagram.

a. *Democrats* and *Republicans* (party affiliations)
b. *Nobel Prize winners* and *Pulitzer Prize winners*

Solution

a. A person can be registered for only one political party, so the sets *Democrats* and *Republicans* are disjoint. Figure 1.14a shows the Venn diagram. The region outside both circles represents people who are neither Democrats nor Republicans—that is, people who are registered for other political parties, who are independent, or who are not registered.
b. It is possible for a person to win both a Nobel Prize and a Pulitzer Prize, so these are overlapping sets. Figure 1.14b shows the Venn diagram. The region outside both circles represents people who have not won either prize, which is most of humanity.

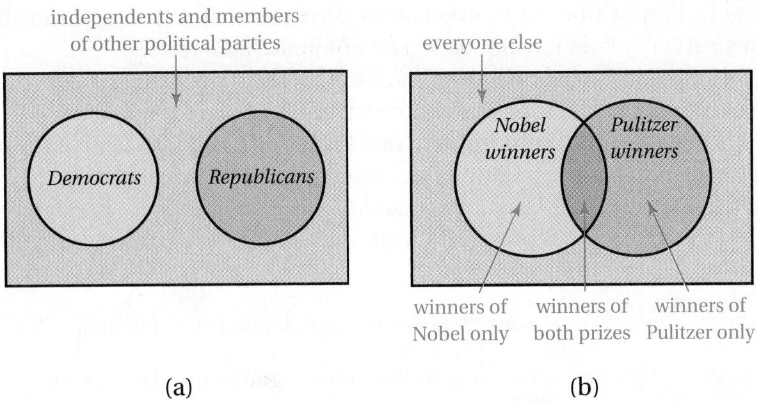

FIGURE 1.14

Now try Exercises 37–42.

BY THE WAY

Among the people who have won both a Nobel Prize (in literature) and a Pulitzer Prize are Toni Morrison, Ernest Hemingway, William Faulkner, John Steinbeck, and Saul Bellow.

Example 3 Sets of Numbers

Draw a Venn diagram showing the relationships among the sets of *natural numbers, whole numbers, integers, rational numbers,* and *real numbers.* Where are irrational numbers found in this diagram? (If you've forgotten the meanings of these number sets, see *A Brief Review* on p. 36.)

Solution Natural numbers are also whole numbers, which means that the natural numbers are a subset of the whole numbers. Similarly, all whole numbers are integers, so the whole numbers are a subset of the integers. The integers, in turn, are a subset of the rational numbers, and the rational numbers are a subset of the real numbers. Figure 1.15 shows these relationships with a set of nested circles. Because irrational numbers are real numbers that are not rational, they are represented by the region outside the *rational numbers* circle but inside the *real numbers* circle.

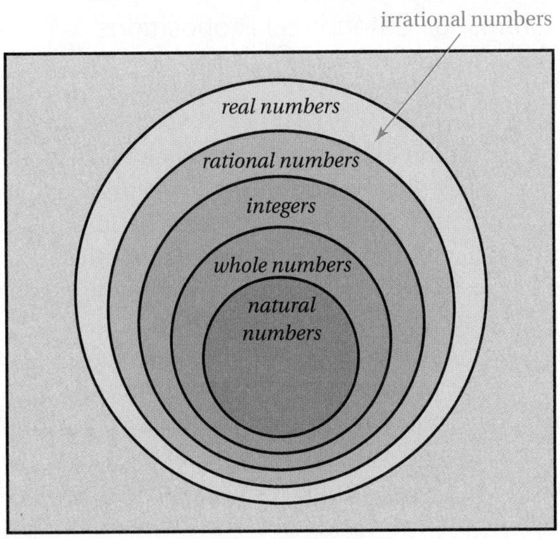

FIGURE 1.15

Now try Exercises 43–44.

BY THE WAY

Are you wondering what goes outside the real numbers circle in Figure 1.15? The answer is numbers that are not real, called *imaginary numbers.* The imaginary number i is defined as $\sqrt{-1}$, which has no real number answer. Despite their name, imaginary numbers are actually quite useful in science and engineering.

Categorical Propositions

Now that we have discussed general relationships between sets, we are ready to study propositions that make claims about sets. For example, the proposition *all whales are mammals* makes a very specific claim—namely, that the set *whales* is a subset of the set *mammals*. Propositions of this type are called **categorical propositions** because they claim a particular relationship between two categories or sets.

Like all propositions, categorical propositions must have the structure of a complete sentence. Categorical propositions also have another important general feature. Of the two sets in a categorical proposition, one set appears in the subject of the sentence and the other appears in the predicate. For example, in the proposition *all whales are mammals*, the set *whales* is the **subject set** and the set *mammals* is the **predicate set**. We usually use the letter *S* to represent the subject set and *P* for the predicate set, so we can rewrite *all whales are mammals* as

all S are P, where S = whales and P = mammals

Categorical propositions come in the following four standard forms.

THE FOUR STANDARD CATEGORICAL PROPOSITIONS

Form	Example	Subject Set (*S*)	Predicate Set (*P*)
All *S* are *P*	All whales are mammals	whales	mammals
No *S* are *P*	No fish are mammals	fish	mammals
Some *S* are *P*	Some doctors are women	doctors	women
Some *S* are not *P*	Some teachers are not men	teachers	men

Because categorical propositions express a relationship between two sets, we can use what we've already learned about Venn diagrams to make visual representations of categorical propositions. However, in the case of overlapping sets, we must be specific in stating which parts of the overlap are addressed by the proposition. The following example should make this idea clear.

Example 4 Venn Diagrams for Categorical Propositions

Draw a Venn diagram to represent each of the four sample propositions in the box above.

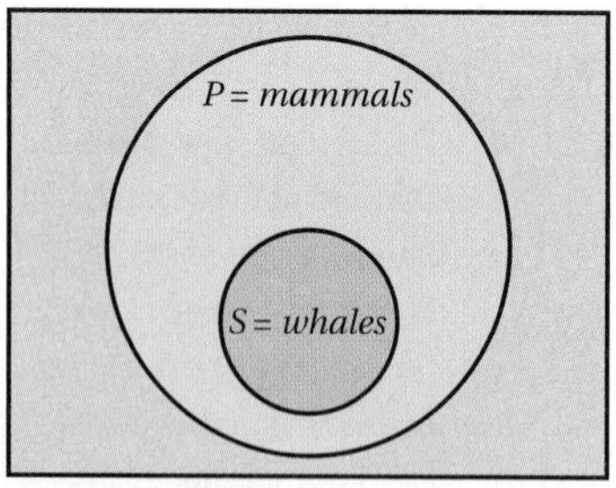

FIGURE 1.16 The Venn diagram for *all S are P*.

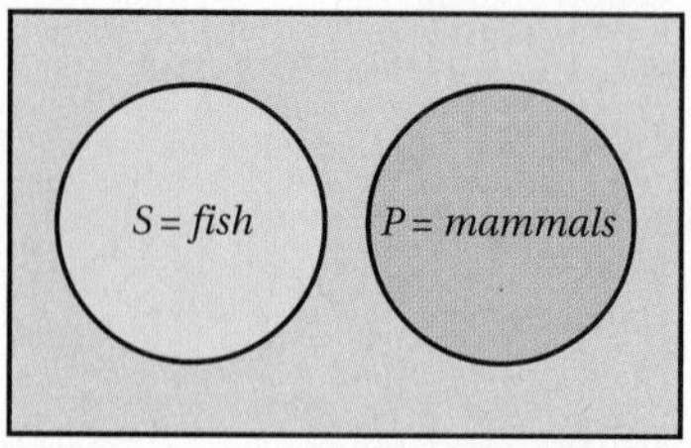

FIGURE 1.17 The Venn diagram for *no S are P*.

Solution The proposition *all whales are mammals* claims that the set *S* = *whales* is a subset of *P* = *mammals*. Figure 1.16 shows the Venn diagram. Note that all propositions of the form *all S are P* would have the same basic Venn diagram.

The proposition *no fish are mammals* tells us that the set *S* = *fish* is disjoint from the set *P* = *mammals*. That is, they have no common members. The Venn diagram therefore shows two separated circles (Figure 1.17).

The Venn diagram for the proposition *some doctors are women* requires overlapping circles for *S* = *doctors* and *P* = *women*. However, we must be specific about the claim made in the proposition. In this case, the proposition asserts that there *are* some people (at least one) who are both doctors and women. We indicate this fact by putting an X in the overlapping region of the diagram (Figure 1.18). Note that the proposition does not tell us whether there are also doctors who are not women, nor does it tell us whether there are women who are not doctors. Without further information, we do not know whether the non-overlapping regions contain any members.

The proposition *some teachers are not men* also requires overlapping circles (Figure 1.19). This proposition asserts that there are some people (at least one) who are in the *S* = *teachers* circle but not in the *P* = *men* circle. Therefore, we put an X in the non-overlapping region of the *teachers* circle. No claim is made about whether there are teachers who are also men or men who are not teachers.

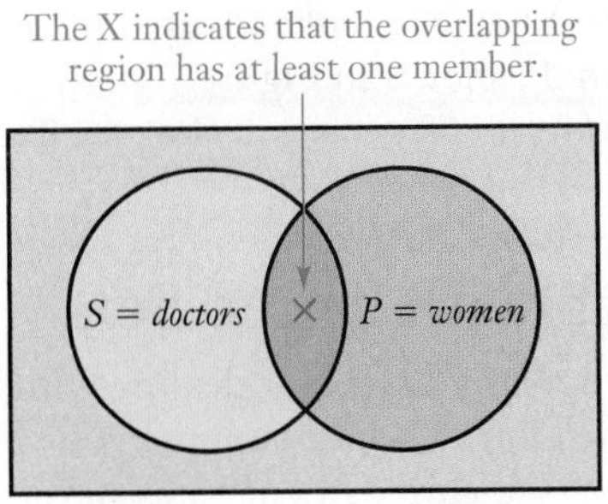

FIGURE 1.18 The Venn diagram for *some S are P.*

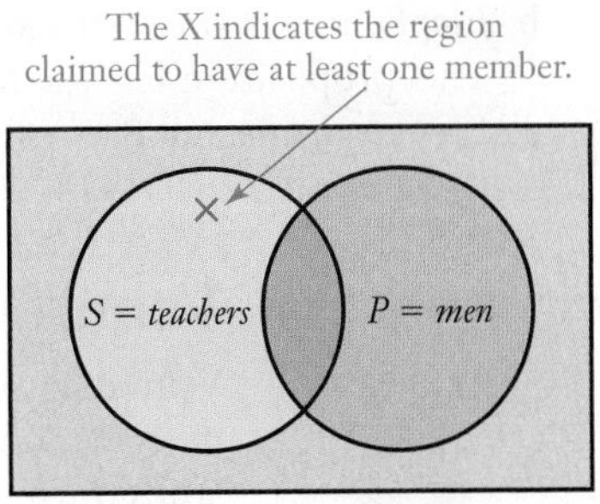

FIGURE 1.19 The Venn diagram for *some S are not P.*

Now try Exercises 45–46.

Time Out to Think

The principal of an elementary school states that at her school some teachers are not men. Can you conclude that some of the teachers *are* men? Why or why not? Can you conclude that *none* of the teachers are men? Why or why not?

Putting Categorical Propositions in Standard Form

Many statements in everyday speech make claims about relationships between two categories, but don't look precisely like one of the four standard forms for categorical propositions. It's often useful to rephrase such statements in one of the standard forms. For example, the statement *all diamonds are valuable* can be rephrased to read *all diamonds are things of value.* Now the statement has the form *all S are P,* where S = *diamonds* and P = *things of value.*

Example 5 Rephrasing in Standard Form

Rephrase each of the following statements in one of the four standard forms for categorical propositions. Then draw the Venn diagram.

a. Some birds can fly.
b. Elephants never forget.

Solution

a. *Some birds can fly* can be rephrased as *some birds are animals that can fly.* It now has the form *some S are P*, where S = *birds* and P = *animals that can fly.* Figure 1.20a shows the Venn diagram, with an X in the overlapping region to indicate the claim that there *are* some birds that can fly.

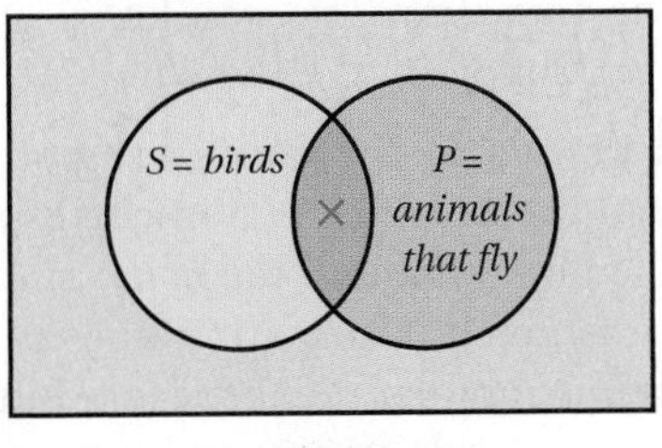

(a)

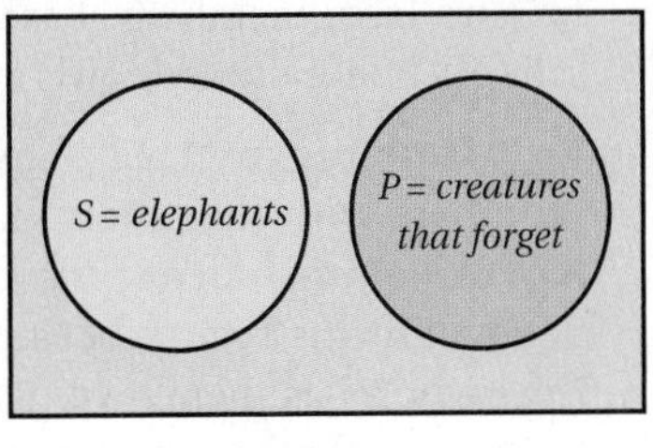

(b)

FIGURE 1.20

b. *Elephants never forget* can be rephrased as *no elephants are creatures that forget.* This proposition has the form *no S are P*, shown in Figure 1.20b (on p. 41), where S = *elephants* and P = *creatures that forget.* **Now try Exercises 47–52.**

Venn Diagrams with Three Sets

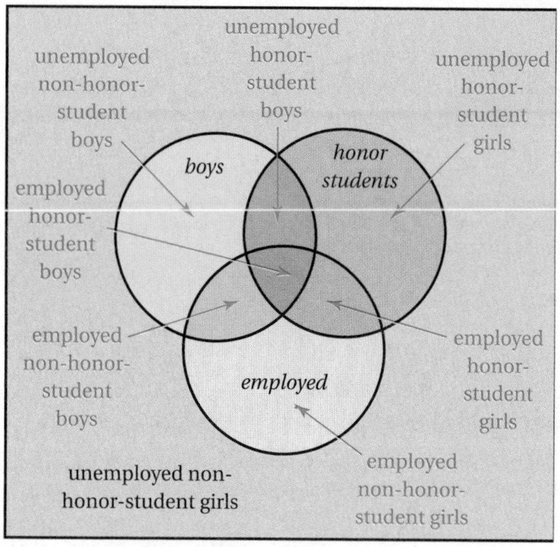

FIGURE 1.21 A Venn diagram for three overlapping sets has $2^3 = 8$ regions.

Venn diagrams are particularly useful for dealing with three sets that may overlap one another. For example, suppose you are conducting a study to learn how teenage employment rates differ between boys and girls and between honor students and others. For each teenager in your study, you need to record the answers to these three questions:

- Is the teenager a boy or a girl?
- Is the teenager an honor student or not?
- Is the teenager employed or not?

Figure 1.21 shows a Venn diagram that can help you organize this information. Notice that it has three circles, representing the sets *boys, honor students,* and *employed.* Because the circles overlap one another, they form a total of eight regions (including the region outside all three circles). Be sure that you understand the labels shown for each region.

Time Out to Think

Could the same information be recorded in a diagram in which the three circles represent the sets *girls* (rather than boys), *honor students,* and *employed?* Could it be recorded in a diagram with the three circles representing the sets *girls, boys,* and *unemployed?* Explain.

Example 6 Makeup of the Study

You hire an assistant to help you with the study of teenage employment described above. He focuses on a small group of teenagers who are all enrolled in the same school. He reports the following facts about this group:

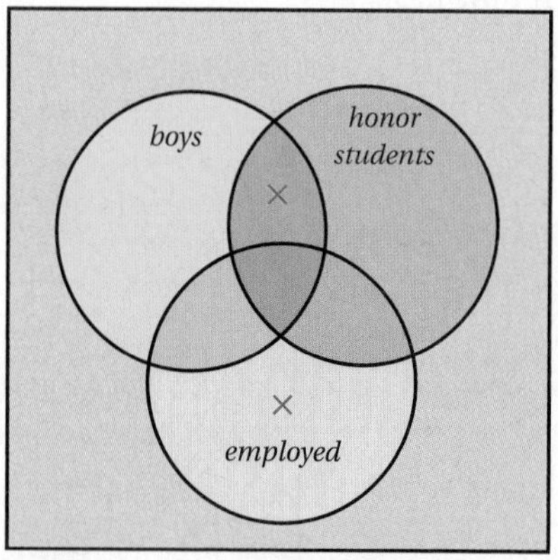

FIGURE 1.22 The X's mark regions known to have members.

- Some of the honor-student boys are unemployed.
- Some of the non-honor-student girls are employed.

Put X's in the appropriate places in Figure 1.21 to indicate the regions that you can be sure have members. Based on this report, do you know whether any of the school's honor-student girls are unemployed? Why or why not?

Solution Figure 1.22 shows the X's in the correct regions of the diagram (compare with the labels in Figure 1.21). The region corresponding to unemployed honor-student girls is the pink region of the *honor students* circle. There is no X in this region because the given information does not tell us whether this region has members. Therefore, among the teenagers in the school, we do not know whether any honor-student girls are unemployed.

Now try Exercises 53–55.

Example 7 Color Monitors

Color television and computer monitors make all the colors you see by combining *pixels* (short for *picture elements*) that display just three colors: red, green, and blue. In pairs, these combinations of colors give the following results (with colors at equal strength):

Combination	Result
Red-green	Yellow
Red-blue	Purple (or magenta)
Blue-green	Light blue (or cyan)

White is made by combining all three colors, and black is made by using none of the colors. Draw a Venn diagram to represent all this color information.

Solution The Venn diagram in Figure 1.23 represents the color combinations with three overlapping circles. The basic colors (red, green, and blue) appear in regions where there is no overlap. The red-green, red-blue, and blue-green combinations appear in regions where two circles overlap. White appears in the central region, where all three colors are present, while black appears outside all three circles, where no colors are present. A real monitor can make a much wider range of colors by varying the relative strengths of the colors. **Now try Exercises 56–58.**

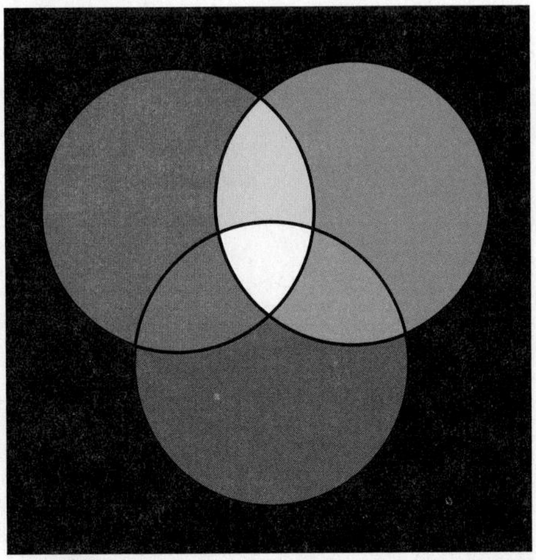

FIGURE 1.23 The color combinations possible from red, green, and blue (in equal strength).

Time Out to Think

If you have a magnifying glass, hold it close to your television to see the individual red, blue, and green dots. How do you think a high-resolution monitor (such as a monitor for HDTV) differs from a lower-resolution one?

More Uses of Venn Diagrams

So far we have used Venn diagrams only to describe relationships, such as whether two sets overlap or whether overlapping sets share common members. Venn diagrams can be even more useful when we add specific information, such as the number of members in each set or overlapping region.

Consider the study summarized in Table 1.1, which is an example of a **two-way table.** This study was designed to learn whether a pregnant mother's status as a smoker or

BY THE WAY

Over 400,000 premature or low birth weight babies are born each year in the United States. These babies are much more likely than others to suffer health problems. They often require weeks or months of intensive high-technology outpatient care.

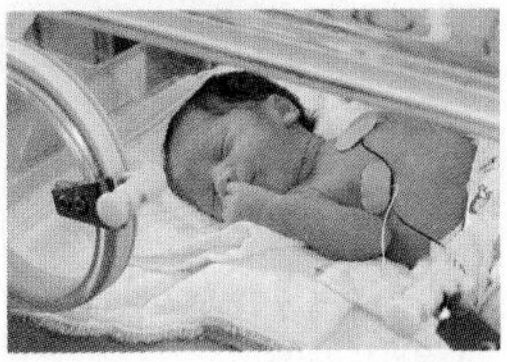

TABLE 1.1 Distribution of 350 Births by Birth Weight Status and Mother's Smoking Status

		Baby's Birth Weight Status	
		Low Birth Weight	**Normal Birth Weight**
Mother's Smoking Status	**Smoker**	18	132
	Nonsmoker	14	186

Source: U.S. National Center for Health Statistics.

nonsmoker affects whether she delivers a low or normal birth weight baby. Notice that the table shows four numbers, which correspond to the four possible combinations of the baby's birth weight status and the mother's smoking status. To be sure that you are reading the table correctly, make sure you see how it shows the following facts:

- 18 babies were born with low birth weight to smoking mothers.
- 132 babies were born with normal birth weight to smoking mothers.
- 14 babies were born with low birth weight to nonsmoking mothers.
- 186 babies were born with normal birth weight to nonsmoking mothers.

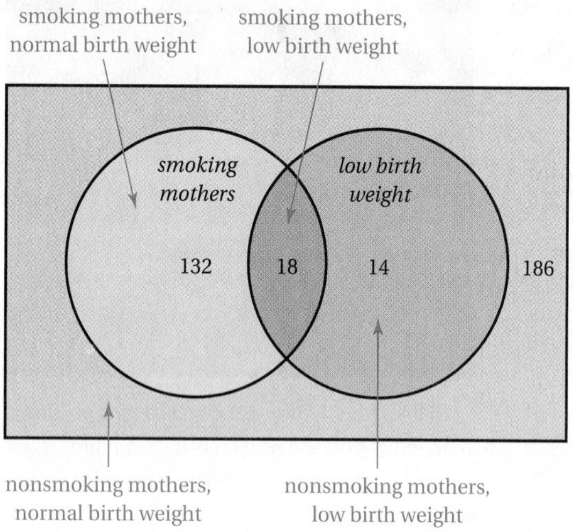

FIGURE 1.24 Venn diagram for the data in Table 1.1.

Although a two-way table is a good way to summarize data, a pictorial representation may be easier to understand. Because there are four combinations of birth weight and smoking status, we can use a Venn diagram with two overlapping circles (creating four regions on the diagram). Figure 1.24 shows one way of making the diagram. The circles represent the sets *smoking mothers* and *low birth weight babies*. The labels show how each region corresponds to one of the combinations in Table 1.1. This Venn diagram differs from those we have studied earlier in that it also shows the number of members in each region, taken from Table 1.1.

The Venn diagram makes it easy to see how smoking affected babies in the study. Notice that normal birth weight babies were much more common than low birth weight babies among both smokers and nonsmokers. However, the smoking mothers had a lower proportion of normal birth weight babies and a higher proportion of low birth weight babies. This suggests that smoking increases the risk of having a low birth weight baby, a fact that has been borne out by careful statistical analysis of this and other studies.

Time Out to Think

Explain why the Venn diagram also could be drawn with circles for the sets *nonsmoking mothers* and *normal birth weight babies*. Draw the diagram for this case, and put the four numbers in the right places.

Example 8 Blood Types

TABLE 1.2 Blood Types in U.S. Population

Blood Type	Percentage of Population
A positive	34%
B positive	8%
AB positive	3%
O positive	35%
A negative	8%
B negative	2%
AB negative	1%
O negative	9%

Human blood is often classified according to whether three antigens, A, B, and Rh, are present or absent. Blood type is stated first in terms of the antigens A and B: Blood containing only A is called type A, blood containing only B is called type B, blood containing both A and B is called type AB, and blood containing neither A nor B is called type O. The presence or absence of Rh is indicated by adding the word *positive* (present) or *negative* (absent) or its symbol. Table 1.2 shows the eight blood types that result and the percentage of people with each type in the U.S. population. Draw a Venn diagram to illustrate these data.

Solution We can think of the three antigens as three sets *A*, *B*, and *Rh* (positive) and draw a Venn diagram with three overlapping circles. Figure 1.25 shows the eight regions, each labeled with its type and percentage of the population. For example, the central region corresponds to the presence of all three antigens (AB positive), so it is labeled with 3%. You should check that all eight regions are labeled according to the data from Table 1.2.

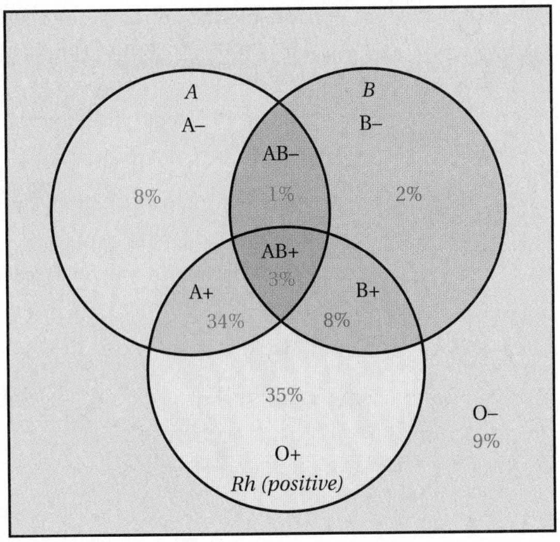

FIGURE 1.25 Venn diagram for blood types.

Historical Note

Human blood groups were discovered in 1901 by Austrian biochemist Karl Landsteiner. In 1909, he classified the groups he had discovered as A, B, AB, and O. He also showed that blood transfusions could be done successfully if the donor and recipient were of the same blood type. For this work, he was awarded the 1930 Nobel Prize in Medicine.

Now try Exercises 59–64.

QUICK QUIZ

Choose the best answer to each of the following questions. Explain your reasoning with one or more complete sentences.

1. Consider the set {Alabama, Alaska, Arizona, . . . , Wyoming}. The ". . . " represents
   a. the fact that we don't know the other members of the set.
   b. the other 46 states of the United States.
   c. Colorado, California, Florida, and Mississippi.
2. Which of the following is *not* a member of the set of integers?
   a. -107 b. 481 c. $3\frac{1}{2}$
3. Based on the Venn diagram below, we conclude that

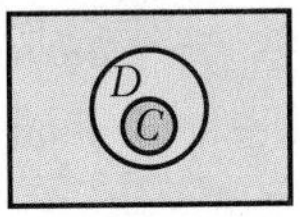

   a. *C* is a subset of *D*.
   b. *D* is a subset of *C*.
   c. *C* is disjoint from *D*.
4. Suppose that *A* represents the set of all boys and *B* represents the set of all girls. The correct Venn diagram for the relationship between these sets is

a. 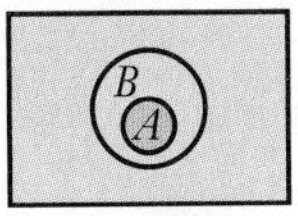

b. 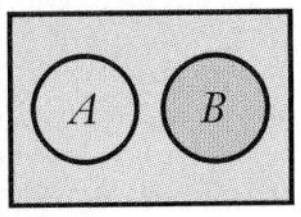

c. 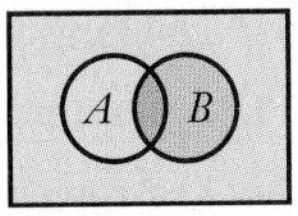

5. Suppose that *A* represents the set of all apples and *B* represents the set of all fruit. The correct Venn diagram for the relationship between these sets is

a. 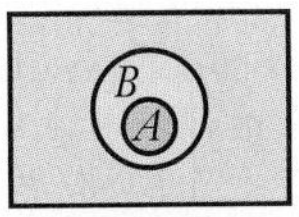

b. 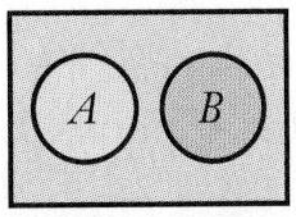

c. 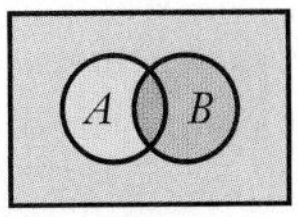

6. Suppose that *A* represents the set of all high school cross country runners and *B* represents the set of all high school swimmers. The correct Venn diagram for the relationship between these sets is

a. 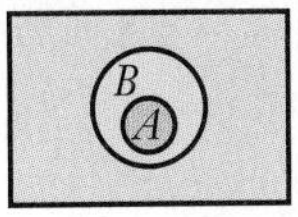

b. 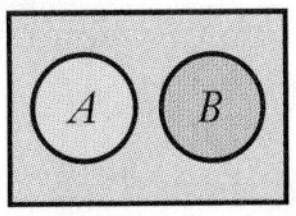

c. 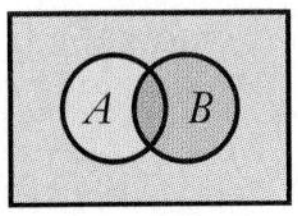

7. In the Venn diagram below, the X tells us that

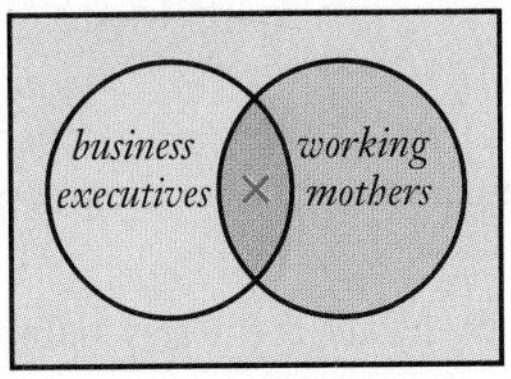

   a. some working mothers are business executives.
   b. no working mothers are business executives.
   c. some working mothers are not business executives.

8. The region with the X in the Venn diagram below represents

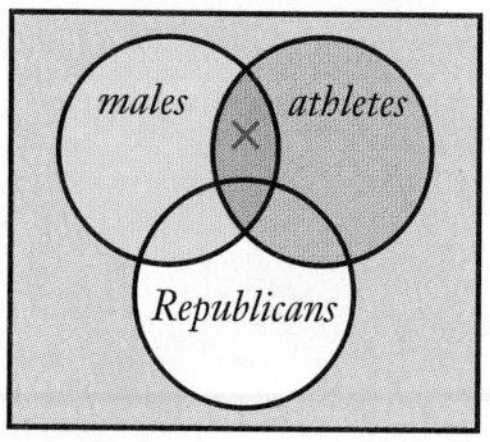

a. male Republican athletes.

b. male Republicans who are not athletes.

c. male athletes who are not Republicans.

9. Consider again the Venn diagram from Exercise 8. The central region of the diagram represents people who are

a. male and Republican and athletes.

b. male or Republican or athletes.

c. neither male nor Republican nor athletes.

10. Look at the data in Table 1.1 (p. 43). The total number of babies born with low birth weight was

a. 14.

b. 18.

c. 32.

Exercises 1C

REVIEW QUESTIONS

1. What is a set? Describe the use of braces for listing the members of a set.
2. What is a Venn diagram? How do we show that one set is a subset of another in a Venn diagram? How do we show disjoint sets? How do we show overlapping sets?
3. List the four standard categorical propositions. Give an example of each type, and draw a Venn diagram for each of your examples.
4. Briefly discuss how you can put a categorical proposition into one of the standard forms if it is not in such a form already.
5. Explain how to draw a Venn diagram for three overlapping sets. Discuss the types of information that can be shown in such diagrams.
6. Explain how to read a table such as Table 1.1 and how to show the information in a Venn diagram.

DOES IT MAKE SENSE?

Decide whether each of the following statements makes sense (or is clearly true) or does not make sense (or is clearly false). Explain your reasoning.

7. The payments we make to the electric company are a subset of the payments we make to the phone company.
8. I don't know what you mean by the sets "jabbers" and "wocks," but I can still draw a Venn diagram for them if you just tell me if and how they share members.
9. I counted an irrational number of students in my class.
10. The number of students in my class is a real number.
11. My professor asked me to draw a Venn diagram for a categorical proposition, but I couldn't do it because the proposition was clearly false.
12. I used a Venn diagram to prove that your opinion is false.

BASIC SKILLS & CONCEPTS

13–28: Classifying Numbers. Choose the first set in the list *natural numbers, whole numbers, integers, rational numbers, and real numbers* that describes the following numbers.

13. 23
14. −45
15. 2/3
16. −5/2
17. 1.2345
18. 0
19. π
20. $\sqrt{8}$
21. −34.25
22. $\sqrt{98}$
23. $\pi/4$
24. 123/456
25. −13/3
26. −145.01
27. $\pi/129$
28. 13,579,023

29–36: Set Notation. Use set notation (braces) to write the members of the following sets, or state that the set has no members. You may use "..." to indicate patterns.

29. The days of the week
30. The even numbers between, but not including, 8 and 64
31. The states that share a border with Texas
32. Every third number between 4 and 20 beginning with 4
33. The perfect squares (such as 1^2, 2^2, 3^2) between 30 and 130
34. The kings of America
35. Odd numbers between 2 and 30 that are multiples of 3
36. The vowels of the English alphabet

37–44: **Venn Diagrams for Two Sets.** Draw Venn diagrams with two circles showing the relationship between the following pairs of sets. Provide an explanation of the diagram you drew.

37. veterinarians and women
38. nurses and skydivers
39. words and verbs
40. reptiles and bacteria
41. musicians and painters
42. atheists and Catholic bishops
43. negative integers and natural numbers
44. limericks and poems

45–52: **Categorical Propositions.** For the given categorical propositions, do the following.

a. If necessary, rephrase the statement in standard form.

b. State the subject and predicate sets.

c. Draw a Venn diagram for the proposition and label all regions of the diagram.

45. All widows are women.
46. No worms are birds.
47. All U.S. presidents have been over 30 years old.
48. Every child can sing.
49. Monkeys don't gamble.
50. Plumbers don't cheat.
51. Winners smile.
52. Some movie stars are redheads.

53–58: **Venn Diagrams for Three Sets.** Draw Venn diagrams with three overlapping circles (eight regions) for the following groups of three sets. Describe the members of each region or state that a region has no members.

53. women, dentists, and kindergarten teachers
54. hockey players, figure skaters, and women
55. published works, novels, and songs
56. oceans, bodies of salt water, and bodies of fresh water
57. words that begin with S, verbs, and words with fewer than 4 letters
58. teachers, swimmers, and tall people

59–60: **Venn Diagram with Numbers.** Use the Venn diagram to answer the following questions.

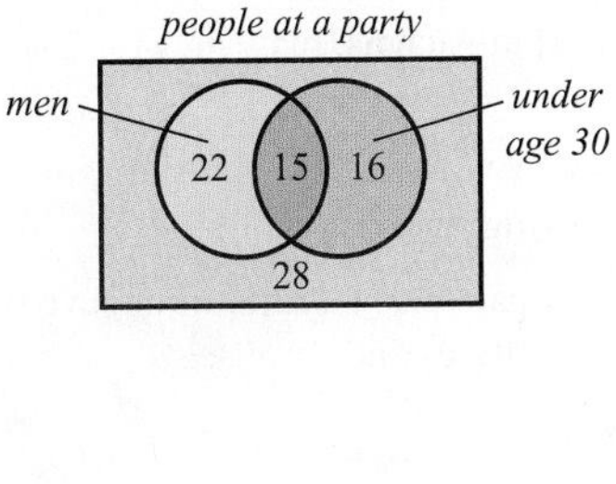

59. a. How many women at the party are under 30?

    b. How many men at the party are not under 30?

    c. How many women are at the party?

    d. How many people are at the party?

60. a. How many men at the party are under 30?

    b. How many women at the party are over 30?

    c. How many men are at the party?

    d. How many people at the party are not under 30?

61–62: **Venn Diagram with Numbers.** Use the Venn diagram to answer the following questions.

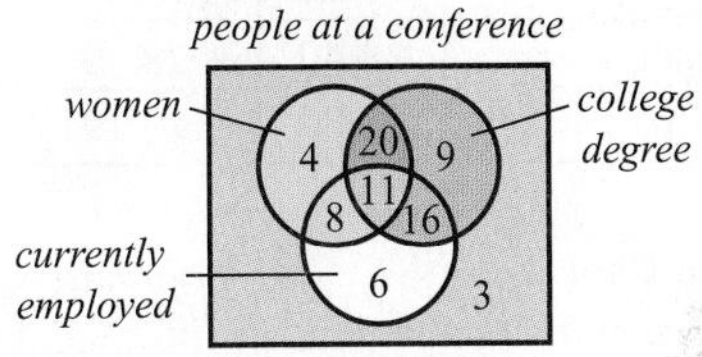

61. a. How many people at the conference are unemployed women with a college degree?

    b. How many people at the conference are employed men?

    c. How many people at the conference are employed women without a college degree?

    d. How many men are at the conference?

62. a. How many people at the conference are employed men without a college degree?

    b. How many people at the conference are unemployed women?

    c. How many people at the conference are unemployed men without a college degree?

    d. How many people are at the conference?

63–64: **Venn Diagrams from Data.** Draw Venn diagrams that represent the following situations. Mark each region of the diagram with the correct number.

63. One hundred people who grew up in either New York or Los Angeles were surveyed to determine whether they preferred hip-hop music or rock music (*both* and *neither* were not acceptable responses). Of those who grew up in Los Angeles, 20 preferred hip-hop and 40 preferred rock. Of those who grew up in New York, 30 preferred hip-hop.
64. In a trial of a new allergy medicine, 120 people were given the medicine and 80 were given a placebo. Of those given the medicine, 90 showed improvement in their allergies. Of those given the placebo, 20 did not show improvement.

FURTHER APPLICATIONS

65–66: **Venn Diagram Analysis.** Draw two-circle Venn diagrams for the following situations and answer the questions.

65. Of the 45 theater performances that a critic reviewed, 23 were comedies. She gave favorable reviews to 8 of the comedies and unfavorable reviews to 12 of the non-comedies.

How many comedies received unfavorable reviews? How many non-comedies received favorable reviews?

66. All cyclists who competed in a race were given a drug test. Of the 18 who tested positive, 3 finished in the top 10. Twenty-five cyclists tested negative. How many cyclists who tested negative did not finish in the top 10? How many cyclists were tested?

67. **Election Results.** The following table gives popular vote counts (in millions) for the two leading candidates in the 2008 U.S. presidential election. Draw a two-circle Venn diagram that represents the results.

	Obama	McCain
Women voters	38.40	28.49
Men voters	29.80	29.19

68. **Tomatoes and Cancer.** A study by the Harvard Medical School (*Journal of the National Cancer Institute*, February 17, 1999) reviewed 72 previous studies of the effect of tomatoes on cancer. The data showed convincingly that "high consumers of tomatoes and tomato products are at substantially decreased risk of numerous cancers, although probably not all cancers." Consider the following table that shows the incidence of oral cancer for a group of people who ate an average of one tomato a day and another group of people who ate fewer than three tomatoes per week. Draw a Venn diagram for the data.

	No oral cancer	Oral cancer
One tomato per day	191	9
Fewer than three tomatoes per week	164	16

69. **Coffee and Gallstones.** A study on the effect of coffee on gallstones (*Journal of the American Medical Association*, June 9, 1999) resulted (in small part) in the data shown below. The category *Coffee* means more than four cups of caffeinated coffee per day. The category *No coffee* means no caffeinated coffee. Draw a Venn diagram for the data.

	Gallstone disease	No disease
No coffee	385	14,068
Coffee	91	4,806

70. **Readership Survey.** A (hypothetical) survey revealed the following results about the news sources that a sample of 130 people use:

TV/radio only	20	TV/radio and Internet only	12
Internet only	29	TV/radio and newspapers only	18
Newspapers only	15	Internet and newspapers only	22
None	6	All three sources	8

a. Draw a three-circle Venn diagram that summarizes the results of the survey.

b. How many people use (at least) TV/radio and newspapers?

c. How many people use TV/radio or Internet?

d. How many people use TV/radio or Internet, but not newspapers?

e. How many people use Internet, but not TV/radio?

f. How many people use TV/radio, but not newspapers?

71. **Hospital Drug Use.** Patients in a (hypothetical) hospital on a single day were taking antibiotics (A), blood pressure medication (BP), and pain medication (P) in the following numbers:

A only	12	A and BP only	15
BP only	8	A and P only	24
P only	22	BP and P only	16
None	2	All three	20

a. Draw a three-circle Venn diagram that summarizes the results in the table.

b. How many patients took antibiotics or blood pressure medication?

c. How many patients took blood pressure medication, but not pain medication?

d. How many patients took (at least) pain medication?

e. How many patients took antibiotics and blood pressure medicine, but not pain medication?

f. How many patients took antibiotics or blood pressure medicine or pain medication?

72. **Is It Possible?** In a taste test, shoppers are asked to sample three brands of vanilla ice cream. Each shopper is allowed to choose *all* of the brands that she or he finds acceptable (a shopper could list 0, 1, 2, or 3 brands). Is it possible to use a two-circle Venn diagram to display how many shoppers find each combination of brands acceptable? Is it possible to use a three-circle Venn diagram? Explain.

73–76: More Than Three Sets. Draw a Venn diagram that illustrates the relationships among the following sets. The diagram should have one circle for each set. In this case, a circle may lie entirely inside of other circles, it may overlap other circles, or it may be completely separate from other circles.

73. animals, house pets, dogs, cats, canaries

74. athletes, women, professional soccer players, amateur golfers, sedentary doctors

75. things that fly, birds, jets, hang gliders, eagles

76. painters, artists, musicians, pianists, violinists, abstract painters

77–78: Completing Two-Way Tables. Fill in the remaining entries in the following two-way tables.

77. A survey of 120 patrons at a restaurant gave the following preferences for entrees and drinks.

	Vegetarian	Meat/fish	Total
Wine	20		60
No wine		15	
Total			120

78. A car insurance company issued a monthly report showing the following numbers of claims filed by clients.

	Women	Men	Total
No claims			50
At least one claim		40	
Total	50	60	

79. **TV Demographics.** According to Nielsen Media Research, of the 113.1 million U.S. households with at least one television set in 2008, 53% have three or more television sets, 73% have a VCR player, and 88% receive basic cable service. Assume that a television set is needed in order to have a VCR or receive cable service. Answer the following questions or state that not enough information is given.

a. What is the percentage of households (in the survey) with fewer than three television sets?

b. What is the percentage of households with VCRs and basic cable?

c. What is the percentage of households without a VCR?

d. What is the percentage of households with three or more television sets and basic cable?

e. How many households have three or more television sets?

80. **Health Clinic Data.** The records for a student health clinic show that during one month

- Of the 120 men who visited with flu or anemia, 60 had flu only and 10 had flu and anemia.
- Of the 150 women who visited with flu or anemia, 80 had flu only and 50 had anemia only.

a. Fill in the following table.

	Women	Men
Flu		
Anemia		
Both		
Total		

b. Draw a three-circle Venn diagram that represents the data. Which two regions of the diagram have no members?

81. **Obama Vote Breakdown.** The popular vote received by Barak Obama in the 2008 presidential election can be divided according to gender and party as follows (vote counts in millions are approximate).

	Women	Men
Democrats	23.80	21.11
Republicans	2.19	1.95
Independents and others	10.34	9.17

a. Show how a three-circle Venn diagram can be used to display the data in the table. Which regions of the diagram are not used? Label the regions and insert the numbers in the correct regions.

b. Show how all regions of the diagram below can be used to display the data in the table. Label the regions and insert the numbers in the correct regions.

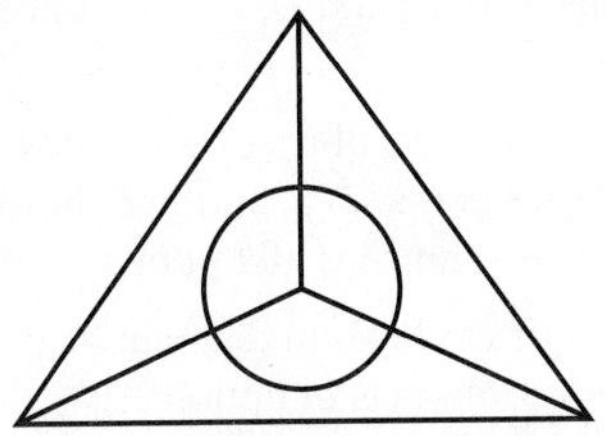

82–84: **Organizing Propositions.** Draw a Venn diagram that represents the information in the following statements. Use the diagram (and no other information) to answer the questions that follow. Explain your reasoning.

82. All hairy animals are mammals. No mammals are fish. Some mammals can swim. No fish can walk on land.

Questions: Could there be hairy fish? Could there be hairy animals that swim? Could there be walking mammals? Could there be hairy animals that walk on land?

83. All meat has protein. All dairy products have protein. Some beans have protein. All beans, but no meat or dairy products, are plants.

Questions: Could there be beans that are dairy products? Could there be meat that is a dairy product? Could there be dairy products that are plants? Could there be plants with protein?

84. No Republicans are Democrats. No Republicans are Green Party members. All Republicans are conservative. Some liberals are Democrats. No liberals are conservatives.

Questions: Could there be conservative Democrats? Could there be liberal Green Party members? Could there be liberal Republicans?

85. **Organizing Politicos.** You are at a conference attended by men and women of various political parties. The conference organizer tells you that none of the women are Republicans and some (but not all) of the Democrats are women.

a. Draw a Venn diagram to organize the given information.

b. Based on the given information, is it possible to meet a woman who is neither a Republican nor a Democrat?

c. Based on the given information, is it possible that there are any male Republicans?

86. **Organizing Literature.** In reviewing for an exam in your literature survey course, you notice the following facts about the writers that you studied:

- Some of the novelists are also poets.
- None of the novelists are playwrights.
- All of the novelists were born in the 20th century.
- All of the writers born in the 19th century are playwrights.

a. Organize these facts in a Venn diagram.

b. Could you have studied a novelist born in the 19th century?

c. Could you have studied a poet born in the 19th century?

d. Could you have studied a writer born in the 20th century who was both a playwright and a poet?

87. **N-set Diagrams.** A computer store offers a basic computer with four options A, B, C, and D, any or none of which buyers can select.

a. How many different sets of options can buyers choose? For example, one choice is A and C, another choice is no options, and another choice is all options.

b. Consider the four-circle Venn diagram below. Label the regions with the various sets of options.

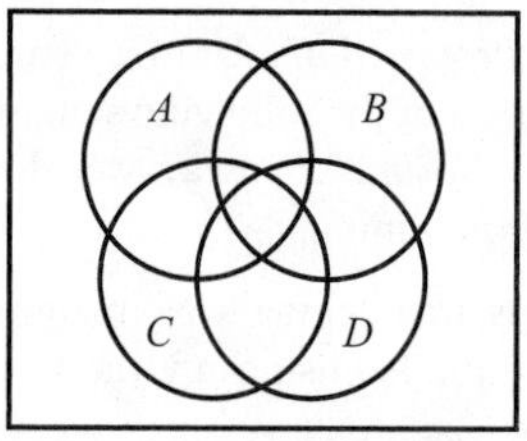

c. Does the diagram in part b represent all the sets of options? If not, which sets of options are missing?

d. Suppose the computer store offered five options A, B, C, D, and E. How many different sets of options would be available?

e. Generalizing from parts a–d, how many different sets of options are available if the store offers N options, where $N = 2, 3, 4, \ldots$?

WEB PROJECTS

88. **State Politics.** Determine from the Web how many states have a Republican majority in the State House and how many states have a Republican majority in the State Senate. Draw a Venn diagram to illustrate the situation.

89. **U.S. Presidents.** Use the Web to learn the following facts about each past American president:

- Bachelor or married (classify as married if married for part of the term)
- Inaugurated before or after age 50
- Served one term (or less) or more than one term

Make a three-circle Venn diagram to represent your results.

90. **Web Venn Diagrams.** You can find many Venn diagrams on the Web (an image search may help). Choose one with interesting categories, and describe what it shows.

IN YOUR WORLD

91. **Categorical Propositions.** Find at least three examples of categorical propositions in news articles or advertisements. State the sets involved in each proposition and draw a Venn diagram for each proposition.

92. **Venn Diagrams in Your Life.** Describe a situation in your own life that could be described or organized using a Venn diagram.

93. **Quantitative Diagram.** Find a news article or research report with a table similar to Table 1.1 or Table 1.2. Draw a Venn diagram to represent the data in the table.

UNIT 1D Analyzing Arguments

With the skills acquired in the previous units, we are now ready to analyze arguments. Recall that an argument begins with a set of premises that are intended to support one or more conclusions (see Unit 1A). If an argument is well constructed, its conclusions follow from its premises in a compelling way. But how do we determine whether an argument is well constructed and compelling? We'll examine this question in this unit.

Two Types of Argument: Inductive and Deductive

Arguments come in two basic types, known as *inductive* and *deductive*. The following two arguments illustrate the two types. As you read each one carefully, ask yourself whether its premises lead to its conclusion in a compelling way.

Argument 1 (Inductive)

Premise:	Birds fly into the air but eventually come back down.
Premise:	People who jump into the air fall back down.
Premise:	Rocks thrown into the air come back down.
Premise:	Balls thrown into the air come back down.
Conclusion:	What goes up must come down.

Argument 2 (Deductive)

Premise: All politicians are married.
Premise: Senator Harris is a politician.
Conclusion: Senator Harris is married.

Note that Argument 1 begins with a set of fairly specific premises, each of which makes a claim about a specific type of object. The conclusion of Argument 1 is a more general statement about how *any* object might behave. This type of argument, in which the conclusion is formed by *generalizing* from more specific premises, is called an **inductive argument.** (The term *inductive* has the root *induce,* which means "to lead by persuasion.")

In contrast, Argument 2 begins with a general statement about politicians and then draws a specific conclusion about a particular politician. Argument 2 is called a **deductive argument** because it allows us to *deduce* a specific conclusion from more general premises.

I think, therefore I am.

—René Descartes (1596–1650), French philosopher and mathematician

DEFINITIONS

An **inductive argument** makes a case for a general conclusion from more specific premises.

A **deductive argument** makes a case for a specific conclusion from more general premises.

Evaluating Inductive Arguments

Let's examine Argument 1 in greater detail. Its premises are clearly true, and each premise lends support to the conclusion. The variety of specific examples cited by its premises makes the argument appear quite compelling—and, indeed, people long believed the conclusion *what goes up must come down* to be true. Nevertheless, we now know that the conclusion is false because a rocket launched with sufficient speed can leave Earth permanently. We thereby see a key fact about inductive arguments: No matter how strong an inductive argument may seem, it does not *prove* that its conclusion is true.

Speaking more formally, we evaluate an inductive argument in terms of its **strength.** A strong argument makes the case for its conclusion seem quite convincing, even though it does not prove the conclusion true. A weak argument is one in which the premises do not seem to lend much support to the conclusion. Note that evaluating strength involves personal judgment. An argument that one person finds strong might appear weak to someone else.

Note also that the strength of an inductive argument is not necessarily related to the truth of its conclusion. Argument 1 was strong enough to convince people throughout most of history, but its conclusion turned out to be false. Conversely, a weak argument may have a true conclusion. For example, the simple argument *the sky is blue because I said so* is extremely weak, even though its conclusion is true.

BY THE WAY

The first artificial satellite to leave Earth was *Sputnik 1,* launched by the Soviet Union on October 4, 1957. *Sputnik 1* orbited Earth for several months before atmospheric drag caused it to fall back to Earth. By early 1959, both the United States and the Soviet Union had launched satellites that would never return to Earth.

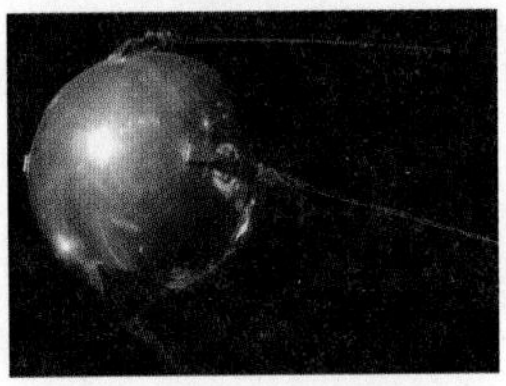

EVALUATING AN INDUCTIVE ARGUMENT

An inductive argument cannot prove its conclusion true, so it can be evaluated only in terms of its **strength.** An argument is strong if it makes a compelling case for its conclusion. It is weak if its conclusion is not well supported by its premises.

Example 1 Hit Movie

A movie director tells her producer (who pays for the movie) not to worry—her film will be a hit. As evidence, she cites the following facts: She's hired big stars for the lead roles, she has a great advertising campaign planned, and it's a sequel to her last hit movie. Explain why this argument is inductive, and evaluate its strength.

Solution Each of the three pieces of evidence is a specific characteristic of her movie. She uses them to support the more general conclusion that her movie will be a hit. Because the conclusion is more general than the premises, the argument is inductive. In this case, her argument is relatively weak. As all producers know, even the best-planned movies can flop. **Now try Exercises 15–22.**

Time Out to Think

Suppose you are the director, and the producer says she needs more evidence that your movie will be a hit. How might you gather additional evidence to strengthen the case for your movie?

Example 2 Earthquake

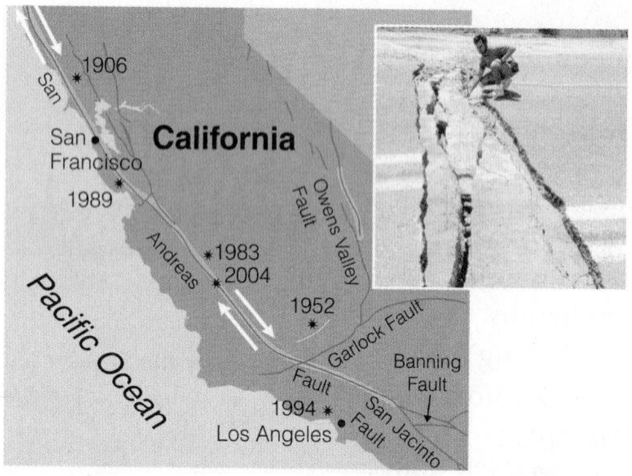

Source: Data from U.S. Geological Survey.

Evaluate the following argument and discuss the truth of its conclusion.

Geological evidence shows that, for thousands of years past, the San Andreas Fault has suffered a major earthquake at least once every hundred years. Therefore, we should expect another earthquake on the fault during the next one hundred years.

Solution This argument is inductive because it cites many specific past events as evidence that another earthquake will occur. The fact that the pattern has held for thousands of years suggests a strong likelihood that it will continue to hold. The argument does not prove that another earthquake will occur, but it makes another earthquake seem quite likely. The argument is strong. **Now try Exercises 23–28.**

Evaluating Deductive Arguments

Now let's turn to Argument 2 (p. 51). You may have the sense that it is a "solid" argument and that the conclusion follows in a convincing way from the premises. That is, if you accept its two premises—*all politicians are married* and *Senator Harris is a politician*—then it follows necessarily that Senator Harris is married.

Of course, you are not required to accept the premises, in which case you might not accept the conclusion either. For example, the first premise is clearly false: It is not true that all politicians are married. As a result, we cannot be sure that the conclusion (*Senator Harris is married*) is true. More generally, evaluating a deductive argument requires answering *two* key questions:

- Does the conclusion follow *necessarily* from the premises?
- Are the premises true?

We can be sure that the conclusion is true only if the answer to both questions is yes.

Let's put this discussion in more formal terms. The first question above deals with the **validity** of the argument. A deductive argument is **valid** if its conclusion follows necessarily from its premises. Note that validity is concerned only with the logical structure of the argument. Validity involves no personal judgment and has nothing to do with the truth of the premises or conclusions.

If a deductive argument is valid *and* its premises are true, then we say that the argument is **sound**. Soundness represents the highest test of reliability of a deductive argument because, at least in principle, a sound argument proves its conclusion true beyond all doubt. However, soundness often involves personal judgment, because people may disagree about the truth of an argument's premises.

> **EVALUATING A DEDUCTIVE ARGUMENT**
>
> We apply two criteria when evaluating a deductive argument. The argument is **valid** if its conclusion follows necessarily from its premises, regardless of the truth of the premises or conclusions. The argument is **sound** if it is valid *and* its premises are all true.

Argument 2 is valid because the conclusion that Senator Harris is married follows necessarily from its premises. But it is not sound, because the first premise (*all politicians are married*) is false.

Time Out to Think

Consider several decisions you made recently. For each case, decide whether the reasoning you used to reach the decision was inductive or deductive, and explain your reasoning process.

KEY DISTINCTIONS: INDUCTIVE AND DEDUCTIVE ARGUMENTS

Inductive Arguments	Deductive Arguments
A conclusion is formed by *generalizing* from a set of more specific premises.	A *specific* conclusion is deduced from a set of more general (or equally general) premises.
An inductive argument can be analyzed only in terms of its *strength*. Evaluating strength involves personal judgment about how well the premises support the conclusion.	A deductive argument can be analyzed in terms of its *validity* and *soundness*. It is valid if its conclusion follows necessarily from its premises. It is sound if it is valid *and* its premises are true.
An inductive argument cannot prove its conclusion true. At best, a strong inductive argument shows that its conclusion *probably* is true.	Validity concerns only logical structure; a deductive argument can be valid even when its conclusion is blatantly false.

Tests of Validity

We used intuition to determine the validity of the argument about Senator Harris. But deductive arguments can be subtle, and it's not always wise to rely on intuition alone. Instead, we can test validity by examining the structure of a deductive argument in a systematic way. We can use Venn diagrams (see Unit 1C) to help us conduct such a test.

Let's begin with a Venn diagram test of Argument 2 on page 51. The first premise, *all politicians are married*, tells us that all members of the set *politicians* are also

The premise *All politicians are married* tells us to draw the *politicians* circle as a subset of the *married people* circle.

We represent the premise *Senator Harris is a politician* by placing an X inside the *politicians* circle to indicate that he is a member of that set.

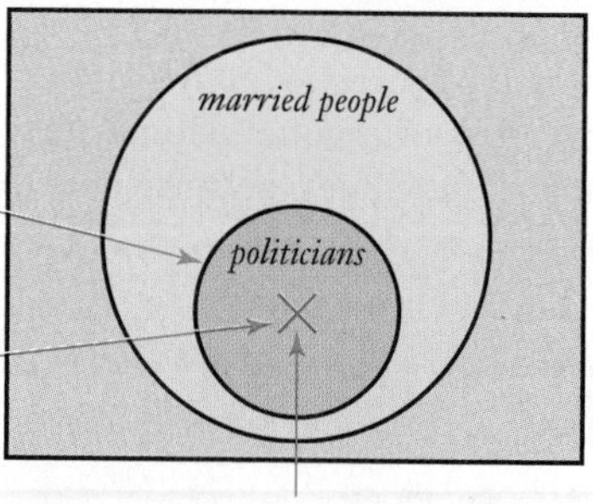

The X is also inside the *married people* circle, which supports the conclusion *Senator Harris is married.*

FIGURE 1.26 This Venn diagram shows the two premises of Argument 2. Because the diagram also contains the information in the conclusion, the argument is valid.

members of the set *married people;* that is, it claims that *politicians* is a subset of *married people.* We represent this proposition by drawing the circle for *politicians* inside the circle for *married people* (Figure 1.26). The second premise tells us that Senator Harris is a member of the set *politicians.* We indicate this fact by putting an X, representing the Senator, inside the *politicians* circle. We test validity by checking to see whether the conclusion is contained within the Venn diagram for the premises. In this case, the X is also inside the *married people* circle, meaning that Senator Harris is a married person—just as the conclusion claims. Thus, the Venn diagram shows that the premises lead necessarily to the conclusion, demonstrating that the argument is valid.

A VENN DIAGRAM TEST OF VALIDITY

To test the validity of a deductive argument with a Venn diagram:

1. Draw a Venn diagram that represents all the information contained in the premises.
2. Check to see whether the Venn diagram also contains the conclusion. If it does, then the argument is valid. Otherwise, the argument is not valid.

Example 3 Invalid Argument

Evaluate the validity and soundness of the following argument.

Premise: All fish live in the water.
Premise: Whales are not fish.
Conclusion: Whales do not live in the water.

The premise *All fish live in the water* tells us to draw the *fish* circle as a subset of the *things that live in water* circle.

The premise *Whales are not fish* tells us to put an X (for *whales*) outside the *fish* circle. But it does not tell us whether the X should be inside or outside the *things that live in water* circle, so we place it on the border of this circle.

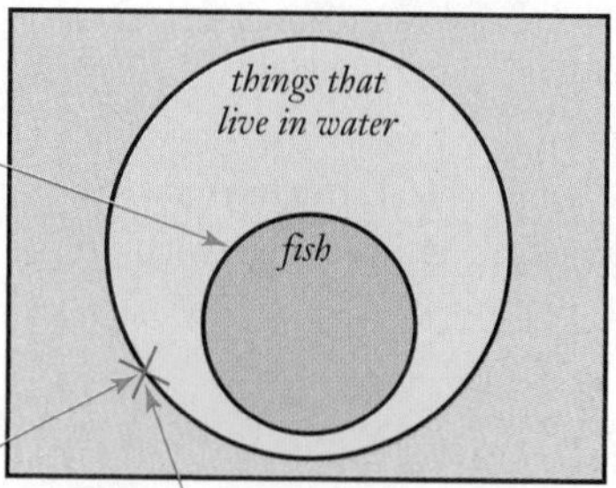

The conclusion *Whales do not live in the water* would require an X *outside* the *things that live in water* circle. But the X from the premises is on the border of this circle, which means the premises do not automatically support the conclusion.

FIGURE 1.27 This Venn diagram shows the two premises of Example 3. The information in the premises does not automatically support the conclusion, so the argument is invalid.

Solution Both premises are true, but the conclusion is false. The argument must therefore have a flaw in its logical structure, making it invalid. We can see the flaw by drawing a Venn diagram. The first premise tells us that the set *fish* is a subset of the set *things that live in water,* so we draw the *fish* circle inside the circle for *things that live in water.* The second premise tells us that whales are not fish. We can indicate this fact by putting an X, representing whales, outside the *fish* circle. However, because the second premise does not tell us whether whales live in the water, we do not know whether the X should be inside or outside the *things that live in water* circle. Therefore, to be as general as possible, we place the X on the border of this circle, indicating that it may actually be either inside or outside (Figure 1.27).

We have now captured all the information in the two premises, so we check whether the diagram contains the information in the conclusion. The conclusion states that whales do not live in the water, which means the X representing whales should be outside the circle for *things that live in water.* But it isn't; it is on the border, which means we don't have enough information to know whether it is inside or outside the circle. Therefore, the conclusion does not follow necessarily from the premises, and the argument is invalid. **Now try Exercises 29–32.**

Example 4 Invalid but True Conclusion

Evaluate the validity and soundness of the following argument.

Premise: All 20th-century U.S. presidents were men.

Premise: John Kennedy was a man.

Conclusion: John Kennedy was a 20th-century U.S. president.

Solution We start by drawing a Venn diagram for the first premise, which requires placing the circle for *20th-century presidents* inside the circle for *men*. The second premise tells us to put an X, representing John Kennedy, inside the *men* circle. However, it does *not* tell us whether the X also belongs inside the *20th-century presidents* circle, so we place it on the border of this circle (Figure 1.28). The conclusion states that the X should be inside the *20th-century presidents* circle, but its border location means we lack the information needed to reach this conclusion. The argument is invalid and therefore cannot be sound.

Note that this argument is invalid even though its premises and conclusion are all true. If you are not convinced, try substituting another man, such as Albert Einstein, for John Kennedy. The argument then reads

Premise: All 20th-century U.S. presidents were men.

Premise: Albert Einstein was a man.

Conclusion: Albert Einstein was a 20th-century U.S. president.

The premises are still true, but the conclusion is now false, showing that the argument's structure is invalid. **Now try Exercises 33–36.**

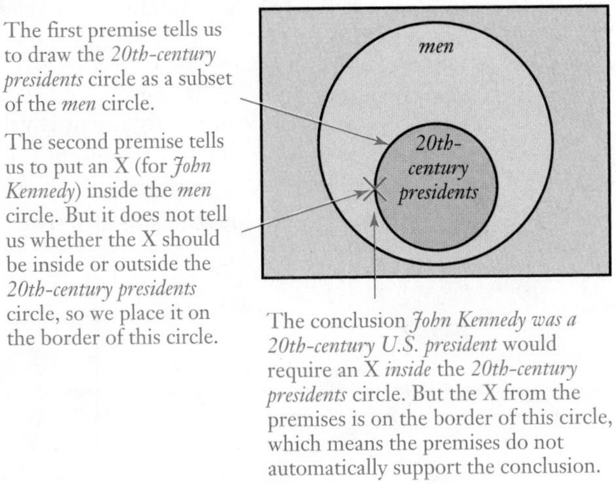

FIGURE 1.28 This Venn diagram shows the two premises of Example 4. The information in the premises does not automatically support the conclusion, so the argument is invalid.

Conditional Deductive Arguments

Consider the following argument:

Premise: If a person lives in Chicago, then the person likes windy days.

Premise: Carlos lives in Chicago.

Conclusion: Carlos likes windy days.

This type of deductive argument, in which the first premise is a conditional statement *if p, then q*, is among the most common and important types of argument. In this case, p = *a person lives in Chicago* and q = *the person likes windy days*. The second premise asserts that, for the person named Carlos, p is true. The conclusion asserts that q is also true for Carlos. You can probably see that this argument is valid. If it is really true that people who live in Chicago like windy days and that Carlos lives in Chicago, then it must be true that Carlos likes windy days.

Conditional arguments come in four basic forms. Each has a special name, which will make sense if you remember that p is the hypothesis and q is the conclusion in *if p, then q*. For example, the second premise of the above argument about Carlos asserts the truth of the hypothesis, so the argument is called *affirming the hypothesis.* Arguments with this form are always valid. The following box summarizes the four forms of conditional arguments and states their validity.

Take Note

The two valid forms are also known by Latin terms. Affirming the hypothesis is called *modus ponens,* and denying the conclusion is called *modus tollens.*

FOUR BASIC CONDITIONAL ARGUMENTS

	Affirming the Hypothesis	Affirming the Conclusion	Denying the Hypothesis	Denying the Conclusion
Structure	If p, then q. p is true. q is true.	If p, then q. q is true. p is true.	If p, then q. p is not true. q is not true.	If p, then q. q is not true. p is not true.
Validity	Valid	Invalid	Invalid	Valid

We can use a variation on standard Venn diagrams to show why each type of conditional argument is valid or invalid. Instead of using the circles to represent sets, we use them to represent the propositions p and q. We then draw a Venn diagram for *if p, then q* by putting the p circle inside the q circle (Figure 1.29). This tells us that whenever p is true, q is also true.

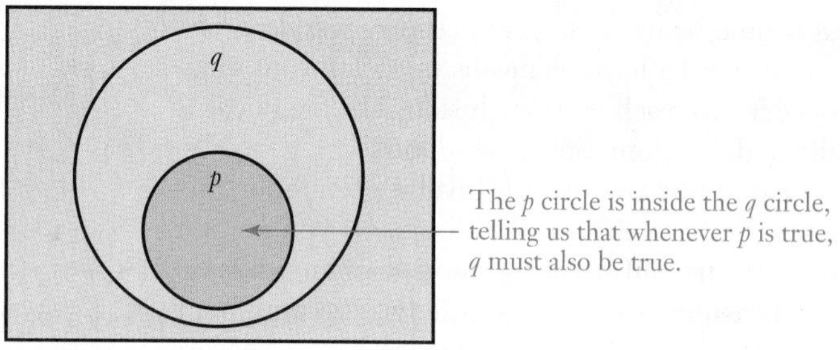

FIGURE 1.29 A Venn diagram for *if p, then q.*

Example 5 Affirming the Hypothesis (Valid)

Use a Venn diagram test to show that the argument above, concerning Carlos and Chicago, is valid.

Solution We begin with the Venn diagram shown in Figure 1.29 for *if p, then q*. In this case, p = *a person lives in Chicago* and q = *the person likes windy days*. The second premise asserts that p is true for the person named Carlos. We show this by putting an X in the p circle (Figure 1.30). We next check whether this diagram of the premises contains the conclusion. Notice that the X is also inside the q circle, meaning that q is also true for Carlos—that is, he *does* like windy days, just as the conclusion claims. The Venn diagram shows that the premises lead necessarily to the conclusion, so the argument is valid.

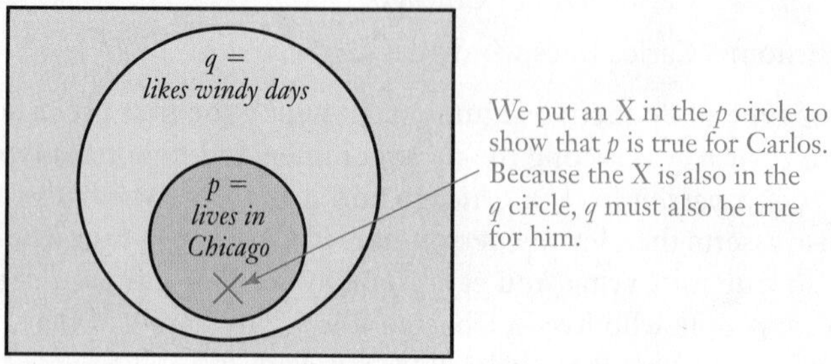

FIGURE 1.30 The Venn diagram for Example 5, showing that affirming the hypothesis is a valid conditional argument.

Now try Exercises 37–38.

Example 6 Affirming the Conclusion (Invalid)

Use a Venn diagram to test the validity of the following argument.

Premise: If an employee is regularly late, then the employee will be fired.

Premise: Sharon was fired.

Conclusion: Sharon was regularly late.

Solution We begin with the Venn diagram for *if p, then q*. In this case, p = *an employee is regularly late* and q = *the employee will be fired*. The second premise asserts that Sharon was fired, meaning that q is true for the person named Sharon. We can show this by putting an X in the q circle. However, the premise says nothing about whether Sharon was regularly late. We therefore put the X on the border of the p circle to indicate that we don't know whether the X belongs inside or outside this circle (Figure 1.31). Now we check whether the diagram contains the conclusion. The conclusion states that Sharon was regularly late, meaning that p is true for Sharon. Therefore, if the conclusion is supported by the premises, our diagram should have an X in the p circle. But it doesn't—the X is on the border. The argument is invalid, and we cannot conclude that Sharon was fired because she was regularly late. She might have been fired for some other reason.

Now try Exercises 39–40.

The X must be inside the q circle to show that q is true for Sharon. But because the premises do not tell us whether p is also true for her, we place the X on the border of the p circle.

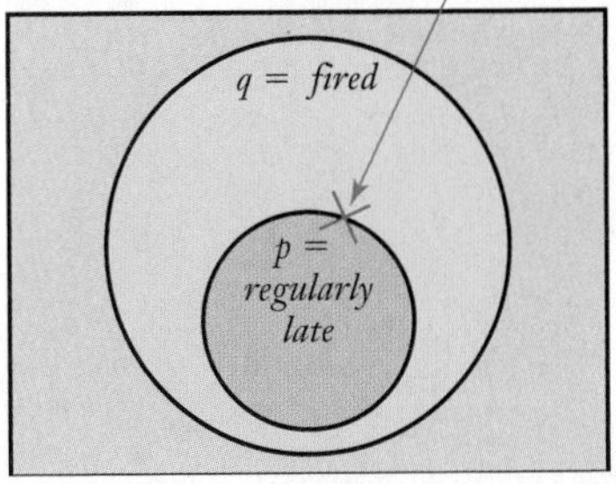

FIGURE 1.31 Venn diagram for Example 6. Because the conclusion demands an X *inside* the p circle, it does not follow from the premises.

Example 7 Denying the Hypothesis (Invalid)

Use a Venn diagram to test the validity of the following argument.

Premise: If you liked the book, then you'll love the movie.

Premise: You did not like the book.

Conclusion: You will not love the movie.

Solution We have p = *you liked the book* and q = *you'll love the movie*. The second premise asserts that p is false for you, which we can show by putting an X outside the p circle. However, we do not know whether the X should also be outside the q circle, because the premise says nothing about q (that is, it says nothing about *you'll love the movie*). We therefore put the X on the border of the q circle (Figure 1.32). Now we check whether the diagram contains the conclusion. The conclusion states that you will not love the movie, meaning that q is false for you. For the conclusion to be supported by the premises, the X must be outside the q circle, not on the border. Therefore, the argument is invalid. It's possible that, despite not liking the book, you will still love the movie.

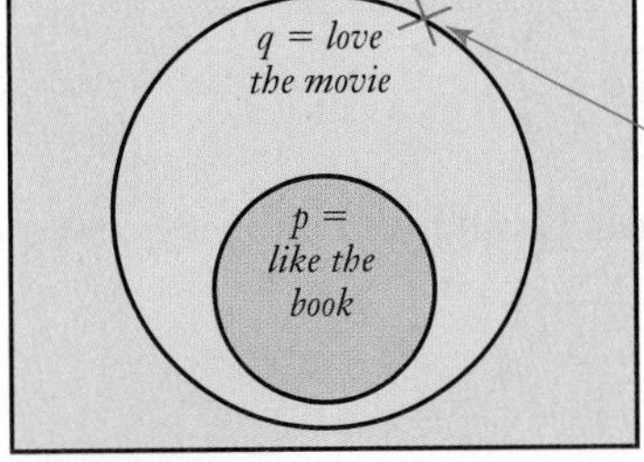

The X must be outside the p circle to show that p is false for you. But we are not given enough information to determine whether the X should also be outside the q circle, so we place it on the border.

FIGURE 1.32 Venn diagram for Example 7. Because the X is on the border of the q circle, we *cannot* conclude that q is also false for you.

Now try Exercises 41–42.

Example 8 Denying the Conclusion (Valid)

Analyze the following argument:

Premise: A narcotic is habit-forming.
Premise: Heroin is not habit-forming.
Conclusion: Heroin is not a narcotic.

Solution The first premise can be rephrased to read *if a substance is a narcotic, then it is habit-forming*. We identify p = *a substance is a narcotic* and q = *the substance is habit-forming* in the Venn diagram (Figure 1.33). We illustrate the second premise by placing an X, representing heroin, outside the q circle. This placement indicates that heroin is *not* habit-forming. We now ask whether this diagram is consistent with the conclusion. The diagram shows the X outside the *narcotic* circle, meaning that heroin is not a narcotic—just as the conclusion claims. The argument is valid.

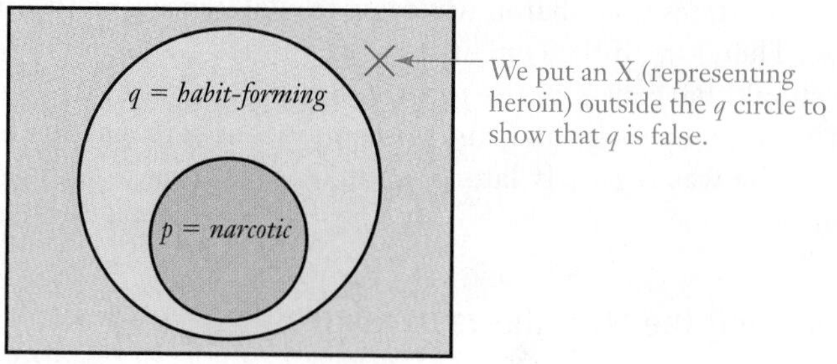

FIGURE 1.33 Venn diagram for Example 8. Because the X is also outside the p circle, p must also be false.

To test for soundness, we must assess the truth of the premises. The first premise is generally true, because narcotics are habit-forming for most people. But the second premise is false. Heroin *is* habit-forming. Because it has a false premise, the argument is not sound.

Now try Exercises 43–44.

Time Out to Think

Suppose you replace heroin with aspirin in Example 8. Is the argument valid? Is it sound?

Deductive Arguments with a Chain of Conditionals

Another common type of deductive argument involves a chain of three or more conditionals. Such arguments have the following form:

Premise: If p, then q.
Premise: If q, then r.
Conclusion: If p, then r.

This particular chain of conditionals is valid: If p implies q and q implies r, it must be true that p implies r.

Example 9 A Chain of Conditionals

Analyze this argument: "If elected to the school board, Maria Lopez will force the school district to raise academic standards, which will benefit my children's education. Therefore, my children will benefit if Maria Lopez is elected."

Solution This argument can be rephrased as a chain of conditionals:

Premise: If Maria Lopez is elected to the school board, then the school district will raise academic standards.

Premise: If the school district raises academic standards, then my children will benefit.

Conclusion: If Maria Lopez is elected to the school board, then my children will benefit.

Cast in this form, the conditional propositions form a clear chain from p = *Maria Lopez is elected* to q = *the district will raise academic standards* to r = *my children will benefit*. Therefore, the argument is valid. **Now try Exercises 45–46.**

Example 10 Invalid Chain of Conditionals

Analyze the following argument: "We agreed that if you shop, I make dinner. We also agreed that if you take out the trash, I make dinner. Therefore, if you shop, you should take out the trash."

Solution Let's assign p = *you shop*, q = *I make dinner*, r = *you take out the trash*. Then this argument has the following form:

Premise: If p, then q.

Premise: If r, then q.

Conclusion: If p, then r.

The conclusion is invalid, because there is no chain from p to r.

Now try Exercises 47–48.

Induction and Deduction in Mathematics

Perhaps more than any other subject, mathematics relies on the idea of *proof*. A mathematical proof is a deductive argument that demonstrates the truth of a certain claim, or *theorem*. A theorem is considered proven if it is supported by a valid and sound proof. Although mathematical proofs use deduction, theorems are often discovered by induction.

Consider the Pythagorean theorem, which applies to right triangles (those with one 90° angle). It says $a^2 + b^2 = c^2$, where c is the length of the longest side, or **hypotenuse**, and a and b are the lengths of the other two sides (Figure 1.34a). A geometric construction in the case $a = 3$, $b = 4$, and $c = 5$ shows how the squares of the sides are related (Figure 1.34b). The same relationship can be found in *any* right triangle, so there is good inductive evidence to suggest that the theorem is true for *all* right triangles.

The Pythagorean theorem is named for the Greek philosopher Pythagoras (c. 580–500 B.C.E.) because he was the first person known to have proved it deductively. However, the theorem was known to many ancient cultures and already had been used for at least a thousand years before the time of Pythagoras. These ancient cultures probably never bothered to prove it. Instead, they simply noticed that it was true

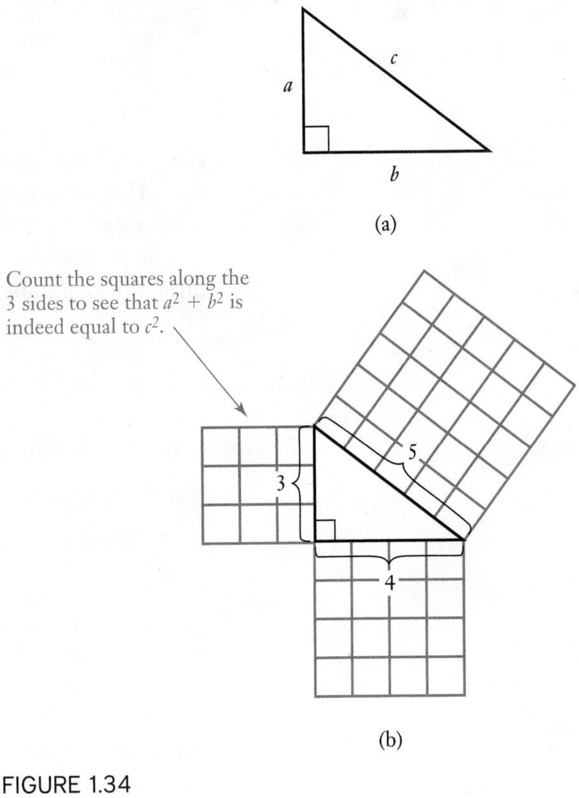

FIGURE 1.34

Thinking About...

Deductive Proof of the Pythagorean Theorem

Over the centuries, mathematicians found many different ways to prove the Pythagorean theorem deductively. One of the simplest proofs is attributed to a 12th-century Hindu mathematician named Bhaskara. His proof begins with a large square, inside of which is a smaller square surrounded by four identical right triangles (Figure 1.35). Note that the diagram divides the large square into five separate regions (the small square and the four triangles) so that

$$\begin{array}{c}\text{area of}\\ \textit{large}\text{ square}\end{array} = \left(\begin{array}{c}\text{area of}\\ \textit{small}\text{ square}\end{array}\right) + 4 \times \left(\begin{array}{c}\text{area of}\\ \text{triangle}\end{array}\right)$$

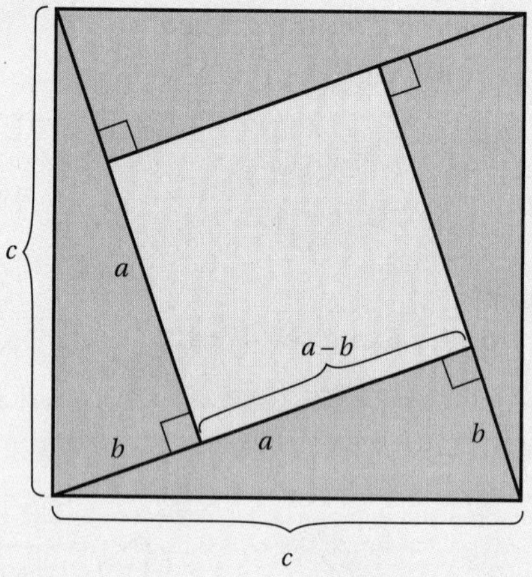

FIGURE 1.35

Now we can write each of these areas as follows:

- The side length of the *large* square is c, so its area is c^2.
- The side length of the *small* square is $a - b$, so its area is $(a - b)^2$.
- The area of any triangle is given by the formula $\frac{1}{2} \times \text{base} \times \text{height}$ (see Unit 10A). Each of the four triangles has base length a and height b, so each has area $ab/2$.

Substituting these areas into the preceding equation gives

$$\underbrace{c^2}_{\text{area of large square}} = \underbrace{(a - b)^2}_{\text{area of small square}} + 4 \times \underbrace{\frac{ab}{2}}_{\text{area of triangle}} = (a - b)^2 + 2ab$$

We continue by using a bit of algebra to show that $(a - b)^2 = a^2 - 2ab + b^2$. Substituting this expression into the previous equation, we get

$$\begin{aligned} c^2 &= (a - b)^2 + 2ab \\ &= a^2 - 2ab + b^2 + 2ab \\ &= a^2 + b^2 \end{aligned}$$

We have arrived at the Pythagorean theorem by following a deductive chain of logic from the starting diagram. Legend has it that, when Bhaskara showed his proof to others, he accompanied it with just a single word: "Behold!"

every time they tested it and that it was very useful in art, architecture, and construction. The many test cases essentially formed an inductive argument, each one lending more support to the conclusion that the theorem is true.

The principle of seeking inductive evidence can be very useful when you are having difficulty remembering whether a particular theorem or mathematical rule applies. It often helps to try a few test cases and see if the rule works. Although test cases can never constitute a proof, they often are enough to satisfy yourself of a rule's truth. However, the rule cannot be true if even one test case fails.

Example 11 Inductively Testing a Mathematical Rule

Test the following rule: For all numbers a and b, $a \times b = b \times a$.

Solution We begin with some test cases, using a calculator as needed.

Does $7 \times 6 = 6 \times 7$? $\Rightarrow$ Yes!
Does $(-23.8) \times 9.2 = 9.2 \times (-23.8)$? $\Rightarrow$ Yes!
Does $4.33 \times \left(-\frac{1}{3}\right) = \left(-\frac{1}{3}\right) \times 4.33$? $\Rightarrow$ Yes!

The three test cases are each somewhat different (mixing fractions, decimals, and negative numbers), yet the rule works for all three. This outcome offers a strong inductive argument in favor of the rule. Although we have not proved the rule $a \times b = b \times a$, we have good reason to believe that it is true. Our belief would be strengthened by additional test cases that confirm the rule. **Now try Exercises 49–50.**

Example 12 Invalidating a Proposed Rule

Suppose you cannot recall whether adding the same amount to both the numerator and the denominator (top and bottom) of a fraction such as $\frac{2}{3}$ is legitimate. That is, you are wondering whether it is true that, for any number a,

$$\frac{2}{3} \stackrel{?}{=} \frac{2+a}{3+a}$$

Solution Again, we can check the rule with test cases.

Suppose that $a = 0$. Is it true that $\frac{2}{3} = \frac{2+0}{3+0}$? ⇒ Yes!

Suppose that $a = 1$. Is it true that $\frac{2}{3} = \frac{2+1}{3+1}$? ⇒ No!

Although the rule worked in the first test case, it failed in the second. Generalizing (inductively), we conclude that it is not legitimate to add the same value to the top and bottom of *any* fraction. **Now try Exercises 51–52.**

QUICK QUIZ

Choose the best answer to each of the following questions. Explain your reasoning with one or more complete sentences.

1. To prove a statement true, you must use
   a. an inductive argument. b. a deductive argument.
   c. a conditional argument.
2. If a deductive argument is valid, its conclusion is
   a. true. b. sound.
   c. an automatic consequence of its premises.
3. A deductive argument *cannot* be
   a. both valid and sound. b. valid but not sound.
   c. sound but not valid.
4. Consider an argument in which Premise 1 is "All knights are heroes" and Premise 2 is "Paul is a hero." If X represents Paul, which Venn diagram correctly represents the two premises?

a.

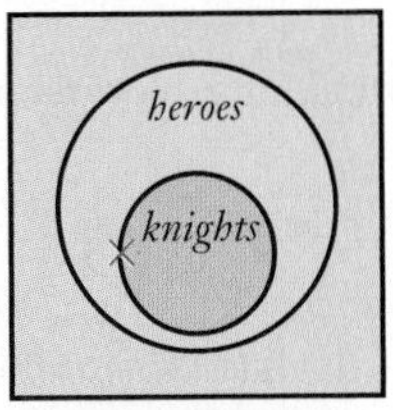

b.

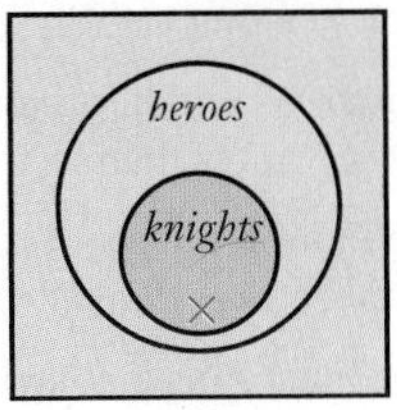

c.

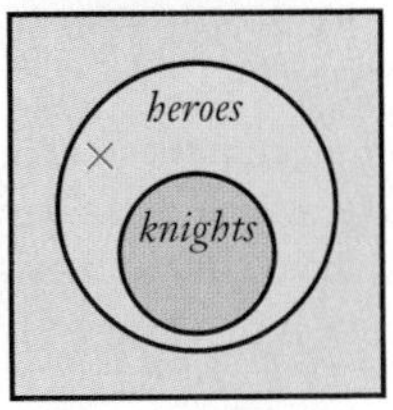

5. Consider again the argument from question 4. Which of the following conclusions is true?
   a. Paul is a knight.
   b. Paul is not a knight.
   c. Paul may or may not be a knight.
6. Consider an argument in which Premise 1 is "If p, then q" and Premise 2 is "q is not true." What can you conclude about p?
   a. p is true.
   b. p is not true.
   c. We cannot conclude anything about p.
7. Consider an argument in which Premise 1 is "If p, then q" and Premise 2 is "q is true." What can you conclude about p?
   a. p is true.
   b. p is not true.
   c. We cannot conclude anything about p.
8. The first premise of an argument is *if a, then b.* The conclusion is *if a, then d.* In order for this argument to be valid, there must be a second premise that reads
   a. *if a, then c.*
   b. *if c, then d.*
   c. *if b, then d.*

9. The longest side of a right triangle is called the
   a. Pythagorean theorem.
   b. hypotenuse.
   c. slant.

10. Consider the right triangle below, with the two known side lengths indicated and the unknown side length c. Which statement is true?
    a. $c = 6$
    b. $c^2 = 41$
    c. $c = 41$

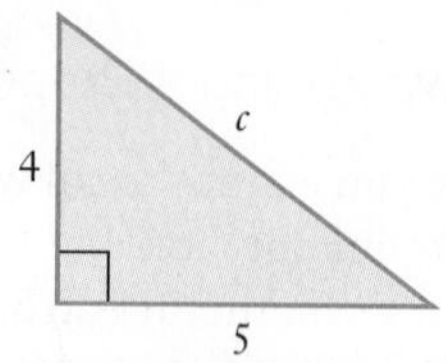

Exercises 1D

REVIEW QUESTIONS

1. Summarize the differences between deductive and inductive arguments. Give an example of each type.
2. Briefly explain the idea of strength and how it applies to inductive arguments. Can an inductive argument prove its conclusion true? Can an inductive argument be valid? Can it be sound?
3. Briefly explain the ideas of validity and soundness and how they apply to deductive arguments. Can a valid deductive argument be unsound? Can a sound deductive argument be invalid? Explain.
4. Describe the procedure used to test the validity of a deductive argument with a Venn diagram.
5. Create your own example of each of the four basic conditional arguments. Then explain why your argument is valid or invalid.
6. What is a chain of conditionals? Give an example of a valid argument made from such a chain.
7. Can inductive logic be used to prove a mathematical theorem? Explain.
8. How can inductive testing of a mathematical rule be useful? Give an example.

DOES IT MAKE SENSE?

Decide whether each of the following statements makes sense (or is clearly true) or does not make sense (or is clearly false). Explain your reasoning.

9. Based on the testimonials of dozens of people who have lost weight following my diet, I will prove to you that my diet works for everyone.
10. The many examples of people whose cancer went away following chemotherapy make a strong case for the idea that chemotherapy can cure cancer.
11. Through the logic of deduction, I will show you that if you accept the truth of my premises, you must also accept the truth of my conclusion.
12. You can see that my argument is valid, and you must therefore accept the truth of my conclusion.
13. If you use logic, then your life will be organized. Therefore, if your life is organized, you must be using logic.
14. Even before Fermat's Last Theorem was proved deductively, mathematicians were sure it was true.

BASIC SKILLS & CONCEPTS

15–22: Everyday Logic. Explain whether the following arguments are deductive or inductive.

15. I have never found mail in my mailbox on a Sunday. The Postal Service must not have Sunday deliveries.
16. Because of a budget cutback, postal workers will no longer work on Saturdays. Therefore, I will not expect Saturday deliveries in the future.
17. Eminem's first five CDs were outstanding. His next CD is bound to be good, so I will buy it without even listening to it.
18. If I eat spicy food before noon, then I get indigestion in the afternoon. Whenever I get indigestion, I have no appetite for the next six hours. Therefore, if I eat spicy food before noon, then I cannot eat dinner.
19. January is windier than July. The wind must blow more often in the winter than in the summer.
20. If a natural number is divisible by 2, then it is even. The number 24 is divisible by 2. Therefore, 24 is even.
21. The Flanagans are having their fourth child. Their other three children are musically gifted, so the youngest child is bound to be musically gifted as well.
22. If I have breakfast at Sid's Café, then I can park free; but then I walk to work, which makes me late, which makes my boss mad. So if I have breakfast at Sid's Café, I save money and make my boss mad.

23–28: Analyzing Inductive Arguments. Determine the truth of the premises of the following arguments. Then assess the strength of the argument and discuss the truth of the conclusion.

23. Premise: $2 + 3 = 5$
Premise: $5 + 4 = 9$
Premise: $7 + 6 = 13$
Conclusion: The sum of an even integer and an odd integer is an odd integer.

24. Premise: If I pay more for a pair of running shoes, they last longer.
Premise: If I pay more for an automobile, it requires fewer repairs.
Conclusion: Quality goes with high prices.

25. Premise: Trout and bass swim and they are fish.
Premise: Sharks and marlin swim and they are fish.
Premise: Tuna and salmon swim and they are fish.
Conclusion: Whales swim and they are fish.

26. Premise: Apes and baboons have hair and they are mammals.
Premise: Mice and rats have hair and they are mammals.
Premise: Tigers and lions have hair and they are mammals.
Conclusion: Animals with hair are mammals.

27. Premise: $(-6) \times (-4) = 24$
Premise: $(-2) \times (-1) = 2$
Premise: $(-27) \times (-3) = 81$
Conclusion: Whenever we multiply two negative numbers, the result is a positive number.

28. Premise: Bach, Buxtehude, Beethoven, Brahms, Berlioz, and Britten are great composers.
Conclusion: Composers with names that begin with B are great.

29–36: Analyzing Deductive Arguments. Consider the following arguments.

a. If necessary, rephrase the first premise so that it has the form *all S are P*.

b. Draw a Venn diagram to determine whether the argument is valid.

c. Discuss the truth of the premises and state whether the argument is sound.

29. Premise: All European countries use the euro as currency.
Premise: Great Britain is a European country.
Conclusion: Great Britain uses the euro as currency.

30. Premise: All dairy products contain protein.
Premise: Soybeans contain protein.
Conclusion: Soybeans are dairy products.

31. Premise: No states west of the Mississippi River are in the eastern time zone.
Premise: Utah is west of the Mississippi River.
Conclusion: Utah is not in the eastern time zone.

32. Premise: All U.S. presidents have been men.
Premise: George Washington was a man.
Conclusion: George Washington was a U.S. president.

33. Premise: All Best Actor Academy Award winners have been men.
Premise: Sean Penn is a man.
Conclusion: Sean Penn won a Best Actor Academy Award.

34. Premise: All fruit is fat-free.
Premise: Avocados are fruit.
Conclusion: Avocados are fat-free.

35. Premise: All opera singers can whistle a Mozart tune.
Premise: Pavarotti was an opera singer.
Conclusion: Pavarotti could whistle a Mozart tune.

36. Premise: No country is an island.
Premise: Iceland is a country.
Conclusion: Iceland is not an island.

37–44: Deductive Arguments with Conditional Propositions. Consider the following arguments.

a. If necessary, rephrase the first premise so that it has the form *if p, then q*.

b. Identify the type of argument and determine its validity with a Venn diagram.

c. Discuss the truth of the premises and state whether the argument is sound.

37. Premise: If an animal is a dog, then it is a mammal.
Premise: Setters are dogs.
Conclusion: Setters are mammals.

38. Premise: If it is a bird, then its young are hatched from eggs.
Premise: Condors are birds.
Conclusion: Condor chicks are hatched from eggs.

39. Premise: If you live in Boston, you live in Massachusetts.
Premise: Amanda does not live in Boston.
Conclusion: Amanda does not live in Massachusetts.

40. Premise: If you live in Boston, you live in Massachusetts.
Premise: Bruno lives in Massachusetts.
Conclusion: Bruno lives in Boston.

41. Premise: If a figure is a triangle, then it has three sides.
Premise: Squares have four sides.
Conclusion: Squares are not triangles.

42. Premise: It's necessary for nurses to know CPR.
Premise: Tom is a nurse.
Conclusion: Tom knows CPR.

43. Premise: Novels written in the 19th century were not written on a word processor.
Premise: Jake finished his first novel last year.
Conclusion: Jake's first novel was written on a word processor.

44. Premise: If we can put a man on the Moon, we can build a computer operating system that works.
    Premise: We can build a computer operating system that works.
    Conclusion: We can put a man on the Moon.

45–48: **Chains of Conditionals.** Write the given argument as a chain of conditional propositions that have the form *if p, then q*. Then determine the validity of the entire argument.

45. Premise: If a natural number is divisible by 8, then it is divisible by 4.
    Premise: If a natural number is divisible by 4, then it is divisible by 2.
    Conclusion: If a natural number is divisible by 8, then it is divisible by 2.
46. Premise: If a creature is a reptile, then it is an animal.
    Premise: If a creature is an animal, then it is alive.
    Conclusion: If a creature is alive, then it is a reptile.
47. Premise: If taxes are increased, then taxpayers will have less disposable income.
    Premise: With less disposable income, spending will decrease and the economy will slow down.
    Conclusion: A tax increase will slow down the economy.
48. Premise: If taxes are cut, the U.S. government will have less revenue.
    Premise: If there is less revenue, then the deficit will be larger.
    Conclusion: Tax cuts will lead to a larger deficit.

49–51: **Testing Mathematical Rules.** Test the following rules with several different sets of numbers. If possible, try to find a counterexample (a set of numbers for which the rule is not true). State whether you think the rule is true.

49. Is it true for all real numbers a and b that $a + b = b + a$?
50. Is it true for all nonzero real numbers a, b, and c that
$$\frac{a}{b+c} = \frac{a}{b} + \frac{a}{c}?$$
51. It is true for all positive real numbers a and b that $\sqrt{a+b} = \sqrt{a} + \sqrt{b}$?
52. It is true for all positive integers n that
$$1 + 2 + 3 + \cdots + n = \frac{n \times (n+1)}{2}?$$

FURTHER APPLICATIONS

53–57: **Validity and Soundness.** State whether it is possible for a deductive argument to have the following properties. If so, make a simple three-proposition argument that demonstrates your conclusion.

53. Valid and sound
54. Not valid and sound
55. Valid and not sound
56. Valid with false premises and a true conclusion
57. Not valid with true premises and a true conclusion

58–61: **Make Your Own Argument.** Create simple three-proposition arguments that have the following forms.

58. Affirming the hypothesis
59. Affirming the conclusion
60. Denying the hypothesis
61. Denying the conclusion
62. **The Goldbach Conjecture.** Recall that a prime number is a natural number whose only factors are itself and 1 (for example, 2, 3, 5, 7, 11, . . .). The Goldbach conjecture, posed in 1742, claims that every even number greater than 2 can be expressed as the sum of two primes. For example, $4 = 2 + 2$, $6 = 3 + 3$, and $8 = 5 + 3$. A *deductive* proof of this conjecture has never been found. Test the conjecture for at least 10 even numbers and present an *inductive* argument for its truth. Do you think the conjecture is true? Why or why not?

63–65: **Conditionals in the Literature.** Consider the following propositions and answer the questions that follow.

63. "If Toyota takes market share from Ford by manufacturing hybrids while Ford is still making SUVs, Ford is punished by the market." —Thomas Friedman, *Hot, Flat, and Crowded*

    a. What is the logical conclusion (if any) in the event that Toyota takes market share from Ford by manufacturing hybrids while Ford is still making SUVs?

    b. What is the logical conclusion (if any) in the event that Ford is not punished by the market?

    c. Can you draw any conclusion about what happens if Toyota makes SUVs and Ford makes hybrids?

64. "If floods have not occurred in the immediate past, people who live on the flood plains are far less likely to purchase flood insurance." —Cass Sunstein, *Worst-Case Scenarios*

    a. What is the logical conclusion (if any) in the event that floods have not occurred in the immediate past?

    b. What is the logical conclusion (if any) in the event that people who live on the flood plains purchase flood insurance?

    c. Can you draw any conclusion about what happens if floods *have* occurred in the immediate past?

65. "If Chinese officials started pulling assets out of the U.S. and touched off a run on the dollar, their vast remaining dollar holdings would plummet in value." —James Fallows, *The Atlantic*, December 2008

a. What is the logical conclusion (if any) in the event that Chinese officials pull assets out of the U.S.?

b. What is the logical conclusion (if any) in the event that the dollar holdings of the Chinese do not plummet?

c. Can you draw any conclusion about what happens if the dollar holdings of the Chinese plummet?

WEB PROJECTS

66. **Fermat's Last Theorem.** One of the most famous mathematical theorems of all times is called Fermat's Last Theorem. For over 350 years, the proof eluded mathematicians; it was finally cracked by Andrew Wiles in the 1990s. Through Web research, learn what the theorem claims and why it became so famous. Briefly summarize how inductive evidence suggested its truth for centuries before Wiles finally found a deductive proof.

67. **The Pythagorean Theorem.** Learn more about the history of the Pythagorean theorem, and write a short report on one aspect of its history. For example, you might write about its use in cultures that predated Pythagoras or describe another proof of the theorem with its historical context.

IN YOUR WORLD

68. **Deductive Reasoning in Your Life.** Given an example of a situation in which you used deductive reasoning in everyday life. Explain the situation, describe the steps in your thinking, and explain why it was deductive reasoning.

69. **Inductive Reasoning in Your Life.** Give an example of a situation in which you used inductive reasoning in everyday life. Explain the situation, describe the steps in your thinking, and explain why it was inductive reasoning.

70. **Editorial Arguments.** Find three simple arguments in editorials. State whether each is deductive or inductive and evaluate it accordingly.

71. **Arguing Your Side.** Choose an issue that you feel strongly about and create an argument in support of your position. Is your argument inductive or deductive? Evaluate your argument.

72. **Arguing the Other Side.** Choose an issue that you feel strongly about and create an argument that tends to *contradict* your position. That is, try to create an argument for the other side. Can you make the argument convincing? Does the argument help you understand the other side of the issue?

UNIT 1E Critical Thinking in Everyday Life

The skills discussed in the preceding units are all useful in their own right. But critical thinking involves much more than isolated skills. It also involves knowing when to use particular skills and when to invent entirely new strategies to analyze an argument or make a decision. Specifically, critical thinking involves careful reading (or listening), sharp thinking, logical analysis, good visualization, and healthy skepticism.

Because it is so wide-ranging, critical thinking cannot be described by any simple step-by-step procedure. Instead, it is developed through experience and by questioning and analyzing every argument or decision you face. Nevertheless, a few general guidelines or hints can be useful. In this unit, we offer a few such hints.

Hint 1: Read (or Listen) Carefully

Language can be used in complex ways that require careful effort to understand. Always read (or listen) carefully to make sure you've grasped precisely what was said. Also be sure that you've distinguished what was actually said, what was assumed, and what must be determined.

Example 1 Confusing Ballot Wording

Colorado voters were asked to vote *yes* or *no* on the following ballot question.

Shall there be an amendment to the Colorado constitution to prohibit the state of Colorado and any of its political subdivisions from adopting or enforcing any law

BY THE WAY

Despite passing, the Colorado amendment never took effect and was declared unconstitutional by the U.S. Supreme Court. The justices said the amendment denied gays a political right enjoyed by everyone else—the chance to seek protection from discrimination in employment, housing, and public accommodations.

> *or policy which provides that homosexual, lesbian, or bisexual orientation, conduct, or relationships constitutes or entitles a person to claim any minority or protected status, quota preferences, or discrimination?*

Explain the meaning of *yes* and *no* votes.

Solution The legalistic wording of the question makes it difficult to see the key point. But, if we read carefully, we find that the question essentially asks: *Should the state prohibit laws that grant gay people minority status or protection from discrimination?* Even in this simplified form, the question may be confusing because it is asked in negative terms: A *yes* vote is a vote *against* gay rights, while a *no* vote is a vote *for* gay rights. Some evidence suggests that the wording confused voters. Pre-election polls indicated that the proposed amendment would be defeated. However, the amendment passed (53% to 47%), which means either that the polls were inaccurate or that voters were confused and voted opposite to their beliefs.

Now try Exercises 11–24.

Time Out to Think

If voters really did misunderstand the wording of the Colorado ballot initiative, would the confusion have affected both sides equally, or would it have favored one side more than the other? Explain.

Hint 2: Look for Hidden Assumptions

The arguments we studied in Unit 1D consisted of clear premises leading to the conclusion. But many real arguments lack such clarity, relying instead on ambiguous terms or hidden assumptions. Often, the speaker (or writer) may think these premises are "obvious," but listeners (or readers) may not agree. Indeed, an argument that seems very convincing to the speaker may actually be quite weak to a listener who is not aware of the hidden assumptions.

Example 2 Building More Prisons

Analyze the following argument:

> *We should build more prisons because incarcerating more criminals will reduce the crime rate.*

Solution: This argument looks deceptively simple because it is so short. Its conclusion is based on a single premise—that incarcerating more criminals will reduce the crime rate. If we recognize the premise as a conditional statement, the argument has the form

Premise: If we incarcerate more criminals, then the crime rate will be reduced.
Conclusion: We should build more prisons.

Viewed this way, the argument hardly makes any sense at all, because the premise says nothing about building prisons. Clearly, the speaker must have intended some hidden assumptions to be "obvious" to the listeners.

We can begin to make sense of the argument by identifying possible hidden assumptions. For example, a plausible argument might begin like this:

Hidden Assumption 1: If we build more prisons, then more criminals can be incarcerated.
Stated Premise: If we incarcerate more criminals, then the crime rate will be reduced.

Hidden Assumption 2:	If the crime rate is reduced, then we will have a more desirable society.
Hidden Assumption 3:	If a policy will lead to a more desirable society, then it should be enacted.
Conclusion:	We should build more prisons.

With the three hidden assumptions, the argument is a long chain of conditionals that is deductively valid. But even if we assume the speaker intended these assumptions to be "obvious," the argument is sound only if you accept the truth of both the single stated premise and the three hidden assumptions. All are debatable.

For example, many people would argue with the first hidden assumption, because incarcerating more criminals requires not only more prison space, but also a more efficient court system. The stated premise is also open to debate: Studies do not agree on whether a higher incarceration rate reduces the crime rate. One could counter the second hidden assumption by arguing that crime reduction might not make a more desirable society if it comes at the price of less personal freedom. Even the last hidden assumption is debatable, because we might not choose to implement a beneficial policy if it has a high cost.

In summary, the original argument makes sense only if we add several hidden assumptions, and these assumptions are open to debate. As a result, the truth of the conclusion is also debatable. **Now try Exercises 25–28.**

Hint 3: Identify the Real Issue

It can be difficult to identify the real issue in a debate because people may be attempting to hide their true intentions. Fortunately, by analyzing arguments carefully, we can often determine whether the real issue is hidden, even if we don't know exactly what it is.

Example 3 Banning Concerts

Analyze the following segment of an editorial from a local newspaper.

> *With last Saturday's sellout crowd at the Moonlight Amphitheater, it is clear that the parking problem has become hopeless. Concert goers parked along residential streets up to a mile away from the amphitheater, badly overcrowding sidewalks, blocking driveways, and disrupting traffic. In light of this parking problem, future concerts should be banned.*

Solution: The argument makes several claims about parking problems, but stripped of the details the argument boils down to this:

Premise:	There is a parking problem for concerts at the theater.
Conclusion:	Future concerts at the theater must be banned.

The rest of the argument simply lists reasons why the parking problem is serious. But is a parking problem really a good enough reason to ban all future concerts? After all, a parking problem could have many solutions. For example, it might be possible to create new parking lots, to use shuttle buses, to step up enforcement of parking violations, or to encourage carpooling. The weakness of the argument should make us wonder whether the editorial writers are *really* concerned about parking or whether they are using this issue to oppose the concerts themselves. Or perhaps they are responding to a few vocal residents who complained about the parking problem. It's hard to know for sure, but it seems unlikely that parking is the real issue.

Now try Exercises 29–30.

Historical Note

Can logic settle all arguments? The German mathematician Gottfried Wilhelm von Leibniz (1646–1716) thought so and took the first steps in a two-century search for a "calculus of reasoning." An outgrowth of this search called symbolic logic is now used extensively in mathematics and computing. But Leibniz's dream of resolving arguments through logic was not to be. In 1931, the Austrian mathematician Kurt Gödel discovered that no system of logic can solve all mathematical problems, let alone problems of ethics or morality.

Hint 4: Understand All the Options

We regularly make decisions in situations where we have several options. For example, we face decisions about which insurance policy to choose, which auto loan to take, or which model of new computer to buy. The key to such decisions is making sure that you understand how each option would affect you.

Example 4 Which Airline Ticket to Buy?

Airlines typically offer many different prices for the same trip. Suppose you are planning a trip six months in advance and discover that you have two choices in purchasing an airline ticket:

(A) The lowest fare is \$400, but 25% of the fare is nonrefundable if you change or cancel the ticket.
(B) A fully refundable ticket is available for \$800.

Analyze the situation.

Solution We can think of each of the two options as a pair of conditional propositions. Under option A, you will lose 25% of \$400, or \$100, if you cancel your trip. Thus, option A represents the following pair of conditional propositions:

(1A) If you purchase ticket A and *go* on the trip, then you will pay \$400.
(2A) If you purchase ticket A and *cancel* the trip, then you will pay \$100.

Similarly, option B represents the following pair of conditional propositions:

(1B) If you purchase ticket B and *go* on the trip, then you will pay \$800.
(2B) If you purchase ticket B and *cancel* the trip, then you will pay \$0.

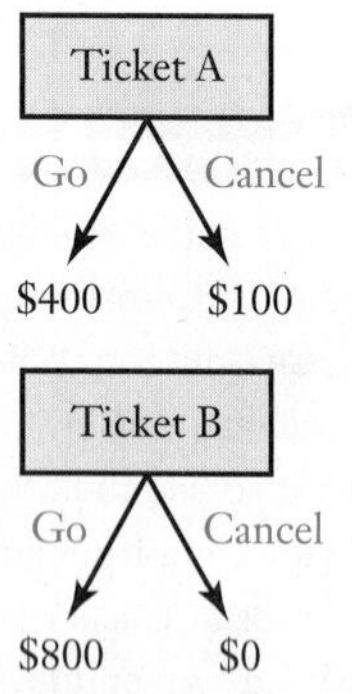

FIGURE 1.36

Figure 1.36 represents the four possibilities. Clearly, option A is the better buy if you go on the trip, and option B is the better buy if you end up canceling your trip. However, because you are planning six months in advance, it's impossible to foresee all the circumstances that might lead you to cancel your trip. Therefore, you might want to analyze the *difference* between the two tickets under the two possibilities (going on the trip or canceling).

If you go on the trip: ticket B costs \$400 more than ticket A.
If you cancel the trip: ticket A costs \$100 more than ticket B.

In effect, you must decide which ticket to purchase by balancing the risk of spending an extra \$400 if you go on the trip against spending an extra \$100 if you cancel. How would *you* decide? **Now try Exercises 31–35.**

Time Out to Think

Consider the two ticket options in Example 4 from the point of view of the airline. How does offering the two options help the airline maximize its revenue?

Hint 5: Watch for Fine Print and Missing Information

There's an old saying that "the devil is in the details," and it is probably nowhere more applicable than in the fine print of offers, deals, and contracts. What looks like a great deal without the fine print may be a poor one with it. Worse yet, sometimes even the fine print neglects to state important information. Use your powers of critical thinking to decide what information you need. If anything is missing, be sure to ask before you act.

Example 5 A Safe Investment?

Marshall was nearing retirement age and was concerned about his retirement savings. He thought the stock market was too risky, so he put his money into a certificate of deposit (CD) at his local bank. Like most CDs, the one at his local bank was federally insured by the F.D.I.C. (which insures bank deposits in the United States), but its interest rate was quite low. Then he received this offer in the mail:

> *Our certificates of deposit have the highest interest rates you'll find anywhere—more than double that of most other banks! For a combination of investment safety and high interest, there's no better choice.*
>
> **Our high yields come from our unique ability to invest in valuable offshore assets.*

Marshall transferred all his savings into one of these high-yield CDs. Two years later, the bank offering these CDs failed, and Marshall learned that he would not be able to recover any of the money he had lost. What happened?

Solution Marshall lost his retirement savings because, unlike most CDs, this one was *not* insured by the F.D.I.C. Losses like this have affected millions of people in recent years, but these losses could have been avoided with additional thought. First, Marshall should have wondered how one bank could possibly have offered a rate so much higher than that of other banks. Second, the fine print stating that investments were "offshore" should have been a clue to the fact that this was not a normal CD. Third, because the offer did not say that the CD was insured, he should have inquired further before assuming that it was. **Now try Exercise 36.**

BY THE WAY

Example 5 is based on a real fraud case involving "certificates of deposit" sold by the Stanford Financial Group, which claimed to offer safe investments but actually invested in risky assets held in a lightly regulated bank outside the United States. The 2009 failure of the Stanford bank cost investors more than $8 billion, with thousands of people losing their lifelong retirement savings.

Hint 6: Are Other Conclusions Possible?

You should never accept the first argument or choice you hear. Even when an argument proves its conclusion, it's still possible that there are other conclusions that have been left unstated. And remember that many real arguments are inductive, which means the conclusion is never proved no matter how strong the argument may seem.

Example 6 Nuclear Deterrence

Evaluate the following historical argument and discuss its conclusion.

> *The development of nuclear weapons changed the way world leaders think about potential conflicts. A single nuclear weapon can kill millions of people, and the arsenals of the United States and the Soviet Union contained enough power to kill everyone on Earth many times over. This potential for catastrophic damage led to the idea of nuclear deterrence, which held that the United States and the Soviet Union would be deterred from direct warfare by the fear of nuclear war. For the more than 45 years of the Cold War, the United States and the Soviet Union never did fight directly. This was one of the longest periods in human history during which two major enemies avoided direct war. We can only conclude that nuclear deterrence prevented war between the United States and the Soviet Union.*

Solution The conclusion of this argument is the claim that nuclear deterrence prevented war between the United States and the Soviet Union. The facts cited in support of this conclusion are all true and all appear relevant to the conclusion. Thus, the argument appears quite strong. Nevertheless, it does not *prove* that nuclear deterrence worked, and we can imagine other possible explanations for why the United States and the Soviet Union avoided war. For example, it might have been because of economic factors, or the emergence of a united Western Europe after World War II, or changes in non-nuclear weaponry. Indeed, because the argument concerns why history unfolded in a particular way, it is probably impossible for us to ever know for certain whether the conclusion is true or false.

Time Out to Think

Can you think of any facts that would tend to undercut the argument that nuclear deterrence prevented war between the United States and the Soviet Union? Overall, in your judgment, is the argument in Example 6 convincing? Why or why not?

Hint 7: Don't Miss the Big Picture

You've probably heard the expression "not seeing the forest for the trees," which means missing out on the big picture (the fact that there is a forest in front of you) because you are too focused on details (the individual trees). The details may be very important to a debate or argument, but you should always step back as you consider them to make sure you have not lost sight of the forest.

Example 7 Burst of the Housing Bubble

Look back at the chapter-opening activity ("Bursting Bubble") about the collapse in the housing market that helped trigger a global recession. Economists and real estate professionals collected vast amounts of data as home prices rose, so everyone was well aware that prices were increasing at a rapid rate from 2000 to 2005. But people continued to buy and invest in real estate at ever-higher prices, and lenders continued to loan money for those purchases, because so many people convinced themselves that real estate was a "safe" investment. Were these arguments reasonable, or did they miss the big picture?

Solution The data on the home price to income ratio (see the figure on p. 14) suggest that the big picture was missed. Remember that the rise in this ratio that occurred during the housing bubble meant that families had to spend larger percentages of their income on housing, and the only way they could do that was through some combination of higher income, reduced expenses in other areas, and increased borrowing. Other data show that the average income (adjusted for inflation) of working families did *not* rise during the housing bubble, nor did families cut back significantly on other expenses. We can therefore conclude that many families were buying homes that were more expensive than they could really afford, and that lenders were lending them the money anyway. In light of this big picture, a significant drop in housing prices seems to have been inevitable; the main debate among economists today is over whether it was also inevitable that the drop would occur suddenly or whether it might have occurred more slowly under other circumstances.

Putting It All Together

The examples we've studied show only a few of the many ways in which critical thinking affects our daily lives. We live in a complex world, and unless you are careful in all your thinking and decision making, you are liable to be led astray. Learn to pick apart every argument or choice you are given. With time, you will gain the experience needed to make wise decisions in school, in your career, and in your life.

PRACTICAL MATTERS

Beware of "Up To" Deals

You've probably heard special cell phone offers such as "get up to 1000 free text messages per month." These offers can be good deals if you are able to take full advantage of them. But the words "up to" hold hidden danger. In this case, the text messages may be free only during certain hours of the day, or they may not include roaming charges. If you are not careful, this special deal may turn out to be quite expensive.

More generally, you should beware of any deal that contains the words "up to." For example, an offer of "up to five free oil changes if you pay for two now" may be structured to make it difficult for you to take advantage of all of them. "Up to" may also mean "no more than"; for example, when you hear that you can "earn up to $5000 a month while working from home," it probably means you're likely to earn far less. Until you've carefully thought through the full meaning of the offer, it's best to assume that "up to" deals are up to no good.

QUICK QUIZ

Choose the best answer to each of the following questions. Explain your reasoning with one or more complete sentences.

1. "If you want to save the social services that would be lost with a property tax reduction, then vote against Proposition C." Based on this quote, a vote *for* Proposition C presumably means that

   a. you favor an increase in property taxes.

   b. you favor a decrease in property taxes.

   c. you support social services.

2. Suppose that an argument is deductively valid only if you assume that it contains one or more unstated, hidden assumptions. In that case, the original argument

   a. is also deductively valid. b. is inductively strong.

   c. is probably weak.

3. You need to buy a car and are considering loans from two banks. The loan terms are otherwise identical, but Bank 1 is offering a loan at 7% interest plus an application fee and Bank 2 is at 7.5% interest plus an application fee. Based on this, you can conclude that

   a. Bank 1 is the better deal.

   b. Bank 2 is probably the better deal, since it probably has a lower application fee.

   c. there is no way to tell which deal is better without knowing the application fees.

4. You get your hair cut at a shop that charges $30. They offer you a deal: If you prepay $150 for five haircuts, they'll give you a punch card that entitles you to a sixth haircut free. The punch card expires in one year. Is this a good deal?

   a. Yes, because you'll get a free haircut.

   b. It depends on whether you'll get six haircuts at this shop in the next year.

   c. No, because no one ever gives anything that's really free.

5. You buy a cell phone plan that gives you up to 1000 minutes of calling for $20 per month. During a particular month, you use only 100 minutes. Your per-minute cost for that month is

   a. 2¢. b. 5¢. c. 20¢.

6. You are planning a trip in six months. You can buy a fully refundable airline ticket for $600 or a $400 ticket of which only 50% is refundable if you cancel your trip. If you purchase the $400 ticket and end up canceling the trip, you will have spent

   a. $200.

   b. $400.

   c. $600.

7. Jack reasons, "Every movie I have ever seen at the Deluxe Theater was outstanding, so all movies at the Deluxe Theater must be outstanding." Which one of the following arguments most closely resembles Jack's argument?

   a. I received a bonus at work for the last three years, so I will get a bonus next year.

   b. If I am salesman-of-the-month twice in a row, I will get a bonus at the end of the year.

   c. Every mathematics teacher I have ever had was great, so all mathematics teachers are great.

8. Auto insurance policy A has an annual premium of $500 and a $200 deductible for collision (meaning *you* pay the first $200 for a collision claim). Auto insurance policy B has an annual premium of $300 and a $1000 deductible for collision. Which one of the following conclusions does *not* follow?

   a. You will spend less on premiums with policy B.

   b. Your expense for insurance and collision repairs over a year will be less with policy B.

   c. You will spend less for a $900 collision repair with policy A.

9. A teacher claims that because spell checkers have weakened students' spelling skills, middle school students should not be allowed to use them. What assumption is made in this argument?
   a. Traditional methods of teaching spelling are effective.
   b. Students should know how to spell as well as a spell checker.
   c. Spell checkers are not reliable.

10. The Smiths have a picnic every Saturday provided it does not rain. What can be concluded if today the Smiths did not have a picnic?
   a. Today is not Saturday.
   b. Today it rained.
   c. If it did not rain, then today is not Saturday.

Exercises 1E

REVIEW QUESTIONS

1. Describe critical thinking and why it is important to everyone.
2. Summarize the hints given in this unit and explain how each is important to critical thinking.
3. Give a few examples of situations in which you used critical thinking in your own life.
4. Give at least one case you know of in which a poor decision was made (by you or someone else) because of a lack of good critical thinking.

DOES IT MAKE SENSE?

Describe whether each of the following statements makes sense (or is clearly true) or does not make sense (or is clearly false). Explain your reasoning.

5. Reed was relieved because his insurance company chose not to deny his claim.
6. Although the plane crashed in Nevada, the survivors were buried in California.
7. Sue prefers the Red Shuttle because it gets her to the airport in an hour and a half, while the Blue Shuttle takes 80 minutes.
8. Alan decided to buy his ticket from Ticketmaster for $33 plus a 10% surcharge rather than from the box office, where it costs $35 with no additional charges.
9. There was no price difference, so Michael chose the tires with a 5-year, 40,000-mile warranty over the tires with a 50-month, 35,000-mile warranty.
10. Auto policy A has $30,000 worth of collision insurance with an annual premium of $400. Auto policy B has $25,000 worth of collision insurance with an annual premium of $300. Clearly policy B is the better policy.

BASIC SKILLS & CONCEPTS

11–22: Read and Think Carefully. Give an answer and an explanation for the following questions.

11. José had six bagels and ate all but four of them. How many bagels were left?
12. Is it possible for a man to marry his widow's sister?
13. Paris Hilton's rooster laid an egg in Brittany Spears' yard. Who owns the egg?
14. Three kinds of apples are all mixed up in a basket. How many apples must you draw (without looking) from the basket to be sure of getting at least two of one kind?
15. Suppose you go to a party with four Americans and four Canadians, none of whom you have met. How many people must you meet to be sure of meeting one Canadian and one American?
16. Suppose you go to a party with four Americans and four Canadians, none of whom you have met. How many people must you meet to be sure of meeting two people of the same nationality?
17. Suppose you go to a party with four Americans and four Canadians, none of whom you have met. How many people must you meet to be sure of meeting two Canadians?
18. A boy and his father were in a car crash and were taken to the emergency room. The surgeon looked at the boy and said, "I can't operate on this boy; he is my son!" How is this possible?
19. Suzanne goes bowling at least one day per week, but never on two consecutive days. List all the numbers of days per week that Suzanne could go bowling.
20. A race car driver completed the first lap in one minute and forty seconds. Despite a crosswind, driving at the same speed, he completed the second lap in 100 seconds. Give a possible explanation.
21. Half of the class consists of communications majors, and half of the class consists of men. Does it follow that one quarter of the class is male communications majors?
22. Half of a country's exports consist of corn, and half of the corn is from the state of Caldonia. Does it follow that one quarter of the exports consist of corn from Caldonia?
23. **Interpreting Policies.** A city charter's sole policy on reelection states

    A person who has served three consecutive terms of four years each shall be eligible for appointment, nomination for or election to the office of councilmember no sooner than for a term beginning eight years after completion of that councilmember's third consecutive full term.

    a. What is the maximum number of consecutive years that a councilmember could serve?
    b. How many years must a councilmember who has served three consecutive full terms wait before running for office again?

c. Suppose a councilmember has served two consecutive full terms and is then defeated for reelection. According to this provision, is she or he required to wait 8 years before running for office again?

d. Suppose a councilmember serves three consecutive full terms and is reelected 10 years later. According to this provision, how many consecutive terms can she or he serve at that time?

24. **Reading a Ballot Initiative.** Consider the following ballot initiative that appeared in a statewide election:

Shall there be an amendment to the state constitution stating that the state and any city, town, or county may control the promotion of obscenity to the full extent permitted by the First Amendment to the U.S. Constitution, and thereby preventing the state courts from interpreting the right of free expression more broadly under the state constitution than under the First Amendment to the U.S. Constitution in the area of obscenity?

a. According to the text of this initiative, is the state constitution currently more or less strict about obscenity than the First Amendment to the U.S. Constitution? Explain.

b. Explain the effect of a *yes* vote on this initiative.

c. True or false: If the initiative passed, then the state would have a stricter law on obscenity than specified in the U.S. Constitution. Explain.

25–28: Hidden Assumptions. Identify at least two hidden assumptions in the following arguments.

25. The bank teller made a calculation and told me that if I deposit \$500 today in a savings plan at a 2.3% interest rate, I will have about \$703 in 15 years.

26. I recommend giving to the United Way because it supports so many worthwhile causes.

27. I voted for Senator McCoy because she campaigned with a promise to overhaul the health care system.

28. I support increased military spending because we need a strong America.

29–30: Unstated Issues. The following arguments give several reasons for a particular political position. Identify at least one unstated issue that may, for at least some people, be the real issue of concern.

29. I oppose the President's spending proposal. Taxpayer money should not be used for programs that many taxpayers do not support. Excessive spending also risks increasing budget deficits. Greater deficits increase the federal debt, which in turn increases our reliance on foreign investors.

30. People who eliminate meat from their diet risk severe nutritional deficiencies. Eating meat is by far the easiest way to consume complete protein plus many other essential nutrients all in one food source. It makes sense: our ancestors have been meat-eaters for thousands of years.

31. **IRS Guidelines on Who Must File a Federal Tax Return.** When must a single person who is claimed as a dependent by someone else file a tax return? Assuming the single person is not age 65 or older and not blind, that person must file a return if any of the following apply:

(i) unearned income was more than \$900; or

(ii) earned income was more than \$5450; or

(iii) gross income was more than the larger of \$900 or your earned income (up to \$5150) plus \$300.

Determine whether the following single dependents (under age 65 and not blind) must file a return.

a. Maria had unearned income of \$750, earned income of \$5700, and gross income of \$6450.

b. Van had unearned income of \$200, earned income of \$3000, and gross income of \$3500.

c. Walt had no unearned income and had earned and gross income of \$5400.

d. Helena had unearned income of \$200, earned income of \$5200, and gross income of \$5500.

32. **IRS Guidelines on Dependents on Federal Tax Returns.** You may claim a person as a dependent on your tax return if that person is a *qualifying child* or a *qualifying relative*. A qualifying child must meet the following requirements.

(i) The child must be your son, daughter, stepchild, foster child, brother, sister, half-brother, half-sister, stepbrother, stepsister, or a descendant of any of them.

(ii) The child must be under age 19 at the end of the year, under age 24 at the end of the year and a full-time student, or any age if permanently disabled.

(iii) The child must have lived with you for more than half of the year, unless the absence is "temporary" for education, illness, vocation, business, or military service.

(iv) The child must not have provided more than half of his/her support for the year.

Determine whether you could claim a child as a dependent in the following situations.

a. You have a 22-year-old stepdaughter who is a full-time student, lives year-round in another state, and receives full support from you.

b. You have an 18-year-old son who works full-time writing software, lives with you, and supports himself.

c. Your nephew (who cannot be claimed by anyone else) is a 20-year-old full-time student who lives with and is supported by you.

d. Your half-brother is an 18-year-old part-time student who lived with you for eight months of the tax year and received two-thirds of his support from you.

33. **Reading a Lease.** Consider the following excerpt from the contract for the lease of an apartment:

Landlord shall return the security deposit to resident within one month after termination of this lease or surrender and acceptance of the premises, whichever occurs first.

Suppose your lease terminates on June 30, and you move out of the apartment on June 5. Explain whether or not the landlord has complied with the terms of the lease if you receive your security deposit back on

a. June 28. b. July 2. c. July 7.

34. **Airline Options.** In planning a trip to New Zealand six months in advance, you find that an airline offers two options:

- Plan A: You can buy a fully refundable ticket for $2200.
- Plan B: You can buy a $1200 ticket, but you forfeit 25% of the price if the ticket is changed or canceled.

Describe your options in the events that you do and do not make the trip. How would you decide which ticket to buy?

35. **Buy vs. Lease.** You are deciding whether to buy a car for $18,000 or to accept a lease agreement. The lease entails a $1000 initiation fee plus monthly payments of $240 for 36 months. Under the lease agreement, you are responsible for service on the car and insurance. At the end of the lease, you may purchase the car for $9000.

a. Should the cost of service and insurance determine which option you choose?

b. Does the total cost of purchasing the car at the end of the lease agreement exceed the cost of purchasing the car at the outset?

c. What are some possible advantages of leasing the car?

36. **You've Won!** You receive the following e-mail notification: "Through a random selection from more than 20 million e-mail addresses, you've been selected as the winner of our grand prize—a two-week vacation in the Bahamas. To claim your prize, please call our toll free number. Have your credit card ready for identification and a small processing fee." Does this sound like a deal worth taking? Explain.

FURTHER APPLICATIONS

37–40: **Ambiguity in the News.** Explain how the following direct quotes from news sources are ambiguous. What additional information is needed to remove the ambiguity?

37. LOS ANGELES—Two jumbo jets with more than 350 people aboard nearly collided over the city during a landing attempt . . .

38. After Governor Baldridge watched the lion perform, he was taken to Main Street and fed twenty-five pounds of red meat in front of the Fox Theater.

39. France must decrease its public deficit from 6% of its gross domestic product, or $83 billion, to 3%.

40. Anti-nuclear protestors released live cockroaches inside the White House Friday, and these were arrested when they left and blocked a security gate.

41. **Comparing Candidates.** Two assistant district attorneys, Alice and Zack, are running for the position of district attorney. The candidates make the following statements:

Zack: In the last five years, Alice has prosecuted 126 defendants charged with sexual assault on children. Of those, only nine cases even went to trial, and of those, only four cases resulted in conviction and a prison sentence.

Alice: I have prosecuted 253 cases involving sexual assault on children. More than 40% of the 253 cases resulted in prison or jail sentences as part of the original plea agreement.

a. Comment on whether the two candidates' numbers for cases prosecuted by Alice are consistent.

b. Would you use these statements as grounds for making a decision on whom to vote for in the district attorney race? If not, what would you do to obtain more complete information?

42. **Credit Card Agreement.** The following rules are among the many provisions of a particular credit card agreement.

For the regular plan, the minimum payment due is the greater of $10.00 or 5% of the new balance shown on your statement (rounded to the nearest $1.00) plus any unpaid late fees and returned check fees, and any amounts shown as past due on your statement.

If you make a purchase under a regular plan, no finance charges will be imposed in any billing period in which (i) there is no previous balance or (ii) payments received and credits issued by the payment due date, which is 25 days after the statement closing date shown on your last statement, equal or exceed the previous balance. If the new balance is not satisfied in full by the payment due date shown on your last statement, there will be a finance charge on each purchase from the date of purchase.

a. If the new balance in your account is $8 and you have $35 in unpaid late fees, what is your minimum payment due?

b. Suppose you have a previous balance of $150 and you pay $200 one month after the statement closing date. Will you be assessed a finance charge?

c. In part b, if you make a purchase on the same day that you make the $200 payment, will a finance charge be assessed on that purchase?

43. **Alaska Nepotism Rule.** The Alaska state law on nepotism states

It is unlawful for a person who is the spouse of or is related by blood within and including the second degree of kindred to the executive head of a principal state department or agency to be employed in that department or agency.

a. Suppose you were an Alaska state senator and hired a stepson (son of your spouse by a previous marriage) as a staff assistant. Explain why you believe that this hire would or would not conform with the law.

b. Describe at least two hiring situations the legality of which you feel is not resolved by this statute. (For example, is it legal for a state senator to hire a former spouse as a staff member?)

44. **Texas Ethics.** In its Guide to Ethics Laws, the Texas Ethics Commission states

A state officer or employee should not accept or solicit any gift, favor, or service that might reasonably tend to influence the officer or employee in the discharge of official duties or that the officer or employee knows or should know is being offered with the intent to influence the officer's or employee's official conduct.

a. Imagine that you are a state representative. Do you believe it would be legal to accept a maximum campaign contribution from a person if you knew nothing about the person except her name?

b. Describe a situation in which you (as a state representative) *would* accept a contribution because it clearly conforms with this guideline. Then describe a situation in which you *would not* accept a contribution because it clearly violates this guideline.

45–48: Decision Making. Analyze the following situations and explain how you would make the decision.

45. You and your spouse are expecting a baby. Your current health insurance costs \$115 per month, but doesn't cover prenatal care or delivery. You can upgrade to a policy that will cover your prenatal care and delivery, but your new premium will be \$275 per month. The cost of prenatal care and delivery is approximately \$4000.

46. You own a small business and need to be in another city on Monday for a meeting. You could fly to the meeting on Monday morning and return Monday evening on a ticket priced at \$750. However, if you arrive on Saturday night (spending nothing on meals that day), the ticket price would be only \$335. A hotel will cost \$105 per night, and you estimate that meals away from home will cost you \$55 per day.

47. You fly frequently between two cities 1500 miles apart. Average round-trip cost on Airline A is \$350. Airline B offers the same trip for only \$325. However, Airline A has a frequent flyer program in which you earn a free round-trip ticket after you fly 25,000 miles. Airline B does not have a frequent flyer program.

48. One day your auto insurance company calls and says that your insurance rates will be increased. You have a choice of keeping your current deductible of \$200 with a new premium of \$450 per year or going to a higher deductible of \$1000 with a premium of \$200 per year. In the past 10 years, you have filed claims of \$100, \$200, and \$600.

49–52: Alternative Explanation. Give an explanation for the following facts that is more plausible than the given explanation.

49. An AFC (American Football League) team has won five out of the last six Superbowls (2004–2009). *Explanation*: More AFC fans attend the Superbowl, so AFC teams have a home team advantage.

50. The (Australian) paradise parrot has not been observed in the wild since the early 1900s. *Explanation*: Bird watchers are less observant than they used to be.

51. In the first decade of the 2000s, violent crime decreased, while the number of inmates in custody increased. *Explanation:* There was an increase in false convictions.

52. Between 2000 and 2010, the annual number of hours of TV watched (ages 12 and over) increased by about 15%, while the annual number of hours of video games played (ages 12 and over) increased by about 25%. *Explanation:* Watching TV leads to playing video games.

53–56: Multiple Explanation. Describe at least one way in which both of the statements in the following pairs could be true.

53. A: In some countries, the number of deaths per year has been increasing.
    B: In those same countries, the annual death rate (deaths per 100,000 people in the population) has been decreasing.

54. A: The total number of assaults on campus increased during the last five years.
    B: The number of reported assaults on campus decreased during the last five years.

55. A: The gun homicide rate is greater in country X than in country Y.
    B: The gun fatality rate is greater in country Y than in country X.

56. A: The birth rate (births per 100,000 people in the population) in a country is increasing.
    B: The population of the same country is decreasing.

57–65: Critical Thinking. Consider the following short arguments that support a conclusion (which may only be implied). Use critical thinking methods to analyze the arguments and determine whether the conclusion is convincing. Write out your analysis carefully.

57. Newspapers have been a mainstay of American life for two centuries. However, their very existence is being threatened by Internet news sources. There is no substitute for newspapers as a local news source. Furthermore, for national issues, citizens need the investigative reporting of trained and independent newspaper journalists, rather than the biased opinions of Internet bloggers.

58. "Just as Tiger Woods forever changed the country-club culture of golf, and Will Smith confounded stereotypes about the Hollywood leading man, hip-hop's rise is helping redefine the American Mainstream, which no longer aspires toward a single iconic image of style or class." —Hua Hsu, *The Atlantic*

59. "Since 1992, ... there has been a growing global consensus that the Earth's changing climate, our patterns of resource consumption, and our soaring population are combining to threaten the web of biodiversity that sustains all species, including our own. Therefore, we need to redefine our relationship with the natural world." —Thomas Friedman, *Hot, Flat, and Crowded*

60. That we have a health care crisis is clear: Large numbers of Americans are uninsured, and the cost of health care to our nation is skyrocketing. I believe that only the government has the power to step in and solve this crisis, so I urge you to support candidates who will make health care reform their top priority.

61. "Smoking has no causal relationship to crime, has little effect on others, and ... looks cool. Controlling for income, education and occupation, it causes about 200,000 deaths per year, mostly of people in their 70s. Single motherhood, by contrast, directly harms children, occurs at a rate of about 1.5 million a year and has a causal relationship to criminal behavior, substance abuse, juvenile delinquency, sexual victimization and almost every other social disorder." —Ann Coulter, HumanEvents.com

62. "We fret about proliferating nanobots and instant cosmic doom when we ought to be devoting our time and energy to confirmed worries like 41 million Americans without health insurance. A high-calorie, low exertion lifestyle is far more likely to harm you than a vagrant black hole. . . . It makes far more sense to focus on mundane troubles that are all too real." —Gregg Easterbrook, *Wired*

63. "Another difference between airline crashes and asteroid collisions . . . is that one can do something about the risk of being killed in an airline crash—not fly or fly less frequently . . . —and one cannot do anything about asteroid collisions. Yet most people who are afraid to fly substitute another means of transportation, namely driving, that is more dangerous than flying." —Richard Posner, *Catastrophe*

64. "There is no universal solution to the problem of decision-making. The real world is just too complex. . . . Sometimes we need to reason through our options and carefully analyze the possibilities. And sometimes, we need to listen to our emotions. The secret is knowing when to use these different styles of thought. We always need to be thinking about how we think." —Jonah Lehrer, *How We Decide*

65. American public universities are approaching a crisis. State funding is declining as priorities shift to public school systems and prisons. At the same time, population projections indicate a 30% increase in high school graduates in the next 15 years. Many universities are at capacity and could not expand even if funds were available. If the number of university graduates remains level, the United States will still have one of the highest university graduation rates of any country in the world. The solution is to raise both admission standards and tuition at four-year colleges and universities, thereby limiting the number of students admitted to these institutions.

66. **Poetry and Mathematics.** Consider the following poem by the English poet A.E. Housman (1859–1936).

LOVELIEST OF TREES

Loveliest of trees, the cherry now
Is hung with bloom along the bough

And stands about the woodland ride
Wearing white for Eastertide.

Now, of my threescore years and ten,
Twenty will not come again,

And take from seventy springs a score,
It only leaves me fifty more.

And since to look at things in bloom
Fifty springs are little room,

About the woodlands I will go
To see the cherry hung with snow.

How old was the poet at the time he wrote this poem? (Hint: A score is 20.) Based on your reading of this poem, how much longer does the poet expect to live? Explain.

WEB PROJECTS

67. **Interpreting the Second Amendment.** Much of the debate over gun control revolves around interpretations of the Second Amendment to the U.S. Constitution. It reads:

A well-regulated militia being necessary to the security of a free state, the right of the people to keep and bear arms shall not be infringed.

Gun rights advocates tend to focus on the "right of the people to keep and bear arms." Gun control advocates tend to focus on "a well-regulated militia." Visit a few of the many Web sites on each side of this issue to find interpretations of the Second Amendment that both support and oppose gun control. Based on what you learn, do you believe that the Second Amendment allows for gun control laws? Defend your opinion.

68. **Ballot Initiatives.** Investigate a particular ballot initiative in your state, county, or city (or choose one in another area from a Web site). Explain the important arguments on each side of the issue. If possible, find a statement of the initiative as it appeared on the ballot. Is the statement of the initiative clear? Explain.

69. **Fine Print.** Several Web sites, including mouseprint.org, give recent examples of deceptive uses of fine print. Describe one case that you think is particularly deceptive or dangerous. Describe the case in detail, and explain how the fine print is important to understanding the situation.

IN YOUR WORLD

70. **Argument Analysis.** Find a news article or editorial in which a clear position is taken on a controversial issue. Analyze the argument using the hints and strategies given in this unit. Whether or not you agree with the final conclusion, state whether the argument is effective.

71. **Personal Decisions.** Discuss a situation in your own life in which you needed to think carefully before making a critical decision. Did you use critical thinking strategies? In retrospect, would you have made a different decision using critical thinking strategies?

72. **Ambiguous Terms.** Many arguments and promotions are difficult to analyze because of vague, ambiguous, or overused terms (for example, "natural food" or "human rights"). In news articles or advertising, find three terms that you believe are vague or ambiguous. Explain how the terms could be more clearly defined.

CHAPTER 1 Summary

UNIT	KEY TERMS	KEY IDEAS AND SKILLS
1A	logic argument premises, conclusions fallacy	**Identify** an argument's premises and conclusions. **Recognize** fallacious arguments, which contain logical flaws so that their conclusions are not well supported by their premises.
1B	proposition truth values, truth tables negation: *not p* conjunction: *p and q* disjunction: *p or q* conditional: *if p, then q* logical equivalence	**Understand** truth tables for negation, conjunction, disjunction, conditional. **Inclusive versus exclusive *or*** Inclusive *or* means *either or both.* Exclusive *or* means *one or the other, but not both.* **Variations on the conditional** *if p, then q* **Converse:** *if q, then p* **Inverse:** *if not p, then not q* **Contrapositive:** *if not q, then not p*
1C	set categorical propositions Venn diagrams	**Set relationships** Subsets, disjoint sets, overlapping sets **Four categorical propositions** All *S* are *P*; No *S* are *P*; Some *S* are *P*; Some *S* are not *P* **Uses of Venn diagrams** Illustrating set relationships Organizing information
1D	inductive argument strength deductive argument validity soundness	**Evaluating arguments** Inductive arguments in terms of strength Deductive arguments in terms of validity and soundness Venn diagram tests of validity Chains of conditionals **Induction and deduction in mathematics** Propose a theorem inductively. Prove a theorem deductively.
1E	critical thinking	1. Read (or listen) carefully. 2. Look for hidden assumptions. 3. Identify the real issue. 4. Understand the options. 5. Watch for fine print and missing information. 6. Are other conclusions possible?

2

Nothing in life is to be feared. It is only to be understood.
—Marie Curie

UNIT 2A

The Problem-Solving Power of Units: We explore the powerful technique of working with units, both to solve problems and to check answers.

UNIT 2B

Standardized Units: More Problem-Solving Power: We review standardized units of both the U.S. customary and the metric systems and investigate units for problems involving temperature, energy, density, and concentration.

UNIT 2C

Problem-Solving Guidelines and Hints: We extend the techniques of the previous units to form a general set of guidelines and hints for effective problem solving.

Approaches to Problem Solving

In your past mathematics classes, it might have seemed that mathematical problems involved only numbers and symbols. But the mathematical problems that you encounter in other classes, in jobs, and in daily life are almost always posed in words. That's why Chapter 1 focused on logic and critical thinking: These skills help you find the key ideas buried in problems that are posed in words. In this chapter, we begin a study of *quantitative* problem solving, in which the problems involve words *and* numbers.

ACTIVITY Global Melting

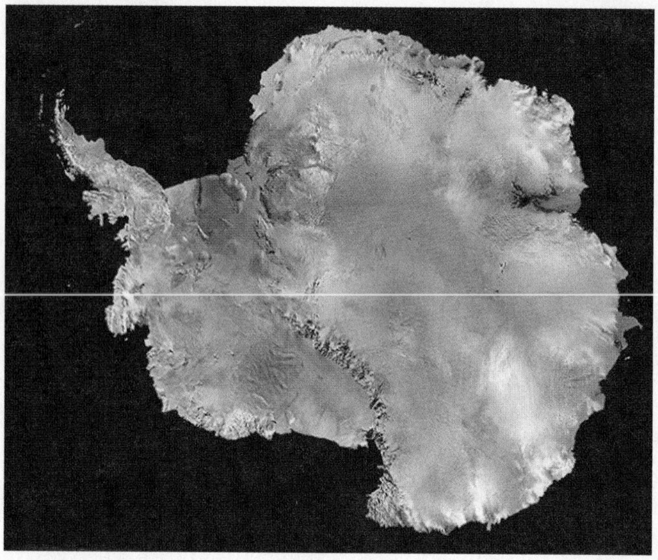

Use this activity to gain a sense of the kinds of problems this chapter will enable you to study. Try working through it before you begin the chapter, then return to it after you've learned the chapter material.

The photo to the left shows a view of Antarctica from space, as it appears without cloud cover. Notice that the continent is covered almost everywhere with thick white ice. What would happen to sea level if all this ice were to melt? This is an important question, because continued global warming will increase the rate of melting, though scientists suspect it would take thousands of years for the ice to melt entirely. This question represents the kind of "real-life" problem solving for which mathematics is so useful.

To solve a problem like this one, we first need to gather some data. A quick Web search will tell you the following:

- The total land area of Antarctica is about 14 million square kilometers.
- The mean (average) thickness of Antarctic ice is about 2.15 kilometers.
- Earth's oceans cover a total surface area of about 340 million square kilometers.
- When ice melts into water, the resulting water volume is about 5/6 of the original ice volume.

Working individually or in small groups, try to answer the following questions. If you have difficulty, you might want to read ahead through parts of this chapter.

1. What is the total volume of the ice sheet on Antarctica in cubic kilometers? (*Hint:* You need only two of the pieces of data listed above.)
2. If all this ice were to melt, what volume of liquid water would it represent?
3. Suppose all the water from the melted ice flowed into Earth's oceans. Assume that the total surface area of the oceans does not change—that is, the oceans stay in the same basin, rather than spreading out over the continents. How much would sea level rise? Give your answer in kilometers, meters, and feet. (Bonus: Do you think the assumption of the ocean surface area staying constant is valid? Why or why not?)
4. The Greenland ice sheet contains about 10% as much ice as the Antarctic ice sheet. How much would sea level rise if the Greenland ice sheet melted?
5. Discuss: While melting of the Antarctic or Greenland ice sheet would raise sea level, melting of ice in the Arctic Ocean would not. Why? Can you think of any other potential consequences of melting of ice in the Arctic Ocean?
6. Discuss: Global warming is expected to cause melting of the polar ice sheets, but scientists cannot yet predict how fast the ice will melt. Given this uncertainty, how should the danger of polar melting be dealt with in political discussions of global warming?

UNIT 2A The Problem-Solving Power of Units

Just as critical thinking can be approached in different ways, there's no single best approach to solving quantitative problems. However, people have spent lifetimes coming up with strategies and guidelines that can help. The overall goal of this chapter is to help you learn some of these strategies and guidelines.

We will begin with a technique sometimes called *unit analysis*, in which we use the units of a problem to help figure out how to solve it. As you will see, unit analysis is a simple yet powerful idea that can be applied to a wide range of problems.

You Can't Add Apples and Oranges

It may be a cliché, but mathematically it is true that you can't add apples and oranges. The reason is that we can add or subtract only quantities of the same type. For example, we can add 5 apples and 3 apples to get 8 apples. But apples and oranges are different things, so if we try to add 5 apples and 3 oranges, all we can say is that we have 5 apples and 3 oranges.

More generally, numbers in real problems usually represent a quantity of *something*, which we can describe by its **units.** If we count the number of apples in a basket, the result has units of *apples*. If we measure the length of a room, the result may have units of *feet*. If we ask how fast a car is traveling, the answer may have units of *miles per hour*.

> **DEFINITION**
>
> The **units** of a quantity describe what is being measured or counted.

We can add or subtract numbers only when they have the same units. However, we can multiply and divide quantities with the same or different units, much as we multiply and divide numbers. A few examples should clarify the idea:

- If you drive 100 miles in two hours, your average speed is the distance traveled (100 mi) divided by the time it took (2 hr):

$$\frac{100 \text{ mi}}{2 \text{ hr}} = \frac{50 \text{ mi}}{1 \text{ hr}} = 50\,\frac{\text{mi}}{\text{hr}}$$

  We read this answer as "50 miles per hour." Note that the word *per* means "divided by" (or "for every").

- To find the *area* of a room, we multiply its length by its width (Figure 2.1). If the room is 12 feet long and 10 feet wide, its area is

$$12 \text{ ft} \times 10 \text{ ft} = 120\,(\text{ft} \times \text{ft}) = 120 \text{ ft}^2$$

  We read this area as "120 square feet," remembering that the word *square* implies something raised to the second power. Note that we multiply the numbers ($12 \times 10 = 120$) separately from the units ($\text{ft} \times \text{ft} = \text{ft}^2$) but keep track of both.

Take Note

When abbreviating units, we do not distinguish between singular and plural. For example, we use *mi* for both mile and miles.

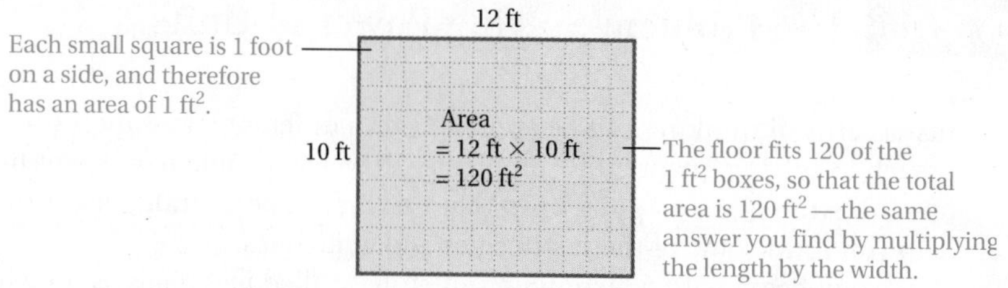

FIGURE 2.1 Multiplying a length in feet by a width in feet gives an area in *square feet* (ft^2).

- To find the *volume* of a box, we multiply its width, depth, and height (Figure 2.2). If the box is 6 inches wide, 4 inches deep, and 10 inches high, its volume is

$$6 \text{ in.} \times 4 \text{ in.} \times 10 \text{ in.} = 240 \text{ (in.} \times \text{in.} \times \text{in.)} = 240 \text{ in.}^3$$

We read this volume as "240 cubic inches," remembering that the word *cubic* implies something raised to the third power. (The abbreviation "in." includes a period.)

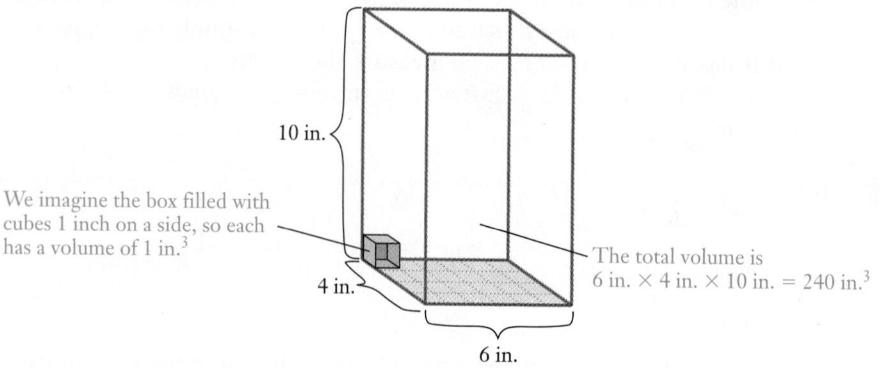

FIGURE 2.2 If we measure the side lengths of a box in inches, we calculate its volume in *cubic inches* (in.^3).

- To find the energy used by a light bulb, we multiply its power rating (in watts or kilowatts) by the length of time it is turned on. If a movie set uses a 0.5-kilowatt light bulb for 6 hours, its energy usage is

$$0.5 \text{ kilowatt} \times 6 \text{ hr} = 3 \text{ kilowatt} \times \text{hr}$$

We read this answer as "3 kilowatt-hours," where the hyphen between the units implies multiplication. (See Unit 2B for further discussion of energy units.)

READING UNITS

Operation	Key word or symbol	Example
Division	*per*	Read miles ÷ hours as "miles per hour."
Raising to second power	*square*	Read ft × ft, or ft^2, as "square feet" or "feet squared."
Raising to third power	*cube* or *cubic*	Read ft × ft × ft, or ft^3, as "cubic feet" or "feet cubed."
Multiplication	hyphen	Read kilowatts × hours as "kilowatt-hours."

Example 1 Identifying Units

Identify the units of the answer for each of the following cases.

a. The price you paid for gasoline, found by dividing its total cost in dollars by the number of gallons of gas that you bought.
b. The area of a circle, found with the formula πr^2, where the radius r is measured in centimeters. (Note that π is a pure number and has no units.)
c. A volume found by multiplying an area measured in acres by a depth measured in feet.

Solution

a. The price of the gasoline has units of dollars divided by gallons, which we write as \$/gal and read as "dollars per gallon."
b. The area of the circle has units of centimeters to the second power, which we write as cm^2 and read as "square centimeters."
c. In this case, the volume has units of acres $\times$ feet, which we read as "acre-feet." This unit of volume is commonly used by hydrologists (water engineers) in the United States.

Now try Exercises 19–26.

Time Out to Think

Look for numbers in a newspaper or magazine. For at least five cases, identify the units of the numbers.

Unit Conversions

Many everyday problems involve nothing more than converting one set of units to another. For example, you might want to convert a distance from kilometers to miles or a recipe measure from quarts to cups.

The basic "trick" of unit conversions is to devise an appropriate way of multiplying by 1. For example, the following are all different ways of writing 1.

$$1 = \frac{1}{1} = \frac{8}{8} = \frac{\frac{1}{4}}{\frac{1}{4}} = \frac{1\text{ kilogram}}{1\text{ kilogram}} = \frac{1\text{ week}}{7\text{ days}} = \frac{12\text{ inches}}{1\text{ foot}}$$

The last expression shows the necessity of stating units: $12 \div 1$ is *not* 1, but 12 in. $\div$ 1 ft *is* 1 because 12 inches and 1 foot are equal.

Conversion Factors

The statement 12 in. = 1 ft is an example of a **conversion factor.** We can write this conversion factor in three equivalent ways:

$$12\text{ in.} = 1\text{ ft} \quad \text{or} \quad \frac{12\text{ in.}}{1\text{ ft}} = 1 \quad \text{or} \quad \frac{1\text{ ft}}{12\text{ in.}} = 1$$

The key to unit conversions is to use the correct form of the conversion factor for the problem at hand.

A Brief Review Working with Fractions

We can express a fraction in three basic ways: as a *common fraction* such as $\frac{1}{2}$; as a fraction in *decimal form* such as 0.5; and as a *percentage* such as 50%. Here, we review the first two forms (see p. 129 for a review of percentages).

Common Fractions

Common fractions have the form a/b, where a and b can be any numbers as long as b is not zero. The number on top is called the **numerator** and the number on the bottom is called the **denominator**. A fraction represents division:

$$\begin{array}{r} \text{numerator} \rightarrow a \\ \text{denominator} \rightarrow b \end{array} \quad \text{means} \quad a \div b$$

We can write an integer as a fraction with a denominator of 1. For example:

$$3 = \frac{3}{1} \quad \text{or} \quad -4 = \frac{-4}{1}$$

Adding and Subtracting Fractions

If two fractions have the same denominator (a *common denominator*), we can add or subtract them by adding or subtracting their numerators. For example:

$$\frac{1}{5} + \frac{2}{5} = \frac{1+2}{5} = \frac{3}{5} \quad \text{or} \quad \frac{7}{9} - \frac{2}{9} = \frac{7-2}{9} = \frac{5}{9}$$

Otherwise, we must rewrite the fractions with the same denominator before adding or subtracting. For example, we can add $\frac{1}{2} + \frac{1}{3}$ by rewriting them as $\frac{3}{6}$ and $\frac{2}{6}$ (so both have a denominator of 6), respectively:

$$\frac{1}{2} + \frac{1}{3} = \frac{3}{6} + \frac{2}{6} = \frac{3+2}{6} = \frac{5}{6}$$

Multiplying Fractions

To multiply fractions, we multiply the numerators and denominators separately. For example:

$$\frac{1}{3} \times \frac{2}{5} = \frac{1 \times 2}{3 \times 5} = \frac{2}{15}$$

Sometimes we can simplify fractions at the same time we multiply them by *canceling* terms that occur in both the numerator and the denominator. For example:

$$\frac{3}{4} \times \frac{5}{3} = \frac{3 \times 5}{4 \times 3} = \frac{5}{4}$$

Reciprocals and Division

Two numbers are **reciprocals** if their product is 1. For example:

$$2 \text{ and } \frac{1}{2} \text{ are reciprocals because } 2 \times \frac{1}{2} = 1$$

$$\frac{4}{3} \text{ and } \frac{3}{4} \text{ are reciprocals because } \frac{4}{3} \times \frac{3}{4} = 1$$

We find the reciprocal of any fraction by inverting it (interchanging the numerator and the denominator). For an integer like 2, we think of it as $\frac{2}{1}$ to find that its reciprocal is $\frac{1}{2}$. In general:

- The reciprocal of a is $\frac{1}{a}$ $(a \neq 0)$.
- The reciprocal of $\frac{a}{b}$ is $\frac{b}{a}$ $(a \neq 0, b \neq 0)$.

To divide fractions, we replace the division with multiplication by the reciprocal. This process is sometimes called *invert and multiply*, as shown in the following examples:

$$10 \div \frac{1}{2} = \underbrace{10 \times \frac{2}{1}}_{\text{invert and multiply}} = 20$$

$$\frac{3}{4} \div \frac{2}{5} = \underbrace{\frac{3}{4} \times \frac{5}{2}}_{\text{invert and multiply}} = \frac{15}{8}$$

Rules Summary

Addition/subtraction (same denominator required):

$$\frac{a}{c} + \frac{b}{c} = \frac{a+b}{c} \quad \text{or} \quad \frac{a}{c} - \frac{b}{c} = \frac{a-b}{c}$$

Multiplication:

$$\frac{a}{b} \times \frac{c}{d} = \frac{a \times c}{b \times d}$$

Division (invert and multiply):

$$\frac{a}{b} \div \frac{c}{d} = \frac{a}{b} \times \frac{d}{c}$$

Decimal Form

For a fraction in decimal form, each digit corresponds to a certain place value, which is always a power of 10 (such as 10, 100, 1000, ...). The following example shows values for the decimal places in the number 3.141.

3	.	1	4	1
ones		tenths	hundredths	thousandths
(1)		$\left(0.1 = \frac{1}{10}\right)$	$\left(0.01 = \frac{1}{100}\right)$	$\left(0.001 = \frac{1}{1000}\right)$

Converting to Common Form

Converting a fraction from decimal to common form requires recognizing the value of the last digit in the decimal. For example:

$$0.4 = \frac{4}{10} \qquad 3.15 = \frac{315}{100}$$

$$0.097 = \frac{97}{1000}$$

Converting to Decimal Form

To convert a common fraction into decimal form, we carry out the division implied by the fraction. For example:

$$\frac{1}{4} = 1 \div 4 = 0.25$$

Many common fractions cannot be written *exactly* in decimal form, but instead have an endless repeating pattern of digits. For example, the decimal form of $\frac{1}{3}$ contains an endless string of 3s:

$$\frac{1}{3} = 0.3333333\ldots$$

Mathematically, we represent the repeating digits by putting a bar over them. For example, the bar in $0.\overline{3}$ means that the 3 repeats indefinitely. In practice, we usually round repeating decimals to one or a few digits. For example, we might round the decimal form of $\frac{1}{3}$ to 0.33. **Now try Exercises 13–18.**

Example 2 Feet to Inches

Convert a distance of 7 feet into inches.

Solution We begin with *feet* and want to end up with *inches*. We therefore need the conversion factor between *inches* and *feet* in a form that has *feet* in the denominator, so that *feet* cancel:

$$7\text{ ft} = 7\text{ ft} \times \underbrace{\frac{12\text{ in.}}{1\text{ ft}}}_{1} = 84\text{ in.}$$

Note that we really just multiplied 7 feet by 1 in a form that allowed us to change the units. Seven feet is the same as 84 inches. **Now try Exercises 27–28.**

Example 3 Inches to Feet

Convert a length of 102 inches to feet.

Solution This time we use the conversion factor in the form with *inches* in the denominator, so that *inches* cancel:

$$102\text{ in.} = 102\text{ in.} \times \underbrace{\frac{1\text{ ft}}{12\text{ in.}}}_{1} = 8.5\text{ ft}$$

Thus, 102 inches is equivalent to 8.5 feet. **Now try Exercises 29–30.**

Example 4 Using a Chain of Conversions

How many seconds are there in one day?

Solution Most of us don't immediately know the answer to this question, but we do know that 1 day = 24 hr, 1 hr = 60 min, and 1 min = 60 s. We can answer the

FOXTROT © 1995 by Bill Amend. Reprinted with permission of UNIVERSAL PRESS SYNDICATE.

question by setting up a *chain* of unit conversions in which we start with *day* and end up with *seconds:*

$$1\ \text{day} \times \frac{24\ \text{hr}}{1\ \text{day}} \times \frac{60\ \text{min}}{1\ \text{hr}} \times \frac{60\ \text{s}}{1\ \text{min}} = 86{,}400\ \text{s}$$

By using the conversion factors needed to cancel the appropriate units, we are left with the answer in *seconds.* There are 86,400 seconds in one day. **Now try Exercises 31–38.**

Conversions with Units Raised to Powers

We must take special care when converting units raised to powers. For example, suppose we want to know the number of square feet in a square yard. We may not know the conversion factor between square yards (yd^2) and square feet (ft^2), but we know that 1 yd = 3 ft. Therefore, we can replace 1 yard by 3 feet when we write out 1 square yard:

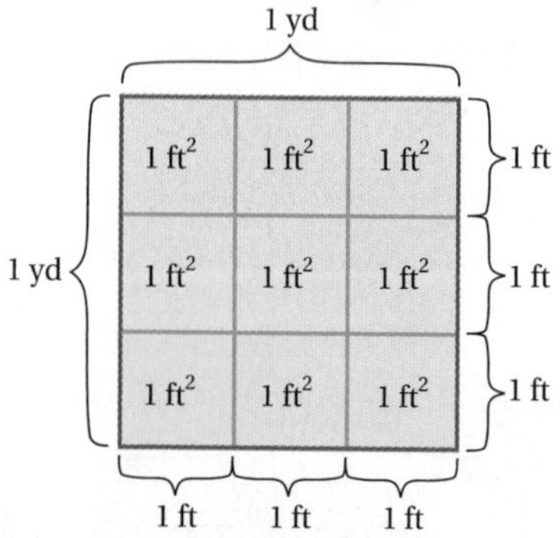

FIGURE 2.3 Notice that 1 square yard contains 9 square feet.

$$1\ \text{yd}^2 = 1\ \text{yd} \times 1\ \text{yd} = 3\ \text{ft} \times 3\ \text{ft} = 9\ \text{ft}^2$$

That is, 1 square yard is the same as 9 square feet. We can also find this conversion factor by squaring both sides of the yards-to-feet conversion:

$$1\ \text{yd} = 3\ \text{ft} \xrightarrow[\text{both sides}]{\text{square}} (1\ \text{yd})^2 = (3\ \text{ft})^2 \xrightarrow[\text{each term}]{\text{square}} 1\ \text{yd}^2 = 9\ \text{ft}^2$$

Figure 2.3 confirms that 9 square feet fit exactly into 1 square yard. As usual, we can write the conversion factor in three equivalent forms:

$$1\ \text{yd}^2 = 9\ \text{ft}^2 \quad \text{or} \quad \frac{1\ \text{yd}^2}{9\ \text{ft}^2} = 1 \quad \text{or} \quad \frac{9\ \text{ft}^2}{1\ \text{yd}^2} = 1$$

Example 5 Carpeting a Room

You want to carpet a room that measures 10 feet by 12 feet, making an area of 120 square feet. But carpet is usually sold by the square yard rather than by the square foot. How many square yards of carpet do you need?

Solution We need to convert the room's area from units of *square feet* to *square yards,* so we use the conversion factor in the form that has square feet (ft^2) in the denominator:

$$120\ \text{ft}^2 \times \frac{1\ \text{yd}^2}{9\ \text{ft}^2} = \frac{120}{9}\text{yd}^2 \approx 13.3\ \text{yd}^2$$

The symbol ≈ means "approximately equal to."

Note that we rounded the answer to the nearest 0.1 square yard. Most stores will not sell fractions of a square yard, so you will need to buy 14 square yards of carpet.

Now try Exercises 39–42.

Example 6 Cubic Units: Purchasing Garden Soil

You are preparing a vegetable garden that is 40 feet long and 16 feet wide, and you need enough soil to fill it to a depth of 1 foot. The landscape supply store sells soil by the cubic yard. How much soil should you order?

Solution To find the volume of soil that you need, we multiply the garden's length (40 feet), width (16 feet), and depth (1 foot):

$$40 \text{ ft} \times 16 \text{ ft} \times 1 \text{ ft} = 640 \text{ ft}^3$$

Because soil is sold by the cubic yard, we need to convert this volume from units of *cubic feet* to *cubic yards*. We know that 1 yd = 3 ft, so we find the cubic conversion factor by cubing both sides of this equation:

$$1 \text{ yd} = 3 \text{ ft} \xrightarrow[\text{both sides}]{\text{cube}} (1 \text{ yd})^3 = (3 \text{ ft})^3 \xrightarrow[\text{each term}]{\text{cube}} 1 \text{ yd}^3 = 27 \text{ ft}^2$$

In the last step, we recognized that $3^3 = 3 \times 3 \times 3 = 27$. As usual, we can write this conversion factor in three equivalent forms:

$$1 \text{ yd}^3 = 27 \text{ ft}^3 \quad \text{or} \quad \frac{1 \text{ yd}^3}{27 \text{ ft}^3} = 1 \quad \text{or} \quad \frac{27 \text{ ft}^3}{1 \text{ yd}^3} = 1$$

To convert the soil volume from cubic feet to cubic yards, we use the conversion factor that has cubic feet (ft^3) in the denominator:

$$640 \text{ ft}^3 \times \frac{1 \text{ yd}^3}{27 \text{ ft}^3} = \frac{640}{27} \text{yd}^3 \approx 23.7 \text{ yd}^3$$

You will need to order about 24 cubic yards of soil for your garden.

Now try Exercises 43–46.

Currency Conversions

Different countries use different money, or **currency.** If you travel internationally, you'll need to change money from one currency to another. Converting between currencies is a unit conversion problem in which the conversion factors are the exchange rates.

Table 2.1 shows a typical table of currency exchange rates. The *Dollars per Foreign* column gives the conversion factor in the form useful for converting from foreign currency into U.S. dollars. For example, the row for Mexico shows 0.06584 in this column, which means

$$1 \text{ peso} = \$0.06584$$

TABLE 2.1 Sample Currency Exchange Rates (March 2009)

Currency	Dollars per Foreign	Foreign per Dollar
British pound	1.414	0.7072
Canadian dollar	0.7834	1.277
European euro	1.256	0.7965
Japanese yen	0.01007	99.34
Mexican peso	0.06584	15.19

USING TECHNOLOGY

Currency exchange rates are constantly changing, but you can always get current rates by typing "exchange rates" into any search engine. Google will also do direct conversions; for example, typing "25 euros in dollars" will tell you today's dollar value of 25 euros.

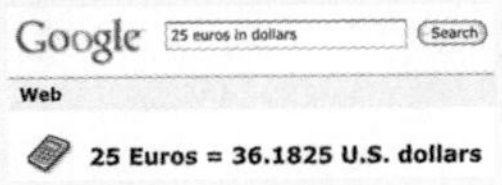

Historical Note

Until the creation of the euro, each European country had its own currency. The euro was first adopted by 11 countries in 1999, though coins and notes did not circulate until 2002. By 2009, the euro was used in 21 countries of the European Union, and several other countries were working to adopt it.

The *Foreign per Dollar* column gives the conversion factor in the form useful for converting U.S. dollars into foreign currency. In this case,

$$\$1 = 15.19 \text{ pesos}$$

Time Out to Think

Find the reciprocals of the numbers in the *Dollars per Foreign* column of Table 2.1. Are your results the numbers in the *Foreign per Dollar* column? Explain.

Example 7 Price Conversion

At a French department store, the price for a pair of jeans is 45 euros. What is the price in U.S. dollars? Use the exchange rates in Table 2.1.

Solution From the *Dollars per Foreign* column in Table 2.1, we see that

$$1 \text{ euro} = \$1.256$$

As usual, we can write this conversion factor in two other equivalent forms:

$$\frac{1 \text{ euro}}{\$1.256} = 1 \quad \text{or} \quad \frac{\$1.256}{1 \text{ euro}} = 1$$

We use the latter form to convert the price from euros to dollars:

$$45 \cancel{\text{euro}} \times \frac{\$1.256}{1 \cancel{\text{euro}}} \approx \$56.52$$

The price of 45 euros is equivalent to $56.52. **Now try Exercises 47–50.**

Example 8 Buying Currency

You are on holiday in Mexico and need cash. How many pesos can you buy with $100? Use the exchange rates in Table 2.1 and ignore any transaction fees.

Solution From the *Foreign per Dollar* column in Table 2.1, we see that

$$\$1 = 15.19 \text{ pesos}$$

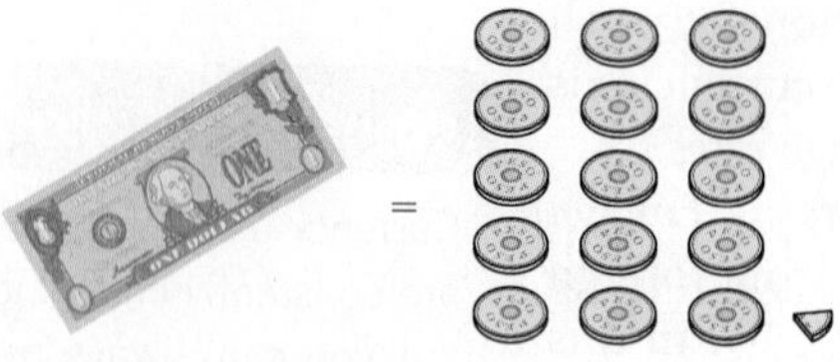

$1 = 15.19 pesos

Two other equivalent forms of this conversion are

$$\frac{15.19 \text{ peso}}{\$1} = 1 \quad \text{or} \quad \frac{\$1}{15.19 \text{ peso}} = 1$$

The first form allows us to convert dollars to pesos:

$$\$100 \times \frac{15.19 \text{ peso}}{\$1} = 1519 \text{ peso}$$

1 peso = $0.06584

Your $100 will buy 1519 pesos. **Now try Exercises 51–54.**

Time Out to Think

Look up the current value and historical values over the past 10 years for one of the currencies in Table 2.1. Can you identify any economic or political changes that might explain the changes in the currency's value relative to the dollar?

PRACTICAL MATTERS

Changing Money in Foreign Countries

It costs money to change currency, so you should always look for the best deal. Two factors affect the cost of changing currency: (1) the exchange rate and (2) fees for the exchange.

Published exchange rates are usually "wholesale" rates available only to banks. Most money changers—including airport change stations, hotels, and exchange booths on streets—make money by giving you a rate that is not as good as the wholesale rate. For example, if the wholesale rate is 15.2 pesos to the dollar, a money changer might give you only 14.6 pesos per dollar.

Fees can also affect the cost of changing currency. Many money changers (especially in hotels, stores, and street booths) charge a fee every time you make an exchange. Here are a few general hints for changing currency:

- Before you travel, get a small amount of your destination's currency from your local bank. That way, if you need cash upon arrival, you won't be forced to accept a poor exchange rate or high fees.
- Once you get to your destination, banks usually offer better exchange rates than other money changers. The best deal may be your ATM card, at least in countries where ATM machines are common, but be sure to find out whether your bank charges a fee for foreign ATM transactions.
- Consider using a credit card for purchases and hotel and restaurant bills. Credit cards generally offer good exchange rates and, unlike cash, can be replaced if lost or stolen. But be sure to check whether your credit card company adds fees for foreign purchases. And avoid using your credit card to get cash, unless it is an emergency, because most credit cards charge high fees and interest for cash advances.

Problem Solving with Units

We have covered basic ideas of units and conversions, so we are ready to apply them to problem solving. In some cases, units can help us decide how to solve a problem. In all cases, units offer a way of checking answers. The following box summarizes how we work with units. Notice how these ideas are applied in the following examples and throughout the rest of this book.

WORKING WITH UNITS

Step 1: Identify the units involved in the problem. Use the units to help you decide how to approach the problem and what units to expect in the answer.

Step 2: Perform any operations (such as multiplication or division) on both the numbers and their associated units. Remember:

- You cannot add or subtract numbers with different units (such as apples and oranges), but you can combine different units through multiplication, division, or raising to powers.
- It is easier to keep track of units if you replace division with multiplication by the reciprocal. For example, instead of dividing by $60\frac{\text{s}}{\text{min}}$, multiply by $\frac{1\text{ min}}{60\text{ s}}$.

Step 3: When you complete your calculations, make sure that your answer has the units you expected. If it doesn't, then you've done something wrong.

BY THE WAY

By remembering that a speed in *miles per hour* is a distance (miles) divided by a time (hours), you can always remember this general relationship:

$$\text{speed} = \frac{\text{distance}}{\text{time}}$$

Then, by rearranging this equation, you can find that distance = speed × time, and that

$$\text{time} = \text{distance} \div \text{speed}.$$

Example 9 Distance, Time, and Speed

A car is traveling 25 miles every half-hour. How fast is it going?

Solution The "how fast" suggests that the final answer should be a speed. In this case, since the problem involves units of miles and hours, we should expect a speed in *miles per hour.* Knowing that these units mean miles *divided by* hours tells us that we should divide the distance traveled by the time it takes:

$$25 \text{ mi} \div \frac{1}{2}\text{hr} = 25 \text{ mi} \times \frac{2}{1 \text{ hr}} = 50\frac{\text{mi}}{\text{hr}}$$

Note that we replaced the division with multiplication by the reciprocal; be sure you understand why the reciprocal of $\frac{1}{2}$ hr is $\frac{2}{1 \text{ hr}}$. The car is traveling at a speed of 50 miles per hour. **Now try Exercises 55–58.**

Example 10 Buying Farm Land

You are buying 30 acres of farm land at $12,000 per acre. What is the total cost?

Solution The question asks about total cost, so the answer should be in *dollars.* We multiply the acreage by the cost per acre:

$$30 \text{ acres} \times \frac{\$12{,}000}{1 \text{ acre}} = \$360{,}000$$

Note how the unit *acre* cancels on the left side to leave the answer in units of dollars, as we expected. The land will cost $360,000. **Now try Exercises 59–68.**

BY THE WAY

An *acre* was originally defined as the amount of land a pair of oxen could plow in a day. Today it is defined as 43,560 square feet, or 1/640 of a square mile.

Using Units to Check Answers

Checking answers is one of the most important reasons for using units. If the answer does not come out with the expected units, then something has gone wrong. Of course, you should always check your method and your calculations as well as your units. An answer with the correct units could still contain other errors.

Example 11 Exam Check

You are a grader for a math course. An exam question reads: "Eli purchased 5 pounds of apples at a price of 50 cents per pound. How much did he pay for the apples?" On the paper you are grading, a student has written: "50 ÷ 5 = 10. He paid 10 cents." Write a note to the student explaining what went wrong.

Solution Dear student—First, notice that your answer does not make sense. If one pound of apples costs 50¢, how could five pounds cost only 10¢? You could have prevented your error by keeping track of the units. In the exam question, the number 50 has units of *cents per pound* and the number 5 has units of *pounds.* Thus, your calculation of "50 ÷ 5 = 10" means

$$50\frac{¢}{\text{lb}} \div 5 \text{ lb} = 50\frac{¢}{\text{lb}} \times \frac{1}{5 \text{ lb}} = 10\frac{¢}{\text{lb}^2}$$

(As usual, we replaced the division with multiplication by the reciprocal.) Your calculation gives units of "cents per square pound," so it cannot be correct for a question that asks for a simple price. The correct calculation multiplies the price per pound by the weight in pounds:

$$50\frac{¢}{\text{lb}} \times 5 \text{ lb} = 250¢ = \$2.50$$

The units now work out as they should: The 5 pounds of apples cost $2.50.

Now try Exercises 69–72.

BY THE WAY

The abbreviation for pound, *lb,* comes from the Latin *libra,* meaning "scales."

Unit Analysis as a Problem-Solving Tool

Thinking about units can often point the way to the solution to a problem that you may not initially know how to solve. Even scientists and applied mathematicians often start analyzing a problem by looking at its units. The following two examples show the basic idea.

Example 12 Gas Mileage

Your destination is 90 miles away, and your fuel gauge shows that your gas tank is only one-quarter full. You know that your tank holds 12 gallons of gas and that your car averages about 25 miles per gallon. Do you need to stop for gas?

Solution There are several ways to think about this problem, but using unit analysis makes it particularly easy. The question relates to "how much gas," so we need units of *gallons*. We are given the distance you need to drive (90 miles) and the gas mileage (25 miles per gallon), so we look for a way to combine these pieces of information and end up with an answer in gallons. We can do so by dividing the distance by the mileage:

$$90 \text{ mi} \div \frac{25 \text{ mi}}{1 \text{ gal}} = 90 \cancel{\text{mi}} \times \frac{1 \text{ gal}}{25 \cancel{\text{mi}}} = 3.6 \text{ gal}$$

You will need 3.6 gallons of gas for the 90-mile trip, but one-quarter of a 12-gallon tank is only 3 gallons. Therefore, you should stop for gas.

Now try Exercises 73–76.

Example 13 Melting Ice

The chapter-opening activity asked about the impact of melting of ice in Antarctica and Greenland. If you succeeded in answering it, you found that melting the Antarctic ice would release about 25 million cubic kilometers of water, which would spread out over Earth's 340 million square kilometers of ocean surface. Use unit analysis to find the amount that sea level will rise.

Solution A rise in sea level has units of length. We are given a volume, which has units of length^3, and an area, which has units of length^2. Notice that dividing length^3 by length^2 results in a length, which tells us that we can find an answer with the correct units by dividing the volume of water by the surface area of the oceans:

$$\frac{25 \text{ million km}^{\cancel{3}}}{340 \text{ million } \cancel{\text{km}^2}} \approx 0.074 \text{ km} = 74 \text{ m}$$

We have found the correct answer simply by working with the units. Note that although unit analysis does not always guarantee a correct answer, it often points us in the right direction.

Now try Exercise 77.

Time Out to Think

Come up with your own example of a problem that you can solve through unit analysis, preferably a problem that you may not have known how to solve before.

QUICK QUIZ

Choose the best answer to each of the following questions. Explain your reasoning with one or more complete sentences.

1. What does the word *per* mean?
   a. divided by
   b. multiplied by
   c. in addition to
2. Which of the following represents 4 square miles?
   a. a line of small squares that is 4 miles long
   b. a square 2 miles on a side
   c. a square 4 miles on a side
3. If you multiply an area in square feet by a height in feet, the result will have units of
   a. feet.
   b. $feet^2$.
   c. $feet^3$.
4. There are 1760 yards in a mile. Therefore, one cubic mile represents
   a. 1760 square yards.
   b. 1760^3 $yards^3$.
   c. 1760 yard-miles.
5. The fact that 1 liter = 1.06 quarts can be written as the conversion factor
   a. 1.06 quarts/liter.
   b. 1.06 liters/quart.
   c. 1 quart/1.06 liters.
6. To end up with units of speed, you need to
   a. multiply a distance by a time.
   b. divide a distance by a time.
   c. divide a time by a distance.
7. If the current exchange rate is $1.20 per euro, then
   a. $1 is worth more than 1 euro.
   b. 1 euro is worth more than $1.
   c. 1 euro is equal to $0.80.
8. One square foot is equivalent to
   a. 12 square inches.
   b. 120 square inches.
   c. 144 square inches.
9. You are given two pieces of information: (1) the volume of a lake in cubic feet and (2) the average depth of the lake in feet. You are asked to find the surface area of the lake in square feet. You should
   a. multiply the volume by the depth.
   b. divide the volume by the depth.
   c. divide the depth by the volume.
10. You are given two pieces of information: (1) the price of gasoline in dollars per gallon and (2) the gas mileage of a car in miles per gallon. You are asked to find the cost of driving this car in dollars per mile. You should
    a. divide the price of gas by the car's gas mileage.
    b. multiply the price of gas by the car's gas mileage.
    c. divide the car's gas mileage by the price of gas.

Exercises 2A

REVIEW QUESTIONS

1. What are units? Describe how to read units that involve division, multiplication, squares, and cubes.
2. Explain why a unit conversion really involves just multiplying by 1.
3. Describe the three forms in which we can write any conversion factor. Given the conversion in one form, such as 1 lb = 16 oz, how do you find the other two forms?
4. Explain in words or with a picture why there are 9 square feet in 1 square yard and 27 cubic feet in 1 cubic yard. Then describe generally how to find conversion factors involving squares or cubes.
5. Describe how to read and use the currency data in Table 2.1.
6. Briefly describe how units can help you check your answers and solve problems. Give examples.

DOES IT MAKE SENSE?

Decide whether each of the following statements makes sense (or is clearly true) or does not make sense (or is clearly false). Explain your reasoning.

7. I drove at a speed of 35 miles for the entire trip.
8. Our house has a floor area of 1500 square feet.
9. I have a box with a volume of 2 square feet.
10. We own 2 square acres of farm land.
11. I figured out how long the airplane will take to reach Beijing by dividing the airplane's speed by the distance to Beijing.
12. I figured out how long the airplane will take to reach Beijing by dividing the distance to Beijing by the airplane's speed.

BASIC SKILLS & CONCEPTS

13–18: Working with Fractions. The following exercises require the skills covered in the Brief Review on pp. 84–85.

13. Evaluate the following expressions.

a. $\frac{3}{4} \times \frac{1}{2}$ b. $\frac{2}{3} \times \frac{3}{5}$ c. $\frac{1}{2} + \frac{3}{2}$ d. $\frac{2}{3} + \frac{1}{6}$

e. $\frac{2}{3} \times \frac{1}{4}$ f. $\frac{1}{4} + \frac{3}{8}$ g. $\frac{5}{8} - \frac{1}{4}$ h. $\frac{3}{2} \times \frac{2}{3}$

14. Evaluate the following expressions.

a. $\frac{1}{3} + \frac{1}{5}$ b. $\frac{10}{3} \times \frac{3}{7}$ c. $\frac{3}{4} - \frac{1}{8}$ d. $\frac{1}{2} + \frac{2}{3} + \frac{3}{4}$

e. $\frac{6}{5} + \frac{4}{15}$ f. $\frac{3}{5} \times \frac{2}{7}$ g. $\frac{1}{3} + \frac{13}{6}$ h. $\frac{3}{5} \times \frac{10}{3} \times \frac{3}{2}$

15. Write each of the following as a common fraction.

a. 3.5 b. 0.3 c. 0.05 d. 4.1

e. 2.15 f. 0.35 g. 0.98 h. 4.01

16. Write each of the following as a common fraction.

a. 2.75 b. 0.45 c. 0.005 d. 1.16

e. 6.5 f. 4.123 g. 0.0003 h. 0.034

17. Convert the following fractions to decimal form; round to the nearest thousandth if necessary.

a. $\frac{1}{4}$ b. $\frac{3}{8}$ c. $\frac{2}{3}$ d. $\frac{3}{5}$

e. $\frac{13}{2}$ f. $\frac{23}{6}$ g. $\frac{103}{50}$ h. $\frac{42}{26}$

18. Convert the following fractions to decimal form; round to the nearest thousandth if necessary.

a. $\frac{1}{5}$ b. $\frac{4}{9}$ c. $\frac{4}{11}$ d. $\frac{12}{7}$

e. $\frac{28}{9}$ f. $\frac{56}{11}$ g. $\frac{102}{49}$ h. $\frac{15}{4}$

19–26: Identifying Units. Identify the units of the following quantities. State the units mathematically (for example, mi/hr) and in words (for example, miles per hour).

19. Your average speed on a long walk, found by dividing distance traveled in miles by time elapsed in hours

20. The unit price of oranges, found by dividing the price in dollars by the weight in pounds

21. The cost of a piece of carpet, found by dividing its price in dollars by its area in square yards

22. The flow rate of a river in which 5000 cubic feet of water flow past a particular location every second

23. The unit price of rice in Japan, found by dividing the price in yen by the weight in kilograms

24. The production rate of a bagel bakery, found by dividing the number of bagels produced by the time required in hours

25. The per capita daily oil consumption by the residents of a town, found by dividing the amount of oil used per day in gallons by the population of the town

26. The density of a rock, found by dividing its weight in grams by its volume in cubic centimeters

27–36: Unit Conversions. Carry out the following unit conversions.

27. Convert 24 feet to inches.

28. Convert 24 feet to yards.

29. Convert 25 minutes to seconds.

30. Convert 2.5 hours to seconds.

31. Convert 15 gallons to quarts.

32. Convert 4 acres to units of square feet.

33. Convert 140 weeks to days.

34. Convert 60 miles per hour to units of miles per minute.

35. Convert 3 years to hours (neglecting leap years).

36. Convert 1 ton (2000 pounds) to ounces.

37. **Area and Volume Calculations.** Show clearly your use of units for the following calculations.

a. A large box-shaped arena has a rectangular floor that measures 200 feet by 150 feet, and a flat ceiling that is 35 feet above the floor. Find the area of the floor and the volume of the arena.

b. A flat-bottom reflecting pool has length 30 yards, width 10 yards, and depth 0.3 yard. Find the surface area of the pool and the volume of water it holds.

c. A raised flower bed is 25 feet long, 8 feet wide, and 1.5 feet deep. Find the area of the bed and the volume of soil it holds.

38. **Area and Volume Calculations.** Clearly show the use of units in the following exercises.

a. A warehouse is 40 yards long and 25 yards wide, and it is piled with cartons to a height of 3 yards. What is the area of the warehouse floor? What is the total volume of the cartons? (Assume there is no space between cartons.)

b. The bed of a truck is 3.5 feet deep, 12 feet long, and 5 feet wide. What is the area of the bed's floor? What is the volume of the bed?

c. A can has a circular base with an area of 6 square inches and is 4 inches tall. What is its total volume?

39–46: Conversions with Square and Cubic Units.

39. Find a conversion factor between square feet and square inches. Write it in three forms.

40. Find a conversion factor between cubic feet and cubic inches. Write it in three forms.

41. Given that 1 meter = 100 centimeters, find a conversion factor between square meters and square centimeters. Write it in three forms.

42. Find the area in square feet of a rectangular yard that measures 20 yards by 12 yards.

43. A new sidewalk will be 4 feet wide, 200 feet long, and filled to a depth of 6 inches (0.5 foot) with concrete. How many cubic yards of concrete are needed?

44. How many cubic inches are there in 2.3 cubic yards?

45. An air conditioning system can circulate 320 cubic feet of air per minute. How many cubic yards of air can it circulate per minute?

46. A hot tub pump circulates 4 cubic feet of water per minute. How many cubic inches of water does it circulate each minute?

47–54: **Currency Conversions.** Use the currency exchange rates in Table 2.1 for the following questions.

47. You arrive in London with $400. How many pounds can you buy?

48. As you leave Paris, you convert 4500 euros to dollars. How many dollars do you receive?

49. You return from Mexico with 3000 pesos. How much are they worth in U.S. dollars?

50. Which is worth more: $1 U.S. or $1 Canadian?

51. Which is worth more: 1 yen or 1 peso?

52. Bottled water costs 0.75 euro per liter in Paris. What is the price in units of U.S. dollars per quart? (1 quart = 0.9464 liter)

53. Gasoline sells for 1.2 euros/liter in Bonn. What is the price in U.S. dollars per gallon? (1 gallon = 3.785 liters)

54. Cantaloupes sell for 1.80 euros per kilogram in Belgium. What is the price in units of U.S. dollars per pound? (1 kilogram = 2.205 pounds)

55–68: **Working with Units.** Use unit conversions to answer the following questions.

55. An airliner travels 45 miles in 5 minutes. What is its speed in miles per hour?

56. What is the total cost of 1.2 cubic yards of soil if it sells for $24 per cubic yard?

57. A hose fills a hot tub at a rate of 3.2 gallons per minute. How many hours will it take to fill a 300-gallon hot tub?

58. Competition speed skydivers have reached record speeds of 614 miles per hour. At this speed, how many feet would you fall every second?

59. How much would you pay for 2.5 ounces of gold at a price of $920 per ounce?

60. Suppose you earn $8.50 per hour and work 24 eight-hour days in a month. How much do you earn in that month?

61. In 2008, 565,650 Americans died of (all forms of) cancer. Assuming a population of 305 million, what was the mortality rate in units of deaths per 100,000 people?

62. In 2008, about 310,000 Americans died of sudden cardiac death (about half of all deaths from coronary heart disease). Assuming a population of 305 million, what was the mortality rate in units of deaths per 100,000 people?

63. There are approximately 3 million births in the United States each year. Find the birth rate in units of births per minute.

64. During a long road trip, you drive 420 miles on a 12-gallon tank of gas. What is your gas mileage (in miles per gallon)?

65. If your car gets 28 miles per gallon, how much does it cost to drive 250 miles when gasoline costs $2.90 per gallon?

66. The median salary for the New York Yankees in 2008 was $1,875,000. Assuming a 160-game season, express this salary in dollars per game.

67. If you sleep an average of 8 hours each night, how many hours do you sleep in a year?

68. A human heart beats about 70 times per minute. If an average human being lives to the age of 80, how many times does the average heart beat in a lifetime?

69–72: **What Went Wrong?** Consider the following exam questions and student solutions. Determine whether the solution is correct. If it is not correct, write a note to the student explaining why it is wrong and give a correct solution.

69. *Exam Question:* A candy store sells chocolate for $7.70 per pound. The piece you want to buy weighs 0.11 pound. How much will it cost, to the nearest cent? (Neglect sales tax.)

Student Solution: 0.11 ÷ 7.70 = 0.014. It will cost 1.4¢.

70. *Exam Question:* You ride your bike up a steep mountain road at 5 miles per hour. How far do you go in 3 hours?

Student Solution: 5 ÷ 3 = 1.7. I ride 1.7 miles.

71. *Exam Question:* You can buy a 50-pound bag of flour for $11 or you can buy a 1-pound bag for $0.39. Compare the per pound cost for the large and small bags.

Student Solution: The large bag price is 50 ÷ $11 = $4.55 per pound, which is much more than the 39¢ per pound price of the small bag.

72. *Exam Question:* The average person needs 1500 Calories a day. A can of Coke contains 140 Calories. How many Cokes would you need to drink to fill your daily caloric needs? (Note: This diet may not meet other nutritional needs!)

Student Solution: 1500 × 140 = 210,000. You would need to drink 210,000 Cokes to meet your daily caloric needs.

73–76: **Gas Mileage.** Answer the following practical gas mileage questions.

73. You plan to take a 2000-mile trip in your car, which averages 32 miles per gallon. How many gallons of gasoline should you expect to use? Would a car that has only half the gas mileage (16 miles per gallon) require twice as much gasoline for the same trip? Explain.

74. Two friends take a 3000-mile cross-country trip together, but they drive their own cars. Car A has a 12-gallon gas tank and averages 40 miles per gallon, while car B has a 20-gallon gas tank and averages 30 miles per gallon. Assume both drivers pay an average of $2.90 per gallon of gas.

a. What is the cost of one full tank of gas for car A? For car B?

b. How many tanks of gas do cars A and B each use for the trip?

c. How much do the drivers of cars A and B each pay for gas for the trip?

75. Gas mileage actually varies slightly with the driving speed of a car (as well as with highway vs. city driving). Suppose your car averages 38 miles per gallon on the highway if your average speed is 55 miles per hour, and it averages 32 miles per gallon on the highway if your average speed is 70 miles per hour.

a. What is the driving time for a 2000-mile trip if you drive at an average speed of 55 miles per hour? What is the driving time at 70 miles per hour?

b. Assume a gasoline price of $2.90 per gallon. What is the gasoline cost for a 2000-mile trip if you drive at an average speed of 55 miles per hour? What is the gasoline cost at 70 miles per hour?

76. Suppose your car averages 32 miles per gallon on the highway if your average speed is 60 miles per hour, and it averages 25 miles per gallon on the highway if your average speed is 75 miles per hour.

a. What is the driving time for a 1500-mile trip if you drive at an average speed of 60 miles per hour? What is the driving time at 75 miles per hour?

b. Assume a gasoline price of $2.90 per gallon. What is the gasoline cost for a 1500-mile trip if you drive at an average speed of 60 miles per hour? What is the gasoline cost at 75 miles per hour?

77. **Greenland Ice Sheet.** The Greenland ice sheet contains about 3 million cubic kilometers of ice. If completely melted, this ice would release about 2.5 million cubic kilometers of water, which would spread out over Earth's 340 million square kilometers of ocean surface. How much would sea level rise?

78. **Practical Carpet Problem.** Suppose you want to install carpet in a room that measures 18 feet by 22 feet. The carpet you want costs $28.50 per square yard and comes only in rolls that are 12 feet wide (and at least 100 feet long). If you allow only one seam (where two pieces of carpet meet), what is the most efficient way to lay the carpet and how much will the carpet cost?

FURTHER APPLICATIONS

79. **Professional Basketball Salaries.** In the 2009 season, Kevin Garnett of the Boston Celtics earned $24,750,000 to play 80 games, each lasting 48 minutes. (Assume no overtime games.)

a. How much did Garnett earn per game?

b. Assuming that Garnett played every minute of every game, how much did he earn per minute?

c. Assuming that Garnett played 2/3 of every game, how much did he earn per minute?

d. Suppose that, averaged over the course of a year, Garnett practiced or trained 40 hours for every game. Including this training time, what was his hourly salary?

80. **Full of Hot Air.** The average person breathes 6 times per minute (at rest), inhaling and exhaling half a liter of air each time. How much "hot air" (air warmed by the body), in liters, does the average person exhale each day?

81. **Kindle 2.** Amazon's Kindle 2 wireless reading device has a capacity of 1.4 gigabytes (1.4 billion bytes). Assume that one byte corresponds to one character and that an average page consists of 2000 characters.

a. How many pages of text can one Kindle hold?

b. How many 500-page books can one Kindle hold?

82. **Volcanic Eruption.** The greatest volcanic eruption in recorded history took place in 1815 on the Indonesian island of Sumbawa, when the volcano Tambora expelled an estimated 100 cubic kilometers of molten rock. Suppose all of the ejected material fell on a region with an area of 600 square kilometers. Find the average depth of the resulting layer of ash and rock.

83. **Shower vs. Bath.** Assume that when you take a bath, you fill a tub to the halfway point and the tub measures 6 feet by 3 feet by 2.5 feet. When you take a shower, you use a shower head with a flow rate of 1.75 gallons per minute, and you typically spend 10 minutes in the shower. There are 7.5 gallons in one cubic foot.

a. Do you use more water taking a shower or taking a bath?

b. How long would you need to shower in order to use as much water as you use taking a bath?

c. Assuming your shower is in a bath tub, propose a nonmathematical way to compare, in one experiment, the amounts of water you use taking a shower and a bath.

84. **Hurricane Katrina.** Experts estimate that when the levees around New Orleans broke in the aftermath of Hurricane Katrina, water flowed into the city at a peak rate of 9 billion gallons per day. There are 7.5 gallons in one cubic foot.

a. Find the flow rate in units of cubic feet per second (cfs). Compare this flow rate to the average flow rate of the Colorado River in the Grand Canyon: 30,000 cfs.

b. Assume that the flooded part of the city had an area of 6 square miles. Estimate how much (in feet) the water level rose in one day at the given flow rate.

85. **Glen Canyon Flood.** The Department of the Interior periodically releases a "spike flood" from the Glen Canyon Dam into the Colorado River. The purpose is to restore the river and the habitats along its banks, particularly in the Grand Canyon. The reservoir behind the dam (Lake Powell) holds approximately 1.2 trillion (1,200,000,000,000) cubic feet of water. During a recent week-long spike flood, water was released at a rate of 25,800 cubic feet per second. How much water was released during the 1-week flood? What percentage of the total water in the reservoir was released during the flood?

86. **Landscaping Project.** Suppose that you are planning to landscape a portion of your yard that measures 60 feet by 35 feet. Determine the price of the needed items at a local store, and use those prices to answer the following questions.

a. How much would it cost to plant the region with grass seed (which is rated by the number of square feet that can be covered per pound of seed)?

b. How much would it cost to cover the region with sod?

c. How much would it cost to cover the region with high-quality topsoil and then plant two flowering bulbs per square foot?

WEB PROJECTS

87. **South American Adventure.** Suppose you are planning an extended trip through many countries in South America. Use one of the many currency exchange sites on the Web to get all the exchange rates you'll need. Make a brief table showing each currency you'll need and the value of each currency in dollars.

88. **Polar Ice Melting.** Starting with a search on "glaciers" or "glaciology" (the study of glaciers), use the Web to learn more about polar ice melting. Focus on one aspect of the issue, such as whether global warming is causing melting, or the environmental impacts of melting, or the geological history of ice ages. Write a one-page summary of what you learn.

IN YOUR WORLD

89. **Are the Units Clear?** Find a news story that involves numerical data. Are all the numbers in the story given with meaningful units, or is the meaning of some of the units unclear? Briefly summarize how well (or how poorly) the article uses units.

90. **Units on the Highway.** Next time you are on the highway, look for three signs that use numbers (such as speed limits or distances to nearest exits). Are the units of the numbers given? If not, how are you expected to know the units? In cases where the units are not given, do you think the units would be obvious to everyone? Why or why not?

91. **False Advertising?** A Goodyear tire commercial began by stating that the Goodyear Aquatread tire can "channel away" 1 gallon of water per second. The announcer then said: "One gallon per second—that's 396 gallons per mile." What's wrong with this statement? What point do you think the advertisement was trying to make? Can you find other examples of advertisements that misstate units?

UNIT 2B Standardized Units: More Problem-Solving Power

Working with units can be a powerful problem-solving technique—but only if the units are clear and meaningful. When units (such as feet, miles, or kilograms) are *standardized,* everyone agrees on their meaning. Having a good understanding of standardized units will allow you to study a broader range of problems.

Standardized Unit Systems: U.S. and Metric

Today, only one system of standardized units enjoys wide international use: the international metric system, also known as SI (from the French *Système International d'Unités*). However, in the United States we commonly use a different measurement system that is sometimes called the English system, but is more formally known as the *U.S. customary system* (USCS). Let's briefly review each system.

The U.S. Customary System

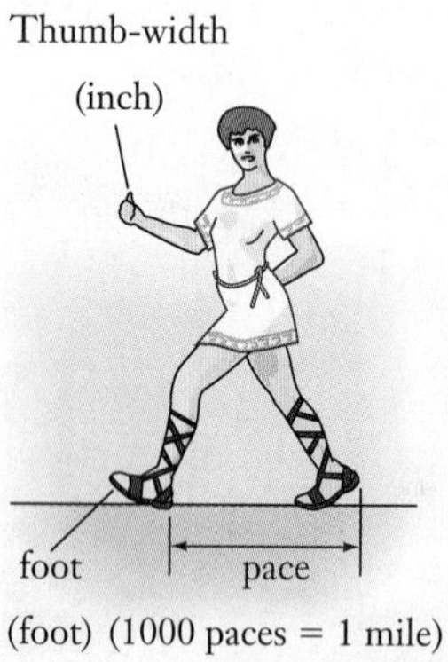

The roots of U.S. customary units reach back to ancient Middle Eastern civilizations, including the Egyptians, Sumerians, Babylonians, and Hebrews. Units of length were based on individual body measurements. For example, the *foot* was once the length of the foot of whoever was doing the measuring, and our word *inch* comes from the Latin *uncia,* meaning "thumb-width." There are 12 inches in one foot because the Romans discovered that most adult feet are about 12 thumb-widths long. The Romans paced out longer distances. Our word *mile* comes from the Latin *milia passum,* meaning "one thousand paces."

Time Out to Think

How many of *your* thumb-widths fit along your bare foot? Were the Romans correct in believing there are 12 thumb-widths in a foot?

TABLE 2.2 USCS Lengths (common abbreviations in parentheses)

1 inch (in.)	= 2.54 centimeters	1 furlong	= 40 rods = $\frac{1}{8}$ mile
1 foot (ft)	= 12 inches	1 mile (mi)	= 1760 yards = 5280 feet
1 yard (yd)	= 3 feet	1 nautical mile	= 1.852 km ≈ 6076.1 feet
1 rod	= 5.5 yards	1 land league	= 3 miles
1 fathom	= 6 feet	1 marine league	= 3 nautical miles

TABLE 2.3 USCS Weights (common abbreviations in parentheses)

Avoirdupois Measures		Troy Measures		Apothecary Measures	
1 grain	= 0.0648 gram	1 grain	= 0.0648 gram	1 grain	= 0.0648 gram
1 ounce (oz)	= 437.5 grains	1 carat = 0.2 gram	= 3.086 grains	1 scruple	= 20 grains
1 pound (lb)	= 16 ounces	1 pennyweight	= 24 grains	1 dram	= 3 scruples
1 ton	= 2000 pounds	1 troy ounce	= 480 grains	1 apoth. ounce	= 8 drams
1 long ton	= 2240 pounds	1 troy pound	= 12 troy ounces	1 apoth. pound	= 12 ounces

TABLE 2.4 USCS Volumes (common abbreviations in parentheses)

Liquid Measures		Dry Measures	
1 tablespoon (tbsp or T)	= 3 teaspoons (tsp or t)	1 in.^{3}	≈ 16.387 cm^3
1 fluid ounce (fl oz)	= 2 tablespoons = 1.805 in.^{3}	1 ft^3	= 1728 in.^{3} = 7.48 gallons
1 cup (c)	= 8 fluid ounces	1 yd^3	= 27 ft^3
1 pint (pt)	= 16 fluid ounces = 28.88 in.^{3}	1 dry pint (pt)	= 33.60 in.^{3}
1 quart (qt)	= 2 pints = 57.75 in.^{3}	1 dry quart (qt)	= 2 dry pints = 67.2 in.^{3}
1 gallon (gal)	= 4 quarts	1 peck	= 8 dry quarts
1 barrel of petroleum	= 42 gallons	1 bushel	= 4 pecks
1 barrel of liquid	= 31 gallons	1 cord	= 128 ft^3

As you might imagine, lengths that vary from person to person can lead to difficulties. For example, if you are buying 10 feet of rope, is it the length of your foot or the seller's foot that should be used to measure the rope? Many cultures therefore standardized units according to body measures of one particular person, such as a king. But such measures still changed every time one king was replaced by another. The first permanent standardization began when English King Henry I (1100–1135) set the *yard* as the measurement from the tip of *his* nose to the tip of *his* thumb on *his* outstretched arm. A few centuries later, the English brought their units to the American colonies, and they have since undergone further modification and standardization. Today, all lengths in the U.S. customary system are based on the inch, which is defined by law to be exactly 2.54 centimeters. Table 2.2 summarizes units of length in the U.S. customary system.

For measuring weight, the U.S. customary system actually has three distinct sets of units. Traditionally, jewelers used *troy* measures of weight, pharmacists used *apothecary* measures of weight, and most other commerce was conducted with *avoirdupois* measures of weight. Table 2.3 summarizes all three systems, but only the avoirdupois measures are commonly used today. The basic unit of weight in all three sets is the *grain*, an ancient unit originally based on the weight of a typical grain of wheat.

Historical Note

The avoirdupois measures were standardized by London merchants around the year 1300. The term *avoirdupois* comes from the French for "goods of weight." The troy system was probably named for the town of Troyes, France, and was established in the 15th century. The apothecary system was developed by medieval pharmacists (*apothecary* is a synonym for *pharmacy*).

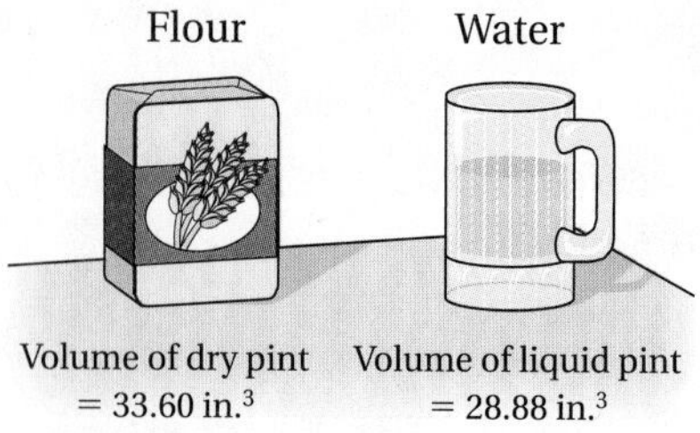

FIGURE 2.4

The basic U.S. customary unit of volume is the cubic inch (in.^{3}), but from here the system becomes complicated, because units with the same name represent different volumes depending on whether we're working with dry or liquid materials. For example, a *dry* pint is 33.60 cubic inches, while a *liquid* pint is only 28.88 cubic inches (Figure 2.4). In other words, a container that holds one pint of water is too small for one pint of flour. (If you travel, it can be even more complicated, because British customary measures differ from U.S. measures. For example, a British pint of beer is about 20% larger than a U.S. pint of beer.) Table 2.4 (p. 97) summarizes USCS measures of volume.

Example 1 The Kentucky Derby

The length of the Kentucky Derby horse race is 10 furlongs. How long is the race in miles?

Solution From Table 2.2, 1 furlong $= \frac{1}{8}$ mi, which is the same as 0.125 mile. As always, we can write this conversion factor in two other equivalent forms:

$$\frac{1 \text{ furlong}}{0.125 \text{ mi}} = 1 \quad \text{or} \quad \frac{0.125 \text{ mi}}{1 \text{ furlong}} = 1$$

The second form allows us to convert furlongs to miles:

$$10 \cancel{\text{furlong}} \times \frac{0.125 \text{ mi}}{1 \cancel{\text{furlong}}} = 1.25 \text{ mi}$$

The Kentucky Derby is a race of 1.25 miles. **Now try Exercises 23–26.**

PRACTICAL MATTERS

Gems and Gold Jewelry

If you've ever bought jewelry, you've probably seen labels stating *karats* or *carats*. But you may be surprised to know that these are not just alternative spellings of the same word. A *carat* is a unit of weight defined to be exactly 0.2 gram (see Table 2.3). A *karat* is a measure of the purity of gold: 24-karat gold is 100% pure, 18-karat gold is 75% pure, 14-karat gold is 58% pure (because $\frac{14}{24} \approx 0.58$), and so on.

If you are buying gold jewelry, look for a label stating both its purity in karats and its weight (usually given in grams); the amount of gold you are actually buying depends on both. For example:

- Ten grams of 18-karat gold contains 7.5 grams of pure gold, since 18-karat gold is 75% pure.
- Ten grams of 14-karat gold contains 5.8 grams of pure gold, since 14-karat gold is 58% pure.

Although a higher karat value is purer, it comes with an important practical tradeoff. Gold is a soft metal, and the metals (usually silver and copper) mixed into lower-karat gold give it added strength. For example, a 14-karat gold ring is stronger and more durable than an 18-karat gold ring.

You'll deal with carats rather than karats if you are buying gems such as diamonds or emeralds. Because 1 carat is 0.2 gram, the number of carats tells you the precise weight of the gem. However, several factors besides weight are important to the price, such as the gem's shape and color.

If you are gem shopping, you'll need to make tradeoffs among weight, color, and clarity (and sometimes other factors as well) to stay within your budget. For example, if you are looking for a round diamond, $10,000 might buy either a 1-carat diamond with good color and clarity or a 2-carat diamond with poorer color and clarity. Given the cost of most gems, you should spend some time doing price comparisons before buying.

Example 2 20,000 Leagues Under the Sea

In Jules Verne's novel *20,000 Leagues Under the Sea* (published in 1870), does the title refer to an ocean depth? How do you know?

Solution From Table 2.2, 1 marine league = 3 nautical miles. Therefore, 20,000 leagues is

$$20{,}000 \text{ leagues} \times \frac{3 \text{ naut. mi}}{1 \text{ league}} = 60{,}000 \text{ naut. mi}$$

This distance is several times the diameter of Earth, so 20,000 leagues cannot possibly refer to an ocean depth. The book's title refers to the distance traveled by Captain Nemo's submarine, the *Nautilus*. **Now try Exercises 27–30.**

BY THE WAY

The deepest point in the oceans is the *Challenger Deep,* which lies in the Marianas Trench in the western Pacific Ocean. Its depth is 36,198 feet (11,033 m), or almost 7 miles.

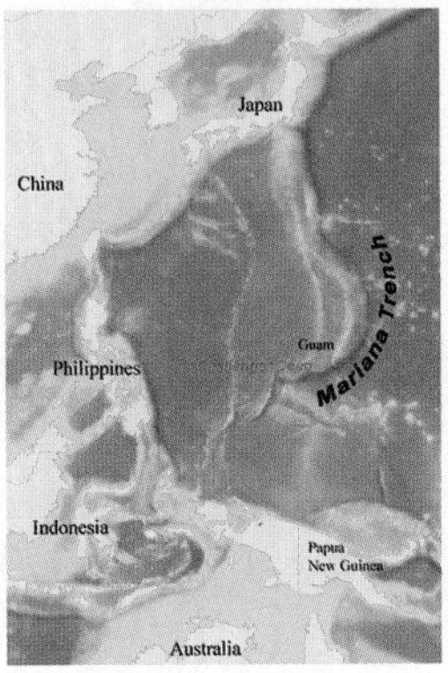

The International Metric System

The international metric system was invented in France late in the 18th century and is now used throughout the world. The metric system was designed for two primary reasons: (1) to replace many customary units with just a few basic units and (2) to simplify conversions through use of a decimal (base 10) system. Similar ideas had already been applied to currency. For example, in 1785, the United States replaced the customary currencies of the individual states with a national currency, the dollar (devised by Thomas Jefferson). Like the metric system, the dollar is based on a decimal relationship (because 100¢ = $1).

The basic units of length, mass, time, and volume in the metric system are

- the **meter** for length, abbreviated m
- the **kilogram** for mass, abbreviated kg
- the **second** for time, abbreviated s
- the **liter** for volume, abbreviated L

These basic units can be combined with a prefix that indicates multiplication by a power of 10. For example, *kilo* means 1000 so a kilometer is 1000 meters, and *micro* means *one-millionth* so a microgram is a millionth of a gram. Table 2.5 lists common metric prefixes.

TABLE 2.5 Common Metric Prefixes

Small Values			Large Values		
Prefix	**Abbrev.**	**Value**	**Prefix**	**Abbrev.**	**Value**
deci	d	10^{-1} (one-tenth)	deca	da	10^{1} (ten)
centi	c	10^{-2} (one-hundredth)	hecto	h	10^{2} (hundred)
milli	m	10^{-3} (one-thousandth)	kilo	k	10^{3} (thousand)
micro	μ	10^{-6} (one-millionth)	mega	M	10^{6} (million)
nano	n	10^{-9} (one-billionth)	giga	G	10^{9} (billion)
pico	p	10^{-12} (one-trillionth)	tera	T	10^{12} (trillion)

Note: The abbreviation for micro, μ, is the Greek letter mu.

Historical Note

In 1790, Thomas Jefferson (then Secretary of State) proposed adoption of the metric system to Congress. Had Congress agreed, the United States would have been the *first* country to adopt the metric system—ahead of France, which adopted it in 1795.

Time Out to Think

People often say that expensive things cost "megabucks." What does this statement mean literally? Can you think of other cases where metric prefixes have entered popular language?

Example 3 Using Metric Prefixes

a. Convert 2759 centimeters to meters.
b. How many nanoseconds are in a microsecond?

Solution

a. Table 2.5 shows that *centi* means 10^{-2}, so $1\text{ cm} = 10^{-2}\text{ m}$ or, equivalently, $1\text{ m} = 100\text{ cm}$. Therefore, 2759 centimeters is the same as

$$2759\ \cancel{\text{cm}} \times \frac{1\text{ m}}{100\ \cancel{\text{cm}}} = 27.59\text{ m}$$

A Brief Review Powers of 10

Powers of 10 indicate how many times to multiply 10 by itself. For example:

$$10^2 = 10 \times 10 = 100$$
$$10^6 = 10 \times 10 \times 10 \times 10 \times 10 \times 10 = 1{,}000{,}000$$

Negative powers indicate reciprocals of corresponding positive powers. For example:

$$10^{-2} = \frac{1}{10^2} = \frac{1}{100} = 0.01$$
$$10^{-6} = \frac{1}{10^6} = \frac{1}{1{,}000{,}000} = 0.000\,001$$

Notice that powers of 10 follow two basic rules:

1. A positive exponent tells how many 0s follow the 1. For example, 10^0 is a 1 followed by no 0s; 10^8 is a 1 followed by eight 0s.
2. A negative exponent tells how many places are to the right of the decimal point, including the 1. For example, $10^{-1} = 0.1$ has one place to the right of the decimal point; $10^{-6} = 0.000\,001$ has six places to the right of the decimal point.

Multiplying and Dividing Powers of 10

Multiplying powers of 10 simply requires adding exponents. For example:

$$10^4 \times 10^7 = \underbrace{10{,}000}_{10^4} \times \underbrace{10{,}000{,}000}_{10^7} = \underbrace{100{,}000{,}000{,}000}_{=10^{4+7}=10^{11}}$$

$$10^5 \times 10^{-3} = \underbrace{100{,}000}_{10^5} \times \underbrace{0.001}_{10^{-3}} = \underbrace{100}_{=10^{5+(-3)}=10^2}$$

$$10^{-8} \times 10^{-5} = \underbrace{0.00000001}_{10^{-8}} \times \underbrace{0.00001}_{10^{-5}} = \underbrace{0.0000000000001}_{=10^{-8+(-5)}=10^{-13}}$$

Dividing powers of 10 requires subtracting exponents. For example:

$$\frac{10^5}{10^3} = \underbrace{100{,}000}_{10^5} \div \underbrace{1000}_{10^3} = \underbrace{100}_{=10^{5-3}=10^2}$$

$$\frac{10^3}{10^7} = \underbrace{1000}_{10^3} \div \underbrace{10{,}000{,}000}_{10^7} = \underbrace{0.0001}_{=10^{3-7}=10^{-4}}$$

$$\frac{10^{-4}}{10^{-6}} = \underbrace{0.0001}_{10^{-4}} \div \underbrace{0.000001}_{10^{-6}} = \underbrace{100}_{=10^{-4-(-6)}=10^2}$$

Powers of Powers of 10

We can use the multiplication and division rules to raise powers of 10 to other powers. For example:

$$(10^4)^3 = 10^4 \times 10^4 \times 10^4 = 10^{4+4+4} = 10^{12}$$

Note that we get the same result by simply multiplying the two powers:

$$(10^4)^3 = 10^{4\times3} = 10^{12}$$

Adding and Subtracting Powers of 10

There is no shortcut for adding or subtracting powers of 10, as there is for multiplication or division. The values must be written in longhand notation. For example:

$$10^6 + 10^2 = 1{,}000{,}000 + 100 = 1{,}000{,}100$$
$$10^8 + 10^{-3} = 100{,}000{,}000 + 0.001 = 100{,}000{,}000.001$$
$$10^7 - 10^3 = 10{,}000{,}000 - 1000 = 9{,}999{,}000$$

Summary

- To *multiply* powers of 10, *add* exponents:
$$10^n \times 10^m = 10^{n+m}$$
- To *divide* powers of 10, *subtract* exponents:
$$\frac{10^n}{10^m} = 10^{n-m}$$
- To *raise* powers of 10 to other powers, multiply exponents:
$$(10^n)^m = 10^{n\times m}$$
- To add or subtract powers of 10, first write them out longhand.

Now try Exercises 19–22.

b. We compare the quantities by dividing the longer time (microsecond) by the shorter time (nanosecond):

$$\frac{1\mu s}{1\text{ ns}} = \frac{10^{-6}\cancel{s}}{10^{-9}\cancel{s}} = 10^{-6-(-9)} = 10^{-6+9} = 10^3$$

A microsecond is 10^3, or 1000, times as long as a nanosecond, so there are 1000 nanoseconds in a microsecond. **Now try Exercises 31–36.**

Metric–USCS Conversions

We carry out conversions between metric and USCS units like any other unit conversions. Table 2.6 lists a few handy conversion factors. It's useful to memorize approximate conversions, particularly if you plan to travel internationally or if you work with metric units in sports or business. For example, if you remember that a kilometer is about 0.6 mile, you will know that a 10-kilometer road race is about 6 miles. Similarly, if you remember that a meter is about 10% longer than a yard, you'll know that a 100-meter race is about the same as a 110-yard race.

TABLE 2.6 USCS–Metric Conversions

USCS to Metric	Metric to USCS
1 in. = 2.540 cm	1 cm = 0.3937 in.
1 ft = 0.3048 m	1 m = 3.28 ft
1 yd = 0.9144 m	1 m = 1.094 yd
1 mi = 1.6093 km	1 km = 0.6214 mi
1 lb = 0.4536 kg	1 kg = 2.205 lb
1 fl oz = 29.574 mL	1 mL = 0.03381 fl oz
1 qt = 0.9464 L	1 L = 1.057 qt
1 gal = 3.785 L	1 L = 0.2642 gal

Historical Note

People around the world use the same base 10 *(decimal)* counting system. This may seem natural because we have 10 fingers, but various ancient cultures used base 2, base 3, base 5, base 20, and other bases. Vestiges of other bases remain in our language. For example, we have 60 seconds in a minute and 60 minutes in an hour because the ancient Babylonians used base 60. Similarly, a dozen is 12 and a gross is $12 \times 12 = 144$, presumably because base 12 was once common in northern Europe.

Example 4 Gas Price per Liter

A gas station in Canada sells gasoline for CAD 1.10 per liter. (CAD is an abbreviation for Canadian dollars.) What is the price in dollars per gallon? Use the currency exchange rate in Table 2.1.

Solution We use a chain of conversions to convert from CAD to dollars and then from liters to gallons. From Table 2.1, the currency conversion is \$0.7834 per CAD, and from Table 2.6, there are 3.785 liters per gallon.

$$\frac{1.10\ \cancel{\text{CAD}}}{1\ \cancel{\text{L}}} \times \frac{\$0.7834}{1\ \cancel{\text{CAD}}} \times \frac{3.785\ \cancel{\text{L}}}{1\text{ gal}} \approx \frac{\$3.26}{1\text{ gal}}$$

The price of the gasoline is about \$3.26 per gallon. **Now try Exercises 37–41.**

Take Note

The liter is defined as 1 cubic decimeter (or, equivalently, 1000 cubic centimeters); this makes it a *derived* unit in the metric system, because its value can be found from the standard definition of a meter.

Example 5 Square Kilometers to Square Miles

How many square kilometers are in one square mile?

Solution We square both sides of the conversion factor, 1 mi = 1.6093 km.

$$(1\text{ mi})^2 = (1.6093\text{ km})^2 \quad \Rightarrow \quad 1\text{ mi}^2 = 2.5898\text{ km}^2$$

One square mile is 2.5898 square kilometers. **Now try Exercises 42–46.**

BY THE WAY

Technically, pounds are a unit of *weight* and kilograms are a unit of *mass,* so the given conversions between pounds and kilograms are valid only on Earth. For example a 50-kilogram astronaut weighs about 110 pounds on Earth; in Earth orbit, the astronaut is weightless but still has a mass of 50 kilograms.

USING TECHNOLOGY

Metric Conversions

You can always do unit conversions just by using the appropriate conversion factors on your calculator. However, some technologies make it even easier.

Microsoft Excel The built-in function CONVERT enables you to do basic unit conversions. Simply enter the number you want to convert along with the correct unit abbreviations in quotes. The following screen shot shows how you convert 35 kilometers to miles in an Excel spreadsheet cell.

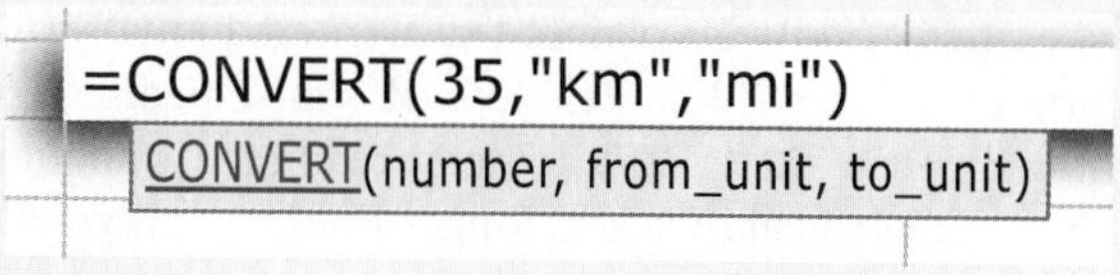

Clicking Return will put the correct numerical answer in the cell (in this case, 21.75). You can find all the necessary unit abbreviations by typing "convert" into the search box on the Help menu of Excel.

Google You can do basic unit conversions simply by typing what you want to convert into the Google search box. The screen shot below shows how Google converts 50 liters into gallons. When you hit Return, the result shows up below the search box.

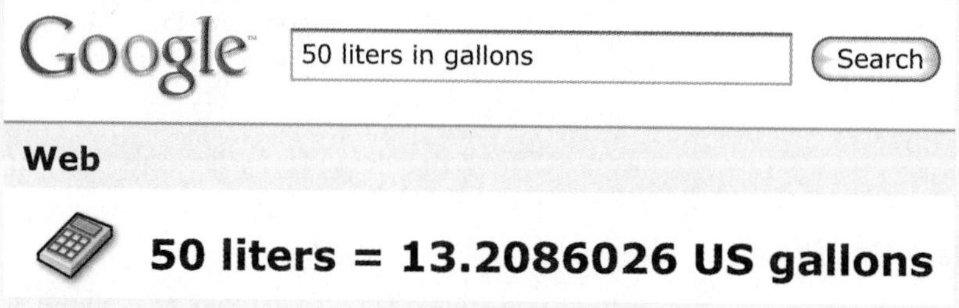

Temperature Units: Fahrenheit, Celsius, and Kelvin

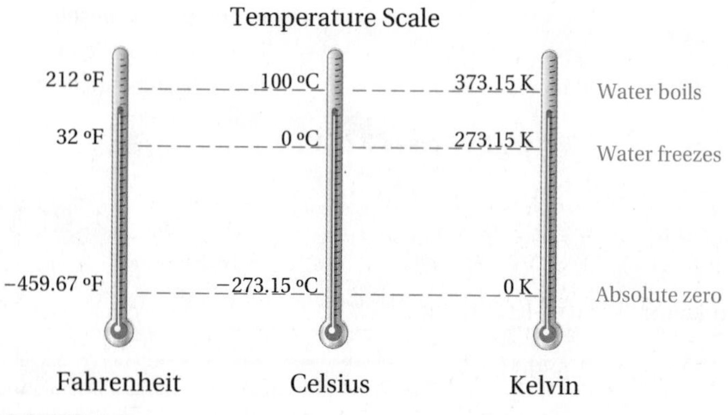

FIGURE 2.5

Three temperature scales are commonly used today (Figure 2.5). The **Fahrenheit** scale is used in the United States. It is defined so that water freezes at 32°F and boils at 212°F. Internationally, temperature is usually measured on the **Celsius** scale, which places the freezing point of water at 0°C and the boiling point at 100°C. In science, temperature is usually measured on the **Kelvin** scale, which is the same as the Celsius scale except for its zero point. A temperature of 0 K is the coldest possible temperature, known as **absolute zero**. It is approximately −273.15°C or −459.67°F. The following box summarizes conversions among the three scales.

TEMPERATURE CONVERSIONS

The conversions are given both in words and with formulas in which C, F, and K are Celsius, Fahrenheit, and Kelvin temperatures, respectively.

To Convert from	Conversion in Words	Conversion Formula
Celsius to Fahrenheit	Multiply by 1.8 (or $\frac{9}{5}$). Then add 32.	$F = 1.8C + 32$
Fahrenheit to Celsius	Subtract 32. Then divide by 1.8 (or multiply by $\frac{5}{9}$).	$C = \frac{F - 32}{1.8}$
Celsius to Kelvin	Add 273.15.	$K = C + 273.15$
Kelvin to Celsius	Subtract 273.15.	$C = K - 273.15$

Where do these conversion formulas come from? It's easy to see their origin by studying Figure 2.5. For conversions between Kelvin and Celsius, note that the scales are the same except for the 273.15° difference in their zero points. Therefore, we simply add 273.15 to a Celsius temperature to get a Kelvin temperature. For conversions between Celsius and Fahrenheit, look at the differences in temperature between the freezing and boiling points of water. The Celsius scale has 100°C between these points, while the Fahrenheit scale has 212°F − 32°F = 180°F between them. Each Celsius degree therefore represents $\frac{180}{100} = 1.8$ Fahrenheit degrees, which explains the factor of 1.8 (or $\frac{9}{5}$) in the conversions. The 32 appears in the Celsius–Fahrenheit conversions to account for the difference in their zero points.

Example 6 Human Body Temperature

Average human body temperature is 98.6°F. What is it in Celsius and Kelvin?

Solution We convert from Fahrenheit to Celsius by subtracting 32 and then dividing by 1.8:

$$C = \frac{F - 32}{1.8} = \frac{98.6 - 32}{1.8} = \frac{66.6}{1.8} = 37.0°\text{C}$$

We find the Kelvin equivalent by adding 273.15 to the Celsius temperature:

$$K = C + 273.15 = 37 + 273.15 = 310.15\text{ K}$$

Human body temperature is 37°C or 310.15 K. **Now try Exercises 47–50.**

Time Out to Think

The local weather report says that tomorrow's temperature will be 59°, but does not specify whether it is in Celsius or Fahrenheit. Can you tell which it is? How?

Units of Energy and Power

We pay energy bills to power companies, we use energy from gasoline to run our cars, and we argue about whether nuclear energy is a sensible alternative to fossil fuels. But what *is* energy?

Broadly speaking, energy is what makes matter move or heat up. We need energy from food to keep our hearts beating, to maintain our body temperatures, and to walk or run. A car needs energy to move the pistons in its engine, which turn the wheels. A light bulb needs energy to generate light.

For Americans, the most familiar energy unit is the food *Calorie* (uppercase C) used to measure the energy our bodies can draw from food. A typical adult uses

Historical Note

The Fahrenheit scale was invented by German-born scientist Gabriel Fahrenheit in 1714. He originally defined the scale with 0°F representing the coldest temperature he could create with a mixture of ice and salt, and 100°F representing a rough estimate of human body temperature. The Celsius scale was invented by Swedish astronomer Anders Celsius in 1742. The Kelvin scale was invented in 1848 by British physicist William Thomson, later known as Lord Kelvin.

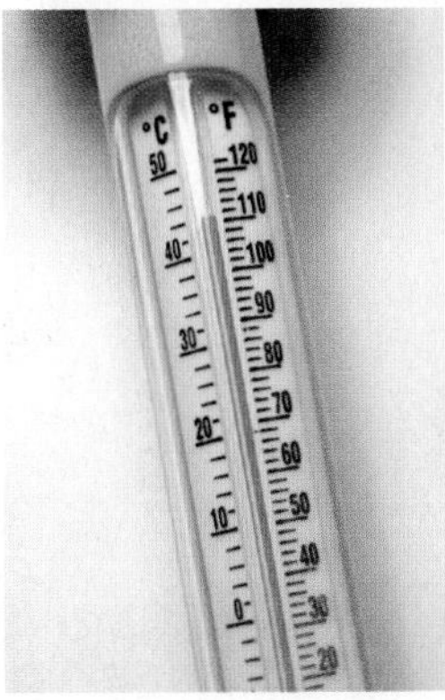

Take Note

A food Calorie (uppercase C) is 1000 calories (lowercase c). The lowercase calorie was once used commonly in science, but scientists today almost always measure energy in joules.

about 2500 Calories of energy each day. The international metric unit of energy is the **joule.** Outside the United States, most foods and beverages are labeled with their energy content in joules (or kilojoules) rather than Calories. One Calorie is equivalent to 4184 joules.

The words *energy* and *power* are often used together, but they are not the same. Power is the *rate* at which energy is used, which means it has units of energy divided by time. The most common unit of power is the **watt**, defined as 1 joule per second.

> **ENERGY AND POWER**
>
> **Energy** is what makes matter move or heat up. The international metric unit of energy is the **joule.**
>
> **Power** is the *rate* at which energy is used. The international metric unit of power is the **watt**, defined as
>
> $$1 \text{ watt} = 1\frac{\text{joule}}{\text{s}}$$

Example 7 Pedal Power

You are riding an exercise bicycle at a fitness center. The readout states that you are using 500 Calories per hour. Are you generating enough power to light a 100-watt bulb? (Note that 1 Calorie = 4184 joules.)

Solution We use a chain of conversions to go from Calories per hour to joules per second:

$$\frac{500\ \cancel{\text{Cal}}}{1\ \cancel{\text{hr}}} \times \frac{4184\text{ joule}}{1\ \cancel{\text{Cal}}} \times \frac{1\ \cancel{\text{hr}}}{60\ \cancel{\text{min}}} \times \frac{1\ \cancel{\text{min}}}{60\text{ s}} \approx 581\frac{\text{joule}}{\text{s}}$$

Your pedaling generates energy at a rate of 581 joules per second, which is a power of 581 watts—enough to light five (almost six) 100-watt bulbs.

Now try Exercises 51–52.

Electric Utility Bills

If you check an electric utility bill, you'll probably find that it refers to electric usage in units of **kilowatt-hours**. The hyphen in this unit tells us that it means 1 kilowatt × 1 hour, which is equivalent to 1000 watts × 1 hour. Replacing 1000 watts with 1000 joule/s, we find

$$1 \text{ kilowatt-hour} = \frac{1000\text{ joule}}{1\ \cancel{\text{s}}} \times 1\ \cancel{\text{hr}} \times \frac{60\ \cancel{\text{min}}}{1\ \cancel{\text{hr}}} \times \frac{60\ \cancel{\text{s}}}{1\ \cancel{\text{min}}} = 3{,}600{,}000\text{ joule}$$

> **BY THE WAY**
>
> If you purchase a gas appliance, such as a gas stove or a kerosene heater, its energy requirements may be labeled in *British thermal units,* or BTUs. One BTU is equivalent to 1055 joules.

> **DEFINITION**
>
> A **kilowatt-hour** is a unit of energy:
>
> $$1 \text{ kilowatt-hour} = 3.6 \text{ million joules}$$

Example 8 Operating Cost of a Light Bulb

Your utility company charges 12¢ per kilowatt-hour of electricity. How much does it cost to keep a 100-watt light bulb on for a week?

Solution One watt is one joule per second, so a 100-watt light bulb requires 100 joules per second. The energy used by the bulb in a week is 100 joule/s × 1 week. Using a chain of conversions to convert a week to seconds, we have

$$\frac{100\ \text{joule}}{1\ \cancel{\text{s}}} \times 1\ \cancel{\text{week}} \times \frac{7\ \cancel{\text{day}}}{1\ \cancel{\text{week}}} \times \frac{24\ \cancel{\text{hr}}}{1\ \cancel{\text{day}}} \times \frac{60\ \cancel{\text{min}}}{1\ \cancel{\text{hr}}} \times \frac{60\ \cancel{\text{s}}}{1\ \cancel{\text{min}}} = 60{,}480{,}000\ \text{joule}$$

Next, we convert this result to kilowatt-hours, remembering that 1 kilowatt-hour is 3,600,000 joules:

$$60{,}480{,}000\ \cancel{\text{joule}} \times \frac{1\ \text{kilowatt-hour}}{3{,}600{,}000\ \cancel{\text{joule}}} = 16.8\ \text{kilowatt-hour}$$

The light bulb uses 16.8 kilowatt-hours of energy in a week. At a price of 12¢ per kilowatt-hour, the total cost is

$$16.8\ \cancel{\text{kilowatt-hr}} \times 12\frac{¢}{\cancel{\text{kilowatt-hr}}} = 201.6¢ \approx \$2.02$$

The electricity to keep the 100-watt light bulb on all week costs about $2.02 (assuming a price of 12¢ per kilowatt-hour). **Now try Exercises 53–54.**

Time Out to Think

Check a utility bill (yours or a friend's). Is the electricity usage metered in units of kilowatt-hours (often abbreviated kWh)? If not, what units are used? If so, what is the price per kilowatt-hour?

PRACTICAL MATTERS

Save Money and Save the Earth

You can save both money and energy by replacing standard (incandescent) light bulbs with more efficient bulbs, such as compact fluorescents or LEDs (light emitting diodes). These bulbs save energy because virtually all the energy they use goes into making light, whereas most of the energy used by standard bulbs goes into heat (which is why they get so hot). As a result, compact fluorescents and LEDs typically need only about one-quarter as much energy as standard bulbs to generate the same amount of light. For example, a 25-watt compact fluorescent can produce as much light as a 100-watt standard bulb.

To see how much you can save, consider a 100-watt light bulb that is left on all the time. At an energy cost of 12¢ per kilowatt-hour, this light bulb costs $2.02 to operate for a week (see Example 8), or more than $100 per year. Replacing the 100-watt bulb with a 25-watt compact fluorescent or LED means your energy cost will be only one-fourth as much, saving you more than $75 per year. This savings more than makes up for the higher cost of compact fluorescents and LEDs; these bulbs also last much longer than standard bulbs, which further increases your savings.

Of course, you shouldn't leave 100-watt light bulbs on all the time, so your savings for a single light bulb will be less than that calculated above. Nevertheless, the total savings for a household can be substantial; nationally and globally, more efficient lighting could lead to huge energy savings and reduced carbon emissions. In the United States, legislation passed in 2007 requires manufacturers to begin phasing out standard light bulbs in 2012, with all sales of them ending in 2014.

Units of Density and Concentration

You'll encounter many other standardized units in everyday life. In most cases, these units will be variations on units with which you are already familiar, so you should be able to make sense of them from their context. Units that describe various types of density or concentration are particularly common.

Density describes compactness or crowding. Here are a few of the many ways that the idea of density is used:

- *Material density* is given in units of mass per unit volume, such as grams per cubic centimeter (g/cm^3). A useful reference is the density of water—about 1 g/cm^3. Objects with densities less than 1 g/cm^3 float in water, while higher-density objects sink.
- *Population density* is given by the number of people per unit area. For example, if 750 people live in a square region that is 1 mile on a side, the population density of the area is 750 $people/mi^2$.
- *Information density* is often used to describe how much memory can be stored by digital media. For example, each square inch on the surface of a dual-layer Blu-ray disk holds about 1 gigabyte of information, so we say that the disk has an information density of 1 $GB/in.^2$.

Historical Note

A king once asked the famed Greek scientist Archimedes (c. 287–212 B.C.E.) to test whether a crown was made of pure gold, as claimed by its goldsmith, or a mixture of silver and gold. Archimedes was at first unsure how to do it, but had a sudden insight while taking a bath one day. Knowing that silver is less dense than gold, he realized he could compare the rise in water level for the crown and for an equal weight of pure gold. Thrilled at this insight, he ran naked through the streets shouting "Eureka!" (meaning "I have found it"). For the goldsmith, the news wasn't so great: The crown was partly silver, so the king had him executed.

Time Out to Think

Use the concept of density to explain why you float better in a swimming pool when your lungs are filled with air than when you fully exhale.

Concentration describes the amount of one substance mixed with another. Here are two of the many ways in which concentration is used:

- The *concentration of an air pollutant* is often measured by the number of molecules of the pollutant per million molecules of air. For example, if there are 12 molecules of carbon monoxide in each 1 million molecules of air, we state the carbon monoxide concentration as 12 parts per million (ppm). (The U.S. Environmental Protection Agency says that air is unhealthy if the carbon monoxide concentration is above 9 ppm.)
- **Blood alcohol content** (BAC) describes the concentration of alcohol in a person's body. It is usually measured in units of grams of alcohol per 100 milliliters of blood. For example, in most states a person is considered legally intoxicated if his or her blood alcohol content is at or above 0.08 gram of alcohol per 100 milliliters of blood (written as 0.08 g/100 mL).

Example 9 New York City

Manhattan Island has a population of about 1.5 million people living in an area of about 57 square kilometers. What is its population density? If there were no high-rise apartments, how much space would be available per person?

Solution We divide the population by the area to find that

$$\text{population density} = \frac{1{,}500{,}000 \text{ people}}{57 \text{ km}^2} \approx 26{,}000 \frac{\text{people}}{\text{km}^2}$$

Manhattan's population density is about 26,000 people per square kilometer. If there were no high rises, each resident would have 1/26,000 square kilometer of land. This number is easier to interpret if we convert from square kilometers to square meters:

$$\frac{1\ \text{km}^2}{26{,}000\ \text{people}} \times \left(\frac{1000\ \text{m}}{1\ \text{km}}\right)^2 = \frac{1\ \text{km}^2}{26{,}000\ \text{people}} \times \frac{1{,}000{,}000\ \text{m}^2}{1\ \text{km}^2} \approx 38\frac{\text{m}^2}{\text{person}}$$

Without high rises, each person would have only 38 square meters, equivalent to a room about 6 meters, or 20 feet, on a side—and this does not include any space for roads, schools, or other common properties. Clearly, Manhattan Island could not fit so many residents without high rises. **Now try Exercises 55–60.**

Example 10 Blood Alcohol Content

An average-sized man has about 5 liters (5000 milliliters) of blood, and an average 12-ounce can of beer contains about 15 grams of alcohol (assuming the beer is about 6% alcohol by volume). If all the alcohol were immediately absorbed into the bloodstream, what blood alcohol content would we find in an average-sized man who quickly drank a single can of beer?

Solution If the alcohol were absorbed immediately, the man's 5000 milliliters of blood would contain the entire 15 grams of alcohol from the beer. We express this concentration as

$$\frac{15\ \text{g alcohol}}{5000\ \text{mL blood}}$$

We convert this concentration to the standard units for blood alcohol (g/100 mL) in two steps. First, we first carry out the division to find the concentration in grams per milliliter:

$$\frac{15\ \text{g}}{5000\ \text{mL}} = 0.003\frac{\text{g}}{\text{mL}}$$

Now, we multiply both the top and the bottom of the fraction by 100 to find the concentration in grams per 100 milliliters:

$$0.003\frac{\text{g}}{\text{mL}} \times \frac{100}{100} = 0.3\frac{\text{g}}{100\ \text{mL}}$$

The man's blood alcohol concentration would be 0.3 gram per 100 milliliters of blood—almost four times the legal limit of 0.08 g/100 mL. In reality, the man's blood alcohol content won't get this high from a single beer, because it takes some time for all the alcohol to be absorbed into the bloodstream (typically 30 minutes on an empty stomach and up to 2 hours on a full stomach) and because metabolic processes gradually eliminate the absorbed alcohol (at a rate of about 10 to 15 grams per hour). Nevertheless, a single beer is enough to cause impaired brain function—making it unsafe to drive—and this example points out how quickly and easily a person can become dangerously intoxicated. **Now try Exercises 61–62.**

BY THE WAY

According to the American Medical Association, brain function is impaired when the blood alcohol content reaches 0.04 g/100 mL of blood—which is half the legal limit of 0.08 g/100 mL. A blood alcohol content at or above 0.4 g/100 mL usually leads to coma and sometimes leads to death.

Time Out to Think

Many college students have lost their lives by rapidly consuming several "shots" of strong alcoholic drinks. Explain why such rapid consumption of alcohol can lead to death, even when the total amount of alcohol consumed may not sound like a lot.

QUICK QUIZ

Choose the best answer to each of the following questions. Explain your reasoning with one or more complete sentences.

1. One kilometer is
   a. 10 meters.
   b. 100 meters.
   c. 1000 meters.
2. A megaton is
   a. 100 tons.
   b. 1000 tons.
   c. 1 million tons.
3. A millimeter is approximately the size of
   a. the ball point in a pen.
   b. a golf ball.
   c. a basketball.
4. You are buying apples while traveling in Europe. The price is most likely to be quoted in
   a. euros per kilogram.
   b. euros per milliliter.
   c. euros per kilometer.
5. A liter is approximately equivalent to
   a. a mile.
   b. a pound.
   c. a quart.
6. A temperature of 105°C is
   a. typical of Phoenix in the summer.
   b. typical of Antarctica in the winter.
   c. hot enough to boil water.
7. Which of the following is *not* a unit of energy?
   a. joules
   b. watts
   c. kilowatt-hours
8. You want to know how much total energy is required to operate a 100-watt light bulb. Do you need any more information?
   a. No.
   b. Yes; you need to know the temperature of the light bulb when it is on.
   c. Yes; you need to know how long the light bulb is on.
9. New Mexico has a population density of about 12 people per square mile and an area of about 120,000 square miles. To find its actual population, you should
   a. multiply the population density by the area.
   b. divide the population density by the area.
   c. divide the area by the population density.
10. The concentration of carbon dioxide in Earth's atmosphere might be stated in
    a. grams per meter.
    b. parts per million.
    c. joules per watt.

Exercises 2B

REVIEW QUESTIONS

1. Briefly describe the origin and use of common units in the U.S. customary system.
2. Briefly describe the origin and use of metric units.
3. What are the basic metric units of length, mass, time, and volume? How are the metric prefixes used?
4. Using examples, show how to convert among the Fahrenheit, Celsius, and Kelvin temperature scales.
5. What is *energy*? List at least three common units of energy. Under what circumstances do the different units tend to be used?
6. What is the difference between *energy* and *power*? What are the standard units for power?
7. What do we mean by *density*? What do we mean by *concentration*? Describe common units of density and concentration, including blood alcohol content, with examples.

DOES IT MAKE SENSE?

Decide whether each of the following statements makes sense (or is clearly true) or does not make sense (or is clearly false). Explain your reasoning. Hint: Be sure to consider whether the units are appropriate to the statement, as well as whether the stated amount makes any sense. For example, a statement that someone is 15 feet tall uses the units (feet) appropriately, but does not make sense because no one is that tall.

8. I drank 2 liters of water today.
9. I know a professional bicyclist who weighs 300 kilograms.
10. I drove along the highway at 100 kilometers per hour.
11. I know someone who can run 35 liters per second.
12. A guy on our track team can high-jump 7 meters.
13. My friend ran 10,000 meters in less than an hour.
14. The book I sent you weighs 3 milligrams.
15. My car's gas tank holds 12 meters of gasoline.

16. My daily food intake gives me about 10 million joules of energy.
17. Our utility company charges 10¢ per watt for the electricity we use.
18. The beach ball we played with had a density of 10 grams per cubic centimeter.

BASIC SKILLS & CONCEPTS

19–22: Powers of 10. Evaluate the following expressions using skills covered in the Brief Review on p. 100.

19. a. $10^4 \times 10^7$ b. $10^5 \times 10^{-3}$ c. $\frac{10^6}{10^2}$ d. $\frac{10^8}{10^{-4}}$
20. a. $10^{-2} \times 10^{-6}$ b. $\frac{10^{-6}}{10^{-8}}$ c. $10^{12} \times 10^{23}$ d. $\frac{10^{-4}}{10^5}$
21. a. $\frac{10^{25}}{10^{15}}$ b. $10^1 + 10^0$ c. $10^2 + 10^{-1}$ d. $10^2 - 10^1$
22. a. $\frac{10^{12}}{10^{-4}}$ b. $10^{23} \times 10^{-23}$ c. $10^4 + 10^2$ d. $\frac{10^{15}}{10^{-5}}$

23–30: USCS Units. Answer the following questions involving conversions within the USCS system.

23. What is the height in inches of a 6'10" basketball player?
24. What is the weight in tons of a 345-pound lineman?
25. One cubic foot holds 7.48 gallons of water, and one gallon of water weighs 8.33 pounds. How much does a cubic foot of water weigh in pounds? in ounces (avoirdupois)?
26. Suppose you bought 10 six-packs of soda, each six-pack containing six 12-ounce cans. How many gallons of soda did you buy?
27. A speed boat has a top speed of 46 knots (nautical miles per hour). What is this speed in miles per hour?
28. How many quarts does an 18-gallon gasoline tank hold? How many pints? How many ounces?
29. How many cords of wood could you fit in a room that is 4 yards long, 4 yards wide, and 2 yards high? (See Table 2.4.)
30. A small city produces 500,000 cubic feet of garbage per week. If all of this garbage were stacked neatly (in a nice vertical pile) on a 100-yard by 60-yard football field, how high would the pile be (in feet)?

31–36: Metric Prefixes. Complete the following sentences with a number. All answers should be greater than 1.

31. A meter is _____ times as large as a millimeter.
32. A kilogram is _____ times as large as a milligram.
33. A liter is _____ times as large as a milliliter.
34. A kilometer is _____ times as large as a micrometer.
35. A square meter is _____ times as large as a square centimeter.
36. A cubic meter is _____ times as large as a cubic millimeter.

37–46: USCS–Metric Conversions. Convert the following quantities to the indicated units.

37. 22 kilograms to pounds
38. 160 centimeters to inches
39. 16 quarts to liters
40. 2 square kilometers to square miles
41. 55 miles per hour to kilometers per hour
42. 120 kilometers per hour to miles per hour
43. 18 meters per second to miles per hour
44. 20 square meters to square feet
45. 300 cubic inches to cubic centimeters
46. 18 grams per cubic centimeter to pounds per cubic inch

47–48: Celsius–Fahrenheit Conversions. Convert the following temperatures from Fahrenheit to Celsius or vice versa.

47. a. 45°F b. 20°C c. −15°C d. −30°C e. 70°F
48. a. −8°C b. 15°F c. 15°C d. 75°F e. 20°F

49–50: Celsius–Kelvin Conversions. Convert the following temperatures from Kelvin to Celsius or vice versa.

49. a. 50 K b. 240 K c. 10°C
50. a. −40°C b. 400 K c. 125°C

51. **Running Power.** Assume that running consumes 100 Calories per mile. If you run 10-minute miles, what is your average power output, in watts, during a 1-hour run?
52. **Bicycle Power.** A 1-hour bike ride at a pace of 15 miles per hour consumes about 750 Calories. What is your average power output, in watts, during a 45-minute bike ride?

53–54: Electric Bills. Consider the following electric bills.
a. Calculate the total electrical energy use in joules.
b. Calculate your average power use in watts.
c. Assume that your power supplier generates electricity by burning oil. Note that 1 liter of oil releases 12 million joules of energy. How much oil is needed to generate the electricity you use? Give your answer in both liters and gallons.

53. In May you used 900 kilowatt-hours of energy for electricity.
54. In October you used 1050 kilowatt-hours of energy for electricity.

55–60: Densities. Compute the following densities using the appropriate units.

55. A cube of wood measures 3 centimeters on a side and it weighs 20 grams. What is its density? Will it float in water?
56. At room temperature, a 0.1-cubic-centimeter sample of plutonium weighs 1.98 grams. What is its density? Will it float in water?
57. The land area of the United States is about 3.5 million square miles, and the population is about 306 million people. What is the average population density?
58. The country with the greatest population density is Monaco, where approximately 32,500 people live in an area of

1.95 square kilometers. What is the population density of Monaco in people per square kilometer? Compare this density to that of the United States, which is approximately 31 people per square kilometer.

59. New Jersey and Alaska have populations of 8.7 million and 680,000, respectively (U.S. Census Bureau, 2008). Their areas are 7417 and 571,951 square miles, respectively. Compute the population densities of both states.

60. A standard DVD has a surface area of 134 square centimeters. Depending on formatting, it holds either 4.7 or 8.5 gigabytes. Find the data density in both cases.

61. **Blood Alcohol Content: Wine.** A typical glass of wine contains about 20 grams of alcohol. Consider a 110-pound woman, with approximately 4 liters (4000 milliliters) of blood, who drinks two glasses of wine.

a. If all the alcohol were immediately absorbed into her bloodstream, what would her blood alcohol content be? Explain why it is fortunate that, in reality, the alcohol is not absorbed immediately.

b. Again assume that all the alcohol is absorbed immediately, but now assume that her body eliminates the alcohol (through metabolism) at a rate of 10 grams per hour. What is her blood alcohol content 3 hours after drinking the wine? Is it safe for her to drive at this time? Explain.

62. **Blood Alcohol Content: Hard Liquor.** Eight ounces of a hard liquor (such as whiskey) typically contain about 70 grams of alcohol. Consider a 200-pound man, with approximately 6 liters (6000 milliliters) of blood, who quickly drinks 8 ounces of hard liquor.

a. If all the alcohol were immediately absorbed into his bloodstream, what would his blood alcohol content be? Explain why it is fortunate that, in reality, the alcohol is not absorbed immediately.

b. Again assume that all the alcohol is absorbed immediately, but now assume that his body eliminates the alcohol (through metabolism) at a rate of 15 grams per hour. What is his blood alcohol content 4 hours after drinking the liquor? Is it safe for him to drive at this time? Explain.

FURTHER APPLICATIONS

63–68: **Currency Conversions.** Use the currency exchange rates in Table 2.1 in Unit 2A to answer the following questions. State all of the conversion factors that you use.

63. Apples in a French market cost 2.50 euros per kilogram. What is the price in dollars per pound?

64. Gasoline at a Belgian gas station costs 1.40 euros per liter. What is the price in dollars per gallon?

65. Suppose that a new fuel-efficient German car travels an average of 26 kilometers on 1 liter of gasoline. If gasoline costs 1.50 euros per liter, how much will it cost to drive 300 kilometers?

66. Carpet at a British home supply store sells for 16 pounds (currency) per square meter. What is the price in dollars per square yard?

67. An 0.8-liter bottle of Mexican wine costs 100 pesos. What is the price in dollars per ounce?

68. The monthly rent on an 80-square-meter apartment in Nice, France, is 1040 euros. The monthly rent on a 500-square-foot apartment in Santa Fe, New Mexico, is $800. In terms of price per area, which apartment is less expensive?

69. **The Metric Mile.** Two historic races in track and field are the mile (1 USCS mile) and the metric mile (1500 meters).

a. Complete the sentence: The metric mile is _____% of the USCS mile in length.

b. Consider the following world records in the two events (as of 2009).

	Men	Women
Mile	3:43:13	4:12:56
Metric mile	3:26:00	3:50:46

Compute and compare the average speed in the men's mile and metric mile races.

c. Compute and compare the average speed in the women's mile and metric mile races.

d. If the average speed for the metric mile were run for the entire length of a mile race, would it result in a world record? Answer for both men and women.

70. **Supertankers.** An oil supertanker of the Very Large Crude Carrier (VLCC) class has a deadweight tonnage (the total amount that it can carry in crew, supplies, and cargo) of 300,000 long tons.

a. How many kilograms can the tanker carry?

b. Assume that the tonnage consists entirely of oil. If the density of oil is 850 kilograms per cubic meter, how many cubic meters of oil can the tanker carry?

c. Assume that 1000 liters of oil has a volume of 1 cubic meter. How many barrels of oil can the tanker carry? (See Tables 2.4 and 2.6.)

d. Find the current price of oil in dollars per barrel. What is the value of the oil carried by a full tanker?

71. **Lake Victoria.** Lake Victoria is Africa's largest lake and the second largest fresh-water lake in the world in terms of surface area. Its volume is approximately 2750 cubic kilometers and its surface area is 68,800 square kilometers.

a. What is the average depth of the lake (the depth of a box with the volume and surface area of the lake)?

b. In the last six years, the water level of the lake has dropped 10 feet (from the depth computed in part a). Approximately how much water has the lake lost?

c. What percentage of the volume (2750 cubic kilometers) has been lost?

72. **The Cullinan Diamond and the Star of Africa.** The largest single rough diamond ever found, the Cullinan diamond, weighed 3106 carats. It was used to cut the world's largest diamond gem, the Star of Africa (530.2 carats), which is part of the British crown jewels collection. How much did the Cullinan diamond weigh in milligrams? in (avoirdupois) pounds? How much does the Star of Africa weigh in milligrams? in (avoirdupois) pounds?

73–76: Gems and Gold. Use carats and karats, as discussed in the Practical Matters box on p. 98, to answer the following questions.

73. What is the weight of the 45.52-carat Hope diamond in grams and ounces?
74. What is the purity (as a percentage) of a 14-karat gold ring?
75. How many ounces of gold are in a 16-karat gold chain that weighs 2.2 ounces?
76. What is the weight in carats of a diamond that weighs 0.15 ounce?
77. **Power Spa.** An outdoor spa (hot tub) draws 1500 watts to keep the water warm. If the utility company charges \$0.10 per kilowatt-hour, how much does it cost to operate the spa for 4 months during the winter (24 hours per day)?
78. **Hair Dryer Cost.** You have an 1800-watt hair dryer that you use for an average of 10 minutes per day. Your utility company charges 12¢ per kilowatt-hour of energy (including taxes and fees). How much does it cost to run the hair dryer each day? each year?
79. **Compact Fluorescent Light Bulbs.** You replace a 100-watt standard light bulb with a 25-watt compact fluorescent bulb that supplies the same light. Over a 10,000-hour life (typical for a compact fluorescent bulb), how much energy, in kilowatt-hours, do you save? If electricity costs 12¢ per kilowatt-hour, how much money do you save?
80. **Human Wattage.** Suppose you require 2500 food Calories per day.

    a. What is your average power, in watts? Compare your answer to the wattage of some familiar appliance.

    b. How much energy, in joules, do you require from food in a year? Counting all forms of energy (such as gasoline, electricity, and energy for heating), the average U.S. citizen consumes about 400 billion joules of energy each year. Compare this value to the energy needed from food alone.
81. **Coal Power Plant.** A new coal-burning power plant can generate 1.5 gigawatts (billion watts) of power. Burning 1 kilogram of coal yields about 450 kilowatt-hours of energy. How much energy, in kilowatt-hours, can the plant generate each month? How much coal, in kilograms, is needed by this power plant each month? If a typical home uses 1000 kilowatt-hours per month, how many homes can this power plant supply with energy?
82. **Nuclear Power Plant.** Operating at full capacity, the Columbia Generating Station, a nuclear power plant near Richland, Washington, can generate 1190 megawatts of power. Nuclear fission of 1 kilogram of uranium (in the form of uranium-235) releases 16 million kilowatt-hours of energy. How much energy, in kilowatt-hours, can the plant generate each month? How much uranium, in kilograms, is needed by this power plant each month? If a typical home uses 1000 kilowatt-hours per month, how many homes can this power plant supply with energy?

83–84: Solar Energy. Use these facts in the following exercises: Solar (photovoltaic) cells convert sunlight directly into electricity. If solar cells were 100% efficient, they would generate about 1000 watts of power per square meter of surface area when exposed to direct sunlight. With lower efficiency, they generate proportionally less power. For example, 10% efficient cells generate 100 watts of power in direct sunlight.

83. Suppose a 1-square-meter panel of solar cells has an efficiency of 20% and receives the equivalent of 6 hours of direct sunlight per day. How much energy, in joules, can it produce each day? What average power, in watts, does the panel produce?
84. Suppose you want to supply 1 kilowatt of power to a house (the average household power requirement) by putting solar panels on its roof. For the solar cells described in Exercise 83, how many square meters of solar panels would you need? Assume that you can make use of the average power from the solar cells (by, for example, storing the energy in batteries until it is needed).
85. **Wind Power: One Turbine.** Modern wind energy "farms" use large wind turbines to generate electricity from the wind. At a typical installation, a single modern turbine can produce an average power of about 200 kilowatts. (This average takes wind variations into account.) How much energy, in kilowatt-hours, can such a turbine generate in a year? Given that the average household uses about 10,000 kilowatt-hours of energy each year, how many households can be powered by a single wind turbine?
86. **California Wind Power.** California currently has wind farms capable of generating a total of 2500 megawatts (2.5 gigawatts) of power (roughly 2% of the state's total electricity).

    a. Assuming that wind farms typically generate 30% of their capacity, how much energy, in kilowatt-hours, can the California wind farms generate in one year? Given that the average household uses about 10,000 kilowatt-hours of energy each year, how many households can be powered by these wind farms?

    b. One of the great advantages of wind power is that it does not produce the carbon dioxide emissions that contribute to global warming. On average, energy produced from fossil fuels generates about 1.5 pounds of carbon dioxide for every kilowatt-hour of energy. Suppose California did not have its wind farms and the energy were instead produced from fossil fuels. How much more carbon dioxide would be entering the atmosphere each year?

WEB PROJECTS

87. **Energy Issues.** The question of how we will continue to meet our energy needs is one of the most important issues of our time. Research one aspect of this issue, such as the potential of various alternative energy resources, using information available at the Web site for the U.S. Energy Information Administration. Write a short report on your findings.

88. **Pollution Progress.** Investigate the average concentrations of various pollutants in a major city of your choice. Find the EPA standards for each pollutant, and find some of the hazards associated with exposure to each pollutant. Track how the levels of pollution in this city have changed over the past 20 years. Based on your findings, do you think it is likely that pollution in this city will get better or worse over the next decade? Summarize your findings and your conclusions in a one- or two-page report.

89. **Alcohol Poisoning.** Research some aspect of the dangers of alcohol, such as drunk driving or alcohol poisoning. Find statistics related to this issue, especially data that relate blood alcohol content to specific dangers. Summarize your findings in a short report about how society might combat the danger.

90. **Should the United States Go Metric?** Research the history of attempts to convert the United States to the metric system. Do you think it will ever happen? Do you think it would be a good idea?

IN YOUR WORLD

91. **Everyday Metric.** Describe three ways that you use metric units in your everyday life.

92. **Energy.** Look for a news article concerning energy or power. What units are used to describe energy or power? Summarize the article and explain the meaning of the units.

93. **Density and Concentration.** Look for a news article that uses units of density or concentration in any context. Summarize the article and explain the meaning of the units.

94. **Utility Bill.** Analyze a utility bill. Explain all the units shown, and determine the relative costs of different energy uses. What changes would you recommend if the recipient of the bill wanted to lower energy costs?

USING TECHNOLOGY

95. **Unit Conversions.** Given what you have learned in this chapter and the appropriate conversion factors, you can do any unit conversion problem. The following problems have somewhat obscure conversion factors. Use Google or Excel (or any other means) to make the following conversions.

    a. Convert 100 furlongs to kilometers.

    b. How fast does a snail crawl? Convert 23 inches per day to miles per hour.

    c. Convert 100 drams to ounces.

    d. Convert 1 hectare to acres.

    e. Convert 1000 pascals to pounds per square inch (units of pressure).

    f. Convert 1 hectoliter to gallons.

96. **Currency Conversions.** Use the Internet to convert $100 to the following currencies.

    a. Brazilian reals
    b. Israeli shekels
    c. Moroccan dirhams
    d. Russian rubles
    e. Turkish lira
    f. Chinese yuan
    g. Colombian pesos
    h. Indian rupees

UNIT 2C Problem-Solving Guidelines and Hints

If you look back through the examples we've studied, you'll see that we studied each problem in order to find a good strategy for solving it, and we carefully interpreted our results to make sure they had the correct units and made sense. In a few cases, we used pictures or diagrams to help us understand a problem. You may have noticed that while every problem is different, the *process* of problem solving has a few common features.

The four-step process on the next page provides a useful guide to problem solving. Study it carefully and look back to see how these steps were applied in earlier examples. Keep in mind that the four steps offer *general* advice, so they will not automatically lead to a solution. In this sense, problem solving is more of an art than a science, and the four steps are more like instructions for painting than a recipe for the Mona Lisa. Note also that while these steps apply to virtually all problem solving, it is not necessary (or particularly useful) to write them out step by step in solutions.

A FOUR-STEP PROBLEM-SOLVING PROCESS

Step 1: Understand the problem. Be sure that you understand the nature of the problem. For example:

- Think about the context of the problem (that is, how it relates to other problems in the real world) to gain insight into its purpose.
- Make a list or table of the specific information given in the problem, including units for numerical data.
- Draw a picture or diagram to help you make sense of the problem.
- Restate the problem in different ways to clarify its question.
- Make a mental or written model of the solution, into which you can insert details as you work through the problem.

Step 2: Devise a strategy for solving the problem. Finding an appropriate strategy requires creativity, organization, and experience. In seeking a strategy, try any or all of the following:

- Obtain needed information that is not provided in the problem statement, using recall, estimation, or research.
- Make a list of possible strategies and hints that will help you select your overall strategy.
- Map out your strategy with a flow chart or diagram.

Step 3: Carry out your strategy, and revise it if necessary. In this step you are likely to use analytical and computational tools. As you work through the mathematical details of the problem, be sure to do the following:

- Keep an organized, neat, and written record of your work, which will be helpful if you later need to review your solution.
- Double-check each step so that you do not risk carrying errors through to the end of your solution.
- Constantly reevaluate your strategy as you work. If you find a flaw in your strategy, return to step 2 and create a revised strategy.

Step 4: Look back to check, interpret, and explain your result. Although you may be tempted to think you have finished after you find a result in step 3, this final step is the most important. After all, a result is useless if it is wrong or misinterpreted or cannot be explained to others. Always do all of the following:

- Be sure that your result makes sense. For example, be sure that it has the expected units, that its numerical value is sensible, and that it is a reasonable answer to the original problem.
- Once you are sure that your result is reasonable, recheck your calculations or find an independent way of checking the result.
- Identify and understand potential sources of uncertainty in your result.
- Write your solution clearly and concisely, including discussion of any relevant uncertainties or assumptions.
- Consider and discuss any pertinent implications of your result.

Historical Note

These four steps are modified from the process in *How to Solve It*, by George Polya (Princeton University Press, Princeton, N.J., 1957). First published in 1945, this book has sold more than 1 million copies and is available in at least 17 different languages.

Time Out to Think

Choose two examples from Units 2A and 2B, and identify how the four-step process was carried out in those examples. More generally, explain how the four steps are implicit in the solutions to the examples we've studied, even though we have not written them out in a step-by-step list.

Using the four-step process will help you become better organized. But the only sure way to become more creative and improve your problem solving is through practice. We now offer several hints about problem solving, each illustrated with an example. The hints themselves relate more to *attitudes* about problem solving than to actual techniques. Indeed, their primary purpose is to help you develop a "mind set" that is conducive to enjoyable and successful problem solving.

"I THINK YOU SHOULD BE MORE EXPLICIT HERE IN STEP TWO."

Hint 1: There May Be More Than One Answer

How can society best reduce the total amount of greenhouse gases emitted into the atmosphere? We won't even attempt to answer this question, but it should make the point that no *single* best answer may be available. Indeed, many different political and economic strategies could yield similar reductions in greenhouse gas emissions.

Most people recognize that policy questions do not have unique answers, but the same is true of many mathematical problems. For example, both $x = 4$ and $x = -4$ are solutions to the equation $x^2 = 16$. Without further information and context, we have no way to determine whether both solutions are valid for a particular problem. Nonunique solutions often occur because not enough information is available to distinguish among a variety of possibilities.

Example 1 Box Office Receipts

Tickets for a fundraising event were priced at \$10 for children and \$20 for adults. Sally worked the first shift at the box office, selling a total of \$130 worth of tickets. However, she did not keep careful count of how many tickets she sold for children and adults. How many tickets of each type (child and adult) did she sell?

Solution Let's proceed by trial and error. Suppose Sally sold just one \$10 child ticket. In that case, she would have sold \$130 − \$10 = \$120 worth of adult tickets. Because the adult tickets cost \$20 apiece, this means she would have sold \$120 ÷ (\$20 per adult ticket) = 6 adult tickets. We have found an answer to the question: Sally could have collected the \$130 by selling 1 child and 6 adult tickets. But it is not the only answer, as we can see by testing other values. For example, suppose she sold three of the \$10 child tickets, for a total of \$30. Then she would have sold \$130 − \$30 = \$100 worth of adult tickets, which means 5 of the \$20 adult tickets. We have a second possible answer—3 child and 5 adult tickets—and have no way to know which answer tells us the actual number of tickets sold.

In fact, there are seven possible answers to the question. In addition to the two answers we've already found, other possible answers are 5 child tickets and 4 adult tickets; 7 child tickets and 3 adult tickets; 9 child tickets and 2 adult tickets; 11 child tickets and 1 adult ticket; and 13 child tickets with 0 adult tickets. Without further information, we do not know which combination represents the actual ticket sales. **Now try Exercises 7–8.**

Time Out to Think

Verify that each of the child/adult ticket combinations listed as a possible solution in Example 1 does indeed total to \$130. Then explain why there aren't any solutions that have an even number of child tickets.

Hint 2: There May Be More Than One Strategy

Just as we must often admit more than one right answer, we should also expect more than one strategy for finding an answer. Given how rich and diverse mathematics and the human mind are, it would be unreasonable to expect everyone to follow the same path to a solution. As illustrated in the following example, an efficient strategy can save a lot of time and work.

Example 2 Jill and Jack's Race

Jill and Jack ran a 100-meter race. Jill won by 5 meters; that is, Jack had run only 95 meters when Jill crossed the finish line. They decide to race again, but this time Jill starts 5 meters behind the starting line. Assuming that both runners run at the same pace as before, who will win?

Solution Strategy 1 One approach to this problem is analytical—we analyze each race quantitatively. We were not told how fast either Jill or Jack ran, so we can choose some reasonable numbers. For example, we might assume that Jill ran the 100 meters in the first race in 20 seconds. In that case, her pace was $100 \text{ m} \div 20 \text{ s} = 5$ meters per second (5 m/s). Because Jack ran only 95 meters in the same 20 seconds, his pace was $95 \text{ m} \div 20 \text{ s} = 4.75 \text{ m/s}$.

For the second race, Jill must run 105 meters (because she starts 5 meters behind the starting line) to Jack's 100 meters. We predict their times by dividing their respective race distances by their speeds from the first race:

$$\textit{Jill:} \quad 105 \text{ m} \div 5\frac{\text{m}}{\text{s}} = 105 \cancel{\text{m}} \times \frac{1 \text{ s}}{5 \cancel{\text{m}}} = 21 \text{ s}$$

$$\textit{Jack:} \quad 100 \text{ m} \div 4.75\frac{\text{m}}{\text{s}} = 100 \cancel{\text{m}} \times \frac{1 \text{ s}}{4.75 \cancel{\text{m}}} \approx 21.05 \text{ s}$$

Jill will win the second race by a slim margin.

Strategy 2 Although the analytical method works, we can use a much more intuitive and direct solution. In the first race, Jill runs 100 meters in the same time that Jack runs 95 meters. Therefore, in the second race, Jill will pull even with Jack 95 meters from the starting line. In the remaining 5 meters, Jill's faster speed will allow her to pull away and win. Note how this insight avoids the calculations needed in Strategy 1.

Now try Exercise 9.

Hint 3: Use Appropriate Tools

You don't need a computer to check your tab in a restaurant, and you don't need calculus to find the area of a rectangular room. For any given task there is an appropriate level of power that is needed, and it is a matter of style and efficiency neither to underestimate nor to overestimate that level. You usually will have a choice of tools to use in any problem. Choosing the tools most suited to the job will make your task much easier.

Example 3 The Cars and the Canary

Two cars, 120 miles apart, begin driving toward each other on a long straight highway. One car travels 20 miles per hour and the other 40 miles per hour (Figure 2.6). At the same time, a canary, starting on one car, flies back and forth between the two cars as they approach each other. If the canary always flies 150 miles per hour and turns around instantly at each car, how far has it flown when the cars collide?

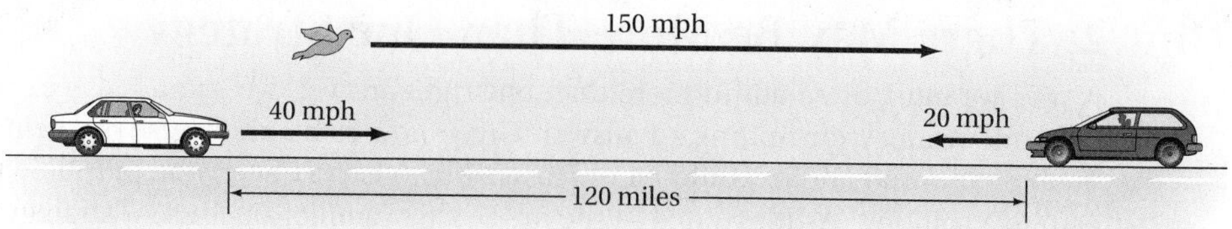

FIGURE 2.6 Set-up for the cars and canary problem.

Solution Because the problem asks "how far," we might be tempted to calculate the *distance* traveled by the canary on each back and forth trip between the cars. However, these trips get shorter as the cars approach each other and we would have to add up all the individual distances. In principle, we would need to add up an *infinite* number of ever-smaller distances—a task that involves the mathematics of calculus.

But note what happens if we focus on *time* rather than distance. The cars will collide with each other at a speed of 60 mi/hr (because one car is traveling at 20 mi/hr and the other is traveling in the opposite direction at 40 mi/hr). Because they initially are 120 miles apart, they will collide in precisely 2 hours:

$$120 \text{ mi} \div 60\frac{\text{mi}}{\text{hr}} = 120 \cancel{\text{mi}} \times \frac{1 \text{ hr}}{60 \cancel{\text{mi}}} = 2 \text{ hr}$$

The canary is flying at a speed of 150 miles per hour, so in 2 hours it flies

$$2 \cancel{\text{hr}} \times 150\frac{\text{mi}}{\cancel{\text{hr}}} = 300 \text{ mi}$$

The canary flies 300 miles before the cars collide. We could have found the answer with calculus, but why bother when we were able to do it with just multiplication and division?

Now try Exercise 10.

Hint 4: Consider Simpler, Similar Problems

Sometimes you are confronted with a problem that at first seems daunting. Our fourth hint is to consider a simpler, but similar, problem. The insight gained from solving the easier problem may help you understand the original problem.

Example 4 Coffee and Milk

Suppose you have two cups in front of you: One holds coffee and one holds milk (Figure 2.7). You take a teaspoon of milk from the milk cup and stir it into the coffee cup. Next, you take a teaspoon of the mixture in the coffee cup and put it back into the

FIGURE 2.7 Set-up for the coffee and milk problem.

Thinking About...

Zeno's Paradox

The Greek philosopher Zeno of Elea (c. 460 B.C.E.) posed several paradoxes that defied solution for thousands of years. (A *paradox* is a situation or statement that seems to violate common sense or to contradict itself.) One paradox begins with an imaginary race between the warrior Achilles and a slow-moving tortoise. The tortoise is given a head start, but our common sense says that the swift Achilles will soon overtake the tortoise and win.

Zeno suggested a different way to look at the race. Suppose that, as shown in the figure, Achilles starts from point P0 and the tortoise starts from P1. During the time it takes Achilles to reach P1, the slow-moving tortoise will move ahead a little bit to P2. While Achilles continues on to P2, the tortoise will move ahead to P3. And so on. That is, Achilles must cover an infinite set of ever-smaller distances to catch the tortoise (that is, from P0 to P1, from P1 to P2, etc.). From this point of view, it seems that Achilles will never catch the tortoise.

This paradox puzzled philosophers and mathematicians for more than 2000 years. Its resolution depends on a key insight that became clear only with the invention of calculus in the 17th century: It does not necessarily require an infinite amount of time to cover an infinite set of distances. For example, imagine that the infinite set of distances covered by Achilles begins with 1 mile, then $\frac{1}{2}$ mile, then $\frac{1}{4}$ mile, and so on. Then the total distance he covers, in miles, is

$$1 + \frac{1}{2} + \frac{1}{4} + \frac{1}{8} + \frac{1}{16} + \frac{1}{32} + \frac{1}{64} + \frac{1}{128} + \frac{1}{256} + \frac{1}{512} + \frac{1}{1024} + \frac{1}{2048} + \cdots$$

This sum is called an **infinite series** because it is the sum of an infinite number of terms. You might guess that an infinite series would sum to infinity. But note what happens when we add just the first four terms, then the first eight terms, and then the first twelve terms. You can confirm the following results with a calculator.

$$1 + \frac{1}{2} + \frac{1}{4} + \frac{1}{8} = 1.875$$

$$1 + \frac{1}{2} + \frac{1}{4} + \frac{1}{8} + \frac{1}{16} + \frac{1}{32} + \frac{1}{64} + \frac{1}{128} = 1.9921875$$

$$1 + \frac{1}{2} + \frac{1}{4} + \frac{1}{8} + \frac{1}{16} + \frac{1}{32} + \frac{1}{64} + \frac{1}{128} + \frac{1}{256} + \frac{1}{512} + \frac{1}{1024} + \frac{1}{2048} = 1.99951171875$$

If you continue to add more terms in this infinite series, you will find that the sum gets closer and closer to 2, but never exceeds it. In fact, it can be proven deductively that the sum of this infinite series is 2. Therefore, even though the paradox has Achilles covering an infinite number of ever-shorter distances, the *total* distance he runs is finite—in this example, it is 2 miles. Clearly, it won't take him long to run a finite distance of 2 miles, so he will pass the slower tortoise and win the race.

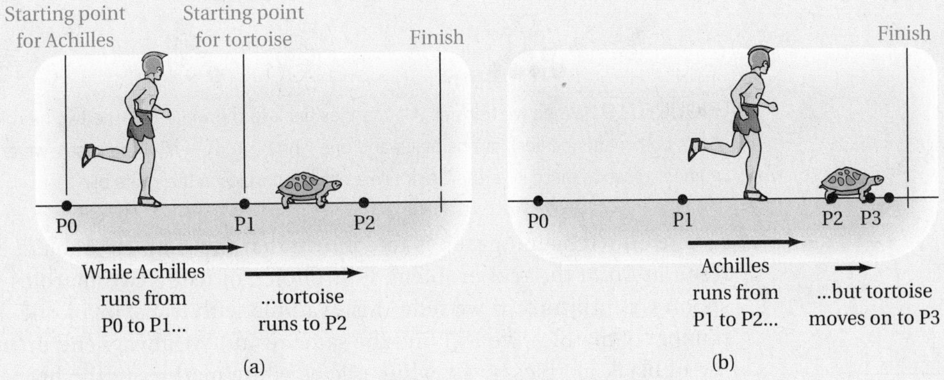

milk cup. After the two transfers, there will be either (1) more coffee in the milk cup than milk in the coffee cup, (2) less coffee in the milk cup than milk in the coffee cup, or (3) equal amounts of coffee in the milk cup and milk in the coffee cup. Which of these three possibilities is correct?

Solution A cup of either milk or coffee contains something like a *trillion trillion* molecules of liquid. Clearly, it would be difficult to visualize how such enormous numbers of molecules mix together, let alone to calculate the result. However, the essence of this problem is the *mixing* of two things. So one approach is to try a similar mixing problem that is much easier: mixing two piles of marbles.

Suppose that the black pile in Figure 2.8 has ten black marbles and represents the coffee. The white pile has ten white marbles and represents the milk. In this simpler problem, we can represent the first transfer—one teaspoon of milk into the coffee cup—by moving two white marbles to the black pile. This leaves the white pile with just eight white marbles, while the black pile now has ten black and two white marbles.

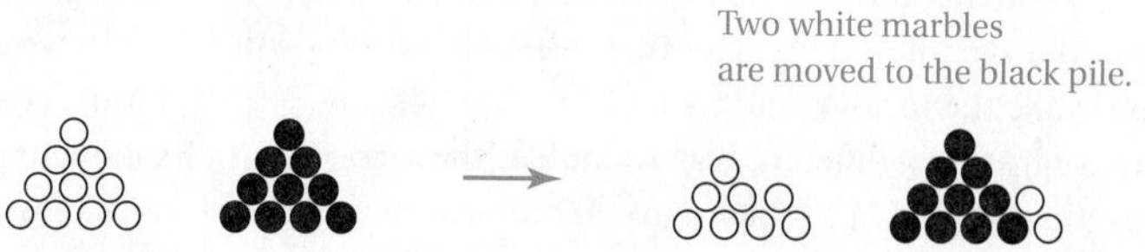

FIGURE 2.8 The white and black piles of marbles represent the milk and coffee, respectively. Moving two white marbles to the black pile represents putting a teaspoon of milk in the coffee.

Representing the second transfer—of one teaspoon from the coffee cup into the milk cup—involves taking any two marbles from the black pile and putting them in the white pile. We can then ask a question analogous to the original question: Are there more black marbles in the white pile or white marbles in the black pile?

Because the marbles represent molecules that mix thoroughly, the two marbles for the second transfer must be drawn at random, which presents three possible cases: The two marbles in the second transfer can be either both black, both white, or one of each. But, as shown in Figure 2.9, in all three cases we end up with the same number of white marbles in the black pile as black marbles in the white pile. By analogy, we have the answer to our original question: After the two transfers, the amounts of coffee in the milk cup and milk in the coffee cup are equal.

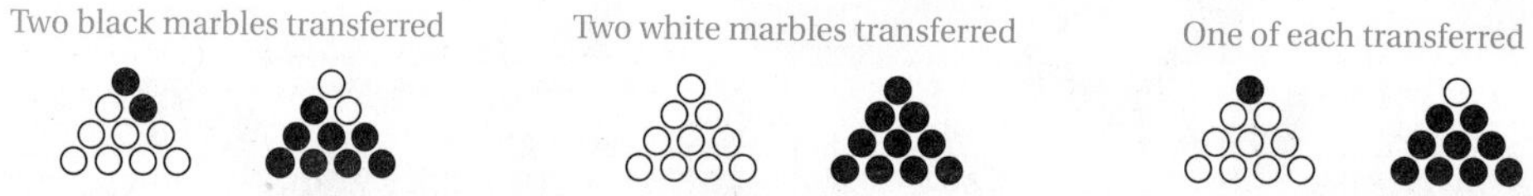

FIGURE 2.9 When we transfer two marbles back to the white pile, the two marbles may be both black (left), both white (center), or one black and one white (right). In all three cases, we end up with the same number of white marbles in the black pile as black marbles in the white pile.

The only remaining step is to confirm that the simpler problem is a reasonable representation of the real problem. Our choice of using two marbles to represent a teaspoon was arbitrary. If we redo this example with transfers of one, three, or any other number of marbles, we will find the same result: We always end up with the same number of black marbles in the white pile as white marbles in the black pile. Starting with ten marbles in each pile also was arbitrary; the conclusion remains the same if we start with twenty, fifty, or a trillion trillion marbles. Because molecules can be thought of as tiny marbles for the purpose of this problem, the real problem has no essential differences from the marble problem. **Now try Exercise 11.**

Time Out to Think

Most people are surprised by the result of the coffee and milk problem. Are you? Now that you know the solution, can you give a simple explanation of the real problem that would satisfy surprised friends?

Hint 5: Consider Equivalent Problems with Simpler Solutions

Replacing a problem with a similar, simpler problem can reveal essential insights about a problem, as we've just seen. However, "similar" is not good enough when we need a numerical answer. In that case, a useful approach to a difficult problem is to look for an *equivalent* problem. An equivalent problem will have the same numerical answer but may be easier to solve.

Example 5 Party Decorations

Juan is decorating for a party in a room that has ten large cylindrical posts. The posts are 8 feet high and have a circumference of 6 feet. His plan is to wrap eight turns of ribbon around each post. How much ribbon does Juan need?

Solution The problem is difficult because it involves three-dimensional geometry. However, we can convert it to a simpler equivalent problem. Assume that each wrapped post is a hollow cylinder, and imagine cutting it down its length and unfolding it into a flat rectangle (Figure 2.10). The width of the rectangle is the 6-foot circumference of the post, and its length is the 8-foot length of the post.

Now, instead of dealing with ribbon wrapped around a three-dimensional post, we have a simple rectangle with eight diagonal segments of ribbon. The total length of the eight segments will be the length of the ribbon required for one of the posts in the original problem. The height of each triangle is $\frac{1}{8}$ of the length of the rectangle, or $8\text{ ft} \div 8 = 1\text{ ft}$. The base of each triangle is the 6-foot width of the rectangle. The Pythagorean theorem tells us that

$$\text{base}^2 + \text{height}^2 = \text{hypotenuse}^2 \quad \text{or} \quad \text{hypotenuse} = \sqrt{\text{base}^2 + \text{height}^2}$$

Substituting the 6-foot base and 1-foot height yields

$$\text{hypotenuse} = \sqrt{(6\text{ ft})^2 + (1\text{ ft})^2} \approx 6.1\text{ ft}$$

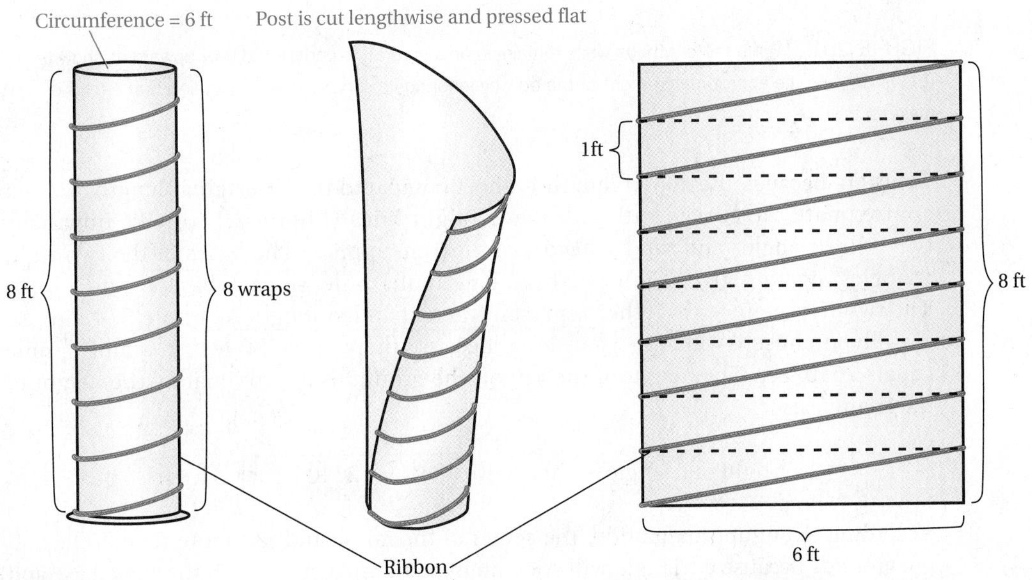

FIGURE 2.10 We want to know the length of ribbon needed to coil around a post (left). We can simplify the problem by imagining that we cut the wrapped post lengthwise (center). When the post is pressed flat, the ribbon lies in straight segments, each of which is the hypotenuse of a right triangle.

The length of each ribbon segment is 6.1 feet, and the total length of the ribbon is 8×6.1 ft $= 48.8$ ft. To decorate 10 posts, Juan needs 10×48.8 ft $= 488$ feet of ribbon. Note how much easier it was to solve this equivalent problem than the original one.

Now try Exercise 12.

Hint 6: Approximations Can Be Useful

Another useful strategy is to make problems easier by using approximations. Most real problems involve approximate numbers to begin with, so an approximation often is good enough for a final answer. In other cases, an approximation will reveal the essential character of a problem, making it easier to reach an exact solution. Approximations also provide a useful check: If you come up with an "exact solution" that isn't close to the approximate one, something may have gone wrong.

Example 6 A Bowed Rail

Imagine a mile-long bar of metal such as the rail along railroad tracks. Suppose that the rail is anchored on both ends (a mile apart) and that, on a hot day, its length expands by 1 foot. If the added length causes the rail to bow upward in a circular arc as shown in Figure 2.11a, about how high would the center of the rail rise above the ground?

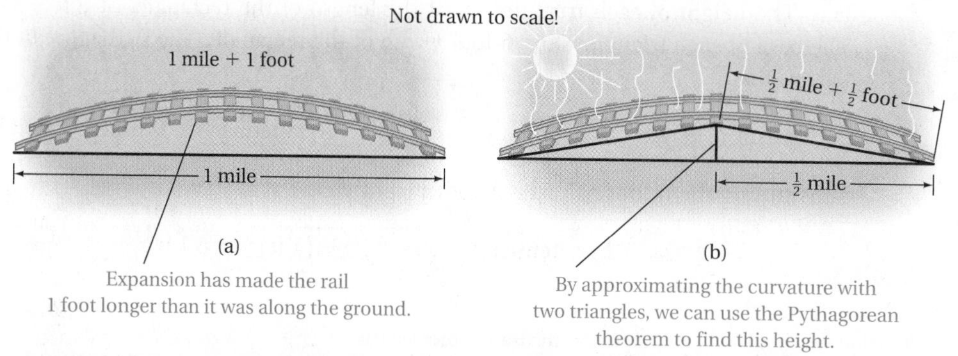

FIGURE 2.11 (a) If a rail lengthens while remaining anchored at its ends, it will bow upward as shown. (b) We can find the approximate height of the bow by ignoring its curvature and assuming that each side makes a triangle.

Solution Because the added length is short compared to the original length, we can approximate the curved rail with two straight lines (Figure 2.11b). We now have two right triangles and the Pythagorean theorem applies. The bases of the two right triangles together give the original rail length of 1 mile, so each base is $\frac{1}{2}$ mile long. The two hypotenuses together represent the expanded length of 1 mile + 1 foot, so each hypotenuse is $\frac{1}{2}$mile + $\frac{1}{2}$foot long. Because there are 5280 feet in a mile, $\frac{1}{2}$ mile equals 2640 feet. The height of the rail off the ground is approximately the height of the triangles:

$$\text{height of triangle} = \sqrt{(2640.5\text{ ft})^2 - (2640\text{ ft})^2} \approx 51.4\text{ ft}$$

According to our approximation, the center of the rail would rise more than 50 feet off the ground! Because a triangle will stick up higher than a curve with the same base and length, the actual height is less than the approximate height. An exact solution shows that the top of the curved rail would be about 48 feet off the ground.

Now try Exercise 13.

Time Out to Think

Are you surprised by the answer to Example 6? How does the use of the approximation tell you that the original question contained at least some unrealistic assumptions? Which assumptions do you think were unrealistic?

Hint 7: Try Alternative Patterns of Thought

Try to avoid rigid patterns of thought that tend to suggest the same ideas and methods over and over again. Instead, approach every problem with an openness that allows innovative ideas to percolate. In its most wondrous form, this approach is typified by what Martin Gardner, a well-known popularizer of mathematics, has called "aha!" problems. These are problems whose best solution involves a penetrating insight that reduces the problem to its essential parts.

Example 7 China's Population Policy

In an effort to reduce population growth, in 1978 China instituted a policy that allows only one child per family. One unintended consequence has been that, because of a cultural bias toward sons, China now has many more males than females (presumably because of selective abortions or, in some cases, infanticide). To solve this problem, some people have suggested replacing the one-child policy with a *one-son* policy. That is, if a family's first child is a boy, the family has met its limit of children. But if the first child is a girl, the family can have additional children until one is a boy. Suppose that the one-son policy were implemented and birth rates returned to their natural levels (half boys and half girls). Compared to the one-child policy, how would this affect the overall birth rate and the numbers of boys and girls?

Solution Most people initially approach this problem by considering the families. Half the families would have a boy as their first and only child. Of the remaining families, half would have a boy as their second child (reaching their one-son limit), while the other half would have a girl and go on to a third child. Half of these families would have a boy on this third try, while the other half would continue on after a third girl. And so on.

However, a moment of insight makes the problem much easier. Neither policy, by itself, affects the natural probability that any child will be a boy or a girl. If the one-son policy restores natural birth rates, then equal numbers of boys and girls must be born. Moreover, nearly all families would have exactly one boy under this policy. Because there must be equal numbers of boys and girls overall, there must also be one girl per family, on average. Therefore, the average number of children per family is two (one boy and one girl) under a one-son policy. In summary, a one-son policy would lead to equal numbers of boys and girls but, compared to a one-child policy, would double the average number of children per family from one to two. **Now try Exercises 14–15.**

BY THE WAY

Hospital birth records show that boys and girls are born in nearly, but not precisely, equal numbers: Roughly 106 boys are born for every 100 girls. However, males have higher mortality rates than females at every age, so the numbers even out in adulthood and women outnumber men in old age.

Time Out to Think

China occupies roughly the same amount of land as the United States, but has almost four times as many people. Given these circumstances, do you think that the one-child policy is a good idea? Would a one-son policy be better? Defend your opinions.

Hint 8: Do Not Spin Your Wheels

Finally, everyone has had the experience of getting "bogged down" with a problem. When your wheels are spinning, let up on the gas! Often the best strategy in problem solving is to put a problem aside for a few hours or days. You may be amazed at what you see (and what you overlooked) when you return to it.

QUICK QUIZ

Choose the best answer to each of the following questions. Explain your reasoning with one or more complete sentences.

1. A quantitative problem from daily life
   a. always has exactly one solution.
   b. may have more than one algebraic solution, but only one of these solutions can make sense.
   c. may have more than one correct answer.
2. You are asked to calculate gas mileage for a car, and your answer comes out with units of mi/gal^2. This means that
   a. you have done something wrong.
   b. you have calculated the area the car can cover per gallon of gas, rather than the distance.
   c. you have found the reciprocal of the correct answer.
3. You are asked to calculate how long a new battery will last in a flashlight when the flashlight is turned on. You should expect your answer to be
   a. a few minutes. b. between a few hours and a few days.
   c. at least several years.
4. You are asked to calculate the weight that a hotel elevator can safely carry. You should expect your answer to be
   a. less than 10 kilograms.
   b. several hundred kilograms.
   c. tens of thousands of kilograms.
5. If you add up an infinite number of ever-smaller fractions, the answer
   a. must be infinity. b. may be finite or infinite.
   c. must be zero.
6. The exterior surface of a cylinder with a circumference of 10 inches and a length of 20 inches (and no end caps) is the same as the area of
   a. a rectangle measuring 10 inches by 20 inches.
   b. a circle with a circumference of 10 inches.
   c. a right triangle with its two shorter sides measuring 10 inches and 20 inches.
7. Is it legal for a man to marry his widow's sister?
   a. Yes. b. It depends on which state you live in.
   c. It is impossible.
8. Forty balls numbered 1 through 40 are mixed up in a barrel. How many balls must you draw from the barrel (without looking) to be sure that you have two even-numbered balls?
   a. 3 b. 40 c. 22
9. Karen arrives at the subway station every day at a random time and takes the first train that arrives. If she takes the A train, which arrives regularly every hour, she goes to the museum. If she takes the B train, which also arrives regularly every hour, she goes to the beach. A month after starting this game, she has gone to the beach 25 times and to the museum 5 times. Of the following options, which is the most likely explanation?
   a. The A train arrives on the hour and the B train always arrives 30 minutes later.
   b. The A train always arrives 10 minutes after the B train.
   c. The A train always arrives 10 minutes before the B train.
10. A small grill can hold two hamburgers at a time. If it takes 5 minutes to cook one side of a hamburger, what is the *shortest* time needed to cook both sides of three hamburgers?
   a. 20 minutes b. 15 minutes c. 10 minutes

Exercises 2C

REVIEW QUESTIONS

1. Describe the four basic steps of problem solving.
2. Summarize the strategic hints for problem solving given in this unit, and give an example of the meaning of each one.

DOES IT MAKE SENSE?

Decide whether each of the following statements makes sense (or is clearly true) or does not make sense (or is clearly false). Explain your reasoning.

3. My simple problem-solving recipe will enable you to solve any mathematical problem easily.
4. Whether it's a problem in mathematics or something else, it's best to start by taking time to make sure you understand the nature of the problem.
5. The four-step problem-solving method given in this section is probably not useful for everyday problems in life.
6. Kids are often taught to draw pictures for simple math problems, but grownups should be able to solve problems without any pictures.

BASIC SKILLS & CONCEPTS

7. A Toll Booth. A toll collector on a highway receives \$2 for cars and \$3 for buses. At the end of a 1-hour period, she collected \$32. How many cars and buses passed through the toll booth during that period? List all possible solutions.
8. Donations. A public radio station offers two levels of support during a fundraiser. Level 1 membership requires a \$25 donation and Level 2 membership requires a \$50 donation. At the end of the day, a fundraiser had pledges for \$350. How many Level 1 and Level 2 pledges were received during this fundraiser? List all possible solutions.

9. **A Second Race.** Jordan and Amari run a 200-meter race, and Jordan wins by 10 meters. They decide to run the 200-meter race again with Jordan starting 10 meters behind the starting line.

   a. Assuming both runners run at the same pace as they did in the first race, who wins the second race?

   b. Suppose that Jordan starts 5 meters behind the starting line in the second race. Who wins the race?

   c. Suppose that Jordan starts 15 meters behind the starting line in the second race. Who wins the race?

   d. How far behind the starting line must Jordan start so that the second race is a tie? First estimate the distance as closely as possible. Then try to find it exactly.

10. **Cars and Canaries.** Two cars, 360 kilometers apart, begin driving toward each other on a long, straight highway. One car travels 80 kilometers per hour and the other 100 kilometers per hour. At the same time, a canary, starting on one car, flies back and forth between the two cars as they approach each other. If the canary flies 120 kilometers per hour and spends no time to turn around at each car, how far has it flown when the cars collide?

11. **Mixing Marbles.** Consider the case in which each of two piles initially contains fifteen marbles (see Example 4). Suppose that on the first transfer, three black marbles are moved to the white pile. On the second transfer, any three marbles are taken from the white pile and put into the black pile. Demonstrate, with diagrams and words, that you will always end up with as many white marbles in the black pile as black marbles in the white pile.

12. **Coiling Problems.** Eight turns of a wire are wrapped around a pipe with a length of 20 centimeters and a circumference of 6 centimeters. What is the length of the wire?

13. **Bowed Rail.** Suppose a railroad rail is 1 kilometer long, and it expands on a hot day by 10 centimeters in length. Approximately how high would the center of the rail rise above the ground?

14. **China's Population.** To convince yourself that a one-son policy would lead to an average of two children per family, with equal numbers of boys and girls, do the following. Suppose that 10,000 families are having children according to the one-son policy. Describe the general makeup of all of the families (that is, start with the fact that 5000 families have a boy as their first and therefore only child, and continue on). Use this process to show that the average number of children is two and that boys and girls are equal in number.

15. **China's Missing Girls.** Suppose that, as the current generation matures, China's population of young adults has more men than women by a ratio of 120 to 100. With 450 million young adults in China, how many men will be unable to find a spouse?

FURTHER APPLICATIONS

16. **Fencing a Yard.** Suppose you are designing a rectangular garden and you have 20 meters of fencing with which to enclose the garden.

   a. Can you enclose a garden that is 7 meters long and 3 meters wide with the available fencing? What is the area of the garden?

   b. Can you enclose a garden that is 8 meters long and 2 meters wide with the available fencing? What is the area of the garden?

   c. By computing the area of other possible gardens that can be enclosed with 20 meters of fencing, find or estimate the dimensions of the garden that has the most area.

17. **Traffic Counter.** A thin tube stretched across a street counts the number of pairs of wheels that pass over it. A car with two axles registers two counts. A light truck with three axles registers three counts. During a 1-hour period, a traffic counter registered 35 counts. How many cars and light trucks passed over the traffic counter? List all possible solutions.

18. **Stereo Wire.** A stereo system is being installed in a room with a rectangular floor measuring 12 feet by 10 feet and an 8-foot ceiling. The stereo amplifier is on the floor in one corner of the room. A speaker is at the ceiling in the opposite corner of the room. You must run a wire from the amplifier to the speaker, and the wire must run along the floor or walls (not through the air). What is the shortest length of wire you can use for the connection? (*Hint:* Turn the problem into an equivalent but simpler problem by imagining cutting the room along its vertical corners and unfolding it so that it is flat. You will be able to apply the Pythagorean theorem.)

19. **A Common Error: Averaging Speeds.** Suppose you run 2 miles from your house to a friend's house at a speed of 4 miles per hour. When the time comes to return home, you are tired and walk the same 2-miles home at 2 miles per hour.

   a. How long did you spend running to your friend's house?

   b. How long did you spend walking home?

   c. Is it true that the average speed for the round trip is the average of 4 miles per hour and 2 miles per hour (which is 3 miles per hour)? (*Hint:* Did you spend more time traveling 4 miles per hour or 2 miles per hour?)

   d. What is your average speed for the round trip?

20–39: Puzzle Problems. The following puzzle problems require careful reading and thinking. *Aha!* solutions are possible.

20. It takes you 30 seconds to walk from the first (ground) floor of a building to the third floor. How long will it take to walk from the first floor to the sixth floor (at the same pace, assuming that all floors have the same height)?

21. Reuben says, "Two days ago I was 20 years old. Later next year I will be 23 years old." How is this possible?

22. There are three kinds of apples all mixed up in a basket. How many apples must you draw (without looking) from the basket to be sure of getting at least two of one kind?

23. "Brothers and sisters I have none, but that man's father is my father's son." Who is "that man"?

24. "I am the brother of the blind fiddler, but brothers I have none." How can this be?

25. A woman bought a horse for $500 and then sold it for $600. She bought it back for $700 and then sold it again for $800. How much did she gain or lose on these transactions?

26. Three boxes of fruit are labeled *Apples*, *Oranges*, and *Apples and Oranges*. Each label is wrong. By selecting just one fruit from just one box, how can you determine the correct labeling of the boxes?

27. Each of ten large barrels is filled with golf balls that all look alike. The balls in nine of the barrels weigh 1 ounce and the balls in one of the barrels weigh 2 ounces. With only *one* weighing on a scale, how can you determine which barrel contains the heavy golf balls?

28. A woman is traveling with a wolf, a goose, and a mouse. She must cross a river in a boat that will hold only herself and one other animal. If left to themselves, the wolf will eat the goose and the goose will eat the mouse. How many crossings are required to get all four creatures across the river alive?

29. How do you measure 9 minutes with a 7-minute and a 4-minute hourglass? Assume the hourglasses can only measure 7-minute and 4-minute intervals and cannot be used to measure other time intervals (for example, you can't tell when 2 minutes have gone by).

30. A rope ladder hanging over the side of a boat has rungs 1 foot apart. Ten rungs are showing. If the tide rises 5 feet, how many rungs will be showing?

31. You are considering buying 12 gold coins that look alike, but you have been told that one of them is a heavy counterfeit. How can you find the heavy coin in three weighings on a balance scale?

32. Suppose you have 40 blue socks and 40 brown socks in a drawer. How many socks must you take from the drawer (without looking) to be sure of getting a pair of the same color?

33. Five books of five different colors are placed on a shelf. The orange book is between the gray and pink books, and these three books are consecutive. The gold book is not leftmost on the shelf and the pink book is not rightmost on the shelf. The brown book is separated from the pink book by two books. If the gold book is not next to the brown book, what is the complete ordering of the books?

34. Three prisoners know that the jailer has three white hats and two red hats. The jailer gives one hat to each prisoner and says, "If you can deduce the color of your own hat, you will be freed." Each prisoner can see the hats of the other two prisoners, but not his own. The first prisoner says (honestly), "I cannot tell the color of my hat." The second prisoner says (honestly), "I cannot tell the color of my hat." The third prisoner is blind, but he is freed because he knows the color of his hat. What color hat does he have and how did he know?

35. A visitor arrived in a small Nevada town in need of a haircut. He discovered that there were exactly two barbers in town. One was well groomed, with splendidly cut hair; the other was unkempt, with an unattractive haircut. Which barber should the visitor patronize?

36. Two quarters rest next to each other on a table. One coin is held fixed while the second coin is rolled around the edge of the first coin with no slipping. When the moving coin returns to its original position, how many times has it revolved?

37. If a clock takes 5 seconds to strike 5:00 (chiming five times), how long does it take to strike 10:00 (chiming ten times)? Assume each chime occurs simultaneously (takes no time).

38. One day in the maternity ward, the name tags for four girl babies become mixed up.

a. In how many different ways could two babies be tagged correctly and two babies be tagged incorrectly?

b. In how many different ways could three of the babies be tagged correctly and one baby be tagged incorrectly?

39. Three guests checked into a hotel and paid $30 for their shared room. A while later, the desk clerk realized that the room should have cost only $25, so she gave the bellhop $5 to return to the three guests. The bellhop realized that $5 couldn't be divided evenly among the three guests, so he kept $2 and gave $1 to each of the guests. It seems that each guest has spent $9 for the room (which makes $27) and the bellhop has $2, for a total of $29. Where is the missing dollar?

40–48: Projects: Real-World Problems. Consider the following complex problems, which do not have a single straightforward solution. Describe how you would apply the four-step problem-solving process described in the text (without actually carrying out the process). List the assumptions and information needed to carry out your solution. Assess the uncertainty in these assumptions and data. Determine whether you believe the problem can be solved and whether a particular solution might generate controversy.

40. You are asked to calculate the cost of installing enough bike racks on campus to solve a bicycle parking problem.

41. What is the cost and what are the risks involved in installing enough battery-charging stations (for cell phones and other small electronic devices) to serve the students on your campus?

42. You want to know whether having a top-quality football program means more or less money for academic programs at your university.

43. Your grandfather recently left you $10,000, which you are determined to save and not spend. Where should you invest your money so that it is as safe *and* profitable as possible?

44. You decide that, in the interest of protecting the environment, you will convert your home heating and hot water system to solar power. How much will this conversion cost or save over the next ten years?

45. Suppose that China and India decide to use their extensive coal reserves to supply energy to their populations at the same per capita level as in the United States. How much carbon dioxide would be added to the atmosphere?

46. Are automobile insurance companies gouging drivers? Suppose that you want to figure out whether they are justified in raising insurance rates as rapidly as they have during the past few years.

47. Suppose that you cook for yourself. How should you design your meals for one week so that they are as nutritious, appealing, and economical as possible?

48. Suppose that a city added new bus routes and handed out free bus passes. How many people would give up driving in favor of the bus? How much money, overall, would this cost or save the city?

Hell's library

49. **Project: Textbook Analysis.** Although research shows that most adults today have difficulty with "story problems," we might hope that the next generation will have less difficulty. Find a current textbook in mathematics that is used in middle schools. Read through the "story problems" in the textbook. Write a critical analysis of the problems and conclude with an opinion as to whether the problems make mathematics meaningful.

WEB PROJECTS

50. **China's Population.** Find current statistics regarding China's population, such as its total population and average number of children per family, and projections of its future population. Is China's population policy achieving its goals? Explain.

51. **Polya and Problem Solving.** Many Web sites discuss George Polya's work and other problem-solving strategies. Explore a few such sites. Write a one- or two-paragraph summary of something you learn about problem solving that you think would be useful to many people.

IN YOUR WORLD

52. **Multiple Solutions.** Find an example of a real problem for which, because of insufficient data, we cannot distinguish between two or more possible solutions. The problem might come from a news report or from your own experiences. What additional data would be useful?

53. **Multiple Strategies.** Find an example of a real problem that could potentially be solved by two or more competing strategies. The problem might come from a news report or from your own experiences. Describe each strategy. Which one do you think is better? Why?

54. **Novel Solution.** Find a news report concerning a problem in business or science that was solved by a surprising method. Describe the method and why it was useful.

CHAPTER 2 Summary

UNIT	KEY TERMS	KEY IDEAS AND SKILLS
2A	units conversion factor currency conversions	**Identify** units with key words *per, square,* or *cube* or with hyphens. **Write** conversion factors in three equivalent forms. **Work** with units to check answers and help solve problems.
2B	U.S. customary system (USCS) metric system (SI) Celsius, Fahrenheit, Kelvin absolute zero energy units: Calorie, joule, kilowatt-hour power units: $1 \text{ watt} = 1 \text{ joule/s}$ density concentration blood alcohol content	**Understand** and convert basic USCS and metric units. **Know** metric prefixes. **Know** temperature units and convert between °F, °C, and Kelvin. **Understand** energy units and power units. Energy is what makes matter move or heat up. Power is the rate at which energy is used. **Apply** the concept of density to materials, population, and information. **Apply** the concept of concentration to pollution and blood alcohol content.
2C	four-step problem-solving process	**Apply** eight strategic hints for problem solving.

The concept of number is the obvious distinction between the beast and man. Thanks to number, the cry becomes song, noise acquires rhythm, the spring is transformed into a dance, force becomes dynamic, and outlines figures.

—Joseph de Maistre, 19th-century French philosopher

Numbers in the Real World

Life is filled with numbers that may at first seem incomprehensible: a population measured in billions of people, national budgets measured in trillions of dollars, and distances ranging from nanometers to light-years. Moreover, numbers come in many forms, including percentages and index numbers (such as the Consumer Price Index), and nearly always involve uncertainties. In this chapter, we will discuss the use and interpretation of numbers we encounter in our daily lives.

ACTIVITY Big Numbers

Use this activity to gain a sense of the kinds of problems this chapter will enable you to study. Try working through it before you begin the chapter, then return to it after you've learned the chapter material.

As a warm-up for thinking about the many ways in which we use numbers in the real world, let's investigate some large numbers that play key roles in all of our lives. Use the Web to find the numbers you need to answer the following questions. If possible, work with two or three other students, with each of you looking up all the numbers. You may find that you and your colleagues find different results; if that happens, discuss how each of you found your numbers, why they differ, and which estimate is likely to be the best one.

1. What are the current populations of the United States and the world? What fraction of the world's population lives in the United States?
2. What is the federal government's deficit expected to be for this fiscal year? How much does that amount represent for each person in the United States?
3. What is the current value of the total federal debt of the United States? How much does the debt represent for each person in the United States? (Note: See Unit 4F if you are unsure of the difference between *deficit* and *debt*.)
4. How much oil, in gallons, does the United States import each year? How much imported oil is used, and how much does it cost, for each person in the United States?
5. Find the total annual budget and the total enrollment for your college or university. Then divide the budget by the enrollment to determine the average cost of educating each student. How does this number compare to what you actually pay in tuition? Can you explain why the two numbers are different?
6. How many videos are currently posted on YouTube? How many views does the average video receive? How many views does the most popular video receive?

UNIT 3A Uses and Abuses of Percentages

News reports frequently express quantitative information with percentages. Unfortunately, while percentages themselves are rather basic—they are just an alternative form of fractions—they are often used in very subtle ways. For example, consider the following quote from a front-page article in the *New York Times:*

> *The rate [of smoking] among tenth graders jumped 45 percent, to 18.3 percent, and the rate for eighth graders is up 44 percent, to 10.4 percent.*

All the percentages in this statement are used correctly, but they are quite confusing. For instance, what does it mean to say "up 44%, to 10.4%"? In this unit, we will investigate some of the uses and abuses of percentages.

Three Ways of Using Percentages

Consider the following statements from news reports:

- A total of 13,000 newspaper employees, 2.6% of the newspaper work force, lost their jobs.
- Citigroup stock fell 48% last week, to $3.50.
- The advanced battery lasts 125% longer than the standard one, but costs 200% more.

On close examination, each statement uses a percentage in a different way. The first uses a percentage to express a *fraction* of the total work force. The second uses a percentage to describe a *change* in stock price. The third uses percentages to *compare* the performance and costs of batteries.

Using Percentages as Fractions

Percent is just a fancy way of saying "divided by 100," so $P\%$ simply means $P/100$. For example, 10.4% means 10.4/100, or 0.104. Therefore, if 10.4% of eighth-graders smoke and there are 100,000 eighth-graders, then the number who smoke is 10.4% *of* 100,000, or

$$10.4\% \times 100{,}000 = 0.104 \times 100{,}000 = 10{,}400$$

Note that the word *of* implies multiplication. We've found that if 10.4% of 100,000 eighth-graders smoke, there are 10,400 smokers.

Example 1 Newspaper Survey

A newspaper reports that 64% of 1069 people surveyed said that the president is doing a good job. How many said the president is doing a good job?

Solution The 64% represents the fraction of respondents who said the president is doing a good job. Because *of* indicates multiplication, we find that 64% of 1069 is

$$64\% \times 1069 = 0.64 \times 1069 = 684.16 \approx 684$$

A Brief Review Percentages

The words *per cent* simply mean "per 100" or "divided by 100." We use the symbol % as a shorthand for the words *per cent*. For example, we read 50% as "50 percent" and its meaning is

$$50\% = \frac{50}{100} = 0.5$$

More generally, for a number P,

$$P\% = \frac{P}{100}$$

For example:

$$100\% = \frac{100}{100} = 1 \qquad 200\% = \frac{200}{100} = 2$$

$$350\% = \frac{350}{100} = 3.5$$

Note that multiplying a number by 100% does not change its meaning, because 100% is just another way of writing 1. For example, multiplying 1.25 by 100% gives

$$1.25 \times 100\% = 125\%$$

This shows that 125% is just another way of writing 1.25. These basic ideas lead to the following rules for converting between percentages and decimals or common fractions.

- **To convert a percentage to a common fraction:** Replace the % symbol with division by 100; simplify the fraction if necessary.

  Example: $25\% = \frac{25}{100} = \frac{1}{4}$

- **To convert a percentage to a decimal:** Drop the % symbol and move the decimal point two places to the left (that is, divide by 100).

  Example: $25\% = 0.25$

- **To convert a decimal to a percentage:** Move the decimal point two places to the right (that is, multiply by 100) and add the % symbol.

  Example: $0.43 = 43\%$

- **To convert a common fraction to a percentage:** First convert the common fraction to decimal form, using a calculator if necessary; then convert the decimal to a percentage.

  Example: $\frac{1}{5} = 0.2 = 20\%$

Now try Exercises 17–32.

About 684 people said the president is doing a good job. We rounded the answer to 684 to obtain a whole number of people. **Now try Exercises 45–50.**

Using Percentages to Describe Change

Percentages are often used to describe how a quantity changes with time. As an example, suppose the population of a town was 10,000 in 1980 and 15,000 in 2010. We can express the change in population in two basic ways:

- Because the population rose by 5000 people (from 10,000 to 15,000), we say that the **absolute change** in the population was 5000 people.
- Because the increase of 5000 people was 50% of the starting population of 10,000, we say that the **relative change** in the population was 50%, or 0.5.

In general, calculating an absolute or relative change always involves two numbers: a starting number, or **reference value**, and a **new value.** Once we identify these two values, we can calculate the absolute and relative change with the formulas in the following box. Note that the absolute and relative changes are *positive* if the new value is greater than the reference value and *negative* if the new value is less than the reference value.

ABSOLUTE AND RELATIVE CHANGE

The **absolute change** describes the actual increase or decrease from a reference value to a new value:

$$\text{absolute change} = \text{new value} - \text{reference value}$$

The **relative change** is a fraction that describes the size of the absolute change in comparison to the reference value:

$$\text{relative change} = \frac{\text{absolute change}}{\text{reference value}} = \frac{\text{new value} - \text{reference value}}{\text{reference value}}$$

The relative change can be converted from a fraction to a percentage by multiplying by 100%.

As the next example shows, the relative change formula leads to the following important rules:

- When a quantity *doubles* in value, its relative change is 1, or 100%.
- When a quantity *triples* in value, its relative change is 2, or 200%.
- When a quantity *quadruples* in value, its relative change is 3, or 300%. And so on.

Example 2 Stock Price Rise

During a 6-month period, Nokia's stock doubled in price from \$10 to \$20. What were the absolute and relative changes in the stock price?

Solution The reference value is the starting stock price of \$10 and the new value is the later stock price of \$20. The absolute change is the difference between the new and starting stock prices:

$$\begin{aligned}\text{absolute change} &= \text{new value} - \text{reference value}\\ &= \$20 - \$10 = \$10\end{aligned}$$

The absolute change divided by the reference value gives the relative change:

$$\text{relative change} = \frac{\text{absolute change}}{\text{reference value}} = \frac{\$10}{\$10} = 1 = 100\%$$

That is, the doubling of the stock price means a relative increase in value of 100%.

Now try Exercises 51–52.

Time Out to Think

In your own words, explain why doubling in value means a relative increase of 100% (as opposed to, say, 200%). Extend this thinking to explain why tripling means a 200% increase, quadrupling means a 300% increase, and so on.

Example 3 World Population Growth

World population was 2.6 billion in 1950 and 6.0 billion in 2000. Describe the absolute and relative change in world population from 1950 to 2000.

Solution The reference value is the 1950 population of 2.6 billion and the new value is the 2000 population of 6.0 billion.

$$\begin{aligned}\text{absolute change} &= \text{new value} - \text{reference value}\\ &= 6.0 \text{ billion} - 2.6 \text{ billion} = 3.4 \text{ billion}\\ \text{relative change} &= \frac{\text{new value} - \text{reference value}}{\text{reference value}}\\ &= \frac{6.0 \text{ billion} - 2.6 \text{ billion}}{2.6 \text{ billion}} \approx 1.3 = 130\%\end{aligned}$$

World population increased by 3.4 billion people, or by 130%, from 1950 to 2000.

Now try Exercises 53–54.

BY THE WAY

According to United Nations and U.S. Census Bureau estimates, world population passed 6 billion in late 1999—only 12 years after passing the 5 billion mark. World population reached 6.75 billion in 2009 and will probably reach the 7 billion mark by the end of 2012.

Example 4 Depreciating a Computer

You bought a computer three years ago for \$1000. Today, it is worth only \$300. Describe the absolute and relative change in the computer's value.

Solution The reference value is the original price of \$1000 and the new value is its current worth of \$300. The absolute change in the computer's value is

$$\begin{aligned}\text{absolute change} &= \text{new value} - \text{reference value}\\ &= \$300 - \$1000 = -\$700\end{aligned}$$

The negative sign tells us that the computer's current worth is \$700 *less than* the price you paid three years ago. The relative change is

$$\begin{aligned}\text{relative change} &= \frac{\text{new value} - \text{reference value}}{\text{reference value}}\\ &= \frac{\$300 - \$1000}{\$1000}\\ &= -0.7 = -70\%\end{aligned}$$

Again, the negative sign tells us that the computer is now worth 70% *less than* it was three years ago.

Now try Exercises 55–56.

Using Percentages for Comparisons

Percentages are also commonly used to compare two numbers. Suppose we want to compare the price of a \$50,000 Mercedes to the price of a \$40,000 Lexus. The difference between the Mercedes and Lexus prices is

$$\$50{,}000 - \$40{,}000 = \$10{,}000$$

That is, the Mercedes costs \$10,000 *more than* the Lexus. We can also express this difference as a percentage of the Lexus price:

$$\frac{\$10{,}000}{\$40{,}000} = 0.25 = 25\%$$

In relative terms, the Mercedes costs 25% *more than* the Lexus.

Because we are *comparing to* the Lexus price, we say that the Lexus price is the **reference value.** Notice that the reference value follows the word *than.* The Mercedes price is the **compared value.** We can now define the absolute and relative *difference* between the quantities, much as we defined absolute and relative change. The absolute and relative differences are *positive* if the compared value is greater than the reference value and *negative* if the compared value is less than the reference value.

ABSOLUTE AND RELATIVE DIFFERENCE

The **absolute difference** is the actual difference between the compared value and the reference value:

$$\text{absolute difference} = \text{compared value} - \text{reference value}$$

The **relative difference** describes the size of the absolute difference as a fraction of the reference value:

$$\text{relative difference} = \frac{\text{absolute difference}}{\text{reference value}} = \frac{\text{compared value} - \text{reference value}}{\text{reference value}}$$

Like the relative change formula, the relative difference formula above gives a fraction. We can convert the answer to a **percent difference** by multiplying it by 100%.

That's essentially all there is to comparisons, except for one subtlety: There's no particular reason why we chose the Lexus price as the reference value. We can just as easily use the Mercedes price as our reference value. In that case, the Lexus price is the compared value and the absolute difference is

$$\text{Lexus price} - \text{Mercedes price} = \$40{,}000 - \$50{,}000 = -\$10{,}000$$

The negative sign tells us that the Lexus costs \$10,000 *less than* the Mercedes. The relative difference is

$$\frac{\text{absolute difference}}{\text{Mercedes price}} = \frac{-\$10{,}000}{\$50{,}000} = -0.20 = -20\%$$

The negative sign indicates that the Lexus costs 20% *less than* the Mercedes.

We now have two ways to express the relative difference:

- The Mercedes costs 25% more than the Lexus; or
- the Lexus costs 20% less than the Mercedes.

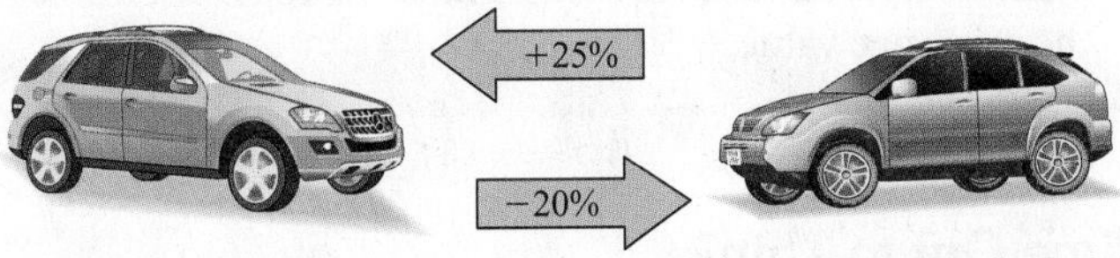

$50,000 Mercedes $40,000 Lexus

Both statements are correct, yet they contain *different* percentages. That is why it is so important to keep careful track of the reference and compared values.

For those who like formulas, we can write the following rule: If quantity A is $P\%$ more than quantity B, then quantity B is $\frac{100P}{100 + P}$ percent less than quantity A.

Example 5 Pay Comparison

Average pay for full-time wage earners varies from state to state. Recent data (2006 data, compiled in 2009) showed that New York ranked first in average pay, at $55,479 per person. South Dakota had the lowest average pay, at $30,291 per person. Compare average pay in South Dakota to that in New York in both absolute and relative terms.

Solution Based on the wording of the statement, we use South Dakota pay as the compared value and New York pay as the reference value.

$$\begin{aligned} \text{absolute difference} &= \text{compared value} - \text{reference value} \\ &= \$30{,}291 - \$55{,}479 \\ &= -\$25{,}188 \\ \text{relative difference} &= \frac{\text{compared value} - \text{reference value}}{\text{reference value}} \\ &= \frac{\$30{,}291 - \$55{,}479}{\$55{,}479} \\ &\approx -0.454 = -45.4\% \end{aligned}$$

In absolute terms, average pay in South Dakota is $25,188 *less than* average pay in New York. In relative terms, average pay in South Dakota is about 45% less than average pay in New York. (You might want to verify that this also means that average pay in New York is 83.2% more than average pay in South Dakota.) **Now try Exercises 57–62.**

BY THE WAY

Although South Dakota had the lowest average pay, Mississippi ranked lowest in per capita (per person) income. Average pay is the total amount of wages earned in the state divided by the total number of wage earners. Per capita income is all income earned, divided by the total number of people, employed or not. Per capita income is a better measure of poverty or wealth, which is why Mississippi is generally considered the poorest state. But jobs there pay better, on average, than those in South Dakota.

Of versus *More Than*

Consider a population that triples in size from 200 to 600. There are two equivalent ways to state this change with percentages:

- Using *more than:* The new population is 200% *more than* the original population. Here we are stating the *relative change* in the population. We find the increase of 200% by using the relative change formula.
- Using *of:* The new population is 300% *of* the original population, which means it is three times the size of the original population. Here, we are looking at the *ratio* of the new population to the original population, which is 3 to 1.

Notice that the percentages in the *of* and *more than* statements are related by 300% = 100% + 200%. Generalizing, we find the relationships in the following box.

OF VERSUS MORE THAN (OR LESS THAN)

- If the compared value is P% *more than* the reference value, it is $(100 + P)$% *of* the reference value.
- If the compared value is P% *less than* the reference value, it is $(100 - P)$% *of* the reference value.

Time Out to Think

Use the relative change formula to confirm that a population that grows from 200 to 600 increases in size by 200%.

Example 6 Salary Difference

Carol earns 50% more than William. How many times larger is her income than his?

Solution We use the rule that P% *more than* means $(100 + P)$% *of*. Because Carol's income is 50% more than William's, we set $P = 50$. Therefore, Carol's income is $(100 + 50)\% = 150\%$ of William's income. Because $150\% = 1.5$, Carol earns 1.5 times as much as William. **Now try Exercises 63–66.**

Example 7 Sale!

A store is having a "25% off" sale. How does an item's sale price compare to its original price?

Solution The "25% off" means that an item's sale price is "25% *less than* its original price. The sale price is $(100 - 25)\% = 75\%$ *of* the original price. For example, if the original price is \$100, the sale price is \$75. **Now try Exercises 67–70.**

A Brief Review What Is a Ratio?

Suppose we want to compare two quantities, such as the prices of a BMW that costs \$80,000 and a Honda that costs \$20,000. We can, of course, find the absolute or relative difference in the quantities. But another way to make the comparison is by dividing, which tells us the *ratio* of the two quantities. In this case, the two quantities are \$80,000 and \$20,000, so their ratio is

$$\frac{\$80{,}000}{\$20{,}000} = \frac{4}{1} = 4$$

We can state this result in several equivalent ways:

- The ratio of the BMW price to the Honda price is 4 to 1. (The ratio can also be stated as 4, but "4 to 1" is more common.)
- The BMW price is 4 times the price of the Honda.
- The ratio of the Honda price to the BMW price is 1 to 4, which we can also state as $\frac{1}{4}$, 0.25, or 25%.

Notice how the units of *dollars* canceled on the top and bottom of the fraction. This is a general characteristic of ratios: Because comparisons make sense only when we compare quantities with the same units, ratios always end up without units.

Example: Earth's average density is about 5.5 grams per cubic centimeter and the average density of Saturn is about 0.7 gram per cubic centimeter. What is the ratio of their densities?

Solution: We divide Earth's density by Saturn's density:

$$\frac{\text{average density of Earth}}{\text{average density of Saturn}} = \frac{5.5\ \cancel{\text{g/cm}^3}}{0.7\ \cancel{\text{g/cm}^3}} \approx 8$$

The ratio of Earth's average density to Saturn's average density is about 8 to 1. Alternatively, we can say that Earth's density is about 8 times that of Saturn, or that Saturn's density is about $\frac{1}{8}$ that of Earth. Again, notice how the units canceled, leaving the ratio without units.

Now try Exercises 33–44.

Time Out to Think

One store advertises "30% off everything!" Another store advertises "Sale prices are 30% of original prices!" Which store is having the bigger sale? Explain.

Percentages of Percentages

Percentage changes or comparisons can be particularly confusing when the values *themselves* are percentages. Suppose your bank increases the interest rate on your savings account from 3% to 4%. It's tempting to say that the interest rate increased by 1%, but this statement is ambiguous at best. The interest rate increased by 1 *percentage point,* but the relative change in the interest rate was

$$\frac{\text{new value} - \text{reference value}}{\text{reference value}} = \frac{4\% - 3\%}{3\%} = 0.33 = 33\%$$

In other words, you can say that the bank raised your interest rate by 33%, even though the actual rate increased by only 1 percentage point. More specifically, the *absolute change* in the interest rate was 1 percentage point, while the *relative change* in the interest rate was 33%.

PERCENTAGE POINTS VERSUS %

When you see a change or difference expressed in *percentage points,* you can assume it is an *absolute* change or difference. If it is expressed with the % sign or the word *percent,* it should be a *relative* change or difference.

Take Note

Be cautious with the *of* versus *more than* rule, which may fail if we convert the percentages to ordinary fractions or numbers. For example, the statement "50 is 100% more than 25" makes sense, but the statement "50 is 1 more than 25" does not—even though 100% = 1. Similarly, most people would say that "50 is two times larger than 25," but it is not correct to say that "50 is 200% larger than 25" (it is 200% *of* 25, or 100% more than 25). Because ordinary language can be ambiguous, it's important to examine context.

Example 8 Newspaper Readership Declines

The percentage of adults who report reading a daily newspaper fell from about 78% in 1980 to 49% in 2009. Describe this change in newspaper readership.

Solution The drop in readership from 78% to 49% represents a decline of 78 − 49 = 29 percentage points. This is the *absolute change* in the percentage of adults who read a daily newspaper. The *relative change* in readership is

$$\frac{\text{new value} - \text{reference value}}{\text{reference value}} = \frac{49\% - 78\%}{78\%} = -0.37 = -37\%$$

The negative sign indicates a *decrease* in readership. We say that readership dropped by 37% in relative terms or by 29 percentage points in absolute terms.

Now try Exercises 71–74.

Example 9 Care in Wording

Assume that 40% of the registered voters in Carson City are Republicans. Read the following questions carefully, and give the most appropriate answers.

a. The percentage of voters registered as Republicans is 25% higher in Freetown than in Carson City. What percentage of the registered voters in Freetown are Republicans?

b. The percentage of voters registered as Republicans is 25 percentage points higher in Freetown than in Carson City. What percentage of the registered voters in Freetown are Republicans?

If you can't convince them, confuse them.

—Harry S Truman

Solution

a. We are told that the percentage of registered Republicans in Carson City is 40%, and that the percentage in Freetown is 25% higher. We interpret the 25% as a relative difference. Because 25% of 40% is 10% ($0.25 \times 0.40 = 0.10$), we add this value to the Carson City percentage to find that the percentage of registered Republicans in Freetown is $40\% + 10\% = 50\%$.

b. We interpret 25 *percentage points* as an absolute difference, so we add this value to the percentage of Republicans in Carson City. The percentage of registered Republicans in Freetown is $40\% + 25\% = 65\%$. **Now try Exercises 75–76.**

Solving Percentage Problems

Consider this statement:

Retail prices are 25% more than wholesale prices.

If you knew a wholesale price, how would you calculate the retail price? One way to begin is by translating the *more than* statement into an *of* statement. The statement becomes

Retail prices are $(100 + 25)\% = 125\%$ *of wholesale prices.*

Replacing *of* with multiplication, we write this statement mathematically as

$$\text{retail price} = 125\% \times \text{wholesale price}$$

With this equation, we can find a retail price from a wholesale price. For example, if the wholesale price is \$10, the retail price is $125\% \times \$10 = 1.25 \times \$10 = \$12.50$.

Now suppose we want to find a wholesale price from a retail price. In this case, we must divide both sides of the equation by 125%:

$$\frac{\text{retail price}}{125\%} = \frac{\cancel{125\%} \times \text{wholesale price}}{\cancel{125\%}}$$

We then interchange the left and right sides to write the result:

$$\text{wholesale price} = \frac{\text{retail price}}{125\%}$$

For example, if the retail price is \$15, the wholesale price is $\$15/1.25 = \$12$. We can now generalize our results.

BY THE WAY

Percentages are often called *rates.* For example, a sales tax of 6% is called a *tax rate* of 6%. If 15% of high school students smoke, we say that the *smoking rate* among high school students is 15%.

SOLVING PERCENTAGE PROBLEMS

If the compared value is P% *more than* the reference value, then

$$\text{compared value} = (100 + P)\% \times \text{reference value}$$

and

$$\text{reference value} = \frac{\text{compared value}}{(100 + P)\%}$$

If the compared value is *less than* the reference value, then use $(100 - P)$ instead of $(100 + P)$ in the above equations.

Example 10 Tax Calculations

a. You purchase a shirt with a labeled (pre-tax) price of \$17. The local sales tax rate is 5%. What is your final cost (including tax)?

b. Your receipt shows that you paid \$19.26 for a Blu-ray disc, tax included. The local sales tax rate is 7%. What was the labeled (pre-tax) price of the disc?

Solution

a. The final cost of an item is its labeled price plus the sales tax. For a tax rate of $P\% = 5\%$, the final cost is

$$\text{final cost} = \text{labeled price} + (5\% \times \text{labeled price})$$

In other words, the final cost is 5% more than the labeled price. Changing from a *more than* statement to an *of* statement, we have

$$\text{final cost} = (100 + 5)\% \times \text{labeled price} = 105\% \times \text{labeled price}$$

When we substitute the given labeled price of \$17, the final cost is

$$\text{final cost} = 105\% \times \$17 = 1.05 \times \$17 = \$17.85$$

The final cost for the shirt is \$17.85.

b. This time the tax rate is $P\% = 7\%$, so the relation between labeled price and final cost is

$$\text{final cost} = (100 + 7)\% \times \text{labeled price} = 107\% \times \text{labeled price}$$

We are given the final cost of \$19.26. We find the labeled price by dividing both sides by 107%:

$$\text{labeled price} = \frac{\text{final cost}}{107\%} = \frac{\$19.26}{107\%} = \frac{\$19.26}{1.07} = \$18.00$$

The labeled price of the Blu-ray disc was \$18. **Now try Exercises 77–82.**

Example 11 Up 44%, to 10.4%

Consider the following statement from the introduction to this unit:

The rate [of smoking] for eighth graders is up 44 percent, to 10.4 percent.

What was the previous smoking rate for eighth-graders?

Solution The "10.4 percent" means that 10.4% of all eighth-graders now smoke. The "44 percent" expresses the relative change from the previous smoking rate to the new rate. It tells us that the new rate is 44% *more than* the previous rate, which means it is $(100 + 44)\% = 144\%$ *of* the previous rate:

$$\text{new rate} = 144\% \times \text{previous rate}$$

We solve for the previous rate by dividing both sides by $144\% = 1.44$:

$$\text{previous rate} = \frac{\text{new rate}}{144\%} = \frac{\text{new rate}}{1.44}$$

Now we find the previous rate by substituting 10.4% for the new rate:

$$\text{previous rate} = \frac{10.4\%}{1.44} \approx 7.2\%$$

The previous smoking rate for eighth-graders was 7.2%. Note that we left the numerator as a percentage in the above equation (rather than converting it to decimal form) so that our answer would be a percentage. **Now try Exercises 83–84.**

Abuses of Percentages

Because percentages can be so subtle, many people misuse percentages—sometimes inadvertently and sometimes deliberately. In the rest of this unit, we'll investigate a few common abuses of percentages.

Beware of Shifting Reference Values

Consider the following situation: Because of losses by your employer, you agree to accept a temporary 10% pay cut. Your employer promises to give you a 10% pay raise after six months. Will the pay raise restore your original salary?

We can answer this question by assuming some arbitrary number for your original weekly pay, such as $200. A 10% pay cut means that your pay will decrease by 10% of $200, or $20, so your weekly pay after the cut is

$$\$200 - \$20 = \$180$$

The subsequent raise increases your pay by 10% of $180, or $18, making your weekly pay

$$\$180 + \$18 = \$198$$

Notice that the 10% pay cut followed by the 10% pay raise leaves you with *less* money than you started with. This result arises because the reference value for the calculations shifted during the problem: It was $200 in the first calculation and $180 in the second.

Example 12 Shifting Investment Value

A stockbroker offers the following defense to angry investors: "I admit that the value of your investments fell 60% during my first year on the job. This year, however, their value has increased by 75%, so you are now 15% ahead!" Evaluate the stockbroker's defense.

Solution Imagine that you began with an investment of $1000. During the first year, your investment lost 60% of its value, or $600, leaving you with $400. During the second year, your investment gained 75% of $400, or $0.75 \times \$400 = \$300$. Thus, at the end of the second year, your investment was worth $\$400 + \$300 = \$700$. This is *less* than your original investment of $1000 and certainly not a 15% gain overall. We can trace the problem with the stockbroker's defense to a shifting reference value: It was $1000 for the first calculation and $400 for the second. **Now try Exercises 85–86.**

Example 13 Tax Cuts

A politician promises, "If elected, I will cut your taxes by 20% for each of the first three years of my term, for a total cut of 60%." Evaluate the promise.

Solution The politician neglected the effects of the shifting reference value. A cut of 20% in each of three years will *not* make an overall cut of 60%. To see what really happens, suppose that you currently pay $1000 in taxes. The following table shows how your taxes change over the three years.

Year	Tax Paid in Previous Year	20% of Previous Year Tax	New Tax This Year
1	$1000	$200	$800
2	$800	$160	$640
3	$640	$128	$512

Over three years, your taxes decline by $1000 − $512 = $488. Because this is only 48.8% of $1000, over the three years your tax bill declines by 48.8%, not by 60%.

Now try Exercises 87–88.

Less Than Nothing

We often see numbers that represent large "more than" percentages. For example, a price of $40 is 300% more than a price of $10. However, in most cases it is not possible to have a "less than" percentage that is greater than 100%. To see why, consider an advertisement claiming that replacing standard light bulbs with energy-efficient ones would use "200 percent less energy." If you think about it, you'll realize that such a savings is impossible. If the new light bulbs used 100% less energy, they'd be using no energy at all. The only way they could use 200% less would be if they actually *produced* energy. Clearly, whoever wrote the advertisement made a mistake.

BY THE WAY

The light bulb example related here was used as the title story in the book *200% of Nothing* by A. K. Dewdney (Wiley, 1993). The book contains many other interesting stories of misuses of numbers.

Example 14 Impossible Sale

A store advertises that it will take "150% off" the price of all merchandise. What should happen when you go to the counter to buy a $500 item?

Solution If the price were 100% off, the item would be free. So if the price is 150% off, the store should *pay you* half the item's cost, or $250. More likely, the store manager did not understand percentages.

Now try Exercises 89–94.

Time Out to Think

Can an athlete give a 110% effort? Can a glass of juice have 110% of the minimum daily requirement for vitamin C? Explain.

Don't Average Percentages

Suppose you got 70% of the questions correct on a midterm exam and 90% correct on the final exam. Can we conclude that you answered 80% of all the questions correctly? It might be tempting to say yes—after all, 80% is the average (mean) of 70% and 90%. But it would be wrong, unless both tests happened to have the same number of questions.

To see why, let's say that the midterm had 10 questions and the final had 100 questions, for a total of 110 questions. Your 70% score on the midterm means you answered 7 questions correctly, while your 90% score on the final means you answered 90 questions

BY THE WAY

We usually think of the average of two numbers as their sum divided by 2. Technically, this type of average is called a *mean*. We'll discuss other definitions of *average* in Unit 6A.

correctly. Therefore, on the two exams combined, you answered 97 out of 110 questions correctly, which is 88.2% (because $97/110 = 0.882$). This is much higher than the 80% "average" of the two individual exam percentages.

This example carries a very important lesson: As a general rule, *you should never average percentages.*

Example 15 Batting Average

In baseball, a player's batting average represents the percentage of at-bats in which he got a hit. For example, a batting average of .350 means the player got a hit 35% of the times he batted. Suppose a player had a batting average of .200 during the first half of the season and .400 during the second half of the season. Can we conclude that his batting average for the entire season was .300 (the average of .200 and .400)? Why or why not? Give an example that illustrates your reasoning.

Solution No. For example, suppose he had 300 at-bats during the first half of the season and 200 at-bats during the second half, for a total of 500 at-bats. His first-half batting average of .200 means he got hits on 20% of his 300 at-bats, or $0.2 \times 300 = 60$ hits. His second-half batting average of .400 means he got hits on 40% of his 200 at-bats, or $0.4 \times 200 = 80$ hits. For the season, he got a total of $60 + 80 = 140$ hits in his 500 at-bats, so his season batting average was $140/500 = 28\%$, or .280—not the .300 found by averaging his first-half and second-half batting percentages. (In fact, the only case in which his season average would be .300 is if he had precisely the same number of at-bats in each half of the season.) **Now try Exercises 95–96.**

QUICK QUIZ

Choose the best answer to each of the following questions. Explain your reasoning with one or more complete sentences.

1. The price of a four-star meal, only $100 per couple decades ago, has since increased 200%. The current price of a four-star meal is

   a. $200. b. $300. c. $400.

2. The population of a town increases from 50,000 to 75,000. What are the absolute and relative changes in the population?

   a. absolute change = 25,000; relative change = 25%

   b. absolute change = 25,000; relative change = 50%

   c. absolute change = −25,000; relative change = −25%

3. Suppose the value of a home changed by −20% over the past five years. This means that

   a. a mistake was made in the calculation, because relative change cannot be negative.

   b. the house increased in value over the past five years.

   c. the house decreased in value over the past five years.

4. Emily scored 50% higher on the SAT than Joshua. This means that

   a. Joshua's score was 50% lower than Emily's.

   b. Joshua's score was half of Emily's.

   c. Joshua's score was two-thirds of Emily's.

5. The price of a movie ticket increased from $10 to $12. This means that the new price is

   a. 20% of the old price.

   b. 80% of the old price.

   c. 120% of the old price.

6. Your receipt shows that you paid $47.96 for a new shirt, including sales tax. The sales tax rate is 9%. The amount you paid in sales tax was

   a. $\$47.96 \times 0.09$. b. $\dfrac{\$47.96}{1.09}$. c. $\$47.96 - \dfrac{\$47.96}{1.09}$.

7. Consider the statement "The interest rate on auto loans has increased 50% over the past decade and now stands at 9%." What can you conclude?

   a. The interest rate a decade ago was 6%.

   b. The interest rate a decade ago was 41%.

   c. You can't conclude anything, because the statement makes no sense.

8. A friend has a textbook that originally cost $150. The friend says that you can have it for 100% less than he paid for it. Your price will be

   a. $50.

   b. $75.

   c. $0 (free).

9. You currently earn \$1000 per month, but you are expecting your earnings to rise 10% per year. This means that in five years you expect to be earning
   a. somewhat less than \$1500 per month.
   b. exactly \$1500 per month.
   c. somewhat more than \$1500 per month.

10. During high school, Elise won 30% of the swim races she entered. During college, Elise won 20% of the swim races she entered. We can conclude that, in high school and college combined, Elise won
    a. 25% of the races she entered.
    b. more than 20% but less than 30% of the races she entered.
    c. more than 26% but less than 28% of the races she entered.

Exercises 3A

REVIEW QUESTIONS

1. Describe the three basic uses of percentages. Give a sample statement that uses percentages in each of the three ways.
2. Distinguish between absolute and relative change. Give an example that illustrates how we calculate a relative change.
3. Distinguish between absolute and relative difference. Give an example that illustrates how we calculate a relative difference.
4. Explain the difference between the key words *of* and *more than* when dealing with percentages. How are their meanings related?
5. Explain the difference between the terms *percent* (%) and *percentage points*. Give an example of how they can differ for the same situation.
6. Give an example to explain why, in general, it is not legitimate to average percentages.

DOES IT MAKE SENSE?

Decide whether each of the following statements makes sense (or is clearly true) or does not make sense (or is clearly false). Explain your reasoning.

7. In many European countries, the percentage change in population has been negative in recent decades.
8. The price of tuition has tripled since my parents went to school—that's a 200% increase in price!
9. My older child weighs 25% more than my younger child.
10. I've decreased my caloric intake by 125%, which has helped me lose weight.
11. If you earn 20% more than I do, then I must earn 20% less than you do.
12. If they raise taxes by 10% every year, in a decade we'll be paying everything we earn to taxes.
13. We found that these rare cancers were 700% more common in children living near the toxic landfill than in the general population.
14. I have a 60% average on our assignments going into the final exam, but I still hope to raise my course average to 70% by getting an 80% on the final. (The final is worth 25% of the final grade.)
15. The rate of return on our fund increased by 50%, to 15%.
16. My bank increased the interest rate on my savings account 100%, from 2% to 4%.

BASIC SKILLS & CONCEPTS

17–32: Fractions, Decimals, Percentages. Express the following numbers in three forms: as a reduced fraction, as a decimal, and as a percentage. (Refer to the Brief Review on p. 129.)

17. 2/5	18. 30%	19. 0.20	20. 0.85
21. 150%	22. 2/3	23. 4/9	24. 1.25
25. 5/8	26. 44%	27. 69%	28. 4.25
29. 7/5	30. 121%	31. 4/3	32. 0.6 . . .

33–44: Review of Ratios. Compare the following pairs of numbers A and B in three ways:

a. Find the ratio of A to B.
b. Find the ratio of B to A.
c. Complete the sentence: A is ______ percent of B. (Refer to the Brief Review on p. 134.)

33. $A = 8$ and $B = 4$
34. $A = 10$ and $B = 30$
35. $A = 150$ and $B = 400$
36. $A = 450$ and $B = 400$
37. $A = 52{,}252$ is the number of deaths due to AIDS in the United States in 1995 and $B = 16{,}268$ is the number of deaths due to AIDS in the United States in 2005 (most recent data available).
38. $A = 40{,}229{,}000$ is the number of Americans over age 65 in 2010 and $B = 88{,}458{,}000$ is the projected number of Americans over age 65 in 2050.
39. $A = 3.9$ million is the population of Los Angeles and $B = 2.9$ million is the population of Chicago.
40. $A = 466$ is the average mathematics SAT score in Maine and $B = 523$ is the average mathematics SAT score in Vermont.
41. $A = 2{,}290{,}000$ is the 2009 daily circulation of *USA Today* (highest in the nation) and $B = 2{,}010{,}000$ is the 2009 daily circulation of the *Wall Street Journal* (second highest in the nation).
42. $A = \$87{,}000$ is the median price of a single-family home in Davenport, Iowa, in 2008 and $B = \$636{,}000$ is the median price of a single-family home in Honolulu, Hawaii, in 2008.
43. $A = 100$ square meters is the area of a square with sides of length 10 meters and $B = 25\pi$ square meters is the area of a circle with a diameter of 10 meters.
44. $A = 87.8\%$ is the high school graduation rate in Nebraska (first in the nation) and $B = 55.8\%$ is the high school graduation rate in Nevada (last in the nation).

45–50: Percentages as Fractions. In the following statements, express the first number as a percentage of the second number.

45. 28 pounds of recyclable trash in a barrel of 52 pounds of trash

46. 12.0 million metric tons of beef produced annually in the United States out of 65.1 million metric tons of beef produced annually worldwide

47. The median salary for U.S. men in 2007 was $33,196 and the median salary for U.S. women in 2007 was $20,922 (most recent data).

48. 40.4 million Americans under age 15 out of 305 million Americans

49. 70.3 Americans per square mile in 1990 and 86.4 Americans per square mile in 2010

50. An estimated 10,000 U.S. nuclear weapons out of an estimated 27,000 nuclear weapons worldwide (as of 2010)

51. **Salary Comparisons.** Clint's salary increased from $20,000 to $28,000 over a three-year period. Helen's salary increased from $25,000 to $35,000 over the same period. Whose salary increased more in absolute terms? In relative terms? Explain.

52. **Population Comparison.** Between 2000 and 2010, the population of Las Vegas increased from 478,000 to 565,000. Over the same decade, the population of Dallas increased from 1,189,000 to 1,245,000. Which city had the greater absolute growth in population? Which city had the greater percentage growth in population?

53–56: Percentage Change. Find the absolute change and the percentage change in the following cases.

53. The population of the United States increased from 249 million in 1990 to 308 million in 2010.

54. The congressional delegation of California increased from 30 in 1950 to 53 in 2010.

55. The number of daily newspapers in the United States was 2226 in 1900 and 1420 in 2010.

56. The number of music CDs shipped in the United States decreased from 942 million in 2000 to 511 million in 2008.

57–62: Percentage Difference. Complete the following sentences.

57. The gestation period of humans (266 days) is _____ percent longer than the gestation period of grizzly bears (220 days).

58. The 2009 life expectancy in Canada (81.2 years) is _____ percent greater than the 2009 life expectancy in Russia (65.9 years).

59. The main span of the Tacoma Narrows bridge (2800 feet) is _____ percent shorter than the main span of the Golden Gate bridge (4200 feet).

60. The median age at first marriage of U.S. women (25.9 years) is _____ percent less than the median age at first marriage of U.S. men (27.5 years).

61. The number of deaths due to poisoning in the United States in a year (25,500) is _____ percent greater than the number of deaths due to falls (21,400).

62. The amount of rice produced by China in 2007 (190 million metric tons) was _____ percent greater than the amount of rice produced by India in 2007 (127 million metric tons).

63–66: *Of* vs. *More Than*. Fill in the blanks in the following statements.

63. Will is 22% taller than Wanda, so Will's height is _____ % of Wanda's height.

64. The area of Norway is 24% more than the area of Colorado, so Norway's area is _____ % of Colorado's area.

65. The population of Virginia is 18% less than the population of Georgia, so Virginia's population is _____ % of Georgia's population.

66. The net worth of Zelda is 6.4% less than the net worth of Alicia, so Zelda's net worth is _____ % of Alicia's net worth.

67–70: Prices and Sales. Fill in the blanks in the following statements.

67. The wholesale price of a TV is 40% less than the retail price. Therefore, the wholesale price is _____ times the retail price.

68. A store is having a 50% off sale. Therefore, the original price of an item is _____ times as much as the sale price.

69. The retail cost of a TV is 30% more than its wholesale cost. Therefore, the retail cost is _____ times the wholesale cost.

70. A store is having a 40% off sale. The sale price for an item with a regular cost of $80 is _____.

71–74: Percentages of Percentages. Describe each of the following changes in two ways: as an absolute change in terms of percentage points and as a relative change in terms of a percentage.

71. The annual interest rate for Jack's savings account increased from 2.3% to 2.8%.

72. The percentage of Republicans in the House of Representatives decreased from 53.3% in 2007 to 46.4% in 2009.

73. The percentage of Americans accessing the Internet increased from 66.9% in 2000 to 78.5% in 2010.

74. The percentage of fifth-graders who scored at or above the national average on the reading test rose to 44 percent from 25 percent.

75. **Care in Wording.** Assume that 30% of city employees in Carson City ride the bus to work. Consider the following two statements:

- The percentage of city employees who ride the bus to work is 10% higher in Freetown than in Carson City.
- The percentage of city employees who ride the bus to work is 10 percentage points higher in Freetown than in Carson City.

For each case, state the percentage of city employees in Freetown who ride the bus to work. Briefly explain why the two statements have different meanings.

76. **Ambiguous News.** The average annual precipitation on Mt. Washington, New Hampshire, is 90 inches. During one

particularly wet year, different news reports carried the following statements.

- The precipitation this year is 200% of normal.
- The precipitation this year is 200% above normal.

What does each of these statements imply about the precipitation during this year? Do the two statements have the same meaning? Explain.

77–84: Solving Percentage Problems. Solve the following percentage problems.

77. You purchase a bicycle with a retail (pre-tax) price of $760. The local sales tax rate is 7.6%. What is the final cost?

78. The final cost of your new shoes is $107.69. The local sales tax rate is 6.2%. What was the retail (pre-tax) price?

79. The 2410 women undergraduates at the college comprise 54% of all undergraduates. How many undergraduates attend the college?

80. The number of housing foreclosures in 2008 was 3.98 million, up 81% over 2007. How many foreclosures were there in 2007?

81. Your total cost for dinner in a restaurant after the tip was $76.40. Assuming you left a 20% tip, what was the bill for food and taxes?

82. Your dinner bill is $42.50. You leave $50. What percent tip did you leave? (Ignore taxes in this question.)

83. Simon's monthly take-home pay (after taxes) is $2200. If he pays 21% of his gross pay (before taxes) in tax, what is his gross pay?

84. Eileen earned $45 in annual interest from a savings account with a 3.5% annual interest rate. Assuming she made no deposits or withdrawals during the year, what is the balance in the account?

85–88: Shifting Reference Value. State whether the following statements are true or false, and explain why. If a statement is false, state the true change.

85. If the national economy shrank at an annual rate of 4% per year for three consecutive years, then the economy shrank by 12% over the three-year period.

86. You receive a pay raise of 5%, then receive a pay cut of 5%. After the two changes in pay, your salary is unchanged.

87. If the profits in your consulting business increase by 4% one year and decrease by 2% the following year, your profits are up by 2% over two years.

88. A high school reports that its students' SAT scores were down by 20% for one year. The next year, however, SAT scores rose by 30%. The high school principal announces, "Overall, test scores have improved by 10% over the past two years."

89–94: Is It Possible? Determine whether the following claims could be true. Explain your answer.

89. By turning off her lights and closing her windows at night, Maria saved 120% on her monthly energy bill.

90. Scott is 140% taller than his son.

91. Restaurant prices have increased 100% in the last 20 years.

92. Through hard training, Renee improved her 10-kilometer running time by 100%.

93. Your computer is 500% faster than mine.

94. Your computer is 250% slower than mine.

95. **Average Percentages.** You are a teacher. Your first-period class, with 25 students, had a mean score of 86% on the midterm exam. Your second-period class, with 30 students, had a mean score of 84% on the same exam. Does it follow that the mean score for both classes combined is 85%? Explain.

96. **Average Percentages.** A player has a batting average over many games of .400. In his next game, he goes 2 for 4, which is a batting average of .500 for the game. Does it follow that his new batting average is $(.400 + .500)/2 = .450$? Explain.

FURTHER APPLICATIONS

97–100: Analyzing Percentage Statements. Assuming the given information is accurate, determine whether the following statements are true. Provide an explanation.

97. The class is 60% women and 10% of the women have blond hair, so blond women comprise $60\% \times 10\% = 6\%$ of the class.

98. The class is 40% men and 20% of the men are bald, so bald men comprise $40\% \times 20\% = 80\%$ of the class.

99. 70% of the hotels have a restaurant and 20% have a swimming pool, so 90% of the hotels in town have a restaurant or a pool.

100. 40% of the class drives to school and 15% takes a bus to school, so 45% of the class neither drives nor takes a bus.

101–106: Percentages in the News. Answer the question that follows each quote from a news source.

101. "Some 80% of the estimated $62 trillion in credit default swaps outstanding in 2008 were speculative." What is the value of the speculative credit default swaps?

102. ". . . the median annual income for adults with bachelor's degrees was $37,729, compared with $20,718 for those with only a high school diploma." The annual income for adults with bachelor's degrees is what precent greater than that for adults with a high school diploma only?

103. "The unemployment rate has risen more than a percentage point, to 8.5% in February from 7.1% last November." What is the relative change in the unemployment rate expressed as a percentage?

104. "The American Booksellers Association, which represents independent booksellers, includes 1500 businesses at 2500 locations. Twenty years ago it represented 4700 businesses at 5500 locations." What is the percent change in the number of businesses and locations represented?

105. "At the Gates Family Foundation, investment losses last year were 43 percent, or $222 million of its endowment." How much was the endowment worth before the losses?

106. "The rate of new [cancer] diagnoses among men dropped 1.8% per year between 2001 and 2005." What is the net percentage decrease in diagnoses over this four-year period?

107. **Stock Market Losses.**

a. The largest single-day *point* loss of the Dow Jones Industrial Average occurred on September 29, 2008, when the market lost 778 points and closed at 10,365. What was the percentage loss?

b. The largest single-day *percentage* loss of the Dow Jones Industrial Average occurred on October 19, 1987, when the market closed down 22.6% at 1739. What was the point loss?

IN YOUR WORLD

108. **Percentages.** Find three recent news reports that quote percentages. In each case, describe the use of the percentage (as a fraction, to describe change, or for comparison) and explain its context.

109. **Percentage Change.** Find a recent news report that quotes a percentage change. Describe the meaning of the change.

110. **Abuse of Percentages.** Find a news article or report in which the use of a percentage is either suspicious or wrong. If possible, clarify or correct the statement.

UNIT 3B Putting Numbers in Perspective

What is a billion dollars or how much is a trillion dollars? For many people, these numbers are just words—so large that they hardly seem to mean anything. But we hear numbers like these every day, and we cannot truly understand the major issues of our time unless we have some understanding of the numbers that are involved. In this unit, we will study several techniques for putting large or small numbers into a perspective that gives them real meaning.

Writing Large and Small Numbers

Working with large and small numbers is much easier when we write them in a special format known as **scientific notation**. We express numbers in this format by writing a number *between* 1 and 10 multiplied by a power of 10. (See the Brief Review on p. 100 for a review of powers of 10.) For example, a billion is ten to the ninth power, or 10^9, so we write 6 billion in scientific notation as 6×10^9. Similarly, we write 420 in scientific notation as 4.2×10^2, and 0.67 as 6.7×10^{-1}.

BY THE WAY

In the United States, a *billion* is a thousand million, or 10^9, and a *trillion* is a thousand billion, or 10^{12}. But in Great Britain and Germany, a billion is a million million, or 10^{12}, and a trillion is 10^{18}. We will use only the U.S. meanings in this book.

DEFINITION

Scientific notation is a format in which a number is expressed as a number *between* 1 and 10 multiplied by a power of 10.

Scientific notation makes it easy to write numbers no matter how large or small. We must be careful, however, not to let this ease of writing deceive us. For example, it's so easy to write the number 10^{80} that we might think it's not all that big—but, in fact, it is larger than the total number of atoms in the known universe.

Example 1 Numbers in Scientific Notation

Rewrite each of the following statements using scientific notation.

a. Total spending in the new federal budget is $3,500,000,000,000.
b. The diameter of a hydrogen nucleus is about 0.000000000000001 meter.

Solution Notice how much easier it is to read the numbers with scientific notation.

a. Total spending in the new federal budget is $\$3.5 \times 10^{12}$, or $3.5 trillion.
b. The diameter of a hydrogen nucleus is about 1×10^{-15} meter.

Now try Exercises 23–28.

Approximations with Scientific Notation

Another advantage of scientific notation is that it makes it easy to *approximate* answers without a calculator. For example, we can quickly approximate the answer to 5795 × 326 by rounding 5795 to 6000 and 326 to 300. Writing the rounded numbers in scientific notation, we then see that

$$5795 \times 326 \approx (6 \times 10^3) \times (3 \times 10^2) = 18 \times 10^5 = 1{,}800{,}000$$

Because the exact answer is 1,889,170, this approximation provides a good estimate.

A Brief Review: Working with Scientific Notation

Converting to Scientific Notation

To convert a number from ordinary notation to scientific notation:

Step 1. Move the decimal point to come after the *first* nonzero digit.

Step 2. For the power of 10, use the number of places the decimal point moves; the power is *positive* if the decimal point moves to the left and *negative* if it moves to the right.

Examples:

$$3042 \xrightarrow[\text{3 places to left}]{\text{decimal moves}} 3.042 \times 10^3$$

$$0.00012 \xrightarrow[\text{4 places to right}]{\text{decimal moves}} 1.2 \times 10^{-4}$$

$$226 \times 10^2 \xrightarrow[\text{2 places to left}]{\text{decimals moves}} (2.26 \times 10^2) \times 10^2 = 2.26 \times 10^4$$

Converting from Scientific Notation

To convert a number from scientific notation to ordinary notation:

Step 1. The power of 10 indicates how many places to move the decimal point; move it to the *right* if the power of 10 is positive and to the *left* if it is negative.

Step 2. If moving the decimal point creates any open places, fill them with zeros.

Examples:

$$4.01 \times 10^2 \xrightarrow[\text{2 places to right}]{\text{move decimal}} 401$$

$$3.6 \times 10^6 \xrightarrow[\text{6 places to right}]{\text{move decimal}} 3{,}600{,}000$$

$$5.7 \times 10^{-3} \xrightarrow[\text{3 places to left}]{\text{move decimal}} 0.0057$$

Multiplying or Dividing with Scientific Notation

Multiplying or dividing numbers in scientific notation simply requires operating on the powers of 10 and the other parts of the number separately.

Examples:

$$(6 \times 10^2) \times (4 \times 10^5) = (6 \times 4) \times (10^2 \times 10^5) = 24 \times 10^7 = 2.4 \times 10^8$$

$$\frac{4.2 \times 10^{-2}}{8.4 \times 10^{-5}} = \frac{4.2}{8.4} \times \frac{10^{-2}}{10^{-5}} = 0.5 \times 10^{-2-(-5)} = 0.5 \times 10^3 = 5 \times 10^2$$

Note that, in both examples, we first found an answer in which the number multiplied by a power of 10 was *not* between 1 and 10. We then followed the process for converting the final answer into scientific notation.

Addition and Subtraction with Scientific Notation

In general, we must write numbers in ordinary notation before adding or subtracting.

Examples:

$$(3 \times 10^6) + (5 \times 10^2) = 3{,}000{,}000 + 500 = 3{,}000{,}500 = 3.0005 \times 10^6$$

$$(4.6 \times 10^9) - (5 \times 10^8) = 4{,}600{,}000{,}000 - 500{,}000{,}000 = 4{,}100{,}000{,}000 = 4.1 \times 10^9$$

When both numbers have the *same* power of 10, we can factor out the power of 10 first.

Examples:

$$(7 \times 10^{10}) + (4 \times 10^{10}) = (7 + 4) \times 10^{10} = 11 \times 10^{10} = 1.1 \times 10^{11}$$

$$(2.3 \times 10^{-22}) - (1.6 \times 10^{-22}) = (2.3 - 1.6) \times 10^{-22} = 0.7 \times 10^{-22} = 7.0 \times 10^{-23}$$

Now try Exercises 15–22.

Example 2 Checking Answers with Approximations

You and a friend are doing a rough calculation of how much garbage New City residents produce every day. You estimate that, on average, each of the 8 million residents produces 1.8 pounds, or 0.0009 ton, of garbage each day. The total amount of garbage is

$$8{,}000{,}000 \cancel{\text{persons}} \times 0.0009 \frac{\text{ton}}{\cancel{\text{person}}}$$

Your friend quickly presses calculator buttons and tells you that the answer is 225 tons. Without using your calculator, determine whether this answer is reasonable.

Solution You can write 8 million as 8×10^6, which is nearly 10^7. You can write 0.0009 as 9×10^{-4}, which is nearly 10^{-3}. Thus, the product should be approximately

$$10^7 \times 10^{-3} = 10^{7-3} = 10^4 = 10{,}000$$

Clearly, your friend's answer of 225 tons is too small. This simple approximation technique provided a useful check, even though it did not tell us the exact answer. (You should confirm that the exact answer is 7200 tons.) **Now try Exercises 29–30.**

Giving Meaning to Numbers

Now that we have a method for writing large and small numbers, we can move toward our goal of putting numbers in perspective. As we found for problem solving in Chapter 2, there's no single recipe for giving meaning to numbers. Nevertheless, a few techniques are particularly useful. Here, we will study three of them: putting numbers in perspective through estimation, through comparisons, and through scaling.

Perspective Through Estimation

Making estimates is one of the best techniques for putting numbers into perspective. For example, how high is 1000 feet? For most people, the quantity 1000 feet has little meaning by itself. However, we know that each story in a building is typically about 10 feet from floor to ceiling. Therefore, we can put 1000 feet in perspective by thinking of it as the approximate height of a 100-story building.

Keep in mind that estimates are not meant to be exact. For example, the 102-story Empire State Building stands 1250 feet tall (not counting its needle), which means our estimate of 1000 feet for a 100-story building was off by about 250 feet, or 25%, in this case. But if we started with no idea about what 1000 feet looks like, this 25% difference is not very important—picturing a 100-story building still gives us a good sense of 1000 feet.

Often, estimates are useful even if they only get us within a very broad range of an exact value. For example, you can infer a lot about the character of a town or city simply by knowing whether its population is in the ten thousands or the millions—the former is the size of a small college town and the latter is a huge city. Estimates that give only a broad range of values, such as "in the millions," are called **order of magnitude** estimates.

DEFINITION

An **order of magnitude** estimate specifies only a broad range of values, such as "in the ten thousands" or "in the millions."

In ordinary language, we usually indicate an order of magnitude estimate by actually using the word *order.* For example, we might say that the population of the United States is "on the order of 300 million," by which we mean it is nearer to 300 million than to, say, 200 million or 400 million. Note that the context determines how we interpret an order of magnitude estimate. When astronomers say that the number of stars in a galaxy is "of order 100 billion," they mean it could be anywhere within about a factor of 10 of this number—that is, between about 10 billion and 1 trillion. This is a much wider range than the range implied when we say "on the order of 300 million" for the population of the United States, but it is appropriate to the context.

BY THE WAY

To make it *convincingly* taller than all other buildings in the world at the time, the architects of the Empire State Building designed a 200-foot cap and needle for the top of the building. The original purpose of the needle was to serve as a docking station for air ships. While the needle was never used for this purpose, it has served as a good radio and TV antenna.

Example 3 Order of Magnitude of Ice Cream Spending

Make an order of magnitude estimate of total annual spending on ice cream in the United States.

Solution We begin by devising a strategy for the problem. Clearly, we can calculate total annual ice cream spending if we know how much the average person spends each year. We simply multiply the per person spending by the population to find the total spending. We can find the per person annual spending by multiplying the average cost of a serving of ice cream by the average number of servings a person eats in a year. Putting these ideas together, we can find the total annual ice cream spending with the following equation:

$$\underbrace{\text{total annual spending}}_{\text{units of } \frac{\$}{\text{yr}}} = \underbrace{\text{servings per person per year}}_{\text{units of } \frac{\cancel{\text{servings}}}{\cancel{\text{person}} \times \text{yr}}} \times \underbrace{\text{price per serving}}_{\text{units of } \frac{\$}{\cancel{\text{serving}}}} \times \underbrace{\text{population}}_{\text{units of } \cancel{\text{persons}}}$$

Notice how the units work out, telling us that our equation will indeed give us the units of dollars per year that we expect for the answer.

Now we need a value for each term in the equation. We can reasonably guess that an average person has something like 50 servings of ice cream per year (which means about one a week). The price of ice cream is of order \$1 per serving (as opposed to, say, 10¢ or \$10). The U.S. population is of order 300 million (3×10^8) people. Using those numbers, a reasonable estimate is

$$\text{total annual spending} = 50 \frac{\cancel{\text{servings}}}{\cancel{\text{person}} \times \text{yr}} \times \frac{\$1}{\cancel{\text{serving}}} \times (3 \times 10^8 \ \cancel{\text{persons}})$$
$$= \frac{\$1.5 \times 10^{10}}{1 \text{ yr}}$$

Take Note

In science, the term *order of magnitude* refers specifically to powers of 10. For example, 10^{23} is said to be five orders of magnitude larger than 10^{18}, because it is 10^5 times larger ($10^{23} = 10^{18} \times 10^5$).

USING TECHNOLOGY

Scientific Notation

Calculators and computers usually use a special format for numbers in scientific notation. Consider the number 3.5 million, which we write in scientific notation as 3.5×10^6. On a calculator or computer, this number will usually be written in a format like 3.5E6. The E is meant to stand for "exponent," but it's easier to think of it as follows:

3.5×10^6 → 3.5E6

Calculator/computer uses "E" to mean "times 10 to the power that follows"

3.5×10^6: the "correct" way to write 3.5 million in scientific notation

3.5E6: the same number on a calculator or computer

Be sure to notice that "E" stands for "times 10 to the power that follows," which means that you do not need to enter the 10. Remembering this fact will help you avoid common mistakes. For example:

- To enter a power of 10, such as the number 1 million, or 10^6, you must put it in scientific notation (1×10^6) by entering 1E6 on your calculator or computer. Many people mistakenly enter 10E6, but that really means $10 \times 10^6 = 10^7$.
- Another common mistake is trying to enter a number like 3.5×10^6 as $3.5 \times 10\text{E}6$, but that actually means $3.5 \times 10 \times 10^6 = 3.5 \times 10^7$.

Standard Calculators Most calculators have a key labeled either "E," "EE," or "exp" for entering the power of 10 (the "exponent"). For example, enter the number 3.5×10^6 with the key sequence

[3.5] (EE) [6]

Microsoft Excel Type the letter E as above when you enter a number in scientific notation into a spreadsheet cell. For example, enter the number 3.5×10^6 by typing "= 3.5E6" into the cell, as shown in the screen shot on the left below.

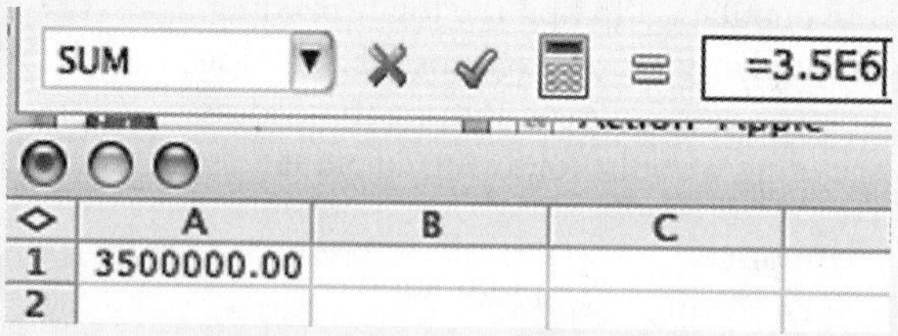

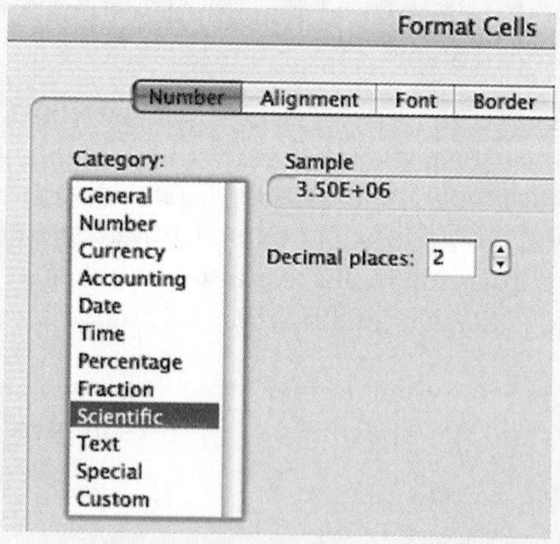

Note that, by default, Excel will format the number without scientific notation in the cell. To change that option, select "scientific" format for the cell, as indicated in the screen shot on the right above. Excel then shows the exponent as "+06," with the "+" indicating that it is a positive exponent.

Google Google has a built-in calculator, which you can use simply by typing your calculations into the search box. The screen shown below illustrates how to multiply $3.5 \times 10^6 \times 7$. The result is shown after you hit Return:

Total annual spending on ice cream in the United States is of order $\$1.5 \times 10^{10}$, or \$15 billion, per year. The actual number could be up to a few times larger or smaller. For example, actual spending might be anywhere between about \$5 billion and \$50 billion. Nevertheless, we've learned a lot—before we started, we had no idea how much Americans spend on ice cream, and now we know that they spend billions of dollars on ice cream each year. **Now try Exercises 31–40.**

Time Out to Think

Suppose you work for a company that distributes ice cream to stores throughout the United States. Market research tells you that a \$5 million advertising campaign could give you an additional 5% of the total U.S. market for ice cream. Based on the estimate in Example 3, would the advertising campaign be worth its cost? Explain.

Perspective Through Comparisons

A second general way to put numbers in perspective is by making comparisons. Consider \$100 billion, a number that you may find in the news almost any day. It's easy to say, but how big is it? Let's think of it in terms of counting. Suppose you were asked to count \$100 billion in \$1 bills. How long would it take? Clearly, if we assume you can count 1 bill each second, it would take 100 billion seconds. We can put 100 billion (10^{11}) seconds in perspective by converting to years, using a chain of conversions:

$$10^{11}\,\cancel{s} \times \left(\frac{1\,\cancel{\text{min}}}{60\,\cancel{s}}\right) \times \left(\frac{1\,\cancel{\text{hr}}}{60\,\cancel{\text{min}}}\right) \times \left(\frac{1\,\text{day}}{24\,\cancel{\text{hr}}}\right) \times \left(\frac{1\,\text{yr}}{365\,\text{days}}\right) \approx 3171\,\text{yr}$$

In other words, you would need *more than three thousand years* just to count \$100 billion in \$1 bills (at a rate of 1 bill per second). And that assumes that you never take a break: no sleeping, no eating, and absolutely no dying!

Comparisons are particularly useful in dealing with units that are relatively unfamiliar, such as energy units. Table 3.1 lists various energies that you can use in comparisons. For example, we immediately see that U.S. annual energy consumption is about $\frac{1}{5}$ of world annual energy consumption.

TABLE 3.1 Selected Energy Comparisons

Item	Energy (joules)
Energy released by metabolism of 1 average candy bar	1×10^{6}
Energy needed for 1 hour of running (adult)	4×10^{6}
Energy released by burning 1 liter of oil	1.2×10^{7}
Electrical energy used in an average home daily	5×10^{7}
Energy released by burning 1 kilogram of coal	1.6×10^{9}
Energy released by fission of 1 kilogram of uranium-235	5.6×10^{13}
Energy released by fusion of hydrogen in 1 liter of water	7×10^{13}
U.S. annual energy consumption	1×10^{20}
World annual energy consumption	5×10^{20}
Annual energy generation of Sun	1×10^{34}

Note: Consumption data (2009) from the U.S. Energy Information Administration.

Example 4 U.S. versus World Energy Consumption

Compare the U.S. population to the world population and U.S. energy consumption to world energy consumption. What does this tell you about energy usage by Americans?

Solution The world population is of order 7 billion (7×10^9) and the U.S. population is of order 300 million (3×10^8). Comparing the two quantities, we find

$$\frac{\text{U.S. population}}{\text{world population}} \approx \frac{3 \times 10^8}{7 \times 10^9} = \frac{3}{7} \times 10^{-1} \approx 0.043$$

The U.S. population is only about 4% of the world's population but, as shown in Table 3.1, the United States uses roughly $\frac{1}{5}$, or 20%, of the world's energy. This tells us that Americans use much more energy per person (more than four times as much) than the world average. **Now try Exercises 41–44.**

BY THE WAY

Nuclear *fission* means splitting large atomic nuclei into smaller ones, while nuclear *fusion* means combining small nuclei into larger ones. Current nuclear power plants use fission of uranium or plutonium, but nuclear bombs generate most of their destructive force through fusion of hydrogen into helium. The Sun generates energy by fusion.

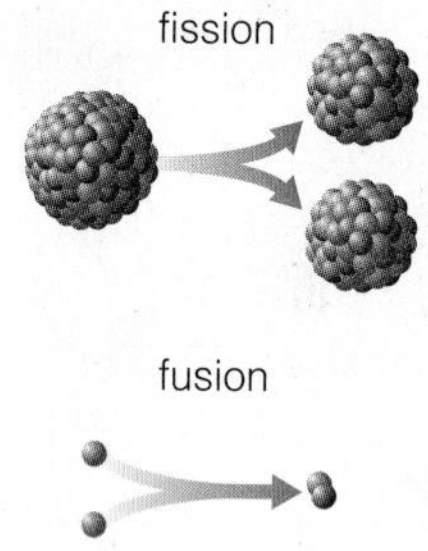

Example 5 Fusion Power

No one has yet succeeded in creating a commercially viable way to produce energy through nuclear fusion. However, suppose that at some time in the future we are able to build fusion power plants that are safe and cost-efficient. If we could extract all the hydrogen from water and use it for fusion, how much water would we need each minute to meet U.S. energy needs?

Solution We find the amount of water needed each year by dividing the U.S. annual energy consumption by the amount of energy available through fusion of 1 liter of water (from Table 3.1):

$$\frac{10^{20} \text{ joule}}{7 \times 10^{13} \frac{\text{joule}}{\text{L}}} = 1.4 \times 10^6 \text{ L}$$

That is, we would need about 1.4 million liters of water *per year.* Now we convert 1.4 million liters per year to units of liters per minute (note how the units work out).

$$\frac{1.4 \times 10^6 \text{ L}}{\text{yr}} \times \frac{1 \text{ yr}}{365 \text{ days}} \times \frac{1 \text{ day}}{24 \text{ hr}} \times \frac{1 \text{ hr}}{60 \text{ min}} \approx \frac{2.7 \text{ L}}{\text{min}}$$

In other words, it would take less than 3 liters of water per minute—less than the rate at which water flows from a typical kitchen faucet—to meet *all* U.S. energy needs through nuclear fusion. **Now try Exercises 45–48.**

BY THE WAY

Scientists working on fusion power actually use a rare form of hydrogen called *deuterium.* (Ordinary hydrogen nuclei contain just a single proton; deuterium also contains a neutron.) About 1 in 50,000 hydrogen atoms is deuterium, so the flow rate needed to power the United States would be 50,000 times higher than that calculated in Example 5–about the flow rate of a small creek.

Time Out to Think

Scientists have been working to achieve viable nuclear fusion power plants for decades, but so far without success. Nevertheless, it's conceivable that nuclear fusion will eventually become a realistic source of energy. Based on what you've learned in Example 5, how do you think this would change our world?

Perspective Through Scaling

A third general technique for giving meaning to numbers uses *scaling* or scale models. You are probably familiar with three common ways of expressing scales:

- *Verbally:* A scale can be described in words such as "One centimeter represents one kilometer" or, more simply, as "1 cm = 1 km."

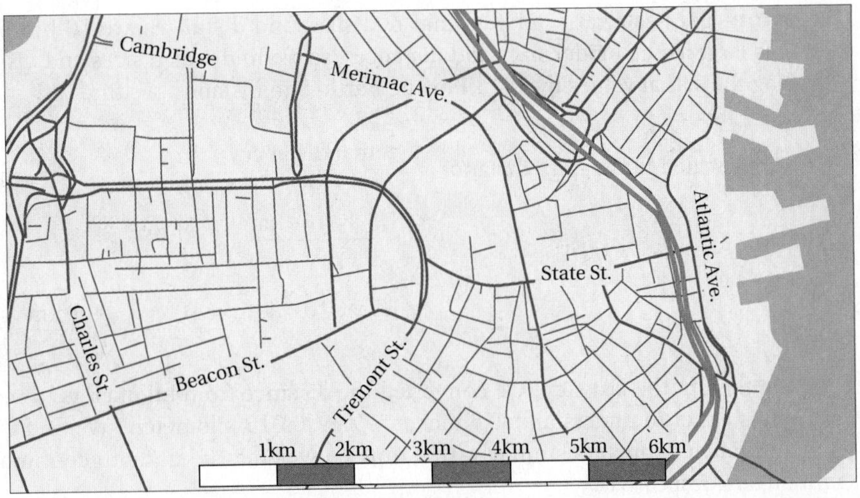

FIGURE 3.1 The miniruler acts as the map scale. In this case, 1 cm on the map represents 1 km in the city.

- *Graphically:* A marked miniruler can show the scale visually (Figure 3.1).
- *As a ratio:* We can state the ratio of a scaled size to an actual size. For example, there are 100,000 centimeters in a kilometer (because there are 100 centimeters in 1 meter and 1000 meters in 1 kilometer), so a scale where 1 centimeter represents 1 kilometer can be described as a **scale ratio** of 1 to 100,000 (or 1/100,000).

Scales have many uses other than maps. Architects and engineers build scale models to visualize their plans. *Timelines* represent the scale of time; a given distance along a timeline represents a certain number of years. *Time-lapse photography* and computer simulations allow us to represent large blocks of time in short periods. For example, in a 4-second time-lapse video clip that shows 24 hours of weather, each second of the video represents 6 hours of real time. Similarly, a computer simulation of continental drift might represent 1 billion years of geographical change in just 1 minute.

Example 6 Scale Ratio

A city map states, "One inch represents one mile." What is the scale ratio for this map?

Solution We find the ratio by converting 1 mile into inches:

$$1\ \cancel{\text{mi}} \times 5280\ \frac{\cancel{\text{ft}}}{\cancel{\text{mi}}} \times 12\ \frac{\text{in.}}{\cancel{\text{ft}}} = 63{,}360\ \text{in.}$$

One inch on the map represents 1 mile, or 63,360 inches. Therefore, the scale ratio for this map is 1 to 63,360, meaning that real distances are 63,360 times the distances on the map. Note that scale ratios never have units. **Now try Exercises 49–52.**

Example 7 Earth and Sun

The distance from the Earth to the Sun is about 150 million kilometers. The diameter of the Sun is about 1.4 million kilometers and the diameter of the Earth is about 12,760 kilometers. Put these numbers in perspective by using a scale model of the solar system with a 1 to 10 billion scale.

BY THE WAY

The Voyage scale model solar system (proposed by the first author of this textbook and located on the National Mall in Washington, D.C.) uses the 1 to 10 billion scale described in Example 7. The photo below shows the author's son touching the model Sun. Visible to the left are the pedestals that hold the inner planets Mercury, Venus, Earth, and Mars.

Solution The scale ratio tells us that real sizes and distances are 10 billion (10^{10}) times as large as the model sizes and distances, so we find scaled sizes and distances by dividing the actual values by 10^{10}. For the Earth–Sun distance, we find

$$\begin{aligned}\text{scaled Earth–Sun distance} &= \frac{\text{actual distance}}{10^{10}}\\ &= \frac{1.5 \times 10^8 \text{ km}}{10^{10}}\\ &= 1.5 \times 10^{-2} \cancel{\text{km}} \times 10^3 \frac{\text{m}}{\cancel{\text{km}}} = 15 \text{ m}\end{aligned}$$

Note that, in the last step, we converted the distance from kilometers to meters because it is easier to understand "15 meters" than "0.015 kilometer." We find the scaled Sun and Earth diameters similarly, this time converting the units to centimeters and millimeters, respectively:

$$\begin{aligned}\text{scaled Sun diameter} &= \frac{\text{actual Sun diameter}}{10^{10}}\\ &= \frac{1.4 \times 10^6 \text{ km}}{10^{10}}\\ &= 1.4 \times 10^{-4} \cancel{\text{km}} \times 10^5 \frac{\text{cm}}{\cancel{\text{km}}} = 14 \text{ cm}\\ \text{scaled Earth diameter} &= \frac{\text{actual Earth diameter}}{10^{10}}\\ &= \frac{1.276 \times 10^4 \text{ km}}{10^{10}}\\ &= 1.276 \times 10^{-6} \cancel{\text{km}} \times 10^6 \frac{\text{mm}}{\cancel{\text{km}}} = 1.276 \text{ mm}\end{aligned}$$

The model Sun, at 14 centimeters in diameter, is roughly the size of a grapefruit. The model Earth, at about 1.3 millimeters in diameter, is about the size of the ball point in a pen, and the distance between them is 15 meters. At this scale, it is easy to visualize relative sizes and distances.

Now try Exercise 53.

BY THE WAY

Light travels so fast that it could circle Earth nearly 8 times in just one second, so you can imagine that light can go a long way in a year. In fact, light can go a *light-year* in one year, which is where this unit gets its name. Be sure to note that a light-year is a unit of *distance*, not of time.

Time Out to Think

Find a grapefruit or similar-sized ball and the ball point from a pen. Set them 15 meters apart to represent the Sun and Earth with a 1 to 10 billion scale. How does a scale model like this one make it easier to understand our solar system? Discuss.

Example 8 Distances to the Stars

The distance from the Earth to the nearest stars besides the Sun (the three stars of the Alpha Centauri system) is about 4.3 light-years. On the 1 to 10 billion scale of Example 7, how far are these stars from the Earth? *Note:* A light-year is the distance that light can travel in one year; 1 light-year = 9.5×10^{12} km.

Solution Because a light-year is about 9.5×10^{12} kilometers, 4.3 light-years is equivalent to

$$4.3 \cancel{\text{light-years}} \times \frac{9.5 \times 10^{12} \text{ km}}{1 \cancel{\text{light-year}}} = 4.1 \times 10^{13} \text{ km}$$

We divide this actual distance by 10 billion to find the scaled distance to the nearest stars:

$$\text{scaled distance} = \frac{\text{actual distance}}{10^{10}} = \frac{4.1 \times 10^{13}\ \text{km}}{10^{10}}$$
$$= 4.1 \times 10^{3}\ \text{km} = 4100\ \text{km}$$

The distance to even the nearest stars on this scale is more than 4000 kilometers, or approximately the distance across the United States. **Now try Exercise 54.**

Time Out to Think

Suppose that an Earth-like planet is orbiting a nearby star. Based on the results of Examples 7 and 8, discuss the challenge of trying to detect such a planet. How is the *Kepler* mission, launched in 2009, searching for such planets?

Example 9 Timeline

Human civilization, at least since the time of ancient Egypt, is on the order of 5000 years old. The age of the Earth is on the order of 5 billion years. Suppose we use the length of a football field, or about 100 meters, as a timeline to represent the age of the Earth. If we put the birth of the Earth at the start of the timeline, how far from the line's end would human civilization begin?

Solution First, we compare the 5000-year history of human civilization to the 5 billion-year age of the Earth:

$$\frac{5000\ \text{yr}}{5\ \text{billion yr}} = \frac{5 \times 10^{3}\ \cancel{\text{yr}}}{5 \times 10^{9}\ \cancel{\text{yr}}} = 10^{-6}$$

That is, 5000 years is about 10^{-6}, or one *millionth*, of the age of the Earth. One millionth of a 100-meter (10^2 m) timeline is

$$10^{-6} \times 10^{2}\ \text{m} = 10^{-6+2}\ \text{m} = 10^{-4}\ \cancel{\text{m}} \times \frac{10^{3}\ \text{mm}}{1\ \cancel{\text{m}}} = 0.1\ \text{mm}$$

On a timeline where the Earth's history stretches the length of a football field, human civilization shows up only in the final tenth of a millimeter. **Now try Exercises 55–56.**

BY THE WAY

According to modern science, Earth and our solar system formed just over $4\frac{1}{2}$ billion years ago from the collapse of a large cloud of interstellar gas. Powerful telescopes allow us to observe similar clouds in which stars are forming today.

Putting It All Together: Case Studies

We've studied several techniques for putting numbers in perspective, but in many cases we gain more perspective by using two or more techniques together. Sometimes we need additional creativity to think of ways to make sense of a particular number. The following case studies illustrate a few more of the many ways of putting numbers in perspective. As you study them, ask whether the numbers now have more meaning and how else you might give meaning to the numbers.

Case Study How Big Is a University?

Consider a large university with 25,000 students. The number 25,000 is small compared to many of the numbers we've dealt with in this chapter, but it still takes thought to put it in perspective. Here's one way: Imagine that the new university president wants to get to know the students. She proposes to meet for lunch with groups of 5 students at a time. Is it possible for her to have lunch with *all* the students?

To answer, let's assume she holds the lunch meetings five days per week. With five students at each lunch, she will meet $5 \times 5 = 25$ students per week. Since there are 25,000 students at the school, it would take her 1000 weeks to have lunch with everyone. If we now assume that she has the lunches for 50 weeks each year (out of the total of 52 weeks in a year), it would take her 1000 weeks $\div$ 50 weeks/yr = 20 years to meet all the students. But after only 4 years, most of the 25,000 students would have graduated and been replaced by a new group of 25,000 students, so she could never keep up. It would *not* be possible to meet all the students at these small group lunches. The lesson from this example is that while 25,000 people might not sound like much, you could not get to know all of them in 4 years—or even a lifetime.

Time Out to Think

Today, a typical congressional representative represents about 700,000 constituents. Is it possible for a representative to campaign by going door to door to meet everyone in his or her district? Explain.

A billion here, a billion there; soon you're talking real money.

—Former Illinois Senator Everett Dirksen

Case Study What Is a Billion Dollars?

One way to put \$1 billion in perspective is to ask a question like "How many people can you employ with \$1 billion per year?" Let's suppose that employees receive a fairly high average salary of \$75,000, and that it costs a business an additional \$25,000 per year in overhead for each employee (costs for office space, computer services, health insurance, and other benefits). The total cost of an employee is therefore \$100,000, so \$1 billion would allow a business to hire

$$\frac{\$1 \text{ billion}}{\$100{,}000 \text{ per employee}} = \frac{\$10^9}{\$10^5/\text{employee}} = 10^4 \text{ employees}$$

One billion dollars per year could support a work force of some 10,000 employees.

Another way to put \$1 billion in perspective also points out how different numbers can be, even when they sound similar (like million, billion, and trillion). Suppose you become a sports star and earn a salary of \$1 million per year. How long would it take you to earn a billion dollars? We simply divide \$1 billion by your salary of \$1 million/year:

$$\frac{\$1 \text{ billion}}{\$1 \text{ million/yr}} = \frac{\$10^9}{\$10^6/\text{yr}} = 10^3 \text{ yr} = 1000 \text{ yr}$$

Even at a salary of \$1 million per year, earning a billion dollars would take a thousand years.

BY THE WAY

The size of an atom is determined by the size of its electron cloud, but most of the mass of an atom is contained in its nucleus. Because the nucleus is so tiny compared to the atom itself, we have the surprising fact that atoms consist mostly of empty space!

Case Study The Scale of the Atom

Everything is made from *atoms,* which consist of a nucleus (made from *protons* and *neutrons*) surrounded by a "cloud" of *electrons.* A typical atom has a diameter of about 10^{-10} meter (as defined by its electron cloud), while its nucleus is about 10^{-15} meter in diameter. Can we put these numbers in perspective?

Let's begin with the atom itself. Because its diameter is 10^{-10} meter, or one *ten-billionth* of a meter, we could fit 10 billion (10^{10}) atoms in a line along a meter stick. A centimeter is 1/100 (or $1/10^2$) of a meter, so we could fit $10^{10}/10^2 = 10^8$, or 100 million, atoms in a 1-centimeter line. Therefore, if we could shrink people down to the size of atoms, the roughly 300 million people in the United States could fit in a line only about 3 centimeters—just over an inch—long.

Next, let's compare the diameter of the atom to the diameter of its nucleus:

$$\frac{\text{diameter of atom}}{\text{diameter of nucleus}} = \frac{10^{-10}\ \cancel{\text{m}}}{10^{-15}\ \cancel{\text{m}}} = 10^{-10-(-15)} = 10^5$$

The atom itself is about 10^5, or 100,000, times as large as its nucleus. That is, if we made a scale model of an atom in which the nucleus were the size of a marble (1 cm), the atom would have a diameter of about 100,000 centimeters, which is 1 kilometer, or more than half a mile.

Case Study Until the Sun Dies

We can hope that living things will flourish on Earth until the Sun dies, which astronomers estimate will be in about 5 billion (5×10^9) years. How long is 5 billion years? First, let's compare the Sun's remaining lifetime to a long human lifetime of 100 years:

$$\frac{5 \times 10^9\ \cancel{\text{yr}}}{100\ \cancel{\text{yr}}} = 5 \times 10^7$$

The Sun's remaining lifetime is equivalent to about 5×10^7, or 50 million, human lifetimes. We can add perspective by dividing a human lifetime of 100 years by 50 million and converting the result from years to minutes:

$$\frac{100\ \text{yr}}{5 \times 10^7} = 2 \times 10^{-6}\ \cancel{\text{yr}} \times \frac{365\ \cancel{\text{days}}}{1\ \cancel{\text{yr}}} \times \frac{24\ \cancel{\text{hr}}}{1\ \cancel{\text{day}}} \times \frac{60\ \text{min}}{1\ \cancel{\text{hr}}} \approx 1\ \text{min}$$

Therefore, a human lifetime in comparison to the Sun's remaining life is roughly the same as *one minute* in comparison to a human lifetime.

How about human creations? The Egyptian pyramids are often described as "eternal." But they are slowly eroding because of wind, rain, air pollution, and the impact of tourists. All traces of them will have vanished within a few million years. If we estimate the lifetime of the pyramids as 5 million (5×10^6) years, then

$$\frac{\text{Sun's remaining lifetime}}{\text{lifetime of pyramids}} \approx \frac{5 \times 10^9\ \cancel{\text{yr}}}{5 \times 10^6\ \cancel{\text{yr}}} = 10^3 = 1000$$

A few million years may seem like a long time, but the Sun's remaining lifetime is a thousand times as long.

On a more somber note, we can gain perspective on the Sun's remaining 5 billion years by considering evolutionary time scales. During the past century, we have acquired sufficient technology and power to destroy human life totally, if we so choose. However, even if we make that unfortunate choice, some species (including many insects) are likely to survive. Would another intelligent species ever emerge on the Earth? There is no way to know, but we can look to the past for guidance. It's been 65 million years since the dinosaurs were wiped out in what many scientists believe was a sudden cataclysm caused by the impact

I met a traveller from an antique land
Who said: Two vast and trunkless legs of stone
Stand in the desert . . . Near them, on the sand,
Half sunk, a shattered visage lies, whose frown,
And wrinkled lip, and sneer of cold command,
Tell that its sculptor well those passions read
Which yet survive, stamped on these lifeless things,
The hand that mocked them, and the heart that fed.
And on the pedestal these words appear:
"My name is Ozymandias, king of kings:
Look on my works, ye Mighty, and despair!"
Nothing beside remains. Round the decay
Of that colossal wreck, boundless and bare,
The lone and level sands stretch far away.

—Percy Bysshe Shelley, *Ozymandias*

of an asteroid, so we might imagine it would take a similar amount of time for the next intelligent species to emerge; to keep the numbers simple, let's assume the required time is 50 million years. Then, if this next species also destroyed itself, another species might emerge 50 million years after that, and so on. If this pattern continued, how many intelligent species would eventually emerge on Earth? We divide the Sun's remaining 5 billion years by the 50 million years between successive intelligent species:

$$\frac{5 \text{ billion years}}{50 \text{ million years}} = \frac{5 \times 10^9 \cancel{\text{years}}}{5 \times 10^7 \cancel{\text{years}}} = 100$$

Even at 50 million years per shot, the Earth would have time for some 100 more intelligent species to emerge. Perhaps one of those species will not destroy itself, and descendants of the Earth might move on to other star systems by the time the Sun finally dies. Perhaps that species will be ours.

QUICK QUIZ

Choose the best answer to each of the following questions. Explain your reasoning with one or more complete sentences.

1. The number 70,000,000 is the same as

   a. 7×10^7. b. 7×10^8. c. 7×10^9.

2. You are multiplying 1277 times 14,385. You expect the answer to be a number between 1 and 10 times

   a. 10^3. b. 10^5. c. 10^7.

3. Fill in the blank: $\$10^9$ is ______ times as much money as $\$10^5$.

   a. four

   b. one thousand

   c. ten thousand

4. You are asked to estimate the total amount of gasoline that will be used by all Americans this year. As an order of magnitude estimate, you determine that the answer should be somewhere around

   a. 1 million gallons.

   b. 100 million gallons.

   c. 100 billion gallons.

5. You are wondering how many dollar bills you'd need to lay end to end to stretch the 400,000-kilometer distance from Earth to the Moon. You find a Web site that says the answer is 8 million dollar bills. With a quick estimate, you conclude that this answer is

   a. a reasonable order of magnitude estimate.

   b. way too large (the actual number would be much less than 8 million).

   c. way too small (the actual number would be much more than 8 million).

6. You are given some data and asked to calculate how long the Sun can continue to shine before it dies. Your answer is 1.2×10^{-10} years. Based on this answer, you conclude that

   a. the Sun will die within just a few centuries.

   b. the death of the Sun is something we do not need to worry about for a very long time.

   c. your answer is wrong.

7. You are looking at a map with a scale of 1 inch = 20 miles. If two towns are separated on the map by 6 inches, the actual distance between them is

   a. 6 miles. b. 120 miles. c. 120 inches.

8. An outstanding quarterback receives a new contract paying him \$10 million per year. How long would it take him at this rate to earn \$1 billion?

   a. 10 years b. 100 years c. 1000 years

9. You are running for mayor this year in a city with 300,000 households. You decide to campaign by going door to door and spending a few minutes talking with members of every household in the town. This plan will

   a. allow you to speak personally with everyone who must vote for you if you hope to win.

   b. occupy about six months of your time.

   c. be impossible to carry out.

10. A lottery ticket on which the odds of winning are 1 in 1 million is given to every person in attendance at a college football game. The most likely result is that there will be

    a. no winners in the stadium.

    b. one winner in the stadium.

    c. many winners in the stadium.

Exercises 3B

REVIEW QUESTIONS

1. Briefly describe scientific notation. How is it useful for writing large and small numbers? How is it useful for making approximations?
2. Explain how we can use estimation to put numbers in perspective. Give an example.
3. What is an order of magnitude estimate? Explain why such an estimate can be useful even though it may be as much as 10 times too large or too small.
4. Explain how we can use comparisons to put numbers in perspective. Give an example.
5. Describe three common ways of expressing the scale of a map or model. How would you show a scale of 1 cm = 100 km graphically? How would you describe it as a ratio?
6. Explain how we can use scaling to put numbers in perspective. Give an example.
7. Suppose that the Sun were the size of a grapefruit. How big and how far away would the Earth be on this scale? How far would the nearest stars (besides the Sun) be?
8. Describe several ways of putting each of the following in perspective: the size of a large university; $1 billion; the size of an atom; the Sun's remaining lifetime.

DOES IT MAKE SENSE?

Decide whether each of the following statements makes sense (or is clearly true) or does not make sense (or is clearly false). Explain your reasoning.

9. I read a book that had 10^5 words in it.
10. I've seen about 10^{50} commercials on TV.
11. I live in an apartment building that is 200 feet tall.
12. In total, Americans spend about a billion dollars per year on housing costs (rent and home mortgage payments).
13. After a recent NFL football game, the star player signed autographs for every person in attendance.
14. The CEO of the company earned more money last year than the company's 500 lowest paid employees combined.

BASIC SKILLS & CONCEPTS

15–20: Review of Scientific Notation. In the following exercises, use the skills covered in the Brief Review on p. 145.

15. Convert each of the following numbers from scientific to ordinary notation and write its name.

    Example: $2 \times 10^3 = 2000 =$ two thousand

    a. 3×10^3 b. 6×10^6 c. 3.4×10^5
    d. 2×10^{-2} e. 2.1×10^{-4} f. 4×10^{-5}

16. Convert each of the following numbers from scientific to ordinary notation and write its name.

    a. 8×10^2 b. 5×10^3 c. 9.6×10^4
    d. 2×10^{-3} e. 3.3×10^{-5} f. 7.66×10^{-2}

17. Write each of the following numbers in scientific notation.

    a. 233 b. 126,547 c. 0.11
    d. 9736.23 e. 124.58 f. 0.8642

18. Write each of the following numbers in scientific notation.

    a. 4327 b. 984.35 c. 0.0045
    d. 624.87 e. 0.1357 f. 98.180004

19. Do the following operations without a calculator and show your work clearly. Be sure to express answers in scientific notation. You may round your answers to one decimal place (as in 3.2×10^5).

    a. $(3 \times 10^3) \times (2 \times 10^2)$ b. $(4 \times 10^2) \times (3 \times 10^8)$
    c. $(3 \times 10^3) + (2 \times 10^2)$ d. $(8 \times 10^{12}) \div (4 \times 10^4)$

20. Do the following operations without a calculator and show your work clearly. Be sure to express answers in scientific notation. You may round your answers to one decimal place (as in 3.2×10^5).

    a. $(4 \times 10^7) \times (2 \times 10^8)$ b. $(3.2 \times 10^5) \times (2 \times 10^4)$
    c. $(4 \times 10^3) + (5 \times 10^2)$ d. $(9 \times 10^{13}) \div (3 \times 10^{10})$

21–22: They Don't Look That Different! Compare the numbers in each pair and give the factor by which the numbers differ. *Example:* 10^6 is 10^2, or 100, times as large as 10^4.

21. a. 10^{35}, 10^{26} b. 10^{17}, 10^{27}
    c. 1 billion, 1 million d. 7 trillion, 7 thousand
    e. 2×10^{-6}, 2×10^{-9} f. 6.1×10^{27}, 6.1×10^{29}

22. a. 250 million, 5 billion b. 9.3×10^2, 3.1×10^{-2}
    c. 10^{-8}, 2×10^{-13} d. 3.5×10^{-2}, 7×10^{-8}
    e. 1 thousand, 1 thousandth f. 10^{12}, 10^{-9}

23–28: Using Scientific Notation. Rewrite the following statements using a number in scientific notation.

23. My new music player has a capacity of 340 gigabytes. (Recall that *giga* means billion.)
24. The estimated (2009) world nuclear energy production is 2608 billion kilowatt-hours.
25. As of 2009, U.S. consumer credit (total amount borrowed) was $2564 billion.
26. The number of different eight-character passwords that can be made with 26 letters and 10 numerals is approximately 2.8 trillion.
27. The diameter of a typical bacterium is about 0.000001 meter.
28. A beam of light can travel the length of a football field in about 30 nanoseconds. Express your answer in seconds. (*Hint:* Recall that *nano* means one billionth.)

29–30: Approximation with Scientific Notation. Estimate the following quantities without using a calculator. Then find the exact result, using a calculator if necessary. Discuss whether your approximation technique worked.

29. a. $300{,}000 \times 100$

b. 5.1 million × 1.9 thousand

c. $4 \times 10^9 \div 2.1 \times 10^6$

d. 33 million × 3.1 thousand

e. $4{,}288{,}364 \div 2132$

f. $(6.129845 \times 10^6) \div (2.198 \times 10^4)$

30. a. 5.6 billion ÷ 200

b. 4 trillion ÷ 260 million

c. $9000 \times 54{,}986$

d. 3 billion ÷ 25,000

e. 5987×341

f. $43 \div 765$

31–34: Perspective Through Estimation. Use estimation to make the following comparisons. Discuss your conclusion.

31. Which is greater: the amount you spend in a month on coffee or the amount you spend in a month on gasoline?

32. Could a person walk across the United States (New York to California) in a year? If not, about how long would it take?

33. Which is greater: the time you spend in a year studying or the time you spend in a year sleeping?

34. Which is greater: the amount you spend in a year on transportation or the amount you spend in a year on food?

35–40: Order of Magnitude Estimates. Make order of magnitude estimates of the following quantities. Explain the assumptions you use in your estimates.

35. The number of times your heart beats in a day

36. The number of steps you take in an average day

37. The amount of water you drink in a year

38. The total number of words in this textbook

39. The number of miles you travel in a car in a year (as either driver or passenger)

40. The number of hours per month that you listen to music

41–48: Energy Comparisons. Use Table 3.1 to answer the following questions.

41. How many average candy bars would you have to eat to supply the energy needed for 6 hours of running?

42. How many liters of oil are required to supply the electrical energy needs of an average home for a month?

43. Compare the energy released by burning 1 kilogram of coal to that released by fission of 1 kilogram of uranium-235.

44. Compare the energy released by burning 1 liter of oil to that released by fusion of the hydrogen in 1 liter of water.

45. If you could generate energy by fusing the hydrogen in ordinary tap water, how much water would you need to generate the electrical energy used daily by a typical home?

46. If you could generate energy by fusing the hydrogen in ordinary tap water, how much water would you need to supply all the energy currently consumed worldwide?

47. How many kilograms of uranium would be required to supply the energy needs of the United States for 1 year using fission?

48. Suppose that we could somehow capture all the energy released by the Sun for just 1 second. Would this energy be enough to supply U.S. energy needs for a year? Explain.

49–52: Scale Ratios. Find the scale ratios for the following maps.

49. 2 centimeters on the map represents 100 kilometers.

50. 1 inch on the map represents 10 miles.

51. 1 cm (map) = 500 km (actual)

52. 0.5 in. (map) = 1 km (actual)

53. **Scale Model Solar System.** The following table gives size and distance data for the planets. Calculate the scaled size and distance for each planet using a 1 to 10 billion scale model solar system. Give your results in table form. Then write one or two paragraphs that describe your findings in words and give perspective to the size of our solar system.

Planet	Diameter	Average Distance from Sun
Mercury	4880 km	57.9 million km
Venus	12,100 km	108.2 million km
Earth	12,760 km	149.6 million km
Mars	6790 km	227.9 million km
Jupiter	143,000 km	778.3 million km
Saturn	120,000 km	1427 million km
Uranus	52,000 km	2870 million km
Neptune	48,400 km	4497 million km

54. **Interstellar Travel.** The fastest spaceships launched to date are traveling away from Earth at speeds of about 50,000 kilometers per hour. How long would such a spaceship take to reach Alpha Centauri? (*Hint:* See Example 8.) Based on your answer, write one or two paragraphs discussing whether interstellar travel is a realistic possibility today.

55. **Universal Time Line.** According to modern science, Earth is about 4.5 billion years old and written human history extends back about 10,000 years. Suppose you represent the entire history of Earth with a 100-yard-long timeline, with the birth of Earth on one end and today at the other end.

a. What distance represents 1 billion years?

b. How far from the end of the timeline does written human history begin?

56. **Universal Clock.** According to modern science, Earth is about 4.5 billion years old and written human history extends back about 10,000 years. Suppose you represent the entire history of Earth by 12 hours on a clock, with the birth of Earth at the stroke of midnight and today at the stroke of noon.

a. How much time on the clock represents 1 billion years?

b. At what time on the clock does written human history begin?

FURTHER APPLICATIONS

57–64: **Making Numbers Understandable.** Restate the following facts as indicated.

57. There are approximately 2.4 million deaths per year in the United States. Express this quantity in deaths per minute.

58. There are approximately 2.2 million marriages per year in the United States. Express this quantity in marriages per hour.

59. Approximately 40,000 Americans are killed each year in automobile accidents. Express this quantity in deaths per day.

60. In 2007, Walmart had profits of \$12.7 billion. Express this profit in terms of dollars per minute.

61. There were 305 million crimes (either violent or property crimes) committed in the United States in 2008. Express this quantity in terms of crimes per second and crimes per American.

62. The 2008 prison population in the United States was approximately 1.6 million. How many arenas with a capacity of 50,000 would this population fill?

63. Americans consume an estimated 7.6 billion pounds of candy (excluding chewing gum) per year. Express this quantity in terms of pounds per person per month. (Use a population of 305 million.)

64. In 2007, Procter and Gamble spent \$5.2 billion on advertising. Express this quantity in terms of the height in kilometers of a stack of \$1 bills. Assume 10 bills per millimeter.

65. **Cells in the Human Body.** Estimates of the number of cells in the human body vary over an order of magnitude. Indeed, the precise number varies from one individual to another and depends on whether you count bacterial cells. Here is one way to make an estimate.

    a. Assume that an average cell has a diameter of 6 micrometers (6×10^{-6} meter), which means it has a volume of 100 cubic micrometers. How many cells are there in a cubic centimeter?

    b. Estimate the number of cells in a liter, using the fact that a cubic centimeter equals a milliliter.

    c. Estimate the number of cells in a 70-kilogram (154-pound) person, assuming that the human body is 100% water (actually it is about 60–70% water) and that 1 liter of water weighs 1 kilogram.

66. **CO_2 Emissions.** For every gallon of gasoline burned by an automobile, approximately 10.2 kilograms of carbon dioxide are emitted into the atmosphere. Estimate the total amount of carbon dioxide added to the atmosphere by all automobile travel in the United States over the past year.

67. **The Amazing Amazon.** An issue of *National Geographic* contained the following statement:

    > *Dropping less than two inches per mile after emerging from the Andes, the Amazon drains a sixth of the world's runoff into the ocean. One day's discharge at its mouth—4.5 trillion gallons—could supply all U.S. households for five months.*

    Based on this statement, determine how much water an average U.S. household uses each month. Does this answer seem reasonable? Explain any estimates you make.

68. **Wood for Energy?** A total of about 180,000 terawatts of solar power reaches Earth's surface, of which about 0.06% is used by plants for photosynthesis. Of the energy that goes to photosynthesis, about 1% ends up stored in plant matter (including wood). (Recall that 1 watt = 1 joule/s; 1 terawatt = 10^{12} watts.)

    a. Calculate the total amount of energy that becomes stored in plant matter each second.

    b. Suppose that power stations generated electricity by burning plant matter. If all the energy stored in plants could be converted to electricity, what average power, in terawatts, would be possible? Would it be enough to meet world electricity demand, which is of order 10 terawatts?

    c. Based on your answer to b, can you draw any conclusions about why humans depend on fossil fuels, such as oil and coal, which are the remains of plants that died long ago? Explain.

69. **Stellar Corpses: White Dwarfs and Neutron Stars.** A few billion years from now, after exhausting its nuclear engines, the Sun will become a type of remnant star called a *white dwarf*. It will still have nearly the same mass (about 2×10^{30} kg) as the Sun today, but its radius will be only about that of Earth (about 6400 km).

    a. Calculate the average density of the white dwarf in units of kilograms per cubic centimeter.

    b. What is the mass of a teaspoon of material from the white dwarf? (*Hint*: A teaspoon is about 4 cubic centimeters.) Compare this mass to the mass of something familiar (for example, a person, a car, a tank).

    c. A neutron star is a type of stellar remnant compressed to even greater densities than a white dwarf. Suppose that a neutron star has a mass 1.4 times the mass of the Sun but a radius of only 10 kilometers. What is its density? Compare the mass of 1 cubic centimeter of neutron star material to the total mass of Mt. Everest (about 5×10^{10} kg).

70–73: **Sampling Problems.** Sampling techniques can be used to estimate physical quantities. To estimate a large quantity, you might measure a representative small sample and find the total quantity by "scaling up." To estimate a small quantity, you might measure several of the small quantities together and "scale down".

Example: How thick is a sheet of a paper?

Solution: One way to estimate the thickness of a sheet of paper is to measure the thickness of a ream (500 sheets) of paper. A particular ream was 7.5 centimeters thick. Thus, a sheet of paper from this ream was 7.5 cm ÷ 500 = 0.015 cm thick, or 0.15 millimeter.

70. How much does a sheet of paper weigh?

71. How thick is a penny? a nickel? a dime? a quarter? Would you rather have your height stacked in pennies, nickels, dimes, or quarters? Explain.

72. How much does a grain of sand weigh? How many grains of sand are in a typical playground sand box?

73. How many stars are visible in the sky on the clearest, darkest nights? How could astronomers estimate the total number of stars in the universe?

WEB PROJECTS

74. **Energy Comparisons.** Using data available from the Energy Information Administration Web site, choose a few measures of U.S. or world energy consumption or production. Make comparisons that put these numbers in perspective.
75. **Nuclear Fusion.** Learn about the current state of research into building commercially viable fusion power plants. What obstacles must still be overcome? Do you think fusion power will be a reality in your lifetime? Explain.
76. **Scale Model Solar System.** Visit the Web site for the Voyage scale model solar system on the National Mall in Washington, D.C. Write a brief report on what you learn.
77. **Richest People.** Find the net worth of the world's three richest people. Put these monetary values in perspective through any techniques you wish.

IN YOUR WORLD

78. **Large Numbers.** Search today's newspaper for as many numbers larger than 100,000 as you can find. Briefly explain the context within which each large number is used.
79. **Perspective in the News.** Find an example in the recent news in which a reporter uses a technique to put a number in perspective. Describe the example. Do you think the technique is effective? Can you think of a better way to put the number in perspective? Explain.
80. **Putting Numbers in Perspective.** Find at least two examples of very large or small numbers in recent news reports. Use a technique of your choosing to put each number in perspective in a way that you believe most people would find meaningful.

TECHNOLOGY EXERCISE

81. **Scientific Notation with Technology.** Use a calculator or Excel to do the following calculations.

   a. Find the distance that light travels in a year at a speed of 186,000 miles/second (a distance called a *light-year*).

   b. Evaluate $\frac{52 \cdot 51 \cdot 50 \cdot 49 \cdot 48}{5 \cdot 4 \cdot 3 \cdot 2 \cdot 1}$, the number of different 5-card hands that can be dealt from a 52-card deck of cards.

   c. Annual worldwide emissions of carbon dioxide are estimated to be 30,000 million metric tons (2009). Express this quantity in per capita terms (metric tons per person in the world). Assume a world population of 6.8 billion.

   d. Earth's mass is 6.0×10^{24} kilograms. Its volume is 1.1×10^{12} cubic kilometers. Find the density of Earth (mass/volume) in units of grams per cubic centimeter. (For comparison, the density of water is 1 gram per cubic centimeter.)

   e. The universe is estimated to be about 14 billion years old. What is its age in seconds?

UNIT 3C Dealing with Uncertainty

> None of us really understands what's going on with all these numbers.
>
> —David Stockman, Budget Director for President Reagan, 1981

The rosy outlook for the United States federal budget was big news in early 2001. Government economists projected a cumulative surplus of $5.6 *trillion* for the coming decade. Politicians argued about whether this windfall should be returned to taxpayers, spent on new programs, or used to pay down the federal debt.

Two years later, the projected surplus not only had vanished, but had been replaced by huge deficits. By 2009, rather than having gained trillions in surplus money, the government had instead gone another $6 trillion into debt. How did the nearly $6 trillion surplus—some $20,000 for every man, woman, and child in the United States—disappear?

It didn't really disappear, of course. Rather, it never existed in the first place—it was only an estimate. Like all estimates, it was only as good as the assumptions that went into it, and these assumptions included highly uncertain predictions about the future of the economy, future tax rates, and future spending. The government economists who made the projection were well aware of the uncertainties, but the news media and politicians tended to report the surplus projection as an indisputable fact.

This story of vanishing trillions holds an important lesson. Many of the numbers we encounter in daily life are far less certain than we are told, and we can therefore be severely misled unless we learn to examine and interpret uncertainties for ourselves. In this unit, we will discuss ways of dealing with uncertainty properly. Understanding the nature of uncertainty will make you better equipped to assess the reliability of numbers as they are typically reported in the news.

Significant Digits

One key consideration in dealing with uncertainty is how we state measurements. For example, suppose you measure your weight to be 132 pounds on a scale that can be read only to the nearest pound. Saying that you weigh 132.00 pounds would be misleading, because it would incorrectly imply that you know your weight to the nearest *hundredth* of a pound, rather than to the nearest pound. In other words, 132 pounds and 132.00 pounds do *not* have the same meaning.

The digits in a number that represent actual measurements and therefore have meaning are called **significant digits.** For example, 132 pounds has 3 significant digits and implies a measurement to the nearest pound, while 132.00 pounds has 5 significant digits and implies a measurement to the nearest hundredth of a pound.

Note that zeros are significant when they represent actual measurements, but not when they serve only to locate the decimal point. We assume that the zeros in 132.00 pounds are significant because there was no reason to include them unless they represented an actual measurement. In contrast, we assume that the zeros in 600 centimeters are *not* significant, because they serve only to tell us that the decimal point comes to their right. Rewriting 600 centimeters as 6 meters makes it easier to see that only the 6 is a significant digit.

The only subtlety in counting significant digits arises when we cannot be sure whether zeros are truly significant. For example, suppose your professor states that there are 200 students in your class. Without further information, you have no way to know whether she means exactly 200 students or roughly 200. We can avoid this kind of ambiguity by writing numbers in scientific notation. In that case, zeros appear only when they are significant. For example, an enrollment of 2×10^2 implies a measurement to the nearest hundred students, while 2.00×10^2 implies exactly 200 students.

SUMMARY When Are Digits Significant?

Type of Digit	Significance
Nonzero digits	Always significant
Zeros that follow a nonzero digit *and* lie to the right of the decimal point (as in 4.20 or 3.00)	Always significant
Zeros *between* nonzero digits (as in 4002 or 3.06) or other significant zeros (such as the first zero in 30.0)	Always significant
Zeros to the *left* of the first nonzero digit (as in 0.006 or 0.00052)	Never significant
Zeros to the *right* of the last nonzero digit but before the decimal point (as in 40,000 or 210)	Not significant unless stated otherwise

Example 1 Counting Significant Digits

State the number of significant digits and the implied meaning of the following numbers.

a. a time of 11.90 seconds
b. a length of 0.000067 meter
c. a population reported as 240,000
d. a population reported as 2.40×10^5

Solution

a. The number 11.90 seconds has 4 significant digits and implies a measurement to the nearest 0.01 second.
b. The number 0.000067 meter has 2 significant digits and implies a measurement to the nearest 0.000001 meter. Note that we can rewrite this number as 67 micrometers, showing clearly that it has only 2 significant digits.

A Brief Review Rounding

The basic process of rounding numbers takes just two steps.

Step 1. Decide which decimal place (e.g., tens, ones, tenths, or hundredths) is the smallest that should be kept.

Step 2. Look at the number in the next place to the *right* (for example, if rounding to tenths, look at hundredths). If the value in the next place is *less than* 5, round *down;* if it is *5 or greater,* round *up.*

For example, the number 382.2593 is given to the nearest ten-thousandth. It can be rounded in the following ways:

382.2593 rounded to the nearest thousandth is 382.259.

382.2593 rounded to the nearest hundredth is 382.26.

382.2593 rounded to the nearest tenth is 382.3.

382.2593 rounded to the nearest one is 382.

382.2593 rounded to the nearest ten is 380.

382.2593 rounded to the nearest hundred is 400.

(Some statisticians use a more complex rounding rule if the value in the next column is exactly 5: They round up if the last digit being kept is odd and down if it is even. We won't use that rule in this book.) **Now try Exercises 15–16.**

c. We assume that the zeros in 240,000 people are not significant. Therefore, the number has 2 significant digits and implies a measurement to the nearest 10,000 people.
d. The number 2.40×10^5 has 3 significant digits. Although this number means 240,000, the scientific notation shows that the first zero is significant, so it implies a measurement to the nearest 1000 people. **Now try Exercises 17–28.**

Example 2 Rounding with Significant Digits

For each of the following operations, give your answer with the specified number of significant digits.

a. 7.7 mm × 9.92 mm; give your answer with 2 significant digits
b. 240,000 × 72,106; give your answer with 4 significant digits

Solution

a. $7.7 \text{ mm} \times 9.92 \text{ mm} = 76.384 \text{ mm}^2$. Because we are asked to give the answer with 2 significant digits, we round to 76 mm^2.
b. $240{,}000 \times 72{,}106 = 1.730544 \times 10^{10}$. Because we are asked to give the answer with 4 significant digits, we round to 1.731×10^{10}. **Now try Exercises 29–34.**

Understanding Errors

We are now ready to deal with errors themselves. We'll begin by describing two types of error. Then we'll discuss how to quantify the sizes of errors and how to report final results to account for errors.

Types of Error: Random and Systematic

Broadly speaking, measurement errors fall into two categories: random errors and systematic errors. The difference between them can be illustrated with an example.

Suppose you work in a pediatric office and use a digital scale to weigh babies. If you've ever worked with babies, you know that they usually aren't very happy about being put on a scale. Their thrashing and crying tends to shake the scale, making the readout jump around. For the case shown in Figure 3.2a, you could equally well record the baby's weight as anything between about 14.5 and 15.0 pounds. We say that the shaking of the scale introduces a **random error**, because any particular measurement may be either too high or too low.

Now suppose you have weighed babies all day. At the end of the day, you notice that the scale reads 1.2 pounds when there is nothing on it (Figure 3.2b). In that case, every

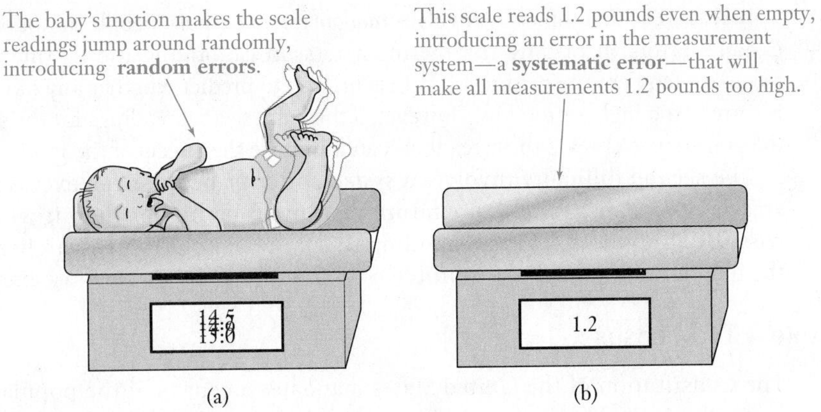

FIGURE 3.2

measurement you made was too high by 1.2 pounds. This type of error is called a **systematic error**, because it is caused by an error in the measurement *system*—that is, an error that consistently (systematically) affects all measurements.

> **TWO TYPES OF MEASUREMENT ERROR**
>
> **Random errors** occur because of random and inherently unpredictable events in the measurement process.
>
> **Systematic errors** occur when there is a problem in the measurement system that affects all measurements in the same way, such as making them all too low or too high by the same amount.

A systematic error affects all measurements in the same way, such as making them all too high or all too low. Thus, if you discover a systematic error, you can go back and adjust the affected measurements. In contrast, the unpredictable nature of random errors makes it impossible to correct for them. However, you can minimize the effects of random errors by making many measurements and averaging them. For example, if you measure the baby's weight ten times, your measurements will probably be too high in some cases and too low in others. Thus, when you average the ten measurements, you are likely to get a value that better represents the true weight.

BY THE WAY

The fact that urban areas tend to be warmer than they would be in the absence of human activity is often called the *urban heat island effect.* Major causes of it include heat released by burning fuel in automobiles, homes, and industry and the fact that pavement and buildings tend to retain heat from sunlight.

Time Out to Think

Go to a Web site that gives the precise current time. How far off is your clock or watch? Describe possible sources of random and systematic errors in your time-keeping.

Example 3 Errors in Global Warming Data

Scientists studying global warming need to know how the average temperature of the entire Earth, or the *global average temperature,* has changed with time. Consider two difficulties (among many others) in trying to interpret historical temperature data from the early 20th century: (1) temperatures were measured with simple thermometers and the data were recorded by hand; and (2) most temperature measurements were recorded in or near urban areas, which tend to be warmer than surrounding rural areas because of heat released by human activity. Discuss whether each of these two difficulties produces random or systematic errors, and consider the implications of these errors.

Solution The first difficulty involves *random errors* because people undoubtedly made occasional errors in reading the thermometers, in calibrating the thermometers, and in recording temperature readings. There is no way to predict whether any individual reading is correct, too high, or too low. However, if there are several readings for the same region on the same day, averaging these readings can minimize the effects of the random errors.

The second difficulty involves a *systematic error* because the excess heat in urban areas always causes the temperature reading to be higher than it would be otherwise. By studying and understanding this systematic error, researchers can correct the temperature data for this problem. **Now try Exercises 35–42.**

BY THE WAY

Between census years, the U.S. Census Bureau *estimates* population based on statistical data for the birth rate, death rate, and immigration rate. The Bureau estimates that the U.S. population reached 300 million in late 2006 and is growing at a rate of 1 person every 11 seconds, or nearly 3 million people per year.

U.S. population
(in millions)

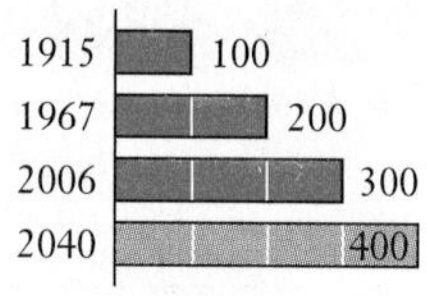

Example 4 The Census

The Constitution of the United States mandates a census of the population every 10 years. The United States Census Bureau conducts the census by distributing household surveys through the mail or through personal visits. Suggest several sources of both random and systematic error in the census.

Solution The surveys are useful if they are properly filled out and recorded. However, some people make errors when they complete the surveys, and Census Bureau employees may make errors when they enter the data into their computers. These kinds of errors are random errors because too few or too many people may end up being counted for any individual household.

Systematic errors arise from problems in the surveying process. For example, it is very difficult to deliver surveys to the homeless, and it is difficult to count undocumented aliens, who may be reluctant to reveal their presence in the United States. The homeless and undocumented aliens therefore tend to be systematically undercounted. Other systematic errors lead to overcounts. For example, college students often get counted both by their parents and in the households where they reside at school, and children of divorced parents are sometimes counted in both parents' households.

Although there is no way to determine the overall effects of random errors, statistical studies can estimate the effects of systematic errors. For example, the 2000 census originally counted about 281.4 million people. However, follow-up statistical studies suggested that the surveys had missed about 7.6 million people and counted 4.3 million people twice. Overall, then, the census undercounted the population by more than 3 million people. **Now try Exercises 43–46.**

Time Out to Think

The question of whether the Census Bureau should be allowed to adjust its "official" count on the basis of statistical surveys is very controversial. The Constitution calls for an "actual enumeration" of the population (Article 1, Section 2, Subsection 2). Do you believe this wording precludes or allows the use of statistical surveys in the official count? Defend your opinion. Also discuss reasons why Democrats tend to favor the use of sampling methods while Republicans tend to oppose it.

Size of Errors: Absolute versus Relative

Besides wanting to know whether an error is random or systematic, we often want to know something about the overall size of the error. For example, is the error big enough to be of concern or small enough to be unimportant? Let's explore the concept of error size.

Suppose you go to the store and ask for 6 pounds of hamburger. However, because the store's scale is poorly calibrated, you actually get only 4 pounds. You'd probably be upset by this 2-pound error. Now suppose you buy a car which the owner's manual says weighs 3132 pounds, but you find that it really weighs 3130 pounds. The error is the same 2 pounds as before, but this error probably doesn't seem very important for the car. This simple example shows that the importance of an error can depend on how you look at it.

In more technical language, the 2-pound error in both the hamburger weight and the car weight is an **absolute error**—it describes how far the measured value (or the claimed value, in the case of the car) lies from the true value. A **relative error** compares the size of an absolute error to the true value. The relative error for the hamburger is fairly large because the absolute error of 2 pounds is half the true weight of 4 pounds. Thus, the relative error for the hamburger is 2/4, or 50%. In contrast, the relative error for the car is quite small, because 2 pounds is very small in comparison to the car's true weight of 3130 pounds. Here, the relative error is 2/3130, which is about 0.0006, or 0.06%. Note the similarity between the ideas of absolute and relative error and those of absolute and relative change or difference (see Unit 3A).

Take Note

Notice that when someone *claims* a value—such as when the owner's manual claims that the car weighs 3132 pounds—we treat the claimed value as the *measured* value in these formulas. The true value is always the actual value, which we may or may not know; that is, it is the value that we would find if a *perfect* measurement were possible.

ABSOLUTE AND RELATIVE ERROR

The **absolute error** describes how far a measured (or claimed) value lies from the true value:

$$\text{absolute error} = \text{measured value} - \text{true value}$$

The **relative error** compares the size of the error to the true value:

$$\text{relative error} = \frac{\text{absolute error}}{\text{true value}} = \frac{\text{measured value} - \text{true value}}{\text{true value}}$$

The absolute and relative errors are *positive* when the measured or claimed value is greater than the true value and *negative* when the measured or claimed value is less than the true value. Note that the above formula gives the relative error as a fraction, which can be converted to a percentage.

Example 5 Absolute and Relative Error

Find the absolute and relative error in each case.

a. Your true weight is 125 pounds, but a scale says you weigh 130 pounds.
b. The government claims that a program costs $49.0 billion, but an audit shows that the true cost is $50.0 billion.

Solution

a. The measured value is the scale reading of 130 pounds, and the true value is your true weight of 125 pounds. The absolute and relative errors are

$$\begin{aligned}\text{absolute error} &= \text{measured value} - \text{true value}\\ &= 130\text{ lb} - 125\text{ lb}\\ &= 5\text{ lb}\end{aligned}$$

$$\text{relative error} = \frac{\text{absolute error}}{\text{true value}} = \frac{5\text{ lb}}{125\text{ lb}} = 0.04 = 4\%$$

The measured weight is too high by 5 pounds, or 4%.

b. We treat the claimed cost of $49.0 billion as the measured value. The true value is the true cost of $50.0 billion. The absolute and relative errors are

$$\begin{aligned}\text{absolute error} &= \$49.0\text{ billion} - \$50.0\text{ billion}\\ &= -\$1.0\text{ billion}\end{aligned}$$

$$\begin{aligned}\text{relative error} &= \frac{\$49.0\text{ billion} - \$50.0\text{ billion}}{\$50.0\text{ billion}}\\ &= -0.02 = -2\%\end{aligned}$$

The claimed cost is too low by $1.0 billion, or 2%. **Now try Exercises 47–54.**

And now for some temperatures around the nation: 58, 72, 85, 49, 77.

—George Carlin, comedian

DILBERT reprinted by permission of United Feature Syndicate, Inc.

BY THE WAY

In 1999, NASA lost the $160 million *Mars Climate Orbiter* when engineers sent it very precise computer instructions in English units (pounds) and the spacecraft software interpreted them in metric units (kilograms). In other words, the loss occurred because the very precise instructions were actually quite inaccurate!

Describing Results: Accuracy and Precision

Once a measurement is reported, we should evaluate it to see whether it is believable in light of any potential errors. In particular, we should consider two key ideas about any reported value: its *accuracy* and its *precision*. The terms are often used interchangeably in English, but mathematically they are different.

The goal of any measurement is to obtain a value that is as close as possible to the *true value*. The closer the measured value lies to the true value, the greater is the **accuracy** of the measurement. If a census says that the population of your home town is 72,453 but the true population is 96,000, then the census report is not very accurate. In contrast, if a company projects sales of $7.30 billion and true sales turn out to be $7.32 billion, we would say that projection is quite accurate.

The **precision** of a number describes the amount of detail in a measurement. That is, it describes how *precisely* a number is measured. For example, a distance given as 2.345 kilometers is more precise than a distance given as 2.3 kilometers, because the first number gives detail to the nearest 0.001 kilometer while the second number gives detail only to the nearest 0.1 kilometer. Similarly, an income of $45,678.90 has greater precision than one of $46,000, because the first income is precise to the nearest penny whereas the second income is precise only to the nearest thousand dollars.

DEFINITIONS

Accuracy describes how closely a measurement approximates a true value. An accurate measurement is very close to the true value.

Precision describes the amount of detail in a measurement.

Example 6 Accuracy and Precision in Your Weight

Suppose your true weight is 102.4 pounds. The scale at the doctor's office, which can be read only to the nearest quarter pound, says that you weigh $102\frac{1}{4}$ pounds. The scale at the gym, which gives a digital readout to the nearest 0.1 pound, says that you weigh 100.7 pounds. Which scale is more *precise?* Which is more *accurate?*

Solution The scale at the gym is more *precise,* because it gives your weight to the nearest tenth of a pound while the doctor's scale gives your weight only to the nearest quarter pound. However, the scale at the doctor's office is more *accurate,* because its value is closer to your true weight. **Now try Exercises 55–58.**

Time Out to Think

In Example 6, we needed to know your *true* weight in order to determine which scale was more accurate. But how would we know your true weight? Can we ever be *sure* that we know your true weight? Explain.

Case Study Does the Census Measure the True Population?

Upon completing the 2000 census, the U.S. Census Bureau reported a population of 281,421,906 (on April 1, 2000), thereby implying an exact count of everyone living in the United States. Unfortunately, such a precise count could not possibly be accurate.

Even in principle, the only way to get an exact count of the number of people living in the United States would be to count everyone *instantaneously.* Otherwise, the count would be off because the number of people changes very rapidly. An average of about eight births and four deaths occur every minute in the United States, and a new immigrant enters the United States about every three minutes on average. Moreover, random and systematic errors can easily make the census inaccurate by a few million people (see Example 4).

In reality, the Census Bureau did *not* know the exact population and only found an estimate of the population to within a few million people. Given these facts, it is dishonest to report the population as an exact count. A more honest report would use much less precision—for example, stating the population as "about 280 million." In fairness to the Census Bureau, their detailed reports explained the uncertainties in the population count, but these uncertainties were rarely mentioned by the press.

Time Out to Think

The 2010 census should be under way or completed by the time you read this book. How are the census results being reported? Is the official result precise? Do you think it is accurate? Explain.

Summary: Dealing with Errors

Let's briefly summarize what we have discussed about measurement and errors.

Mistakes are the portals of discovery.

—James Joyce

- Errors can occur in many ways, but generally can be classified as one of two basic types: random errors or systematic errors.
- Whatever the source of an error, its size can be described in two different ways: as an absolute error or as a relative error.
- Once a measurement is reported, we can evaluate it in terms of its accuracy and its precision.

Combining Measured Numbers

Suppose you live in a city with a population of 300,000. One day, your best friend moves to your city to share an apartment with you. What is the population of your city now?

You might be tempted to add your friend to the city's population, making the new population 300,001. However, the number 300,000 has only 1 significant digit, implying that the population is known only to the nearest 100,000 people. The number 300,001 has 6 significant digits, which implies that you know the population *exactly.*

USING TECHNOLOGY

Rounding in Excel

You can specify the precision to which numbers are rounded in Excel. On the "Format" menu, choose "cells." You will then see an option to format numbers in the cell, which allows you to choose how many decimal places are displayed.

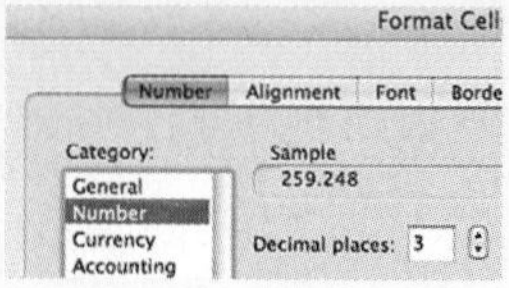

Clearly, your friend's move cannot change the fact that the population is known only to the nearest 100,000. The population is still 300,000, despite the addition of your friend.

As this example illustrates, we must be very careful when we combine measured numbers. Otherwise, we may state answers with more certainty than they deserve. In scientific or statistical work, researchers conduct careful analyses to determine how to combine numbers properly. For most purposes, however, we can use two simple rounding rules.

COMBINING MEASURED NUMBERS

Rounding rule for addition or subtraction: Round your answer to the same precision as the *least precise* number in the problem.

Rounding rule for multiplication or division: Round your answer to the same number of *significant digits* as the measurement with the *fewest significant digits*.

Note: To avoid errors, you should do the rounding only after completing all the operations, not during intermediate steps.

Remember that these rounding rules tell you the *most* precision that can be justified. In many cases, the justified precision may actually be less than these rules imply.

Example 7 Combining Measured Numbers

a. A book written in 1962 states that the oldest Mayan ruins are 2000 years old. How old are they now?

b. The government in a town of 82,000 people plans to spend $41.5 million this year. Assuming all this money must come from taxes, what average amount must the city collect from each resident?

Solution

a. A book written in 1962 is almost 50 years old, so we might be tempted to add 50 years to 2000 years to get 2050 years for the age of the ruins. However, 2000 years is the less precise of the two numbers: It is precise only to the nearest 1000 years, while 50 years is precise to the nearest 10 years. Therefore, the answer also should be precise only to the nearest 1000 years:

$$\underbrace{2000\text{ yr}}_{\text{precise to nearest 1000}} + \underbrace{50\text{ yr}}_{\text{precise to nearest 10}} = \underbrace{2050\text{ yr}}_{\text{must round to nearest 1000}} \approx \underbrace{2000\text{ yr}}_{\text{correct final answer}}$$

To the precision with which we know the age of the ruins, they are still 2000 years old, despite the 50-year age of the book.

b. We find the average tax by dividing the $41.5 million, which has 3 significant digits, by the population of 82,000, which has 2 significant digits. The population has the fewest significant digits, so the answer should be rounded to match it, with 2 significant digits.

$$\underbrace{\$41{,}500{,}000}_{\text{3 significant digits}} \div \underbrace{82{,}000\text{ persons}}_{\text{2 significant digits}} = \underbrace{\$506.10\text{ per person}}_{\text{must round to 2 significant digits}} \approx \underbrace{\$510\text{ per person}}_{\text{correct final answer}}$$

The average resident must pay about $510 in taxes. **Now try Exercises 59–66.**

QUICK QUIZ

Choose the best answer to each of the following questions. Explain your reasoning with one or more complete sentences.

1. The $5.6 trillion surplus that government economists had projected in 2001 never materialized because the people who made this projection

   a. didn't really understand how the government budget works.

   b. based it on assumptions about the future economy that turned out to be untrue.

   c. made basic errors in their calculations.

2. Under the standard rules for counting significant digits, which of the following numbers has the *most* significant digits?

   a. 5.0×10^{-1} b. 5×10^{3} c. 500,000

3. Under the standard rules for counting significant digits, which of the following numbers has the *most* significant digits?

   a. 1.02 b. 1.020 c. 0.000020

4. You are trying to measure the outside temperature at a particular time. You are likely to get better results if you average readings on three different thermometers rather than using just a single thermometer, because the averaging will

   a. reduce the effects of any random errors.

   b. eliminate the effects of systematic errors.

   c. increase the precision of your measurements.

5. You are trying to measure the outside temperature at a particular time. If you use three thermometers and place all three in direct sunlight, the sunlight is likely to cause your measurements to suffer from

   a. random errors.

   b. systematic errors.

   c. a decrease in precision.

6. A testing service makes an error that causes the SAT scores for several thousand students all to be too low by 50 points. This is an example of

   a. poor precision.

   b. scores being affected by random errors.

   c. scores being affected by a systematic error.

7. A testing service makes an error that causes the SAT scores for several thousand students all to be too low by 50 points. Which statement is true?

   a. All the scores had the same relative error, but the absolute errors varied.

   b. All the scores had the same absolute error, but the relative errors varied.

   c. Both the absolute and relative errors were the same in all cases.

8. A digital scale shows that you weigh 112.7 pounds, but you actually weigh 146 pounds. Which statement is true?

   a. The scale was fairly precise but not very accurate.

   b. The scale was fairly accurate but not very precise.

   c. The scale had a small absolute error but a large relative error.

9. At a particular moment, the U.S. National Debt Clock says that the federal debt is $11,952,496,384.69. This reading is

   a. very precise but not necessarily accurate.

   b. very accurate but not necessarily precise.

   c. both very precise and very accurate.

10. Your car gets 29 miles per gallon and has a gas tank that can hold 10.0 gallons of gas. According to the standard rules for combining measured numbers, the distance this car can go on a full tank of gas is

    a. 290 miles.

    b. 290.0 miles.

    c. 300 miles.

Exercises 3C

REVIEW QUESTIONS

1. What are significant digits? How can you tell whether zeros are significant?
2. Distinguish between random errors and systematic errors. Give an example of how each type might affect measurements of weight. How can we minimize the effects of random errors? How can we account for the effects of a systematic error?
3. Distinguish between the absolute error and the relative error in a measurement. Give an example in which the absolute error is large but the relative error is small and another example in which the absolute error is small but the relative error is large.
4. Distinguish between accuracy and precision. Give an example of a measurement that is precise but inaccurate and another example of a measurement that is accurate but imprecise.
5. Why can it be misleading to give measurements with more precision than is justified by the measurement process?
6. State the rounding rules for adding and subtracting measured numbers and for multiplying and dividing measured numbers. Give examples of their use.

DOES IT MAKE SENSE?

Decide whether each of the following statements makes sense (or is clearly true) or does not make sense (or is clearly false). Explain your reasoning.

7. Next year's federal deficit will be $675.734 billion.
8. In many developing nations, official estimates of the population may be off by 10% or more.
9. I weigh 110.3627 pounds.
10. The 2009 presidential inauguration brought 1.822 million people to the National Mall.
11. Wilma used a yard stick to measure the length of her kitchen to the nearest micrometer.
12. More precision is useless if the measurement is inaccurate.
13. A $1 million error may sound like a lot, but when compared to our company's revenue it represents a relative error of only 0.1%.
14. Once we corrected the measurements for all known systematic errors, we were sure that our results had perfect accuracy.

BASIC SKILLS & CONCEPTS

15–16: Review of Rounding. In the following exercises, use the skills covered in the Brief Review on p. 162.

15. Round the following numbers to the nearest whole number.

a. 3.45	b. 87.737	c. 0.12
d. 184.73	e. 1945.1	f. 2.5001
g. 6.495	h. 1499.5	i. −13.6

16. Round the following numbers to the nearest tenth and nearest ten.

a. 567.52	b. 23.49	c. 34.5001
d. 123.4567	e. −34.8	f. 45.499
g. −76.34	h. 32.5	i. 0.012

17–28: Counting Significant Digits. State the number of significant digits and the implied precision of the following numbers.

17. 2454 dollars per acre
18. 90.001 miles per hour
19. 90 miles per hour
20. 0.01 centimeter
21. 3.32234 miles
22. 450,000 years
23. 1.2×10^4 seconds
24. 0.000203 meter
25. 154.1234 pounds
26. 0.00001 liter
27. 134.3 kilometers per second
28. 2.123×10^{12} kilograms

29–34: Rounding with Significant Digits. Carry out the indicated operations and give your answer with the specified number of significant digits.

29. 45×32.1; 3 significant digits
30. 45×32.1; 5 significant digits
31. $231.89 \div 0.034$; 2 significant digits
32. $231.89 \div 0.034$; 4 significant digits
33. $(2.3 \times 10^5) \times (7.963 \times 10^{-3})$; 6 significant digits
34. $(6.667 \times 10^3) \times (8.9421 \times 10^{-2})$; 4 significant digits

35–42: Sources of Error. Describe possible sources of random and systematic errors in the following measurements.

35. A count of every different meadowlark that visits a three-acre region over a 2-hour period
36. The population of a Michigan town obtained by a census count
37. Weights of 25 adult women obtained by asking each woman her weight
38. Running times at a 10-kilometer race
39. Weight of a can of spaghetti sauce with a labeled weight of 28 ounces
40. Number of M&Ms® in a 1-pound bag
41. The high temperature of the day in Tucson measured by an outdoor thermometer
42. The number of votes cast for two candidates in a U.S. Senate race
43. **Tax Audit.** A tax auditor reviewing a tax return looks for several kinds of problems, including (1) mistakes made in entering or calculating numbers on the tax return and (2) places where the taxpayer reported income dishonestly. Discuss whether each problem involves random or systematic errors.
44. **AIDS Epidemic.** Researchers studying the progression of the AIDS epidemic need to know how many people are suffering from AIDS, which they try to determine by studying medical records. Two of the many problems they face in this research are that (1) some people who are suffering from AIDS are misdiagnosed as having other diseases, and vice versa, and (2) some people with AIDS never seek medical help and therefore do not have medical records. Discuss whether each problem involves random or systematic errors.
45. **Safe Air Travel.** Before taking off, a pilot is supposed to set the aircraft altimeter to the elevation of the airport. A pilot leaves Denver (altitude 5280 ft) with her altimeter set to 2500 feet. Explain how this affects the altimeter readings throughout the flight. What kind of error is this?
46. **Cutting Lumber.** A lumber yard employee cuts 30 three-foot boards by measuring a three-foot length and then making a cut (30 times). Later, careful measurements show that all of the boards are either slightly more than or less than 37 inches in length. What kind of measurement errors are involved in this case?

47–54: Absolute and Relative Errors. Find the absolute and relative errors in the following situations.

47. Your true height is 68.0 inches (5'8"), but a nurse in your doctor's office measures your height as 67.5 inches.
48. The label on a bag of dog food says "30 pounds," but the true weight is only 29 pounds.
49. Your speedometer reads 60 miles per hour when you are actually traveling 58 miles per hour.

50. An order of fish and chips is supposed to cost $8.95, but the server accidentally keys in a price of $9.95.

51. Your homemade pasta sauce recipe calls for 5 ounces of olive oil. You mistakenly use $4\frac{3}{4}$ ounces.

52. The actual distance to Paradise is 13.34 miles, but your odometer reads 13.0 miles.

53. The diameter of a gear must be 24.5 centimeters in order for it to fit in a transmission. Instead, it is manufactured with a diameter of 24.65 centimeters.

54. The vote count in a precinct is 2563. It is later discovered that two voters were double counted.

55–58: **Accuracy and Precision.** For each pair of measurements, state which one is more accurate and which one is more precise.

55. Your true height is 70.50 inches. A tape measure that can be read to the nearest $\frac{1}{8}$ inch gives your height as $70\frac{3}{8}$ inches. A new laser device at the doctor's office that gives readings to the nearest 0.05 inch gives your height as 70.90 inches.

56. Your true height is 62.50 inches. A tape measure that can be read to the nearest $\frac{1}{8}$ inch gives your height as $62\frac{5}{8}$ inches. A new laser device at the doctor's office that gives readings to the nearest 0.05 inch gives your height as 62.50 inches.

57. Your weight is 52.55 kilograms. A scale at a health clinic that gives weight measurements to the nearest half kilogram gives your weight as 53 kilograms. A digital scale at the gym that gives readings to the nearest 0.01 kilogram gives your weight as 52.88 kilograms.

58. Your weight is 52.55 kilograms. A scale at a health clinic that gives weight measurements to the nearest half kilogram gives your weight as $52\frac{1}{2}$ kilograms. A digital scale at the gym that gives readings to the nearest 0.01 kilogram gives your weight as 51.48 kilograms.

59–66: **Combining Numbers.** Use the appropriate rounding rules to do the following calculations. Express the result with the correct precision or correct number of significant digits.

59. Subtract 0.1 pound from 12 pounds to find the weight of your chihuahua before he ate dinner.

60. Multiply 43 miles per hour by 0.25 hour.

61. Divide 102 miles by 0.65 hour.

62. Each of 60,000 households in a city pays an average of $445.79 in property taxes. What is the total tax revenue?

63. As you drive down the freeway, a sign tells you that it is 36 miles to city hall. Your destination lies 2.2 miles beyond city hall. How much farther do you have to drive?

64. At the hardware store, you buy a 50-kilogram bag of sand. You also buy 1.25 kilograms of nails. What is the total weight of your purchases?

65. What is the per capita cost of a $2.1 million recreation center in a city with 120,345 people?

66. You buy 450 pounds of sand for $21.43 (not including tax). What is the price of the sand per pound?

FURTHER APPLICATIONS

67–74: **Believable Facts?** Discuss possible sources of error in the following measurements. Then state whether you think the measurement is believable, given the precision with which it is stated.

67. In 2007, 5,253,350 domestic cars and 2,365,063 imported cars were sold in the United States.

68. John McCain and Sarah Palin received 55,729,124 votes in the 2008 presidential election.

69. The tallest building in the world is Burj Dubai in the United Arab Emirates, with a height of 818 meters (2683 feet).

70. The most common last name in the U.S. population is *Smith*, which is the last name of 0.881% of the population.

71. The Caspian Sea (considered the largest lake on Earth) has an area of 143,244 square miles.

72. The population of the United States in 1920 was 106,021,568.

73. The May 2008 earthquake in Sichuan province, China, killed 69,227 people.

74. The U.S. magazine with the greatest number of paid subscriptions is *AARP The Magazine*, with a circulation of 24,444,293.

75. **Propagation of Error.** Suppose you want to cut 20 identical boards of length 4 feet. The procedure is to measure and cut the first board, then use the first board to measure and cut the second board, then use the second board to measure and cut the third board, and so on.

a. What are the possible lengths of the 20th board, if each time you cut a board there is a maximum error of $\pm\frac{1}{4}$ inch?

b. What are the possible lengths of the 20th board, if each time you cut a board there is a maximum error of ±0.5%?

WEB PROJECTS

76. **The 2010 Census.** Learn about the 2010 census on the U.S. Census Bureau Web site. Choose one issue relating to the census that involves accuracy or precision. Write a short report about the issue, and discuss whether you think the Census Bureau handled it well.

77. **Global Warming.** Find current estimates regarding how much Earth has warmed over the past century and how much human activity contributes to that warming. Based on what you learn, write a one- to two-page essay about how scientists account for uncertainties in past temperature data.

IN YOUR WORLD

78. **Random and Systematic Errors.** Find a recent news report that gives a measured quantity (for example, a report of population, average income, or the number of homeless people). Write a short description of how the quantity was measured, and describe any likely sources of either random or systematic errors. Overall, do you think that the reported measurement was accurate?

79. **Absolute and Relative Errors.** Find a recent news report that describes some mistake in a measured, estimated, or projected number (for example, a budget projection that turned out to be incorrect). In words, describe the size of the error in terms of both absolute error and relative error.

80. **Accuracy and Precision.** Find a recent news article that causes you to question accuracy or precision. For example, the article might report a figure with more precision than you think is justified, or it may cite a figure that you know is inaccurate. Write a short summary of the report and explain why you question its accuracy or precision.

81. **Uncertainty in the News.** Look for news articles from the past week to find at least two numbers from each of the following: national/international news, local news, sports news, and business news. In each case, describe the number and its context, and discuss any uncertainty that you think is associated with the number.

82. **Real-World Rounding.** Find at least three different examples of numbers that were rounded in news stories. Explain how and why each number was rounded. (*Hint:* You might consider baseball batting averages, times in athletic events, or the stock market.)

UNIT 3D Index Numbers: The CPI and Beyond

If you follow economic news, you've probably heard about **index numbers** such as the Consumer Price Index, the Producer Price Index, and the Consumer Confidence Index. Index numbers are common because they provide a simple way to compare measurements made at different times or in different places. In this unit, we'll investigate the meaning and use of index numbers. We'll focus special attention on the Consumer Price Index (CPI), because it plays such an important role in modern economics.

What Is an Index Number?

Let's start with an example using gasoline prices. Table 3.2 shows the average prices of gasoline in the United States every 10 years from 1955 to 2005. Suppose that, instead of the prices themselves, we want to find out how the price of gasoline in different years compared to the 1975 price. One way to do this would be to express each year's price as a percentage of the 1975 price. For example, by dividing the 1965 price by the 1975 price, we find that the 1965 price was 55.0% of the 1975 price:

$$\frac{1965\text{ price}}{1975\text{ price}} = \frac{31.2¢}{56.7¢} = 0.550 = 55.0\%$$

BY THE WAY

The gas prices in Table 3.2 are year-long averages that do not show how much the prices varied. During 2005, for example, gas prices peaked shortly after Hurricane Katrina at a high of $3.13 per gallon.

Proceeding similarly for the other years, we can calculate all the prices as percentages of the 1975 price. The third column of Table 3.2 shows the results. Note that the percentage for 1975 is 100%, because we chose the 1975 price as the reference value.

TABLE 3.2 Average Gasoline Prices (per gallon)

Year	Price	Price as a Percentage of 1975 Price	Price Index (1975 = 100)
1955	29.1¢	51.3%	51.3
1965	31.2¢	55.0%	55.0
1975	56.7¢	100.0%	100.0
1985	119.6¢	210.9%	210.9
1995	120.5¢	212.5%	212.5
2005	231.0¢	407.4%	407.4

Source: U.S. Department of Energy.

Now look at the last column of Table 3.2. It is identical to the third column, except we dropped the % signs. This simple change converts the numbers from percentages to a *price index*, which is one type of index number. The statement "1975 = 100" in the column heading shows that the reference value is the 1975 price. In this case, there's really no difference between stating the comparison in terms of percentages and in terms of index numbers—it's a matter of choice and convenience. However, as we'll see shortly, it's traditional to use index numbers rather than percentages in cases where many factors are considered simultaneously.

INDEX NUMBERS

An **index number** provides a simple way to compare measurements made at different times or in different places. The value at one particular time (or place) must be chosen as the *reference value*. The index number for any other time (or place) is

$$\text{index number} = \frac{\text{value}}{\text{reference value}} \times 100$$

Example 1 Finding an Index Number

During 2008, the average gasoline price reached a record high of \$4.10 per gallon. Using the 1975 price as the reference value, find the price index number for gasoline at \$4.10 per gallon.

Solution Table 3.2 shows that the price of gas was 56.7¢, or \$0.567, per gallon in 1975. If we use the 1975 price as the reference value, the index number for the 2008 record price is

$$\frac{\text{2008 price}}{\text{1975 price}} \times 100 = \frac{\$4.10}{\$0.567} \times 100 = 723.1$$

The index number for gasoline at the 2008 record price is 723.1, meaning that the price was 723.1% of the 1975 price. **Now try Exercises 11–12.**

Time Out to Think

What is the price of gasoline today? What is the gasoline price index for today's price, with the 1975 price as the reference value?

Making Comparisons with Index Numbers

The primary purpose of index numbers is to facilitate comparisons. For example, suppose we want to know how much more expensive gas was in 2005 than in 1975. We can get the answer easily from Table 3.2, which uses the 1975 price as the reference value. This table shows that the price index for 2005 was 407.4, which means that the price of gasoline in 2005 was 407.4% of the 1975 price. Equivalently, we can say that the 2005 price was 4.074 times the 1975 price.

We can also do comparisons when neither value is the reference value. For example, suppose we want to know how much more expensive gas was in 1995 than in 1965. We find the answer by dividing the index numbers for the two years:

$$\frac{\text{index number for 1995}}{\text{index number for 1965}} = \frac{212.5}{55.0} = 3.86$$

That is, the 1995 price was 3.86 times the 1965 price, or 386% of the 1965 price. The same amount of gas that cost \$1.00 in 1965 would have cost \$3.86 in 1995.

Example 2 Using the Gas Price Index

Use Table 3.2 to answer the following questions:

a. Suppose it cost \$7.00 to fill a gas tank in 1975. How much would it have cost to fill the same tank in 2005?
b. Suppose it cost \$20.00 to fill a gas tank in 1995. How much would it have cost to fill the same tank in 1955?

Solution

a. Table 3.2 shows that the price index for 2005 was 407.4, which means that the price of gasoline in 2005 was 407.4% of the 1975 price. Therefore, the 2005 price of gas that cost \$7.00 in 1975 would have been

$$407.4\% \times \$7.00 = 4.074 \times \$7.00 = \$28.52$$

b. Table 3.2 shows that the price index for 1995 was 212.5 and the index for 1955 was 51.3. Therefore, the cost of gasoline in 1955 compared to the cost in 1995 was

$$\frac{\text{index number for 1955}}{\text{index number for 1995}} = \frac{51.3}{212.5} = 0.2414$$

A tank of gas that cost \$20.00 in 1995 would have cost only $0.2414 \times \$20.00 =$ \$4.83 in 1955. **Now try Exercises 13–14.**

Changing the Reference Value

There's no particular reason why we chose the 1975 price as the reference value in Table 3.2, and it is easy to recast the table with a different reference value. For example, let's compute the gasoline price index with the 1985 price as the reference value.

The first two columns of the table do not change because they give actual years and prices of gasoline. But this time, the reference value is the 1985 price of 119.6¢. We use this value to find the index numbers for the other years. For example, the index number for the 1955 price of 29.1¢ is

$$\frac{\text{1955 price}}{\text{1985 price}} \times 100 = \frac{29.1¢}{119.6¢} \times 100 = 24.3$$

As we should expect, the index number is *not* the same as it was when we used 1975 as the reference year. Table 3.3 shows the index numbers with both 1975 and 1985 as the reference year. Both sets of numbers are equally valid, but meaningful only when we know the reference value. Thus, including the reference year is crucial.

TABLE 3.3 The Gasoline Price Index with Two Different Reference Years

Year	Price	Price Index (1975 = 100)	Price Index (1985 = 100)
1955	29.1¢	51.3	24.3
1965	31.2¢	55.0	26.1
1975	56.7¢	100.0	47.4
1985	119.6¢	210.9	100.0
1995	120.5¢	212.5	100.8
2005	231.0¢	407.4	193.1

Time Out to Think

For practice in finding index numbers, use the index number formula to confirm the rest of the values in the last column of Table 3.3.

Example 3 1985 Index

Consider the 2008 record gasoline price of $4.10 per gallon. Using the 1985 price as the reference value, find its price index number. Compare this number to the answer in Example 1, where 1975 was the reference year.

Solution Table 3.3 shows that the price of gas was 119.6¢, or $1.196, per gallon in 1985. With the 1985 price as the reference value, the index number for the 2008 record price is

$$\frac{\text{2008 price}}{\text{1985 price}} \times 100 = \frac{\$4.10}{\$1.196} \times 100 = 342.8$$

As we should expect, this index number is different from the value of 723.1 found in Example 1, where we used 1975 as the index year. Both numbers are valid, but meaningful only when we know the reference value. Specifically, the 1985 index number tells us that the 2008 record price was 342.8% of the 1985 price, while the 1975 index number tells us that it was 723.1% of the 1975 price. **Now try Exercises 15–16.**

The Consumer Price Index

We've seen that the price of gas has risen substantially with time. Most other prices and wages have also risen, a phenomenon we call **inflation.** (Prices and wages occasionally decline with time, which is *deflation.*) Changes in actual prices therefore are not very meaningful unless we compare them to the overall rate of inflation, which is measured by the **Consumer Price Index (CPI).**

The Consumer Price Index is computed and reported monthly by the U.S. Bureau of Labor Statistics. It represents an average of prices for a sample of goods, services, and housing. The monthly sample consists of more than 60,000 items. The details of the data collection and index calculation are fairly complex, but the CPI itself is a simple index number. Table 3.4 shows the average annual CPI over a 33-year period. Currently, the reference value for the CPI is an average of prices during the period 1982–1984, which is why the table says "1982–1984 = 100."

THE CONSUMER PRICE INDEX

The **Consumer Price Index (CPI)** is based on an average of prices for a sample of more than 60,000 goods, services, and housing costs. It is computed and reported monthly.

TABLE 3.4 Average Annual Consumer Price Index (1982–1984 = 100)

Year	CPI	Year	CPI	Year	CPI
1976	56.9	1987	113.6	1998	163.0
1977	60.6	1988	118.3	1999	166.6
1978	65.2	1989	124.0	2000	172.2
1979	72.6	1990	130.7	2001	177.1
1980	82.4	1991	136.2	2002	179.9
1981	90.9	1992	140.3	2003	184.0
1982	96.5	1993	144.5	2004	188.9
1983	99.6	1994	148.2	2005	195.3
1984	103.9	1995	152.4	2006	201.6
1985	107.6	1996	156.9	2007	207.3
1986	109.6	1997	160.5	2008	215.3

Take Note

The government measures two consumer price indices. The *CPI-U* is based on products thought to reflect the purchasing habits of all urban consumers. The *CPI-W* is based on the purchasing habits of only wage earners. (Table 3.4 shows the CPI-U.)

The CPI allows us to see how prices have changed with time. For example, to find out how much higher typical prices were in 2005 than in 1995, we compute the ratio of the CPIs for the two years, using the shorthand CPI_{2005} to represent the CPI for 2005 (and similar notation for other years):

$$\frac{CPI_{2005}}{CPI_{1995}} = \frac{195.3}{152.4} = 1.28$$

Based on the CPI, typical prices in 2005 were 1.28 times those in 1995, or 28% higher. For example, a typical item that cost \$1.00 in 1995 would have cost \$1.28 in 2005.

BY THE WAY

The FutureGen project, designed to demonstrate a zero-emission coal-burning power plant, was canceled in 2008 when the Energy Department claimed its projected cost had doubled. In 2009, auditors discovered that this claim did not account for inflation over the project's development period, and the real budget increase was only 39%. As one auditor put it, the cancellation was based on "fundamental budget math errors." The project was then revived.

Example 4 CPI Changes

Suppose you needed \$30,000 to maintain a particular standard of living in 2000. How much would you have needed in 2008 to maintain the same standard of living? Assume that the average price of your typical purchases has risen at the same rate as the Consumer Price Index (CPI).

Solution We compare prices for two different years by comparing the CPIs for those years:

$$\frac{CPI_{2008}}{CPI_{2000}} = \frac{215.3}{172.2} = 1.250$$

That is, typical prices in 2008 were 1.25 times those in 2000. If you needed \$30,000 for your standard of living in 2000, then in 2008 you would have needed $1.25 \times \$30,000 = \$37,500$ for the same standard of living. **Now try Exercises 17–18.**

The Rate of Inflation

The **rate of inflation** refers to the relative change in the CPI from one year to the next. For example, the inflation rate from 1980 to 1981 was the relative increase in the CPI between those two years:

$$\text{inflation rate 1980 to 1981} = \frac{CPI_{1981} - CPI_{1980}}{CPI_{1980}} = \frac{90.9 - 82.4}{82.4} = 0.103 = 10.3\%$$

As measured by the CPI, the rate of inflation from 1980 to 1981 was 10.3%.

> **THE RATE OF INFLATION**
>
> The **rate of inflation** from one year to the next is usually defined as the relative change in the Consumer Price Index.

Example 5 Inflation Comparison

Find the inflation rate from 2007 to 2008. How does it compare to the inflation rate in the late 1970s?

Solution The inflation rate from 2007 to 2008 was

$$\frac{CPI_{2008} - CPI_{2007}}{CPI_{2007}} = \frac{215.3 - 207.3}{207.3} = 0.039 = 3.9\%$$

This rate of 3.9% is much lower than the rate of inflation in the late 1970s.

Now try Exercises 19–20.

If I had to populate an asylum with people certified insane, I'd just pick 'em from all those who claim to understand inflation.

—Will Rogers

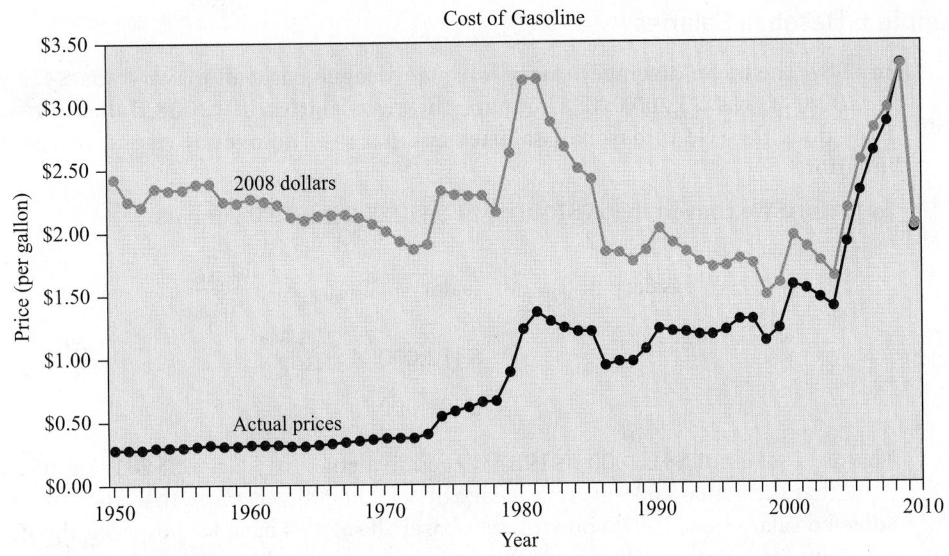

FIGURE 3.3 Gasoline prices, 1950–2009. Note that, because we use 2008 dollars for the adjusted prices, the actual and adjusted prices are the same for 2008. That is why the two curves converge at 2008. (Note: 2009 value was a mid-year estimate.) *Source:* U.S. Energy Information Administration.

Adjusting Prices for Inflation

During the spring and summer of 2008, a sudden jump in gasoline prices became a hot consumer and political issue. Pump prices peaked at \$4.10 per gallon (U.S. average), and the average price for the entire year came in at \$3.31. Some reporters noted that gas had sold for only \$0.65 in 1978, implying that gas prices had more than quintupled in the 30-year span.

But was the 2008 price really more than five times as high as the price 30 years earlier? For a fair comparison of historical prices, we must take inflation into account. We can see how typical prices in 2008 compared to typical prices in 1978 by finding the ratio of the CPIs for those years:

$$\frac{CPI_{2008}}{CPI_{1978}} = \frac{215.3}{65.2} \approx 3.30$$

Therefore, the 1978 price of \$0.65 per gallon for gasoline was equivalent to a 2008 price of $3.30 \times \$0.65 = \$2.15$ per gallon. In the language of economics, we say that \$0.65 in "1978 dollars" is equivalent to \$2.15 in "2008 dollars." The 2008 average price of \$3.31 per gallon was indeed higher, but it was less than twice as high—*not* more than five times as high. Figure 3.3 shows gasoline prices going back to 1950. Note that, adjusted for inflation, the 2008 peak was barely higher than the previous peak in the early 1980s.

USING TECHNOLOGY

The Inflation Calculator

The U.S. Bureau of Labor Statistics (BLS), which compiles CPI data for the United States, provides an online inflation calculator that allows you to adjust prices for any pair of years. Find it by searching for "inflation calculator" on the BLS Web site.

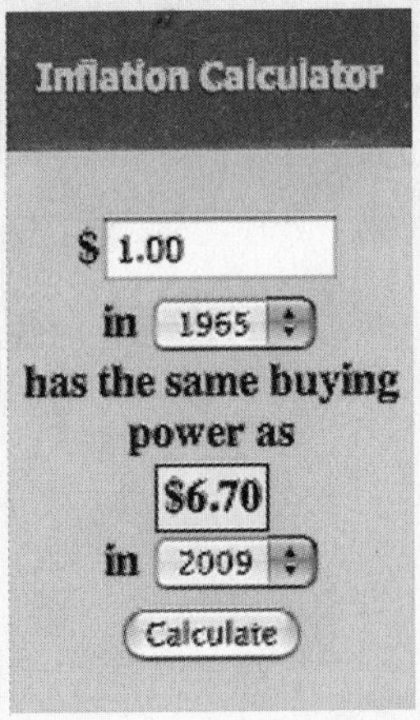

Time Out to Think

Suppose that adjusted prices in Figure 3.3 were adjusted to 1982 dollars rather than 2008 dollars. Where would the two curves cross in that case? Would the general trends look the same or different? Explain.

ADJUSTING PRICES FOR INFLATION

Given a price in dollars for year *X* ($\$_X$), the equivalent price in dollars for year *Y* ($\$_Y$) is

$$\text{price in } \$_Y = (\text{price in } \$_X) \times \frac{CPI_Y}{CPI_X}$$

where *X* and *Y* represent years, such as 1992 and 2008.

BY THE WAY

Salaries of professional athletes were once kept low because the players were not allowed to offer their skills in the free market ("free agency"). That changed after star baseball player Curt Flood filed suit against Major League Baseball in 1970. Flood ultimately lost when the Supreme Court ruled in favor of baseball management in 1972, but the process he set in motion (toward free agency) was unstoppable.

Example 6 Baseball Salaries

In 1987, the mean (average) salary for major league baseball players was \$412,000. In 2008, it was \$3,200,000. Compare the two salaries in "2008 dollars" ($\$_{2008}$). How does the rise in baseball salaries compare to the overall rise in prices with inflation?

Solution We convert the 1987 salary of \$412,000 into 2008 dollars:

$$\begin{aligned}\text{salary in } \$_{2008} &= (\text{salary in } \$_{1987}) \times \frac{\text{CPI}_{2008}}{\text{CPI}_{1987}} \\ &= \$412{,}000 \times \frac{215.3}{113.6} \\ &\approx \$781{,}000\end{aligned}$$

That is, a salary of \$412,000 in 1987 was equivalent to a salary of \$781,000 in 2008. Note that the actual 2008 average salary of \$3,200,000 was more than four times the adjusted salary from 1987, showing that baseball salaries have far outpaced the rate of inflation. More specifically, we say that average baseball salaries more than quadrupled in "real terms" (terms adjusted for inflation) from 1987 to 2008. In other words, the average baseball salary in 2008 has more than four times the buying power of the average baseball salary in 1987.

Now try Exercises 21–22.

Example 7 Computer Prices

According to computer performance tests, a Macintosh computer that cost \$1000 in 2008 had computing power greater than that of a supercomputer that sold for \$30 million in 1985. If computer prices had risen with inflation, how much would the computing power of the 1985 supercomputer have cost in 2008? What does this tell us about the cost of computers?

Solution We convert the 1985 price of \$30 million into 2008 dollars:

$$\begin{aligned}\text{price in } \$_{2008} &= (\text{price in } \$_{1985}) \times \frac{\text{CPI}_{2008}}{\text{CPI}_{1985}} \\ &= \$30 \text{ million} \times \frac{215.3}{107.6} \\ &\approx \$60 \text{ million}\end{aligned}$$

If computer prices had risen with inflation, the computing power of the 1985 supercomputer would have cost \$60 million in 2008. Instead, it cost only \$1000—or about 1/60,000 as much. In real terms, the price of computing power fell by a factor of about 60,000 from 1985 to 2008. In other words, in less than 25 years, computing power that had been affordable only by government agencies and large corporations became cheaper than a typical used car.

Now try Exercises 23–26.

Other Index Numbers

The Consumer Price Index is only one of many index numbers you'll see in news reports. Some are also price indices, such as the Producer Price Index (PPI), which measures the prices that producers (manufacturers) pay for the goods they purchase (rather than the prices that consumers pay). Other indices attempt to measure more qualitative variables. For example, the Consumer Confidence Index is based on a survey designed to measure consumer attitudes so that businesses can gauge whether people are likely to be spending or saving. New indices are created frequently by groups attempting to provide simple comparisons.

Note that the term *index* is also often used for other types of numbers that provide useful comparisons, even when the numbers are not standard index numbers. For example, Body Mass Index (BMI) provides a way of comparing people by height and weight, but it is defined without any reference value. (Specifically, Body Mass Index is defined as weight in kilograms divided by the square of height in meters.)

PRACTICAL MATTERS

Does the CPI Really Measure Inflation?

The Consumer Price Index affects everyone because it plays such a huge role in modern economics. For example:

- Your tax rate depends on the CPI. Each year, the government raises the levels of income at which different income tax rates take effect (*tax brackets*) by the amount that the CPI changes. This annual adjustment is supposed to protect you from the effects of inflation. If the brackets did not change, then people with no change in their living standards would gradually move to higher tax brackets.
- If you receive government payments from Social Security or other programs, your monthly benefits are raised each year to keep up with the CPI. These increases are supposed to make sure that benefits increase enough that recipients can maintain the same standard of living.
- Spending on all government programs, from education to the military, is largely determined by the CPI. Just as maintaining your standard of living requires that you receive pay increases to keep up with inflation, government programs must keep up with inflation if they are to maintain their same level of commitment. Thus, for example, increasing education spending by less than the increase in the CPI is considered a "cut" in real spending. One result is that total spending generally rises each year just to keep up with the CPI, even before decisions about new programs are made.

The CPI also influences how we perceive nearly all economic data. For example, over the past two to three decades, the rise in wages for lower-income people has been less than the rise in the CPI. This is taken to mean that the "real" spending power of lower-income people has decreased—that is, the poor are getting poorer.

But what if the CPI does not really measure the true rate of inflation? In that case, all the decisions and beliefs that are pegged to the CPI could be wrong. In fact, many economists argue that the CPI overstates the true rate of inflation.

The thrust of the argument is that the standard calculation of the CPI contains systematic errors that tend to overstate the increase in the cost of living. One problem is that, from one month to the next, the CPI is based on changes in the prices of particular items at particular stores. However, consumers may not experience an increase in their cost of living if they can find the same item for a lower price at a different store or if they can substitute a similar but lower-priced item. Another problem arises because the CPI tracks prices of items purchased by "typical" consumers. Today's CPI includes items that were not available just a couple of decades ago, such as Blu-ray recorders, high-speed Internet access, and iPods. The CPI does not factor in any improvement in the standard of living that these items represent. For example, consider the fact that the average person can now afford computing power that would have cost \$30 million in 1985 (see Example 7). Economists would say that this represents a significant improvement in our standard of living, but the CPI does not take it into account.

The implications of an overstated CPI are immense. For example, it would mean that Social Security benefits have been rising more than necessary to keep pace with inflation, thereby affecting the amount of money available for all other government programs. In fact, if the CPI overstates the rate of inflation by 1 percentage point per year, the total cost for Social Security over the next decade will be more than *\$1 trillion* higher than it would be otherwise.

Clearly, knowing the truth about the CPI and inflation is very important to all of us. Unfortunately, the CPI remains a topic of hot debate. Given the huge economic and political implications of changes to the CPI, it's unlikely that the debate will end soon.

QUICK QUIZ

Choose the best answer to each of the following questions. Explain your reasoning with one or more complete sentences.

1. Look at the gasoline price index in Table 3.2. What does the 1985 index of 210.9 tell us?

   a. Gas in 1985 cost 210.9 times as much as gas in 1975.

   b. Gas in 1985 cost a little more than twice as much as gas in 1975.

   c. Gas in 1985 cost 210.9¢ per gallon.

2. Consider a gasoline price index with 1970 = 100 chosen as the reference. If the price of gas today is \$3.40, do you need any additional information to compute the index number for today's price?

   a. No.

   b. Yes; you need to know the current CPI.

   c. Yes; you need to know the price of gas in 1970.

3. The Consumer Price Index is designed to

   a. tell us the current cost of living for an average person.

   b. provide a fair comparison of how prices change with time.

   c. describe how the cost of gasoline has changed with time.

4. As shown in Table 3.4, the CPI was 163.0 for 1998 and 184.0 for 2003. This tells us that typical prices in 2003 were

   a. 21¢ higher than prices in 1998.

   b. 21% higher than prices in 1998.

   c. 184.0/163.0 times prices in 1998.

5. The Consumer Price Index (CPI) is currently published with a reference value of 100 for the years 1982–1984. Suppose the CPI were recalculated with 1995 as the reference year. Then the CPI for 2008 would be

   a. the same (215.3) as it is with 1982–1984 as the reference period.

   b. higher than 215.3.

   c. lower than 215.3.

6. Suppose we created a price index for computers, remembering that computer prices have fallen with time. If we used 1990 = 100 as the reference value for the computer price index, the price index today would be

   a. still about 100.

   b. much less than 100.

   c. much more than 100.

7. Over the past three decades, the cost of college has increased at a much greater rate than the CPI. This tells us that for the average family

   a. college has become more difficult to afford.

   b. college has become easier to afford.

   c. a college education is more valuable today than ever before.

8. Suppose your salary has been rising at a greater rate than the CPI. In principle, this should mean that

   a. your standard of living has improved.

   b. your standard of living has declined.

   c. you must now be working more hours.

9. Study Figure 3.3. Adjusted for inflation, gasoline was cheaper than at any other time since 1950 during the period

   a. 1950–1952.

   b. 1980–1982.

   c. 1998–1999.

10. Assume that, from 1985 to 2005, housing prices in San Diego tripled. If we created a housing price index for San Diego with 1985 = 100 as the reference value, the index for 2005 would be

    a. 3.

    b. 130.

    c. 300.

Exercises 3D

REVIEW QUESTIONS

1. What is an index number? Briefly describe how index numbers are calculated and what they mean.

2. What is the Consumer Price Index (CPI)? How is it supposed to be related to inflation?

3. In making price comparisons, why is it important to adjust prices for the effects of inflation? Briefly describe how we use the CPI to adjust prices.

4. List a few other uses of index numbers besides the CPI. Why is it important to understand an index before deciding whether to trust it?

DOES IT MAKE SENSE?

Decide whether each of the following statements makes sense (or is clearly true) or does not make sense (or is clearly false). Explain your reasoning.

5. The price per gallon of gasoline has risen from only a quarter in 1918 to nearly $3 today, thereby making it much more difficult for the poor to afford fuel for their cars.
6. Even though my salary has remained the same for the past 7 years, my standard of living has fallen.
7. Benjamin Franklin said, "A penny saved is a penny earned," but if he were alive today, he would be talking about a dollar rather than a penny.
8. The prices of cars have risen steadily, but when the prices are adjusted for inflation, cars are actually cheaper today than they were a couple of decades ago.
9. When we chart the price of milk in 1995 dollars we find that it has become slightly more expensive, but when we chart it in 1975 dollars we find that it has become cheaper.
10. The Consumer Price Index is a nice theoretical idea, but it has no impact on me, as a student on financial aid.

BASIC SKILLS & CONCEPTS

11–16: Gasoline Price Index. Use Table 3.2 to answer the following questions.

11. Suppose the current price of gasoline is $2.50. Find the current price index number, using the 1975 price as the reference value.
12. Suppose the current price of gasoline is $2.80. Find the current price index number, using the 1975 price as the reference value.
13. If it cost $8 to fill a gas tank in 1975, how much would it have cost to fill the same tank in 2005?
14. If it cost $12 to fill a gas tank in 1995, how much would it have cost to fill the same tank in 2005?
15. If it cost $10 to fill a gas tank in 1985, what fraction of the same tank could you fill with $10 in 2005?
16. Recast the gasoline price indices in Table 3.2 using the 1995 price as the reference value.

17–26: Understanding the CPI. Use Table 3.4 to answer the following questions. Assume that all prices have risen at the same rate as the CPI.

17. If someone needed $20,000 to maintain a certain standard of living in 1976, how much would be needed to maintain the same standard of living in 2008?
18. If someone needed $40,000 to maintain a certain standard of living in 1985, how much would be needed to maintain the same standard of living in 2006?
19. What was the net inflation rate between 1980 and 1985?
20. What was the net inflation rate between 2000 and 2008?
21. A box of macaroni and cheese cost $0.25 in 1976. What was its price in 2005 dollars?
22. A car cost $1500 in 1980. What was its price in 2006 dollars?
23. If a movie ticket cost $9.00 in 2008, what was its price in 1980 dollars?
24. If a ski lift ticket cost $85 in 2008, what was its price in 1985 dollars?
25. What was the purchasing power of $1 in 1976 in terms of 2006 dollars?
26. What was the purchasing power of $1 in 1979 in terms of 2008 dollars?

FURTHER APPLICATIONS

27–30: Housing Price Index. The following table shows a housing index that can be used to compare housing prices in different cities. If you know the price of a particular house in your town, you can use the index to find the price of a comparable house in another town, using the following formula:

$$\text{price (other town)} = \text{price (your town)} \times \frac{\text{index (other town)}}{\text{index (your town)}}$$

Use this index to answer the following questions.

City	Index	City	Index
Juneau, AK	100	Manhattan, NY	495
Palo Alto, CA	365	Tulsa, OK	52
Denver, CO	87	Providence, RI	91
Sioux City, IA	47	Spokane, WA	78
Boston, MA	182	Cheyenne, WY	75

27. Suppose you see a house valued at $300,000 in Denver. Find the price of a comparable house in Palo Alto, Sioux City, and Boston.
28. Suppose you see a house valued at $570,000 in Boston. Find the price of a comparable house in Juneau, Manhattan, and Tulsa.
29. Suppose you see a house valued at $250,000 in Cheyenne. Find the price of a comparable house in Spokane, Denver, and Juneau.
30. Suppose you see a house valued at $1,000,000 in Manhattan. Find the price of a comparable house in Providence, Spokane, and Tulsa.
31. **Health Care Spending.** Total spending on health care in the United States rose from $85 billion in 1976 to $2.4 trillion in 2007. Compare this rise in health care spending to the overall rate of inflation as measured by the Consumer Price Index.
32. **Airfare.** The average price for a low-fare airline ticket between New York and Los Angeles rose from $230 in 1980 to $420 in 2008. Calculate the relative change in cost from 1980 to 2008, and compare this change to the overall rate of inflation as measured by the Consumer Price Index.
33. **Private College Costs.** The average tuition and fees at private 4-year colleges and universities increased from $14,857 in 1989 to $25,143 in 2008. Calculate the relative change in cost over this time period, and compare it to the overall rate of inflation as measured by the CPI.

34. **Public College Cost.** The average tuition and fees at public 4-year colleges and universities increased from $2929 in 1989 to $6585 in 2008. Calculate the relative change in cost over this time period, and compare it to the overall rate of inflation as measured by the CPI.

35. **Home Prices, South.** The typical (median) price of a single-family home in the South (United States) rose from $75,300 in 1990 to $170,000 in 2008. Calculate the relative change in price from 1990 to 2008, and compare it to the overall rate of inflation as measured by the Consumer Price Index.

36. **Home Prices, West.** The typical (median) price of a single-family home in the West (United States) rose from $129,600 in 1990 to $275,000 in 2008. Calculate the relative change in price from 1990 to 2008, and compare it to the overall rate of inflation as measured by the Consumer Price Index.

37–44: **Federal Minimum Wage.** Use the following table, showing federal minimum wages over the past 70 years, to answer the following questions.

Year	Actual Dollars	1996 Dollars
1938	$0.25	$2.78
1939	$0.30	$3.39
1945	$0.40	$3.49
1950	$0.75	$4.88
1956	$1.00	$5.77
1961	$1.25	$6.41
1967	$1.40	$6.58
1968	$1.60	$7.21
1974	$2.00	$6.37
1976	$2.30	$6.34
1978	$2.65	$6.38
1979	$2.90	$6.27
1981	$3.35	$5.78
1990	$3.50	$4.56
1991	$4.25	$4.90
1996	$4.75	$4.75
1997	$5.15	$5.03
2007	$5.85	$4.42
2008	$6.55	$4.77
2009	$7.25	$5.12

Note: 1996 dollars based on CPI-U; entries in table are years in which the minimum wage changed.
Source: Department of Labor.

37. According to this table, how much is a quarter ($0.25) in 1938 dollars worth in 1996 dollars?

38. According to this table, how much is $1.00 in 1956 dollars worth in 1996 dollars?

39. Explain why the minimum wage for 1996 is the same in actual and 1996 dollars.

40. Explain why the 2009 minimum wage in actual dollars is greater than the 2009 minimum wage in 1996 dollars.

41. Use Table 3.4 to convert the 1979 minimum wage from actual dollars to 1996 dollars. Is the result consistent with the entry in the minimum wage table above?

42. In terms of purchasing power, would you rather have earned the minimum wage in 1968 or 2009?

43. In what year was the purchasing power of the minimum wage the highest? Explain.

44. You are listening to an argument in which Paul claims that the minimum wage has never been higher, because it has been rising for the past 70 years. Paula counters that the minimum wage actually needs to be increased, because it has been decreasing almost consistently since 1968. Based on the data in the minimum wage table above, write a one-paragraph explanation of each argument. Which argument do you think is stronger? Why?

WEB PROJECTS

45. **Consumer Price Index.** Go to the Consumer Price Index home page and find the latest news release with updated figures for the CPI. Summarize the news release and any important ongoing trends in the CPI.

46. **Producer Price Index.** Go to the Producer Price Index (PPI) home page. Read the overview and recent news releases. Write a short summary describing the purpose of the PPI and how it is different from the CPI. Also summarize any important recent trends in the PPI.

47. **Consumer Confidence Index.** Use a search engine to find recent news about the Consumer Confidence Index. After studying the news, write a short summary of what the Consumer Confidence Index attempts to measure and describe any recent trends in the Consumer Confidence Index.

48. **Human Development Index.** The United Nations Development Programme regularly releases its Human Development Report. A closely watched finding of this report is the Human Development Index (HDI), which measures the overall achievements in a country in three basic dimensions of human development: life expectancy, educational attainment, and adjusted income. Find the most recent copy of this report and investigate exactly how the HDI is defined and computed.

49. **Does the CPI Overstate Inflation?** Find arguments on both sides of the question of whether the CPI overstates inflation. Write a short summary of the arguments. Then state and defend your own opinion as to whether the CPI overstates inflation.

IN YOUR WORLD

50. **Consumer Price Index.** Find a recent news report that includes a reference to the Consumer Price Index. Briefly describe how the Consumer Price Index is important in the story.

51. **Index Numbers.** Find a recent news report that includes an index number *other than* the Consumer Price Index. Describe the index number and its meaning, and discuss how the index is important in the story.

52. **Accurate CPI?** Find a news story that talks about some long-term economic change that is tied to inflation, such as change in personal income over the past few decades. Briefly

explain the report. How would the story be different if it turned out that the Consumer Price Index overstated inflation by, say, 1 percentage point per year?

TECHNOLOGY EXERCISES

53–58: Inflation Calculator. Use the Bureau of Labor Statistics inflation calculator to complete the following sentences.

53. $100 in 1980 has the same buying power as $_____ in 2009.

54. $10 in 2009 has the same buying power as $_____ in 1920.

55. $25 in 1930 has the same buying power as $_____ in 2009.

56. $1000 in 2008 has the same buying power as $_____ in 1915.

57. Suppose that Y is the year in which you were born and that $\$A$ in year Y is worth $\$B$ today. Is A greater than or less than B?

58. Suppose that Y is the year in which you were born and that $\$C$ today is worth $\$D$ in year Y. Is C greater than or less than D?

UNIT 3E How Numbers Deceive: Polygraphs, Mammograms, and More

The government administers polygraph tests ("lie detectors") to new applicants for sensitive security jobs. The polygraph tests are reputed to be 90% accurate. That is, they supposedly catch 90% of the people who are lying and validate 90% of the people who are truthful. Most people therefore guess that only 10% of the people who fail a polygraph test have been falsely identified as lying. In fact, the actual percentage of false accusations can be *much* higher—in some cases, more than 90% of those who fail a test have been falsely accused! How can this be?

We'll discuss the answer soon, but first let's draw the important moral of this story: Numbers may not lie, but they can be deceiving if we do not interpret them carefully. In this unit, we'll discuss several common ways in which numbers can deceive.

Better in Each Case, but Worse Overall

Suppose a pharmaceutical company creates a new treatment for acne. To decide whether the new treatment is better than an older treatment, the company conducts a test. The old treatment is given to 90 patients, and the new treatment is given to 110 patients. Here are the results after four weeks of treatment (summarized in Table 3.5):

- Among patients with mild acne, 10 received the old treatment and 90 received the new treatment. Among the 10 receiving the old treatment, 2 were cured, for a 20% cure rate. Among the 90 receiving the new treatment, 30 were cured, for a 33% cure rate. The new treatment had a higher cure rate among patients with mild acne.
- Among patients with severe acne, 80 received the old treatment and 20 received the new treatment. Among the 80 receiving the old treatment, 40 were cured, for a 50% cure rate. Among the 20 receiving the new treatment, 12 were cured, for a 60% cure rate. The new treatment had a higher cure rate among patients with severe acne.

TABLE 3.5 Results of Acne Treatments

	Mild Acne		Severe Acne	
	Cured	**Not Cured**	**Cured**	**Not Cured**
Old Treatment	2	8	40	40
New Treatment	30	60	12	8

Notice that the new treatment had a higher cure rate both for patients with mild acne and for patients with severe acne. Is it fair for the company to claim that its new treatment is better than the old treatment?

At first, this might seem to make sense. But let's look at the overall results:

- Among the total of 90 patients receiving the old treatment, 42 were cured—2 out of 10 with mild acne and 40 out of 80 with severe acne. Therefore, the overall cure rate for the old treatment was $42/90 = 46.7\%$.
- Among the total of 110 patients receiving the new treatment, 42 were cured—30 out of 90 with mild acne and 12 out of 20 with severe acne. Therefore, the overall cure rate for the new treatment was $42/110 = 38.2\%$.

Historical Note

Simpson's paradox gets its name from Edward Simpson, who described it in 1951. However, the same idea was actually described much earlier, by Scottish statistician George Yule around 1900.

Overall, the old treatment had the higher cure rate, despite the fact that the new treatment had a higher rate for both mild and severe acne cases.

This example illustrates that it is possible for a set of data to give different results in each of several groups than it does when the groups are taken together. This situation is an example of **Simpson's paradox.** If you look carefully, you'll see that it occurs because of the way in which the overall results were divided into unequally sized groups (in this case, the groups were mild acne patients and severe acne patients, with no clear rationale given for how "mild" and "severe" were defined). Simpson's paradox arises surprisingly often and is one way in which numbers can deceive unless they are examined with great care.

Example 1 Who Played Better?

Table 3.6 gives the shooting performance of two players in a basketball game during the two halves. Shaq had a higher shooting percentage both in the first half (40% to 25%) and in the second half (75% to 70%). Does this mean that Shaq had the better shooting percentage for the game?

TABLE 3.6 Basketball Shots

	First Half			Second Half		
Player	**Baskets**	**Attempts**	**Percent**	**Baskets**	**Attempts**	**Percent**
Shaq	4	10	40%	3	4	75%
Vince	1	4	25%	7	10	70%

Solution No, and we can see why by looking at the overall game statistics. Shaq made a total of 7 baskets (4 in the first half and 3 in the second half) on 14 shots (10 in the first half and 4 in the second half), for an overall shooting percentage of $7/14 = 50\%$. Vince made a total of 8 baskets on 14 shots, for an overall shooting percentage of $8/14 = 57.1\%$. Even though Shaq had a higher shooting percentage in both halves, Vince had a better overall shooting percentage for the game. Now try Exercises 11–12.

Is It Discrimination?—and Other Cases of Simpson's Paradox

Variations on Simpson's paradox arise in many situations. One famous case involved an investigation of possible gender discrimination in graduate programs at the University of California, Berkeley. Examining graduate admissions for 1973, university officials found that male applicants were being admitted at a significantly higher rate than female applicants. Assuming that male and female applicants were equally qualified, the university appeared to be engaging in discrimination against women.

The university began investigating individual departments to see which ones were responsible for the discrimination. Table 3.7 shows the results for the six departments

TABLE 3.7 Admissions for Six Graduate Programs at UC Berkeley, 1973

	Men			Women		
Department	**Applied**	**Admitted**	**Percent**	**Applied**	**Admitted**	**Percent**
A	825	512	62%	108	89	82%
B	560	353	63%	25	17	68%
C	325	120	37%	593	202	34%
D	417	138	33%	375	131	35%
E	191	53	28%	393	94	24%
F	373	22	6%	341	24	7%
Total	2691	1198	44.5%	1835	557	30.4%

Source: P. Bickel and J. W. O'Connell, *Science*, Vol. 187, 1975, pp. 398–404.

BY THE WAY

A National Science Foundation study once found that, on average, women in science and engineering earned only 77% as much as men. But when the data were examined within each field, in every case the average salary for women was at least 92% of the average salary for men. The explanation for this case of Simpson's paradox: Women were more highly represented in life sciences and social sciences, which tend to be lower paying than physical sciences and engineering.

with the largest numbers of graduate applicants. (University policy requires that departments not be named, so we refer to them as Departments A through F.)

Note that the admission rates (percentages) for women were actually higher than those for men in all but Departments C and E, and the rates were quite close in those cases. Nevertheless, the totals confirm a much higher overall admission rate for men than for women. We are seeing Simpson's paradox in action again: While women were admitted at a significantly lower rate overall, no individual department was guilty of this practice.

Time Out to Think

Look closely at the data in Table 3.7. Would it be reasonable to conclude that Department A discriminates against men? Why or why not?

Example 2 Does Smoking Make You Live Longer?

In the early 1970s, a medical study in England involved many adult residents from a district called Wickham. Twenty years later, a follow-up study looked at the survival rates of the people from the original study. The follow-up study found the following surprising results (D. R. Appleton, J. M. French, and M. P. Vanderpump, *American Statistician*, Vol. 50, 1996, pp. 340–341):

- Among the adults who smoked, 24% died during the 20 years since the original study.
- Among the adults who did not smoke, 31% died during the 20 years since the original study.

Do these results suggest that smoking can make you live longer?

Solution Not necessarily, because the given results don't tell us the ages of the smokers and nonsmokers. It turned out that, in the original study, the nonsmokers were older on average than the smokers. The higher death rate among nonsmokers simply reflected the fact that death rates tend to increase with age. When the results were broken into age groups, they showed that for any given age group, nonsmokers had a higher 20-year survival rate than smokers. That is, 55-year-old smokers were less likely to reach age 75 than 55-year-old nonsmokers, and so on. Rather than suggesting that smoking prolongs life, a careful study of the data showed just the opposite.

Now try Exercises 13–16.

BY THE WAY

The mammogram example and the polygraph example that follow illustrate cases in which *conditional probabilities* (discussed in Unit 7B) lead to confusion. The proper way of handling conditional probabilities was discovered by the Reverend Thomas Bayes (1702–1761) and is often called *Bayes rule*.

Does a Positive Mammogram Mean Cancer?

We often associate tumors with cancers, but most tumors are not cancers. Medically, any kind of abnormal swelling or tissue growth is considered a tumor. A tumor caused by cancer is said to be *malignant* (or *cancerous*), while others are said to be *benign*.

Imagine you are a doctor or nurse treating a patient who has a breast tumor. The patient will be understandably nervous, but you can give her some comfort by telling her that only about 1 in 100 breast tumors turns out to be malignant. But, just to be safe, you order a mammogram to determine whether her tumor is one of the 1% that are malignant.

Now, suppose the mammogram comes back positive, suggesting the tumor is malignant. Mammograms are not perfect, so even the positive result does not necessarily mean that your patient has breast cancer. More specifically, let's assume that the mammogram screening is 85% accurate. It will correctly identify 85% of malignant tumors as malignant and 85% of benign tumors as benign. (Most real cancer tests have different accuracy rates for malignant and benign tumors.) When you tell your patient that her mammogram was positive, what should you tell her about the chance that she actually has cancer?

Because the mammogram screening is 85% accurate, most people guess that the positive result means that the patient probably has cancer. Studies have shown that in this situation most doctors also believe this to be the case, and would tell the patient to be prepared for cancer treatment. But a more careful analysis shows otherwise. In fact, the chance that the patient has cancer is still quite small—about 5%. We can see why by analyzing some numbers.

Consider a study in which mammograms are given to 10,000 women with breast tumors. Assuming that 1% of tumors are malignant, $1\% \times 10{,}000 = 100$ of the women actually have cancer; the remaining 9900 women have benign tumors. Table 3.8 summarizes the mammogram results. Note the following:

- The mammogram screening correctly identifies 85% of the 100 malignant tumors as malignant. That is, it gives positive (malignant) results for 85 of the malignant tumors. These cases are called **true positives.** In the other 15 malignant cases, the result is negative, even though the women actually have cancer. These cases are **false negatives.**
- The mammogram screening correctly identifies 85% of the 9900 benign tumors as benign. That is, it gives negative (benign) results for $85\% \times 9900 = 8415$ of the benign tumors. These cases are **true negatives.** The rest of the 9900 women with benign tumors ($9900 - 8415 = 1485$ women) get positive results in which the mammogram incorrectly suggests their tumors are malignant. These cases are **false positives.**

Overall, the mammogram screening gives positive results to 85 women who actually have cancer and to 1485 women who do *not* have cancer. The total number of positive

BY THE WAY

The accuracy of mammograms is improving with technology, and some newer technologies can achieve accuracy rates of over 98%. However, studies show that the the accuracy also depends greatly on the physician or radiologist who interprets the results. Women seeking mammograms should go to a facility with a good reputation, where doctors have extensive experience reading mammograms.

TABLE 3.8 Summary of Results for 10,000 Mammograms (in which 100 of the women have malignant tumors and 9900 have benign tumors)

	Tumor Is Malignant	Tumor Is Benign	Total
Positive Mammogram	85 true positives	1485 false positives	1570
Negative Mammogram	15 false negatives	8415 true negatives	8430
Total	100	9900	10,000

results is $85 + 1485 = 1570$. Because only 85 of these are true positives (the rest are false positives), the chance that a positive result really means cancer is only $85/1570 = 0.054$, or 5.4%. Therefore, when your patient's mammogram comes back positive, you should reassure her that there's still only a small chance that she has cancer.

Example 3 False Negatives

Suppose you are a doctor seeing a patient with a breast tumor. Her mammogram comes back negative. Based on the numbers in Table 3.8, what is the chance that she has cancer?

Solution For the 10,000 cases summarized in Table 3.8, the mammograms are negative for 15 women with cancer and for 8415 women with benign tumors. The total number of negative results is $15 + 8415 = 8430$. The fraction of women with false negatives is $15/8430 = 0.0018$, or slightly less than 2 in 1000. In other words, the chance that a woman with a negative mammogram has cancer is only about 2 in 1000.

Now try Exercise 17.

Time Out to Think

While the chance of cancer with a negative mammogram is small, it is not zero. Therefore, it might seem like a good idea to biopsy all tumors, just to be sure. However, biopsies involve surgery, which means they can be painful and expensive, among other things. Given these facts, do you think that biopsies should be routine for all tumors? Should they be routine for cases of positive mammograms? Defend your opinion.

Polygraphs and Drug Tests

We're now ready to return to the question asked at the beginning of this unit, about how a 90% accurate polygraph test can lead to a surprising number of false accusations. The explanation is very similar to that found in the case of the mammograms.

Suppose the government gives the polygraph test to 1000 applicants for sensitive security jobs. Further suppose that 990 of these 1000 people tell the truth on their polygraph test, while only 10 people lie. For a test that is 90% accurate, we find the following results:

- Of the 10 people who lie, the polygraph correctly identifies 90%, meaning that 9 fail the test (they are identified as liars) and 1 passes.
- Of the 990 people who tell the truth, the polygraph correctly identifies 90%, meaning that $90\% \times 990 = 891$ truthful people pass the test and the other $10\% \times 990 = 99$ people fail the test.

Figure 3.4 summarizes these results. The total number of people who fail the test is $9 + 99 = 108$. Of these, only 9 were actually liars; so the other 99 were falsely accused of lying. That is, 99 out of 108, or $99/108 = 91.7\%$, of the people who fail the test were actually telling the truth.

The percentage of people who are falsely accused in any real situation depends on both the accuracy of the test and the proportion of people who are lying. Nevertheless, for the numbers given here, we have an astounding result: Assuming the government rejects applicants who fail the polygraph test, then almost 92% of the rejected applicants were actually being truthful and may have been highly qualified for the jobs.

BY THE WAY

A polygraph, often called a "lie detector," measures a variety of bodily functions including heart rate, skin temperature, and blood pressure. Polygraph operators look for subtle changes in these functions that typically occur when people lie. However, polygraph results have never been allowed as evidence in criminal proceedings, because 90% accuracy is far too low for justice. In addition, studies show that polygraphs are easily fooled by people who train to beat them.

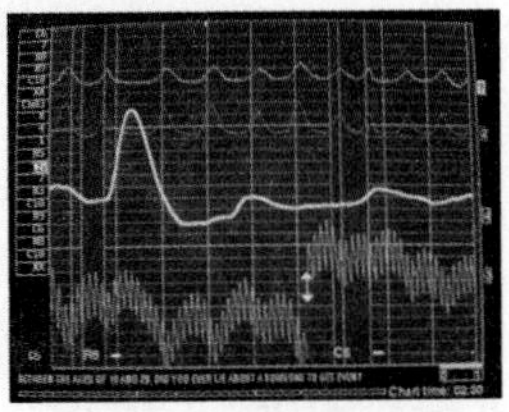

Time Out to Think

Imagine that you are falsely accused of a crime. The police suggest that, if you are truly innocent, you should agree to take a polygraph test. Would you do it? Why or why not?

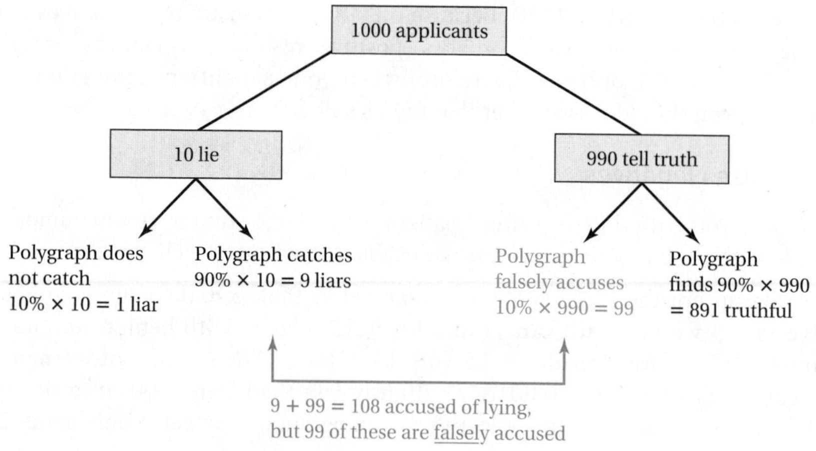

FIGURE 3.4 A tree diagram summarizes results of a 90% accurate polygraph test for 1000 people, of whom only 10 are lying.

Example 4 High School Drug Testing

All athletes participating in a regional high school track and field championship must provide a urine sample for a drug test. Those who fail are eliminated from the meet and suspended from competition for the following year. Studies show that, at the laboratory selected, the drug tests are 95% accurate. Assume that 4% of the athletes actually use drugs. What fraction of the athletes who fail the test are falsely accused and therefore suspended without cause?

Solution The easiest way to answer this question is by using some sample numbers. Suppose there are 1000 athletes in the meet. We are told to assume that 4%, or 40 athletes, actually use drugs. The remaining 960 athletes do not use drugs. In that case, the 95% accurate drug test should return the following results:

- 95% of the 40 athletes who use drugs, or $0.95 \times 40 = 38$ athletes, fail the test. The other 2 athletes who use drugs pass the test.
- 95% of the 960 athletes who do not use drugs pass the test, but 5% of these 960 athletes fail. The number of athletes who fail despite not using drugs is $0.05 \times 960 = 48$.

The total number of athletes who fail the test is $38 + 48 = 86$. But 48 of these athletes, or $48/86 = 56\%$, are actually nonusers. Despite the 95% accuracy of the drug test, more than half of the suspended students are innocent of drug use.

Now try Exercises 18–19.

Political Math

Another type of deception occurs when two sides in a debate argue with different sets of numbers. Some of the classic cases arise in the politics of taxes and tax cuts.

Both of the charts in Figure 3.5 purport to show the effects of the *same* proposed tax cut. Figure 3.5a reflects numbers supplied by Republicans, who supported the tax cut. It suggests that the tax cut would benefit families of all incomes similarly in percentage terms, with slightly greater benefits going to middle-income families than to the poor or the rich. Figure 3.5b reflects numbers supplied by Democrats, who opposed the cut. This chart suggests that the benefits would go disproportionately to the rich. If we assume that neither side is lying outright, how can they make such remarkably different claims? The answer lies in how each side chose to calculate "benefits" of the tax cut.

ON THE OTHER HAND . . .

Two Views of a Tax Cut

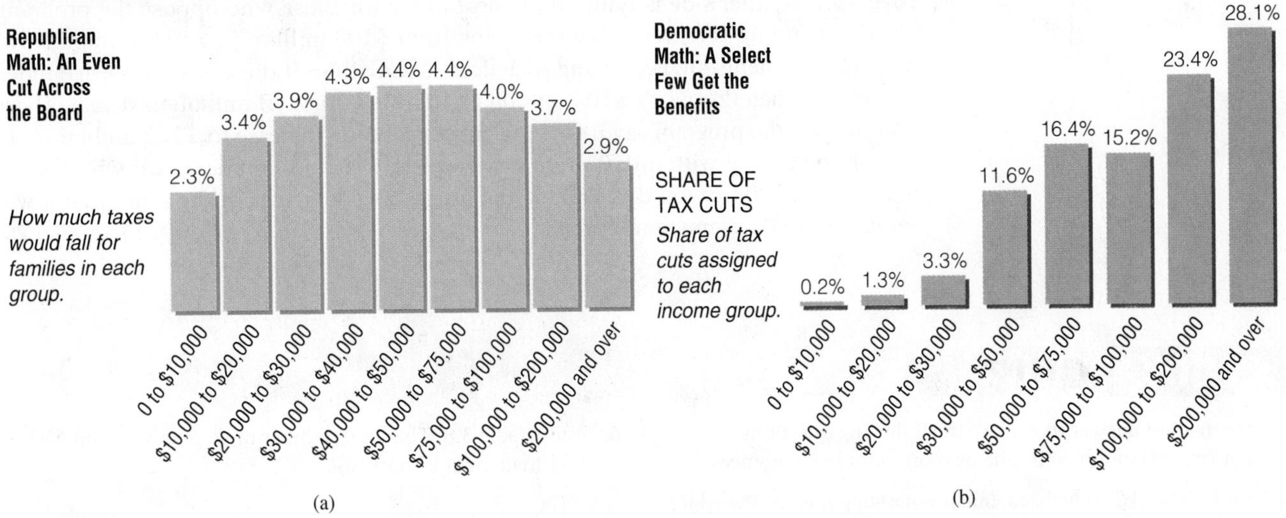

FIGURE 3.5 *Source:* Adapted from the *New York Times.*

The Republicans calculated the *average* tax cut that would be received by families in each group. For example, the last bar in Figure 3.5a shows that families with incomes over $200,000 would get an average tax cut of 2.9%. Of course, a 2.9% tax cut means many more actual dollars to someone paying a lot in taxes than to someone paying a little. For example, someone who pays $100,000 in taxes would save $2900 with a 2.9% tax cut, while someone paying $1000 in taxes would save only $29.

The Democrats calculated the percentage of *total* benefits that would go to each group. For example, the last bar in Figure 3.5b shows that families with an income over $200,000 would receive 28.1% of the total benefits from the tax cut. But this does *not* mean that these families get a 28.1% tax cut. To see why, consider the effects of an across-the-board tax cut of the same percentage for everyone. Because families with incomes above $200,000 pay more than one-fourth of the total income taxes collected by the U.S. government, these families would receive about one-fourth of the total benefit of *any* across-the-board cut. For example, if the government collected $1 trillion in taxes, a 10% across-the-board cut would mean savings of $100 billion for taxpayers as a whole. In that case, because one-fourth of the $1 trillion was paid by families with income over $200,000, one-fourth of the $100 billion in savings would go to these same families. In other words these families would get 25% of the *benefits* of the tax cut, even though their actual tax cut would be only 10%.

Which side was being more fair? Neither, really. The Republicans chose to neglect the fact that most of the total tax savings would go to the wealthy, while the Democrats chose to neglect the fact that the wealthy already pay most of the taxes. Unfortunately, this type of "selective truth" is very common when it comes to numbers, bringing home the necessity of listening carefully to quantitative arguments.

Example 5 A Cut or an Increase?

Government spending for a popular education program was $100 million last year. When Congress prepares its budget for next year, spending for the program is slated to rise to $102 million. Lobbyists immediately go into action. Those who support the program complain about the planned cut in the program. Those who oppose the program complain that it is being increased when it should be cut. Is one side lying? Explain. Assume that the Consumer Price Index is expected to rise by 3% over the next year.

Solution Neither side is lying. It's easiest to see for those who oppose the program: Clearly, spending *is* rising, since it is going from $100 million to $102 million. However, the opponents are neglecting the effects of inflation. If the Consumer Price Index rises by 3%, then this year's $100 million is equivalent to $103 million next year. Those who support the program say it is being cut because the increase to $102 million is not enough to keep up with inflation. In other words, $102 million next year will not buy as much as $100 million this year, so the program is being cut in the sense that it will not be able to do as much next year. **Now try Exercise 20.**

QUICK QUIZ

Choose the best answer to each of the following questions. Explain your reasoning with one or more complete sentences.

1. Study Table 3.5. Which statement is *not* supported by the table?
   a. The new treatment cured a higher percentage of the people with any kind of acne than did the old treatment.
   b. The new treatment cured a higher percentage of the people with mild acne than did the old treatment.
   c. The new treatment cured a higher percentage of the people with severe acne than did the old treatment.
2. Study Table 3.7. What does the 63% in row B mean?
   a. 63% of the men who applied to Department B were admitted.
   b. 63% of the women who applied to Department B were admitted.
   c. 63% of all people who applied to Department B were admitted.
3. During their freshman year, Derek's GPA was 3.4 and Terry's was 3.2. During their sophomore year, Derek's GPA was 3.6 and Terry's was 3.5. Which of the following statements is *not* necessarily true?
   a. Derek had a higher GPA than Terry during their freshman year and again during their sophomore year.
   b. Derek's overall GPA for the two-year period was higher than Terry's.
   c. Derek's overall GPA for the two-year period was somewhere between 3.4 and 3.6.
4. A *false negative* in a cancer screening test means that
   a. a person tested negative but actually has cancer.
   b. a person tested negative and does not have cancer.
   c. a person tested positive but does not actually have cancer.
5. A *false positive* in a test for steroids means that
   a. a person tested negative but actually took steroids.
   b. a person tested positive and actually took steroids.
   c. a person tested positive but did not actually take steroids.
6. Study Table 3.8. The total number of women who did *not* have malignant tumors was
   a. 100.
   b. 8415.
   c. 9900.
7. Study Table 3.8. The total number of women whose tests gave *incorrect* results was
   a. 100.
   b. 1500.
   c. 1570.
8. Suppose that a home pregnancy test is 99% accurate. Which statement is *not* necessarily true?
   a. The test will give correct results to 99% of the women.
   b. Among the women who actually are pregnant, only 1% will get a result saying they're not pregnant.
   c. Among the women who test negative, 99% really are not pregnant.
9. Study the "Republican Math" graph in Figure 3.5. Which of the following is *not* true according to this graph?
   a. The largest percentage tax cuts will go to people earning between about $40,000 and $75,000.
   b. People earning more than $200,000 will save fewer total dollars with this tax cut than people earning between $40,000 to $50,000.
   c. All groups will get a tax cut of at least 2%.
10. Study the "Democratic Math" graph in Figure 3.5. Which of the following is *not* true according to this graph?
    a. A little over half the total value of the tax cuts will go to people earning more than $100,000.
    b. A little less than half the total value of the tax cuts will go to people earning less than $100,000.
    c. People earning more than $200,000 will see their tax bills fall by 28.1%.

Exercises 3E

REVIEW QUESTIONS

1. What is Simpson's paradox? Give an example to show how it can make something look different in individual cases than when the cases are taken together.
2. Briefly explain why a positive result on a cancer test such as a mammogram does not necessarily mean that a patient has cancer.
3. Explain how it is possible for a very accurate polygraph or drug test to result in a large proportion of false accusations.
4. Give an example explaining how politicians on both sides of an issue can use numbers to support their case without actually lying.

DOES IT MAKE SENSE?

Decide whether each of the following statements makes sense (or is clearly true) or does not make sense (or is clearly false). Explain your reasoning.

5. Despite the fact that the new drug lowered blood pressure more than the old drug did in both the men and the women in the study, an overall analysis shows that the old drug was actually more effective.
6. I clearly played a better basketball game than you, because I had a higher shooting percentage in both the first and the second half.
7. Baggage screening machines are 98% accurate in identifying bags that contain banned materials. Therefore, if the screening shows a bag contains banned materials, then it almost certainly does.
8. The polygraph test showed that the suspect was lying when he claimed to be innocent, so he must be guilty.
9. The Republicans claim the tax cut benefits everyone equally, but the Democrats say it favors the rich. Clearly, one side must be lying.
10. The agency suffered a real cut in its annual budget, even though it got a higher dollar amount this year than last.

BASIC SKILLS & CONCEPTS

11. **Batting Percentages.** The table below shows the batting records of two baseball players in the first half (first 81 games) and last half of a season.

	First Half		
Player	Hits	At-bats	Batting Average
Josh	50	150	.333
Jude	10	50	.200

	Second Half		
Player	Hits	At-bats	Batting Average
Josh	35	70	.500
Jude	70	150	.467

a. Which player had the higher batting average in the first half of the season?

b. Which player had the higher batting average in the second half of the season?

c. Which player had the higher overall batting average for the season?

d. Explain how these results illustrate Simpson's paradox.

12. **Jeter and Justice.** The following table shows the number of hits (H), number of at-bats (AB), and batting average (AVG = H/AB) for major leaguers Derek Jeter and David Justice in 1995 and 1996.

	1995	1996
Jeter	12 H, 48 AB, AVG = .250	183 H, 582 AB, AVG = .310
Justice	104 H, 411 AB, AVG = .253	45 H, 140 AB, AVG = .321

Source: Ken Ross, *A Mathematician at the Ballpark: Odds and Probabilities for Baseball Fans*, Pi Press, 2004.

a. Which player had the higher batting average in both 1995 and 1996?

b. Compute the batting average for each player for the two years combined.

c. Which player had the higher combined batting average for 1995 and 1996?

d. Explain how these results illustrate Simpson's paradox.

13. **Test Scores.** The table below shows eighth-grade mathematics test scores in Nebraska and New Jersey. The scores are separated according to the race of the students. Also shown are the state averages for all races.

	White	Nonwhite	Average for All Races
Nebraska	281	250	277
New Jersey	283	252	272

Source: National Assessment of Educational Progress scores for 1992, from *Chance*, Spring 1999.

a. Which state had the higher scores in both racial categories? Which state had the higher overall average across both racial categories?

b. Explain how a state could score lower in both categories and still have a higher overall average.

c. Now consider the table below that gives the percentages of whites and nonwhites in each state. Use these percentages to verify that the overall average test score in Nebraska is 277, as claimed in the first table.

	White	Nonwhite
Nebraska	87%	13%
New Jersey	66%	34%

d. Use the racial percentages to verify that the overall average test score in New Jersey is 272, as claimed in the first table.

e. Explain briefly, in your own words, how Simpson's paradox appeared in this case.

14. **Test Scores.** Consider the following table comparing the grade averages and mathematics SAT scores of high school students in 1988 and 1998.

	% Students		SAT Score		
Grade Average	1988	1998	1988	1998	Change
A+	4	7	632	629	−3
A	11	15	586	582	−4
A−	13	16	556	554	−2
B	53	48	490	487	−3
C	19	14	431	428	−3
Overall average			504	514	+10

Source: Cited in *Chance,* Vol. 12, No. 2, 1999, from data in *New York Times,* September 2, 1999.

a. In general terms, how did the SAT scores of the students in the five grade categories change between 1988 and 1998?

b. How did the overall average SAT score change between 1988 and 1998?

c. How is this an example of Simpson's paradox?

15. **Tuberculosis Deaths.** The following table shows deaths due to tuberculosis (TB) in New York City and Richmond, Virginia, in 1910.

	New York	
Race	Population	TB Deaths
White	4,675,000	8400
Nonwhite	92,000	500
Total	4,767,000	8900
	Richmond	
Race	Population	TB Deaths
White	81,000	130
Nonwhite	47,000	160
Total	128,000	290

Source: Cohen and Nagel, *An Introduction to Logic and Scientific Method,* Harcourt, Brace and World, 1934.

a. Compute the death rates for whites, nonwhites, and all residents in New York City.

b. Compute the death rates for whites, nonwhites, and all residents in Richmond.

c. Explain why this is an example of Simpson's paradox and explain how the paradox arises.

16. **Weight Training.** Two cross-country running teams participated in a (hypothetical) study in which a fraction of each team used weight training to supplement a running workout. The remaining runners did not use weight training. At the end of the season, the mean improvement in race times (in seconds) was recorded in the following table.

	Time Improvement with Weight Training	Time Improvement without Weight Training	Team Average Time Improvement
Gazelles	10 s	2 s	6.0 s
Cheetahs	9 s	1 s	6.2 s

Describe how Simpson's paradox arises in this table. Resolve the paradox by finding the percentage of each team that used weight training.

17. **More Accurate Mammograms.** Like Table 3.8, the following table is based on the assumption that 1% of breast tumors are malignant. However, this table assumes that mammogram screening is 90% accurate (versus 85% accurate, as assumed in Table 3.8).

	Tumor Is Malignant	Tumor Is Benign	Total
Positive Mammogram	90 true positives	990 false positives	1080
Negative Mammogram	10 false negatives	8910 true negatives	8920
Total	100	9900	10,000

a. Verify that the numbers in the table are correct.

b. Suppose a patient has a positive mammogram. What is the chance that she really has cancer?

c. What is the chance of a positive mammogram, given that the patient has cancer?

d. Suppose a patient has a negative mammogram. What is the chance that she actually does have cancer?

18. **Polygraph Test.** Suppose that a polygraph is 85% accurate (it will correctly detect 85% of people who are lying and it will correctly detect 85% of people who are telling the truth). The 2000 employees of a company are given a polygraph test during which they are asked whether they use drugs. All of them deny drug use, when, in fact, 1% of the employees actually use drugs. Assume that anyone whom the polygraph operator finds untruthful is accused of lying.

a. Verify that the entries in the table below follow from the given information. Explain each entry.

	Users	Non-users	Total
Test Finds Employee Lying	17	297	314
Test Finds Employee Truthful	3	1683	1686
Total	20	1980	2000

b. How many employees are accused of lying? Of these, how many were actually lying and how many were telling the truth? What percentage of those accused of lying were falsely accused?

c. How many employees are found truthful? Of these, how many were actually truthful? What percentage of those found truthful really were truthful?

19. **Disease Test.** Suppose a test for a disease is 90% accurate for those who have the disease (true positives) and 90% accurate for those who do not have the disease (true negatives). Within a sample of 4000 patients, the incidence rate of the disease is the national average, which is 1.5%.

a. Verify that the entries in the table below follow from the information given and that the overall incidence rate is 1.5%. Explain.

	Disease	No Disease	Total
Test Positive	54	394	448
Test Negative	6	3546	3552
Total	60	3940	4000

b. Of those with the disease, what percentage test positive?

c. Of those who test positive, what percentage have the disease? Compare this result to the one in part b and explain why they are different.

d. Suppose a patient tests positive for the disease. As a doctor using this table, how would you describe the patient's chance of actually having the disease? Compare this figure to the overall incidence rate of the disease.

20. **Political Math.** Government spending for a popular housing program was $1 billion last year. When Congress prepares its budget for next year, spending for the program is slated to rise to $1.01 billion. Assume that the Consumer Price Index is expected to rise by 3% over the next year. Those who support the program complain that the program is being cut. Those who oppose the program complain that the program is being increased. Explain each position.

FURTHER APPLICATIONS

21. **Basketball Records.** Consider the following hypothetical basketball records for Spelman and Morehouse Colleges.

	Spelman College	Morehouse College
Home Games	10 wins, 19 losses	9 wins, 19 losses
Away Games	12 wins, 4 losses	56 wins, 20 losses

a. Give numerical evidence to support the claim that Spelman College has a better team than Morehouse College.

b. Give numerical evidence to support the claim that Morehouse College has a better team than Spelman College.

c. Which claim do you think makes more sense? Why?

22. **Better Drug.** Two drugs, A and B, were tested on a total of 2000 patients, half of whom were women and half of whom were men. Drug A was given to 900 patients, and Drug B to 1100 patients. The results appear in the table below.

	Women	Men
Drug A	5 of 100 cured	400 of 800 cured
Drug B	101 of 900 cured	196 of 200 cured

a. Give numerical evidence to support the claim that Drug B is more effective than Drug A.

b. Give numerical evidence to support the claim that Drug A is more effective than Drug B.

c. Which claim do you think makes more sense? Why?

23. **HIV Risks.** The New York State Department of Health estimates a 10% rate of HIV for the "at risk" population and a 0.3% rate for the general population. Tests for HIV are 95% accurate in detecting both true negatives and true positives. Random selection of 5000 "at risk" people and 20,000 people from the general population results in the following table.

	"At Risk" Population	
	Test Positive	Test Negative
Infected	475	25
Not Infected	225	4275
	General Population	
	Test Positive	Test Negative
Infected	57	3
Not Infected	997	18,943

a. Verify that incidence rates for the general and "at risk" populations are 0.3% and 10%, respectively. Also, verify that detection rates for the general and "at risk" populations are 95%.

b. Consider a patient in the "at risk" category. Of those with HIV, what percentage test positive? Of those who test positive, what percentage have HIV? Explain why these two percentages are different.

c. Suppose a patient in the "at risk" category tests positive for the disease. As a doctor using this table, how would you describe the patient's chance of actually having the disease? Compare this figure to the overall rate of the disease in the "at risk" population.

d. Consider a patient in the general population. Of those with HIV, what percentage test positive? Of those who test positive, what percentage have HIV? Explain why these two percentages are different.

e. Suppose a patient in the general population tests positive for the disease. As a doctor using this table, how would you describe the patient's chance of actually having the disease? Compare this figure to the overall incidence rate of the disease.

24. **Airline Arrivals.** The following table shows real arrival data for two airlines in five cities (airline names have been changed).

	Excelsior Airlines		Paradise Airlines	
Destination	% On Time	Number of Arrivals	% On Time	Number of Arrivals
Los Angeles	88.9	559	85.6	811
Phoenix	94.8	233	92.1	5255
San Diego	91.4	232	85.5	448
San Francisco	83.1	605	71.3	449
Seattle	85.8	2146	76.7	262
Total		3775		7225

Source: Technical Review (1994), p. 3845.

a. Which airline has the higher percentage of on-time flights to the five cities?

b. Compute the percentage of on-time flights for the two airlines over all five cities.

c. Explain how the data illustrate Simpson's paradox.

25. **Hiring Statistics.** (This problem is based on an example in "Ask Marilyn," *Parade Magazine,* April 28, 1996.) A company decided to expand, so it opened a factory, generating 455 jobs. For the 70 white-collar positions, 200 males and 200 females applied. Of the females who applied, 20% were hired, while only 15% of the males were hired. Of the 400 males applying for the blue-collar positions, 75% were hired, while 85% of the 100 females who applied were hired. How does looking at the white-collar and blue-collar positions separately suggest a hiring preference for women? Do the overall data support the idea that the company hires women preferentially? Explain why this is an example of Simpson's paradox and how the paradox can be resolved.

26. **Drug Trials.** (This problem is based on an example in "Ask Marilyn," *Parade Magazine,* April 28, 1996.) A company runs two trials of two treatments for an illness. In the first trial, Treatment A cures 20% of the cases (40 out of 200) and Treatment B cures 15% of the cases (30 out of 200). In the second trial, Treatment A cures 85% of the cases (85 out of 100) and Treatment B cures 75% of the cases (300 out of 400). Which treatment had the better cure rate in the two trials individually? Which treatment had the better overall cure rate? Explain why this is an example of Simpson's paradox and how the paradox can be resolved.

27–30: Income Share vs. Tax Share. Refer to the graph in Figure 3.6, which shows changes in income share and tax share for the 400 Americans who earned the most in each year.

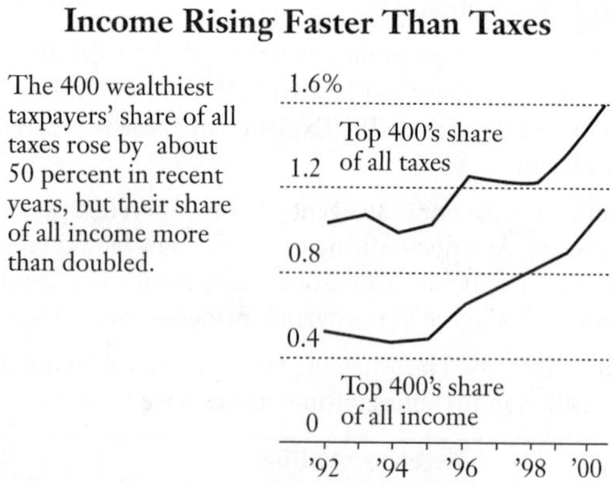

FIGURE 3.6 *Source:* Internal Revenue Service; *New York Times.*

27. Use the data in the graph to support the argument that the highest-income taxpayers are paying more than their fair share of taxes and therefore their taxes should be cut.

28. Use the data in the graph to support the argument that the highest-income taxpayers have seen their tax rates fall sharply in recent years and therefore their taxes should be raised.

29. Use the data in the graph to support the argument that lower tax rates on the rich lead to greater tax revenue for the federal government.

30. Use the data in the graph to support the argument that the rich earn too much money compared to the average person.

31. **A Tax Cut.** According to an analysis of a federal tax cut by the accounting firm Deloitte and Touche, a single person with a household income of \$41,000 would save \$211 in income taxes, while a single person with a household income of \$530,000 would save \$12,838 in taxes. A married couple with two children and a household income of \$41,000 would save \$1208 in income taxes, while a married couple with two children and a household income of \$530,000 would save \$13,442 in taxes.

a. Find the absolute difference in savings between a single person earning \$41,000 and a single person earning \$530,000. Then express the savings as a percentage of earnings for each person.

b. Find the absolute difference in savings between a married couple with two children earning \$41,000 and a married couple with two children earning \$530,000. Then express the savings as a percentage of earnings for each couple.

c. Write a paragraph either defending or disputing the position that the tax cut helps lower-income people.

WEB PROJECTS

32. **Polygraph Arguments.** Visit Web sites devoted to either opposing or supporting the use of polygraph tests. Summarize the arguments on both sides, specifically noting the role that false negative rates play in the discussion.

33. **Drug Testing.** Explore the issue of drug testing either in the workplace or for athletic competitions. Discuss the legality of drug testing in these settings and the accuracy of the tests that are commonly conducted.

34. **Cancer Screening.** Investigate recommendations concerning routine screening for some type of cancer (for example, breast cancer, prostate cancer, colon cancer). Explain how the accuracy of the screening test is measured. How is the test useful? How can its results be misleading?

IN YOUR WORLD

35. **Simpson's Paradox.** Find a recent news article that gives data whose interpretation may be complicated by Simpson's paradox (such as an article about possible discrimination). Explain what additional information you would need in order to reach a definitive conclusion.

36. **Polygraphs.** Find a recent article in which someone or some group proposes a polygraph test to determine whether a person is being truthful. In light of what you know about polygraph tests, do you think the results will be meaningful? Why or why not?

37. **Drug Testing and Athletes.** Find a news report concerning drug testing of athletes. Summarize how the testing is being used, and discuss whether the testing is reliable.

38. **Tax Change.** Find information about a recently proposed tax cut or increase, and find the arguments about fairness being used by both proponents and opponents of the change. Discuss the numerical data cited by each side. Which side do you think has the stronger argument? Why?

CHAPTER 3 Summary

UNIT	KEY TERMS	KEY IDEAS AND SKILLS
3A	absolute change relative change absolute difference relative difference	**Absolute change = new value − reference value** **Relative change** $= \dfrac{\text{absolute change}}{\text{reference value}} = \dfrac{\text{new value} - \text{reference value}}{\text{reference value}}$ **Absolute difference** = compared value − reference value **Relative difference** $= \dfrac{\text{absolute difference}}{\text{reference value}} = \dfrac{\text{compared value} - \text{reference value}}{\text{reference value}}$ **Understand** the *of* versus *more than* rule. **Understand** percentage points versus %. **Solve** percentage problems. **Identify** common abuses of percentages.
3B	scientific notation order of magnitude	**Write** and interpret numbers in scientific notation. **Put numbers in perspective** through estimation, including order of magnitude estimates comparisons scaling
3C	significant digits random error systematic error absolute error relative error accuracy precision	**Distinguish significant digits from nonsignificant zeros.** **Identify and distinguish** between random and systematic errors. **Absolute error** = measured value − true value **Relative error** $= \dfrac{\text{absolute error}}{\text{true value}} = \dfrac{\text{measured value} - \text{true value}}{\text{true value}}$ **Distinguish** between accuracy and precision. **Apply rounding rules** for combining approximate numbers. Addition/subtraction: Round to the precision of the *least precise* number in the problem. Multiplication/division: Round to the same number of significant digits as in the number in the problem with the fewest significant digits.
3D	index number reference value Consumer Price Index (CPI) inflation	**Understand index numbers** and how they are useful for comparisons. **Index number** $= \dfrac{\text{value}}{\text{reference value}} \times 100$ **Understand** how the CPI is used to measure inflation. **Adjust** prices for inflation with the CPI: $\text{price in } \$_Y = (\text{price in } \$_X) \times \dfrac{\text{CPI}_Y}{\text{CPI}_X}$
3E	Simpson's paradox test results: false positive true positive false negative true negative	**Understand and give examples of Simpson's paradox.** **Understand and give examples** of how mammograms and polygraphs can lead to surprising results. **Understand and give examples** of how Democrats and Republicans can make different claims about the same data, even if neither side is lying.

4

Managing Money

A fool and his money are soon parted.

—English proverb

Managing your personal finances is a complex task in the modern world. If you are like most Americans, you already have a bank account and at least one credit card. You may also have student loans, a home mortgage, and various investment plans. In this chapter, we discuss key issues in personal financial management, including budgeting, savings, loans, taxes, and investments. We also explore how the government manages its money, which affects all of us.

UNIT 4A

Taking Control of Your Finances: You cannot achieve financial success unless you know how to make wise decisions about your money. We discuss the basics of personal budgeting.

UNIT 4B

The Power of Compounding: We explore the way in which you can increase your savings through the mathematics of compound interest.

UNIT 4C

Savings Plans and Investments: We calculate the future value of savings plans in which you make monthly deposits and study investments in stocks and bonds.

UNIT 4D

Loan Payments, Credit Cards, and Mortgages: We calculate monthly payments and explore loan issues.

UNIT 4E

Income Taxes: We explore the mathematics of income taxes and a few of the hot political issues that surround them.

UNIT 4F

Understanding the Federal Budget: Personal finances are ultimately tied to government finances. We examine the federal budget process and related political issues.

ACTIVITY Student Loans

Use this activity to gain a sense of the kinds of problems this chapter will enable you to study. Try working through it before you begin the chapter, then return to it after you've learned the chapter material.

If you are like most college students in the United States, you probably have received money through at least one student loan, and you are likely to need more student loans in the future. Even if you don't personally have a student loan, many of your friends probably do. But student loans don't always have the same cost. For example, two students who each borrow $10,000 won't necessarily owe the same amounts at graduation, and they may not have the same interest rate or monthly payments once they take a job. Moreover, rules, fees, and penalties also differ for student loans. Because they are such an important part of most students' lives, let's use student loans to begin thinking about the financial topics that will be covered in this chapter.

1. Do you have a student loan? If you do, did you really need the loan in order to attend college, or did you have other options for paying for your college education? If you don't have a student loan, how have you managed to avoid having one, and do you think you will need one in the future?
2. If you have one or more student loans, look up their terms. What are the interest rates? When will you have to start paying back the loans? How long will you have to make payments, and what will your monthly payments be? If you don't have a student loan, answer these questions for a loan that you could in principle take out.
3. Suppose that you need to borrow $10,000 to pay for your next year of college. Use resources available through your college or the Web to investigate your options for a new $10,000 student loan. Which option seems the best, and why?
4. Whether or not you have student loans, college is expensive. What makes you think that it is worth its cost? How do you expect to benefit from your college education?

UNIT 4A Taking Control of Your Finances

Money can't buy me love . . .

—The Beatles

Money isn't everything, but it certainly has a great influence on our lives. Most people would like to have more money, and there's no doubt that more money allows you to do things that simply aren't possible with less. However, when it comes to personal happiness, studies show that the amount of money you have is less important than having your personal finances under control. People who lose control of their finances tend to suffer from financial stress, which in turn leads to higher divorce rates and other difficulties in personal relationships, higher rates of depression, and a variety of other ailments. In contrast, people who manage their money well are more likely to say they are happy, even when they are not particularly wealthy. So if you want to attain happiness—along with any financial goals you might have—the first step is to make sure you understand *your* personal finances enough to keep them well under control.

Take Control

If you're reading this book, chances are that you are in college somewhere. In that case, you are almost certainly facing financial challenges that you've never had to deal with before. If you are a recent high school graduate, this may be the first time that you are fully responsible for your own financial well-being. If you are coming back to school after years in the work force or as a parent, you now have the challenge of juggling the cost of college with all the other financial challenges of daily life.

The key to success in meeting these financial challenges is to make sure you always control them, rather than letting them control you. And the first step in gaining control is to make sure you keep track of your finances. Unless you happen to be among the superrich, keeping track of your finances probably isn't that difficult, but it requires diligence. For example, you should always know your bank account balance, so that you never have to worry about bouncing a check or having your debit card rejected. Similarly, you should know what you are spending on your credit card—and if it's going to be possible for you to pay off the card at the end of the month or if your spending will dig you deeper into debt. And, of course, you should spend money wisely and at a level that you can afford.

There are lots of books and Web sites designed to help you control your finances, but in the end they all come back to the same basic idea: You need to know how much money you have and how much money you spend, and then find a way to live within your means. If you can do that, as summarized in the following box, you have a good chance at financial success and happiness.

BY THE WAY

College is expensive, but statistically it's worth it: The average college graduate earns nearly $20,000 per year more than a person who graduates only from high school, which adds up to nearly *$1 million* in extra income over the course of a career. Of course, this is only an average: Students who take harder classes and get better grades tend to get higher-paying jobs than those who take an easier route through school.

CONTROLLING YOUR FINANCES

- Know your bank balance. You should never bounce a check or have your debit card rejected.
- Know what you spend; in particular, keep track of your debit and credit card spending.
- Don't buy on impulse. Think first; then buy only if you are sure the purchase makes sense for you.
- Make a budget, and don't overspend it.

Example 1 Latte Money

Calvin isn't rich, but he gets by, and he loves sitting down for a latte at the college coffee shop on a busy day. With tax and tip, he usually spends $5 on his large latte. He gets at least one every day (on average), and about every three days he has a second one. He figures it's not such a big indulgence. Is it?

Solution One a day means 365 per year. A second one every third day adds about $365/3 = 121$ more (rounding down). That means $365 + 121 = 486$ lattes a year. At $5 apiece, this comes to

$$486 \times \$5 = \$2430$$

Calvin's coffee habit is costing him more than $2400 per year. That might not be much if he's financially well off. But it's more than two months of rent for an average college student; it's enough to allow him to take a friend out for a $100 dinner twice a month; and it's enough so that if he saved it, with interest he could easily build a savings balance of more than $25,000 over the next ten years. **Now try Exercises 13–20.**

Example 2 Credit Card Interest

Cassidy has recently begun to keep her spending under better control, but she still can't fully pay off her credit card. She's maintaining an average monthly balance of about $1100, and her card charges a 24% annual interest rate, which it bills at a rate of 2% per month. How much is she spending on credit card interest?

Solution Her average monthly interest is 2% of the $1100 average balance, which is

$$0.02 \times \$1100 = \$22$$

BY THE WAY

Credit card companies sometimes set minimum payments that are less than or equal to the interest alone—in which case you will *never* pay off your credit card if you make only the minimum payments. To avoid this problem, be sure you are always paying at least something toward principal. You can use the "2 by 24" rule: If your interest rate is 24%, be sure you are paying more than 2% of the balance each month. Better yet, pay off the entire balance so that you won't be paying such exorbitant interest.

Multiplying by the 12 months in a year gives her annual interest payment:

$$12 \times \$22 = \$264$$

Interest alone is costing Cassidy more than \$260 per year—a significant amount for someone living on a tight budget. Clearly, she'd be a lot better off if she could find a way to pay off that credit card balance quickly and end those interest payments.

Now try Exercises 21–24.

Master Budget Basics

As you can see from Examples 1 and 2, one of the keys to deciding what you can afford is knowing your personal budget. Making a budget means keeping track of how much money you have coming in and how much you have going out and then deciding what adjustments you need to make. The following box summarizes the four basic steps in making a budget.

A FOUR-STEP BUDGET

1. List all your monthly income. Be sure to include a prorated amount—that is, what it averages out to per month—for any income you do not receive monthly (such as once-per-year payments).
2. List all your monthly expenses. Be sure to include a prorated amount for expenses that don't recur monthly, such as expenses for tuition, books, vacations, and holiday gifts.
3. Subtract your total expenses from your total income to determine your net monthly **cash flow**.
4. Make adjustments as needed.

For most people, the most difficult part of the budget process is making sure you don't leave anything out of your list of monthly expenses. A good technique is to keep careful track of your expenses for a few months. For example, carry a small note pad with you, and write down everything you spend. And don't forget to prorate your occasional expenses, or else you may severely underestimate your average monthly costs.

Once you've made your lists for steps 1 and 2, the third step is just arithmetic: Subtracting your monthly expenses from your monthly income gives you your overall monthly **cash flow**. If your cash flow is positive, you will have money left over at the end of each month, which you can use for savings. If your cash flow is negative, you have a problem: You'll need to find a way to balance it out, either by earning more, spending less, using savings, or taking out a loan.

Example 3 College Expenses

In addition to your monthly expenses, you have the following college expenses that you pay twice a year: \$3500 for your tuition each semester, \$750 in student fees each semester, and \$500 for textbooks each semester. How should you handle these expenses in computing your monthly budget?

Solution Since you pay these expenses twice a year, the total amount you pay over a whole year is

$$2 \times (\$3500 + \$750 + \$500) = \$9500$$

To prorate this total expense for the year on a monthly basis, we divide it by 12:

$$\$9500 \div 12 \approx \$792$$

Your average monthly college expense for tuition, fees, and textbooks comes to just under $800, so you should put $800 per month into your expense list.

Now try Exercises 25–30.

BY THE WAY

The cost of a college education is significantly more than what students actually pay in tuition and fees. On average, tuition and fees cover about two-thirds of the total cost at private colleges and universities, one-third of the cost at public four-year institutions, and 20% of the cost at two-year public colleges. The rest is covered by taxpayers, alumni donations, grants, and other revenue sources.

Example 4 College Student Budget

Brianna is creating a budget. The expenses she pays monthly are $700 for rent, $120 for gas for her car, $140 for health insurance, $75 for auto insurance, $25 for renters' insurance, $110 for her cell phone, $100 for utilities, about $300 for groceries, and about $250 for entertainment, including eating out. In addition, over the entire year she spends $12,000 for college expenses, about $1000 on gifts for family and friends, about $1500 for vacations at spring and winter break, about $800 on clothes, and $600 in gifts to charity. Her income consists of a monthly, after-tax paycheck of about $1600 and a $3000 scholarship that she received at the beginning of the school year. Find her total monthly cash flow.

Solution Step 1 in creating her budget is to come up with her total monthly income. Her $3000 scholarship means an average of $3000/12 = $250 per month on a prorated basis. Adding this to her $1600 monthly paycheck makes her average monthly income $1850.

Step 2 is to look at her monthly expenses. Those paid monthly come to $700 + $120 + $140 + $75 + $25 + $110 + $100 + $300 + $250 = $1820. Her annual expenses come to $12,000 + $1000 + $1500 + $800 + $600 = $15,900; dividing this sum by the 12 months in a year gives $15,900/12 = $1325 on a prorated monthly basis. Thus, her average monthly expenditures are $1820 + $1325 = $3145.

Step 3 is to find her cash flow by subtracting her expenses from her income:

$$\begin{aligned}\text{monthly cash flow} &= \text{monthly income} - \text{monthly expenses}\\ &= \$1850 - \$3145\\ &= -\$1295\end{aligned}$$

Her monthly cash flow is about −$1300. The fact that this amount is negative means she is spending about $1300 per month—or about $1300 × 12 = $15,600 per year—more than she is taking in. Unless she can find a way to earn more or spend less, she will have to cover this excess expenditure either by drawing on past savings (her own or her family's) or by going into debt.

Now try Exercises 31–34.

Time Out to Think

Look carefully at the list of expenses for Brianna in Example 4. Do *you* have any categories of expenses that are *not* covered on her list? If so, what?

Adjust Your Budget

If you're like most people, a careful analysis of your budget will prove very surprising. For example, many people find that they are spending a lot more in certain categories than they had imagined, and that the items they thought were causing their biggest difficulties are small compared to other items. Once you evaluate your current budget, you'll almost certainly want to make adjustments to improve your cash flow for the future.

BY THE WAY

Spending patterns have shifted a great deal over time. At the beginning of the twentieth century, the average American family spent 43% of its income on food and 23% on housing. Today, food accounts for only 13% of the average family's spending, while housing takes 33%. Notice that the *combined* percentage for food and housing has declined from 66% to 46% over the past century, implying that families now spend significantly higher percentages of income on other items, including leisure activities.

There are no set rules for adjusting your budget, so you'll need to use your critical thinking skills to come up with a plan that makes sense for you. If your finances are complicated—for example, if you are a returning college student who is juggling a job and family while attending school—you might benefit from consulting a financial advisor or reading a few books about financial planning.

You might also find it helpful to evaluate your own spending against average spending patterns. For example, if you are spending a higher percentage of your money on entertainment than the average person, you might want to consider finding lower-cost entertainment options. Figure 4.1 summarizes the average spending patterns for people of different ages in the United States.

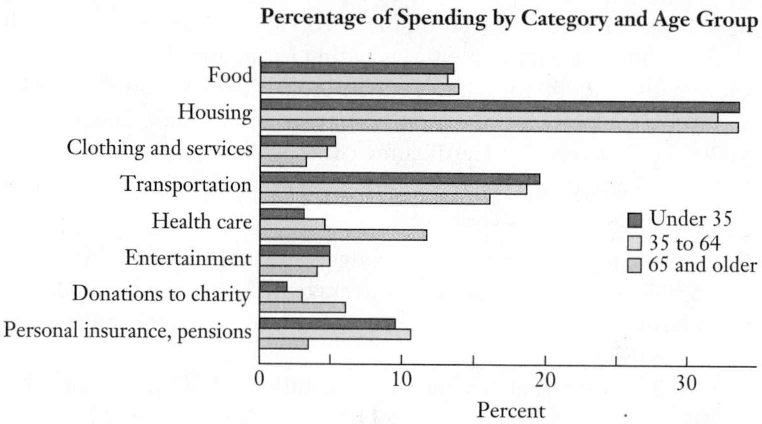

FIGURE 4.1 Average spending patterns by age group. Technical note: The data show spending per "consumer unit," which is defined to be either a single person or a family sharing a household. *Source:* U.S. Department of Labor, Bureau of Labor Statistics.

Example 5 Affordable Rent?

You've worked up a budget and find that you have $1500 per month available for all your personal expenses combined. According to the spending averages in Figure 4.1, how much should you be spending on rent?

Solution Figure 4.1 shows that the percentage of spending for housing varies very little across age groups; it is close to 1/3, or 33%, across the board. Based on this average and your available budget, your rent would be about 33% of $1500, or $500 per month. That's low compared to rents for apartments in most college towns, which means you face a choice: Either you can put a higher proportion of your income toward rent—in which case you'll have less left over for other types of expenditures than the average person—or you can seek a way of keeping rent down, such as finding a roommate. **Now try Exercises 35–40.**

Look at the Long Term

Figuring out your monthly budget is a crucial step in taking control of your personal finances, but it is only the beginning. Once you have understood your budget, you need to start looking at longer-term issues. There are far too many issues to be listed here, and many of them depend on your personal circumstances and choices. But the general principle is always the same: Before making any major expenditure or investment, be sure you figure out how it will affect your finances over the long term.

Example 6 Cost of a Car

Jorge commutes both to his job and to school, driving a total of about 250 miles per week. His current car is fully paid off, but it's getting old. He is spending about $1800 per year on it for repairs, and it gets only about 18 miles per gallon. He's thinking about buying a new hybrid that will cost $25,000 but that should be maintenance-free aside from oil changes over the next five years, and it gets 54 miles per gallon. Should he do it?

Solution To figure out whether the new car expense makes sense, Jorge needs to consider many factors. Let's start with gas. His 250 miles per week of driving means about $250 \text{ mi/wk} \times 52 \text{ wk/yr} = 13{,}000$ miles per year of driving. In his current car that gets 18 miles per gallon, this means he needs about 720 gallons of gas:

$$\frac{13{,}000 \text{ mi}}{18 \dfrac{\text{mi}}{\text{gal}}} \approx 720 \text{ gal}$$

If we assume that gas costs $3 per gallon, this comes to 720 × $3 = $2160 per year. Notice that the 54-miles-per-gallon gas mileage for the new car is three times the 18-miles-per-gallon mileage for his current car, so gasoline cost for the new car would be only 1/3 as much, or about $720. He would therefore save $2160 − $720 = $1440 each year on gas. He would also save the $1800 per year that he's currently spending on repairs, making his total annual savings about $1440 + $1800 = $3240.

Over five years, Jorge's total savings on gasoline and repairs would come to about $3240/yr × 5 yr = $16,200. Although this is still short of the $25,000 he would spend on the new car, the savings are starting to look pretty good, and they will get better if he keeps the new car for more than five years or if he can sell it for a decent price at the end of five years. On the other hand, if he has to take out a loan to buy the new car, his interest payments will add an extra expense; insurance for the new car may cost more as well. What would *you* do in this situation? **Now try Exercises 41–46.**

Example 7 Is a College Class Worth Its Cost?

Across all institutions, the average cost of a three-credit college class is approximately $1500. Suppose that, between class time, commute time, and study time, the average class requires about 10 hours per week of your time. Assuming that you could have had a job paying $10 per hour, what is the net cost of the class compared to working? Is it a worthwhile expense?

Solution A typical college semester lasts 14 weeks, so your "lost" work wages for the time you spend on the class come to

$$14 \text{ wk} \times \frac{10 \text{ hr}}{\text{wk}} \times \frac{\$10}{\text{hr}} = \$1400$$

We find your total net cost of taking the class by adding this to the $1500 that the class itself costs. The result is $2900. Whether this expense is worthwhile is subjective, but remember that the average college graduate earns nearly $1 million more over a career than a high school graduate. And also remember that, on average, students who do better in college do even better in their career earnings. **Now try Exercises 47–48.**

Time Out to Think

Following up on Example 7, suppose that you are having difficulty in a particular class, but believe that you could raise your grade by cutting back on your work hours to allow more time for studying. How would you decide whether you should do this? Explain.

Base Financial Goals on Solid Understanding

These days, it's rare for a financial decision to have a clear "best" answer for everyone. Instead, your decisions will depend on your current circumstances, your goals for the future, and some unavoidable uncertainty. The key to your future financial success is to approach all your financial decisions with a clear understanding of the available choices.

In the rest of this chapter, we'll study several crucial topics in finance, helping you to build the understanding you'll need to reach your financial goals. To prepare yourself for this study, it's worth taking a few moments to think about the impact that each of these topics will have on your financial life. In particular:

- Achieving your financial goals will almost certainly require that you build up savings over time. Although it may be difficult to save while you are still in college, ultimately you will need to find a way to make your budget allow for savings; you'll also need to understand how savings work and how to choose appropriate savings plans. These are the topics of Units 4B and 4C.
- You will probably need to borrow money at various points in your life. You may already have credit cards, or you may be using student loans to help pay for college. In the future, you may need loans for large purchases, such as a car or a home. Because borrowing is very expensive, it's critical that you understand the basic mathematics of loans so that you can make wise choices; this is the topic of Unit 4D.
- Whether we like it or not, many of the financial decisions we make have consequences on our taxes. Sometimes, these tax consequences can be large enough to influence our decisions. For example, the fact that interest on house payments is tax deductible while rent is not may influence your decision to rent or buy. While no one can expect to understand tax law fully, it's important to have at least a basic understanding of how taxes are computed and how they can affect your financial decisions; this is the topic of Unit 4E.
- Finally, we do not live in isolation, and our personal finances are inevitably intertwined with the government's finances. For example, when politicians allow the government to run deficits now, it means that future politicians will have to collect more tax dollars from you or your children. We'll devote Unit 4F to discussing the federal budget and what it may mean for you in the future.

QUICK QUIZ

Choose the best answer to each of the following questions. Explain your reasoning with one or more complete sentences.

1. By evaluating your monthly budget, you can learn how to
   a. keep your personal spending under control.
   b. make better investments.
   c. earn more money.
2. The two things you must keep track of in order to understand your budget are
   a. your income and your spending.
   b. your wages and your bank interest.
   c. your wages and your credit card debt.
3. A *negative* monthly cash flow means that
   a. your investments are losing value.
   b. you are spending more money than you are taking in.
   c. you are taking in more money than you are spending.
4. When you are making your monthly budget, what should you do with your once-a-year expenses for December holiday gifts?
   a. Ignore them.
   b. Include them only in your calculation for December's budget.
   c. Divide them by 12 and include them as a monthly expense.
5. For the average person, the single biggest category of expense is
   a. food.
   b. housing.
   c. entertainment.
6. According to Figure 4.1, which of the following expenses tends to increase the most as a person ages?
   a. housing
   b. transportation
   c. health care

7. Which of the following is *necessary* if you want to make monthly contributions to savings?
   a. You must have a positive monthly cash flow.
   b. You must be spending less than 20% of your income on food and clothing.
   c. You must not owe money on any loans.
8. Trey smokes about $1\frac{1}{2}$ packs of cigarettes per day and pays about $3.50 per pack. His *monthly* spending on cigarettes is closest to
   a. $50. b. $100. c. $150.
9. Kira drinks about 6 cans of soda each day, generally buying them from vending machines at an average price of $1.25. Her *annual* spending on soda is closest to
   a. $500. b. $1500. c. $3000.
10. You drive an average of 400 miles per week in a car that gets 18 miles per gallon. With gasoline priced at $3 per gallon, approximately how much would you save each year on gas if you instead had a car that got 50 miles per gallon?
   a. $500 b. $2200 c. $4500

Exercises 4A

REVIEW QUESTIONS

1. Why is it so important to understand your personal finances? What types of problems are more common among people who do not have their finances under control?
2. List four crucial things you should do if you hope to keep your finances under control, and describe how you can achieve each one.
3. What is a budget? Describe the four-step process of figuring out your monthly budget.
4. What is cash flow? Briefly describe your options if you have a negative monthly cash flow, and contrast them with your options if you have a positive monthly cash flow.
5. Summarize how average spending patterns change with age. How can comparing your own spending to average spending patterns help you evaluate your budget?
6. What items should you include when calculating how much it is costing you to attend college? How can you decide whether this is a worthwhile expense?

DOES IT MAKE SENSE?

Decide whether each of the following statements makes sense (or is clearly true) or does not make sense (or is clearly false). Explain your reasoning.

7. When I figured out my monthly budget, I included only my rent and my spending on gasoline, because nothing else could possibly add up to much.
8. My monthly cash flow was −$150, which explained why my credit card debt kept rising.
9. My vacation travel cost a total of $1800, which I entered into my monthly budget as $150 per month.
10. Emma and Emily are good friends who do everything together, spending the same amounts on eating out, entertainment, and other leisure activities. Yet Emma has a negative monthly cash flow while Emily's is positive, because Emily has more income.
11. Brandon discovered that his daily routine of buying a slice of pizza and a soda at lunch was costing him more than $15,000 per year.
12. I bought the cheapest health insurance I could find, because that's sure to be the best option for my long-term financial success.

BASIC SKILLS & CONCEPTS

13–20: Extravagant Spending? Compute the total cost per year of the following pairs of expenses. Then complete the sentence: On an *annual* basis, the first set of expenses is ______ % of the second set of expenses.

13. Maria spends $20 every week on coffee and spends $130 per month on food.
14. Jeremy buys the *New York Times* from the newsstand for $1 a day (skipping Sundays) and spends $20 per week on gasoline for his car.
15. Suzanne's cell phone bill is $85 per month, and she spends $200 per year on student health insurance.
16. Homer spends $10 per week on lottery tickets and $400 per month on rent.
17. Sheryl spends $9 every week on cigarettes and spends $30 a month on dry cleaning.
18. Ted goes to a club or concert every two weeks and spends an average of $60 each time; he spends $500 a year on car insurance.
19. Vern drinks three 6-packs of beer each week at a cost of $7 each and spends $700 per year on his textbooks.
20. Sandy fills the gas tank of her car an average of once every two weeks at a cost of $35 per tank; her cable TV/Internet service costs $60 per month.

21–24: Interest Payments. Find the *monthly* interest payments in the following situations. Assume that monthly interest rates are 1/12 of annual interest rates.

21. You maintain an average balance of $650 on your credit card, which carries an 18% annual interest rate.
22. Brooke's credit card has an annual interest rate of 21% on her unpaid balance, which averages $900.
23. Vic bought a new plasma TV for $2200. He made a down payment of $300 and then financed the balance through the store. Unfortunately, he was unable to make the first monthly

payments and now pays 3% interest per month on the balance (while he watches his TV).

24. Deanna owes a clothing store $700, but until she makes a payment, she pays 9% interest per month.

25–30: **Prorating Expenses.** Prorate the following expenses and find the corresponding *monthly* expense.

25. During one year, Louisa pays $5600 for tuition and fees, plus $400 for textbooks, for each of two semesters.

26. During one year, Jason takes 15 credit-hours for each of three quarters. Tuition and fees amount to $600 per credit-hour. Textbooks average $350 per quarter.

27. Lan pays a semiannual premium of $650 for automobile insurance, a monthly premium of $125 for health insurance, and an annual premium of $400 for life insurance.

28. Juan pays $500 per month in rent, a semiannual car insurance premium of $800, and an annual health club membership fee of $900.

29. In filing his income tax, Raul reported annual contributions of $200 to a public radio station, $245 to a public TV station, $100 to a local food bank, and $300 to other charitable organizations.

30. Randy spends an average of $25 per week on gasoline and $45 every three months on the daily newspaper.

31–34: **Net Cash Flow.** The following tables show expenses and income for various individuals. Find each person's net monthly cash flow (it could be negative or positive). Assume that salaries and wages are after taxes, and assume 1 month = 4 weeks.

31.

Income	Expenses
Part-time job: $600/month	Rent: $450/month
College fund from grandparents: $400/month	Groceries: $50/week
Scholarship: $5000/year	Tuition and fees: $3000 twice a year
	Incidentals: $100/week

32.

Income	Expenses
Part-time job: $1200/month	Rent: $600/month
Student loan: $7000/year	Groceries: $70/week
Scholarship: $8000/year	Tuition and fees: $7500/year
	Health insurance: $40/month
	Entertainment: $200/month
	Phone: $65/month

33.

Income	Expenses
Salary: $2300/month	Rent: $800/month
	Groceries: $90/week
	Utilities: $125/month
	Health insurance: $360 semiannually
	Car insurance: $400 semiannually
	Gasoline: $25/week
	Miscellaneous: $400/month
	Phone: $85/month

34.

Income	Expenses
Salary: $32,000/year	House payments: $700/month
Pottery sales: $200/month	Groceries: $150/week
	Household expenses: $450/month
	Health insurance: $150/month
	Car insurance: $500 semiannually
	Savings plan: $200/month
	Donations: $600/year
	Miscellaneous: $800/month

35–40: **Budget Allocations.** Determine whether the following spending patterns are equal to, above, or below the national averages given in Figure 4.1. Assume that salaries and wages are after taxes.

35. A single 30-year-old woman with a monthly salary of $3200 spends $900 per month on rent.

36. A couple under the age of 30 has a combined household income of $3500 per month and spends $400 per month on entertainment.

37. A single 42-year-old man with a monthly salary of $3600 spends $200 per month on health care.

38. A 32-year-old couple with a combined household income of $45,500 per year spends $700 per month on transportation.

39. A retired couple (over 65 years old) with a fixed monthly income of $4200 spends $600 per month on health care.

40. A family with a 45-year-old wage earner has an annual household income of $48,000 and spends $1500 per month on housing.

41–46: **Making Decisions.** Consider the following situations, which each involve two options. Determine which option is less expensive. Are there unstated factors that might affect your decision?

41. You currently drive 250 miles per week in a car that gets 21 miles per gallon of gas. You are considering buying a new fuel-efficient car for $16,000 (after trade-in on your current car) that gets 45 miles per gallon. Insurance premiums for the new and old car are $800 and $400 per year, respectively. You anticipate spending $1500 per year on repairs for the old car and having no repairs on the new car. Assume gas costs $3.50 per gallon. Over a five-year period, is it less expensive to keep your old car or buy the new car?

42. You currently drive 300 miles per week in a car that gets 15 miles per gallon of gas. You are considering buying a new fuel-efficient car for $12,000 (after trade-in on your current car) that gets 50 miles per gallon. Insurance premiums for the new and old car are $800 and $600 per year, respectively. You anticipate spending $1200 per year on repairs for the old car and having no repairs on the new car. Assume gas costs $3.50 per gallon. Over a five-year period, is it less expensive to keep your old car or buy the new car?

43. You must decide whether to buy a new car for $22,000 or lease the same car over a three-year period. Under the terms

of the lease, you make a down payment of $1000 and have monthly payments of $250. At the end of three years, the leased car has a residual value (the amount you pay if you choose to buy the car at the end of the lease period) of $10,000. Assume you can sell the new car at the end of three years at the same residual value. Is it less expensive to buy or to lease?

44. You must decide whether to buy a new car for $22,000 or lease the same car over a four-year period. Under the terms of the lease, you make a down payment of $1000 and have monthly payments of $300. At the end of four years, the leased car has a residual value (the amount you pay if you choose to buy the car at the end of the lease period) of $8000. Assume you can sell the new car at the end of four years at the same residual value. Is it less expensive to buy or to lease?

45. You have a choice between going to an in-state college where you would pay $4000 per year for tuition and an out-of-state college where the tuition is $6500 per year. The cost of living is much higher at the in-state college, where you can expect to pay $700 per month in rent, compared to $450 per month at the other college. Assuming all other factors are equal, which is the less expensive choice on an annual (12-month) basis?

46. If you stay in your home town, you can go to Concord College at a reduced tuition of $3000 per year and pay $800 per month in rent. Or you can leave home, go to Versalia College on a $10,000 scholarship (per year), pay $16,000 per year in tuition, and pay $350 per month to live in a dormitory. You will pay $2000 per year to travel back and forth from Versalia College. Assuming all other factors are equal, which is the less expensive choice on an annual (12-month) basis?

47–48: **Choices.** Consider the following pairs of options and answer the questions that follow.

47. You could take a 15-week, three-credit college course, which requires 10 hours per week of your time and costs $500 per credit-hour in tuition. Or during those hours you could have a job paying $10 per hour. What is the net cost of the class compared to working? Given that the average college graduate earns nearly $20,000 per year more than a high school graduate, is paying for the college course a worthwhile expense?

48. You could have a part-time job (20 hours per week) that pays $15 per hour, or you could have a full-time job (40 hours per week) that pays $12 per hour. Because of the extra free time, you will spend $150 per week more on entertainment with the part-time job than with the full-time job. After accounting for the extra entertainment, how much more is your cash flow with the full-time job than with the part-time job? Neglect taxes and other expenses.

FURTHER APPLICATIONS

49. **Laundry Upgrade.** Suppose that you currently own a clothes dryer that costs $25 per month to operate. A new efficient dryer costs $620 and has an estimated operating cost of $15 per month. How long will it take for the new dryer to pay for itself?

50. **Solar Payback Period.** Julie is considering installing photovoltaic panels on the roof of her house. Her monthly electricity bills currently average $85. The cost of installing a photovoltaic system is $18,400; however, she expects to see a 40% reduction in this cost due to tax credits and local rebates. Assuming all of her electrical needs are met by the new system and neglecting possible profits when the system puts electricity back into the grid, what is the approximate payback period on the investment?

51. **Insurance Deductibles.** Many insurance policies carry a deductible provision that states how much of a claim you must pay out of pocket before the insurance company pays the remaining expenses. For example, if you file a claim for $350 on a policy with a $200 deductible, you pay $200 and the insurance company pays $150. In the following cases, determine how much you would pay with and without the insurance policy.

    a. You have a car insurance policy with a $500 deductible provision (per claim) for collisions. During a two-year period, you file claims for $450 and $925. The annual premium for the policy is $550.

    b. You have a car insurance policy with a $200 deductible provision (per claim) for collisions. During a two-year period, you file claims for $450 and $1200. The annual premium for the policy is $650.

    c. You have a car insurance policy with a $1000 deductible provision (per claim) for collisions. During a two-year period, you file claims for $200 and $1500. The annual premium for the policy is $300.

    d. Explain why lower insurance premiums go with higher deductibles.

52. **Car Leases.** Consider the following three lease options for a new car. Determine which lease is least expensive, assuming you buy the car when the lease expires. The residual is the amount you pay if you choose to buy the car when the lease expires. Discuss other factors that might affect your decision.

    - Plan A: $1000 down payment, $400 per month for two years, residual value = $10,000
    - Plan B: $500 down payment, $250 per month for three years, residual value = $9500
    - Plan C: $0 down payment, $175 per month for four years, residual value = $8000

53. **Health Costs.** Assume that you have a (relatively simple) health insurance plan with the following provisions:

    - Office visits require a co-payment of $25.
    - Emergency room visits have a $200 deductible (you pay the first $200).
    - Surgical operations have a $1000 deductible (you pay the first $1000).
    - You pay a monthly premium of $350.

During a one-year period, your family has the following expenses.

Expense	Total Cost (before insurance)
Feb. 18: Office visit	$100
Mar. 26: Emergency room	$580
Apr. 23: Office visit	$100
May 14: Surgery	$6500
July 1: Office visit	$100
Sept. 23: Emergency room	$840

a. Determine your health-care expenses for the year with the insurance policy.

b. Determine your health-care expenses for the year if you did not have the insurance policy.

54. **Health-Care Choices.** You have a choice of two health insurance policies with the following terms.

Plan A	Plan B
Office visits require a co-payment of $25.	Office visits require a co-payment of $25.
Emergency room visits have a $500 deductible (you pay the first $500).	Emergency room visits have a $200 deductible (you pay the first $200).
Surgical operations have a $5000 deductible (you pay the first $5000).	Surgical operations have a $1500 deductible (you pay the first $1500).
You pay a monthly premium of $300.	You pay a monthly premium of $700.

Suppose that during a one-year period your family has the following expenses.

Expense	Total Cost (before insurance)
Jan. 23: Emergency room	$400
Feb. 14: Office visit	$100
Apr. 13: Surgery	$1400
June 14: Surgery	$7500
July 1: Office visit	$100
Sept. 23: Emergency room	$1200

a. Determine your annual health-care expenses if you have Plan A.

b. Determine your annual health-care expenses if you have Plan B.

c. Would having no health insurance be better than either Plan A or Plan B?

55–58: Personal Finances. The following exercises involve analyses of your personal income and expenses. We suggest that students be allowed to fictionalize their data, if they wish.

55. **Daily Expenditures.** Keep a list of everything you spend money on during one entire day. Categorize each expenditure, and then make a table with one column for the categories and one column for the expenditures. Add a third column in which you compute how much you'd spend in a year if you spent the same amount every day.

56. **Weekly Expenditures.** Repeat Exercise 55, but this time make the list for a full week of spending rather than just one day.

57. **Prorated Expenditures.** Make a list of all the major expenses you have each year that you do not pay on a monthly basis, such as college expenses, holiday expenses, and vacation expenses. For each item, estimate the amount you spend in a year, and then determine the prorated amount that you should use when you determine your monthly budget.

58. **Monthly Cash Flow.** Create your complete monthly budget, listing all sources of income and all expenditures, and use it to determine your net monthly cash flow. Be sure to include small but frequent expenditures and prorated amounts for large expenditures. Explain any assumptions you make in creating your budget. When the budget is complete, write a paragraph or two explaining what you learned about your own spending patterns and what adjustments you may need to make to your budget.

WEB PROJECTS

59. **Personal Budgets.** Many Web sites provide personal budget advice and worksheets. Visit several of these sites and choose one to help you organize your budget for at least three months. Is the site effective in helping you plan your finances? Discuss how the site led to insights that you would not have had otherwise.

60. **U.S. Spending Patterns.** Find the complete (two-page) paper from which Figure 4.1 was taken (*Spending Patterns by Age*, U.S. Department of Labor, Bureau of Labor Statistics). Write a summary of the conclusions of the paper and discuss whether your personal finances fit the patterns described in the paper.

IN YOUR WORLD

61. **Personal Bankruptcies.** The rate of personal bankruptcies has been increasing for several years. Find at least three news articles on the subject, document the increase in bankruptcies, and explain the primary reasons for the increase.

62. **Consumer Debt.** Find data on the increase in consumer (credit card) debt in the United States. Based on your reading, do you think consumer debt is (a) a crisis, (b) a significant occurrence but nothing to worry about, or (c) a good thing? Justify your conclusion.

63. **U.S. Savings Rate.** When it comes to saving disposable income, Americans have a remarkably low savings rate. Find sources that compare the savings rates of Asian and European countries to that of the United States. Discuss your observations and put your own savings habits on the scale.

UNIT 4B The Power of Compounding

On July 18, 1461, King Edward IV of England borrowed the modern equivalent of \$384 from New College of Oxford. The King soon paid back \$160, but never repaid the remaining \$224. The debt was forgotten for 535 years. Upon its rediscovery in 1996, a New College administrator wrote to the Queen of England asking for repayment, with interest. Assuming an interest rate of 4% per year, he calculated that the college was owed \$290 billion.

This example illustrates what is sometimes called the "power of compounding": the remarkable way that money grows when interest continues to accumulate year after year. In the New College case, there is no clear record of a promise to repay the debt with interest, and even if there were, the Queen might not feel obliged to pay a debt that had been forgotten for more than 500 years. But anyone can take advantage of compound interest simply by opening a savings account. With patience, the results may be truly astonishing.

Simple versus Compound Interest

Imagine that you deposit \$1000 in Honest John's Money Holding Service, which promises to pay 5% interest each year. At the end of the first year, Honest John's sends you a check for

$$5\% \times \$1000 = 0.05 \times \$1000 = \$50$$

You also get \$50 at the end of the second and third years. Over the 3 years, you receive total interest of

$$3 \times \$50 = \$150$$

Your original \$1000 has grown in value to \$1150. Honest John's method of payment represents **simple interest**, in which interest is paid only on your actual investment, or **principal.**

Now, suppose that you place the \$1000 in a bank account that pays the same 5% interest once a year. But instead of paying you the interest directly, the bank adds the interest to your account. At the end of the first year, the bank deposits \$50 interest into your account, raising your balance to \$1050. At the end of the second year, the bank again pays you 5% interest. This time, however, the 5% interest is paid on the balance of \$1050, so it amounts to

$$5\% \times \$1050 = 0.05 \times \$1050 = \$52.50$$

Adding this \$52.50 raises your balance to

$$\$1050 + \$52.50 = \$1102.50$$

This is the new balance on which your 5% interest is computed at the end of the third year. So your third interest payment is

$$5\% \times \$1102.50 = 0.05 \times \$1102.50 = \$55.13$$

Therefore, your balance at the end of the third year is

$$\$1102.50 + \$55.13 = \$1157.63$$

Despite identical interest rates, you end up with \$7.63 more if you use the bank instead of Honest John's. The difference comes about because the bank pays you *interest on the interest* as well as on the original principal. This type of interest payment is called **compound interest.**

BY THE WAY

The New College administrator did not seriously believe that the Queen would pay \$290 billion. However, he suggested a compromise of assuming a 2% per year interest rate, in which case the college was owed only \$8.9 million. This, he said, would be enough to pay for a modernization project at the College. The Queen has not yet paid.

DEFINITIONS

The **principal** in financial formulas is the balance upon which interest is paid.

Simple interest is interest paid only on the original principal, and not on any interest added at later dates.

Compound interest is interest paid both on the original principal and on all interest that has been added to the original principal.

Example 1 Savings Bond

While banks almost always pay compound interest, bonds usually pay simple interest. Suppose you invest \$1000 in a savings bond that pays simple interest of 10% per year. How much total interest will you receive in 5 years? If the bond paid compound interest, would you receive more or less total interest? Explain.

Solution With simple interest, every year you receive the same interest payment of $10\% \times \$1000 = \$100$. Therefore, you receive a total of \$500 in interest over 5 years. With compound interest, you receive *more* than \$500 in interest because the interest each year is calculated on your growing balance rather than on your original principal.

A Brief Review — Powers and Roots

We have already reviewed powers of 10 (see A Brief Review, p. 100). Now, for our work with financial formulas, we review powers and roots more generally.

Basics of Powers

A number raised to the *n*th power is that number multiplied by itself *n* times (*n* is called an *exponent*). For example:

$$2^1 = 2 \qquad 2^2 = 2 \times 2 = 4 \qquad 2^3 = 2 \times 2 \times 2 = 8$$

A number to the *zero* power is defined to be 1. For example:

$$2^0 = 1$$

Negative powers are the reciprocals of the corresponding positive powers. For example:

$$5^{-2} = \frac{1}{5^2} = \frac{1}{5 \times 5} = \frac{1}{25} \qquad 2^{-3} = \frac{1}{2^3} = \frac{1}{2 \times 2 \times 2} = \frac{1}{8}$$

Power Rules

In the following rules, x represents a number being raised to a power, and n and m are exponents. Note that these rules work only when all powers involve the same number x.

- To multiply powers of the same number, *add* the exponents:

$$x^n \times x^m = x^{n+m}$$

Example: $2^3 \times 2^2 = 2^{3+2} = 2^5 = 32$

- To divide powers of the same number, *subtract* the exponents:

$$\frac{x^n}{x^m} = x^{n-m}$$

Example: $\frac{5^3}{5^2} = 5^{3-2} = 5^1 = 5$

- When a power is raised to another power, *multiply* the exponents:

$$(x^n)^m = x^{n \times m}$$

Example: $(2^2)^3 = 2^{2\times 3} = 2^6 = 64$

Basics of Roots

Finding a root is the reverse of raising a number to a power. Second roots, or square roots, are written with a number under the root symbol $\sqrt{\ }$. More generally, we indicate an *n*th root by writing a number under the symbol $\sqrt[n]{\ }$. For example:

$$\sqrt{4} = 2 \text{ because } 2^2 = 2 \times 2 = 4$$

$$\sqrt[3]{27} = 3 \text{ because } 3^3 = 3 \times 3 \times 3 = 27$$

$$\sqrt[4]{16} = 2 \text{ because } 2^4 = 2 \times 2 \times 2 \times 2 = 16$$

$$\sqrt[6]{1{,}000{,}000} = 10 \text{ because } 10^6 = 1{,}000{,}000$$

Roots as Fractional Powers

The *n*th root of a number is the same as the number raised to the $1/n$ power. That is,

$$\sqrt[n]{x} = x^{1/n}$$

For example:

$$64^{1/3} = \sqrt[3]{64} = 4$$

$$1{,}000{,}000^{1/6} = \sqrt[6]{1{,}000{,}000} = 10$$

Now try Exercises 15–26.

For example, because your first interest payment of \$100 raises your balance to \$1100, your next compound interest payment is $10\% \times \$1100 = \$110$, which is more than the simple interest payment of \$100. For the same interest rate, compound interest always raises your balance faster than simple interest. **Now try Exercises 43–46.**

The Compound Interest Formula

Let's return to King Edward's debt to the New College. We can calculate the amount owed to the College by pretending that the \$224 he borrowed was deposited into an interest-bearing account for 535 years. Let's assume, as did the New College administrator, that the interest rate was 4% per year. For each year, we can calculate the interest and the new balance with interest. The first three columns of Table 4.1 show these calculations for 4 years.

To find the total balance, we could continue the calculations to 535 years. Fortunately, there's a much easier way. The 4% annual interest rate means that each end-of-year balance is 104% of, or 1.04 times, the previous year's balance. As shown in the last column of Table 4.1, we can get each balance as follows:

- The balance at the end of 1 year is the original principal times 1.04:

$$\$224 \times 1.04 = \$232.96$$

- The balance at the end of 2 years is the 1-year balance times 1.04, which is equal to the original principal times $(1.04)^2$:

$$\$224 \times 1.04 \times 1.04 = \$224 \times (1.04)^2 = \$242.28$$

- The balance at the end of 3 years is the 2-year balance times 1.04, which is equal to the original principal times $(1.04)^3$:

$$\$224 \times 1.04 \times 1.04 \times 1.04 = \$224 \times (1.04)^3 = \$251.97$$

Continuing the pattern, we find that the balance after N years is the original principal times 1.04 raised to the Nth power. For example, the balance after $N = 10$ years is

$$\$224 \times (1.04)^{10} = \$331.57$$

We can generalize this result by looking carefully at the last equation above. Notice that the \$224 is the original principal that we began with. The 1.04 is 1 plus the interest rate of 4%, or 0.04. The exponent 10 is the number of times that the interest has been compounded. Let's write the equation again, adding these identifiers and turning it around to put the result on the left:

$$\underbrace{\$331.57}_{\text{accumulated balance, } A} = \underbrace{\$224}_{\text{original principal, } P} \times \underbrace{(1.04)}_{1 + \text{interest rate}}{}^{10} \leftarrow \text{number of compounding periods}$$

When interest is compounded just once a year, as it is in this case, the interest rate is called the **annual percentage rate**, or **APR**. The number of compounding periods is then simply the number of years, which we call Y, over which the principal earns interest. We therefore obtain the following general formula for interest compounded once a year.

USING TECHNOLOGY

Powers

Most calculators have a special key labeled y^x or ^ for raising a number to any power. Most spreadsheets and computer programs use the ^ symbol. For example, to calculate 1.04^{535}, you would enter 1.04^535. The screen shot below shows the calculation in Excel, with the answer in cell A1.

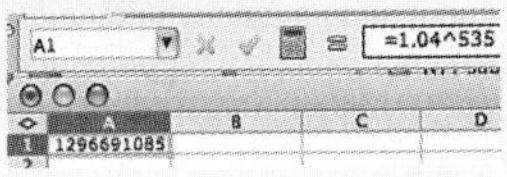

TABLE 4.1 Calculating Compound Interest

After N Years	Interest	Balance	Or Equivalently
1 year	$4\% \times \$224 = \$8.96$	$\$224 + \$8.96 = \$232.96$	$\$224 \times 1.04 = \$232.96$
2 years	$4\% \times \$232.96 = \$9.32$	$\$232.96 + \$9.32 = \$242.28$	$\$224 \times (1.04)^2 = \$242.28$
3 years	$4\% \times \$242.28 = \$9.69$	$\$242.28 + \$9.69 = \$251.97$	$\$224 \times (1.04)^3 = \$251.97$
4 years	$4\% \times \$251.97 = \$10.08$	$\$251.97 + \$10.08 = \$262.05$	$\$224 \times (1.04)^4 = \$262.05$

Take Note

For the more general case in which the interest rate is not necessarily set on an annual (APR) basis, you may see the compound interest formula written

$$A = P \times (1 + i)^N$$

where i is the interest rate and N is the total number of compounding periods.

THE COMPOUND INTEREST FORMULA (FOR INTEREST PAID ONCE A YEAR)

$$A = P \times (1 + \text{APR})^Y$$

where
A = accumulated balance after Y years
P = starting principal
APR = annual percentage rate (as a decimal)
Y = number of years

Notes: (1) The starting principal, P, is often called the **present value** (PV), because we usually begin a calculation with the amount of money in an account at present. (2) The accumulated balance, A, is often called the **future value** (FV), because it is the amount that will be accumulated at some time in the future. (3) When using this formula, you must express the APR as a decimal rather than as a percentage.

In the New College case, the annual interest rate is $APR = 4\% = 0.04$, and interest is paid over a total of 535 years. The accumulated balance after $Y = 535$ years is

$$\begin{aligned} A &= P \times (1 + \text{APR})^Y \\ &= \$224 \times (1 + 0.04)^{535} \\ &= \$224 \times (1.04)^{535} \\ &= \$224 \times 1{,}296{,}691{,}085 \\ &\approx \$2.9 \times 10^{11} = \$290 \text{ billion} \end{aligned}$$

As the administrator claimed, a 4% interest rate means the Queen owes about $290 billion.

Example 2 Simple and Compound Interest

You invest $100 in two accounts that each pay an interest rate of 10% per year. However, one account pays simple interest and one account pays compound interest. Make a table that shows the growth of each account over a 5-year period. Use the compound interest formula to verify the result in the table for the compound interest case.

Solution The simple interest is the same absolute amount each year. The compound interest grows from year to year, because it is paid on the accumulated interest as well as on the starting balance. Table 4.2 summarizes the calculations.

To verify the final entry in the table with the compound interest formula, we use a starting principal $P = \$100$ and an annual interest rate $\text{APR} = 10\% = 0.1$ with interest paid for $Y = 5$ years. The accumulated balance A is

$$\begin{aligned} A &= P \times (1 + \text{APR})^Y \\ &= \$100 \times (1 + 0.1)^5 \\ &= \$100 \times 1.1^5 \\ &= \$100 \times 1.6105 \\ &= \$161.05 \end{aligned}$$

TABLE 4.2 Calculations for Example 2

End of Year	Simple Interest Account: Interest Paid	Simple Interest Account: Old Balance + Interest = New Balance	Compound Interest Account: Interest Paid	Compound Interest Account: Old Balance + Interest = New Balance
1	10% × $100 = $10	$100 + $10 = **$110**	10% × $100 = $10	$100 + $10 = **$110**
2	10% × $100 = $10	$110 + $10 = **$120**	10% × $110 = $11	$110 + $11 = **$121**
3	10% × $100 = $10	$120 + $10 = **$130**	10% × $121 = $12.10	$121 + $12.10 = **$133.10**
4	10% × $100 = $10	$130 + $10 = **$140**	10% × $133.10 = $13.31	$133.10 + $13.31 = **$146.41**
5	10% × $100 = $10	$140 + $10 = **$150**	10% × $146.41 = $14.64	$146.41 + $14.64 = **$161.05**

This result agrees with the one in the table. Overall, the account paying compound interest builds to $161.05 while the simple interest account reaches only $150, even though both pay at the same 10% rate. Although the 10% interest rate that we assumed here is quite high compared to what most banks pay, the basic point should be clear: For the same interest rate, compound interest is always better for the investor than simple interest.
Now try Exercises 47–48.

USING TECHNOLOGY

The Compound Interest Formula

Standard Calculators You can do compound interest calculations on any calculator that has a key for raising numbers to powers (y^x or ∧). The only "trick" is making sure you follow the standard **order of operations:**

1. Parentheses: Do terms in parentheses first.
2. Exponents: Do powers and roots next.
3. Multiplication and Division: Work from left to right.
4. Addition and Subtraction: Work from left to right.

You can remember the order of operations with the mnemonic "Please Excuse My Dear Aunt Sally."

Let's apply this order of operations to the compound interest problem from Example 2, in which we have $P = \$100$, $APR = 0.1$, and $Y = 5$ years.

General Procedure	Our Example	Calculator Steps	Output
$A = P \times (1 + APR)^Y$	$A = 100 \times (1 + 0.1)^5$	Step 1 1 + 0.1 =	1.1
1. parentheses	1. parentheses	Step 2 ∧ 5 =	1.61051
2. exponent	2. exponent	Step 3 × $100 =	161.051
3. multiply	3. multiply		

Note: It is very important that you not round any of the answers in intermediate steps, even though you will round the final answer to the nearest cent.

Excel The built-in function FV (for future value) makes it easy to do compound interest calculations using Excel. The screen shot to the right shows how you use this function for our sample calculation. The table at the bottom explains the inputs that go in the parentheses of the FV function.

Although you can get the result simply by typing in the FV function, as above, we strongly recommend that you show your work more clearly by typing the inputs next to cells that are labeled descriptively. You can then reference the input cells in the FV function, as shown in the screen shot to the right. Note that besides making your work clearer, this approach makes it very easy to do "what if" scenarios—changing the interest rate, for example.

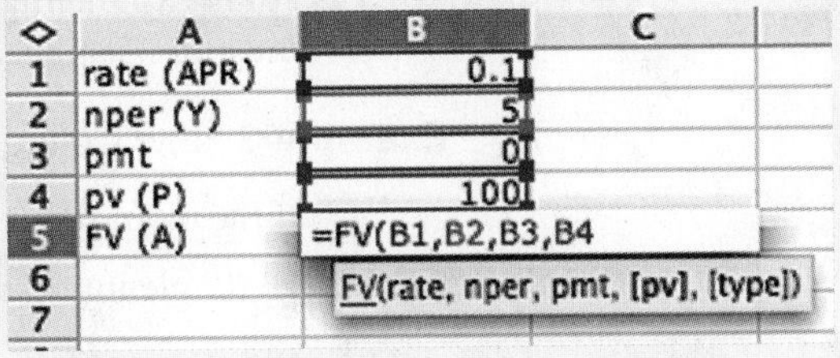

Input	Description	Our Example
rate	The interest rate for each compounding period	Because we are using interest compounded once a year, the interest rate is the annual rate, $APR = 0.1$.
nper	The total number of compounding periods	For interest compounded once a year, the total number of compounding periods is the number of years, $Y = 5$.
pmt	The amount of any payment made each month	No payment is being made monthly in our example, so we enter 0.
pv	The present value, equivalent to the starting principal P	We use the starting principal, $P = 100$.
type	An optional input related to whether monthly payments are made at the beginning $(\text{type} = 0)$ or end $(\text{type} = 1)$ of a month	Type does not apply in this case because there is no monthly payment, so we do not include it.

Compound Interest as Exponential Growth

The New College case demonstrates the remarkable way in which money can grow with compound interest. Figure 4.2 shows how the value of the New College debt rises during the first 100 years, assuming a starting value of \$224 and an interest rate of 4% per year. Note that while the value rises slowly at first, it rapidly accelerates, so in later years the value grows by much more each year than it did during earlier years.

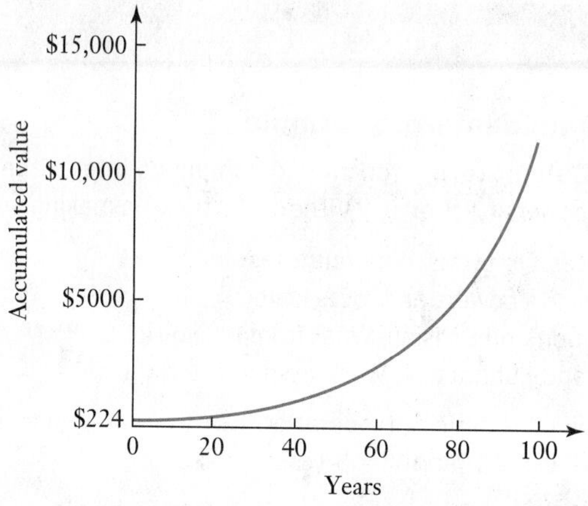

FIGURE 4.2 The value of the debt in the New College case during the first 100 years, at an interest rate of 4% per year. Note that the value rises much more rapidly in later years than in earlier years—a hallmark of exponential growth.

This rapid growth is a hallmark of what we generally call *exponential growth*. You can see how exponential growth gets its name by looking again at the general compound interest formula:

$$A = P \times (1 + \text{APR})^Y$$

Because the principal P and the interest rate APR have fixed values for any particular compound interest calculation, the growth of the accumulated value A depends only on Y (the number of times interest has been paid), which appears in the *exponent* of the calculation.

Exponential growth is one of the most important topics in mathematics, with applications that include population growth, resource depletion, and radioactivity. We will study exponential growth in much more detail in Chapter 8. In this chapter, we focus only on its applications in finance.

Example 3 New College Debt at 2%

If the interest rate is 2%, calculate the amount due to New College using

a. simple interest   b. compound interest

Solution

a. The following steps show the simple interest rate calculation for a principal of \$224 and an interest rate of 2%:

1. The simple interest due each year is 2% of the principal:	$2\% \times \$224 = 0.02 \times \$224 = \$4.48$
2. Over 535 years, this is the total interest due:	$535 \times \$4.48 = \$2396.80$
3. Adding total interest to the original loan principal of \$224 gives the payoff amount:	$\$224 + \$2396.80 = \$2620.80$

With simple interest, the payoff amount after 535 years is \$2620.80.

b. To find the amount due with compound interest, we set the annual interest rate to APR = 2% = 0.02 and the number of years to $Y = 535$. Then we use the formula for compound interest paid once a year:

$$\begin{aligned} A = P \times (1 + \text{APR})^Y &= \$224 \times (1 + 0.02)^{535} \\ &= \$224 \times (1.02)^{535} \\ &\approx \$224 \times 39{,}911 \\ &\approx \$8.94 \times 10^6 \end{aligned}$$

The amount due with compound interest is about \$8.94 million—far higher than the amount due with simple interest. **Now try Exercises 49–50.**

Effects of Interest Rate Changes

You should note the remarkable effects of small changes in the compound interest rate. In Example 3, we found that a 2% compound interest rate leads to a payoff amount of \$8.94 million after 535 years. Earlier, we found that a 4% interest rate for the same 535 years leads to a payoff amount of \$290 billion—which is more than 30,000 times as large as \$8.94 million. Figure 4.3 contrasts the values of the New College debt during the first 100 years at interest rates of 2% and 4%. Note that the rate change doesn't make much difference for the first few years, but over time the higher rate becomes far more valuable.

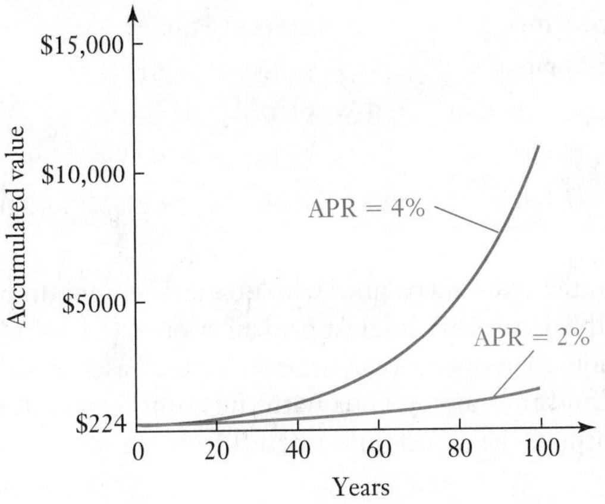

FIGURE 4.3 This figure contrasts the debt in the New College case during the first 100 years at interest rates of 2% and 4%.

Time Out to Think

Suppose the interest rate for the New College debt were 3%. Without calculating, do you think the value after 535 years would be halfway between the values at 2% and 4% or closer to one or the other of these values? Now, check your guess by calculating the value at 3%. What happens at an interest rate of 6%? Briefly discuss why small changes in the interest rate can lead to large changes in the accumulated value.

Example 4 Mattress Investments

Your grandfather put \$100 under his mattress 50 years ago. If he had instead invested it in a bank account paying 3.5% interest compounded yearly (roughly the average U.S. rate of inflation during that period), how much would it be worth now?

Solution The starting principal is $P = \$100$. The annual percentage rate is APR $= 3.5\% = 0.035$. The number of years is $Y = 50$. So the accumulated balance is

$$\begin{aligned} A = P \times (1 + \text{APR})^Y &= \$100 \times (1 + 0.035)^{50} \\ &= \$100 \times (1.035)^{50} \\ &= \$558.49 \end{aligned}$$

Invested at a rate of 3.5%, the \$100 would be worth over \$550 today. Unfortunately, the \$100 was put under a mattress, so it still has a face value of only \$100.

Now try Exercises 51–54.

Compound Interest Paid More Than Once a Year

Suppose you deposit \$1000 into a bank that pays compound interest at an annual percentage rate of APR = 8%. If the interest is paid all at once at the end of a year, you'll receive interest of

$$8\% \times \$1000 = 0.08 \times \$1000 = \$80$$

Thus, your year-end balance will be \$1000 + \$80 = \$1080.

Now, assume instead that the bank pays the interest *quarterly*, or four times a year (that is, once every 3 months). The quarterly interest rate is one-fourth of the annual interest rate:

$$\text{quarterly interest rate} = \frac{\text{APR}}{4} = \frac{8\%}{4} = 2\% = 0.02$$

Table 4.3 shows how quarterly compounding affects the \$1000 starting principal during the first year.

TABLE 4.3 Quarterly Interest Payments

After *N* Quarters	Interest Paid	New Balance
1st quarter (3 months)	2% × \$1000 = \$20	\$1000 + \$20 = \$1020
2nd quarter (6 months)	2% × \$1020 = \$20.40	\$1020 + \$20.40 = \$1040.40
3rd quarter (9 months)	2% × \$1040.40 = \$20.81	\$1040.40 + \$20.81 = \$1061.21
4th quarter (1 full year)	2% × \$1061.21 = \$21.22	\$1061.21 + \$21.22 = \$1082.43

Note that the year-end balance with quarterly compounding (\$1082.43) is *greater* than the year-end balance with interest paid all at once (\$1080). That is, when interest is compounded more than once a year, the balance increases by *more* than the APR in 1 year.

We can find the same results with the compound interest formula. Remember that the basic form of the compound interest formula is

$$A = P \times (1 + \text{interest rate})^{\substack{\text{number of} \\ \text{compoundings}}}$$

where A is the accumulated balance and P is the original principal. In our current case, the starting principal is $P = \$1000$, the quarterly payments have an interest rate of APR/4 = 0.02, and in one year the interest is paid four times. Therefore, the accumulated balance at the end of one year is

$$A = P \times (1 + \text{interest rate})^{\substack{\text{number of} \\ \text{compoundings}}} = \$1000 \times (1 + 0.02)^4 = \$1082.43$$

We see that if interest is paid quarterly, the interest rate at each payment is APR/4. Generalizing, if interest is paid n times per year, the interest rate at each payment is APR/n. The total number of times that interest is paid after Y years is nY. We therefore find the following formula for interest paid more than once each year.

COMPOUND INTEREST FORMULA FOR INTEREST PAID n TIMES PER YEAR

$$A = P\left(1 + \frac{\text{APR}}{n}\right)^{(nY)}$$

where

A = accumulated balance after Y years
P = starting principal
APR = annual percentage rate (as a decimal)
n = number of compounding periods per year
Y = number of years

Note that Y is not necessarily an integer; for example, a calculation for three and a half years would have $Y = 3.5$.

Time Out to Think

Confirm that substituting $n = 1$ into the formula for interest paid n times per year gives you the formula for interest paid once a year. Explain why this should be true.

USING TECHNOLOGY

The Compound Interest Formula for Interest Paid More than Once a Year

Standard Calculators The procedure with interest paid more than once a year is essentially the same as that for the basic compound interest formula (see Using Technology, p. 213), except you'll need to enter APR/n instead of just APR and nY instead of just Y. Let's apply the procedure to Example 5, in which we have $P = \$5000$, $\text{APR} = 0.03$, $n = 12$, and $Y = 5$ years.

General Procedure	Our Example	Calculator Steps*	Output
$A = P \times \left(1 + \frac{\text{APR}}{n}\right)^{(nY)}$ 1. parentheses 2. exponent 3. multiply	$A = 5000 \times \left(1 + \frac{0.03}{12}\right)^{(12 \times 5)}$ 1. parentheses 2. exponent 3. multiply	Step 1 1 (+) 0.03 (÷) 12 (=)	1.0025
		Step 2 (∧) (()12 (×) 5()) (=)	1.1616...
		Step 3 (×) \$5000 (=)	5808.08

*If your calculator does not have parentheses keys, then you will need to do the exponent ($nY = 12 \times 5$) before you start and keep track of it either on paper or in the calculator's memory.

Excel We use the built-in function FV, just as we did for the basic compound interest formula (p. 213), *except*

- because *rate* is the interest rate *for each compounding period*, in this case it is the monthly interest rate $\text{APR}/n = 0.03/12$.
- because *nper* is the total number of compounding periods, in this case it is $nY = 12 \times 5$. (Note that Excel uses an asterisk * for multiplication.)

The following screen shot shows the direct entry of the FV function for our example.

```
fx =FV(0.03/12,12*5,0,5000)
   FV(rate, nper, pmt, [pv], [type])
```

Again, it's best to show your work by referencing clearly labeled cells. In this case, we start with cells for APR, n, and Y, because these are the variables used in the compound interest formula in this book. These are then referenced to create the inputs for the FV function. You should create your own Excel worksheet to confirm that you get the result from Example 5 ($A = \$5808.08$).

	A	B
1	APR	0.03
2	n (monthly compounding)	12
3	Y (number of years)	5
4	rate for each compounding period = APR/n	=B1/B2
5	nper (total number of compounding periods = nY)	=B2*B3
6	pmt (no monthly payment in this case)	0
7	pv (present value = starting principal P)	5000
8	FV (future value = accumulated balance A)	=FV(B4,B5,B6,B7

Example 5 Monthly Compounding at 3%

You deposit $5000 in a bank account that pays an APR of 3% and compounds interest monthly. How much money will you have after 5 years? Compare this amount to the amount you'd have if interest were paid only once each year.

Solution The starting principal is $P = \$5000$ and the interest rate is APR $= 0.03$. Monthly compounding means that interest is paid $n = 12$ times a year, and we are considering a period of $Y = 5$ years. We put these values into the compound interest formula to find the accumulated balance, A.

$$\begin{aligned} A = P \times \left(1 + \frac{\text{APR}}{n}\right)^{(nY)} &= \$5000 \times \left(1 + \frac{0.03}{12}\right)^{(12 \times 5)} \\ &= \$5000 \times (1.0025)^{60} \\ &= \$5808.08 \end{aligned}$$

For interest paid only once each year, we find the balance after 5 years by using the formula for compound interest paid once a year:

$$\begin{aligned} A = P \times (1 + \text{APR})^{Y} &= \$5000 \times (1 + 0.03)^{5} \\ &= \$5000 \times (1.03)^{5} \\ &= \$5796.37 \end{aligned}$$

After 5 years, monthly compounding gives you a balance of $5808.08 while annual compounding gives you a balance of $5796.37. That is, monthly compounding earns $\$5808.08 - \$5796.37 = \$11.71$ more, even though the APR is the same in both cases.

Now try Exercises 55–62.

Annual Percentage Yield (APY)

We've seen that in one year, money grows by *more* than the APR when interest is compounded more than once a year. For example, we found that with quarterly compounding and an 8% APR, a $1000 principal increases to $1082.43 in one year. This represents a relative increase of 8.24%:

$$\text{relative increase} = \frac{\text{absolute increase}}{\text{starting principal}} = \frac{\$82.43}{\$1000} = 0.08243 = 8.243\%$$

This relative increase over one year is called the **annual percentage yield (APY)**. Note that the APY of 8.243% is greater than the APR of 8%.

DEFINITION

The **annual percentage yield (APY)** is the actual percentage by which a balance increases in one year. It is equal to the APR if interest is compounded annually. It is greater than the APR if interest is compounded more than once a year. The APY does not depend on the starting principal. The APY is sometimes also called the *effective yield* or simply the *yield*.

Banks usually list both the annual percentage rate (APR) and the annual percentage yield (APY). However, the APY is what your money really earns and is the more important number when you are comparing interest rates. Banks are required by law to state the APY on interest-bearing accounts.

Example 6 More Compounding Means a Higher Yield

You deposit \$1000 into an account with APR = 8%. Find the annual percentage yield with *monthly* compounding and with *daily* compounding.

Solution The easiest way to find the annual percentage yield is by finding the balance at the end of one year. We have $P = \$1000$, $\text{APR} = 8\% = 0.08$, $Y = 1$ year. For monthly compounding, we set $n = 12$. At the end of one year, the accumulated balance with monthly compounding is

$$\begin{aligned} A = P \times \left(1 + \frac{\text{APR}}{n}\right)^{(nY)} &= \$1000 \times \left(1 + \frac{0.08}{12}\right)^{(12\times1)} \\ &= \$1000 \times (1.006666667)^{12} \\ &= \$1083.00 \end{aligned}$$

Your balance increases by \$83.00, so the annual percentage yield is

$$\text{APY} = \text{relative increase in 1 year} = \frac{\$83.00}{\$1000} = 0.083 = 8.3\%$$

With monthly compounding, the annual percentage yield is 8.3%.

Daily compounding means that interest is paid $n = 365$ times per year. At the end of one year, your accumulated balance with daily compounding is

$$\begin{aligned} A = P \times \left(1 + \frac{\text{APR}}{n}\right)^{(nY)} &= \$1000 \times \left(1 + \frac{0.08}{365}\right)^{(365\times1)} \\ &= \$1000 \times (1.000219178)^{365} \\ &= \$1083.28 \end{aligned}$$

Your balance increases by \$83.28, so the annual percentage yield is

$$\text{APY} = \text{relative increase in 1 year} = \frac{\$83.28}{\$1000} = 0.08328 = 8.328\%$$

With an APR of 8% and daily compounding, the annual percentage yield is 8.328%, slightly higher than the APY for monthly compounding. The same APY would have been found using any starting principal. **Now try Exercises 63–66.**

USING TECHNOLOGY

APY in Excel

The Excel function EFFECT returns APY (the *effective yield*) from APR and the number of compounding periods per year (n); the format is EFFECT(APR, n). *Example:* With APR = 0.08 and $n = 4$, find the APY by entering

	A	B
1	=EFFECT(0.08,4)	

For cases where you know the APY and need to find the APR, use the NOMINAL function. *Example:* With APY = 0.08243 and $n = 4$ (quarterly compounding), find that APR = 0.08 by entering

	A	B
1	=NOMINAL(0.08243,4)	

Take Note

Most banks divide the APR by 360, rather than 365, when calculating the interest rate and APY for daily compounding. Thus, the results found here may not agree exactly with actual bank results.

Continuous Compounding

Suppose that interest were compounded more often than daily—say, every second or every trillionth of a second. How would this affect the annual percentage yield?

Let's examine what we've found so far for APR = 8%. If interest is compounded annually (once a year), the annual yield is simply APY = APR = 8%. With quarterly compounding, we found APY = 8.243%. With monthly compounding, we found APY = 8.300%. With daily compounding, we found APY = 8.328%. Clearly, more frequent compounding means a higher APY (for a given APR).

However, notice that the change gets smaller as the frequency of compounding increases. For example, changing from annual compounding ($n = 1$) to quarterly compounding ($n = 4$) increases the APY quite a bit, from 8% to 8.243%. In contrast, going from monthly ($n = 12$) to daily ($n = 365$) compounding increases the APY only slightly, from 8.300% to 8.328%. You probably won't be surprised to learn that the APY can't get much bigger than it already is for daily compounding.

TABLE 4.4 Annual Yield (APY) for APR = 8% with Various Numbers of Compounding Periods (n)

n	APY	n	APY
1	8.0000000%	1000	8.3283601%
4	8.2432160%	10,000	8.3286721%
12	8.2999507%	1,000,000	8.3287064%
365	8.3277572%	10,000,000	8.3287067%
500	8.3280135%	1,000,000,000	8.3287068%

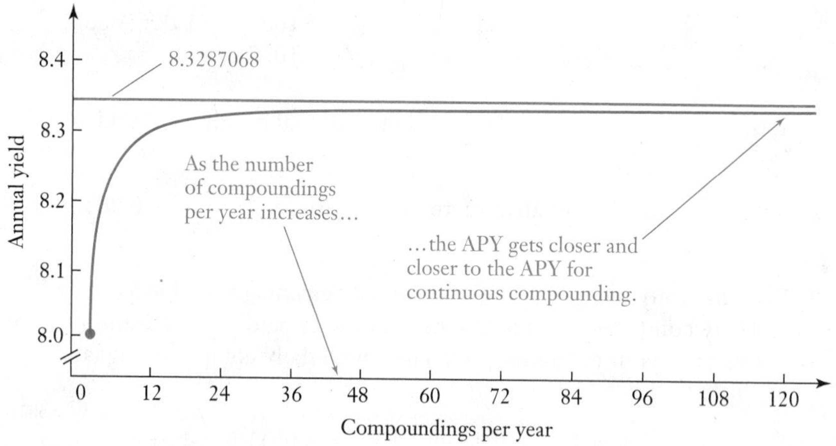

FIGURE 4.4 The annual percentage yield (APY) for APR = 8% depends on the number of times interest is compounded per year.

Table 4.4 shows the APY for various compounding periods and Figure 4.4 is a graph of the results. As expected, the annual yield does *not* grow indefinitely. Instead, it approaches a *limit* that is very close to the APY of 8.3287068% found for $n = 1$ billion. In other words, even if we could compound *infinitely many times* per year, the annual yield would not go much above 8.3287068%. Compounding infinitely many times per year is called **continuous compounding.** It represents the best possible compounding for a particular APR. With continuous compounding, the compound interest formula takes the following special form.

USING TECHNOLOGY

You can find powers of e in Excel with the function EXP(power). *Example:* To find $e^{0.8}$, enter

=EXP(0.8)

In Google, simply type e and use ∧ to raise it to a power.

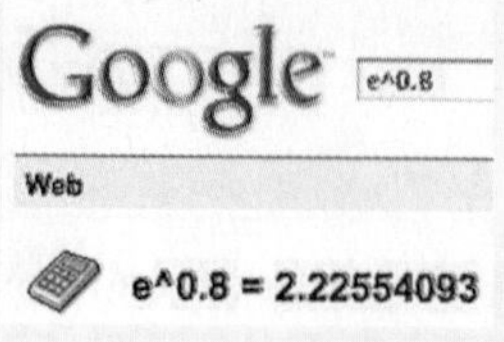

COMPOUND INTEREST FORMULA FOR CONTINUOUS COMPOUNDING

$$A = P \times e^{(\text{APR} \times Y)}$$

where

A = accumulated balance after Y years
P = starting principal
APR = annual percentage rate (as a decimal)
Y = number of years

The number e is a special irrational number with a value of $e \approx 2.71828$. You can compute e to a power with the e^x key on your calculator.

Time Out to Think

Look for the e^x key on your calculator. Use it to enter e^1 and thereby verify that $e \approx 2.71828$. Bonus: Also verify the value in Excel and with Google.

Example 7 Continuous Compounding

You deposit $100 in an account with an APR of 8% and continuous compounding. How much will you have after 10 years?

A Brief Review — Three Basic Rules of Algebra

In prior units, we've already encountered several instances in which we needed to solve an equation by adding, subtracting, multiplying, or dividing both sides by the same quantity. These operations will be useful in this unit and the rest of the book, so it is important to review the basic rules.

Three Basic Rules

The following three rules can always be used:

1. We can add or subtract the same quantity on both sides of an equation.
2. We can multiply or divide both sides of an equation by the same quantity, as long as we do not multiply or divide by zero.
3. We can interchange the left and right sides of an equation. That is, if $x = y$, it is also true that $y = x$.

Adding and Subtracting

The following examples show how adding to or subtracting from both sides can help solve equations that involve unknowns.

Example: Solve the equation $x - 9 = 3$ for x.

Solution: We isolate x by adding 9 to both sides:

$$x - 9 + 9 = 3 + 9 \quad \longrightarrow \quad x = 12$$

Example: Solve the equation $y + 6 = 2y$ for y.

Solution: Because we have y on the left side and $2y$ on the right, we can isolate y on the right by subtracting y from both sides:

$$y + 6 - y = 2y - y \quad \longrightarrow \quad 6 = y$$

We interchange the left and right sides, writing the answer as $y = 6$.

Example: Solve the equation $8q - 17 = p + 4q - 2$ for p.

Solution: We isolate p by subtracting $4q$ from both sides while also adding 2 to both sides:

$$8q - 17 - 4q + 2 = p + 4q - 2 - 4q + 2$$
$$\downarrow$$
$$4q - 15 = p$$

We interchange the left and right sides, writing the answer more simply as $p = 4q - 15$. Note that the equation is solved for p, but we cannot state a numerical value for p until we know the value of q.

Multiplying and Dividing

When we cannot isolate a variable by addition or subtraction alone, we may need to multiply or divide both sides of an equation by the same quantity.

Example: Solve the equation $4x = 24$ for x.

Solution: We isolate x by dividing both sides by 4:

$$\frac{\cancel{4}x}{\cancel{4}} = \frac{24}{4} \quad \longrightarrow \quad x = 6$$

Example: Solve the equation $\frac{3z}{4} - 2 = 10$ for z.

Solution: First, we isolate the term containing z by adding 2 to both sides:

$$\frac{3z}{4} - 2 + 2 = 10 + 2 \quad \longrightarrow \quad \frac{3z}{4} = 12$$

Now we multiply both sides by $\frac{4}{3}$:

$$\frac{\cancel{3}z}{\cancel{4}} \times \frac{\cancel{4}}{\cancel{3}} = \overset{4}{\cancel{12}} \times \frac{4}{\underset{1}{\cancel{3}}} \quad \longrightarrow \quad z = 16$$

Example: Solve the equation $7w = 3s + 5$ for s.

Solution: We isolate the term containing s by subtracting 5 from both sides:

$$7w - 5 = 3s + 5 - 5 \quad \longrightarrow \quad 7w - 5 = 3s$$

Next we divide both sides by 3 to isolate s. To write the final answer more simply, we also switch the left and right sides after dividing.

$$\frac{7w - 5}{3} = \frac{\cancel{3}s}{\cancel{3}} \quad \longrightarrow \quad s = \frac{7w - 5}{3}$$

Remember that you should always check that your solution satisfies the original equation.

Now try Exercises 27–42.

Historical Note

Like the number π that arises so frequently in mathematics, the number e is one of the universal constants of mathematics. It appears in countless applications, most importantly to describe exponential growth and decay processes. The notation e was proposed by the Swiss mathematician Leonhard Euler in 1727. Like π, the number e is not only an irrational number, but also a transcendental number.

Solution We have $P = \$100$, APR = 8% = 0.08, and $Y = 10$ years of continuous compounding. The accumulated balance after 10 years is

$$A = P \times e^{(\text{APR} \times Y)} = \$100 \times e^{(0.08 \times 10)} = \$100 \times e^{0.8} = \$222.55$$

Your balance will be \$222.55 after 10 years. Note: Be sure you can get the above answer by using the number e correctly with your calculator or computer.

Now try Exercises 67–72.

Planning Ahead with Compound Interest

Suppose you have a new baby and want to make sure that you'll have \$100,000 for his or her college education. Assuming your baby will start college in 18 years, how much money should you deposit now?

If we know the interest rate, this problem is simply a "backwards" compound interest problem. We start with the amount, A, needed after 18 years and then calculate the necessary starting principal, P. The following two examples illustrate the calculations.

Example 8 College Fund at 3%

Suppose you put money in an investment with an interest rate of APR = 3%, compounded annually, and leave it there for the next 18 years. How much would you have to deposit now to realize \$100,000 after 18 years?

Solution We know the interest rate (APR = 0.03), the number of years of compounding ($Y = 18$), and the amount desired after 18 years ($A = \$100{,}000$). To find the starting principal (P) that must be deposited now, we solve the compound interest formula for P, then substitute the given values for A, APR, and Y.

1. Start with the compound interest formula for interest paid once a year: $A = P \times (1 + \text{APR})^Y$
2. Interchange the left and right sides and divide both sides by $(1 + \text{APR})^Y$: $P = \dfrac{A}{(1 + \text{APR})^Y}$
3. Substitute the values APR = 0.03, $Y = 18$, and $A = \$100{,}000$: $P = \dfrac{\$100{,}000}{(1 + 0.03)^{18}} = \dfrac{\$100{,}000}{(1.03)^{18}} = \$58{,}739.46$

Depositing \$58,739 now will yield the desired \$100,000 in 18 years—assuming that the 3% APR doesn't change and that you make no withdrawals or additional deposits.

Now try Exercises 73–76.

BY THE WAY

The process of finding the principal (present value) that must be deposited today to yield some particular future amount is called *discounting* by financial planners.

Example 9 College Fund at 5%, Compounded Monthly

Repeat Example 8, but with an interest rate of 5% and monthly compounding. Compare the results.

Solution This time we solve for P in the compound interest formula for interest paid more than once a year, then substitute the given values (APR = 0.05, $Y = 18$, and $A = \$100{,}000$); for monthly compounding, we have $n = 12$.

1. Start with the compound interest formula for interest paid more than once a year: $A = P \times \left(1 + \dfrac{\text{APR}}{n}\right)^{nY}$
2. Interchange the left and right sides and divide both sides by $(1 + \text{APR})^{nY}$: $P = \dfrac{A}{\left(1 + \dfrac{\text{APR}}{n}\right)^{nY}}$

3. Substitute the values APR = 0.05, $Y = 18$, $A = \$100{,}000$, and $n = 12$:

$$P = \frac{\$100{,}000}{\left(1 + \frac{0.05}{12}\right)^{12\times18}} = \frac{\$100{,}000}{(1.004166667)^{216}} = \$40{,}733.06$$

With a 5% APR and monthly compounding, you can reach \$100,000 in 18 years by depositing \$40,733 today. This deposit is about \$18,000 less than the deposit needed to reach the same goal with an interest rate of 3% and annual compounding.

Now try Exercises 77–80.

Time Out to Think

Aside from long-term government bonds, it is extremely difficult to find investments with a constant interest rate for 18 years. Nevertheless, financial planners often make such assumptions when exploring investment options. Explain why such calculations can be useful, despite the fact that you can't be sure of a steady interest rate.

QUICK QUIZ

Choose the best answer to each of the following questions. Explain your reasoning with one or more complete sentences.

1. Consider two bank accounts, one earning simple interest and one earning compound interest. If both start with the same initial deposit (and you make no other deposits or withdrawals) and earn the same annual interest rate, after two years the account with simple interest will have
   a. a greater balance than the account with compound interest.
   b. a smaller balance than the account with compound interest.
   c. the same balance as the account with compound interest.
2. An account with interest compounded annually and an APR of 5% increases in value each year by a factor of
   a. 1.05. b. 1.5. c. 1.005.
3. After five years, an account with interest compounded annually and an APR of 6.6% increases in value by a factor of
   a. 1.66^5. b. 5×1.066. c. 1.066^5.
4. An account with an APR of 4% and quarterly compounding increases in value every three months by
   a. 1%. b. 1/4%. c. 4%.
5. With the same deposit, APR, and length of time, an account with monthly compounding yields
   a. a greater balance than an account with daily compounding.
   b. a smaller balance than an account with quarterly compounding.
   c. a greater balance than an account with annual compounding.
6. The annual percentage yield (APY) of an account is always
   a. less than the APR. b. at least as great as the APR.
   c. the same as the APR.
7. Consider two bank accounts earning compound interest, one with an APR of 4% and the other with an APR of 2%, both with the same initial deposit (and no further deposits or withdrawals). After twenty years, how much more interest will the account with APR = 4% have earned than the account with APR = 2%?
   a. less than twice as much
   b. exactly twice as much
   c. more than twice as much
8. If you deposit \$500 in an account with an APR of 6% and continuous compounding, the balance after two years is
   a. $\$500 \times e^{0.12}$.
   b. $\$500 \times e^2$.
   c. $\$500 \times (1 + 0.06)^2$.
9. Suppose you use the compound interest formula to calculate how much you must deposit into a college fund today if you want it to grow in value to \$20,000 in ten years. Your calculated amount will be the actual amount after ten years only if
   a. the average APR remains as you assumed throughout the ten years.
   b. the account has continuous compounding.
   c. the account earns simple interest rather than compound interest.
10. A bank account with compound interest exhibits what we call
   a. linear growth.
   b. compound growth.
   c. exponential growth.

Exercises 4B

REVIEW QUESTIONS

1. What is the difference between simple interest and compound interest? Why do you end up with more money with compound interest?
2. Explain how New College could claim that a debt of $224 from 535 years ago is worth $290 billion today. How does this show the "power of compounding"?
3. Explain why the term APR/*n* appears in the compound interest formula for interest paid *n* times a year.
4. State the compound interest formula for interest paid once a year. Define APR and *Y*.
5. State the compound interest formula for interest paid more than once a year. Define all the variables.
6. What is an annual percentage yield (APY)? Explain why, for a given APR, the APY is higher if the interest is compounded more frequently.
7. What is continuous compounding? How does the APY for continuous compounding compare to the APY for, say, daily compounding? Explain the formula for continuous compounding.
8. Give an example of a situation in which you might want to solve the compound interest formula to find the principal *P* that must be invested now to yield a particular amount *A* in the future.

DOES IT MAKE SENSE?

Decide whether each of the following statements makes sense (or is clearly true) or does not make sense (or is clearly false). Explain your reasoning.

9. Simple Bank was offering simple interest at 4.5% per year, which was clearly a better deal than the 4.5% compound interest rate at Complex Bank.
10. Both banks were paying the same annual percentage rate (APR), but one had a higher annual percentage yield than the other (APY).
11. The bank that pays the highest annual percentage rate (APR) is always the best deal.
12. No bank could afford to pay interest every trillionth of a second because, with compounding, it would soon owe everyone infinite dollars.
13. My bank paid an annual interest rate (APR) of 5.0%, but at the end of the year my account balance had grown by 5.1%.
14. If you deposit $10,000 in an investment account today, it can double in value to $20,000 in just a couple of decades even at a relatively low interest rate (say, 4%).

BASIC SKILLS & CONCEPTS

15–26: Review of Powers. Use the skills covered in the Brief Review on p. 210 to evaluate or simplify the following expressions.

15. 2^3
16. 3^4
17. 4^3
18. 3^{-2}
19. $16^{1/2}$
20. $81^{1/2}$
21. $64^{-1/3}$
22. $2^3 \times 2^5$
23. $3^4 \div 3^2$
24. $6^2 \times 6^{-2}$
25. $25^{1/2} \div 25^{-1/2}$
26. $3^3 + 2^3$

27–42: Algebra Review. Use the skills covered in the Brief Review on p. 221 to solve the following equations.

27. $x - 3 = 9$
28. $y + 4 = 7$
29. $z - 10 = 6$
30. $2x = 8$
31. $3p = 12$
32. $4y + 2 = 18$
33. $5z - 1 = 19$
34. $1 - 6y = 13$
35. $3x - 4 = 2x + 6$
36. $5 - 4s = 6s - 5$
37. $3a + 4 = 6 + 4a$
38. $3n - 16 = 53$
39. $6q - 20 = 60 + 4q$
40. $5w - 5 = 3w - 25$
41. $t/4 + 5 = 25$
42. $2x/3 + 4 = 2x$

43–46: Simple Interest. Calculate the amount of money you will have in the following accounts after five years, assuming that you earn simple interest.

43. You deposit $700 in an account with an annual interest rate of 4%.
44. You deposit $1200 in an account with an annual interest rate of 2%.
45. You deposit $3200 in an account with an annual interest rate of 2.5%.
46. You deposit $1800 in an account with an annual interest rate of 3.2%.

47–48: Simple vs. Compound Interest. Complete the following tables, which show the performance of two accounts over a 5-year period. Round all figures to the nearest dollar.

47. Suzanne deposits $3000 in an account that earns simple interest at an annual rate of 2.5%. Derek deposits $3000 in an account that earns compound interest at an annual rate of 2.5%.

Year	Suzanne's Annual Interest	Suzanne's Balance	Derek's Annual Interest	Derek's Balance
1				
2				
3				
4				
5				

48. Ariel deposits $5000 in an account that earns simple interest at an annual rate of 3%. Travis deposits $5000 in an account that earns compound interest at an annual rate of 3%.

Year	Ariel's Annual Interest	Ariel's Balance	Travis's Annual Interest	Travis's Balance
1				
2				
3				
4				
5				

49–54: Compound Interest. Use the compound interest formula to compute the balance in the following accounts after the stated period of time, assuming interest is compounded annually.

49. $10,000 is invested at an APR of 4% for 10 years.

50. $10,000 is invested at an APR of 5% for 20 years.

51. $15,000 is invested at an APR of 3.2% for 25 years.

52. $3000 is invested at an APR of 4% for 12 years.

53. $5000 is invested at an APR of 3.1% for 12 years.

54. $40,000 is invested at an APR of 8.5% for 30 years.

55–62: Compounding More Than Once a Year. Use the appropriate compound interest formula to compute the balance in the following accounts after the stated period of time.

55. $10,000 is invested for 10 years with an APR of 2% and quarterly compounding.

56. $2000 is invested for 5 years with an APR of 3% and daily compounding.

57. $25,000 is invested for 5 years with an APR of 3% and daily compounding.

58. $10,000 is invested for 5 years with an APR of 2.75% and monthly compounding.

59. $2000 is invested for 15 years with an APR of 5% and monthly compounding.

60. $30,000 is invested for 15 years with an APR of 4.5% and daily compounding.

61. $25,000 is invested for 30 years with an APR of 3.7% and quarterly compounding.

62. $15,000 is invested for 15 years with an APR of 4.2% and monthly compounding.

63–66: Annual Percentage Yield (APY). Find the annual percentage yield (to the nearest 0.01%) in the following situations.

63. A bank offers an APR of 5.5% compounded daily.

64. A bank offers an APR of 4.5% compounded monthly.

65. A bank offers an APR of 4.2% compounded monthly.

66. A bank offers an APR of 2.25% compounded quarterly.

67–72: Continuous Compounding. Use the formula for continuous compounding to compute the balance in the following accounts after 1, 5, and 20 years. Also, find the APY for each account.

67. A $10,000 deposit in an account with an APR of 3.5%

68. A $2000 deposit in an account with an APR of 3.1%

69. A $7000 deposit in an account with an APR of 4.5%

70. A $3000 deposit in an account with an APR of 7.5%

71. A $3000 deposit in an account with an APR of 6%

72. A $500 deposit in an account with an APR of 2.7%

73–76: Planning Ahead. How much must you deposit today into the following accounts in order to have $25,000 in 8 years for a down payment on a house? Assume no additional deposits are made.

73. An account with annual compounding and an APR of 5%

74. An account with quarterly compounding and an APR of 4.5%

75. An account with monthly compounding and an APR of 6%

76. An account with daily compounding and an APR of 4%

77–80: College Fund. How much must you deposit today into the following accounts in order to have a $120,000 college fund in 15 years? Assume no additional deposits are made.

77. An APR of 4%, compounded daily

78. An APR of 5.5%, compounded daily

79. An APR of 2.8%, compounded quarterly

80. An APR of 3.5% compounded monthly

FURTHER APPLICATIONS

81–82: Small Rate Differences. The following pairs of investment plans are identical except for a small difference in interest rates. Compute the balance in the accounts after 10 and 30 years. Discuss the difference.

81. Chang invests $500 in a savings account that earns 3.5% compounded annually. Kio invests $500 in a different savings account that earns 3.75% compounded annually.

82. José invests $1500 in a savings account that earns 5.6% compounded annually. Marta invests $1500 in a different savings account that earns 5.7% compounded annually.

83. **Comparing Annual Yields.** Consider an account with an APR of 6.6%. Find the APY with quarterly compounding, monthly compounding, and daily compounding. Comment on how changing the compounding period affects the annual yield.

84. **Comparing Annual Yields.** Consider an account with an APR of 5%. Find the APY with quarterly compounding, monthly compounding, and daily compounding. Comment on how changing the compounding period affects the annual yield.

85. **Rates of Compounding.** Compare the accumulated balance in two accounts that both start with an initial deposit of $1000. Both accounts have an APR of 5.5%, but one account compounds interest annually while the other account compounds interest daily. Make a table that shows the interest earned each year and the accumulated balance in both accounts for the first 10 years. Compare the balance in the accounts, in percentage terms, after 10 years. Round all figures to the nearest dollar.

86. **Understanding Annual Percentage Yield (APY).**

    a. Explain why APR and APY are the same with annual compounding.

    b. Explain why APR and APY are different with daily compounding.

c. Does APY depend on the starting principal, P? Why or why not?

d. How does APY depend on the number of compoundings during a year, n? Explain.

87. **Comparing Investment Plans.** Rosa invests \$3000 in an account with an APR of 4% and annual compounding. Julian invests \$2500 in an account with an APR of 5% and annual compounding.

a. Compute the balance in each account after 5 and 20 years.

b. Determine, for each account and for 5 and 20 years, the percentage of the balance that is interest.

c. Comment on the effect of interest rates and patience.

88. **Comparing Investment Plans.** Paula invests \$4000 in an account with an APR of 4.8% and continuous compounding. Petra invests \$3600 in an account with an APR of 5.6% and continuous compounding.

a. Compute the balances in the accounts after 5 and 20 years.

b. Determine, for each account and for 5 and 20 years, the percentage of the balance that is interest.

c. Comment on the effect of interest rates and patience.

89. **Retirement Fund.** Suppose you want to accumulate \$120,000 for your retirement in 30 years. You have two choices: Plan A is a single deposit into an account with annual compounding and an APR of 5%. Plan B is a single deposit into an account with continuous compounding and an APR of 4.8%. How much do you need to deposit in each account in order to reach the goal?

90. **Your Bank Account.** Find the current APR, the compounding period, and the claimed APY for your personal savings account (or pick a rate from a nearby bank if you don't have an account).

a. Calculate the APY on your account. Does your calculation agree with the APY claimed by the bank? Explain.

b. Suppose you receive a gift of \$10,000 and place it in your account. If the interest rate never changes, how much will you have in 10 years?

c. Suppose you find another account that offers interest at an APR that is 2 percentage points higher than yours, with the same compounding period. For the \$10,000 deposit, how much will you have after 10 years? Briefly discuss how this result compares to the result from part b.

91–93: Finding Time Periods. Use a calculator and possibly some trial and error to answer the following questions.

91. How long will it take your money to triple at an APR of 8% compounded annually?

92. How long will it take your money to grow by 50% at an APR of 7% compounded annually?

93. You deposit \$1000 in an account that pays an APR of 7% compounded annually. How long will it take for your balance to reach \$100,000?

94. **Continuous Compounding.** Explore continuous compounding by answering the following questions.

a. For an APR of 12%, make a table similar to Table 4.4 in which you display the APY for $n = 1, 4, 12, 365, 500, 1000$.

b. Find the APY for continuous compounding at an APR of 12%.

c. Show the results of parts a and b on a graph similar to Figure 4.3.

d. In words, compare the APY with continuous compounding to the APY with other types of compounding.

e. You deposit \$500 in an account with an APR of 12%. With continuous compounding, how much money will you have at the end of 1 year? at the end of 5 years?

WEB PROJECT

95. **Rate Comparisons.** Find a Web site that compares interest rates available for ordinary savings accounts at different banks. What is the range of rates currently being offered? What is the best deal? How does your own bank account compare?

IN YOUR WORLD

96. **Bank Advertisement.** Find two bank advertisements that refer to compound interest rates. Explain the terms in each advertisement. Which bank offers the better deal? Explain.

97. **Power of Compounding.** In an advertisement or article about an investment, find a description of how money has grown (or will grow) over a period of many years. Discuss whether the description is correct.

TECHNOLOGY EXERCISES

98. **Evaluating Powers.** Use a calculator or Excel to evaluate the following expressions.

a. 6^{12} b. 1.01^{40} c. 20×1.05^{16}

d. 4^{-5} e. 1.08^{-20}

99. **Compound Interest with Excel: Annual Compounding.** Use the future value (FV) function in Excel to compute the balance in the following accounts.

a. An account with annual compounding, an APR of 10%, and an initial deposit of \$100, after 5 years

b. An account with annual compounding, an APR of 2%, and an initial deposit of \$224, after 535 years

100. **Compound Interest with Excel: Dependence on Parameters.** Suppose you deposit \$500 in an account with an APR of 3% and annual compounding. As explained in the Using Technology box (page 213), fill the cells on an Excel spreadsheet as follows:

	B	C
1	APR	Value
2	Y	Value
3	PMT	0
4	PV	Value
5	FV	= FV(C1, C2, C3, C4)

By changing the input values, answer the following questions.

a. What is the balance after 20 years?

b. If you double the APR in part a, is the balance double, more than double, or less than double the balance in part a?

c. If you double the number of years in part a, is the balance double, more than double, or less than double the balance in part a?

d. If you double the amount of the deposit in part a, is the balance double, more than double, or less than double the balance in part a?

101. **Compound Interest with Excel: Multiple Compoundings per Year.** Use the future value (FV) function in Excel to compute the balance in the following accounts.

a. An account with monthly compounding, an APR of 3%, and an initial deposit of $5000, after 5 years

b. An account with monthly compounding, an APR of 4.5%, and an initial deposit of $800, after 30 years

c. An account with daily compounding, an APR of 3.75%, and an initial deposit of $1000, after 50 years

102. **Effective Yield.** Use the effective yield function (EFFECT) in Excel to compute the APY (or effective yield) in the following accounts.

a. An account with quarterly compounding and an APR of 4%

b. An account with monthly compounding and an APR of 4%

c. An account with daily compounding and an APR of 4%

d. Based on the results of parts a, b, and c, estimate the APY for an account with continuous compounding (in which the number of compoundings becomes very large).

103. **Exponential Function.** Use a calculator, Excel, or Google to evaluate the following quantities.

a. $e^{3.2}$

b. $e^{0.065}$

c. The APY (effective yield) of an account with continuous compounding and an APR of 4%

UNIT 4C Savings Plans and Investments

Suppose you want to save money for retirement, for your child's college expenses, or for any other reason. You could deposit a lump sum of money today and let it grow through the power of compound interest. But what if you don't have a large lump sum to start such an account?

For most people, a more realistic way to save is by depositing smaller amounts on a regular basis. For example, you might put $50 a month into savings. Such long-term **savings plans** are so popular that many have special names—and some even get special tax treatment (see Unit 4E). Popular types of savings plans include Individual Retirement Accounts (IRAs), 401(k) plans, Keogh plans, and employee pension plans.

> **BY THE WAY**
>
> Financial planners call any series of equal, regular payments an *annuity*. Thus, savings plans are a type of annuity, as are loans that you pay with equal monthly payments.

The Savings Plan Formula

We can study savings plans with a simple example. Suppose you deposit $100 into your savings plan at the end of each month. To make the numbers easy to work with, let's suppose that your plan pays interest monthly at an annual rate of APR = 12%, or 1% per month.

- You begin with $0 in the account. At the end of month 1, you make the first deposit of $100.
- At the end of month 2, you receive the monthly interest on the $100 already in the account, which is 1% × $100 = $1. In addition, you make your monthly deposit of $100. Your balance at the end of month 2 is

$$\underbrace{\$100}_{\text{prior balance}} + \underbrace{\$1.00}_{\text{interest}} + \underbrace{\$100}_{\text{new deposit}} = \$201.00$$

- At the end of month 3, you receive 1% interest on the $201 already in the account, or 1% × $201 = $2.01. Adding your monthly deposit of $100, you have a balance at the end of month 3 of

$$\underbrace{\$201.00}_{\text{prior balance}} + \underbrace{\$2.01}_{\text{interest}} + \underbrace{\$100}_{\text{new deposit}} = \$303.01$$

TABLE 4.5 Savings Plan Calculations

End of . . .	Prior Balance	Interest on Prior Balance	End-of-Month Deposit	New Balance
Month 1	\$0	\$0	\$100	\$100
Month 2	\$100	1% × \$100 = \$1	\$100	\$201
Month 3	\$201	1% × \$201 = \$2.01	\$100	\$303.01
Month 4	\$303.01	1% × \$303.01 = \$3.03	\$100	\$406.04
Month 5	\$406.04	1% × \$406.04 = \$4.06	\$100	\$510.10
Month 6	\$510.10	1% × \$510.10 = \$5.10	\$100	\$615.20

Note: The last column shows the new balance at the end of each month, which is the sum of the prior balance, the interest, and the end-of-month deposit.

Table 4.5 continues these calculations through 6 months.

In principle, we could extend this table indefinitely—but it would take a lot of work. Fortunately, there's a much easier way: the **savings plan formula.**

Take Note

The savings plan formula assumes the same payment and compounding periods. For example, if payments are made monthly, interest also is calculated and paid monthly. If the compounding period is different from the payment period, replace the term APR/n by the effective yield for each payment period.

SAVINGS PLAN FORMULA (REGULAR PAYMENTS)

$$A = \text{PMT} \times \frac{\left[\left(1 + \frac{\text{APR}}{n}\right)^{(nY)} - 1\right]}{\left(\frac{\text{APR}}{n}\right)}$$

where
- A = accumulated savings plan balance
- PMT = regular payment (deposit) amount
- APR = annual percentage rate (as a decimal)
- n = number of payment periods per year
- Y = number of years

As with compound interest, the accumulated balance (A) is often called the *future value* (FV); the *present value* is the starting principal (P), which is 0 because we assume the account has no balance before the payments begin.

Example 1 Using the Savings Plan Formula

Use the savings plan formula to calculate the balance after 6 months for an APR of 12% and monthly payments of \$100.

Solution We have monthly payments of PMT = \$100, annual interest rate of APR = 0.12, n = 12 because the payments are made monthly, and $Y = \frac{1}{2}$ because 6 months is a half year. Using the savings plan formula, we can find the balance after 6 months:

$$A = \text{PMT} \times \frac{\left[\left(1 + \frac{\text{APR}}{n}\right)^{(nY)} - 1\right]}{\left(\frac{\text{APR}}{n}\right)} = \$100 \times \frac{\left[\left(1 + \frac{0.12}{12}\right)^{(12\times 1/2)} - 1\right]}{\left(\frac{0.12}{12}\right)}$$

$$= \$100 \times \frac{[(1.01)^6 - 1]}{0.01} = \$615.20$$

Note that this answer agrees with Table 4.5. **Now try Exercises 23–26.**

Thinking About...

Derivation of the Savings Plan Formula

We can derive the savings plan formula by looking at the example in Table 4.5 in a different way. Instead of calculating the balance at the end of each month (as in Table 4.5), let's calculate the value of each individual payment (deposit) and its interest at the end of month 6.

The first \$100 payment was made at the *end* of month 1. Therefore, by the end of 6 months, it has collected interest for $6 - 1 = 5$ months (at the end of months 2, 3, 4, 5, and 6). We can find its value at the end of month 6 with the compound interest formula (Unit 4B). The payment amount is $\text{PMT} = \$100$ and the *monthly* interest rate is $i = 0.01$. Thus, after the collection of 5 interest payments, its value is

$$\text{PMT} \times (1 + i)^5 = \$100 \times 1.01^5$$

Similarly, the second \$100 payment has collected interest for $6 - 2 = 4$ months, so its value at the end of month 6 is

$$\text{PMT} \times (1 + i)^4 = \$100 \times 1.01^4$$

The table below continues the calculations. The last column shows how the compound interest formula applies in general to each individual payment. The accumulated balance A after $N = 6$ months is the sum of the values of the individual payments. Note that the second column sum agrees with the result found in Table 4.5.

End-of-Month Payment	Value After Month 6	Value Generalized for N Months
1	$\$100 \times 1.01^5$	$\text{PMT} \times (1 + i)^{N-1}$
2	$\$100 \times 1.01^4$	$\text{PMT} \times (1 + i)^{N-2}$
3	$\$100 \times 1.01^3$	$\vdots$
4	$\$100 \times 1.01^2$	
5	$\$100 \times 1.01$	$\text{PMT} \times (1 + i)^1$
6	\$100	PMT
Total (accumulated balance, A)	\$615.20	(sum of terms above)

Because the last column contains only general formulas, we can use the sum of its terms as the accumulated balance A for any savings plan after N months:

$$\begin{aligned} A = {} & \text{PMT} \\ & + \text{PMT} \times (1 + i)^1 \\ & + \cdots \\ & + \text{PMT} \times (1 + i)^{N-1} \end{aligned}$$

(We've used "$\cdots$" to indicate a continuing pattern.)

We could use this formula for A, but we can simplify it further with the algebra shown in Equation 1 at the bottom of this box. As shown, we multiply both sides by $(1 + i)^1$, and then subtract the original equation from the result. Note how all but two terms cancel on the right. The last line in Equation 1 contains the formula we seek, except we still need to solve it for A.

We do this by rewriting the term on the left as

$$\underbrace{A(1 + i)}_{= A + Ai} - A = A + Ai - A = Ai$$

The equation becomes

$$\begin{aligned} Ai &= \text{PMT}(1 + i)^N - \text{PMT} \\ &= \text{PMT} \times [(1 + i)^N - 1] \end{aligned}$$

(The last step above comes from factoring out PMT from both terms on the right.) Now, we divide both sides by i to get the savings plan formula:

$$A = \text{PMT} \times \frac{[(1 + i)^N - 1]}{i}$$

To put the savings plan formula in the form given in the text, we substitute $i = \text{APR}/n$ for the interest rate per period and $N = nY$ for the total number of payments (where n is the number of payments per year and Y is the number of years).

Equation 1:

$$\begin{aligned} A(1 + i) &= \cancel{\text{PMT}(1 + i)^1} + \cancel{\cdots} + \cancel{\text{PMT}(1 + i)^{N-1}} + \text{PMT}(1 + i)^N \\ -A &= \text{PMT} + \cancel{\text{PMT}(1 + i)^1} + \cancel{\cdots} + \cancel{\text{PMT}(1 + i)^{N-1}} \\ \hline A(1 + i) - A &= -\text{PMT} + \text{PMT}(1 + i)^N \\ &= \text{PMT}(1 + i)^N - \text{PMT} \end{aligned}$$

Take Note

A savings plan in which payments are made at the end of each month is called an *ordinary annuity.* A plan in which payments are made at the beginning of each period is called an *annuity due.* In both cases, the accumulated amount, *A*, at some future date is called the *future value* of the annuity. The formulas in this unit apply only to ordinary annuities.

Example 2 Retirement Plan

At age 30, Michelle starts an IRA to save for retirement. She deposits \$100 at the end of each month. If she can count on an APR of 6%, how much will she have when she retires 35 years later at age 65? Compare the IRA's value to her total deposits over this time period.

Solution We use the savings plan formula for payments of PMT = \$100, an interest rate of APR = 0.06, and $n = 12$ for monthly deposits. The balance after $Y = 35$ years is

$$A = \text{PMT} \times \frac{\left[\left(1 + \frac{\text{APR}}{n}\right)^{(nY)} - 1\right]}{\left(\frac{\text{APR}}{n}\right)} = \$100 \times \frac{\left[\left(1 + \frac{0.06}{12}\right)^{(12\times35)} - 1\right]}{\left(\frac{0.06}{12}\right)}$$

$$= \$100 \times \frac{[(1.005)^{420} - 1]}{0.005}$$

$$= \$142{,}471.03$$

USING TECHNOLOGY

The Savings Plan Formula

Standard Calculators As with compound interest calculations, the only "trick" to using the savings plan formula on a standard calculator is following the correct order of operations. The following calculation shows the correct order for the numbers from Example 2, in which PMT = \$100, APR = 0.06, $n = 12$, and $Y = 35$ years; as always, be sure that you *do not round any answers until the end of the calculation.*

General Procedure	Our Example	Calculator Steps*	Output
$A = \text{PMT} \times \frac{\left[\left(1 + \frac{\text{APR}}{n}\right)^{(nY)} - 1\right]}{\left(\frac{\text{APR}}{n}\right)}$	$A = 100 \times \frac{\left[\left(1 + \frac{0.06}{12}\right)^{(12\times35)} - 1\right]}{\left(\frac{0.06}{12}\right)}$	Step 1 1 (+) 0.06 (÷) 12 (=)	1.005
1. inner parentheses	1. inner parentheses	Step 2 (^) (() 12 (×) 35 ()) (=)	8.12355...
2. exponent	2. exponent	Step 3 (−) 1 (=)	7.12355...
3. outer parentheses	3. outer parentheses	Step 4 (÷) (() 0.06 (÷) 12 ()) (=)	1424.71029
4. divide	4. divide	Step 5 (×) \$100 (=)	142471.029
5. multiply	5. multiply		

*If your calculator does not have parentheses keys, then you will need to do those steps before you start and keep track of the results either on paper or in the calculator's memory.

Excel We again use the built-in function FV, as we did for the compound interest formula (see Using Technology, pp. 213 and 217). In this case, the input will be as follows:

```
=fv(.06/12,35*12,100)
FV(rate, nper, pmt, [pv], [type])
```

Note:

- *rate* is the interest rate for each compounding period, which in this case is the monthly interest rate APR/n = 0.06/12.

Because 35 years is 420 months ($35 \times 12 = 420$), the total amount of her deposits over 35 years is

$$420\ \cancel{\text{months}} \times \frac{\$100}{\cancel{\text{month}}} = \$42{,}000$$

She will deposit a total of \$42,000 over 35 years. However, thanks to compounding, her IRA will have a balance of more than \$142,000—*more than three times* the amount of her contributions. **Now try Exercises 27–30.**

Planning Ahead with Savings Plans

Most people start savings plans with a particular goal in mind, such as saving enough for retirement or enough to buy a new car in a couple of years. For planning ahead, the important question is this: Given a financial goal (the total amount, A, desired after a certain number of years), what regular payments are needed to reach the goal? The following two examples show how the calculations work.

- *nper* is the total number of compounding periods, which in this case is $nY = 12 \times 35$.
- *pmt* is the monthly payment of \$100.
- *pv* is left blank, because there is no starting principal (present value) in this case.
- *type* is also left blank, which indicates that $\text{type} = 0$. This is the default value; it indicates monthly payments made at the *end* of each period (month), as is the case for all the examples in this book. For the rarer case in which payments are made at the beginning of each payment period, you would set $\text{type} = 1$.

You may find it easier to see the inputs if you use the dialog box that comes up when you choose the FV function from the Insert menu, which will look something like this:

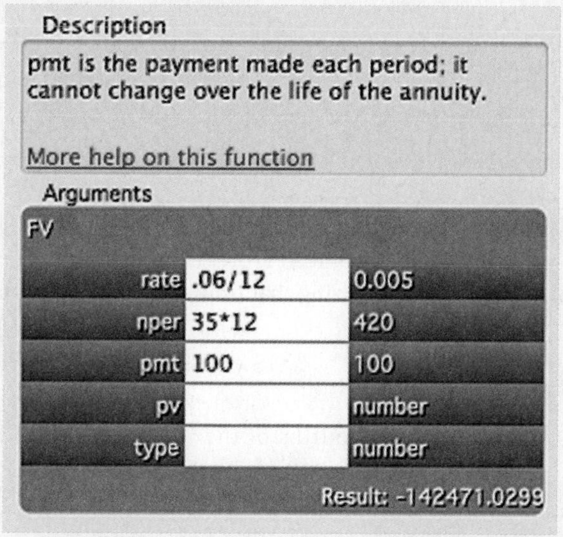

You may wonder why the result (shown at the lower right) is negative. This is an artifact of the way Excel's financial functions handle cash flow. Positive amounts are considered *inflows* of money and negative amounts are *outflows*. In this case, the positive monthly payments of \$100 are inflows into the savings plan. The future value is then negative because it is the amount that you will eventually draw *out* of the savings plan to pay for the home, college, or whatever else you were saving for. Note that, aside from this subtlety, the result is just as we found in Example 2.

Example 3 College Savings Plan at 3%

You want to build a $100,000 college fund in 18 years by making regular, end-of-month deposits. Assuming an APR of 3%, calculate how much you should deposit monthly. How much of the final value comes from actual deposits and how much from interest?

Solution The goal is to accumulate A = $100,000 over Y = 18 years. The interest rate is APR = 0.03 and monthly payments mean n = 12. The goal is to calculate the required monthly payments, PMT. We therefore need to solve the savings plan formula for PMT and then substitute the given values for A, APR, n, and Y. The following steps show the calculation.

1. Start with the savings plan formula:

$$A = \text{PMT} \times \frac{\left[\left(1 + \frac{\text{APR}}{n}\right)^{(nY)} - 1\right]}{\left(\frac{\text{APR}}{n}\right)}$$

2. Multiply both sides by $\left(\frac{\text{APR}}{n}\right)$ and divide both sides by $\left[\left(1 + \frac{\text{APR}}{n}\right)^{(nY)} - 1\right]$:

$$A \times \frac{\left(\frac{\text{APR}}{n}\right)}{\left[\left(1 + \frac{\text{APR}}{n}\right)^{(nY)} - 1\right]} = \text{PMT} \times \frac{\cancel{\left[\left(1 + \frac{\text{APR}}{n}\right)^{(nY)} - 1\right]}}{\cancel{\left(\frac{\text{APR}}{n}\right)}} \times \frac{\cancel{\left(\frac{\text{APR}}{n}\right)}}{\cancel{\left[\left(1 + \frac{\text{APR}}{n}\right)^{(nY)} - 1\right]}}$$

3. Interchange the left and right sides:

$$\text{PMT} = A \times \frac{\left(\frac{\text{APR}}{n}\right)}{\left[\left(1 + \frac{\text{APR}}{n}\right)^{(nY)} - 1\right]}$$

4. Use the values APR = 0.03, n = 12, Y = 18, and A = $100,000:

$$\text{PMT} = \$100{,}000 \times \frac{\left(\frac{0.03}{12}\right)}{\left[\left(1 + \frac{0.03}{12}\right)^{(12\times 18)} - 1\right]}$$

$$= \$100{,}000 \times \frac{0.0025}{[(1.0025)^{216} - 1]}$$

$$= \$349.72$$

Assuming a constant APR of 3%, monthly payments of $349.72 will give you $100,000 after 18 years. During that time, you deposit a total of

$$18\ \cancel{\text{yr}} \times \frac{12\ \cancel{\text{mo}}}{\cancel{\text{yr}}} \times \frac{\$349.72}{\cancel{\text{mo}}} \approx \$75{,}540$$

Just over three-fourths of the $100,000 comes from your actual deposits; the other one-fourth is the result of compound interest. **Now try Exercises 31–34.**

Time Out to Think

Compare the result of Example 3 to that of Example 9 in Unit 4B. Notice that both have the same interest rate of 3% and both allow you to accumulate $100,000 at the end of 18 years, but one does it with a savings plan and the other by starting with a large, lump-sum deposit. Discuss the pros and cons of each approach. How would *you* decide which approach to use?

Example 4 A Comfortable Retirement

You would like to retire 25 years from now, and you would like to have a retirement fund from which you can draw an income of \$50,000 per year—forever! How can you do it? Assume a constant APR of 7%.

Solution You can achieve your goal by building a retirement fund that is large enough to earn \$50,000 per year *from interest alone*. In that case, you can withdraw the interest for your living expenses while leaving the principal untouched (for your heirs!). The principal will then continue to earn the same \$50,000 interest year after year (assuming there is no change in interest rates).

What balance do you need to earn \$50,000 annually from interest? Since we are assuming an APR of 7%, the \$50,000 must be 7% = 0.07 of the total balance. That is,

$$\$50{,}000 = 0.07 \times (\text{total balance})$$

Dividing both sides by 0.07, we find

$$\text{total balance} = \frac{\$50{,}000}{0.07} = \$714{,}286$$

In other words, with a 7% APR, a balance of about \$715,000 allows you to withdraw \$50,000 per year without ever reducing the principal.

Let's assume you will try to accumulate this balance of $A = \$715{,}000$ by making regular, monthly deposits into a savings plan. We have APR = 0.07, $n = 12$ (for monthly deposits), and $Y = 25$ years. As in Example 3, we calculate the required monthly deposits by using the savings plan formula solved for PMT.

$$\text{PMT} = \frac{A \times \left(\frac{\text{APR}}{n}\right)}{\left[\left(1 + \frac{\text{APR}}{n}\right)^{(nY)} - 1\right]} = \frac{\$715{,}000 \times \left(\frac{0.07}{12}\right)}{\left[\left(1 + \frac{0.07}{12}\right)^{(12\times25)} - 1\right]}$$

$$= \frac{\$715{,}000 \times 0.0058333}{[(1.0058333)^{300} - 1]}$$

$$= \$882.64$$

If you deposit about \$882 per month over the next 25 years, you will achieve your retirement goal—assuming you can count on a 7% APR (which is high by historical standards). Although saving almost \$900 per month is a lot, it can be easier than it sounds thanks to special tax treatment for retirement plans (see Unit 4E).

Now try Exercises 35–36.

BY THE WAY

An account that provides a permanent source of income without reducing its principal is called an *endowment*. Many charitable foundations are endowments. They spend each year's interest (or a portion of the interest) on charitable activities, while leaving the principal untouched to earn interest again in future years. Of course, the *value* of a particular dollar amount tends to decline with time, because inflation reduces the value of a dollar.

Total and Annual Return

In the examples so far, we've assumed that you get a constant interest rate for a long period of time. In reality, interest rates usually vary over time. Consider a case in which you invest a starting principal of \$1000 and it grows to \$1500 in 5 years. Although the interest rate may have varied during the 5 years, we can still describe the change in both total and annual terms.

Your **total return** is the relative change in the investment value over the 5-year period (see Unit 3A for a discussion of relative change):

$$\text{total return} = \frac{\text{new value} - \text{starting principal}}{\text{starting principal}} = \frac{\$1500 - \$1000}{\$1000} = 0.5$$

The total return on this investment is 50% over 5 years.

Your **annual return** is the *average annual rate* at which your money grew over the 5 years. That is, it is the constant annual percentage yield (APY) that would give the same result in 5 years. In this case, the annual return is about 8.5%. We can see why by using the compound interest formula for interest paid once a year. We set the interest rate (APR) to the annual yield of APY = 8.5% = 0.085 and the number of years to Y = 5. The compound interest formula confirms that a starting principal $P = \$1000$ grows to about $A = \$1500$ in 5 years:

$$A = P \times (1 + \text{APY})^Y = \$1000 \times (1 + 0.085)^5 = \$1503.66$$

In this case, we "guessed" the APY, then confirmed our guess with the compound interest formula. We can calculate the annual return more directly by solving the compound interest formula for APY. The algebra is shown in the Brief Review below. The result is summarized in the following box.

TOTAL AND ANNUAL RETURN

Consider an investment that grows from an original principal P to a later accumulated balance A.

The **total return** is the relative change in the investment value:

$$\text{total return} = \frac{(A - P)}{P}$$

The **annual return** is the annual percentage yield (APY) that would give the same overall growth. The formula is

$$\text{annual return} = \left(\frac{A}{P}\right)^{(1/Y)} - 1$$

where Y is the investment period in years.

A Brief Review — Algebra with Powers and Roots

The following two rules hold true for working with equations:

1. We can raise both sides of an equation to the same power.
2. We can take the same root of both sides of an equation, which is equivalent to raising both sides to the same fractional power. (Note: This process may produce both positive and negative roots; we consider only positive roots here.)

Example: Find the positive solution of the equation $x^4 = 16$.
Solution: We isolate x by raising both sides to the 1/4 power:

$$(x^4)^{1/4} = 16^{1/4} \rightarrow x^{4\times1/4} = 16^{1/4} \rightarrow x = 16^{1/4} = 2$$

Therefore, one solution of the equation is $x = 2$. Note that, in the last step, we recognized that $x^{4\times1/4} = x^1 = x$.

Example: Solve the equation $A = P \times (1 + \text{APY})^Y$ for APY.

Solution: First, we isolate the term containing APY by dividing both sides of the equation by P:

$$\frac{A}{P} = (1 + \text{APY})^Y$$

Next, we raise both sides of the equation to the $1/Y$ power, then simplify the right side:

$$\left(\frac{A}{P}\right)^{1/Y} = [(1 + \text{APY})^Y]^{1/Y}$$

$$= \underbrace{(1 + \text{APY})^{Y\times1/Y}}_{\substack{\text{This step} \\ \text{from the rule} \\ (x^n)^m = x^{n\times m}}} = \underbrace{1 + \text{APY}}_{\substack{\text{This step} \\ \text{from the rule} \\ x^{n/n} = x^1 = x}}$$

Finally, we isolate APY by subtracting 1 from both sides:

$$\left(\frac{A}{P}\right)^{1/Y} - 1 = 1 + \text{APY} - 1 \rightarrow \text{APY} = \left(\frac{A}{P}\right)^{1/Y} - 1$$

(In the last step, we interchanged the left and right sides.) To get the formula in the box "Total and Annual Return," we replace APY by *annual return*. This replacement is valid because the annual return is the same as the constant APY that would lead to an accumulated balance A.

Now try Exercises 15–22.

Example 5 Mutual Fund Gain

You invest \$3000 in the Clearwater mutual fund. Over 4 years, your investment grows in value to \$8400. What are your total and annual returns for the 4-year period?

Solution You have a starting principal $P = \$3000$ and an accumulated value of $A = \$8400$ after $Y = 4$ years. Your total and annual returns are

$$\text{total return} = \frac{(A - P)}{P} = \frac{(\$8400 - \$3000)}{\$3000} = 1.8 = 180\%$$

and

$$\text{annual return} = \left(\frac{A}{P}\right)^{(1/Y)} - 1 = \left(\frac{\$8400}{\$3000}\right)^{(1/4)} - 1 = \sqrt[4]{2.8} - 1 = 0.294 = 29.4\%$$

Your total return is 1.8, or 180%, meaning that the value of your investment after 4 years is 1.8 times its original value. Your annual return is 0.294, or 29.4%, meaning that your investment has grown by an average of 29.4% each year.

You should check your answer for the annual return by using the compound interest formula. If you use the annual return as the APY, the compound interest formula should give you the correct accumulated value. In this case,

$$A = P \times (1 + \text{APY})^Y = \$3000 \times (1 + 0.294)^4 = \$8411.21$$

This is very close to the correct value of \$8400. The slight difference is due to rounding when we calculated the annual return. **Now try Exercises 37–40.**

Example 6 Investment Loss

You purchased shares in NewWeb.com for \$2000. Three years later, you sold them for \$1100. What were your total return and annual return on this investment?

Solution You had a starting principal $P = \$2000$ and an accumulated value of $A = \$1100$ after $Y = 3$ years. Your total and annual returns were

$$\text{total return} = \frac{(A - P)}{P} = \frac{(\$1100 - \$2000)}{\$2000} = -0.45$$

and

$$\text{annual return} = \left(\frac{A}{P}\right)^{(1/Y)} - 1 = \left(\frac{\$1100}{\$2000}\right)^{(1/3)} - 1 = \sqrt[3]{0.55} - 1 = -0.18$$

The returns are negative because you *lost* money on this investment. Your total return was −0.45, or −45%, meaning that your investment lost 45% of its original value. Your annual return was −0.18, or −18%, meaning that your investment lost an average of 18% of its value each year. **Now try Exercises 41–44.**

USING TECHNOLOGY

Fractional Powers (Roots)

Recall that raising a number to a fractional power such as $1/Y$ is the same as taking the Yth root.

Most standard calculators have a key labeled $x^{1/y}$ or $\sqrt[y]{x}$. *Example*: Calculate $2.8^{1/4} = \sqrt[4]{2.8}$ by pressing 2.8 $\sqrt[y]{x}$ 4 =. Alternatively, you can use parentheses, to enter the calculation directly:

2.8 ^ (1 ÷ 4) =

In Excel, use the ^ symbol to raise to a power, with the fractional power in parentheses, as shown in the screen shot below.

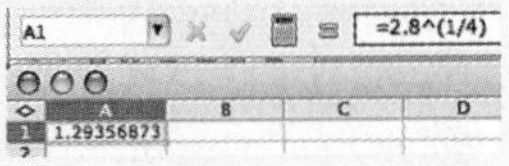

Types of Investments

Savings plans can involve many types of investments. By combining what we've covered about savings plans with the ideas of total and annual return, we can now study investment options. Most investments fall into one of the three basic categories described in the following box.

BY THE WAY

There are many other types of investments besides the basic three, such as rental properties, precious metals, commodities, futures, and derivatives. These investments generally are more complex and often have higher risk than the basic three.

THREE BASIC TYPES OF INVESTMENTS

Stock (or *equity*) gives you a share of ownership in a company. You invest some principal amount to purchase the stock, and the only way to get your money out is to sell the stock. Because stock prices change with time, the sale may give you either a gain or a loss on your original investment.

A **bond** (or *debt*) represents a promise of future cash. You buy a bond by paying some principal amount to the issuing government or corporation. The issuer pays you simple interest (as opposed to compound interest) and promises to pay back your principal at some later date.

Cash investments include money you deposit into bank accounts, certificates of deposit (CD), and U.S. Treasury bills. Cash investments generally earn interest.

There are two basic ways to invest in any of these categories. First, you can invest directly, which means buying individual investments yourself. For example, you can directly purchase individual stocks through a stockbroker and you can buy bonds directly from the government. In general, the only costs associated with direct investments are commissions that you pay to brokers.

Alternatively, you can invest indirectly by purchasing shares in a **mutual fund**, where a professional fund manager invests your money (and the money of others participating in the fund). *Stock mutual funds* invest primarily in stocks, *bond mutual funds* invest primarily in bonds, *money market funds* invest only in cash, and *diversified funds* invest in a mixture of stocks, bonds, and cash.

BY THE WAY

The U.S. Treasury issues bills, notes, and bonds. *Treasury bills* are essentially cash investments that are highly liquid and very safe. *Treasury notes* are essentially bonds with 2- to 10-year terms. *Treasury bonds* have 20- to 30-year terms.

Investment Considerations: Liquidity, Risk, and Return

No matter what type of investment you make, you should evaluate the investment in terms of three general considerations.

- **Liquidity**: How difficult is it to take out your money? An investment from which you can withdraw money easily, such as an ordinary bank account, is said to be **liquid.** The liquidity of an investment like real estate is much lower because real estate can be difficult to sell.
- **Risk:** Is your investment principal at **risk?** The safest investments are federally insured bank accounts and U.S. Treasury bills—there's virtually no risk of losing the principal you've invested. Stocks and bonds are much riskier because they can drop in value, in which case you may lose part or all of your principal.
- **Return**: How much **return** (total or annual) can you expect on your investment? A higher return means you earn more money. In general, low-risk investments offer relatively low returns, while high-risk investments offer the prospects of higher returns—along with the possibility of losing your principal.

Historical Returns

One of the most difficult tasks of investing is trying to balance risk and return. Although there is no way to predict what will happen in the future, historical trends offer at least some guidance. To study historical trends, financial analysts generally look at an *index* that describes the overall performance of some category of investment. The best-known index is the *Dow Jones Industrial Average* (DJIA), which reflects the average prices of the stocks of 30 large companies. The 30 companies are chosen by the editors of the *Wall Street Journal*, who hope these companies will represent the overall market; for that reason, they sometimes change the companies that are part of the "Dow 30." Figure 4.5 shows historical data for the DJIA.

Notice that the long-term trend shown in Figure 4.5 looks quite good, reflecting the fact that stocks have had a high rate of return over many years. In fact, over the long

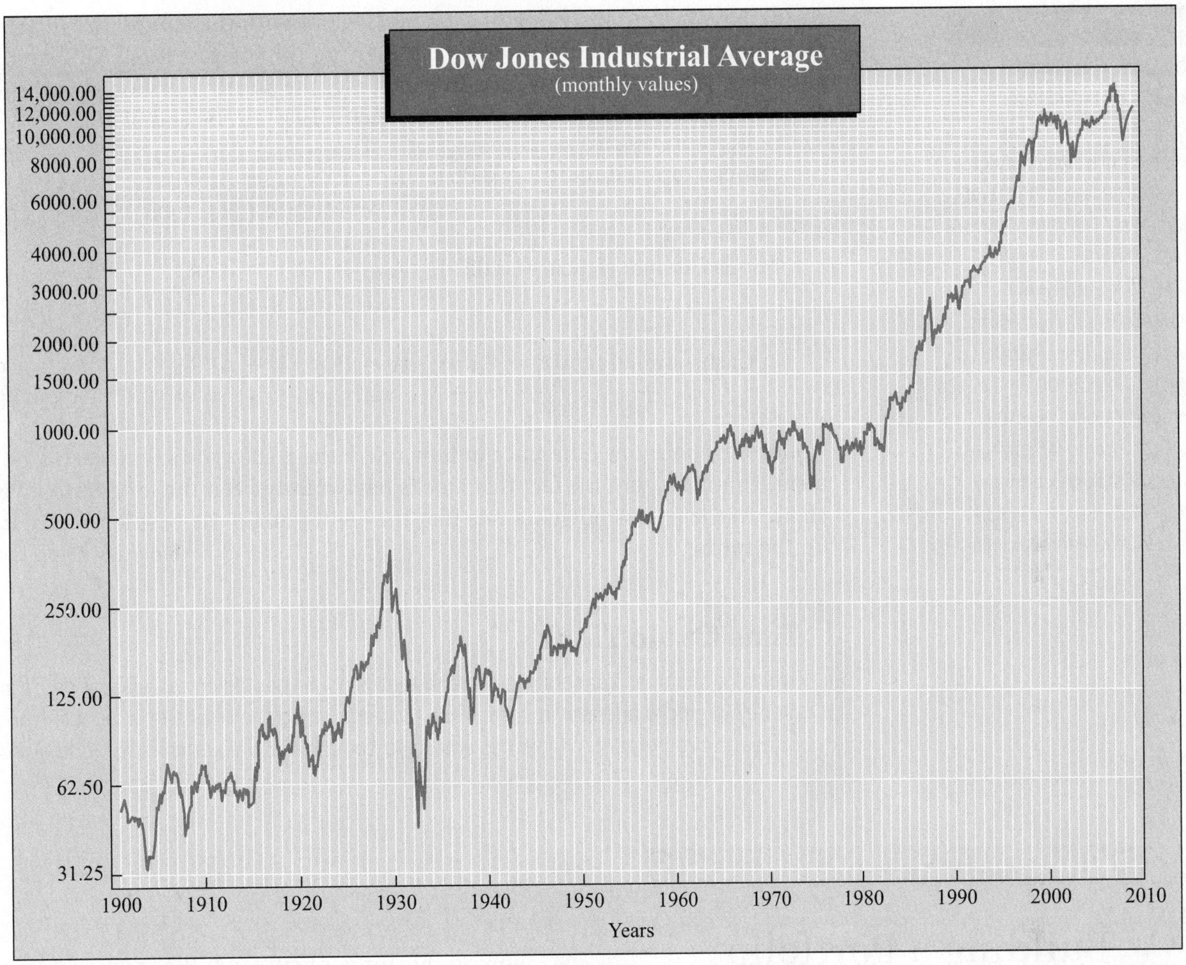

FIGURE 4.5 Historical values of the Dow Jones Industrial Average, 1900 through September 2009. Note that the numbers on the vertical axis double with each equivalent increment in height; this type of exponential graph makes it easier to see the up-and-down trends that occurred when the DJIA was low compared to its value today.
Sources: Dow Jones & Company; StockCharts.com.

term, stocks have proven to be a far better investment than bonds or cash (Table 4.6). Over shorter time periods, however, stocks can be a risky investment. For example, if just before the crash of 1929 you had invested in a mutual fund that tracked the DJIA, you would have had to wait some 25 years before the fund returned to its pre-crash value.

TABLE 4.6 Historical Returns by Category, 1900–2008

Category	Average Annual Return
Stocks	6.0%
Bonds	2.1%
Cash	1.0%

Source: Credit Suisse Global Investment Returns Yearbook 2009.

Time Out to Think

Find today's closing value for the DJIA. How does it compare to the DJIA's all-time high of 14,164, reached on October 9, 2007? If you had invested in a mutual fund that tracked the DJIA in 2000, would your investment be worth more or less today? What if you had invested in 1990? in 2005?

Example 7 Historical Returns

Suppose your great-great-grandmother invested $100 at the end of 1900 in each of three funds that tracked the averages of stocks, bonds, and cash, respectively. Assuming that her investments grew at the rates given in Table 4.6, approximately how much would each investment have been worth at the end of 2008?

BY THE WAY

The DJIA is the most famous stock index, but others that track larger numbers of stocks may give a better picture of the overall market. These include the *Standard and Poor's 500* (S&P 500), which tracks 500 large-company stocks; the *Russell 2000*, which tracks 2000 small-company stocks; and the *NASDAQ composite*, which tracks 100 large-company stocks listed on the NASDAQ exchange.

Solution We find the value of each investment with the compound interest formula (for interest compounded once a year), setting the interest rate (APR) to the average annual return for each category. In each case, the starting principal is $P = \$100$ and $Y = 108$ (the number of years from the end of 1900 to the end of 2008).

$$\text{Stocks (annual return} = 0.06\text{):} \quad A = P \times (1 + \text{APR})^Y = \$100 \times (1 + 0.06)^{108} = \$54{,}079.60$$

$$\text{Bonds (annual return} = 0.021\text{):} \quad A = P \times (1 + \text{APR})^Y = \$100 \times (1 + 0.021)^{108} = \$943.58$$

$$\text{Cash (annual return} = 0.01\text{):} \quad A = P \times (1 + \text{APR})^Y = \$100 \times (1 + 0.01)^{108} = \$292.89$$

Notice the enormous difference in how much the $100 grows with each type of investment. Unfortunately, the fact that stocks have clearly been the long-term investment of choice in the past is no guarantee that they will remain the best long-term investment for the future.

Now try Exercises 45–46.

Time Out to Think

Typically, financial planners recommend that younger people invest a larger proportion of their money in stocks and less in cash, while recommending the opposite to people who are retired or nearing retirement. Why is this advice so common? Do you think it is good advice?

PRACTICAL MATTERS

Building a Portfolio

Before you bought a new television for a few hundred dollars, you'd probably do a fair amount of research to make sure that you were getting a good buy. You should be even more diligent when making investments that may determine your entire financial future.

The best way to plan your savings is to learn about investments by reading financial pages of newspapers and some of the many books and magazines devoted to finance. You may also want to consult a professional financial planner. With this background, you will be prepared to create a personal financial *portfolio* (set of investments) that meets your needs.

Most financial advisors recommend that you create a *diversified* portfolio—that is, a portfolio with a mixture of low-risk and high-risk investments. No single mixture is right for everyone. Your portfolio should balance risk and return in a way that is appropriate for your situation. For example, if you are young and retirement is far in the future, you may be willing to have a relatively risky portfolio that offers the hope of high returns. In contrast, if you are already retired, you may want a low-risk portfolio that promises a safe and steady stream of income.

However you structure your portfolio, the most important step in meeting your financial goals is making sure that you save enough money. You can use the tools in this unit to help you determine what is "enough." Make a reasonable estimate of the annual return you can expect from your overall portfolio. Use this annual return as the interest rate in the savings plan formula, and calculate how much you must invest each month or each year to meet your goals (see Examples 3 and 4). Then make sure you actually put this money in your investment plan. If you need further motivation, consider this: Every $100 you spend today is gone, but even at a fairly low (by historical standards) annual return of 4%, every $100 you invest today will be worth $148 in 10 years, $219 in 20 years, and $711 in 50 years.

Financial Data

If you are investing money, you can track your investments online. Let's look briefly at what you must know to understand commonly published data about stocks, bonds, and mutual funds.

Stocks

In general, there are two ways to make money on stocks:

- You can make money if you sell a stock for more than you paid for it, in which case you have a **capital gain** on the sale of the stock. Of course, you also can lose money on a stock (a capital loss) if you sell shares for less than you paid for them or if the company goes into bankruptcy.
- You can make money while you own the stock if the corporation distributes part or all of its profits to stockholders as **dividends.** Each share of stock is paid the same dividend, so the amount of money you receive depends on the number of shares you own. Not all companies distribute profits as dividends. Some reinvest all profits within the corporation.

Before you invest in any stock, you should check its current stock quote; Figure 4.6 explains the key data that you'll find in a typical stock quote. In addition, you should learn more about the company by studying its annual report and visiting its Web site. You can also get independent research reports from many investment services (usually for a fee) or by working with a stockbroker (to whom you pay commissions when you buy or sell stock).

BY THE WAY

A *corporation* is a legal entity created to conduct a business. Ownership is held through shares of stock. For example, owning 1% of a company's stock means owning 1% of the company. Shares of stock in *privately held* corporations are owned only by a limited group of people. Shares of stock in *publicly held* corporations are traded on a public exchange, such as the New York Stock Exchange or the NASDAQ, where anyone may buy or sell them.

Example 8 Understanding the Microsoft Quote

Answer the following questions based on the Microsoft stock quote in Figure 4.6.

a. What is the symbol for Microsoft stock?
b. What was the price per share at the end of the day yesterday?
c. Based on the current price, what is the total value of the shares that have been traded so far today?
d. What fraction of all Microsoft shares have been traded so far today?
e. Suppose you own 100 shares of Microsoft. Based on the current price and dividend yield, what total dividend should you expect to receive this year?

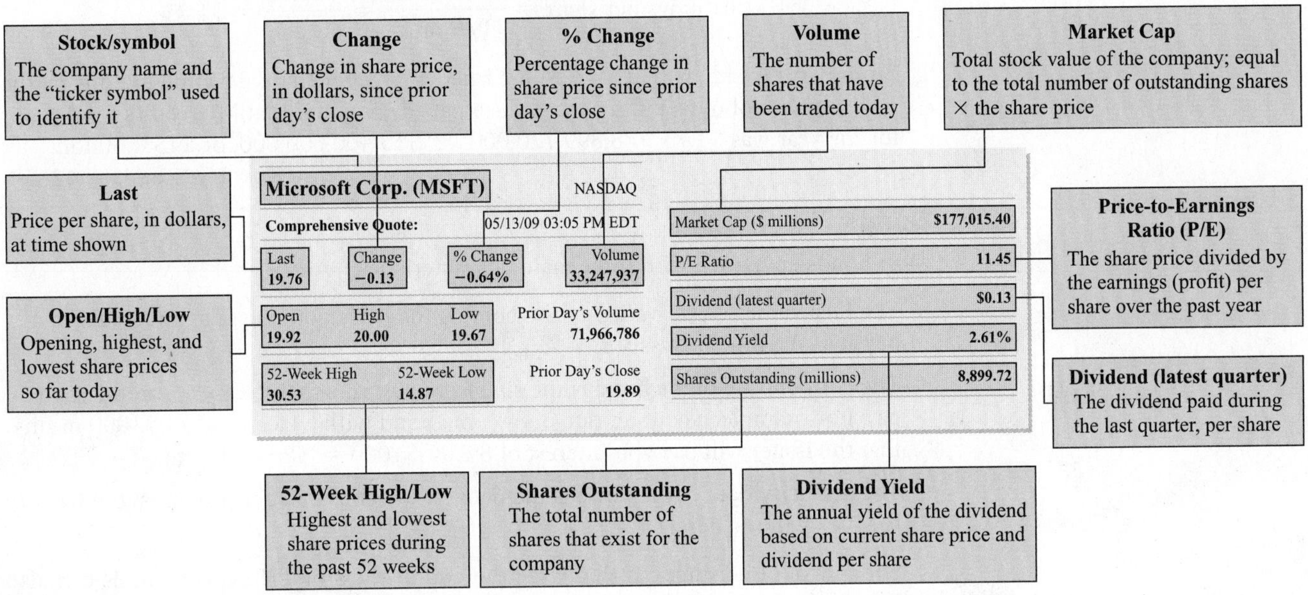

FIGURE 4.6 This figure explains key data that you'll find in an online stock quote.

Frank and Ernest

f. How much profit did Microsoft earn per share in the past year?
g. How much total profit did Microsoft earn in the past year?

BY THE WAY

Historically, most gains from stocks have come from increases in stock prices, rather than from dividends. Stocks in companies that pay consistently high dividends are called *income stocks* because they provide ongoing income to stockholders. Stocks in companies that reinvest most profits in hopes of growing larger are called *growth stocks.* Of course, a so-called "growth stock" can still decline or the company can go out of business.

Solution

a. As shown at the top of the quote, Microsoft's stock symbol is MSFT.

b. The quote shows that the current share price is \$19.76, and the change of −0.13 means that this is \$0.13 *less* than the price at the end of the day yesterday. Therefore, the price at the end of the day yesterday was \$19.76 + \$0.13 = \$19.89.

c. The volume shows that 33,247,937 shares have been traded today. At the current price of \$19.76 per share, the value of these shares is

$$33{,}247{,}937 \text{ shares} \times \$19.76/\text{share} \approx \$657{,}000{,}000$$

So the total value of shares traded today is about \$657 million.

d. The value for shares outstanding, quoted in millions, shows a total of 8899.72, so the actual number of shares outstanding is 8899.72 × 1,000,000 = 8,899,720,000. Therefore, the 33,247,937 shares traded today represent a fraction 33,247,937/8,899,720,000 ≈ 0.0037 of the total, or about 0.37%.

e. At the current price, your 100 shares are worth 100 × \$19.76 = \$1976. The dividend yield is 2.61%, so at that rate you would earn \$1976 × 0.0261 = \$51.57 in dividend payments this year.

f. The P/E ratio of 11.45 indicates that Microsoft's share price is 11.45 times its earnings per share for the past year. Therefore, its earnings per share were

$$\text{earnings per share} = \frac{\text{share price}}{\text{P/E ratio}} = \frac{\$19.76}{11.45} = \$1.73$$

g. From part f we know that Microsoft earned \$1.73 per share. Multiplying this by the total number of outstanding shares (see part d), we find that Microsoft's total profit for the year was \$1.73 × 8,899,720,000 ≈ \$15,400,000,000, or \$15.4 billion.

Now try Exercises 47–54.

Bonds

Most bonds are issued with three main characteristics:

- The **face value** (or *par value*) of the bond is the price you must pay the issuer to buy it at the time it is issued.
- The **coupon rate** of the bond is the *simple interest rate* that the issuer promises to pay. For example, a coupon rate of 8% on a bond with a face value of \$1000 means that the issuer will pay you interest of 8% × \$1000 = \$80 each year.
- The **maturity date** of the bond is the date on which the issuer promises to repay the face value of the bond.

Bonds would be simple if that were the end of the story. However, bonds can also be bought and sold after they are issued, in what is called the *secondary bond market.*

For example, suppose you own a bond with a $1000 face value and a coupon rate of 8%. Further suppose that new bonds with the same level of risk and same time to maturity are issued with a coupon rate of 9%. In that case, no one would pay $1000 for your bond because the new bonds offer a higher interest rate. However, you may be able to sell your bond at a *discount*—that is, for less than its face value. In contrast, suppose that new bonds are issued with a coupon rate of 7%. In that case, buyers will prefer your 8% bond to the new bonds and therefore may pay a *premium* for your bond—a price greater than its face value.

Consider a case in which you buy a bond with a face value of $1000 and a coupon rate of 8% for only $800. The bond issuer will still pay simple interest of 8% of $1000, or $80 per year. However, because you paid only $800 for the bond, *your* return for each year is

$$\frac{\text{amount you earn}}{\text{amount you paid}} = \frac{\$80}{\$800} = 0.1 = 10\%$$

More generally, the **current yield** of a bond is defined as the amount of interest it pays each year divided by the bond's current price (*not* its face value).

CURRENT YIELD OF A BOND

$$\text{current yield} = \frac{\text{annual interest payment}}{\text{current price of bond}}$$

A bond selling at a discount from its face value has a current yield that is higher than its coupon rate. The reverse is also true: A bond selling at a premium over its face value has a current yield that is lower than its coupon rate. These facts lead to the rule that *bond prices and yields move in opposite directions.*

Bond prices are usually quoted in *points*, which means percentage of face value. Most bonds have a face value of $1000. Thus, for example, a bond that closes at 102 points is selling for 102% × $1000 = $1020.

BY THE WAY

Bonds are graded in terms of risk by independent rating services. Bonds with a AAA rating are presumed to have the lowest risk and bonds with a D rating have the highest risk. Unfortunately, during the financial crisis that began in 2007, many bond ratings turned out to have been overstated.

BY THE WAY

A company that needs cash can raise it either by issuing new shares of stock or by issuing bonds. Issuing new shares of stock reduces the ownership fraction represented by each share and hence can depress the value of the shares. Issuing bonds obligates the company to pay interest to bondholders. Companies must balance these factors in deciding whether to raise cash through bond issues or stock offerings.

Example 9 Bond Interest

The closing price of a U.S. Treasury bond with a face value of $1000 is quoted as 105.97 points, for a current yield of 3.7%. If you buy this bond, how much annual interest will you receive?

Solution The 105.97 points means the bond is selling for 105.97% of its face value or

$$105.97\% \times \$1000 = \$1059.70$$

This is the current price of the bond. We are also given its current yield of 3.7%, so we can solve the current yield formula to find the annual interest payment:

1. Start with the current yield formula: $\text{current yield} = \dfrac{\text{annual interest}}{\text{current price}}$
2. Multiply both sides by *current price:* $\text{current yield} \times \text{current price} = \dfrac{\text{annual interest}}{\cancel{\text{current price}}} \times \cancel{\text{current price}}$
3. Simplify and interchange the left and right sides: $\text{annual interest} = \text{current yield} \times \text{current price}$
4. Use the given current yield (3.7% = 0.037) and the value found above for current price ($1059.70): $\text{annual interest} = 0.037 \times \$1059.70 = \$39.21$

The annual interest payments on this bond are $39.21. **Now try Exercises 55–62.**

BY THE WAY

Mutual funds collect fees in two ways. Some funds charge a commission, or *load,* when you buy or sell shares. Funds that do not charge commissions are called *no-load* funds. Nearly all funds charge an *annual fee,* which is usually a percentage of your investment's value. In general, fees are higher for funds that require more research on the part of the fund manager.

Mutual Funds

When you buy shares in a mutual fund, the fund manager takes care of the day-to-day decisions about when to buy and sell individual stocks or bonds. Thus, in comparing mutual funds, the most important factors are the fees charged for investing and measures of how well the manager is doing with the fund's money. Figure 4.7 shows a sample mutual fund quote, in this case for a Vanguard fund that is designed to track the S&P 500 stock index. The quote makes it easy to see the past performance of the fund, which you can compare to that of other funds. Of course, as stated in every mutual fund prospectus, *past performance is no guarantee of future results.*

Most mutual fund tables do not show the fees charged. For that, you must call or check the Web site of the company offering the mutual fund. Because fees are generally withdrawn automatically from your mutual fund account, they can have a big impact on your long-term gains. For example, if you invest $1000 in a fund that charges a 5% annual fee, only $950 is actually invested. Over many years, this can significantly reduce your total return.

Example 10 Understanding the Mutual Fund Quote

Answer the following questions based on the Vanguard 500 mutual fund quote shown in Figure 4.7.

a. Suppose you decide to invest $3000 in this fund today. How many shares will you be able to buy?

b. Suppose you had invested $3000 in this fund 3 years ago. How much would your investment be worth now?

c. Suppose you had invested $3000 in this fund 5 years ago. How much would your investment be worth now?

Solution

a. To find the number of shares you can buy, divide your investment of $3000 by the current share price, which is the NAV of $83.83:

$$\frac{\$3000}{83.83} \approx 35.8$$

Your $3000 investment buys 35.8 shares in the fund.

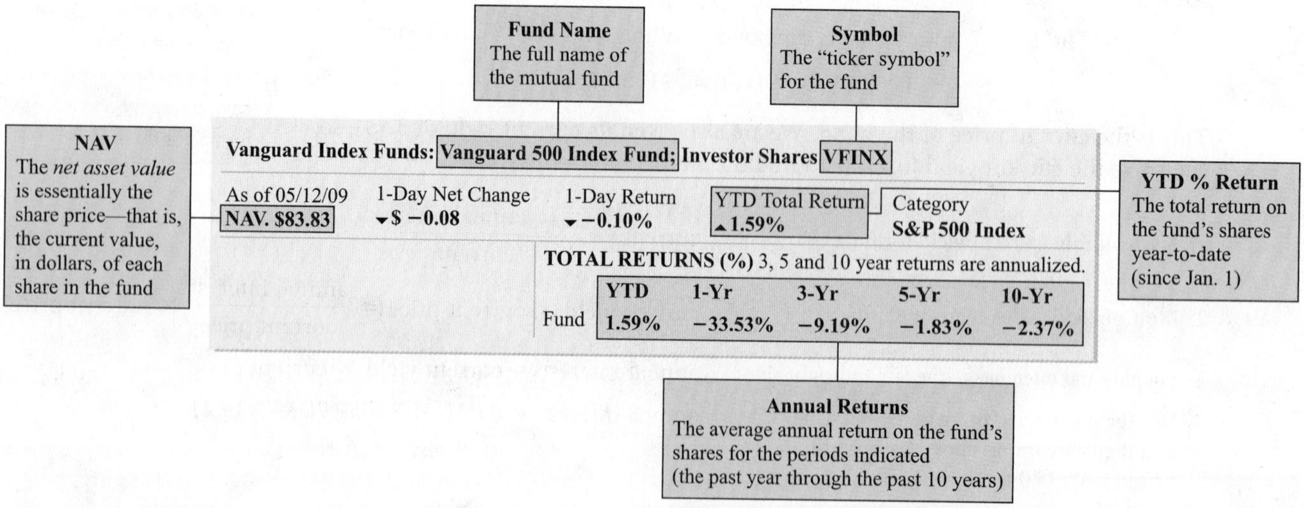

FIGURE 4.7 This figure explains key data that you'll find in an online mutual fund quote.

b. The annual return for the past 3 years was −9.19%, or −0.0919. We use this value as the APR in the compound interest formula with a term of $Y = 3$ years and starting principal of $P = \$3000$:

$$A = P \times (1 + \text{APR})^Y = \$3000 \times (1 - 0.0919)^3 = \$2246.58$$

Your investment would have declined significantly in value because of the negative return over the past 3 years.

c. The annual return for the past 5 years was −1.83%, or −0.0183. We use this value as the APR in the compound interest formula with a term of $Y = 5$ years and starting principal of $P = \$3000$:

$$A = P \times (1 + \text{APR})^Y = \$3000 \times (1 - 0.0183)^5 = \$2735.36$$

Again, your investment would have declined significantly in value because of the negative return over the past 5 years. **Now try Exercises 63–64.**

Time Out to Think

Note that the mutual fund quote in Example 10 is from 2009, and that an investment made 5 years ago (in 2004) would not have declined as much as an investment made just 3 years ago (in 2006). What does this tell you about how the fund performed in 2004 and 2005?

QUICK QUIZ

Choose the best answer to each of the following questions. Explain your reasoning with one or more complete sentences.

1. In the savings plan formula, assuming all other variables are constant, the accumulated balance in the savings account
   a. increases as n increases.
   b. increases as APR decreases.
   c. decreases as Y increases.
2. In the savings plan formula, assuming all other variables are constant, the accumulated balance in the savings account
   a. decreases as n increases.
   b. decreases as PMT increases.
   c. increases as Y increases.
3. The *total return* on a 5-year investment is
   a. the value of the investment after 5 years.
   b. the difference between the final and initial values of the investment.
   c. the relative change in the value of the investment.
4. The *annual return* on a 5-year investment is
   a. the average of the amounts that you earned in each of the 5 years.
   b. the annual percentage yield that gives the same increase in the value of the investment.
   c. the amount you earned in the best of the 5 years.
5. Suppose you deposited \$100 per month into a savings plan for 10 years, and at the end of that period your balance was \$22,200. The amount you earned in interest was
   a. \$10,200.
   b. \$20,200.
   c. impossible to compute without knowing the APR.
6. The best investment would be characterized by which of the following choices?
   a. low risk, high liquidity, and high return
   b. high risk, low liquidity, and high return
   c. low risk, high liquidity, and low return
7. Company A has 1 million shares outstanding and a share price of \$10. Company B has 10 million shares outstanding and a share price of \$9. Company C has 100,000 shares outstanding and a share price of \$100. Which company has the greatest market capitalization?
   a. A
   b. B
   c. C
8. Excalibur's P/E ratio of 75 tells you that
   a. its current share price is 75 times its earnings per share over the past year.
   b. its current share price is 75 times the total value of the company if it were sold.
   c. it offers an annual dividend that is 1/75 of its current share price.
9. The price you pay for a bond with a face value of \$5000 selling at 103 points is
   a. \$5300.
   b. \$5150.
   c. \$5103.
10. The 1-year return on a mutual fund
    a. must be greater than the 3-year return.
    b. must be less than the 3-year return.
    c. could be greater than or less than the 3-year return.

Exercises 4C

REVIEW QUESTIONS

1. What is a savings plan? Explain the savings plan formula.
2. Give an example of a situation in which you might want to solve the savings plan formula to find the payments, PMT, required to achieve some goal.
3. Distinguish between the total return and the annual return on an investment. How do you calculate the annual return? Give an example.
4. Briefly describe the three basic types of investments: stocks, bonds, and cash. How can you invest in these types directly? How can you invest in them indirectly through a mutual fund?
5. Explain what we mean by an investment's liquidity, risk, and return. How are risk and return usually related?
6. Contrast the historical returns for different types of investments. How do financial indices, such as the DJIA, help keep track of historical returns?
7. Define the face value, coupon rate, and maturity date of a bond. What does it mean to buy a bond at a premium? at a discount? How can you calculate the current yield of a bond?
8. Briefly describe the meaning of key data values given in online quotes for stocks and mutual funds.

DOES IT MAKE SENSE?

Decide whether each of the following statements makes sense (or is clearly true) or does not make sense (or is clearly false). Explain your reasoning.

9. If interest rates stay at 4% APR and I continue to make my monthly $25 deposits into my retirement plan, I should be able to retire in 30 years with a comfortable income.
10. My financial advisor showed me that I could reach my retirement goal with deposits of $200 per month and an average annual return of 7%. But I don't want to deposit that much of my paycheck, so I'm going to reach the same goal by getting an average annual return of 15% instead.
11. I'm putting all my savings into stocks because stocks always outperform other types of investment over the long term.
12. I'm hoping to withdraw money to buy my first house soon, so I need to put it into an investment that is fairly liquid.
13. I bought a fund advertised on the Web that says it uses a secret investment strategy to get an annual return twice that of stocks, with no risk at all.
14. I'm already retired, so I need low-risk investments. That's why I put most of my money in U.S. Treasury bills, notes, and bonds.

BASIC SKILLS & CONCEPTS

15–22: Solving with Powers and Roots. Solve the following equations for the unknown quantity.

15. $x^2 = 25$
16. $y^3 = 27$
17. $(x - 4)^2 = 36$
18. $p^{1/3} = 3$
19. $(t/3)^2 = 16$
20. $w^2 + 2 = 27$
21. $u^9 = 512$
22. $v^3 + 4 = 68$

23–26: Savings Plan Formula. Assume monthly deposits and monthly compounding in the following savings plans.

23. Find the savings plan balance after 12 months with an APR of 3% and monthly payments of $150.
24. Find the savings plan balance after 5 years with an APR of 2.5% and monthly payments of $100.
25. Find the savings plan balance after 3 years with an APR of 4% and monthly payments of $400.
26. Find the savings plan balance after 24 months with an APR of 5% and monthly payments of $250.

27–30: Investment Plans. Use the savings plan formula to answer the following questions.

27. At age 25, you set up an IRA (individual retirement account) with an APR of 5%. At the end of each month, you deposit $75 in the account. How much will the IRA contain when you retire at age 65? Compare that amount to the total deposits made over the time period.
28. A friend creates an IRA with an APR of 6.25%. She starts the IRA at age 25 and deposits $50 per month. How much will her IRA contain when she retires at age 65? Compare that amount to the total deposits made over the time period.
29. You put $300 per month in an investment plan that pays an APR of 3.5%. How much money will you have after 18 years? Compare this amount to the total deposits made over the time period.
30. You put $200 per month in an investment plan that pays an APR of 4.5%. How much money will you have after 18 years? Compare that amount to the total deposits made over the time period.

31–34: Planning for the Future. Use the savings plan formula to answer the following questions.

31. Your goal is to create a college fund for your child. Suppose you find a fund that offers an APR of 5%. How much should you deposit monthly to accumulate $85,000 in 15 years?
32. At age 35 you start saving for retirement. If your investment plan pays an APR of 6% and you want to have $2 million when you retire in 30 years, how much should you deposit monthly?
33. You want to purchase a new car in 3 years and expect the car to cost $15,000. Your bank offers a plan with a guaranteed APR of 5.5% if you make regular monthly deposits. How much should you deposit each month to end up with $15,000 in 3 years?
34. At age 20 when you graduate, you start saving for retirement. If your investment plan pays an APR of 4.5% and you want to have $5 million when you retire in 45 years, how much should you deposit monthly?

35. **Comfortable Retirement.** Suppose you are 30 years old and would like to retire at age 60. Furthermore, you would like to have a retirement fund from which you can draw an income of $100,000 per year—forever! How can you do it? Assume a constant APR of 6%.

36. **Very Comfortable Retirement.** Suppose you are 25 years old and would like to retire at age 65. Furthermore, you would like to have a retirement fund from which you can draw an income of $200,000 per year—forever! How can you do it? Assume a constant APR of 6%.

37–44: **Total and Annual Returns.** Compute the total and annual returns on the following investments.

37. Five years after buying 100 shares of XYZ stock for $60 per share, you sell the stock for $9400.

38. You pay $8000 for a municipal bond. When it matures after 20 years, you receive $12,500.

39. Twenty years after purchasing shares in a mutual fund for $6500, you sell them for $11,300.

40. Three years after buying 200 shares of XYZ stock for $25 per share, you sell the stock for $8500.

41. Three years after paying $3500 for shares in a startup company, you sell the shares for $2000 (at a loss).

42. Five years after paying $5000 for shares in a new company, you sell the shares for $3000 (at a loss).

43. Ten years after purchasing shares in a mutual fund for $7500, you sell them for $12,600.

44. Ten years after purchasing shares in a mutual fund for $10,000, you sell them for $2200 (at a loss).

45. **Historical Returns.** Suppose your great-great-grandfather invested $250 at the end of 1900 in each of three funds that tracked the averages of stocks, bonds, and cash, respectively. Assuming that his investments grew at the rates given in Table 4.6, approximately how much would each investment have been worth at the end of 2008?

46. **Historical Returns.** Which investment in 1900 would have been worth more at the end of 2008: $10 invested in stocks, $75 invested in bonds, or $500 invested in cash?

47–48: **Reading Stock Tables.**

47. Answer the following questions, assuming the data for Intel stock come from an online quote you looked at last night.

Intel Corporation (INTC)					
Last **15.48**	Change **+0.43**	% Change **+2.86%**	Volume **64,000,000**	Market Cap ($ millions)	**$86,460**
Open **15.00**	High **15.51**	Low **15.00**		P/E Ratio	**19.77**
52-Week High **24.75**	52-Week Low **12.05**			Dividend (latest quarter)	**$0.14**
				Dividend Yield	**3.62%**
				Shares Outstanding ($ millions)	**5580**

a. What is the symbol for Intel stock?

b. What was the price per share at the end of the day yesterday?

c. Based on the current price, what is the total value of the shares that have been traded so far today?

d. What percentage of all Intel shares have been traded so far today?

e. Suppose you own 100 shares of Intel. Based on the current price and dividend yield, what total dividend should you expect to receive this year?

f. What were the earnings per share for Intel?

g. How much total profit did Intel earn in the past year?

48. Answer the following questions, assuming the data for Walmart stock come from an online quote you looked at last night.

Wal-Mart Stores (WMT)					
Last **50.00**	Change **+0.75**	% Change **+1.52%**	Volume **17,280,000**	Market Cap ($ millions)	**$195,000**
Open **49.18**	High **50.66**	Low **49.16**		P/E Ratio	**14.88**
52-Week High **63.85**	52-Week Low **46.25**			Dividend (latest quarter)	**$0.27**
				Dividend Yield	**2.18%**
				Shares Outstanding ($ millions)	**3910**

a. What is the symbol for Walmart stock?

b. What was the price per share at the end of the day yesterday?

c. Based on the current price, what is the total value of the shares that have been traded so far today?

d. What percentage of all Walmart shares have been traded so far today?

e. Suppose you own 100 shares of Walmart. Based on the current price and dividend yield, what total dividend should you expect to receive this year?

f. What were the earnings per share for Walmart?

g. How much total profit did Walmart earn in the past year?

49–52: **Price-to-Earning Ratio.** For the stocks described below, answer the following questions.

a. How much were earnings per share?

b. Does the stock seem overpriced, underpriced, or about right, given that the historical P/E ratio is 12–14?

49. Costco closed at $48.30 per share with a P/E ratio of 17.25.

50. General Mills closed at $52.65 per share with a P/E ratio of 16.14.

51. IBM closed at $101.89 per share with a P/E ratio of 11.30.

52. Google closed at $393.50 per share with a P/E ratio of 28.78.

53. **Stock Look-Up.** Find a quote for Exxon Mobil on the Web, and locate the closing stock price and the current P/E ratio. How much were the earnings per share during the previous year? Does the stock seem overpriced? Explain.

54. **Stock Look-Up.** Find a quote for Wells Fargo and Company on the Web, and locate the closing stock price and the current P/E ratio. How much were the earnings per share during the previous year? Does the stock seem overpriced? Explain.

55–58: **Bond Yields.** Compute the current yield on the following bonds.

55. A $1000 Treasury bond with a coupon rate of 2.0% that has a market value of $950
56. A $1000 Treasury bond with a coupon rate of 2.5% that has a market value of $1050
57. A $1000 Treasury bond with a coupon rate of 5.5% that has a market value of $1100
58. A $10,000 Treasury bond with a coupon rate of 3.0% that has a market value of $9500

59–62: **Bond Interest.** Compute the annual interest that you would earn on the following bonds.

59. A $1000 Treasury bond with a current yield of 3.9% that is quoted at 105 points
60. A $1000 Treasury bond with a current yield of 1.5% that is quoted at 98 points
61. A $1000 Treasury bond with a current yield of 6.2% that is quoted at 114.3 points
62. A $10,000 Treasury bond with a current yield of 3.6% that is quoted at 102.5 points
63. **Mutual Fund Growth.**

Vanguard Limited-Term Tax-Exempt Fund (VMLTX)

As of 05/12/09	1-Day Net Change	1-Day Return
NAV. $10.93	**▾$0.00**	**▾0.0%**

TOTAL RETURNS (%) 3, 5 and 10 year returns are annualized.

	YTD	1-Yr	5-Yr	10-Yr
Fund	**2.92%**	**3.89%**	**3.20%**	**3.69%**

a. Suppose you invest $5000 in this fund today. How many shares will you buy?

b. Suppose you had invested $5000 in this fund 5 years ago. How much would your investment be worth now?

c. Suppose you had invested $5000 in this fund 10 years ago. How much would your investment be worth now?

64. **Mutual Fund Growth.**

Vanguard Long-Term Bond Index (VBLTX)

As of 05/12/09	1-Day Net Change	1-Day Return
NAV. $10.82	**▴$ 0.07**	**▴0.64%**

TOTAL RETURNS (%) 3, 5 and 10 year returns are annualized.

	YTD	1-Yr	5-Yr	10-Yr
Fund	**−7.71%**	**−0.48%**	**4.82%**	**6.19%**

a. Suppose you invest $2500 in this fund today. How many shares will you buy?

b. Suppose you had invested $2500 in this fund 5 years ago. How much would your investment be worth now?

c. Suppose you had invested $2500 in this fund 10 years ago. How much would your investment be worth now?

FURTHER APPLICATIONS

65–68: **Who Comes Out Ahead?** Consider the following pairs of savings plans. Compare the balances in each plan after 10 years. In each case, which person deposited more money in the plan? Which of the two investment strategies do you believe was better? Assume that the compounding and payment periods are the same.

65. Yolanda deposits $200 per month in an account with an APR of 5%, while Zach deposits $2400 at the end of each year in an account with an APR of 5%.
66. Polly deposits $50 per month in an account with an APR of 6%, while Quint deposits $40 per month in an account with an APR of 6.5%.
67. Juan deposits $400 per month in an account with an APR of 6%, while Maria deposits $5000 at the end of each year in an account with an APR of 6.5%.
68. George deposits $40 per month in an account with an APR of 7%, while Harvey deposits $150 per quarter in an account with an APR of 7.5%.

69–72: **Will It Work?** Suppose you want to accumulate $50,000 for a college fund over the next 15 years. Determine whether the following investment plans will allow you to reach your goal. Assume that the compounding and payment periods are the same.

69. You deposit $50 per month into an account with an APR of 7%.
70. You deposit $75 per month into an account with an APR of 7%.
71. You deposit $100 per month into an account with an APR of 6%.
72. You deposit $200 per month into an account with an APR of 5%.
73. **Total Return on Stock.** Suppose you bought XYZ stock 1 year ago for $5.80 per share and sell it at $8.25. You also pay a commission of $0.25 per share on your sale. What is the total return on your investment?
74. **Total Return on Stock.** Suppose you bought XYZ stock 1 year ago for $46.00 per share and sell it at $8.25. You also pay a commission of $0.25 per share on your sale. What is the total return on your investment?
75. **Death and the Maven (A True Story).** In December 1995, 101-year-old Anne Scheiber died and left $22 million to Yeshiva University. This fortune was accumulated through shrewd and patient investment of a $5000 nest egg over the course of 50 years. In turning $5000 into $22 million, what were Scheiber's total and annual returns? How did her annual return compare to the average annual return for stocks (see Table 4.6)?
76. **Cigarettes to Dollars.** The Web site *MSN Money* claims, "A 40-year-old who quits smoking and puts the savings into a 401(k) earning 9% a year would have nearly $250,000 by age 70." Check the accuracy of this statement for a pack-a-day smoker who spends $4.50 per pack. Assume monthly deposits and monthly compounding.

77. **Get Started Early!** Mitch and Bill are the same age. When Mitch is 25 years old, he begins depositing $1000 per year into a savings account. He makes deposits for 10 years, at which point he is forced to stop making deposits. However, he leaves his money in the account for the next 40 years (where it continues to earn interest). Bill doesn't start saving until he is 35 years old, but for the next 40 years he makes annual deposits of $1000. Assume that both accounts earn interest at an annual rate of 7% and interest in both accounts is compounded once a year.

a. How much money does Mitch have in his account at age 75?

b. How much money does Bill have in his account at age 75?

c. Compare the amounts of money that Mitch and Bill deposit into their accounts.

d. Write a paragraph summarizing your conclusions about this parable.

WEB PROJECTS

78. **Investment Tracking.** Choose three stocks, three bonds, and three mutual funds that you think would make good investments. Imagine that you invest $1000 in each of these nine investments. Use the Web to track the value of your investment portfolio over the next 5 weeks. Based on the portfolio value at the end, find your return for the 5-week period. Which investments fared the best, and which did most poorly?

79. **Dow Jones Industrial Average.** The Dow Jones Company has an extensive Web site that includes its history and functions, as well as information on the Dow Jones Industrial Average (DJIA) and links to the companies that make up the DJIA. Visit the Web site and choose a specific topic related to the DJIA (for example, the history of the DJIA, the original companies in the DJIA, the best and worst days for the DJIA, how the DJIA is computed). Using the Web site and any other resources, write a two-page paper on your topic.

80. **Company Research.** Choose one of the 30 companies in the DJIA and carry out research on that company as if you were a prospective investor. You should consider the following questions: How has the company performed over the last year? 5 years? 10 years? Does the company offer dividends? How do you interpret its P/E ratio? Overall, do you think the company is a good investment? Why or why not?

81. **Financial Web Sites.** Visit one of the many financial news and advice Web sites. Describe the services offered by the Web site. Explain whether, as an active or prospective investor, you find the Web site useful.

82. **Other Averages.** Investigate one of several other stock averages, such as Standard and Poor's or the Russell 2500. How do these averages differ from the Dow Jones Industrial Average?

83. **Online Brokers.** Visit the Web sites of at least two online brokers. How do their services differ? Compare the commissions charged by the brokers.

IN YOUR WORLD

84. **Advertised Investment.** Find an advertisement for an investment plan. Describe some of the cited benefits of the plan. Using what you learned in this unit, identify at least one possible drawback of the plan.

85. **Financial Pages.** Choose a major newspaper and study its financial pages. Can you identify examples of all the investment data described in this unit? If not, what data are missing? What additional financial data are offered? Explain how to read the pages.

86. **Personal Investment Options.** Does your employer offer you the option of enrolling in a savings or retirement plan? If so, describe the available options and discuss the advantages and disadvantages of each.

TECHNOLOGY EXERCISES

87. **Savings Plan Formula with Excel.** Use the future value (FV) function in Excel to answer the following questions.

a. What is the balance in an account after 25 years with monthly deposits of $100 and an APR of 4%?

b. If you double the APR in part a, is the balance double, more than double, or less than double the balance in part a?

c. If you double the number of years in part a, is the balance double, more than double, or less than double the balance in part a?

88. **Savings Plan Formula with Excel.** Abe deposits $50 each month for 40 years in an account with an APR of 5.5%. Beatrice deposits $100 each month for 20 years in an account with an APR of 5.5%.

a. Verify that Abe and Beatrice deposit the same amount of money during the stated periods of time. How much money do they deposit?

b. Compute the balance in each account and explain the results.

89. **Computing Roots.** Use a calculator or Excel to compute the following quantities.

a. $2.8^{1/4}$ b. $120^{1/3}$

c. The annual return on an account in which an initial investment of $250 increases to $1850 over a period of 15 years

UNIT 4D Loan Payments, Credit Cards, and Mortgages

Do you have a credit card? Do you have student loans or a loan for a car? Do you own a house? Chances are that you owe money for at least one of these purposes. If so, you not only have to pay back the money you borrowed but also have to pay interest on the money that you owe. In this unit, we will study the basic mathematics of loans.

Loan Basics

Suppose you borrow \$1200 at an annual interest rate of APR = 12%, or 1% per month. At the end of the first month, you owe interest in the amount of

$$1\% \times \$1200 = \$12$$

If you paid *only* this \$12 in interest, you'd still owe \$1200. That is, the total amount of the loan, called the loan **principal**, would still be \$1200. In that case, you'd owe the same \$12 in interest the next month. In fact, if you paid only the interest from one month to the next, the loan would never be paid off and you'd have to pay \$12 per month forever.

If you hope to make progress in paying off the loan, you need to pay part of the principal as well as interest. For example, suppose that you paid \$200 toward your loan principal each month, plus the current interest. At the end of the first month, you'd pay \$200 toward principal *plus* \$12 for the 1% interest you owe, making a total payment of \$212. Because you've paid \$200 toward principal, your new loan principal would be \$1200 − \$200 = \$1000.

At the end of the second month, you'd again pay \$200 toward principal and 1% interest. But this time the interest is on the \$1000 that you still owe. Your interest payment therefore would be 1% × \$1000 = \$10, making your total payment \$210. Table 4.7 shows how the calculations continue until the loan is paid off after 6 months.

TABLE 4.7 Payments and Principal for a \$1200 Loan with Principal Paid Off at a Constant \$200/Month

End of . . .	Prior Principal	Interest on Prior Principal	Payment Toward Principal	Total Payment	New Principal
Month 1	\$1200	1% × \$1200 = \$12	\$200	\$212	\$1000
Month 2	\$1000	1% × \$1000 = \$10	\$200	\$210	\$800
Month 3	\$800	1% × \$800 = \$8	\$200	\$208	\$600
Month 4	\$600	1% × \$600 = \$6	\$200	\$206	\$400
Month 5	\$400	1% × \$400 = \$4	\$200	\$204	\$200
Month 6	\$200	1% × \$200 = \$2	\$200	\$202	\$0

LOAN BASICS

For any loan, the **principal** is the amount of money owed at any particular time. Interest is charged on the loan principal. To pay off a loan, you must gradually pay down the principal. Therefore, in general, every payment should include all the interest you owe *plus* some amount that goes toward paying off the principal.

Installment Loans

For the case illustrated in Table 4.7, your total payment decreases from month to month because of the declining amount of interest that you owe. There's nothing inherently wrong with this method of paying off a loan, but most people prefer to pay the *same* total amount each month because it makes planning a budget easier. A loan that you pay off with equal regular payments is called an **installment loan** (or *amortized loan*).

Suppose you wanted to pay off your $1200 loan with 6 equal monthly payments. How much should you pay each month? Because the payments in Table 4.7 vary between $202 and $212, it's clear that the equal monthly payments must lie somewhere in this range. The exact amount is not obvious, but we can calculate it with the **loan payment formula.**

BY THE WAY

About two-thirds of all college students take out student loans, with an average debt of about $20,000 at graduation.

LOAN PAYMENT FORMULA (INSTALLMENT LOANS)

$$\text{PMT} = \frac{P \times \left(\frac{\text{APR}}{n}\right)}{\left[1 - \left(1 + \frac{\text{APR}}{n}\right)^{(-nY)}\right]}$$

where

PMT = regular payment amount
P = starting loan principal (amount borrowed)
APR = annual percentage rate
n = number of payment periods per year
Y = loan term in years

In our current example, the starting loan principal is $P = \$1200$, the annual interest rate is APR = 12%, the loan term is $Y = \frac{1}{2}$ year (6 months), and monthly payments mean $n = 12$. The loan payment formula gives

$$\text{PMT} = \frac{P \times \left(\frac{\text{APR}}{n}\right)}{\left[1 - \left(1 + \frac{\text{APR}}{n}\right)^{(-nY)}\right]} = \frac{\$1200 \times \left(\frac{0.12}{12}\right)}{\left[1 - \left(1 + \frac{0.12}{12}\right)^{(-12 \times 1/2)}\right]}$$

$$= \frac{\$1200 \times (0.01)}{[1 - (1 + 0.01)^{-6}]} = \frac{\$12}{1 - 0.942045235} = \$207.06$$

The monthly payments would be $207.06; note that, as we expected, the payment is between $202 and $212.

Because the loan principal is gradually paid down with the installment payments, while the payments remain the same, the interest due each month must decline gradually. And because the payments remain the same, the amount paid toward principal each month gradually rises. We therefore have the general relationship between principal and interest summarized in the following box.

PRINCIPAL AND INTEREST FOR INSTALLMENT LOANS

The portions of installment loan payments going toward principal and toward interest vary as the loan is paid down. Early in the loan term, the portion going toward interest is relatively high and the portion going toward principal is relatively low. As the term proceeds, the portion going toward interest gradually decreases and the portion going toward principal gradually increases.

USING TECHNOLOGY

The Loan Payment Formula (Installment Loans)

Standard Calculators As with compound interest and savings plan calculations, you can do loan payment calculations with a standard calculator, as long as you follow a correct order of operations. The following calculation shows one correct way to handle the numbers from Example 1, in which $P = \$7500$, $\text{APR} = 0.09$, $n = 12$, and $Y = 10$ years; as always, be sure that you *do not round any answers until the end of the calculation.*

General Procedure	Our Example	Calculator Steps*		Output
$\text{PMT} = \dfrac{P \times \left(\dfrac{\text{APR}}{n}\right)}{\left[1 - \left(1 + \dfrac{\text{APR}}{n}\right)^{(-nY)}\right]}$	$\text{PMT} = \dfrac{\$7500 \times \left(\dfrac{0.09}{12}\right)}{\left[1 - \left(1 + \dfrac{0.09}{12}\right)^{(-12\times10)}\right]}$	Step 1	1 (+) 0.09 (÷) 12 (=)	1.0075
1. parentheses	1. parentheses	Step 2	(∧) ((−) 12 (×) 10) (=)	0.407937305
2. exponent	2. exponent	Step 3	1 (−) 0.407937305 (=)	0.592062695
3. complete denominator	3. complete denominator	Step 4	7500 (×) 0.09 (÷) 12 (÷) 0.592062695 (=)	95.0068...
4. do numerator and divide by denominator	4. do numerator and divide by denominator			

*If your calculator does not have parentheses keys, then you will need to keep track of the results of Steps 1–3 either on paper or in the calculator's memory. Do not round intermediate results.

Excel We use the built-in function PMT to compute payments for installment loans. The inputs are shown in the screen shot below.

Note that the variables are similar to those we used earlier with the FV function:

- *rate* is the interest rate for each payment period, which in this case is the monthly interest rate $\text{APR}/n = 0.09/12$.
- *nper* is the total number of payment periods, which in this case is $nY = 12 \times 10$.
- *pv* is the present value, which is the starting loan principal of \$7500.
- *fv* is the future value, which is \$0 because the goal is to pay off the loan completely; note that it is 0 by default, so we can leave *fv* blank.
- *type* is also left blank, because we use the default value ($\text{type} = 0$) to indicate monthly payments made at the *end* of each period (month).

You may find it easier to see the inputs if you use the dialog box that appears when you choose the PMT function from the Insert menu, which will resemble the screen shot at the right.

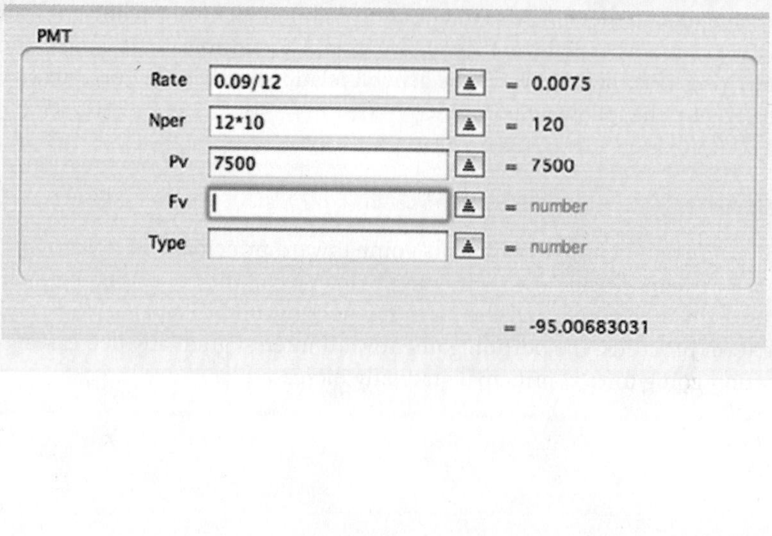

Example 1 Student Loan

Suppose you have student loans totaling \$7500 when you graduate from college. The interest rate is APR = 9% and the loan term is 10 years. What are your monthly payments? How much will you pay over the lifetime of the loan? What is the total interest you will pay on the loan?

Solution The starting loan principal is $P = \$7500$, the interest rate is APR = 0.09, the loan term is $Y = 10$ years, and $n = 12$ for monthly payments. We use the loan payment formula to find the monthly payments:

$$\text{PMT} = \frac{P \times \left(\frac{\text{APR}}{n}\right)}{\left[1 - \left(1 + \frac{\text{APR}}{n}\right)^{(-nY)}\right]} = \frac{\$7500 \times \left(\frac{0.09}{12}\right)}{\left[1 - \left(1 + \frac{0.09}{12}\right)^{(-12\times10)}\right]}$$

$$= \frac{\$7500 \times (0.0075)}{\left[1 - (1.0075)^{-120}\right]}$$

$$= \frac{\$56.25}{[1 - 0.407937305]}$$

$$= \$95.01$$

Take Note

Because we assume the compounding period is the same as the payment period and because we round payments to the nearest cent, the calculated payments may differ slightly from actual payments.

Your monthly payments are \$95.01. Over the 10-year term, your total payments will be

$$10 \text{ yr} \times 12 \frac{\text{mo}}{\text{yr}} \times \frac{\$95.01}{\text{mo}} = \$11{,}401.20$$

Of this amount, \$7500 pays off the principal. The rest, or \$11,401 − \$7500 = \$3901, represents interest payments. **Now try Exercises 13–24.**

Example 2 Principal and Interest Payments

For the loan in Example 1, calculate the portions of your payments that go to principal and to interest during the first 3 months.

Solution The monthly interest rate is APR/12 = 0.09/12 = 0.0075. For a \$7500 starting loan principal, the interest due at the end of the first month is

$$0.0075 \times \$7500 = \$56.25$$

Your monthly payment (calculated in Example 1) is \$95.01. We've found that the interest due is \$56.25, so the rest, or \$95.01 − \$56.25 = \$38.76, goes to principal. Thus, after your first payment, your new loan principal is

$$\$7500 - \$38.76 = \$7461.24$$

Table 4.8 continues the same calculations for months 2 and 3. Note that, as expected, the interest payment gradually decreases and the payment toward principal gradually increases. But also note that, for these first 3 months of a 10-year loan, more than half of each payment goes toward interest. We could continue this table through the life of the loan, but it's generally easier to use software that finds principal and interest payments with built-in functions.

BY THE WAY

A table of principal and interest payments over the life of a loan is called an *amortization schedule.* Most banks will provide an amortization schedule for any loan you are considering.

TABLE 4.8 Interest and Principal Portions of Payments on a \$7500 Loan (10-year term, APR = 9%)

End of . . .	Interest = 0.0075 × Balance	Payment Toward Principal	New Principal
Month 1	0.0075 × \$7500 = \$56.25	\$95.01 − \$56.25 = \$38.76	\$7500 − \$38.76 = \$7461.24
Month 2	0.0075 × \$7461.24 = \$55.96	\$95.01 − \$55.96 = \$39.05	\$7461.24 − \$39.05 = \$7422.19
Month 3	0.0075 × \$7422.19 = \$55.67	\$95.01 − \$55.67 = \$39.34	\$7422.19 − \$39.34 = \$7382.85

Now try Exercises 25–26.

Time Out to Think

In a case such as the student loan in Examples 1 and 2, many people are surprised to find that more than half of their early loan payments goes to interest when the annual interest rate is only 9%. By referring to Table 4.8, explain why this is the case. How will the payments toward principal and interest compare toward the end of the loan?

Choices of Rate and Term

You'll usually have several choices of interest rate and loan term when seeking a loan. For example, a bank might offer a 3-year car loan at 8%, a 4-year loan at 9%, and a 5-year loan at 10%. You'll pay less total interest with the shortest-term, lowest-rate loan, but this loan will have the highest monthly payments. You'll have to evaluate your choices and make the decision that is best for your personal situation.

USING TECHNOLOGY

Principal and Interest Payments

You can use Excel to make a table of principal and interest payments like the one shown in Table 4.8. The most direct way of doing this is shown in the following screen shot.

◇	A	B	C	D	E
1					
2		Month	Interest	Principal	Balance
3					7500
4		1	=0.09*E3/12	=95.01-C4	=E3-D4
5		2	=0.09*E4/12	=95.01-C5	=E4-D5
6		3	=0.09*E5/12	=95.01-C6	=E5-D6
7					

To understand how the program works, note the following:

- The table begins with the starting balance of $7500 in cell E3.
- Cell C4 calculates the interest for month 1, which is the balance from cell E3 times APR/n, which in this case is $0.09/12$.
- Cell D4 calculates the principal for month 1 by subtracting the interest payment (cell C4) from the monthly payment of $95.01.
- Cell E4 calculates the new balance after month 1 by subtracting the principal payment (cell D4) from the prior balance (cell E3).
- Each successive row then repeats the same pattern.

You should make this table for yourself in Excel and confirm that it gives the values shown in Table 4.8.

The only difficulty with this approach is that finding the principal and interest payments in, say, month 25 requires 25 rows in your table. If you only want to know the interest and principal payments for a particular month, you can instead use Excel's functions IPMT and PPMT, as shown in the screen shot below for the 25th month; note that the variable *per* is the period for which you want to know the payments, which is 25 in this case. As with the PMT function (see Using Technology, p. 250), we have left the *fv* and *type* inputs blank.

fx =IPMT(0.09/12,25,120,7500)
IPMT(rate, per, nper, pv, [fv], [type])

fx =PPMT(0.09/12,25,120,7500)
PPMT(rate, per, nper, pv, [fv], [type])

Example 3 Choice of Auto Loans

You need a \$6000 loan to buy a used car. Your bank offers a 3-year loan at 8%, a 4-year loan at 9%, and a 5-year loan at 10%. Calculate your monthly payments and total interest over the loan term with each option.

Solution We are looking for payments on an installment loan, so we use the loan payment formula

$$\text{PMT} = \frac{P \times \left(\frac{\text{APR}}{n}\right)}{\left[1 - \left(1 + \frac{\text{APR}}{n}\right)^{(-nY)}\right]}$$

For all three cases, we have the same principal, $P = \$6000$, and monthly payments for which $n = 12$; the differences are in the APR and the loan term. The following table makes the comparisons easy by using a column for each of the three loan choices. Be sure you see how the numbers in Step 1 correspond to the loan payment formula above.

	Y = 3 years (36 months), APR = 0.08	Y = 4 years (48 months), APR = 0.09	Y = 5 years (60 months), APR = 0.10
1. Use the loan payment formula to find the monthly payment:	$\text{PMT} = \frac{\$6000 \times \left(\frac{0.08}{12}\right)}{\left[1 - \left(1 + \frac{0.08}{12}\right)^{(-12 \times 3)}\right]}$ $= \$188.02$	$\text{PMT} = \frac{\$6000 \times \left(\frac{0.09}{12}\right)}{\left[1 - \left(1 + \frac{0.09}{12}\right)^{(-12 \times 4)}\right]}$ $= \$149.31$	$\text{PMT} = \frac{\$6000 \times \left(\frac{0.10}{12}\right)}{\left[1 - \left(1 + \frac{0.10}{12}\right)^{(-12 \times 5)}\right]}$ $= \$127.48$
2. Multiply the monthly payment by the loan term in months to find the total payments:	\$188.02/month × 36 months = \$6768.72	\$149.31/month × 48 months = \$7166.88	\$127.48/month × 60 months = \$7648.80
3. Subtract the principal from the total payments to find the total interest:	\$6768.72 − \$6000 = \$768.72	\$7166.88 − \$6000 = \$1166.88	\$7648.80 − \$6000 = \$1648.80

Notice that, as we should expect, a longer-term loan leads to lower monthly payments but higher total interest. **Now try Exercises 27–28.**

BY THE WAY

You should always watch out for financial scams, especially when borrowing money. Keep in mind what is sometimes called the first rule of finance: *If it sounds too good to be true, it probably is!*

Time Out to Think

Consider your own current financial situation. If you needed a \$6000 car loan, which option from Example 3 would you choose? Why?

Credit Cards

Credit card loans differ from installment loans in that you are not required to pay off your balance in any set period of time. Instead, you are required to make only a minimum monthly payment that generally covers all the interest but very little principal. As a result, it takes a very long time to pay off your credit card loan if you make only the minimum payments. If you wish to pay off your loan in a particular amount of time, you should use the loan payment formula to calculate the necessary payments.

A word of caution: Most credit cards have very high interest rates compared to other types of loans. As a result, it is easy to get into financial trouble if you get overextended with credit cards. The trouble is particularly bad if you miss your payments. In that case, you will probably be charged a late fee that is added to your principal, thereby increasing the amount of interest due the next month. With the interest charges operating like compound interest in reverse, failure to pay on time can put a person into an ever-deepening financial hole.

BY THE WAY

About three-fourths of American households have at least one credit card, and their average credit card balance is about \$8000. The average credit card interest rate is about 17%—far higher than the interest rate on most other consumer loans.

Example 4 Credit Card Debt

You have a credit card balance of \$2300 with an annual interest rate of 21%. You decide to pay off your balance over 1 year. How much will you need to pay each month? Assume you make no further credit card purchases.

Solution Your starting loan principal is $P = \$2300$, the interest rate is APR = 0.21, and monthly payments mean $n = 12$. Because you want to pay off the loan in 1 year, we set $Y = 1$. The required payments are

$$\text{PMT} = \frac{P \times \left(\frac{\text{APR}}{n}\right)}{\left[1 - \left(1 + \frac{\text{APR}}{n}\right)^{(-nY)}\right]} = \frac{\$2300 \times \left(\frac{0.21}{12}\right)}{\left[1 - \left(1 + \frac{0.21}{12}\right)^{(-12\times 1)}\right]} = \$214.16$$

You must pay \$214.16 per month to pay off the balance in 1 year.

Now try Exercises 29–32.

Thinking About...

Derivation of the Loan Payment Formula

Suppose you borrow a principal P for a loan term of N months at a monthly interest rate i. In most real cases, you would make monthly payments on this loan. However, suppose the lender did not want monthly payments, but instead wanted you to pay back the principal with compound interest in a lump sum at the end of the loan term. We can find this lump sum amount with the compound interest formula:

$$A = P \times (1 + i)^N$$

In financial terms, this lump sum amount, A, is called the *future value* of your loan. (The *present value* is the original loan principal, P.) From the lender's point of view, allowing you to spread your payments out over time should not affect this future value. Thus, in the end, your monthly payments should represent the same future value, A. We already have a formula for determining the future value with monthly payments—it is the general form of the savings plan formula from Unit 4C:

$$A = \text{PMT} \times \frac{\left[(1 + i)^N - 1\right]}{i}$$

We now have two different expressions for A, so we set them equal:

$$\text{PMT} \times \frac{\left[(1 + i)^N - 1\right]}{i} = P \times (1 + i)^N$$

To find the loan payment formula, we need to solve this equation for PMT. We first multiply both sides by the reciprocal of the fraction on the left:

$$\text{PMT} \times \frac{\cancel{\left[(1 + i)^N - 1\right]}}{i} \times \frac{i}{\cancel{\left[(1 + i)^N - 1\right]}}$$

$$= P \times (1 + i)^N \times \frac{i}{\left[(1 + i)^N\right] - 1} = \frac{P \times (1 + i)^N \times i}{\left[(1 + i)^N - 1\right]}$$

Next, we divide both the numerator and the denominator of the fraction on the right by $(1 + i)^N$:

$$\text{PMT} = \frac{\dfrac{P \times \cancel{(1 + i)^N} \times i}{\cancel{(1 + i)^N}}}{\dfrac{\left[(1 + i)^N - 1\right]}{(1 + i)^N}}$$

The numerator simplifies to $P \times i$. To simplify the denominator, note that

$$\frac{\left[(1 + i)^N - 1\right]}{(1 + i)^N} = \frac{\cancel{(1 + i)^N}}{\cancel{(1 + i)^N}} - \frac{1}{(1 + i)^N}$$
$$= 1 - (1 + i)^{-N}$$

Substituting the simplified terms for the numerator and the denominator, we find the loan payment formula:

$$\text{PMT} = \frac{P \times i}{1 - (1 + i)^{-N}}$$

To put the loan payment formula in the form given in the text, we substitute $i = \text{APR}/n$ for the interest rate per period and $N = nY$ for the total number of payments (where n is the number of payments per year and Y is the number of years).

Time Out to Think

Continuing Example 4, suppose you can get a personal loan at a bank at an annual interest rate of 10%. Should you take this loan and use it to pay off your $2300 credit card debt? Why or why not?

BY THE WAY

Americans hold a total of more than 500 million VISA, MasterCard, and American Express cards, plus another 800 million store credit cards and debit cards. Americans charge more than $1 trillion each year to their credit cards, and pay more than $50 billion in interest on these charges.

Example 5 A Deepening Hole

Paul has gotten into credit card trouble. He has a balance of $9500 and just lost his job. His credit card company charges interest of APR = 21%, compounded daily. Suppose the credit card company allows him to suspend his payments until he finds a new job—but continues to charge interest. If it takes him a year to find a new job, how much will he owe when he starts his new job?

Solution Because Paul is not making payments during the year, this is not a loan payment problem. Instead, it is a compound interest problem, in which Paul's balance of $9500 grows at an annual rate of 21%, compounded daily. We use the compound interest formula with a starting balance of $P = \$9500$, APR = 0.21,

PRACTICAL MATTERS

Avoiding Credit Card Trouble

Most adults have credit cards for good reason. Used properly, credit cards offer many conveniences: They are safer and easier to carry than cash, they offer monthly statements that list everything charged to the card, and they can be used as ID to rent a car. But credit card trouble can compound quickly, and many people get into financial trouble as a result. A few simple guidelines can help you avoid credit card trouble.

- Use only one credit card. People who accumulate balances on several cards often lose track of their overall debt. A lost wallet or purse means more credit cards that must be canceled.
- If possible, pay off your balance in full each month. Then there's no chance of getting into a financial hole.
- If you plan to pay off your balance in full each month, be sure that your credit card offers an interest-free "grace period" on purchases (usually of about 1 month) so that you will not have to pay any interest.
- Compare the interest rate and annual fee (if any) of your credit card and others. Fees and rates differ greatly among credit cards, so be sure you are getting a good deal. In particular, if you carry a balance, look for a card with a relatively low interest rate.
- When choosing a credit card, watch out for *teaser rates*. These are low interest rates that are offered for a short period, such as 6 months, after which the card reverts to very high rates.
- Never use your credit card for a cash advance except in an emergency, because nearly all credit cards charge both fees and high interest rates for cash advances. In addition, most credit cards charge interest immediately on cash advances, even if there is a grace period on purchases. When you need cash, get it directly from your own bank account by cashing a check or using an ATM card.
- If you own a home, consider replacing a common credit card with a home equity credit line. You'll generally get a lower interest rate, and the interest may be tax deductible.
- If you find yourself in a deepening financial hole, consult a financial advisor right away. A good place to start is with the National Foundation for Credit Counseling (www.nfcc.org). The longer you wait, the worse off you'll be in the long run.

$Y = 1$ year, and $n = 365$ (for daily compounding). At the end of the year, his loan balance will be

$$A = P \times \left(1 + \frac{\text{APR}}{n}\right)^{(nY)}$$
$$= \$9500 \times \left(1 + \frac{0.21}{365}\right)^{(365\times1)}$$
$$= \$11{,}719.23$$

During his year of unemployment, interest alone will make Paul's credit card balance grow from \$9500 to over \$11,700, an increase of more than \$2200. Clearly, this increase will only make it more difficult for Paul to get back on his financial feet.

Now try Exercises 33–36.

Mortgages

BY THE WAY

By mid-2009, the bursting of the "housing bubble" had caused home values to plummet so much that nearly one-third of Americans owed more money on their mortgages than their homes were worth. Such mortgages are said to be *underwater*, and they can cause great problems for homeowners. For example, someone with an underwater mortgage who has to move for a new job will be unable to sell his or her home for enough money to pay off the loan.

One of the most popular types of installment loans is designed specifically to help you buy a home. It's called a home **mortgage**. Mortgage interest rates generally are lower than interest rates on other types of loans because your home itself serves as a payment guarantee. If you fail to make your payments, the lender (usually a bank or mortgage company) can take possession of your home through the process called *foreclosure* and sell it to recover some or all of the amount loaned to you.

There are several considerations in getting a home mortgage. First, the lender will probably require a **down payment**, typically 10% to 20% of the purchase price. Then the lender will loan you the rest of the money needed to purchase the home. Most lenders also charge fees, or **closing costs**, at the time you take out a loan. Closing costs can be substantial and may vary significantly between lenders, so you should be sure that you understand them. In general, there are two types of closing costs:

- Direct fees, such as fees for getting the home appraised and checking your credit history, for which the lender charges a fixed dollar amount. These fees typically range from a few hundred dollars to a couple thousand dollars.
- Fees charged as **points**, where each point is 1% of the loan amount. Many lenders divide points into two categories: an "origination fee" that is charged on all loans and "discount points" that vary for loans with different rates. For example, a lender might charge an origination fee of 1 point (1%) on all loans, then offer you a choice of adding 1 discount point for a loan at 8% or 2 discount points for a loan at 7.75%. Despite their different names, there is no essential difference between an origination fee and discount points.

As always, you should watch out for any fine print that may affect the cost of your loan. For example, you should check to make sure that there are no *prepayment penalties* if you decide to pay off your loan early. Most people pay off mortgages early, either because they sell the home or because they decide to refinance the loan to get a better interest rate or to change their monthly payments.

DEFINITIONS

A home **mortgage** is an installment loan designed specifically to finance a home.

A **down payment** is the amount of money you must pay up front in order to be given a mortgage or other loan.

Closing costs are fees you must pay in order to be given the loan. They may include a variety of direct costs, or fees charged as **points**, where each point is 1% of the loan amount. In most cases, lenders are required to give you a clear assessment of closing costs before you sign for the loan.

PRACTICAL MATTERS

Choosing or Refinancing a Loan

As you've seen throughout this unit, interest rate and loan term are the primary factors in determining loan payments. But they are not the only factors that are important in choosing a loan. Because you are almost certain to make many loan decisions in your life, it's very important to understand these other factors, regardless of whether you are taking out a new loan (such as a student loan, a car loan, or a home mortgage) or refinancing an existing loan. The following general guidelines should help you get started.

- Be sure that you understand the loan you are taking out. For example, is the interest rate fixed? What is the term of the loan? When are payments due?
- Is a down payment required? If so, how will you afford it? If not, could you get a better interest rate by offering to make a down payment?
- What fees and closing costs will be charged? Be sure you identify *all* closing costs, including origination fees and discount points, since different lenders may quote their fees differently. Also, be sure to consider how these fees and costs affect the overall cost of the loan over its term.
- Watch out for fine print that may make the loan more expensive than it seems on the surface. Be especially wary of any prepayment penalties, since you may later decide to pay the loan off early or to refinance it at a better interest rate.
- Be very careful of offers to refinance loans. Refinancing at a lower interest rate can save you money, but it may not be a good idea in all circumstances. In particular, always consider these two additional factors when deciding whether to refinance a loan:
  1. How long will it take before your monthly savings cover the fees and closing costs you must pay for the new loan? As a general rule, you should not refinance a loan for which these costs will take more than about 2 to 3 years to recoup, unless you are convinced that you will be holding the new loan for a much longer time.
  2. Remember that refinancing "resets the clock" on a loan. For example, suppose you have been paying off a 10-year student loan for 4 years. If you keep this loan, you will pay it off in 6 more years. But if you refinance with a new 10-year loan, you will have payments for 10 years starting from now. So even if the new loan reduces your monthly payments, it may not be worth it because you will be making payments for 10 more years instead of only 6 more years.
- Most important, regardless of what a bank or loan broker might say, be sure that *you* feel confident that you will be able to afford your loan payments throughout the life of the loan, even in the event that you temporarily lose your job or have other unexpected financial difficulties.

Fixed Rate Mortgages

The simplest type of home loan is a **fixed rate mortgage**, in which you are guaranteed that the interest rate will not change over the life of the loan. Most fixed rate loans have a term of either 15 or 30 years, with lower interest rates on the shorter-term loans. We can calculate payments on fixed rate loans with the loan payment formula.

BY THE WAY

The idea of a mortgage contract originated in early British real estate law. The curious word *mortgage* comes from Latin and old French. It literally means "dead pledge."

Example 6 Fixed Rate Payment Options

You need a loan of $100,000 to buy your new home. The bank offers a choice of a 30-year loan at an APR of 8% or a 15-year loan at 7.5%. Compare your monthly payments and total loan cost under the two options. Assume that the closing costs are the same in both cases and therefore do not affect the choice.

Solution Mortgages are installment loans, so we use the loan payment formula

$$\text{PMT} = \frac{P \times \left(\frac{\text{APR}}{n}\right)}{\left[1 - \left(1 + \frac{\text{APR}}{n}\right)^{(-nY)}\right]}$$

For both cases, we have a principal $P = \$100{,}000$ and monthly payments for which $n = 12$; the differences are in the APR and the loan term. Be sure you see how the numbers in Step 1 correspond to the loan payment formula above.

	$Y = 30$ years, APR $= 0.08$	$Y = 15$ years, APR $= 0.075$
1. Use the loan payment formula to find the monthly payment:	$\text{PMT} = \frac{\$100{,}000 \times \left(\frac{0.08}{12}\right)}{\left[1 - \left(1 + \frac{0.08}{12}\right)^{(-12 \times 30)}\right]} = \$733.76$	$\text{PMT} = \frac{\$100{,}000 \times \left(\frac{0.075}{12}\right)}{\left[1 - \left(1 + \frac{0.075}{12}\right)^{(-12 \times 15)}\right]} = \$927.01$
2. Multiply the monthly payment by the loan term in months to find the total payments:	$30 \text{ yr} \times \frac{12 \text{ mo}}{\text{yr}} \times \frac{\$733.76}{\text{mo}} \approx \$264{,}150$	$15 \text{ yr} \times \frac{12 \text{ mo}}{\text{yr}} \times \frac{\$927.01}{\text{mo}} \approx \$166{,}860$

Note that the payments of \$927.01 on the 15-year loan are almost \$200 higher than the payments of \$733.76 on the 30-year loan. However, the 15-year loan saves you almost \$100,000 in total payments. That is, the 15-year loan saves you a lot in the long run, but it's a good plan only if you are confident that you can afford the additional \$200 per month that it will cost you for the next 15 years. (See Example 9 for an alternative payment strategy.)

Now try Exercises 37–40.

Time Out to Think

Do a quick Web search to find today's average interest rate for 15-year and 30-year fixed mortgage loans. How would the payments in Example 6 differ with the current rates?

Example 7 Closing Costs

Great Bank offers a \$100,000, 30-year, 8% fixed rate loan with closing costs of \$500 plus 2 points. Big Bank offers a lower rate of 7.9%, but with closing costs of \$1000 plus 2 points. Evaluate the two options.

Solution In Example 6, we calculated the payments on the 8% loan to be \$733.76. At the lower 7.9% rate, the payments are

$$\text{PMT} = \frac{P \times \left(\frac{\text{APR}}{n}\right)}{\left[1 - \left(1 + \frac{\text{APR}}{n}\right)^{(-nY)}\right]} = \frac{\$100{,}000 \times \left(\frac{0.079}{12}\right)}{\left[1 - \left(1 + \frac{0.079}{12}\right)^{(-12 \times 30)}\right]} = \$726.81$$

You'll save about \$7 per month with Big Bank's lower interest rate. Now we must consider the difference in closing costs. Both banks charge the same 2 points, so this portion of the closing costs won't affect your decision. (Note, however, that 2 points means 2% of the \$100,000 loan, which is a \$2000 fee!) But you must consider Big Bank's extra \$500 in direct fees.

BY THE WAY

When you pay points, most lenders give you a choice between paying them up front and folding them into the loan. For example, if you pay 2 points on a \$100,000 loan, your choice is to pay \$2000 up front or to make the loan amount \$102,000 rather than \$100,000. For the examples in this book, we assume that you pay the points up front.

The choice comes down to this: Big Bank costs you an extra $500 now, but saves you $7 per month in payments. Dividing $500 by $7 per month, we find the time it will take to recoup the extra $500:

$$\frac{\$500}{\$7/\text{mo}} = 71.4 \text{ mo} \approx 6 \text{ yr}$$

It will take you about 6 years to save the extra $500 that Big Bank charges up front. Unless you are sure that you will be staying in your house (and keeping the same loan) for much more than 6 years, you probably should go with the lower closing costs at Great Bank, even though your monthly payments will be slightly higher. **Now try Exercises 41–42.**

Example 8 Points Decision

Continuing Example 7, suppose you've decided to go with Great Bank's lower closing costs. You learn that Great Bank actually offers two options for 30-year loans: an 8% interest rate with 2 points or a 7.5% rate with 4 points. Evaluate your options.

Solution We already know that the monthly payments for the 8% loan are $733.76. For the 7.5% loan, we have $P = \$100{,}000$, $n = 12$, and $Y = 30$. Setting APR = 7.5% = 0.075, we find that the monthly payments are

$$\text{PMT} = \frac{P \times \left(\frac{\text{APR}}{n}\right)}{\left[1 - \left(1 + \frac{\text{APR}}{n}\right)^{(-nY)}\right]} = \frac{\$100{,}000 \times \left(\frac{0.075}{12}\right)}{\left[1 - \left(1 + \frac{0.075}{12}\right)^{(-12 \times 30)}\right]} = \$699.21$$

The 7.5% loan lowers the monthly payments by $733.76 − $699.21 = $34.55. However, this loan has 2 additional points in closing costs, which means 2% of your $100,000 loan, or $2000. You must decide whether it is worth an extra $2000 up front for a monthly savings of just under $35. Let's calculate how long it will take to make up the added up-front costs:

$$\frac{\$2000}{\$34.55/\text{mo}} = 57.9 \text{ mo}$$

This is not quite 5 years. If you think it's likely that you will sell or refinance within 5 years, you should not pay the extra points. However, if you expect to keep the loan for a long time, the added points might be worth it. For example, if you keep the loan for the full 30 years (360 months), you'll save 360 × $34.55 = $12,438 in monthly payments over the life of the loan—far more than the extra $2000 you pay for the lower rate today. **Now try Exercises 43–44.**

Prepayment Strategies

Because of the long loan term, the early payments on a mortgage tend to be almost entirely interest. For example, Figure 4.8 shows the portion of each payment going to principal and interest for a 30-year, $100,000 loan at 8%. In addition, the total interest paid on mortgages is often much more than the principal. In Example 6, we found that the total payments for this $100,000 loan would be about $264,000—more than $2\frac{1}{2}$ times the starting principal!

Clearly, you can save a lot if you can reduce your interest payments. One way to do this is to pay extra toward the principal, particularly early in the term. For example, suppose you pay an extra $100 toward principal in the first monthly payment of your $100,000 loan. That is, instead of paying the required $734 (see Example 6), you pay $834. Because you've reduced your loan balance by $100, you will save the compounded value of this $100 over the rest of the 30-year loan term—which is nearly $1100. In other words, paying an extra $100 in the first month saves you about $1100 in interest over the 30 years.

BY THE WAY

Mortgage rates vary substantially with time. In the 1980s, average U.S. rates for new mortgages (30-year fixed) were almost always above 10%, peaking at more than 18% in 1981. During 2009, average rates dipped below 5%—lower than during any other period in the past 40 years.

BY THE WAY

Although it may seem strange at first, making prepayments on a home loan is not always a good idea even though it reduces the total payments. For example, you should probably first accumulate at least some savings that you can get instant access to, in case you need money for some unexpected financial crisis. In addition, because home mortgage interest is tax deductible (see Unit 4E), your effective interest rate may be much lower than the actual interest rate, so the interest payments might not be costing you quite as much as they seem before you consider the tax implications.

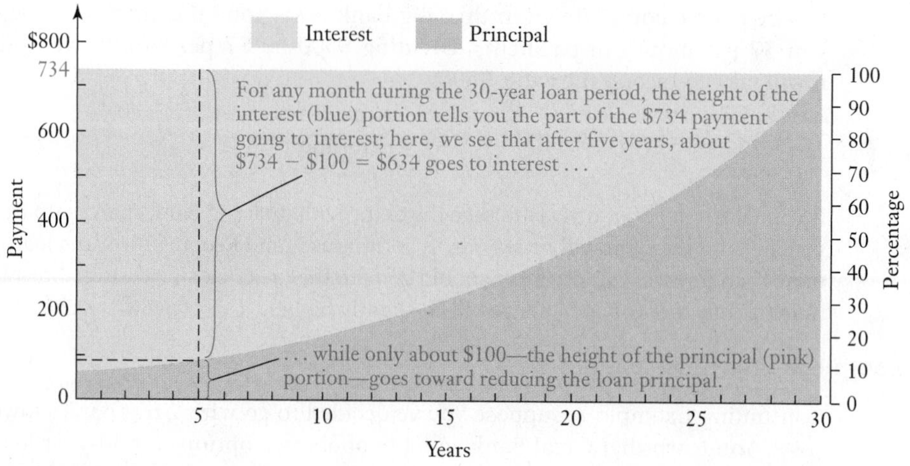

FIGURE 4.8 Portions of monthly payments going to principal and interest over the life of a 30-year, \$100,000 loan at 8%. (The calculations leading to this graph can be done by making a principal and interest table as described in the Using Technology box on p. 252.)

BY THE WAY

We keep things simple in this book by assuming that lenders are honest about costs to borrowers, and that lenders do not sell or transfer the loans they make. Real life is not that simple. During the housing bubble of 2001–2006, many lenders misled borrowers, encouraging them to take out loans that they could not afford. Lenders did this in part because they were able to collect fees for making loans and then sell the loans to other financial institutions, transferring the risk in the loans to the new owners of the loans. The new owners of the loans, in turn, often bundled the loans and used "reinsurers" who supposedly insured the loans against default. One of the largest reinsurers was AIG, which lost more than \$100 billion when the housing bubble burst.

Example 9 An Alternative Strategy

An alternative strategy to the mortgage options in Example 6 is to take the 30-year loan at 8%, but to try to pay it off in 15 years by making larger payments than are required. How much would you have to pay each month? Discuss the pros and cons of this strategy.

Solution To reflect paying off an 8% loan in 15 years, we set $APR = 0.08$ and $Y = 15$; we still have $P = \$100{,}000$ and $n = 12$. The monthly payments are

$$\text{PMT} = \frac{P \times \left(\frac{\text{APR}}{n}\right)}{\left[1 - \left(1 + \frac{\text{APR}}{n}\right)^{(-nY)}\right]} = \frac{\$100{,}000 \times \left(\frac{0.08}{12}\right)}{\left[1 - \left(1 + \frac{0.08}{12}\right)^{(-12\times15)}\right]} = \$955.65$$

In Example 6, we found that the 30-year loan requires payments of \$733.76. Thus, to pay off the loan in 15 years, you must make payments that are more than the minimum required by $\$955.65 - \$733.76 = \$221.89$ per month.

Note that this payment is about \$30 per month *more* than the payment of \$927.01 required with the 15-year loan (see Example 6), because the 15-year loan had a lower interest rate. Clearly, if you *know* you're going to pay off the loan in 15 years, you should take the lower-interest 15-year loan. However, taking the 30-year loan has one advantage: Because your required payments are only \$733.76, you can always drop back to this level if you find it difficult to afford the extra needed to pay off the loan in 15 years.

Now try Exercises 45–46.

Time Out to Think

Consider two options for paying off a loan in 15 years: taking out a 15-year loan or taking out a 30-year loan and making an extra principal payment each month. Assuming that you would like to pay off the loan in 15 years, how would you decide which strategy is better for you?

Adjustable Rate Mortgages

A fixed rate mortgage is advantageous for you because your monthly payments never change. However, it poses a risk to the lender. Imagine that you take out a fixed, 30-year loan of \$100,000 from Great Bank at a 6% interest rate. Initially, the loan may seem like a good deal for Great Bank. But suppose that, 2 years later, prevailing interest rates have risen to 8%. If Great Bank still had the $100,000 that it lent to you, it could lend it out to someone else at this higher 8% rate. Instead, it's stuck with the 6% rate that you are paying. In effect, Great Bank loses potential future income if prevailing rates rise substantially and you have a fixed rate loan.

Lenders can lessen the risk of rising interest rates by charging higher rates for longer-term loans. That is why rates generally are higher for 30-year loans than for 15-year loans. But an even lower-risk strategy for the lender is an **adjustable rate mortgage (ARM)**, in which the interest rate you pay changes whenever prevailing rates change. Because of the reduced long-term risk to lenders, ARMs generally have much lower initial interest rates than fixed rate loans. For example, a bank offering a 6% rate on a fixed 30-year loan might offer an ARM that begins at 4%. Most ARMs guarantee their starting interest rate for the first 6 months or 1 year, but interest rates in subsequent years move up or down to reflect prevailing rates. Most ARMs also include a *rate cap* that cannot be exceeded. For example, if your ARM begins at an interest rate of 4%, you may be promised that your interest rate can never go higher than a rate cap of 10%. Making a decision between a fixed rate loan and an ARM can be one of the most important financial decisions of your life.

BY THE WAY

Watch out for "teaser" rates on adjustable rate mortgages. Under normal circumstances, your rate on an ARM rises only if prevailing interest rates rise. However, some lenders offer low teaser rates—rates below the prevailing rates—for the first few months of an ARM. Teaser rates are certain to rise as soon as the teaser period is over. While teaser rates may be attractive, the longer-term policies of the ARM are far more important.

Example 10 Rate Approximations for ARMs

You have a choice between a 30-year fixed rate loan at 8% and an ARM with a first-year rate of 5%. Neglecting compounding and changes in principal, estimate your monthly savings with the ARM during the first year on a $100,000 loan. Suppose that the ARM rate rises to 11% by the fourth year. How will your payments be affected?

Solution Because mortgage payments are mostly interest in the early years of a loan, we can make approximations by pretending that the principal remains unchanged. For the 8% fixed rate loan, the interest on the $100,000 loan for the first year will be approximately 8% × $100,000 = $8000. With the 5% loan, your first-year interest will be approximately 5% × $100,000 = $5000. The ARM will save you about $3000 in interest during the first year, which means a monthly savings of about $3000 ÷ 12 = $250.

By the fourth year, when rates reach 11%, the situation is reversed. The rate on the ARM is now 3 percentage points above the rate on the fixed rate loan. Instead of saving $250 per month, you'd be paying $250 per month *more* on the ARM than on the 8% fixed rate loan. Moreover, if interest rates remain high on the ARM, you will continue to make these high payments for many years to follow. Thus, while ARMs reduce risk for the lender, they add risk for the borrower. **Now try Exercises 47–48.**

Time Out to Think

In recent years, another type of mortgage loan became popular: the *interest only loan*, in which you pay only interest and pay nothing toward principal. Most financial experts advise against these loans, because your principal never gets paid off, and many think they played a role in creating the housing bubble that burst in 2007. Can you think of any circumstances under which such a loan might make sense for a home buyer? Explain.

QUICK QUIZ

Choose the best answer to each of the following questions. Explain your reasoning with one or more complete sentences.

1. In the loan payment formula, assuming all other variables are constant, the monthly payment

   a. increases as *P* increases.
   b. increases as APR decreases.
   c. increases as *Y* increases.

2. With the same APR and principal, a 15-year loan will have

   a. a higher monthly payment than a 30-year loan.
   b. a lower monthly payment than a 30-year loan.
   c. a payment that could be greater or less than that of a 30-year loan.

3. With the same term and principal, a loan with a higher APR will have
   a. a lower monthly payment than a loan with a lower APR.
   b. a higher monthly payment than a loan with a lower APR.
   c. a payment that could be greater or less than that of a loan with a lower APR.
4. In the early years of a 30-year mortgage loan,
   a. most of the payment goes to the principal.
   b. most of the payment goes to interest.
   c. equal amounts go to principal and interest.
5. If you make monthly payments of $1000 on a 10-year loan, your total payments over the life of the loan amount to
   a. $10,000. b. $100,000. c. $120,000.
6. Credit card loans are different from installment loans in that
   a. credit card loans do not require regular (monthly) payments.
   b. credit card loans do not have an APR.
   c. credit card loans do not have a set loan term.
7. A loan of $200,000 that carries a 2-point origination fee requires an advance payment of
   a. $2000. b. $40,000. c. $4000.
8. A $120,000 loan with $500 in closing costs plus 1 point requires an advance payment of
   a. $1500. b. $1700. c. $500.
9. You are currently paying off a student loan with an interest rate of 9% and a monthly payment of $450. You are offered the chance to refinance the remaining balance with a new 10-year loan with an interest rate of 8% that will give you a significantly lower monthly payment. Refinancing in this way
   a. is always a good idea.
   b. is a good idea if it lowers your monthly payment by at least $100.
   c. may or may not be a good idea, depending on closing costs and how many years are remaining in your current loan term.
10. Consider two mortgage loans with the same principal and the same APR. Loan 1 is fixed for 15 years, and Loan 2 is fixed for 30 years. Which statement is true?
    a. Loan 1 will have higher monthly payments, but you'll pay less total interest over the life of the loan.
    b. Loan 1 will have lower monthly payments, and you'll pay less total interest over the life of the loan.
    c. Both loans will have the same monthly payments, but you'll pay less total interest with Loan 1.

Exercises 4D

REVIEW QUESTIONS

1. Suppose you pay only the interest on a loan. Will the loan ever be paid off? Why not?
2. What is an installment loan? Explain the meaning and use of the loan payment formula.
3. Explain, in general terms, how the portions of loan payments going to principal and interest change over the life of the loan.
4. Suppose that you need a loan of $10,000 and are offered a choice of a 3-year loan at 7% interest or a 5-year loan at 8% interest. Discuss the pros and cons of each choice.
5. How do credit card loans differ from ordinary installment loans? Why are credit card loans particularly dangerous?
6. What is a mortgage? What is a down payment on a mortgage? Explain how closing costs, including points, can affect loan decisions.

DOES IT MAKE SENSE?

Decide whether each of the following statements makes sense (or is clearly true) or does not make sense (or is clearly false). Explain your reasoning.

7. The interest rate on my student loan is only 7%, yet more than half of my payments are currently going toward interest rather than principal.
8. My student loans were all 20-year loans at interest rates of 8% or above, so when my bank offered me a 20-year loan at 7%, I took it and used it to pay off the student loans.
9. I make only the minimum required payments on my credit card balance each month, because that way I'll have more of my own money to keep.
10. I carry a large credit card balance, and I had a credit card that charged an annual interest rate of 12%. So when I found another credit card that promised a 3% interest rate for the first 3 months, it was obvious that I should switch to this new card.
11. I had a choice between a fixed rate mortgage at 6% and an adjustable rate mortgage that started at 3% for the first year with a maximum increase of 1.5 percentage points a year. I took the adjustable rate, because I'm planning to move within three years.
12. Fixed rate loans with 15-year terms have lower interest rates than loans with 30-year terms, so it always makes sense to take the 15-year loan.

BASIC SKILLS & CONCEPTS

13–14: Loan Terminology. Consider the following loans.

a. Identify the loan principal, the annual interest rate, the number of payments per year, the loan term, and the payment amount.

b. How many total payments does the loan require? What is the total amount paid over the full term of the loan?

c. Of the total amount paid, what percentage is paid toward the principal and what percentage is paid for interest?

13. You borrowed $80,000 at an APR of 7%, which you are paying off with monthly payments of $620 for 20 years.
14. You borrowed $15,000 at an APR of 9%, which you are paying off with monthly payments of $190 for 10 years.

15–24: Loan Payments. Consider the following loans.

a. Calculate the monthly payment.

b. Determine the total amount paid over the term of the loan.

c. Of the total amount paid, what percentage is paid toward the principal and what percentage is paid for interest?

15. A student loan of $50,000 at a fixed APR of 10% for 20 years
16. A student loan of $12,000 at a fixed APR of 8% for 10 years
17. A home mortgage of $200,000 with a fixed APR of 7.5% for 30 years
18. A home mortgage of $150,000 with a fixed APR of 7.5% for 15 years
19. A home mortgage of $200,000 with a fixed APR of 9% for 15 years
20. A home mortgage of $100,000 with a fixed APR of 8.5% for 15 years
21. You borrow $10,000 over a period of 3 years at a fixed APR of 12%.
22. You borrow $10,000 over a period of 5 years at a fixed APR of 10%.
23. You borrow $150,000 over a period of 15 years at a fixed APR of 8%.
24. You borrow $100,000 over a period of 30 years at a fixed APR of 7%.

25–26: Principal and Interest. For the following loans, make a table (as in Example 2) showing the amount of each monthly payment that goes toward principal and interest for the first three months of the loan.

25. A home mortgage of $150,000 with a fixed APR of 8.5% for 30 years
26. A student loan of $24,000 at a fixed APR of 8% for 15 years
27. **Choosing a Personal Loan.** You need to borrow $12,000 to buy a car and you determine that you can afford monthly payments of $250. The bank offers three choices: a 3-year loan at 7% APR, a 4-year loan at 7.5% APR, or a 5-year loan at 8% APR. Which loan best meets your needs? Explain your reasoning.
28. **Choosing a Personal Loan.** You need to borrow $4000 to pay off your credit cards and you can afford monthly payments of $150. The bank offers three choices: a 2-year loan at 8% APR, a 3-year loan at 9% APR, or a 4-year loan at 10% APR. Which loan best meets your needs? Explain your reasoning.

29–32: Credit Card Debt. Suppose that on January 1 you have a balance of $5000 on the following credit cards, which you want to pay off in the given amount of time. Assume that you make no additional charges to the card after January 1.

a. Calculate your monthly payments.

b. When the card is paid off, how much will you have paid since January 1?

c. What percentage of your total payment (part b) is interest?

29. The credit card APR is 18% and you want to pay off the balance in 1 year.
30. The credit card APR is 20% and you want to pay off the balance in 2 years.
31. The credit card APR is 21% and you want to pay off the balance in 3 years.
32. The credit card APR is 22% and you want to pay off the balance in 1 year.
33. **Credit Card Debt.** Assume you have a balance of $1200 on a credit card with an APR of 18%, or 1.5% per month. You start making monthly payments of $200, but at the same time you charge an additional $75 per month to the credit card. Assume that interest for a given month is based on the balance for the previous month. The following table shows how you can calculate your monthly balance.

Month	Payment	Expenses	Interest	New Balance
0	—	—	—	$1200
1	$200	$75	1.5% × $1200 = $18	$1200 − $200 + $75 + $18 = $1093
2	$200	$75		
3	$200	$75		

Complete and extend the table to show your balance at the end of each month until the debt is paid off. How long does it take to pay off the credit card debt?

34. **Credit Card Debt.** Repeat the table in Exercise 33 but this time assume that you make monthly payments of $300. Extend the table as long as necessary until your debt is paid off. How long does it take to pay off your debt?
35. **Credit Card Woes.** The following table shows the expenses and payments for 8 months on a credit card account with an initial balance of $300. Assume that the interest rate is 1.5% per month (18% APR) and that interest for a given month is charged on the balance for the previous month. Complete the table. After 8 months, what is the balance on the credit card? Comment on the effect of the interest and the initial balance, in light of the fact that for 7 of the 8 months expenses never exceeded payments.

Month	Payment	Expenses	Interest	Balance
0	—	—	—	$300
1	$300	$175	1.5% × $300 = $4.50	$179.50
2	$150	$150		
3	$400	$350		
4	$500	$450		
5	0	$100		
6	$100	$100		
7	$200	$150		
8	$100	$80		

36. **Teaser Rate.** You have a total credit card debt of \$4000. You receive an offer to transfer this debt to a new card with an introductory APR of 6% for the first 6 months. After that, the rate becomes 24%.

    a. What is the monthly interest payment on \$4000 during the first 6 months? (Assume you pay nothing toward principal and don't charge any further debts.)

    b. What is the monthly interest payment on \$4000 *after* the first 6 months? Comment on the change from the teaser rate.

37–40: **Comparing Loan Options.** Compare the monthly payments and total loan costs for the following pairs of loan options. Assume that both loans are fixed rate and have the same closing costs. Discuss the pros and cons of each loan.

37. You need a \$200,000 loan.
    Option 1: a 30-year loan at an APR of 8%
    Option 2: a 15-year loan at 7.5%

38. You need a \$75,000 loan.
    Option 1: a 30-year loan at an APR of 8%
    Option 2: a 15-year loan at 7%

39. You need a \$60,000 loan.
    Option 1: a 30-year loan at an APR of 7.15%
    Option 2: a 15-year loan at 6.75%

40. You need a \$180,000 loan.
    Option 1: a 30-year loan at an APR of 7.25%
    Option 2: a 15-year loan at 6.8%

41–44: **Closing Costs.** Consider the following pairs of loan options for a \$120,000 mortgage. Calculate the monthly payment and total closing costs for each option. Explain which option you would choose and why.

41. Choice 1: 30-year fixed rate at 8% with closing costs of \$1200 and no points

    Choice 2: 30-year fixed rate at 7.5% with closing costs of \$1200 and 2 points

42. Choice 1: 30-year fixed rate at 8.5% with no closing costs and no points

    Choice 2: 30-year fixed rate at 7.5% with closing costs of \$1200 and 4 points

43. Choice 1: 30-year fixed rate at 7.25% with closing costs of \$1200 and 1 point

    Choice 2: 30-year fixed rate at 6.75% with closing costs of \$1200 and 3 points

44. Choice 1: 30-year fixed rate at 7.5% with closing costs of \$1000 and no points

    Choice 2: 30-year fixed rate at 6.5% with closing costs of \$1500 and 4 points

45. **Accelerated Loan Payment.** Suppose you have a student loan of \$30,000 with an APR of 9% for 20 years.

    a. What are your required monthly payments?

    b. Suppose you would like to pay the loan off in 10 years instead of 20. What monthly payments will you need to make?

    c. Compare the total amounts you'll pay over the loan term if you pay the loan off in 20 years versus 10 years.

46. **Accelerated Loan Payment.** Suppose you have a student loan of \$60,000 with an APR of 8% for 25 years.

    a. What are your required monthly payments?

    b. Suppose you would like to pay the loan off in 15 years instead of 25. What monthly payments will you need to make?

    c. Compare the total amounts you'll pay over the loan term if you pay the loan off in 25 years versus 15 years.

47. **ARM Rate Approximations.** You have a choice between a 30-year fixed rate loan at 7% and an adjustable rate mortgage (ARM) with a first-year rate of 5%. Neglecting compounding and changes in principal, estimate your monthly savings with the ARM during the first year on a \$150,000 loan. Suppose that the ARM rate rises to 8.5% at the start of the third year. Approximately how much extra will you then be paying over what you would have paid if you had taken the fixed rate loan?

48. **ARM Rate Approximations.** You have a choice between a 30-year fixed rate loan at 8.5% and an ARM with a first-year rate of 5.5%. Neglecting compounding and changes in principal, estimate your monthly savings with the ARM during the first year on a \$125,000 loan. Suppose that the ARM rate rises to 10% at the start of the second year. Approximately how much extra will you then be paying over what you would have paid if you had taken the fixed rate loan?

FURTHER APPLICATIONS

49. **How Much House Can You Afford?** You can afford monthly payments of \$500. If current mortgage rates are 9% for a 30-year fixed rate loan, what loan principal can you afford? If you are required to make a 20% down payment and you have the cash on hand to do it, how expensive a home can you afford? (*Hint:* You will need to solve the loan payment formula for P.)

50. **Refinancing.** Suppose you take out a 30-year \$200,000 mortgage with an APR of 6%. You make payments for 5 years (60 monthly payments) and then consider refinancing the original loan. The new loan would have a term of 20 years, an APR of 5.5%, and be in the amount of the unpaid balance on the original loan. (The amount you borrow on the new loan would be used to pay off the balance on the original loan.) The administrative cost of taking out the second loan would be \$2000.

    a. What are the monthly payments on the original loan?

    b. A short calculation shows that the unpaid balance on the original loan after 5 years is \$186,046, which would become the amount of the second loan. What would the monthly payments be on the second loan?

    c. What would the total payout be if you continued with the original 30-year loan without refinancing?

    d. What would the total payout be with the refinancing plan?

    e. Compare the two options and decide which one you would choose. What other factors should be considered in making the decision?

51. **Student Loan Consolidation.** Suppose you have the following three student loans: \$10,000 with an APR of 8% for 15 years, \$15,000 with an APR of 8.5% for 20 years, and \$12,500 with an APR of 9% for 10 years.

a. Calculate the monthly payment for each loan individually.

b. Calculate the total you'll pay in payments during the life of all three loans.

c. A bank offers to consolidate your three loans into a single loan with an APR of 8.5% and a loan term of 20 years. What will your monthly payments be in that case? What will your total payments be over the 20 years? Discuss the pros and cons of accepting this loan consolidation.

52. **Bad Deals: Car-Title Lenders.** Some "car-title lenders" offer quick cash loans in exchange for being allowed to hold the title to your car as collateral (you lose your car if you fail to pay off the loan). In many states, these lenders operate under pawnbroker laws that allow them to charge fees as a percentage of the unpaid balance. Suppose you need $2000 in cash, and a car-title company offers you a loan at an interest rate of 2% per month *plus* a monthly fee of 20% of the unpaid balance.

a. How much will you owe in interest and fees on your $2000 loan at the end of the first month?

b. Suppose that you pay only the interest and fees each month. How much will you pay over the course of a full year?

c. Suppose instead that you obtain a loan from a bank with a term of 3 years and an APR of 10%. What are your monthly payments in that case? Compare these to the payments to the car-title lender.

53. **Other Than Monthly Payments.** Suppose you want to borrow $100,000 and you find a bank offering a 20-year loan with an APR of 6%.

a. Find your regular payments if you pay $n = 1, 12, 26, 52$ times a year.

b. Compute the total payout for each of the loans in part a.

c. Compare the total payouts computed in part b. Discuss the pros and cons of the plans.

54. **13 Payments (Challenge).** Suppose you want to borrow $100,000 and you find a bank offering a 20-year loan with an APR of 6%.

a. What are your monthly payments?

b. Instead of making 12 payments per year, you save enough money to make a 13th payment each year (in the amount of your regular monthly payment of part a). How long will it take to retire the loan?

55. **Project: Choosing a Mortgage.** Imagine that you work for an accounting firm and a client has told you that he is buying a house and needs a loan of $120,000. His monthly income is $4000 and he is single with no children. He has $14,000 in savings that can be used for a down payment. Find the current rates available from local banks for both fixed rate mortgages and adjustable rate mortgages (ARMs). Analyze the offerings and summarize orally or in writing the best options for your client, along with the pros and cons of each option.

WEB PROJECTS

56. **Credit Card Comparisons.** Visit a Web site that gives comparisons between credit cards. Briefly explain the factors that are considered in the comparisons. How does your own credit card compare to other credit cards? Based on this comparison, do you think you would be better off with a different credit card?

57. **Home Financing.** Visit a Web site that offers online home financing. Describe the options offered, and discuss the advantages and disadvantages of each option.

58. **Online Car Purchase.** Find a car online that you might want to buy. Find a loan that you would qualify for, and calculate your monthly payments and total payments over the life of the loan. Next, suppose that you started a savings plan instead of buying the car, depositing the same amounts that would have gone to car payments. Estimate how much you would have in your savings plan by the time you graduate from college. Explain your assumptions.

59. **Student Financial Aid.** There are many Web sites that offer student loans. Visit a Web site that offers student loans and describe the terms of a particular loan. Discuss the advantages and disadvantages of financing a student loan online rather than through a bank or through your university or college.

60. **Scholarship Scams.** The Federal Trade Commission keeps track of many financial scams related to college scholarships. Read about two different types of scams, and report on how they work and how they hurt people who are taken in by them.

61. **Financial Scams.** Many Web sites keep track of current financial scams. Visit some of these sites and report on one scam that has already hurt a lot of people. Describe how the scam works and how it hurts those who are taken in by it.

IN YOUR WORLD

62. **Mortgage Rates.** Find advertisements in the newspaper or on the Web for two different home mortgages companies. Using the ideas of this unit, evaluate the terms of loans from each company and decide which company you would use for a home mortgage.

63. **Credit Card Statement.** Look carefully at the terms of financing explained on your most recent credit card statement. Explain all the important terms, including the interest rates that apply, annual fees, and grace periods.

64. **Bank Rates.** Find the interest rates that your bank (or another local bank) charges for different types of loans, such as auto loans, personal loans, and home mortgages. Why do you think the rates are different in the different cases?

TECHNOLOGY EXERCISES

65. **Loan Payments Using Excel.** Use the PMT function in Excel to answer the following questions.

    a. Find the monthly payment for a $7500 loan with an APR of 9% and a payback period of 10 years.

    b. Describe the change in the monthly payment for the loan in part a if the payback period is doubled.

    c. Describe the change in the monthly payment for the loan in part a if the APR is halved.

66. **Loan Table in Excel.** Consider the loan in Exercise 65 (a $7500 loan with an APR of 9% and a payback period of 10 years).

    a. Follow the guidelines in the Using Technology box on p. 252 to construct a table showing the interest payment and loan balance after each month. Verify that with monthly payments of $95.01, the loan balance reaches $0 after 120 months.

    b. How much interest is paid in the first month of the loan? How much is paid toward the principal in the first month of the loan?

    c. How much interest is paid in the last month of the loan? How much is paid toward the principal in the last month of the loan?

UNIT 4E Income Taxes

There are many types of taxes, including sales tax, gasoline tax, and property tax. But for most Americans, the largest tax burden comes from taxes on wages and other income. In this unit, we explore a few of the many aspects of federal income taxes.

Income Tax Basics

In this world, nothing is certain but death and taxes.

—Benjamin Franklin

The hardest thing in the world to understand is the income tax.

—Albert Einstein

It's quite possible that *no one* fully understands federal income taxes. The complete tax code consists of thousands of pages of detailed regulations. Many of the regulations are difficult to interpret, and disputes about their meaning are often taken to court. Congress frequently tinkers with tax laws and occasionally undertakes major reforms. For example, tax laws were greatly simplified by Congress in 1986. Unfortunately, politicians were unable to resist making modifications to the simplified tax code, so it gradually became more complex once again.

Nevertheless, the many arcane tax laws generally apply only to relatively small segments of the population. Most people not only can file their own taxes—which usually requires little more than filling in a few boxes and looking up numbers in a table—but can understand how their taxes work. This is important, because understanding your taxes not only will allow you to make intelligent decisions about your personal finances but also will help you understand the political issues that you vote on.

Figure 4.9 summarizes the steps in a basic tax calculation. We'll follow the flow of the steps, defining terms as we go along.

- The process begins with your **gross income**, which is *all* your income for the year, including wages, tips, profits from a business, interest or dividends from investments, and any other income you receive.

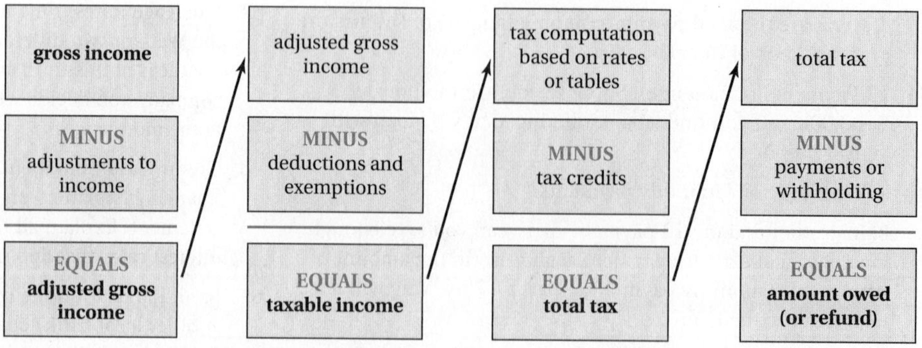

FIGURE 4.9 Flow chart showing the basic steps in calculating income tax.

- Some gross income is not taxed (at least not in the year it is received), such as contributions to IRAs and other tax-deferred savings plans. These untaxed portions of gross income are called *adjustments*. Subtracting adjustments from your gross income gives your **adjusted gross income.**
- Most people are entitled to certain **exemptions** and **deductions**—amounts that you subtract from your adjusted gross income before calculating your taxes. (The amounts you can subtract depend on factors that we'll discuss shortly.) Once you subtract the exemptions and deductions, you are left with your **taxable income.**
- A tax table or tax rate computation allows you to determine how much tax you owe on your taxable income. However, you may not actually have to pay this much tax if you are entitled to any tax credits. For example, you may be entitled to a tax credit of $1000 per child. From your tax rate computation, you subtract the amount of any credits to find your **total tax.**
- Finally, most people have already paid part or all of their tax bill during the year, either through *withholdings* (by your employer) or through paying quarterly *estimated taxes* (if you are self-employed). You subtract the taxes that you've already paid to determine how much you still owe. In many cases, you may have paid more than you owe, in which case you should receive a **tax refund.**

Historical Note

An income tax was first levied in the United States in 1862 (during the Civil War), but was abandoned a few years later. The 16th Amendment to the Constitution, ratified in 1913, gave the federal government full authority to levy an income tax.

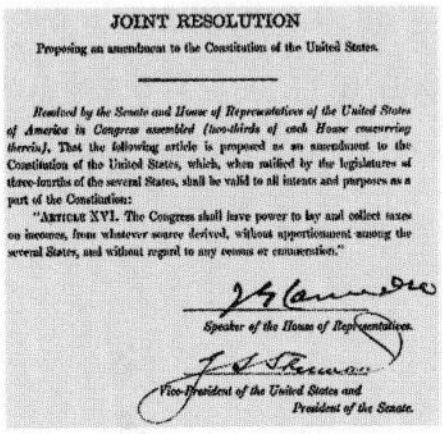
JOINT RESOLUTION

Proposing an amendment to the Constitution of the United States.

Resolved by the Senate and House of Representatives of the United States of America in Congress assembled (two-thirds of each House concurring therein), That the following article is proposed as an amendment to the Constitution of the United States, which, when ratified by the legislatures of three-fourths of the several States, shall be valid to all intents and purposes as a part of the Constitution:

"ARTICLE XVI. The Congress shall have power to lay and collect taxes on incomes, from whatever source derived, without apportionment among the several States, and without regard to any census or enumeration."

Speaker of the House of Representatives.

Vice-President of the United States and President of the Senate.

Example 1 Income on Tax Forms

Karen earned wages of $34,200, received $750 in interest from a savings account, and contributed $1200 to a tax-deferred retirement plan. She was entitled to a personal exemption of $3650 and to deductions totaling $5900. Find her gross income, adjusted gross income, and taxable income.

Solution Karen's gross income is the sum of all her income, which means the sum of her wages and her interest:

$$\text{gross income} = \$34{,}200 + \$750 = \$34{,}950$$

Her $1200 contribution to a tax-deferred retirement plan counts as an adjustment to her gross income, so her adjusted gross income (AGI) is

$$\text{AGI} = \text{gross income} - \text{adjustments} = \$34{,}950 - \$1200 = \$33{,}750$$

To find her taxable income, we subtract her exemptions and deductions:

$$\begin{aligned}\text{taxable income} &= \text{AGI} - \text{exemptions} - \text{deductions}\\ &= \$33{,}750 - \$3650 - \$5900 = \$24{,}200\end{aligned}$$

Her taxable income is $24,200. **Now try Exercises 19–22.**

Filing Status

Tax calculations depend on your **filing status**, such as single or married. Most people fall into one of four filing status categories:

- *Single* applies if you are unmarried, divorced, or legally separated.
- *Married filing jointly* applies if you are married *and* you and your spouse file a single tax return. (In some cases, this category also applies to widows or widowers.)
- *Married filing separately* applies if you are married *and* you and your spouse file two separate tax returns.
- *Head of household* applies if you are unmarried and are paying more than half the cost of supporting a dependent child or parent.

We will use these four categories in the rest of our discussion.

BY THE WAY

United States federal income taxes are collected by the *Internal Revenue Service* (IRS), which is part of the United States Department of the Treasury. Most people file federal taxes by completing a tax form, such as Form 1040, 1040A, or 1040EZ.

BY THE WAY

Not all taxpayers get the full advantage of exemptions and deductions. For example, the amounts of exemptions begin to "phase out" for single people earning more than about \$160,000, and many middle- to high-income taxpayers are subject to the alternative minimum tax (AMT), which disallows most or all deductions.

Exemptions and Deductions

Both exemptions and deductions are subtracted from your adjusted gross income. However, they are calculated differently, which is why they have different names.

Exemptions are a fixed amount per person (\$3650 in 2009 for most people, though some higher income people have a lower exemption due to "phase-out" rules). You can claim the amount of an exemption for yourself and each of your *dependents* (for example, children whom you support).

Deductions vary from one person to another. The most common deductions include interest on home mortgages, contributions to charity, and taxes you've paid to other agencies (such as state income taxes or local property taxes). However, you don't necessarily have to add up all your deductions. When you file your taxes, you have two options for deductions:

- You can choose a **standard deduction**, the amount of which depends on your filing status.
- You can choose **itemized deductions**, in which case you add up all the individual deductions to which you are entitled.

Note that you get *either* the standard deduction *or* itemized deductions, not both. Because deductions lower your tax bill, you should choose whichever option is larger.

Example 2 Should You Itemize?

Suppose you have the following deductible expenditures: \$2500 for interest on a home mortgage, \$900 for contributions to charity, and \$250 for state income taxes. Your filing status entitles you to a standard deduction of \$5700. Should you itemize your deductions or claim the standard deduction?

Solution The total of your deductible expenditures is

$$\$2500 + \$900 + \$250 = \$3650$$

If you itemize your deductions, you can subtract \$3650 when finding your taxable income. But if you take the standard deduction, you can subtract \$5700. You are better off with the standard deduction. **Now try Exercises 23–28.**

Tax Rates

The United States has a **progressive income tax**, meaning that people with higher taxable incomes pay at a higher tax *rate*. The system works by assigning different **marginal tax rates** to different income ranges (or *margins*). For example, suppose you are single and your taxable income is \$25,000. Under 2009 tax rates, you would pay 10% tax on the first \$8350 and 15% tax on the remaining \$16,650. In this case, we say that your *marginal rate* is 15%, or that you are in the 15% *tax bracket*. For each major filing status, Table 4.9 shows the marginal tax rate, standard deduction, and exemptions for 2009.

The income levels for the tax brackets, the standard deductions, and the exemption amounts all rise each year to keep pace with inflation. In addition, Congress and the President tend to change the rates for the tax brackets every few years. If you are calculating taxes for a year other than 2009, you must get an updated tax rate table. You can find current tax rates on the IRS Web site.

BY THE WAY

The tables and calculations in this unit neglect the *alternative minimum tax (AMT)*, a tax originally designed to apply only to very high-income taxpayers. However, because the AMT rates were not indexed to inflation, over time they have come to apply even to many middle-class taxpayers. You can use tax software or consult a tax professional to determine if you are subject to the AMT. The rules for the AMT change almost every year as Congress attempts to mitigate its impact.

Time Out to Think

Find a table of marginal tax rates for the current year. Have the tax brackets (10%, 15%, . . . , 35%) changed since 2009? Have the income thresholds for each tax bracket changed? Briefly summarize the changes you notice.

TABLE 4.9 2009 Marginal Tax Rates, Standard Deductions, and Exemptions

Tax Rate*	Single	Married Filing Jointly	Married Filing Separately	Head of Household
10%	up to $8350	up to $16,700	up to $8350	up to $11,950
15%	up to $33,950	up to $67,900	up to $33,950	up to $45,500
25%	up to $82,250	up to $137,050	up to $68,525	up to $117,450
28%	up to $171,550	up to $208,850	up to $104,425	up to $190,200
33%	up to $372,950	up to $372,950	up to $186,475	up to $372,950
35%	above $372,950	above $372,950	above $186,475	above $372,950
standard deduction	$5700	$11,400	$5700	$8350
exemption (per person)**	$3650	$3650	$3650	$3650

*Each higher marginal rate begins where the prior one leaves off. For example, for a single person, the 15% marginal rate affects income starting at $8350, which is where the 10% rate leaves off, and continuing up to $33,950.

**The exemption amount is reduced for relatively high-income taxpayers. We will ignore this "phase-out" of the exemption for calculations in this book.

Example 3 Marginal Tax Computations

Using 2009 rates, calculate the tax owed by each of the following people. Assume that they all claim the standard deduction and neglect any tax credits.

a. Deirdre is single with no dependents. Her adjusted gross income is $90,000.
b. Robert is a head of household taking care of two dependent children. His adjusted gross income also is $90,000.
c. Jessica and Frank are married with no dependents. They file jointly. They each have $90,000 in adjusted gross income, making a combined income of $180,000.

There is no such thing as a good tax.
—Winston Churchill

I like paying taxes. With them I build civilization.
—Justice Oliver Wendell Holmes

Solution

a. First, we must find Deirdre's taxable income. She is entitled to a personal exemption of $3650 and a standard deduction of $5700. We subtract these amounts from her adjusted gross income to find her taxable income:

$$\text{taxable income} = \$90{,}000 - \$3650 - \$5700 = \$80{,}650$$

Now we calculate her taxes using the *single* rates in Table 4.9. She is in the 25% tax bracket because her taxable income is above $33,950 but below the 28% threshold of $82,250. Therefore she owes 10% on the first $8350 of her taxable income, 15% on her taxable income above $8350 but below $33,950, and 25% on her taxable income above $33,950.

$$\underbrace{(10\% \times \$8350)}_{\text{10\% marginal rate on first \$8350 of taxable income}} + \underbrace{(15\% \times [\$33{,}950 - \$8350])}_{\text{15\% marginal rate on taxable income between \$8350 and \$33,950}} + \underbrace{(25\% \times [\$80{,}650 - \$33{,}950])}_{\text{25\% marignal rate on taxable income above \$33,950}}$$

$$= \$835 + \$3840 + \$11{,}675$$
$$= \$16{,}350$$

Deirdre's tax is $16,350.

b. Robert is entitled to *three* exemptions of $3650 each—one for himself and one for each of his two children. As a head of household, he is also entitled to a standard deduction of \$8350. We subtract these amounts from his adjusted gross income to find his taxable income:

$$\text{taxable income} = \$90{,}000 - (3 \times \$3650) - \$8350 = \$70{,}700$$

We calculate Robert's taxes using the *head of household* rates. His taxable income of \$70,700 puts him in the 25% tax bracket, so his tax is

$$\underbrace{(10\% \times \$11{,}950)}_{\substack{\text{10\% marginal rate on first} \\ \text{\$11,950 of taxable income}}} + \underbrace{(15\% \times [\$45{,}500 - \$11{,}950])}_{\substack{\text{15\% marginal rate on taxable income} \\ \text{between \$11,950 and \$45,500}}} + \underbrace{(25\% \times [\$70{,}700 - \$45{,}500])}_{\substack{\text{25\% marignal rate on taxable} \\ \text{income above \$45,500}}}$$

$$= \$1195 + \$5032.50 + \$6300$$
$$= \$12{,}527.50$$

Rounding up, Robert's tax is \$12,528.

c. Jessica and Frank are each entitled to one exemption of \$3650. Because they are married filing jointly, their standard deduction is \$11,400. We subtract these amounts from their adjusted gross income to find their taxable income:

$$\text{taxable income} = \$180{,}000 - (2 \times \$3650) - \$11{,}700 = \$161{,}300$$

We calculate their taxes using the *married filing jointly* rates. Their taxable income of \$161,300 puts them in the 28% tax bracket, so their tax is

$$\underbrace{(10\% \times \$16{,}700)}_{\substack{\text{10\% marginal rate on first} \\ \text{\$16,700 of taxable income}}} + \underbrace{(15\% \times [\$67{,}900 - \$16{,}700])}_{\substack{\text{15\% marginal rate on taxable income} \\ \text{between \$16,700 and \$67,900}}}$$

$$+ \underbrace{(25\% \times [\$137{,}050 - \$67{,}900])}_{\substack{\text{25\% marginal rate on taxable income} \\ \text{between \$67,900 and \$137,050}}} + \underbrace{(28\% \times [\$161{,}300 - \$137{,}050])}_{\substack{\text{28\% marginal rate on taxable} \\ \text{income above \$137,050}}}$$

$$= \$1670 + \$7680 + \$17{,}287.50 + \$6790$$
$$= \$33{,}427.50$$

Rounding up, Jessica and Frank's combined tax is \$33,428, equivalent to \$16,714 each.

Now try Exercises 29–36.

BY THE WAY

In Example 3, Jessica and Frank (part c) each earned the same amount as Deirdre (part a), but they each paid the equivalent of \$16,714, which is \$364 more than Deirdre paid. This feature of the tax code, whereby people pay more when they are married than they would if they were single, is called the *marriage penalty*. Not all couples are affected the same way by the marriage penalty. Some couples even get a marriage bonus instead, especially if one spouse earns much more than the other (or only one is employed).

Time Out to Think

Note that all four individuals in Example 3 have the same \$90,000 in adjusted gross income, yet they each pay a different amount in taxes. Explain why this is the case. Do you believe the outcomes are fair? Why or why not? (Bonus: Could their *gross incomes* have differed even though their adjusted gross incomes were the same? Explain.)

Tax Credits and Deductions

Tax credits and tax deductions may sound similar, but they are very different. Suppose you are in the 15% tax bracket. A tax *credit* of \$500 reduces your total tax bill by the full \$500. In contrast, a tax *deduction* of \$500 reduces your taxable income by \$500, which means it saves you only $15\% \times \$500 = \$75$ in taxes. As a rule, tax credits are more valuable than tax deductions.

Congress authorizes tax credits for only specific situations, such as a (maximum) \$1000 tax credit for each child (as of 2009). In contrast, your spending determines how much you claim in deductions, at least if you are itemizing. The most valuable deduction for most people is the **mortgage interest tax deduction**, which allows you to deduct the *interest* (but not the principal) you pay on a home mortgage. Many people also get substantial deductions from donating money to charities.

Example 4 Tax Credits vs. Tax Deductions

Suppose you are in the 28% tax bracket. How much does a \$1000 tax credit save you? How much does a \$1000 charitable contribution (which is tax deductible) save you? Answer these questions both for the case in which you itemize deductions and for the case in which you take the standard deduction.

Solution The entire \$1000 tax credit is deducted from your tax bill and therefore saves you a full \$1000, whether you itemize deductions or take the standard deduction. In contrast, a \$1000 deduction reduces your taxable income, not your total tax bill, by \$1000. For the 28% tax bracket, *at best* your \$1000 deduction will save you $28\% \times \$1000 = \$280$. However, you will save this \$280 only if you are itemizing deductions. If your total itemized deductions are less than the standard deduction (see Example 2), you will still be better off with the standard deduction. In that case, the \$1000 contribution will save you nothing at all. **Now try Exercises 37–42.**

Example 5 Rent or Own?

Suppose you are in the 28% tax bracket and you itemize your deductions. You are trying to decide whether to rent an apartment or buy a house. The apartment rents for \$1400 per month. You've investigated your loan options, and you've determined that if you buy the house, your monthly mortgage payments will be \$1600, of which an average of \$1400 goes toward interest during the first year. Compare the monthly rent to the mortgage payment. Is it cheaper to rent the apartment or buy the house? Assume that you have enough other deductions so that you are itemizing deductions rather than taking the standard deduction.

Solution The monthly cost of the apartment is \$1400 in rent. For the house, however, we must take into account the value of the mortgage deduction. The monthly interest of \$1400 is tax deductible. Because you are in the 28% tax bracket, this deduction saves you $28\% \times \$1400 = \$392$. As a result, the true monthly cost of the mortgage is the payment minus the tax savings, or

$$\$1600 - \$392 = \$1208$$

Despite the fact that the mortgage payment is \$200 higher than the rent, its true cost to you is almost \$200 per month less because of the tax savings from the mortgage interest deduction. Of course, as a homeowner, you will have other costs, such as for maintenance and repairs, that you may not have to pay if you rent. Moreover, we have assumed that you are itemizing deductions; if your total deductions are below (or not too far above) the standard deduction, then the deduction for the interest will not provide you with the benefit calculated here. **Now try Exercises 43–44.**

Time Out to Think

Aside from the lower monthly cost, what other factors would affect your decision about whether to rent or buy in Example 5?

Example 6 Varying Value of Deductions

Drew is in the 15% marginal tax bracket. Marian is in the 35% marginal tax bracket. They each itemize their deductions. They each donate \$5000 to charity. Compare their true costs for the charitable donation.

Solution The \$5000 contribution to charity is tax deductible. Because Drew is in the 15% tax bracket, this contribution saves him $15\% \times \$5000 = \$750$ in taxes.

BY THE WAY

In 2009, President Obama proposed that all taxpayers in the 28% tax bracket and above be able to deduct only at the 28% level. The proposal was designed both to raise revenue and to address the fact that deductions are more valuable to people in higher income tax brackets. The proposal was quickly killed in Congress, though the Obama administration planned to continue to push for it.

Therefore, its true cost to him is the contributed amount of $5000 minus his tax savings of $750, or $4250. For Marian, who is in the 35% tax bracket, the contribution saves 35% × $5000 = $1750 in taxes. Therefore, its true cost to her is $5000 − $1750 = $5000 − $1750 = $3250. The true cost of the donation is considerably lower for Marian because she is in a higher tax bracket. **Now try Exercises 45–46.**

Time Out to Think

As shown in Example 6, tax deductions are more valuable to people in higher tax brackets. Some people argue that this is unfair because it means that tax deductions save more money for richer people than for poorer people. Others argue that it is fair, because richer people pay a higher tax rate in the first place. What do you think? Defend your opinion.

Social Security and Medicare Taxes

In addition to being subject to taxes computed with the marginal rates, some income is subject to Social Security and Medicare taxes, which are collected under the obscure name of **FICA** (Federal Insurance Contribution Act) taxes. Taxes collected under FICA are used to pay Social Security and Medicare benefits, primarily to people who are retired.

FICA applies only to income from wages (including tips) and self-employment. It does not apply to income from such things as interest, dividends, or profits from sales of stock. In 2009, the FICA tax rates for individuals who were *not* self-employed were

- 7.65% on the first $106,800 of income from wages
- 1.45% on any income from wages in excess of $106,800

In addition, the individual's employer is required to pay matching amounts of FICA taxes.

Individuals who are self-employed must pay both the employee and the employer shares of FICA. That is, the rates for self-employed individuals are *double* the rates paid by individuals who are not self-employed.

FICA is calculated on *all* wages, tips, and self-employment income. You may not subtract any adjustments, exemptions, or deductions when calculating FICA taxes.

Example 7 FICA Taxes

In 2009, Jude earned $22,000 in wages and tips from her job waiting tables. Calculate her FICA taxes and her total tax bill including marginal taxes. What is her overall tax rate on her gross income, including both FICA and income taxes? Assume she is single and takes the standard deduction.

Solution Jude's entire income of $22,000 is subject to the 7.65% FICA tax:

$$\text{FICA tax} = 7.65\% \times \$22{,}000 = \$1683$$

Now we must find her income tax. We get her taxable income by subtracting her $3650 personal exemption and $5700 standard deduction:

$$\text{taxable income} = \$22{,}000 - \$3650 - \$5700 = \$12{,}650$$

From Table 4.9, her income tax is 10% on the first $8350 of her taxable income and 15% on the remaining amount of $12,650 − $8350 = $4300. Thus, her income tax is (10% × $8350) + (15% × $4300) = $1480. Her total tax, including both FICA and income tax, is

$$\text{total tax} = \text{FICA} + \text{income tax} = \$1683 + \$1480 = \$3163$$

BY THE WAY

The portion of FICA going to Social Security is called OASDI (Old Age, Survivors, and Disability Insurance). The portion going to Medicare is called HI (Hospital Insurance).

Her overall tax rate, including both FICA and income tax, is

$$\frac{\text{total tax}}{\text{gross income}} = \frac{\$3163}{\$22{,}000} \approx 0.144$$

Jude's overall tax rate is 14.4%. Note that she pays over $200 more in FICA tax than in income tax. **Now try Exercises 47–52.**

BY THE WAY

When the portion of FICA taxes paid by employers (and by the self-employed) is taken into account, most Americans pay more in FICA tax than in ordinary income tax.

Dividends and Capital Gains

Not all income is created equal, at least not in the eyes of the tax collector! In particular, dividends (on stocks) and capital gains—profits from the sale of stock or other property—get special tax treatment. **Capital gains** are divided into two subcategories. **Short-term capital gains** are profits on items sold within 12 months of their purchase, and **long-term capital gains** are profits on items held for more than 12 months before being sold.

Long-term capital gains and most dividends are taxed at lower rates than other income such as wages and interest earnings. As of 2009, the rates were

- 0% for income in the 10% and 15% tax brackets
- 15% for income in all higher tax brackets

In a few cases, capital gains get even better tax treatment. For example, capital gains on the sale of your home are often tax exempt. (There are also some special cases in which capital gains are taxed at higher rates.)

Time Out to Think

Under tax laws passed in 2001, capital gains rates are scheduled to undergo dramatic changes in both 2010 and 2011. However, Congress is likely to make changes to that law. Find the current capital gains tax rates. How do they compare to the rates for 2009? Are they scheduled to change again?

Example 8 Dividend and Capital Gains Income

In 2009, Serena was single and lived off an inheritance. Her gross income consisted solely of $90,000 in dividends and long-term capital gains. She had no adjustments to her gross income, but had $12,000 in itemized deductions and a personal exemption of $3650. How much tax does she owe? What is her overall tax rate?

BY THE WAY

The rationale behind a lower tax on capital gains is that it encourages investment in new businesses and products that involve risk on the part of the investor.

Solution She owes no FICA tax because her income is not from wages. She had no adjustments to her gross income, so we find her taxable income by subtracting her itemized deductions and personal exemption:

$$\text{taxable income} = \$90{,}000 - \$12{,}000 - \$3650 = \$74{,}350$$

Because her income is all dividends and long-term capital gains, she pays tax at the special rates for these types of income. The 0% rate for dividends and long-term capital gains applies to the income on which she would have been taxed at 10% or 15% if it had been ordinary income. From Table 4.9, therefore, we see that this means her first $33,950 of income. The rest of her income is taxed at the special 15% rate. Her total tax is

$$\underbrace{(0\% \times \$33{,}950)}_{\text{0\% capital gains rate}} + \underbrace{(15\% \times [\$74{,}350 - \$33{,}950])}_{\text{15\% capital gains rate}} = \$0 + \$6060 = \$6060$$

Her overall tax rate is

$$\frac{\text{total tax}}{\text{gross income}} = \frac{\$6060}{\$90{,}000} \approx 0.067$$

Serena's overall tax rate is 6.7%.

Now try Exercises 53–54.

Time Out to Think

Note that Serena in Example 8 had a gross income more than quadruple that of Jude in Example 7. Compare their tax payments and overall tax rates. Who pays more tax? Who pays at a higher tax rate? Explain.

Tax-Deferred Income

BY THE WAY

With tax-deferred savings, you will eventually pay tax on the money when you withdraw it. With *tax-exempt* investments, you never have to pay tax on the earnings. Some government bonds are tax-exempt. A Roth IRA is a special type of individual retirement account in which you pay taxes on money you deposit now, but all earnings on the account are tax-exempt when you withdraw them.

The tax code tries to encourage long-term savings by allowing you to *defer* income taxes on contributions to certain types of savings plans, called **tax-deferred savings plans.** Money that you deposit into such savings plans is not taxed now. Instead, it will be taxed in the future when you withdraw the money.

Tax-deferred savings plans go by a variety of names, such as *individual retirement accounts* (IRAs), *qualified retirement plans* (QRPs), *401(k) plans,* and more. All are subject to strict rules. For example, you generally are not allowed to withdraw money from any of these plans until you reach age $59\frac{1}{2}$. Anyone can set up a tax-deferred savings plan, and *you should,* regardless of your current age. Why? Because they offer two key advantages in saving for your long-term future.

First, contributions to tax-deferred savings plans count as *adjustments* to your present gross income and are not part of your taxable income. As a result, the contributions cost you less than contributions to savings plans without special tax treatment. For example, suppose you are in the 28% marginal tax bracket. If you deposit \$100 in an ordinary savings account, your tax bill is unchanged and you have \$100 less to spend on other things. But if you deposit \$100 in a tax-deferred savings account, you do not have to pay tax on that \$100. With your 28% marginal rate, you therefore save \$28 in taxes. Thus, the amount you have to spend on other things decreases by only $\$100 - \$28 = \$72$.

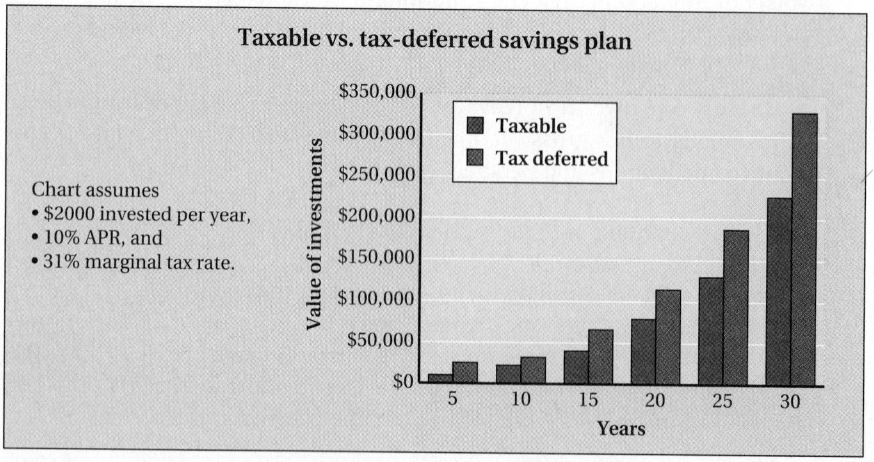

FIGURE 4.10 This graph compares the values of a tax-deferred savings plan and an ordinary savings plan, assuming that tax on the interest is paid from the plan in the latter case. After 30 years, the tax-deferred savings plan is worth over \$100,000 more than the ordinary plan.

The second advantage of tax-deferred savings plans is that their earnings are also tax deferred. With an ordinary savings plan, you must pay taxes on the earnings each year, which effectively reduces your earnings. With a tax-deferred savings plan, *all* of the earnings accumulate from one year to the next. Over many years, this tax saving makes the value of tax-deferred savings accounts rise much more quickly than that of ordinary savings accounts (Figure 4.10).

Example 9 Tax-Deferred Savings Plan

Suppose you are single, have a taxable income of \$65,000, and make monthly payments of \$500 to a tax-deferred savings plan. How do the tax-deferred contributions affect your monthly take-home pay?

Solution Table 4.9 shows that your marginal tax rate is 25%. Each \$500 contribution to a tax-deferred savings plan therefore reduces your tax bill by

$$25\% \times \$500 = \$125$$

In other words, \$500 goes into your tax-deferred savings account each month, but your monthly paychecks go down by only \$500 − \$125 = \$375. The special tax treatment makes it significantly easier for you to afford the monthly contributions needed to build your retirement fund. (The monthly saving found here is your *average* monthly saving for the year, after any tax refund or tax bill. It will be your precise monthly saving only if your withholding is computed so that you have zero tax due at year end.)

Now try Exercises 55–58.

Time Out to Think

In 2009, President Obama appointed a task force on tax reform to investigate ways to simplify and reform the tax code. Find the current status of the task force's work. What have they proposed? Have any of their proposals been implemented? (Bonus: Look up the recommendations made by President Bush's advisory panel on tax reform in 2005. Can you find any important similarities or differences between that group's recommendations and those of the new task force?)

QUICK QUIZ

Choose the best answer to each of the following questions. Explain your reasoning with one or more complete sentences.

1. The total amount of income you receive is called your

   a. gross income. b. net income. c. taxable income.

2. If your taxable income puts you in the 25% marginal tax bracket,

   a. your tax is 25% of your taxable income.

   b. your tax is 25% of your gross income.

   c. your tax is 25% of only a portion of your income; the rest is taxed at a lower rate.

3. Suppose you are in the 25% marginal tax bracket. Then a *tax credit* of \$1000 will reduce your tax bill by

   a. \$1000. b. \$150. c. \$500.

4. Suppose you are in the 15% marginal tax bracket and earn \$25,000. Then a *tax deduction* of \$1000 will reduce your tax bill by

   a. \$1000. b. \$150. c. \$500.

5. Suppose that in the past year your only deductible expenses were \$4000 in mortgage interest and \$2000 in charitable contributions. If you are entitled to a standard deduction of \$5700, then the total deduction you can claim is

   a. \$5700. b. \$6000. c. \$11,150.

6. Assume you are in the 25% tax bracket and you are entitled to a standard deduction of \$5700. If you have no other deductible expenses, by how much will a \$1000 charitable contribution reduce your tax bill?

   a. \$0 b. \$250 c. \$1000

7. What is the FICA tax?

 a. a tax on investment income

 b. another name for the marginal tax rate system

 c. a tax collected primarily to fund Social Security and Medicare

8. Based on the FICA rates for 2009, which of the following people pays the highest *percentage* of his or her income in FICA taxes?

 a. Joe, whose income consists of $12,000 from his job at Burger Joint

 b. Kim, whose income is $150,000 in wages from her job as an aeronautical engineer

 c. David, whose income is $1,000,000 in capital gains from investments

9. Jerome, Jenny, and Jacqueline all have the same *taxable income,* but Jerome's income is entirely from wages at his job, Jenny's income is a combination of wages and short-term capital gains, and Jacqueline's income is all from dividends and long-term capital gains. If you count both income taxes and FICA, how do their tax bills compare?

 a. They all pay the same amount in taxes.

 b. Jerome pays the most, Jenny the second most, and Jacqueline the least.

 c. Jacqueline pays the most, Jenny the second most, and Jerome the least.

10. When you place money into a tax-deferred retirement plan,

 a. you never have to pay tax on this money.

 b. you pay tax on this money now, but not when you withdraw it later.

 c. you do not pay tax on this money now, but you pay tax on money you withdraw from the plan later.

Exercises 4E

REVIEW QUESTIONS

1. Explain the basic process of calculating income taxes, as shown in Figure 4.9. What is the difference between gross income, adjusted gross income, and taxable income?
2. What is meant by filing status? How does it affect tax calculations?
3. What are exemptions and deductions? How should you choose between taking the standard deduction and itemizing deductions?
4. What is meant by a progressive income tax? Explain the use of marginal tax rates in calculating taxes. What is meant by a tax bracket?
5. What is the difference between a tax deduction and a tax credit? Why is a tax credit more valuable?
6. Explain how a deduction, such as the mortgage interest tax deduction, can save you money. Why do deductions benefit people in different tax brackets differently?
7. What are FICA taxes? What type of income is subject to FICA taxes?
8. How are dividends and capital gains treated differently than other income by the tax code?
9. Explain how you can benefit from a tax-deferred savings plan.
10. Why do tax-deferred savings plans tend to grow faster than ordinary savings plans?

DOES IT MAKE SENSE?

Decide whether each of the following statements makes sense (or is clearly true) or does not make sense (or is clearly false). Explain your reasoning.

11. We're both single with no children and we both have the same total (gross) income, so we must both pay the same amount in taxes.
12. The $1000 child tax credit sounds like a good idea, but it doesn't help me because I take the standard deduction rather than itemized deductions.
13. When I calculated carefully, I found that it was cheaper for me to buy a house than to continue renting, even though my rent payments were lower than my new mortgage payments.
14. My husband and I paid $12,000 in mortgage interest this year, but we didn't get any tax benefit from it.
15. Bob and Sue were planning to get married in December of this year, but they postponed their wedding until January when they found it would save them money in taxes.
16. The top marginal tax rate may be 35%, but I never pay more than 15% because I live off the dividends from my inheritance.
17. I didn't owe any ordinary income tax because my business (self-employed) made only a $7000 profit, but my total tax bill still came to 15.3% of my income.
18. I started contributing $400 each month to my tax-deferred savings plan, but my take-home pay declined by only $300.

BASIC SKILLS & CONCEPTS

19–22: **Income on Tax Forms.** Find the gross income, adjusted gross income, and taxable income in the following situations.

19. Antonio earned wages of $47,200, received $2400 in interest from a savings account, and contributed $3500 to a tax-deferred retirement plan. He was entitled to a personal exemption of $3300 and had deductions totaling $5150.
20. Marie earned wages of $28,400, received $95 in interest from a savings account, and was entitled to a personal exemption of $3300 and a standard deduction of $5150.
21. Isabella earned wages of $88,750, received $4900 in interest from a savings account, and contributed $6200 to a tax-deferred retirement plan. She was entitled to a personal exemption of $3300 and had deductions totaling $9050.

22. Lebron earned wages of $3,452,000, received $54,200 in interest from savings, and contributed $30,000 to a tax-deferred retirement plan. He was not allowed to claim a personal exemption (because of his high income) but was allowed deductions totaling $674,500.

23–24: To Itemize or Not. Decide whether you should itemize your deductions or take the standard deduction in the following cases.

23. Your deductible expenditures are $8600 for interest on a home mortgage, $2700 for contributions to charity, and $645 for state income taxes. Your filing status entitles you to a standard deduction of $11,400.

24. Your deductible expenditures are $3700 for contributions to charity and $760 for state income taxes. Your filing status entitles you to a standard deduction of $5700.

25–28: Income Calculations. Compute the gross income, adjusted gross income, and taxable income in the following situations. Use the exemptions and deductions in Table 4.9. Explain how you decided whether to itemize deductions or use the standard deduction.

25. Suzanne is single and earned wages of $33,200. She received $350 in interest from a savings account. She contributed $500 to a tax-deferred retirement plan. She had $450 in itemized deductions from charitable contributions.

26. Malcolm is single and earned wages of $23,700. He had $4500 in itemized deductions from interest on a mortgage.

27. Wanda is married, but she and her husband filed separately. Her salary was $35,400, and she earned $500 in interest. She had $1500 in itemized deductions and claimed three exemptions for herself and two children.

28. Emily and Juan are married and filed jointly. Their combined wages were $75,300. They earned $2000 from a rental property they own, and they received $1650 in interest. They claimed four exemptions for themselves and two children. They contributed $3240 to their tax-deferred retirement plans, and their itemized deductions totaled $9610.

29–36: Marginal Tax Calculations. Use the marginal tax rates in Table 4.9 to compute the tax owed in the following situations.

29. Gene is single and had a taxable income of $35,400.

30. Sarah and Marco are married filing jointly with a taxable income of $87,500.

31. Bobbi is married filing separately with a taxable income of $77,300.

32. Abraham is single with a taxable income of $23,800.

33. Paul is a head of household with a taxable income of $89,300. He is entitled to a $1000 tax credit.

34. Pat is a head of household with a taxable income of $57,000. She is entitled to a $1000 tax credit.

35. Winona and Jim are married filing jointly with a taxable income of $105,500. They also are entitled to a $2000 tax credit.

36. Chris is married filing separately with a taxable income of $127,300.

37–42: Tax Credits and Tax Deductions. Determine how much the following individuals or couples will save in taxes with the specified tax credits or deductions.

37. Midori and Tremaine are in the 28% tax bracket and claim the standard deduction. How much will their tax bill be reduced if they qualify for a $500 tax credit?

38. Vanessa is in the 35% tax bracket and itemizes her deductions. How much will her tax bill be reduced if she qualifies for a $500 tax credit?

39. Rosa is in the 15% tax bracket and claims the standard deduction. How much will her tax bill be reduced if she makes a $1000 contribution to charity?

40. Shiro is in the 15% tax bracket and itemizes his deductions. How much will his tax bill be reduced if he makes a $1000 contribution to charity?

41. Sebastian is in the 28% tax bracket and itemizes his deductions. How much will his tax bill be reduced if he makes a $1000 contribution to charity?

42. Santana is in the 35% tax bracket and itemizes her deductions. How much will her tax bill be reduced if she makes a $1000 contribution to charity?

43–44: Rent or Own? Consider the following choices between paying rent and making house payments. Including savings through the mortgage interest deduction, determine whether the monthly rent is greater than or less than the monthly house payments during the first year. In both cases, assume you itemize deductions.

43. You are in the 33% tax bracket. Your apartment rents for $1600 per month. Your monthly mortgage payments would be $2000, of which an average of $1800 per month goes toward interest during the first year.

44. You are in the 15% tax bracket. Your apartment rents for $600 per month. Your monthly mortgage payments would be $675, of which an average of $600 per month goes toward interest during the first year.

45. **Varying Value of Deductions.** Maria is in the 33% tax bracket. Steve is in the 15% tax bracket. They each itemize their deductions and pay $10,000 in mortgage interest during the year. Compare their true costs for mortgage interest.

46. **Varying Value of Deductions.** Yolanna is in the 35% tax bracket. Alia is in the 10% tax bracket. They each itemize their deductions, and they each donate $4000 to charity. Compare their true costs for charitable donations.

47–52: Fica Taxes. In the following situations, calculate the FICA taxes and income taxes to obtain a total tax bill. Then find the overall tax rate on the gross income, including both FICA and income taxes. Assume that all individuals are single and take the standard deduction. Use the tax rates in Table 4.9.

47. Luis earned $28,000 from wages as a computer programmer and made $2500 in tax-deferred contributions to a retirement fund.

48. Carla earned $34,500 in salary and $750 in interest and made $3000 in tax-deferred contributions to a retirement fund.

49. Jack earned $44,800 in salary and $1250 in interest and made $2000 in tax-deferred contributions to a retirement fund.

50. Alejandro earned $115,200 in salary and $4450 in interest and made $9500 in tax-deferred contributions to a retirement fund.

51. Brittany earned $48,200 in wages and tips. She had no other income and made no contributions to retirement plans.

52. Larae earned $21,200 in wages and tips. She had no other income and made no contributions to retirement plans.

53–54: Dividends and Capital Gains. Calculate the total tax owed by each individual in the following pairs (FICA and income taxes). Compare their overall tax rates. Assume all individuals are single and take the standard deduction. Use the tax rates in Table 4.9 and the special rates for dividends and capital gains given in the text.

53. Pierre earned $120,000 in wages. Katarina earned $120,000, all in dividends and long-term capital gains.

54. Deion earned $60,000 in wages. Josephina earned $60,000, all in dividends and long-term capital gains.

55–58: Tax-Deferred Savings Plans. Calculate the change in monthly take-home pay when the following tax-deferred contributions are made.

55. You are single and have a taxable income of $18,000. You make monthly contributions of $400 to a tax-deferred savings plan.

56. You are single and have a taxable income of $45,000. You make monthly contributions of $600 to a tax-deferred savings plan.

57. You are married filing jointly and have a taxable income of $90,000. You make monthly contributions of $800 to a tax-deferred savings plan.

58. You are married filing jointly and have a taxable income of $200,000. You make monthly contributions of $800 to a tax-deferred savings plan.

FURTHER APPLICATIONS

59–62: Marriage Penalty. Consider the following couples, who are engaged to be married. Calculate their income tax in two ways: (1) if they delay their marriage until next year so that they can file their tax returns as individuals at the single tax rate this year and (2) if they marry before the end of the year and file a joint return. Assume that each person takes one exemption and the standard deduction. Use the tax rates in Table 4.9. Do the couples face a marriage penalty if they marry before the end of the year? (Married rates apply for the entire year, regardless of when during the year the marriage took place.)

59. Gabriella and Roberto have adjusted gross incomes of $44,500 and $33,400, respectively.

60. Joan and Paul have adjusted gross incomes of $32,500 and $29,400, respectively.

61. Mia and Steve each have an adjusted gross income of $185,000.

62. Lisa has an adjusted gross income of $85,000, and Patrick is a student with no income.

WEB PROJECTS

63. **Tax Simplification Plans.** Use the Web to investigate a recent proposal to simplify federal tax laws and filing procedures. What are the advantages and disadvantages of the simplification plan, and who supports it?

64. **Fairness Issues.** Choose a tax question that has issues of fairness associated with it (for example, capital gains rates, the marriage penalty, or the alternative minimum tax [AMT]). Use the Web to investigate the current status of this question. Have new laws been passed that affect it? What are the advantages and disadvantages of recent or proposed changes, and who supports the changes? Summarize your own opinion about whether current tax law is unfair and, if so, what should be done about it.

65. **Consumption Tax.** Some people have proposed that the income tax be replaced by a consumption tax. What is a consumption tax? Find Web reports discussing the pros and cons of a consumption tax, and state your own opinion about whether it should be considered.

IN YOUR WORLD

66. **Alternative Minimum Tax (AMT).** The calculations described in this unit all assume that a person pays taxes according to the "normal" tax code. However, some people will be subject to the alternative minimum tax (AMT) in coming years. The AMT calculates taxes in a very different way, making taxes higher for people who pay it. The AMT is becoming a hot political issue, because more and more people are expected to owe it over the next few years. Find a recent article about the impact of the AMT. Write a short report on what you learn.

67. **Tax Changes.** Find a recent news article about proposed changes to federal tax laws. Briefly describe the proposed changes and their impact. What parties support and oppose the changes?

68. **Your Tax Return.** Briefly describe your own experiences with filing a federal income tax return. Do you file your own returns? If so, do you use a computer software package or a professional tax advisor? Will you change your filing method in the future? Why or why not?

UNIT 4F Understanding the Federal Budget

So far in this chapter, we have discussed issues of financial management that affect us directly as individuals. But we are also affected by the way our government manages its finances. In this unit, we will discuss a few of the basic concepts needed to understand the federal budget.

Federal Budget Basics

In theory, the federal budget works much like your personal budget (Unit 4A) or the budget of a small business. All have **receipts**, or income, and **outlays**, or expenses. **Net income** is the difference between receipts and outlays. When receipts exceed outlays, net income is positive and the budget has a **surplus** (profits). When outlays exceed receipts, net income is negative and the budget has a **deficit** (losses).

> **DEFINITIONS**
>
> **Receipts**, or income, represent money that has been collected.
>
> **Outlays**, or expenses, represent money that has been spent.
>
> **Net income** = receipts − outlays
>
> If net income is positive, the budget has a **surplus**.
>
> If net income is negative, the budget has a **deficit**.

There can be no freedom or beauty about a home life that depends on borrowing and debt.

—Henrik Ibsen, 1879

Note that a deficit means spending more money than was collected. The only way you (or a business or government) can survive a deficit is by spending savings or borrowing money. When you borrow, you accumulate a **debt**. Every year that you borrow to cover a deficit, your debt grows. In addition, the lender will surely charge interest on your debt. Thus, in addition to accumulating a debt, you will also face growing interest payments as your debt rises. In contrast, a surplus means collecting more money than was spent. If you have a surplus, you can use it either to add to your savings or to reduce your debt.

A national debt, if it is not excessive, will be to us a national blessing.

—Alexander Hamilton, 1781

> **DEBT VERSUS DEFICIT**
>
> A **deficit** represents money that is borrowed (or taken from savings) during a *single* year.
>
> The **debt** is the total amount of money owed to lenders, which may result from accumulating deficits over many years.

Example 1 Personal Budget

Suppose your gross income last year was \$40,000. Your expenditures were as follows: \$20,000 for rent and food, \$2000 for interest on your credit cards and student loans, \$6000 for car expenses, and \$9000 for entertainment and miscellaneous expenses. You also paid \$8000 in taxes. Did you have a deficit or a surplus?

Solution The total of your outlays, including tax, was

$$\$20{,}000 + \$2000 + \$6000 + \$9000 + \$8000 = \$45{,}000$$

Because your outlays were greater than your \$40,000 income by \$5000, your personal budget had a \$5000 deficit. Therefore, you must have either withdrawn \$5000 from savings or borrowed \$5000 to cover your expenditures. **Now try Exercises 15–16.**

Trends in the Federal Deficit and Debt

You're probably aware that the U.S. government has been running up huge deficits in recent years, and these accumulating deficits have driven rapid growth in the total federal debt. Deficits are not new; the government has run deficits almost every year since the 1930s (and in many other years before that as well), with notable exceptions from 1947 to 1949 and 1998 to 2001. What's new is the size of the deficits, which have exploded in recent years. Figure 4.11a shows the deficits and surpluses from 1965 through 2009, and Figure 4.11b shows the growth of the national debt during the same period.

There's great debate about how much of a problem these deficits and the growing debt pose for our future, and we'll discuss some of the issues in the rest of this unit. But it's worth noting that the current problems represent a reversal of what appeared to be a very positive trend in the 1990s. As you can see in Figure 4.11a, the deficit reached $290 billion in 1992 (a record high at the time), after which a combination of tax increases and a strong economy led to deficit reductions each year, until the deficit became a surplus in 1998. The surplus continued through 2001, and projections at the time suggested that the surpluses would continue indefinitely and that the debt could be rapidly paid down.

How did the surpluses change back to deficits, and why have the deficits grown so large? Economists cite two major factors: tax cuts passed in early 2001 and the economic impact of the 9/11 terrorist attacks that year. Both factors continued to affect the deficit in the years after 2001, but a third factor fueled further deficit growth: the costs of the wars in Iraq and Afghanistan. Then, an even larger rise in the deficit occurred in 2008–2009. This increase in the deficit was driven by the economic collapse

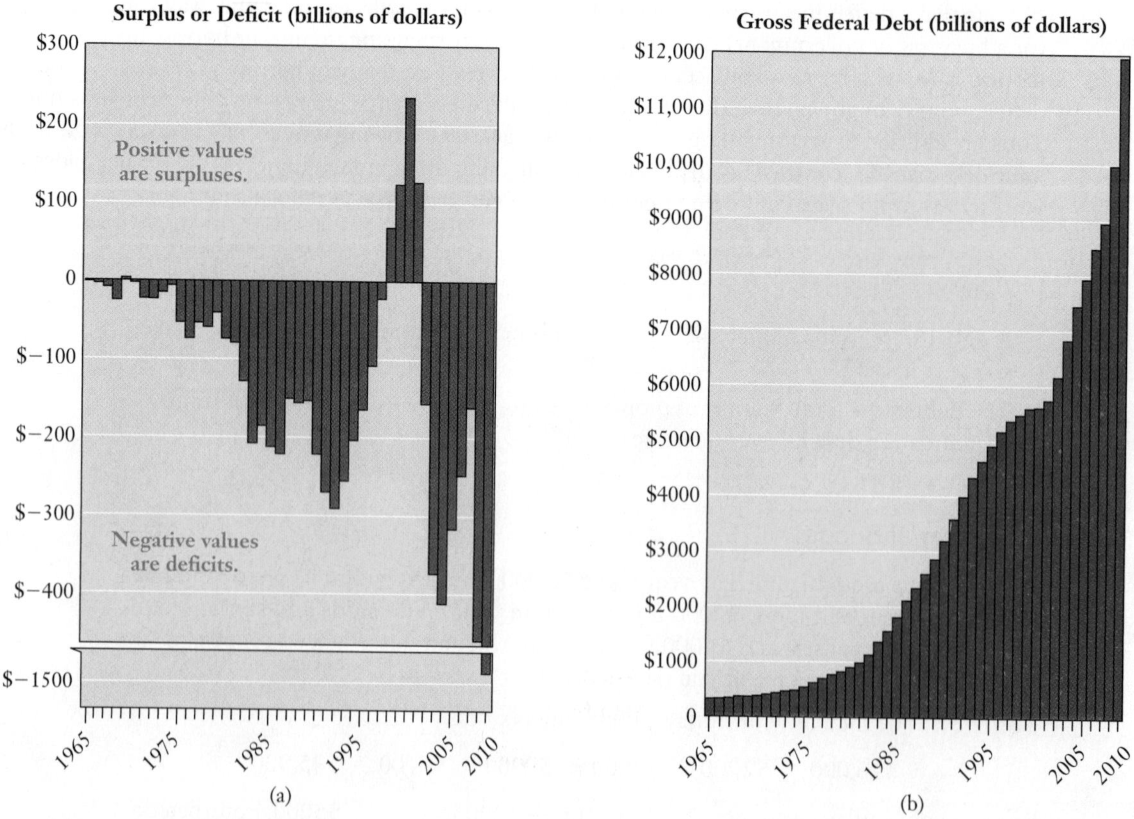

FIGURE 4.11 (a) Annual deficits or surpluses 1965–2009. (b) Accumulated gross federal debt 1965–2009. Data are based on fiscal years, which end on September 30.

Source: United States Office of Management and Budget.

that began with the bursting of the housing bubble, which caused the government to spend hundreds of billions of dollars on a combination of bailouts to financial companies and stimulus spending in hopes of countering the recession.

Time Out to Think

If the bailouts and stimulus spending work as hoped, the government could recoup the huge costs that led to the deficit explosion. Successful bailouts would allow companies to pay back the money they received, perhaps even generating a profit for the government. A successful stimulus would revive the economy, leading to greater tax revenues that would reduce the deficit. Has either of these hoped-for scenarios occurred so far? Do you see any evidence that the deficit will be brought back under control?

Example 2 The Federal Debt

The federal debt at the end of 2009 was nearly \$12 trillion. If this debt were divided evenly among the roughly 300 million citizens of the United States, how much would *you* owe?

Solution This question is easiest to answer by putting the numbers in scientific notation. We divide the debt of \$12 trillion ($\$1.2 \times 10^{13}$) by the 300 million ($3 \times 10^8$) population:

$$\frac{\$1.2 \times 10^{13}}{3 \times 10^8 \text{ persons}} = \$4 \times 10^4/\text{person}$$

Your personal share of the total debt is roughly $\$4 \times 10^4$, or \$40,000.

Now try Exercises 17–18.

Time Out to Think

How does your share of the national debt compare to personal debts that you owe? Explain.

A Small-Business Analogy

Before we focus on the federal budget, let's investigate the simpler books of an imaginary company with not-so-imaginary problems. Table 4.10 summarizes four years of budgets for the Wonderful Widget Company, which started with a clean slate at the beginning of 2007.

The first column shows that, during 2007, the company had receipts of \$854,000 and total outlays of \$1,000,000. The company's net income was

$$\$854{,}000 - \$1{,}000{,}000 = -\$146{,}000$$

TABLE 4.10 Budget Summary for the Wonderful Widget Company (in thousands of dollars)

	2007	2008	2009	2010
Total Receipts	\$854	\$908	\$950	\$990
Outlays				
Operating	525	550	600	600
Employee Benefits	200	220	250	250
Security	275	300	320	300
Interest on Debt	0	12	26	47
Total Outlays	1000	1082	1196	1197
Surplus/Deficit	−146	−174	−246	−207
Debt (accumulated)	**−146**	**−320**	**−566**	**−773**

The negative sign tells us that the company had a *deficit* of \$146,000. The company had to borrow money to cover this deficit and ended the year with a debt of \$146,000. The debt is shown as a negative number because it represents money owed to someone else.

In 2008, receipts increased to \$908,000, while outlays increased to \$1,082,000. These outlays included a \$12,000 interest payment on the debt from the first year. The deficit for 2008 was

$$\$908{,}000 - \$1{,}082{,}000 = -\$174{,}000$$

The company had to borrow \$174,000 to cover this deficit. Further, it had no money with which to pay off the debt from 2007. Thus, the total debt at the end of 2008 was

$$\$146{,}000 + \$174{,}000 = \$320{,}000$$

Here is the key point: Because the company again failed to balance its budget in its second year, its total debt continued to grow. As a result, its interest payment in 2009 increased to \$26,000.

In 2010, the company's owners decided to change strategy. They froze operating expenses and employee benefits (relative to 2009) and actually *cut* security expenses. However, the interest payment rose substantially because of the rising debt. Despite the attempts to curtail outlays and despite another increase in receipts, the company still ran a deficit in 2010 and the total debt continued to grow.

Time Out to Think

Suppose you were a loan officer for a bank in 2011, when the Wonderful Widget Company came asking for further loans to cover its increasing debt. Would you lend it the money? If so, would you attach any special conditions to the loan? Explain.

Example 3 Growing Interest Payments

Consider Table 4.10 for the Wonderful Widget Company. Assume that the \$47,000 interest payment in 2010 was for the prior debt of \$566,000. What was the annual interest rate? If the interest rate remains the same, what will the payment be on the debt at the end of 2010? What will the payment be if the interest rate rises by 2 percentage points?

Solution Paying \$47,000 interest on a debt of \$566,000 means an interest rate of

$$\frac{\$47{,}000}{\$566{,}000} = 0.083$$

The interest rate was 8.3%. At the end of 2010, the debt stands at \$773,000. At the same interest rate, the next interest payment will be

$$0.083 \times \$773{,}000 = \$64{,}159$$

If the interest rate rises by 2 percentage points, to 10.3%, the next interest payment will be

$$0.103 \times \$773{,}000 = \$79{,}619$$

A 2-percentage-point change in the interest rate increases the interest payment by more than \$15,000.

Now try Exercises 19–20.

TABLE 4.11 U.S. Federal Budget Summary, 2001–2009 (all amounts in billions of dollars)

	2001	2002	2003	2004	2005	2006	2007	2008	2009
Total Receipts	\$1991	\$1853	\$1783	\$1880	\$2154	\$2407	\$2568	\$2524	\$2100
Total Outlays	1863	2011	2160	2293	2472	2655	2729	2983	3520
Net Income	128	−158	−378	−413	−318	−248	−161	−459	−1420

Source: United States Office of Management and Budget.

The Federal Budget

The Widget Company example shows that a succession of deficits leads to a rising debt. The increasing interest payments on that debt, in turn, make it even easier to run deficits in the future. The Widget Company story is a mild version of what happened to the U.S. budget. Table 4.11 shows a summary of the federal budget in recent years. Moreover, as the debt has risen, interest payments have increased. Low interest rates have helped ease this burden in recent years, but interest payments still make up close to 10% of federal outlays. For example, interest on the debt cost the government about \$260 billion in 2009—more than double what the government spent on all education, training, and social services combined, and nearly 15 times as much as it spent for NASA.

The future of the federal budget is notoriously difficult to predict. Over the past couple decades, each year's budget projections for the following year have been off by an average of about 11%. Projections more than one year out have been even further off.

Example 4 Budget Projections

As of 2009, the government projected total receipts for 2011 of \$2685 billion (\$2.685 trillion) and a deficit of \$929 billion. How would net income change if the projection of receipts turned out to be too high by 11%? How would it change if the projection of receipts were too low by 11%? Assume that outlays are unchanged.

Solution An error of 11% of the projected receipts of \$2685 billion is

$$0.11 \times \$2685 \text{ billion} = \$295 \text{ billion (rounded to nearest \$1 billion)}$$

If receipts were 11% lower than expected, net income would be \$295 billion less than projected, thereby increasing the deficit from its projected \$929 billion to \$929 billion + \$295 billion = \$1224 billion (\$1.224 trillion). If receipts were 11% higher than expected, net income would be \$295 billion higher than projected, reducing the projected deficit to \$634 billion. **Now try Exercises 21–22.**

BY THE WAY

The government also collects revenues from a few "business-like" activities, such as charging entrance fees at national parks. However, for historical reasons, these revenues are subtracted from outlays instead of being added to receipts when the government publishes its budget. Although this method of accounting may seem odd, it does not affect overall calculations of the surplus or deficit.

Time Out to Think

Do you think it is wise to base long-term spending or taxing plans on long-term budget projections? Why or why not?

Federal Government Receipts

To understand the federal budget more deeply, we need to understand how the government gets its receipts and how it spends its outlays. Figure 4.12 shows the approximate makeup of government receipts as of 2009. The categories are

- Individual income taxes, as we discussed in Unit 4E
- Corporate income taxes, which are income taxes paid by businesses

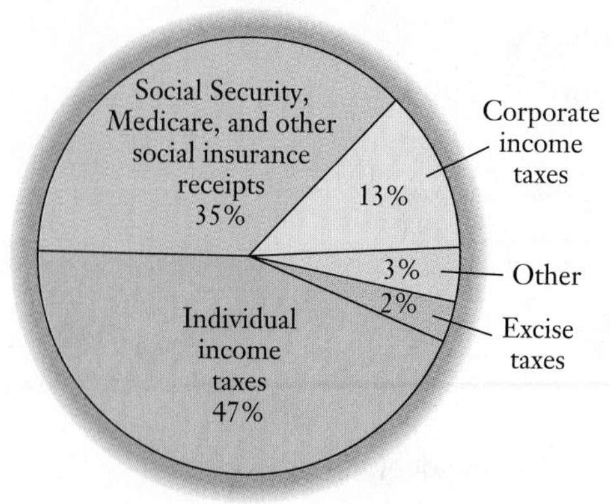

FIGURE 4.12 Approximate makeup of federal government receipts, 2009.
Source: United States Office of Management and Budget.

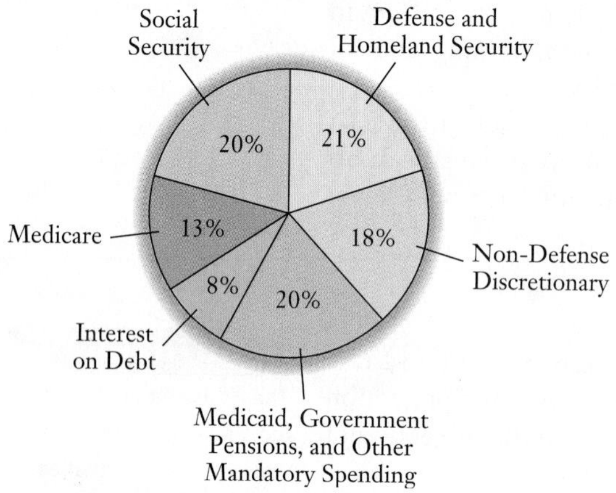

FIGURE 4.13 Approximate makeup of federal government outlays, 2009. All categories *except* "Defense and Homeland Security" and "Non-Defense Discretionary" are considered mandatory.
Source: United States Office of Management and Budget.

- Social insurance taxes, which primarily represent FICA taxes (see Unit 4E) for Social Security and Medicare but also include payments into retirement plans by federal employees and taxes for unemployment insurance
- Excise taxes, which include taxes on alcohol, tobacco, gasoline, and other products
- Other, which includes such things as gift taxes and fines collected by the government

Note that most of the receipts come from income taxes, followed fairly closely by social insurance.

Federal Government Outlays

Figure 4.13 shows the approximate makeup of government outlays as of 2009. For purposes of projecting budgets, the government generally groups spending into two major areas.

- **Mandatory outlays** are expenses that will be paid automatically unless Congress acts to change them. Most of the mandatory outlays are for "entitlements" such as Social Security, Medicare, and other payments to individuals. (They are called *entitlements* because the law specifically states the conditions under which individuals are entitled to them.) Interest on the debt is also a mandatory outlay, because it must be paid to prevent the government from being in default on its loans.
- **Discretionary outlays** are decided on a year-to-year basis. The amounts for discretionary programs must be approved by Congress in authorization bills, which then must be signed by the President to become law. Discretionary outlays are subdivided into programs for defense (military and homeland security) and non-defense. *Non-defense discretionary outlays* include everything except the mandatory outlays and defense. For example, non-defense discretionary outlays include education, transportation, housing, international aid, the space program, and scientific research.

Example 5 Discretionary Squeeze

The portion of the budget going to Social Security is expected to grow as more people retire in coming decades. Suppose that Social Security rises to 30% of total outlays while all other programs except non-defense discretionary spending hold steady at the proportions shown in Figure 4.13. As a percentage of total outlays, how much would non-defense discretionary spending have to decrease to cover the increase in Social Security? Comment on how this scenario would affect Congress's power to control the deficit.

Solution Figure 4.13 shows that 20% of outlays currently go to Social Security, so a rise to 30% would be a rise of 10 percentage points. Then the proportion of spending for all other programs would have to drop by 10 percentage points for the total to remain 100%. If this drop came entirely from non-defense discretionary spending, non-defense discretionary spending would fall from 18% to 8% of total outlays.

If non-defense discretionary spending were only 8% of total outlays, Congress would lose much of its power to control deficits. Here's why: First, remember that Congress authorizes only discretionary spending (as opposed to mandatory spending) on a year-to-year basis. In essence, this is the only portion of the budget that Congress can easily control. Second, 8% is smaller than the average error in budget projections (see Example 4). Therefore, the proportion of the budget that Congress can easily control would be smaller than the uncertainty that Congress must deal with in making a budget. Clearly, this would make it nearly impossible for Congress to predict the deficit accurately. **Now try Exercises 23–28.**

BY THE WAY

If you've ever paid Social Security taxes, then you have your own private Social Security account. The Social Security Administration automatically sends annual statements to wage earners age 25 or older. Your statement should arrive about 3 months before your birthday. If you don't receive an automatic statement, you can request a statement from the Social Security Administration Web site. You should check your statement carefully, to make sure that your Social Security taxes have been properly credited to your account.

Strange Numbers: Publicly Held and Gross Debt

Take another look at Figure 4.11 and you may notice something rather strange: Even in the years when the government ran a surplus (1998–2001), the debt still continued to increase. Why did the debt keep rising, even when the government collected more money than it spent? More generally, why does the debt tend to rise from one year to the next by more than the amount of the deficit for the year? To answer these questions, we must investigate government accounting in a little more detail.

Financing the Debt

Remember that whenever you run a deficit, you must cover it either by withdrawing from savings or by borrowing money. The federal government does both. It withdraws money from its "savings," and it borrows money from people and institutions willing to lend to it.

Let's consider borrowing first. The government borrows money by selling Treasury bills, notes, and bonds (see Unit 4C) to the public. If you buy one of these Treasury issues, you are effectively lending the government money that it promises to pay back with interest. Because Treasury issues are considered to be very safe investments, the government has never had trouble finding people or institutions willing to buy them. By the end of 2009, the government had borrowed a total of about $8 trillion through the sale of Treasury issues. This debt, which the government must eventually pay back to those who hold the Treasury issues, is called the **publicly held debt** (sometimes called the *net debt* or the *marketable debt*). Nearly half of this debt is currently held by foreign individuals and banks, with China as the largest holder of U.S. securities.

The government's "savings" consist of special accounts designed to meet future obligations. These accounts are called *trust funds*. The biggest trust fund by far is for Social Security, which is primarily a retirement program. People "invest" by paying Social Security taxes (most of the FICA taxes; see Unit 4E) and then collect Social Security benefits after they retire.

Currently, the government is collecting more in Social Security taxes than it is paying out in Social Security benefits (see Figures 4.12 and Figure 4.13). This reflects the fact that, today, many more people are working and paying Social Security taxes than are collecting benefits. However, as today's workers retire, the government will have to pay more and more in Social Security benefits. Therefore, to make sure there is enough money to pay future Social Security benefits, the government should invest the excess Social Security taxes that it collects today.

The trust fund more accurately represents a stack of IOUs to be presented to future generations for payment, rather than a build-up of resources to fund future benefits.

—John Hambor, former research director for the Social Security Administration

Legally, the government must invest the excess Social Security money in the Social Security trust fund. It does the same for several other trust funds, including those for the pensions of government workers. In a sense, these trust funds are like the government's savings accounts. But there's a catch: Before the government borrows from the public to finance a deficit, it first tries to cover the deficit by borrowing from its own trust funds.

In fact, the government has to date borrowed every penny it ever deposited into these trust funds. In other words, *there is no money in any of the trust funds, including*

Social Security. Instead, the trust fund is filled with the equivalent of a stack of IOUs (more technically, with Treasury bills), in which the government has promised to return the money it borrowed, with interest.

As of the end of 2009, the government's debt to its own trust funds was approaching \$4.5 trillion. Adding this amount to the publicly held debt of \$8.5 trillion, we get a **gross debt** of almost \$13 trillion. This is the total debt shown in Figure 4.11b, and it represents the total amount that the government is eventually obligated to repay from other government receipts (that is, receipts besides those collected for Social Security and other trust funds).

> **TWO KINDS OF NATIONAL DEBT**
>
> The **publicly held debt** (or *net debt*) represents money the government must repay to individuals and institutions that bought Treasury issues.
>
> The **gross debt** includes both the publicly held debt and money that the government owes to its own trust funds, such as the Social Security trust fund.

On-Budget and Off-Budget: Effects of Social Security

As an example of how trust funds affect the two kinds of debt, consider 2001—when the federal government ran a \$128 billion surplus (see Table 4.11). The government used this surplus money to buy back some of the Treasury notes and bonds it had sold to the public, which reduced the publicly held debt.

However, remember that the government also collected excess Social Security taxes, which legally had to be deposited in the Social Security trust fund. In addition, the government owed the trust fund interest for all the money it had borrowed from the trust fund in the past. When we add both the excess Social Security taxes and the owed interest, it turns out that the government was *supposed to* deposit \$161 billion in the Social Security trust fund in 2001. But the government had already spent the \$161 billion, leaving no cash available to deposit in the trust fund. The government therefore "deposited" \$161 billion worth of IOUs in the trust fund, adding to the stack of IOUs already there from the past. Because IOUs represent loans, the government effectively borrowed \$161 billion from the Social Security trust fund. When we subtract this borrowed amount from the \$128 billion surplus, the government's income for 2001 becomes

$$\underbrace{\$128\text{ billion}}_{\text{unified net income}} - \underbrace{\$161\text{ billion}}_{\text{off-budget net income}} = \underbrace{-\$33\text{ billion}}_{\text{on-budget net income}}$$

With Social Security counted, the \$128 billion surplus turns into a \$33 billion deficit!

In government-speak, Social Security is said to be **off-budget**. Because the government really did collect \$128 billion more than it spent, this number is called the **unified net income**. The **on-budget** net income is what remains after we subtract the portion of the unified net income that came from Social Security. It represents the amount by which the government overspent its revenue when Social Security is included.

Although Social Security is the only major expenditure that is legally considered off-budget, other trust funds also represent future repayment obligations. Because the government borrowed from all these other trust funds as well, the gross debt rose by considerably more than the \$33 billion on-budget deficit. In fact, when all was said and done, the gross debt rose by \$141 billion during 2001. Despite the surplus, the debt to be repaid in the future grew substantially.

BY THE WAY

If you want complete details of debt accounting, you can download the entire federal budget (typically a couple thousand pages) from the Web site for the United States Office of Management and Budget. The site also offers many simplified summaries and other useful data.

UNIFIED BUDGET, ON BUDGET, AND OFF BUDGET

The U.S. government's **unified budget** represents all federal revenues and spending. For accounting purposes, the government divides this unified budget into two parts:

- The portion of the unified budget that is involved in Social Security (that is, revenue from Social Security tax and spending on Social Security benefits) is considered **off-budget.**
- The rest of the unified budget (that is, everything that is not involved in Social Security) is considered **on-budget.**

Thus, the following relationships hold for any surplus or deficit in the budget:

$$\text{unified net income} = \text{on-budget net income} + \text{off-budget net income}$$

Or, equivalently,

$$\text{unified net income} - \text{on-budget net income} = \text{off-budget net income}$$

Example 6 On- and Off-Budget

The federal government ran a $459 billion deficit (unified deficit) in 2008. However, this number does not separate the effects of excess Social Security taxes. For 2008, the government collected $190 billion more in Social Security revenue than it paid out in Social Security benefits. What do we call this excess $190 billion of Social Security revenue, and what happened to it? What was the government's on-budget deficit for 2008? Explain.

Solution The $190 billion excess Social Security revenue represents what we call the off-budget net income (a surplus) for 2008, because it is counted separately from the rest of the budget (that's what makes it "off" budget). By law, this $190 billion had to be added to the Social Security trust fund. Unfortunately, it had already been spent (on programs other than Social Security), so the government instead added $190 billion worth of IOUs (Treasury bills) to the trust fund. Since this $190 billion worth of IOUs will have to be repaid eventually, it should be included in the calculation of what we call the on-budget deficit—the amount by which the government actually overspent in 2008. That is, the on-budget net income for 2008 was

$$\underbrace{-\$459\text{ billion}}_{\text{unified net income}} - \underbrace{\$190\text{ billion}}_{\text{off-budget net income}} = \underbrace{-\$649\text{ billion}}_{\text{on-budget net income}}$$

In summary, the unified deficit of $459 billion means the government's total revenue fell $459 billion short of its outlays. But because the government added $190 billion to its long-term obligation to repay its own Social Security trust fund, the government's future repayment obligations really rose by the on-budget deficit of $649 billion. (In fact, because of the government's other trust funds and other accounting details, the debt rose by even more than this amount.) **Now try Exercises 29–30.**

BY THE WAY

Social Security benefits differ from private retirement benefits in at least two major ways. First, Social Security benefits are guaranteed. Private retirement accounts may rise or fall in value, thereby changing how much you can afford to withdraw during retirement, but Social Security promises a particular benefit payment in any circumstances. Second, Social Security benefits are paid as long as you live, but cannot be passed on to your heirs. In contrast, private retirement accounts can be passed on through your will.

The Future of Social Security

Imagine that you decide to set up a retirement savings plan that will allow you to retire comfortably at age 65. Using the savings plan formula (see Unit 4C), you determine that you can achieve your retirement goal by making monthly deposits of $250 into your retirement plan. So you start the plan today by making your first $250 deposit.

However, in the first month you see a new sound system that looks really cool. Being short on cash, you decide to buy it by withdrawing the $250 that you had put into your retirement plan. Because you don't want to fall behind on your retirement savings, you write yourself an IOU stating that you "owe" your retirement plan $250.

Next month, you again deposit $250 in your retirement plan—but soon withdraw it for a nice weekend getaway. As before, you write an IOU to remind yourself that you owe $250 to your retirement plan. Moreover, recognizing that you would have earned interest on the previous month's deposit if you hadn't withdrawn it, you write yourself an IOU for the lost interest.

Month after month and year after year, you continue in the same way. Because you always spend the money you had planned to put in your retirement plan, you keep writing yourself IOUs for the payments plus interest. When you finally reach age 65, your retirement plan contains IOUs that say you owe yourself enough money to retire on—*but your retirement account contains no actual money.* Obviously, it will be difficult to live off the IOUs you wrote to yourself.

Take Note

Projections are made in current dollars, so it is not necessary to adjust projected numbers for future inflation.

This method of "saving" for retirement may sound silly, but it essentially describes the Social Security trust fund. Officially, the Social Security trust fund is growing larger and larger because of excess Social Security taxes and interest on past IOUs. According to recent projections, its balance will grow to over $3 trillion by 2016. But, in reality, the trust fund contains no cash today and will contain no cash in 2016. It will just be filled with $3 trillion worth of IOUs from the government to itself.

Now comes the bad news. Sometime around or after 2016, the increasing number of retirees will mean that Social Security payments will exceed the receipts from Social Security taxes. In order to pay benefits, the government will have to begin withdrawing money from the trust fund. This means the government will somehow have to start redeeming the IOUs that it has written to itself.

To see the problem vividly, consider the year 2037, when the "intermediate" projections (meaning those that are neither especially optimistic nor especially pessimistic) say the Social Security trust fund will go bankrupt. By then, projected Social Security payments will be about $900 billion more than collections from Social Security taxes. The government will therefore have to redeem $900 billion in IOUs from the Social Security trust fund, which means it will somehow have to find $900 billion in cold, hard cash. Generally speaking, the government could do this through some combination of the following three options:

1. It could cut spending on discretionary programs, such as the military or education, in order to free up money to redeem the IOUs. Unfortunately, $900 billion roughly equals the amount currently spent on *all* discretionary spending. Thus, the government would have to eliminate virtually all discretionary spending—including eliminating the military—in order to cover the Social Security payments.
2. It could borrow the money from the public by issuing more Treasury notes and bonds. But the needed $900 billion would vastly increase any other deficit the government might be running.
3. It could raise taxes to collect extra cash.

You may notice that any of these three possibilities could have a dramatic impact on *you.* Programs such as education for your kids may be cut, or the economy will be hurt by huge deficits, or you'll be taxed much more heavily than you are today. Clearly, something must be done to solve this problem before it arrives. Unfortunately, the politics of Social Security makes a solution hard to come by. Worse yet, Medicare is expected to face a similar crisis, and some economists believe the Medicare problems are even more severe.

Time Out to Think

Some proposals for solving the Social Security problem call for converting part or all of the program to private savings accounts. This would have the advantage of making sure that the government couldn't keep borrowing from Social Security. In addition, private investments have historically grown at a faster rate than the trust fund interest the government pays itself. However, the fact that private accounts can also lose value—as they did in the recent fall of the stock market—makes them risky. What's your opinion of privatizing Social Security? Explain.

BY THE WAY

Social Security is sometimes called the "third rail" of politics. The term comes from the New York City subways, where the trains run on two rails and the third rail carries electricity at very high voltage. Touching the third rail generally causes instant death.

Example 7 Tax Increase

In 2009, individual income taxes made up about 47% of total government receipts of $2.16 trillion. Suppose that the government needed to raise an additional $900 billion through individual income taxes. How much would taxes have to increase? Neglect any economic problems that the tax increase might cause.

Solution To bring in 47% of the $2.16 trillion in receipts for 2009, individual income taxes had to account for about $1.0 trillion in government revenue. Raising an additional $900 billion ($0.9 trillion) would require an additional 90% in revenue from individual income taxes. To generate an extra $900 billion, overall income taxes would have to rise by 90%.

Now try Exercises 31–32.

QUICK QUIZ

Choose the best answer to each of the following questions. Explain your reasoning with one or more complete sentences.

1. In 2009, Bigprofit.com had $1 million more in outlays than in receipts, bringing the total amount it owed lenders to $7 million. We say that at the end of 2009 Bigprofit.com had

   a. a deficit of $7 million and a debt of $1 million.

   b. a deficit of $1 million and a debt of $7 million.

   c. a surplus of $1 million and a deficit of $7 million.

2. If the U.S. government decided to pay off the federal debt by asking for an equal contribution from all U.S. citizens, you'd be asked to pay approximately

   a. $430. b. $4300. c. $43,000.

3. Suppose the government predicts that for next year tax receipts will be $2.5 trillion and net income will be −$100 billion (a deficit). Based on historical errors in predicting the budget for the following year, you can expect next year's actual net income to be

   a. a deficit of between about $90 billion and $110 billion.

   b. a deficit of between about $50 billion and $150 billion.

   c. somewhere between a deficit of $350 billion and a surplus of $150 billion.

4. In terms of the U.S. budget, what do we mean by *discretionary* outlays?

   a. money that the government spends on things that aren't really important

   b. money that the government spends on programs that Congress must authorize every year

   c. programs funded by FICA taxes

5. Which of the following is *not* considered a mandatory expense in the U.S. federal budget?

   a. national defense b. interest on the debt

   c. Medicare

6. Currently, the majority of government spending goes to

   a. mandatory expenses. b. national defense.

   c. science and education.

7. Suppose the government collects $100 billion more in Social Security taxes than it pays out in Social Security benefits. Under current policy, what happens to this "extra" $100 billion?

   a. It is physically deposited into a bank that holds it to be used for future Social Security benefits.

   b. It is used to fund other government programs.

   c. It is returned in the form of rebates to those who paid the excess taxes.

8. If the government were able to pay off the *publicly held debt*, who would receive the money?

   a. The money would be distributed among all U.S citizens.

   b. The money would go to holders of Treasury bills, notes, and bonds.

   c. The money would go to future retirees through the Social Security Trust Fund.

9. Which of the following best describes the *total* amount of money that the government has obligated itself to pay back in the future?

a. the publicly held debt b. the gross debt

c. the off-budget debt

10. By the year 2030, the government is expected to owe several hundred billion dollars more in Social Security benefits each year than it will collect in Social Security taxes. Although all options for covering this shortfall might be politically difficult, which of the following is *not* an option even in principle?

a. The shortfall could be covered by tax increases.

b. The shortfall could be covered by additional borrowing from the public.

c. The shortfall could be covered by reducing the amount of education grants offered.

Exercises 4F

REVIEW QUESTIONS

1. Define receipts, outlays, net income, surplus, and deficit as they apply to annual budgets.
2. What is the difference between a deficit and a debt? How large is the federal debt?
3. Explain why years of running deficits makes it increasingly difficult to get a budget into balance.
4. How large is the deficit at present? Should we assume future deficit projections are correct? Explain.
5. Briefly summarize the makeup of federal receipts and federal outlays. Distinguish between mandatory outlays and discretionary outlays.
6. How does the federal government finance its debt? Distinguish between the publicly held debt and the gross debt.
7. Briefly describe the Social Security trust fund. What's in it? What problems may this cause in the future?
8. Distinguish between an off-budget deficit (or surplus) and an on-budget deficit (or surplus). What is the unified deficit (or surplus)?

DOES IT MAKE SENSE?

Decide whether each of the following statements makes sense (or is clearly true) or does not make sense (or is clearly false). Explain your reasoning.

9. My share of the federal government's debt is greater than the cost of a new car.
10. My share of the federal government's annual *interest* payments on the federal debt is greater than the cost of a new car.
11. Because Social Security is off-budget, we could cut Social Security taxes with no impact on the rest of the federal government.
12. The government collected more money than it spent, but its gross debt still increased.
13. I read today that in 10 years the government will return to surpluses (from deficits), so we should start planning how we'll use the surplus.
14. The Social Security trust fund will have a positive balance for at least 20 years to come, so there's no need to be concerned about how the government will pay Social Security benefits.

BASIC SKILLS & CONCEPTS

15. **Personal Budget Basics.** Suppose your after-tax annual income is \$38,000. Your annual expenses are \$12,000 for rent, \$6000 for food and household expenses, \$1200 for interest on credit cards, and \$8500 for entertainment, travel, and other.

a. Do you have a surplus or a deficit? Explain.

b. Next year, you expect to get a 3% raise. You think you can keep your expenses unchanged, with one exception: You plan to spend \$8500 on a car. Explain the effect of this purchase on your budget.

c. As in part b, assume you get a 3% raise for next year. If you can limit your expenses to a 1% increase (over the prior year), could you afford \$7500 in tuition and fees without going into debt?

16. **Personal Budget Basics.** Suppose your after-tax income is \$28,000. Your annual expenses are \$8000 for rent, \$4500 for food and household expenses, \$1600 for interest on credit cards, and \$10,400 for entertainment, travel, and other.

a. Do you have a surplus or a deficit? Explain.

b. Next year, you expect to get a 2% raise, but plan to keep your expenses unchanged. Will you be able to pay off \$5200 in credit card debt? Explain.

c. As in part b, assume you get a 2% raise for next year. If you can limit your expenses to a 1% increase, could you afford \$3500 for a wedding and honeymoon without going into debt?

17. **Per-Worker Debt.** Suppose the government decided to pay off the \$13 trillion debt with a one-time charge distributed equally among the 160-million-person civilian work force. How much would each worker be charged?

18. **Per-Family Debt.** Suppose the government decided to pay off the $13 trillion debt with a one-time charge distributed equally among all 120 million U.S. families. How much would each family be charged?

19. **The Wonderful Widget Company Future.** Extending the budget summary of the Widget Company (Table 4.10), assume that, for 2011, total receipts are $1,050,000, operating expenses are $600,000, employee benefits are $200,000, and security costs are $250,000.

    a. Based on the accumulated debt at the end of 2010, calculate the 2011 interest payment. Assume an interest rate of 8.2%.

    b. Calculate the total outlays for 2011, the year-end surplus or deficit, and the year-end accumulated debt.

    c. Based on the accumulated debt at the end of 2011, calculate the 2012 interest payment, again assuming an 8.2% interest rate.

    d. Assume that in 2012 the Widget Company has receipts of $1,100,000, holds operating costs and employee benefits to their 2011 levels, and spends no money on security. Calculate the total outlays for 2012, the year-end surplus or deficit, and the year-end accumulated debt.

    e. Imagine that you are the CFO (Chief Financial Officer) of the Wonderful Widget Company at the end of 2012. Write a three-paragraph statement to shareholders about the company's future prospects.

20. **The Wonderful Widget Company Future.** Extending the budget summary of the Widget Company (Table 4.10), assume that, for 2011, total receipts are $975,000, operating expenses are $850,000, employee benefits are $290,000, and security costs are $210,000.

    a. Based on the accumulated debt at the end of 2010, calculate the 2011 interest payment. Assume an interest rate of 8.2%.

    b. Calculate the total outlays for 2011, the year-end surplus or deficit, and the year-end accumulated debt.

    c. Based on the accumulated debt at the end of 2011, calculate the 2012 interest payment, again assuming an 8.2% interest rate.

    d. Assume that in 2012 the Widget Company has receipts of $1,050,000, holds operating costs and employee benefits to their 2011 levels, and spends no money on security. Calculate the total outlays for 2012, the year-end surplus or deficit, and the year-end accumulated debt.

    e. Imagine that you are the CFO (Chief Financial Officer) of the Wonderful Widget Company at the end of 2012. Write a three-paragraph statement to shareholders about the company's future prospects.

21. **Budget Projections.** Refer to the 2009 data in Table 4.11. How would the deficit have been affected by a 1% decrease in total receipts? How would it have been affected by a 0.5% increase in total outlays?

22. **Budget Projections.** Refer to the 2009 data in Table 4.11. How would the deficit have been affected by a 0.5% decrease in total receipts? How would it have been affected by a 1% increase in total outlays?

23–28: **Budget Analysis.** Consider the 2009 federal outlays and receipts shown in Table 4.11 and Figures 4.12 and 4.13.

23. How much income came from individual income taxes?

24. How much income came from social insurance taxes?

25. How much income came from excise taxes?

26. How much was spent on Social Security?

27. How much was spent on Medicare?

28. How much was spent on defense?

29. **On- and Off-Budget.** Suppose the government has a unified net income of $40 billion, but was supposed to deposit $180 billion in the Social Security trust fund. What was the on-budget surplus or deficit? Explain.

30. **On- and Off-Budget.** Suppose the government has a unified net income of −$220 billion, but was supposed to deposit $205 billion in the Social Security trust fund. What was the on-budget deficit? Explain.

31. **Social Security Finances.** Suppose the year is 2020, and the government needs to pay out $350 billion more in Social Security benefits than it collects in Social Security taxes. Briefly discuss the options for finding this money.

32. **Social Security Finances.** Suppose the year is 2025, and the government needs to pay out $525 billion more in Social Security benefits than it collects in Social Security taxes. Briefly discuss the options for finding this money.

FURTHER APPLICATIONS

33. **Counting the Federal Debt.** Suppose you began counting the $13 trillion federal debt, $1 at a time. If you could count $1 each second, how long would it take to complete the count? Specify the answer in years.

34. **Paving with the Federal Debt.** Suppose you began covering the ground with $1 bills. If you had the $13 trillion federal debt in $1 bills, how much total area could you cover? Compare this area to the total land area of the United States, which is about 10 million square kilometers. (*Hint:* Assume that a dollar bill has an area of 100 square centimeters.)

35. **Rising Debt.** Suppose the federal debt increases at an annual rate of 1% per year. Use the compound interest formula to determine the size of the debt in 10 years and in 50 years. Assume that the current size of the debt (the principal for the compound interest formula) is $13 trillion.

36. **Rising Debt.** Suppose the federal debt increases at an annual rate of 2% per year. Use the compound interest formula to determine the size of the debt in 10 years and in 50 years. Assume that the current size of the debt (the principal for the compound interest formula) is $13 trillion.

37. **Budget Projections.** Consider the budget projection described in Example 4. What are the projected outlays? If the outlays turn out to be 5% higher than the projection and receipts 5% lower than the projection, what is the resulting deficit or surplus?

38. **Budget Projections.** Consider the budget projection described in Example 4. What are the projected outlays? If the outlays turn out to be 10% higher than the projection and receipts 10% lower than the projection, what is the resulting deficit or surplus?

39. **Retiring the Public Debt.** Consider the publicly held debt of $8 trillion in 2009. Use the loan payment formula to determine the annual payments needed to pay this debt off in 10 years. Assume an annual interest rate of 4%.

40. **Retiring the Public Debt.** Consider the publicly held debt of $8 trillion in 2009. Use the loan payment formula to determine the annual payments needed to pay this debt off in 15 years. Assume an annual interest rate of 2%.

41. **National Debt Lottery.** Imagine that, through some political or economic miracle, the gross debt stopped rising. To retire the gross debt, the government decided to have a national lottery. Suppose that every U.S. citizen bought a $1 lottery ticket every week, thereby generating about $300 million in weekly lottery revenue. Because lotteries typically use half their revenue for prizes and lottery operations, half the $300 million, or $150 million, would go toward debt reduction each week. How long would it take to retire the debt through this lottery? Use the 2009 gross debt of $13 trillion.

42. **National Debt Lottery.** Suppose the government hopes to pay off the gross debt of $13 trillion with a national lottery. For the debt to be paid off in 50 years, how much would each citizen have to spend on lottery tickets each year? Assume that half of the lottery revenue goes toward debt reduction and that there are 310 million citizens.

WEB PROJECTS

43. **Federal Budget Deficit.** Use the Web to find the most recent projections of the federal deficit for the next 10 years.

44. **Deficit/Debt and GDP.** In this unit we discussed the deficit and debt in dollar amounts, but most economists believe a more meaningful measure is the deficit or debt as a percentage of the *gross domestic product* (GDP), which is a measure of the total size of the economy. Research the current size of the deficit and debt as a percentage of GDP. How does the current size of the deficit and debt compare to historical values of this percentage?

45. **Debt Problem.** How serious a problem is the gross debt? Use the Web to find arguments on both sides of this question. Summarize the arguments and state your own opinion.

46. **Social Security Problems.** Using information available on the Web, research the current status of the Social Security trust fund and potential future problems in paying out benefits. For example, when is the fund projected to start paying out more than it takes in each year? Write a one- to two-page report that summarizes your findings.

47. **Social Security Solutions.** Research various proposals for solving the problems with Social Security. Choose one proposal that you think is worthwhile and write a one- to two-page report summarizing it and describing why you think it is a good idea.

48. **Privatizing Social Security.** One proposal for saving the Social Security program is privatization—removing it from the government and running it like a for-profit business. Find an argument for and an argument against privatization of Social Security. Summarize each argument and discuss which case you think is stronger.

IN YOUR WORLD

49. **Federal Budget.** Choose one of the many current news stories concerning federal finances. Summarize the story and the issues involved.

50. **Social Security.** Find a news article that concerns either the present or the future state of the Social Security system. Briefly summarize the article and interpret it in light of what you learned in this unit.

51. **Relying on Projections.** Find a news story that describes how Congress or the President is relying on projections several years into the future to make a budget today. Report on how the uncertainty in the projections is being dealt with, and discuss whether the decisions are being made wisely.

CHAPTER 4 Summary

UNIT | **KEY TERMS** | **KEY IDEAS AND SKILLS**

4A

Key terms: budget; cash flow

Understand the importance of controlling your finances.
Know how to make a budget.
Be aware of factors that help determine whether your spending patterns make sense for your situation.

4B

Key terms: principal; simple interest; compound interest; annual percentage rate (APR); annual percentage yield (APY); variable definitions: A, P, i, N, n, Y

General form of the compound interest formula:

$$A = P \times (1 + i)^N$$

Compound interest formula for interest paid once a year:

$$A = P \times (1 + \text{APR})^Y$$

Compound interest formula for interest paid n times a year:

$$A = P\left(1 + \frac{\text{APR}}{n}\right)^{(nY)}$$

Compound interest formula for continuous compounding:

$$A = P \times e^{(\text{APR} \times Y)}$$

Know when and how to apply these formulas.

4C

Key terms: savings plan; total return; annual return; mutual fund; investment considerations (liquidity, risk, return); bond characteristics (face value, coupon rate, maturity rate, current yield)

Savings plan formula:

$$A = \text{PMT} \times \frac{\left[\left(1 + \frac{\text{APR}}{n}\right)^{(nY)} - 1\right]}{\left(\frac{\text{APR}}{n}\right)}$$

Return on investments:

$$\text{total return} = \frac{(A - P)}{P}$$

$$\text{annual return} = \left(\frac{A}{P}\right)^{(1/Y)} - 1$$

Understand investment types: stock, bond, cash.
Read financial tables for stocks, bonds, and mutual funds.
Remember important principles of investing, such as
- Higher returns usually involve higher risk.
- High commissions and fees can dramatically lower returns.
- Build an appropriately diversified portfolio.

4D

Key terms: installment loan; mortgages (down payment, closing cost, points, fixed rate mortgage, adjustable rate mortgage)

Loan payment formula:

$$\text{PMT} = \frac{P \times \left(\frac{\text{APR}}{n}\right)}{\left[1 - \left(1 + \frac{\text{APR}}{n}\right)^{(-nY)}\right]}$$

Understand the uses and dangers of credit cards.
Understand strategies for early payment of loans.
Understand considerations in choosing a mortgage.

(*Continued*)

UNIT	KEY TERMS	KEY IDEAS AND SKILLS
4E	gross income adjusted gross income exemptions, deductions, credits taxable income filing status progressive income tax marginal tax rates Social Security, FICA, self-employment tax capital gains	**Define** different types of income as they apply to taxes. **Use** tax rate tables to calculate taxes. **Distinguish between** tax credits and tax deductions. **Calculate** FICA taxes. **Be aware of** special tax rates for dividends and capital gains. **Understand** the benefits of tax-deferred savings plans.

4F	receipts, outlays
	net income
	  surplus
	  deficit
	debt
	mandatory outlays
	discretionary outlays
	publicly held debt
	gross debt
	on budget, off budget
	unified budget
		Distinguish between a deficit and a debt.
		Understand basic principles of the federal budget.
		Distinguish between publicly held debt and gross debt.
		Be familiar with major issues concerning the future of Social Security.

UNIT 5A

Fundamentals of Statistics: We discuss how statistical studies are conducted, with emphasis on the importance of sampling.

UNIT 5B

Should You Believe a Statistical Study? We develop eight useful guidelines for evaluating statistical claims.

UNIT 5C

Statistical Tables and Graphs: We investigate basic tables and graphs, including frequency tables, bar graphs, pie charts, histograms, and line charts.

UNIT 5D

Graphics in the Media: News media go well beyond the basics with fancy statistical graphics. We explore common types of media graphics.

UNIT 5E

Correlation and Causality: One of the most important uses of statistics is to identify cause-and-effect relationships. We investigate how to interpret correlations and how to decide whether a correlation is the result of causality.

5

Statistical thinking will one day be as necessary for efficient citizenship as the ability to read and write.

—H. G. Wells

Statistical Reasoning

Is your drinking water safe? Do most people approve of the President's tax plan? How much is the cost of health care rising? These questions and thousands more like them can be answered only through statistical studies. Indeed, statistical information appears in the news every day, making the ability to understand and reason with statistics crucial to modern life.

ACTIVITY Cell Phones and Driving

Use this activity to gain a sense of the kinds of problems this chapter will enable you to study. Try working through it before you begin the chapter, then return to it after you've learned the chapter material.

Is it safe to use a cell phone while driving? The science of statistics provides a way to approach this question, and the results of many studies now suggest that the answer is no. A study by the Harvard Center for Risk Analysis, for example, found that cell phone use (either talking or texting) is involved in about 6% of all automobile crashes in the United States—which adds up to more than 600,000 crashes, 300,000 injuries, and nearly 3000 deaths each year. As preparation for your study of statistics in this chapter, work individually or in groups to research the issues raised in the following questions. Discuss your findings.

1. Think about the physical process of using a cell phone while driving (either talking or texting), and list possible reasons why it could be distracting and cause accidents.
2. When the link between cell phone use and accidents was first discovered, many people thought the problem could be solved by mandating that only hands-free cell phone systems be allowed in cars, and many localities, states, and nations enacted laws allowing drivers to use only hands-free systems. However, more recent studies show that hands-free systems are nearly as dangerous as regular cell phones—and that talking on a hands-free system is much more dangerous than talking to a passenger sitting next to you. Why don't hands-free systems eliminate the danger of cell phone use while driving?
3. The fact that many accidents involve cell phone use does not necessarily prove that the use of cell phones *caused* the accidents. What kinds of studies might prove that cell phone use is the cause of accidents? How could such studies be conducted? Look for results of actual studies of this issue.
4. Find some actual data, in either tables or graphs, that shed light on the issue of cell phones and driving. Explain what the data show. Do you think the data are summarized clearly, or could they have been displayed in a better way?
5. Have you personally ever had either an accident or a close call in which you think a cell phone played a role? If so, how confident are you that the cell phone use was responsible?
6. Statistical studies are most useful when they lead to intelligent action. Given the apparent link between cell phone use and driving, what do *you* think should be done about the issue? Defend your opinion.

UNIT 5A Fundamentals of Statistics

The subject of statistics plays a major role in modern society. It's used to determine whether a new drug is effective in treating cancer. It's involved when agricultural inspectors check the safety of the food supply. It's used in every opinion poll and survey. In business, it's used for market research. Sports statistics are part of daily conversation for millions of people. Indeed, you'll be hard-pressed to think of a topic that is not linked in some way to statistics.

But what *is* (or *are*) statistics? There are two answers, because the term *statistics* can be either singular or plural. When it is singular, *statistics* refers to the *science* of statistics.

The science of statistics helps us collect, organize, and interpret *data,* which are numbers or other pieces of information about some topic. When it is plural, the word *statistics* refers to the data themselves, especially those that describe or summarize something. For example, if there are 30 students in your class and they range in age from 17 to 64, the numbers "30 students," "17 years," and "64 years" are statistics that describe your class.

BY THE WAY

You'll sometimes hear the word *data* used as a singular synonym for *information,* but technically the word *data* is plural. One piece of information is called a *datum,* and two or more pieces are called *data.*

TWO DEFINITIONS OF STATISTICS

- Statistics is the *science* of collecting, organizing, and interpreting data.
- Statistics are the *data* that describe or summarize something.

How Statistics Works

Statistical studies are conducted in many different ways and for many different purposes, but they all share a few characteristics. To get the basic ideas, consider the *Nielsen ratings,* which are used to estimate the numbers of people watching various television shows. These ratings are used, for example, to determine the most popular television show of the week.

Suppose the Nielsen ratings tell you that *American Idol* was last week's most popular show, with 22 million viewers. You probably know that no one actually counted all 22 million people. But you may be surprised to learn that the Nielsen ratings are based on the television-viewing habits of people in only about 5000 homes. To understand how Nielsen can draw a conclusion about millions of Americans from only a few thousand homes, we need to investigate the principles behind statistical research.

Nielsen's goal is to draw conclusions about the viewing habits of all Americans. In the language of statistics, we say that Nielsen is interested in the **population** of all Americans. The characteristics of this population that Nielsen seeks to learn—such as the number of people watching each television show—are called **population parameters.** Note that, although we usually think of a population as a group of people, in statistics a population can be any kind of group—people, animals, or things. For example, in a study of college costs, the population might be *all colleges and universities,* and the population parameters might include prices for tuition, fees, and housing.

Nielsen seeks to learn about the population of all Americans by studying a much smaller **sample** of Americans in depth. More specifically, Nielsen has devices (called "people meters") attached to televisions in about 5000 homes, so the people who live in these homes make up the sample of Americans that Nielsen studies. The individual measurements that Nielsen collects from the sample, such as who is watching each show at each time, constitute the *raw data.* Nielsen then consolidates these raw data into a set of numbers that characterize the sample, such as the percentage of young male viewers watching *American Idol.* These numbers are called **sample statistics.**

BY THE WAY

Arthur C. Nielsen founded his company and invented market research in 1923. He began producing ratings for radio programs in 1942 and added television ratings in the 1960s. Nielsen's company now also tracks media on the Internet.

DEFINITIONS

The **population** in a statistical study is the *complete* set of people or things being studied. The **sample** is the subset of the population from which the raw data are actually obtained.

Population parameters are specific characteristics of the population that a statistical study is designed to estimate. **Sample statistics** are numbers or observations that summarize the raw data.

Example 1 Population and Sample

For each of the following cases, describe the population, sample, population parameters, and sample statistics.

a. Agricultural inspectors for Jefferson County measure the levels of residue from three common pesticides on 25 ears of corn from each of the 104 corn-producing farms in the county.
b. Anthropologists determine the average brain size of early Neandertals in Europe by studying skulls found at three sites in southern Europe.

Solution

a. The inspectors seek to learn about the population of all ears of corn grown in the county. They do this by studying a sample that consists of 25 ears from each farm. The population parameters are the average levels of residue from the three pesticides on all corn grown in the county. The sample statistics describe the average levels of residue that are actually measured on the corn in the sample.
b. The anthropologists seek to learn about the population of all early Neandertals in Europe. Specifically, they seek to determine the average brain size of all Neandertals, which is the population parameter in this case. The sample consists of the relatively few individual Neandertals whose skulls are found at the three sites. The sample statistic is the average brain size (skull size) of the individuals in the sample.

Now try Exercises 15–20.

The Process of a Statistical Study

Because Nielsen does not study the entire population of all Americans, it cannot actually measure any population parameters. Instead, the company tries to infer reasonable values for population parameters from the sample statistics (which it *did* measure).

The process of inference is simple in principle, though it must be carried out with great care. For example, suppose Nielsen finds that 7% of the people in its sample watched *American Idol*. If this sample accurately represents the entire population of all Americans, then Nielsen can infer that *approximately* 7% of all Americans watched the show. In other words, the sample statistic of 7% is used as an estimate for the population parameter. (By using statistical techniques that we'll discuss in Unit 6D, Nielsen can also estimate the uncertainty in the inferred population parameters.)

Once Nielsen has estimates of the population parameters, it can draw general conclusions about what Americans were watching. The process used by Nielsen Media Research is similar to that used in many statistical studies, summarized in the box below. Figure 5.1 summarizes the general relationships among a population, a sample, the sample statistics, and the population parameters.

BY THE WAY

Statisticians often divide their subject into two major branches. *Descriptive statistics* is the branch that deals with *describing* data in the form of tables, graphs, or sample statistics. *Inferential statistics* is the branch that deals with *inferring* (or estimating) population characteristics from sample data.

BASIC STEPS IN A STATISTICAL STUDY

1. State the goal of your study precisely. That is, determine the population you want to study and exactly what you'd like to learn about it.
2. Choose a representative sample from the population.
3. Collect raw data from the sample and summarize these data by finding sample statistics of interest.
4. Use the sample statistics to infer the population parameters.
5. Draw conclusions: Determine what you learned and whether you achieved your goal.

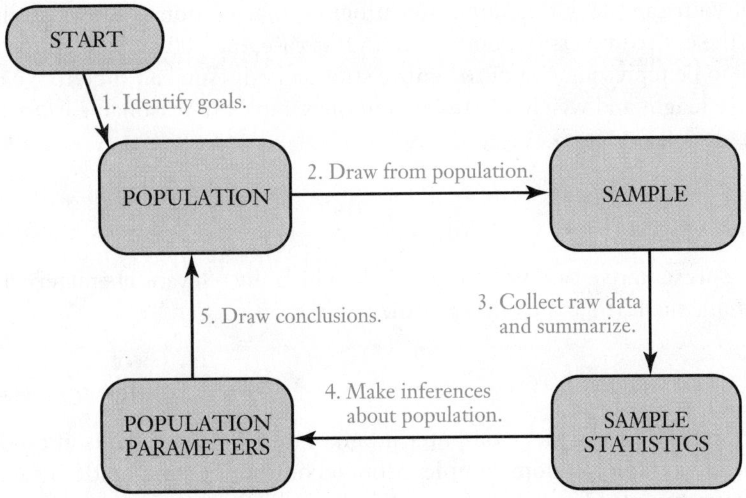

FIGURE 5.1 Elements of a statistical study.

Example 2 Unemployment Survey

Each month, the U.S. Labor Department surveys 60,000 households to determine characteristics of the U.S. work force. One population parameter of interest is the U.S. unemployment rate, defined as the percentage of people who are unemployed among all those who are either employed or actively seeking employment. Describe how the five basic steps of a statistical study apply to this research.

Solution The steps apply as follows.

Step 1. The goal of the research is to learn about the employment (or unemployment) within the population of all Americans who are either employed or actively seeking employment.

Step 2. The Labor Department chooses a sample consisting of people employed or seeking employment in 60,000 households.

Step 3. The Labor Department asks questions of the people in the sample, and their responses constitute the raw data for the research. The Department then consolidates these data into sample statistics, such as the percentage of people in the sample who are unemployed.

Step 4. Based on the sample statistics, the Labor Department makes estimates of the corresponding population parameters, such as the unemployment rate for the entire United States.

Step 5. The Labor Department draws conclusions based on the population parameters and other information. For example, it might use the current and past unemployment rates to draw conclusions about whether jobs have been created or lost.

Now try Exercises 21–26.

BY THE WAY

According to the Labor Department, someone who is not working is not necessarily unemployed. For example, stay-at-home moms and dads are not counted among the unemployed unless they are actively trying to find a job, and people who had been trying to find work but gave up in frustration are not counted as unemployed.

Seasonally Adjusted U.S. Unemployment Rate (percent)

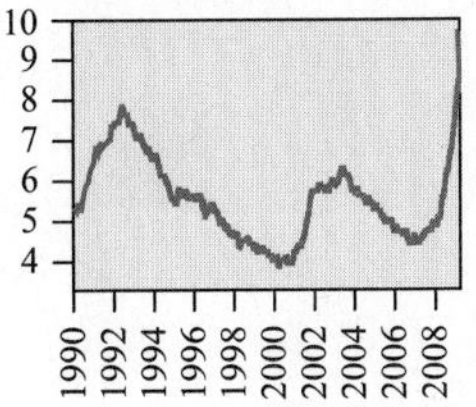

Choosing a Sample

Choosing a sample may be the most important step in any statistical study. If the sample fairly represents the population as a whole, then it's reasonable to make inferences from the sample to the population. But if the sample is *not* representative, then there's little hope of drawing accurate conclusions about the population.

Suppose you want to determine the average height and weight of students at a large university by measuring the heights and weights of a sample of 100 students. A sample consisting only of members of the football and basketball teams would not be reliable, because these athletes tend to be larger than most students. In contrast, suppose you

USING TECHNOLOGY

Random Numbers

Many calculators have a key that generates random numbers, and a Web search will turn up many random number generators. In Excel, the RAND function generates uniformly distributed random numbers between 0 and 1.

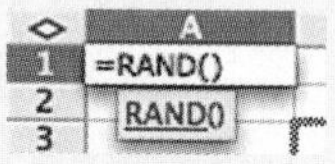

Alternatively, the Excel function RANDBETWEEN generates a random integer between any two given numbers; the example below shows how to generate random numbers between 1 and 25.

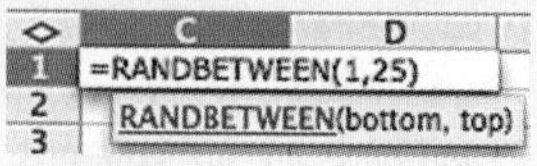

select your sample with a computer program that randomly draws student numbers from the entire university population. In this case, the 100 students in your sample are likely to be representative of the entire student body. You can therefore expect that the average height and weight of students in the sample are reasonable estimates of the averages for all students.

DEFINITION

A **representative sample** is a sample in which the relevant characteristics of the sample members match those of the population.

Now try Exercises 27–28.

A sample drawn with a computer program that selects students at random is an example of a **simple random sample.** More technically, simple random sampling means that every sample of a particular size has the same chance of being selected. In the case of the student sample, every set of 100 students has an equal chance of being selected by the computer program.

Simple random sampling is usually the best way to choose a representative sample. However, it is not always practical or necessary, so other sampling techniques are sometimes used. The following box summarizes four of the most common sampling techniques, and Figure 5.2 illustrates the ideas.

COMMON SAMPLING METHODS

Simple random sampling: We choose a sample of items in such a way that every sample of a given size has an equal chance of being selected.

Systematic sampling: We use a simple system to choose the sample, such as selecting every 10th or every 50th member of the population.

Convenience sampling: We use a sample that is convenient to select, such as people who happen to be in the same classroom.

Stratified sampling: We use this method when we are concerned about differences among subgroups, or *strata,* within a population. We first identify the subgroups and then draw a simple random sample within each subgroup. The total sample consists of all the samples from the individual subgroups.

Regardless of what type of sampling is used, always keep the following two key ideas in mind:

- No matter how a sample is chosen, the study can be successful only if the sample is representative of the population.
- Even if a sample is chosen in the best possible way, it is still just a sample (as opposed to the entire population). We can never be *sure* that a sample is representative of the population. In general, a larger sample is more likely to be representative of the population, as long as it is chosen well.

Example 3 Sampling Methods

Identify the type of sampling used in each of the following cases, and comment on whether the sample is likely to be representative of the population.

a. You are conducting a survey of students in a dormitory. You choose your sample by knocking on the door of every 10th room.

Simple Random Sampling:
Every sample of the same size has an equal chance of being selected. Computers are often used to generate random telephone numbers.

Convenience Sampling:
Use results that are readily available.

Systematic Sampling:
Select every *k*th member.

Stratified Sampling:
Partition the population into at least two strata, then draw a sample from each.

FIGURE 5.2 Common sampling techniques.

b. To survey opinions on a possible property tax increase, a research firm randomly draws the addresses of 150 homeowners from a public list of all homeowners.
c. Agricultural inspectors for Jefferson County check the levels of residue from three common pesticides on 25 ears of corn from each of the 104 corn-producing farms in the county.
d. Anthropologists determine the average brain size of early Neandertals in Europe by studying skulls found at three sites in southern Europe.

Solution

a. Choosing every 10th room makes this a systematic sample. The sample may be representative, as long as students were randomly assigned to rooms.
b. The records presumably list all homeowners, so drawing randomly from this list produces a simple random sample. It has a good chance of being representative of the population.
c. Each farm may have different pesticide use, so the inspectors consider corn from each farm as a subgroup (stratum) of the full population. By checking 25 ears of corn from each of the 104 farms, the inspectors are using stratified sampling. If the ears are collected randomly on each farm, each set of 25 is likely to be representative of its farm.
d. By studying skulls found at selected sites, the anthropologists are using a convenience sample. They have little choice, because only a few skulls remain from the many Neandertals who once lived in Europe. However, it seems reasonable to assume that these skulls are representative of the larger population.

Now try Exercises 29–34.

BY THE WAY

Neandertals lived between about 100,000 and 30,000 years ago in Eurasia and northern Africa. They were physiologically distinct from modern humans, but scientists are not yet sure whether they represented a separate species or could interbreed with Homo sapiens. Neandertals developed many aspects of culture, including caring for the sick and burying their dead. Skull measurements suggest that Neandertals had larger brains than modern humans.

Watching Out for Bias

Consider a study designed to estimate the average weight of all men at a college. As we discussed earlier, a sample consisting only of football players would *not* be representative of the population with respect to weight. We say that this sample is *biased* because the men in the sample differ in a critical way from "typical" men at the college. More generally, the term **bias** refers to any problem in the design or conduct of a statistical study that tends to favor certain results.

Besides occurring in a poorly chosen sample, bias can arise in many other ways. For example, a researcher may be biased if he or she has a personal stake in the outcome of the study. In that case, the researcher might distort (intentionally or unintentionally) the true meaning of the data. You should always be on the lookout for any type of bias that may affect the results or interpretation of a statistical study. We'll discuss sources of bias further in Unit 5B.

DEFINITION

A statistical study suffers from **bias** if its design or conduct tends to favor certain results.

Time Out to Think

Thinking about issues of bias, explain why television networks use Nielsen to measure ratings rather than doing it themselves.

Types of Statistical Study

Historical Note

Statistics originated with the collection of census and tax data, which are affairs of state. That is why the word *state* is at the root of the word *statistics*.

Broadly speaking, most statistical studies fall into one of two categories: observational studies and experiments. Nielsen's studies of television viewing are **observational** because they are designed to *observe* the television-viewing behavior of the people in its 5000 sample homes. Note that observational studies may still involve some interaction. For example, an opinion poll is observational, even though researchers may conduct in-depth interviews, because the poll's goal is to learn (observe) people's opinions, not to change them. Similarly, a study in which individuals in the sample are weighed is also observational, because the measurement process records (observes) but does not change a person's weight.

In contrast, consider a medical study designed to test whether large doses of vitamin C can help prevent colds. To conduct this study, the researchers must ask some people in the sample to take large doses of vitamin C. This type of statistical study is called an **experiment**, because some participants receive a treatment (in this case, vitamin C) that they would not otherwise receive.

TWO BASIC TYPES OF STATISTICAL STUDY

1. In an **observational study**, researchers observe or measure characteristics of the sample members but do not attempt to influence or modify these characteristics.
2. In an **experiment**, researchers apply a treatment to some or all of the sample members and then look to see whether the treatment has any effects.

It is difficult to determine whether an experimental treatment works unless you compare groups that receive the treatment to groups that don't. In the vitamin C study, for example, researchers might create two groups of people: a **treatment group** that takes large doses of vitamin C and a **control group** that does not take vitamin C. The researchers can then look for differences in the numbers of colds among people in the two groups. Having a control group is usually crucial to interpreting the results of experiments.

In an experiment, it is very important for the treatment and control groups to be alike in all respects except for the treatment. For example, if the treatment group consisted of active people with good diets and the control group consisted of sedentary people with poor diets, we could not attribute any differences in colds to vitamin C alone. To avoid this type of problem, assignments to the control and treatment groups must be done randomly.

With proper treatment, a cold can be cured in a week. Left to itself, it may linger for seven days.

—A medical folk saying

TREATMENT AND CONTROL GROUPS

The **treatment group** in an experiment is the group of sample members who receive the treatment being tested.

The **control group** in an experiment is the group of sample members who do *not* receive the treatment being tested.

It is important for the treatment and control groups to be selected randomly and to be alike in all respects except for the treatment.

Time Out to Think

Consider a computer function that generates random numbers between 0 and 100. How could you use this function to assign participants in an experiment to the treatment and control groups?

The Placebo Effect and Blinding

For experiments involving people, using a treatment and a control group might not be enough to get reliable results. The problem is that people can be affected by their beliefs as well as by real treatments. For example, stress and other psychological factors have been shown to affect resistance to colds. If people taking vitamin C get fewer colds than people who don't, we can't conclude that the vitamin C was responsible. It might be that people stayed healthier because they believed that vitamin C works. Therefore, people in the control group should be given a **placebo**—in this case, pills that look like vitamin C pills but don't actually contain vitamin C. As long as the participants don't know whether they are in the treatment or control group (that is, whether they got the real pills or the placebo), any effect arising from psychological factors—known as a **placebo effect**—should affect both groups equally. Then, if people in the vitamin C group get fewer colds than people in the control group, we have evidence that vitamin C really works.

BY THE WAY

The placebo effect can be surprisingly powerful. Consider a drug now used to combat balding, which was tested on balding men. The drug maker was pleased to learn that 86% of the men receiving the drug either stopped balding or grew new hair. But remarkably, so did 42% of the men who received the placebo! In other studies, as many as 75% of participants receiving a placebo have actually improved.

DEFINITIONS

A **placebo** lacks the active ingredients of a treatment being tested in a study, but is identical in appearance to the treatment. Thus, study participants cannot distinguish the placebo from the real treatment.

The **placebo effect** refers to the situation in which patients improve simply because they believe they are receiving a useful treatment.

In statistical terminology, the practice of keeping people in the dark about who is in the treatment group and who is in the control group is called **blinding.** A **single-blind** experiment is one in which the participants don't know which group they belong to, but the experimenters (the people administering the treatment) do know. Using a placebo is one way to create a single-blind experiment. Sometimes, a single-blind experiment can still be unreliable if the experimenters can subtly influence outcomes. For example, in an experiment that involves interviews, the experimenters might speak differently to people who received the real treatment than to those who received the placebo. This type of problem can be avoided by making the experiment **double-blind**, which means neither the participants nor the experimenters know who belongs to each group. (Of course, someone must keep track of the two groups in order to evaluate the results at the end. In typical double-blind experiments, researchers hire experimenters to make any necessary contact with the participants.)

BLINDING IN EXPERIMENTS

An experiment is **single-blind** if the participants do not know whether they are members of the treatment group or members of the control group, but the experimenters do know.

An experiment is **double-blind** if neither the participants nor the experimenters (people administering the treatment) know who belongs to the treatment group and who belongs to the control group.

Example 4 What's Wrong with This Experiment?

For each of the experiments described below, identify any problems and explain how the problems could have been avoided.

a. A chiropractor wants to know if his adjustments relieve back pain. He performs adjustments on 25 patients with back pain. Afterward, 18 of the patients say they feel better. He concludes that the adjustments are an effective treatment.

b. A new drug for attention deficit disorder (ADD) is supposed to make the affected children more polite. Randomly selected children suffering from ADD are divided into treatment and control groups. Those in the control group receive a placebo that looks just like the real drug. The experiment is single-blind. Experimenters interview the children one-on-one to decide whether they became more polite.

Solution

a. The 25 patients who receive adjustments represent a treatment group, but this study lacks a control group. The patients may be feeling better because of a placebo effect rather than any real effect of the adjustments. The chiropractor might have improved his study by hiring an actor to do a fake adjustment (one that feels like a real manipulation, but doesn't actually conform to chiropractic guidelines) on a control group. Then he could have compared the results in the two groups to see whether a placebo effect was involved.

b. Because the experimenters know which children received the real drug, during the interviews they may inadvertently speak differently or interpret behavior differently with these children. In that case, their conclusions might not be valid. The experiment should have been double-blind, so that the experimenters conducting the interviews would not have known which children received the real drug and which children received the placebo.

Now try Exercises 35–40.

Case-Control Studies

Sometimes it may be impractical or unethical to conduct an experiment. For example, suppose we want to study how alcohol consumed during pregnancy affects newborn

DILBERT reprinted by permission of United Feature Syndicate, Inc.

babies. Because it is already known that alcohol can be harmful during pregnancy, it would be unethical to divide a sample of pregnant mothers randomly into two groups and then force the members of one group to consume alcohol. However, we may be able to conduct a **case-control study** (sometimes called a *retrospective study*), in which the participants naturally form groups by choice. In this example, the **cases** consist of mothers who consume alcohol during pregnancy *by choice,* and the **controls** consist of mothers who choose *not* to consume alcohol.

A case-control study is observational because the researchers do not change the behavior of the participants. But it also resembles an experiment because the cases effectively represent a treatment group and the controls represent a control group.

DEFINITIONS

A **case-control study** is an observational study that resembles an experiment because the sample naturally divides into two (or more) groups. The participants who engage in the behavior under study form the **cases**, which makes them like a treatment group in an experiment. The participants who do not engage in the behavior are the **controls**, making them like a control group in an experiment.

Example 5 Which Type of Study?

For each of the following questions, what type of statistical study is most likely to lead to an answer? Why?

a. What is the average income of stock brokers?
b. Do seat belts save lives?
c. Can lifting weights improve runners' times in a 10-kilometer race?
d. Can a new herbal remedy reduce the severity of colds?

Solution

a. An *observational study* can tell us the average income of stock brokers. We need only survey (observe) the brokers.
b. It would be unethical to do an experiment in which some people were told to wear seat belts and others were told *not* to wear them. Instead, we can conduct an observational *case-control study.* Some people choose to wear seat belts (the cases) and others choose not to wear them (the controls). By comparing the death rates in accidents between cases and controls, we can learn whether seat belts save lives. (They do.)
c. We need an *experiment* to determine whether lifting weights can improve runners' 10K times. One group of runners will be put on a weight-lifting program, and a control group will be asked to stay away from weights. We must try to ensure that all

other aspects of their training are similar. Then we can see whether the runners in the lifting group improve their times more than those in the control group. Note that we cannot use blinding in this experiment because there is no way to prevent participants from knowing whether they are lifting weights.

d. We should use a *double-blind experiment,* in which some participants get the actual remedy while others get a placebo. We need double-blind conditions because the severity of a cold may be affected by mood or other factors that experimenters might inadvertently influence. **Now try Exercises 41–46.**

Surveys and Opinion Polls

BY THE WAY

Politicians and marketers often pretend they are trying to conduct a true opinion poll or survey when, in fact, they are deliberately trying to get particular results. These types of surveys are called *push polls* because they try to "push" people's opinions.

Surveys and opinion polls may be the most common types of statistical study, and we must be very careful when we interpret them. Fortunately, survey and poll results usually include something called the **margin of error.**

Suppose a poll finds that 76% of the public supports the President, with a margin of error of 3 percentage points. The 76% is a sample statistic; that is, 76% of the people in a sample said they support the President. The margin of error helps us understand how well this sample statistic is likely to approximate the true population parameter (in this case, the percentage of *all* Americans who support the President). By adding and subtracting the margin of error from the sample statistic, we find a range of values, or a **confidence interval,** *likely* to contain the population parameter. In this case, we add and subtract 3 percentage points to find a confidence interval from 73% to 79%.

DEFINITION

The **margin of error** in a statistical study is used to describe a **confidence interval** that is likely to contain the true population parameter. We find this interval by subtracting and adding the margin of error from the sample statistic obtained in the study. That is, the confidence interval is

from (sample statistic − margin of error)
to (sample statistic + margin of error)

How confident can we be in a poll result? Unless we are told otherwise, we assume that the margin of error is defined to give us 95% confidence that the confidence interval contains the population parameter. We'll discuss the precise meaning of "95% confidence" in Unit 6D, but for now you can think of it as follows: If the poll were repeated 20 times with 20 different samples, 19 of the 20 polls (that is, 95% of the polls) would have a confidence interval that contains the true population parameter.

Example 6 Close Election

An election eve poll finds that 52% of surveyed voters plan to vote for Smith, and she needs a majority (more than 50%) to win without a runoff. The margin of error in the poll is 3 percentage points. Will she win?

Solution We subtract and add the margin of error of 3 percentage points to find a confidence interval

$$\text{from} \quad 52\% - 3\% = 49\% \quad \text{to} \quad 52\% + 3\% = 55\%$$

We can be 95% confident that the actual percentage of people planning to vote for her is between 49% and 55%. Because this confidence interval leaves open the possibility of both a majority and less than a majority, this election is too close to call.

Now try Exercises 47–50.

Time Out to Think

In Example 6, suppose the poll found the candidate had 55% of the vote. Should she be confident of a win?

QUICK QUIZ

Choose the best answer to each of the following questions. Explain your reasoning with one or more complete sentences.

1. You conduct a poll in which you randomly select 1000 registered voters from Texas and ask if they approve of the job their governor is doing. The *population* for this study is

   a. all registered voters in the state of Texas.

   b. the 1000 people that you interview.

   c. the governor of Texas.

2. Results of the poll described in question 1 would most likely suffer from *bias* if you chose the participants from

   a. all registered voters in Texas.

   b. all people with a Texas driver's license.

   c. people who donated money to the governor's campaign.

3. When we say that a sample is *representative* of the population, we mean that

   a. the results found for the sample are similar to those we would find for the entire population.

   b. the sample is very large.

   c. the sample was chosen in the best possible way.

4. Consider an experiment designed to test whether cash incentives improve school attendance. The researcher chooses two groups of 100 high school students. She offers one group $10 for every week of perfect attendance. She tells the other group that they are part of an experiment but does not give them any incentive. The students who do not receive an incentive represent

   a. the treatment group.

   b. the control group.

   c. the observation group.

5. The experiment described in question 4 is

   a. single-blind. b. double-blind. c. not blind.

6. The purpose of a *placebo* is

   a. to prevent participants from knowing whether they belong to the treatment group or the control group.

   b. to distinguish between the cases and the controls in a case-control study.

   c. to determine whether diseases can be cured without any treatment.

7. If we see a *placebo effect* in an experiment to test a new treatment designed to cure warts, we know that

   a. the experiment was not properly double-blind.

   b. the experimental groups were too small.

   c. the warts of those in the control group were cured.

8. An experiment is single-blind if

   a. it lacks a treatment group.

   b. it lacks a control group.

   c. the participants do not know whether they belong to the treatment or the control group.

9. Poll X predicts that Powell will receive 49% of the vote, while Poll Y predicts that he will receive 53% of the vote. Both polls have a margin of error of 3 percentage points. What can you conclude?

   a. One of the two polls must have been conducted poorly.

   b. The two polls are consistent with each other.

   c. Powell will receive 51% of the vote.

10. A survey reveals that 12% of Americans believe Elvis is still alive, with a margin of error of 4 percentage points. The confidence interval for this poll is

    a. from 10% to 14%.

    b. from 8% to 16%.

    c. from 4% to 20%.

Exercises 5A

REVIEW QUESTIONS

1. Why do we say that the term *statistics* has two meanings? Describe both meanings.
2. Define the terms *population, sample, population parameter,* and *sample statistics* as they apply to statistical studies.
3. Describe the five basic steps in a statistical study, and give an example of their application.
4. Why is it so important that a statistical study use a representative sample? Briefly describe four common sampling methods.

5. What is bias? How can it affect a statistical study? Give examples of several forms of bias.
6. Describe and contrast observational studies and experiments. What do we mean by the treatment group and control group in an experiment? What do we mean by the cases and controls in an observational case-control study?
7. What is a placebo? Describe the placebo effect and how it can make experiments difficult to interpret. How can making an experiment single-blind or double-blind help?
8. What is meant by the margin of error in a survey or opinion poll? How is it used to identify a confidence interval?

DOES IT MAKE SENSE?

Decide whether each of the following statements makes sense (or is clearly true) or does not make sense (or is clearly false). Explain your reasoning.

9. In my experimental study, I used a sample that was larger than the population.
10. I followed all the guidelines for sample selection carefully, yet my sample still did not reflect the characteristics of the population.
11. I wanted to test the effects of vitamin C on colds, so I gave the treatment group vitamin C and gave the control group vitamin D.
12. I don't believe the results of the experiment, because the results were based on interviews but the study was not double-blind.
13. The pre-election poll found that Kennedy would get 58% of the vote, with a margin of error of 4%, but he ended up losing the election.
14. By choosing my sample carefully, I can make a good estimate of the average height of Americans by measuring the heights of only 500 people.

BASIC SKILLS & CONCEPTS

15–20: Population and Sample. For the following studies, describe the population, sample, population parameters, and sample statistics.

15. In order to gauge public opinion on how to handle Iran's growing nuclear program, the Pew Research Center surveyed 1001 Americans by telephone.
16. Astronomers typically determine the distance to a galaxy (a huge collection of billions of stars) by measuring the distances to just a few stars within it and taking the mean (average) of these distance measurements.
17. An AP/CBS telephone poll of 998 randomly selected Americans revealed that 6 in 10 people believe there has been progress in finding a cure for cancer in the last 30 years.
18. A Gallup poll of 1051 American adults shows that 32% of Americans say they have been spending less in recent months and 27% say they are saving more now and intend to make this their new, normal pattern in the years ahead.
19. In a *USA Today*/Gallup poll of 1027 Americans surveyed by cell phones and land lines, 62% of those who responded said that there should be an investigation of anti-terror tactics used during the Bush administration.
20. The Higher Education Research Institute conducts an annual study of attitudes of incoming college students by surveying approximately 241,000 first-year students at 340 colleges and universities. There are approximately 1.4 million first-year college students in this country.

21–26: Steps in a Study. Describe how you would apply the five basic steps of a statistical study to the following issues.

21. You want to determine the average number of hours per week that ninth-graders spend on cell phones.
22. A supermarket manager wants to determine whether the variety of products in her store meets customers' needs.
23. You want to know the percentage of male college students in America who play chess at least once per week.
24. You want to know the typical percentage of the bill that is left as a tip in restaurants.
25. You want to know the average time to failure of batteries in a particular model of laptop computer.
26. You want to know the percentage of high school students who are vegetarians.
27. **Representative Sample?** You want to determine the average percentage of classes skipped by first-year students at a small college during a particular semester. Determine, with an explanation, which of the following samples are likely to be representative and which are not likely to be representative.
    - 100 first-year students who belong to a sorority or fraternity
    - 100 first-year students who play a varsity sport
    - The first 100 first-year students whom you meet at the student union
    - 100 first-year students taking honors humanities courses
28. **Representative Sample?** You want to determine the typical dietary habits of students at a college. Which of the following would make the best sample, and why? Also explain why each of the other choices would *not* make a good sample for this study.
    - Students in a single dormitory
    - Students majoring in public health
    - Students who participate in intercollegiate sports
    - Students enrolled in a required mathematics class

29–34: Identify the Sampling Method. Identify the sampling method (simple random sampling, systematic sampling, convenience sampling, or stratified sampling) in the following studies.

29. An IRS (Internal Revenue Service) auditor randomly selects for audits 30 taxpayers in each of the filing status categories: single, head of household, married filing jointly, and married filing separately.
30. *People* magazine chooses its "25 most beautiful women" by looking at responses from readers who voluntarily mail in a survey printed in the magazine.
31. A study of the use of antidepressants selects 50 participants between the ages of 20 and 29, 50 participants between the ages of 30 and 39, and 50 participants between the ages of 40 and 49.

32. Every 100th computer chip that is produced is given a reliability test.

33. A computer randomly selects 400 names from a list of all registered voters. Those selected are surveyed to predict who will win the election for mayor.

34. A taste test for chips and salsa is conducted at the entrance to a supermarket.

35–40: Type of Study. Determine whether the following studies are observational studies or experiments. If the study is an experiment, identify the control and treatment groups, and discuss whether single- or double-blinding is necessary. If the study is observational, state whether it is a case-control study, and if so, identify the cases and controls.

35. A study at the University of Southern California separated 108 volunteers into groups, based on psychological tests designed to determine how often they lied and cheated. Those with a tendency to lie had different brain structures than those who did not lie (*British Journal of Psychiatry*).

36. A National Cancer Institute study of 716 melanoma patients and 1014 cancer-free patients matched by age, sex, and race found that those having a single large mole had twice the risk of melanoma. Having 10 or more moles was associated with a 12 times greater risk of melanoma (*Journal of the American Medical Association*).

37. In a study done at Boston University, researchers took snapshots of 4000 white adults every four years for 30 years and determined that 9 of 10 men and 7 of 10 women will eventually become overweight (*Annals of Internal Medicine*).

38. A breast cancer study began by asking 25,624 women questions about how they spent their leisure time. The health of these women was tracked over the next 15 years. Those women who said they exercised regularly were found to have lower incidence of breast cancer (*New England Journal of Medicine*).

39. A double-blind drug versus placebo study of 103 patients suffering from tinnitus (the perception of ringing in the ears) demonstrated the effectiveness of ginkgo biloba extract. The ginkgo treatment improved the condition of all the tinnitus patients (*Annals of Otology, Rhinology, and Laryngology*).

40. Using a survey of 35,000 Americans, the Pew Forum on Religion and Public Life determined that between 47 and 59 percent of adults switch their religious affiliation at least once in their lives.

41–46: What Type of Study? What type of statistical study is most likely to lead to an answer to the following questions?

41. Is magnet therapy a more effective way to treat headaches than aspirin or doing nothing at all?

42. Which of eight airlines has the lowest percentage of delayed flights?

43. Which National Football League team has the linemen with the greatest average weight?

44. Which of the leading brands of insect repellent provides the best protection from mosquitoes?

45. Does taking a multivitamin a day reduce the incidence of strokes?

46. Are the Sunday horoscopes in a local newspaper more accurate than the weekday horoscopes?

47–50: Margin of Error. The following summaries of statistical studies give a sample statistic and a margin of error. Find the confidence interval and answer any additional questions.

47. A poll is conducted the day before an election for state senator. There are only two candidates running. The poll shows that 53% of the voters surveyed favor the Republican candidate, with a margin of error of ±2.5 percentage points. Should the Republican plan a victory party? Why or why not?

48. In an NBC News/*Wall Street Journal* poll of 500 adults nationwide, 53% of those surveyed answered *yes* to the question, "Do you favor a law to ban the sale of assault weapons and semiautomatic rifles?" The margin of error was ±4.4 percentage points. Would you claim that a majority of American support such a law?

49. A national survey by the Pew Research Center for the People and the Press of 1521 respondents reached on land lines and cell phones found that the percentage of adults who favor legalized abortion has dropped from 54% a year ago to 46%. The study claimed that the error attributable to sampling is ±3 percentage points. Would you claim that a majority of American oppose legalized abortion?

50. In a survey of 1002 people, 701 (which is 70%) said that they voted in the most recent presidential election (based on data from ICR Research Group). The margin of error for the survey was ±3 percentage points. However, actual voting records show that only 61% of all eligible voters actually did vote. Does this necessarily imply that people lied when they answered the survey?

FURTHER APPLICATIONS

51–54: Experimental Results. Consider the following results of experiments designed to measure the efficacy of a new drug. The new drug was given to participants in the treatment group, while a placebo was given to those in the control group. Discuss whether there is evidence that the treatment is effective.

51. 70% of those in the treatment group showed improvement; 30% of those in the placebo group showed improvement.

52. 45% of those in the treatment group showed improvement; 45% of those in the placebo group showed improvement.

53. 90% of those in the treatment group showed improvement; 50% of those in the placebo group showed improvement.

54. 25% of those in the treatment group showed improvement; 50% of those in the placebo group showed improvement.

55–60: Real Studies. Consider the following statistical studies.

a. Identify the population and the population parameter of interest.

b. Describe the sample and sample statistic for the study.

c. Identify the type of study.

d. Discuss what additional facts you would like to know before you believed the study or acted on the results of the study.

55. A study done at the Center for AIDS and STD at the University of Washington tracked the survival rates of 17,517 asymptomatic

North American patients with HIV who started drug therapy at different points in the progression of the infection. It was discovered that asymptomatic patients who postponed antiretroviral treatment until their disease was more advanced faced a higher risk of dying than those who had initiated drug treatment earlier (*New England Journal of Medicine*).

56. A Fox News poll of 900 registered voters found that 19% of Americans "regift" (give gifts that they received as gifts). Women (21%) are more likely to regift than men (16%) and the results are nearly independent of income. The margin of error was ±3 percentage points.

57. One hundred people in the 60–70 and 71–82 age categories were given cognitive tests. It was discovered that those participants who were given a suggestion that their age might affect their performance on the test actually did worse on the test (*Experimental Aging Research*).

58. The Pew Research Center asked 1546 adult Americans whether humans would land on Mars within the next 50 years; 76% of these people said either "definitely yes" or "probably yes." The margin of error for the poll was ±2.5 percentage points.

59. A survey of 16,000 adolescents and a review of smoking laws in 36 states showed that rigorous enforcement of laws on tobacco sales led to a 20.8% decrease in the rate at which 10th-graders became regular smokers (*BMC Public Health*).

60. In a CBS/*New York Times* telephone poll, 973 adult Americans responded to the following question.

> *As you may know, for the past seven years the United States has been holding a number of suspected terrorists at a US military prison in Guantanamo Bay, Cuba. Based on what you have heard or read, do you think the US should continue to operate the prison, or do you think the US should close the prison and transfer the prisoners somewhere else?*

Forty-seven percent said the prison should continue to operate, 44% said the prison should be closed, and 9% said they had no opinion.

WEB PROJECTS

61. **Current Nielsen Ratings.** Find the Nielsen ratings for the past week. What were the three most popular television shows? Explain both the rating and the share for each show.

62. **Attitude Update.** The Pew Research Center for the People and the Press studies public attitudes toward the press, politics, and public policy issues. Go to the center's Web site and find the latest survey about attitudes. Write a one-page summary of what Pew surveyed, how it conducted the survey, and what it found.

63. **Labor Statistics.** Use the Bureau of Labor Statistics Web page to learn about its monthly survey. Choose one aspect of the survey, such as how the sample is chosen or how it is used to compare unemployment rates over time. Write a short summary of what you learn.

64. **Professional Polling.** Visit the Web site of a national polling organization and report on a recent poll. Write a short description of the poll and its results, commenting on features such as sampling technique, sample size, and margin of error.

IN YOUR WORLD

65. **Statistics in the News.** Select three news stories from the past week that involve statistics in some way. For each case, write one or two paragraphs describing the role of statistics in the story.

66. **Statistics in Your Major.** Write two to three paragraphs describing the ways in which you think the science of statistics is important in your major field of study. (If you have not chosen a major, answer this question for a major that you are considering.)

67. **Statistics in Sports.** Choose a sport and describe three different statistics commonly tracked by participants in or spectators of the sport. In each case, briefly describe the importance of the statistic to the sport.

68. **Sample and Population.** Find a report in today's news concerning any type of statistical study. What is the population being studied? What is the sample? Why do you think the sample was chosen as it was?

69. **Poor Sampling.** Find a news article about a study that attempts to describe some characteristic of a population, but that you believe involved poor sampling (for example, a sample that was too small or not representative of the population under study). Describe the population, the sample, and what you think was wrong with the sample. Briefly discuss how you think the poor sampling affected the study results.

70. **Good Sampling.** Find a recent news article that describes a statistical study in which the sample was well chosen. Describe the population, the sample, and why you think the sample was a good one.

71. **Margin of Error.** Find a report of a recent survey or poll. Interpret the sample statistic and margin of error quoted for the survey or poll.

TECHNOLOGY EXERCISES

72. **Generating Random Numbers.** Use a calculator or Excel to generate the following sets of random numbers. (Answers are not unique!)

    a. Ten random numbers between 0 and 1

    b. Ten random numbers between 0 and 10

    c. Ten random numbers between 1 and 2

    d. Ten random numbers between 10 and 20

73. **Average Random Numbers.**

    a. Generate ten random numbers between 0 and 1. What is the average of the numbers (divide the sum of the numbers by 10)?

    b. Repeat part a. What is the average?

    c. Without carrying out the calculation, what number do you think the average of 1000 random numbers between 0 and 1 is near?

UNIT 5B Should You Believe a Statistical Study?

Most statistical research is carried out with integrity and care. Nevertheless, statistical research is sufficiently complex that bias can arise in many different ways. We should always examine reports of statistical research carefully, looking for anything that might make us question the results. In this unit, we discuss eight guidelines that can help you answer the question "Should I believe a statistical study?"

Guideline 1: Identify the Goal, Population, and Type of Study

Before evaluating the details of a statistical study, we must know what it is about. Based on what you hear or read, try to answer basic questions such as these:

- What was the goal of the study?
- What was the population under study? Was the population clearly and appropriately defined?
- What type of study was used? Was the type appropriate for the goal?

If you can't find reasonable answers to these questions, it will be difficult to evaluate other aspects of the study.

BY THE WAY

Surveys show that nearly half of Americans believe their horoscopes. However, in controlled experiments, the predictions of horoscopes come true no more often than would be expected by chance.

Example 1 Appropriate Type of Study?

A newspaper reports: "Researchers gave each of the 100 participants their astrological horoscopes, and asked them whether the horoscopes appeared to be accurate. Eighty-five percent of the participants reported that the horoscopes were accurate. The researchers concluded that horoscopes are valid most of the time." Analyze this study according to Guideline 1.

Solution The goal of the study was to determine the validity of horoscopes. Based on the news report, it appears that the study was *observational:* The researchers simply asked the participants about the accuracy of the horoscopes. However, because the accuracy of a horoscope is somewhat subjective, this study should have been a controlled experiment in which some people were given their actual horoscope and others were given a fake horoscope. Then the researchers could have looked for differences between the two groups. Moreover, because researchers could easily influence the results by how they questioned the participants, the experiment should have been double-blind. In summary, the type of study was inappropriate to the goal and its results are meaningless. **Now try Exercises 9–10.**

BY THE WAY

After decades of arguing to the contrary, in 1999 the Philip Morris Company—the world's largest seller of tobacco products—publicly acknowledged that smoking causes lung cancer, heart disease, emphysema, and other serious diseases. Shortly thereafter, Philip Morris changed its name to Altria.

Guideline 2: Consider the Source

Statistical studies are supposed to be objective, but the people who carry them out and fund them may be biased. Always be sure to consider the source of a study and evaluate the potential for biases that might invalidate its conclusions.

Example 2 Is Smoking Healthy?

By 1963, enough research on the health dangers of smoking had accumulated that the Surgeon General of the United States publicly announced that smoking is bad for health. Research done since that time has built further support for this claim. However,

while the vast majority of studies show that smoking is unhealthy, a few studies found no dangers from smoking, and perhaps even health *benefits*. These studies generally were carried out by the Tobacco Research Institute, funded by the tobacco companies. Analyze the Tobacco Research Institute studies according to Guideline 2.

Solution Tobacco companies had a financial interest in minimizing the dangers of smoking. Because the studies carried out at the Tobacco Research Institute were funded by the tobacco companies, there may have been pressure on the researchers to produce results to the companies' liking. This *potential* for bias does not mean their research *was* biased, but the fact that it contradicted virtually all other research on the subject gave reason for concern. **Now try Exercises 11–12.**

Guideline 3: Look for Bias in the Sample

Look for bias that may prevent the sample from being representative of the population. There are two particularly common forms of bias that can affect sample selection.

> **BIAS IN CHOOSING A SAMPLE**
>
> **Selection bias** occurs whenever researchers *select* their sample in a way that tends to make it unrepresentative of the population. For example, a pre-election poll that surveys only registered Republicans has selection bias because it is unlikely to reflect the opinions of all voters.
>
> **Participation bias** occurs primarily with surveys and polls; it arises whenever people *choose* whether to participate. Because people who feel strongly about an issue are more likely to participate, their opinions may not represent the larger population that is less emotionally attached to the issue. (Surveys or polls in which people choose whether to participate are often called *self-selected* or *voluntary response surveys.*)

Historical Note

A young pollster named George Gallup conducted his own survey prior to the 1936 election. Sending postcards to only 3000 randomly selected people, he correctly predicted not only the outcome of the election, but also the outcome of the *Literary Digest* poll to within 1%. Gallup went on to establish a very successful polling organization.

Case Study The 1936 Literary Digest Poll

The *Literary Digest*, a popular magazine of the 1930s, successfully predicted the outcomes of several elections using large polls. In 1936, editors of the *Literary Digest* conducted a particularly large poll in advance of the presidential election. They randomly chose a sample of 10 million people from various lists, including names in telephone books and rosters of country clubs. They mailed a postcard "ballot" to each of these 10 million people. About 2.4 million people returned the postcard ballots. Based on the returned ballots, the editors of the *Literary Digest* predicted that Alf Landon would win the presidency by a margin of 57% to 43% over Franklin Roosevelt. Instead, Roosevelt won with 62% of the popular vote. How did such a large survey go so wrong?

The sample suffered from both selection bias and participation bias. The selection bias arose because the *Literary Digest* chose its 10 million names in ways that favored affluent people. For example, selecting names from telephone books meant choosing only from those who could afford telephones back in 1936. Similarly, country club members are usually quite wealthy. The selection bias favored Landon because he was the Republican, and affluent voters of the 1930s tended to vote for Republican candidates.

The participation bias arose because return of the postcard ballots was voluntary. People who felt most strongly about the election were more likely to be among those who returned their postcard ballots. This bias also tended to favor Landon because he was the challenger—people who did not like President Roosevelt could express their desire for change by returning the postcards. Together, the two forms of bias made the sample results useless, despite the large number of people surveyed.

Example 3 Self-Selected Poll

The television show *Nightline* conducted a poll in which viewers were asked whether the United Nations headquarters should be kept in the United States. Viewers could respond to the poll by paying 50 cents to call a "900" phone number with their opinions. The poll drew 186,000 responses, of which 67% favored moving the United Nations out of the United States. Around the same time, a poll using simple random sampling of 500 people found that 72% wanted the United Nations to *stay* in the United States. Which poll is more likely to be representative of the general opinions of Americans?

Solution The *Nightline* sample suffered from severe participation bias. Not only did viewers choose whether to call in for the survey, but they had to *pay* to participate. This cost made it even more likely that respondents would be those who felt a need for change. Thus, despite its large number of respondents, the *Nightline* survey was too biased to be trusted. In contrast, a simple random sample of 500 people is quite likely to be representative, so the finding of this small survey has a better chance of representing the true opinions of all Americans. **Now try Exercises 13–14.**

BY THE WAY

More than a third of all Americans routinely shut the door or hang up the phone when contacted for a survey, thereby making self-selection a problem for legitimate pollsters. One reason people hang up may be the proliferation of selling under the guise of market research (often called "sugging"), in which a telemarketer pretends you are part of a survey in order to get you to buy something.

Guideline 4: Look for Problems in Defining or Measuring the Variables of Interest

Statistical studies usually attempt to measure *something,* and we call the things being measured the **variables** of interest in the study. The term *variable* simply refers to an item or quantity that can vary or take on different values. For example, variables in the Nielsen ratings include *show being watched* and *number of viewers.*

DEFINITION

A **variable** is any item or quantity that can vary or take on different values. The *variables of interest* in a statistical study are the items or quantities that the study seeks to measure.

Results of a statistical study may be especially difficult to interpret if the variables under study are difficult to define or measure. For example, imagine trying to conduct a study of how exercise affects resting heart rates. The variables of interest would be *amount of exercise* and *resting heart rate.* However, both variables are difficult to define and measure. In the case of *amount of exercise,* it's not clear what the definition covers: Does it include walking to class? Even if we specify the definition, how can we measure *amount of exercise* given that some forms of exercise are more vigorous than others? The following two examples describe real cases in which defining or measuring variables caused problems in statistical studies.

Time Out to Think

How would you measure your resting heart rate? Describe some difficulties in defining and measuring *resting heart rate.*

Example 4 Can Money Buy Love?

A Roper poll reported in *USA Today* involved a survey of the wealthiest 1% of Americans. The survey found that these people would pay an average of \$487,000 for "true love," \$407,000 for "great intellect," \$285,000 for "talent," and \$259,000 for "eternal youth." Analyze this result according to Guideline 4.

Solution The variables in this study are very difficult to define. How, for example, do you define "true love"? And does it mean true love for a day, a lifetime, or something else? Similarly, does the ability to balance a spoon on your nose constitute "talent"? Because the variables are so poorly defined, it's likely that different people interpreted them differently, making the results very difficult to interpret. **Now try Exercise 15.**

Example 5 Illegal Drug Supply

Law enforcement authorities try to stop illegal drugs from entering the country. A commonly quoted statistic is that they succeed in stopping only about 10% to 20% of the drugs entering the United States. Should you believe this statistic?

Solution There are essentially two variables in the study: *quantity of illegal drugs intercepted* and *quantity of illegal drugs NOT intercepted.* It should be relatively easy to measure the quantity of illegal drugs that law enforcement officials intercept. However, because the drugs are illegal, it's unlikely that anyone is reporting the quantity of drugs that are *not* intercepted. How, then, can anyone know that the intercepted drugs are 10% to 20% of the total? In a *New York Times* analysis, a police officer was quoted as saying that his colleagues refer to this type of statistic as "P.F.A.," for "pulled from the air." **Now try Exercise 16.**

Guideline 5: Watch Out for Confounding Variables

Variables that are *not intended* to be part of the study can sometimes make it difficult to interpret results properly. Such variables are often called *confounding* variables, because they confound (confuse) a study's results.

It's not always easy to discover confounding variables. Sometimes they are discovered years after a study was completed, and sometimes they are not discovered at all. Fortunately, confounding variables are sometimes more obvious and can be discovered simply by thinking hard about factors that may have influenced a study's results.

BY THE WAY

Many hardware stores sell simple kits that you can use to test whether radon gas is accumulating in your home. If it is, the problem can be eliminated by installing an appropriate "radon mitigation" system, which usually consists of a fan that blows the radon out from under the house before it can get in.

Example 6 Radon and Lung Cancer

Radon is a radioactive gas produced by natural processes (the decay of uranium) in the ground. The gas can leach into buildings through the foundation and can accumulate in relatively high concentrations if doors and windows are closed. Imagine a study that seeks to determine whether radon gas causes lung cancer by comparing the lung cancer rate in Colorado, where radon gas is fairly common, with the lung cancer rate in Hong Kong, where radon gas is less common. Suppose the study finds that the lung cancer rates are nearly the same. Is it fair to conclude that radon is *not* a significant cause of lung cancer?

Solution The variables under study are *amount of radon* and *lung cancer rate.* However, because smoking can also cause lung cancer, *smoking rate* may be a confounding variable in this study. In particular, the smoking rate in Hong Kong is much higher than the smoking rate in Colorado, so any conclusions about radon and lung cancer must take the smoking rate into account. In fact, careful studies have shown that radon gas *can* cause lung cancer, and the U.S. Environmental Protection Agency (EPA) recommends taking steps to prevent radon from building up indoors.

Now try Exercises 17–18.

Guideline 6: Consider the Setting and Wording in Surveys

Even when a survey is conducted with proper sampling and with clearly defined terms and questions, it's important to watch out for problems in the setting or wording that might produce inaccurate or dishonest responses. Dishonest responses are particularly likely when the survey concerns sensitive subjects, such as personal habits or income. For example, the question "Do you cheat on your income taxes?" is unlikely to elicit honest answers from those who cheat, especially if the setting does not guarantee complete confidentiality.

In other cases, even honest answers may not be accurate if the wording of questions invites bias. Sometimes just the order of the words in a question can affect the outcome. A poll conducted in Germany asked the following two questions:

- *Would you say that traffic contributes more or less to air pollution than industry?*
- *Would you say that industry contributes more or less to air pollution than traffic?*

With the first question, 45% answered traffic and 32% answered industry. With the second question, only 24% answered traffic while 57% answered industry. Simply changing the order of the words *traffic* and *industry* dramatically changed the survey results.

BY THE WAY

People are more likely to choose the item that comes first in a survey because of what psychologists call the *availability error*—the tendency to make judgments based on what is *available* in the mind. Professional polling organizations must be very careful to avoid this problem, sometimes by posing the question to some people in one order and to others in the opposite order.

Example 7 Do You Want a Tax Cut?

The Republican National Committee commissioned a poll to find out whether Americans supported a tax-cut proposal. Asked whether they favored the tax cut, 67% of respondents answered yes. Should we conclude that Americans supported the proposal?

Solution A question like "Do you favor a tax cut?" is biased because it does not give other options (much like the fallacy of *limited choice* discussed in Unit 1A). In fact, an independent poll conducted at the same time gave respondents a list of options for using surplus revenues. This poll found that 31% wanted the money devoted to Social Security, 26% wanted it used to reduce the national debt, and only 18% favored using it for a tax cut. (The remaining 25% of respondents chose a variety of other options.)

Now try Exercises 19–20.

Guideline 7: Check That Results Are Presented Fairly

Even when a statistical study is done well, it may be misrepresented in graphs or concluding statements. Researchers may occasionally misinterpret the results of their own studies or jump to conclusions that are not supported by the results, particularly when they have personal biases toward certain interpretations. In other cases, news reporters or others may misinterpret a survey or jump to unwarranted conclusions that make a story seem more spectacular. Misleading graphs are an especially common problem (see Unit 5D). In general, you should look for inconsistencies between the interpretation of a study (in pictures and words) and any actual data given with it.

Example 8 Does the School Board Need a Statistics Lesson?

The school board in Boulder, Colorado, created a hubbub when it announced that 28% of Boulder school children were reading "below grade level," and hence concluded that methods of teaching reading needed to be changed. The announcement was based on reading tests on which 28% of Boulder school children scored below the national average for their grade. Do these data support the board's conclusion?

Solution The fact that 28% of Boulder children scored below the national average for their grade implies that 72% scored at or above the national average. Thus, the school board's ominous statement about students reading "below grade level" makes sense only if "grade level" means the national average score for a particular grade. This interpretation of "grade level" is curious because it means that half the students in the nation are always below grade level—no matter how high the scores. The conclusion that teaching methods needed to be changed was not justified by these data.

Now try Exercises 21–22.

Guideline 8: Stand Back and Consider the Conclusions

Extraordinary claims require extraordinary evidence.
—Carl Sagan (1934–1996)

Finally, even if a study seems reasonable according to all the previous guidelines, you should stand back and consider the conclusions. Ask yourself questions such as these:

- Did the study achieve its goals?
- Do the conclusions make sense?
- Can you rule out alternative explanations for the results?
- If the conclusions do make sense, do they have any practical significance?

Example 9 Practical Significance

An experiment is conducted in which the weight losses of people who try a new "Fast Diet Supplement" are compared to the weight losses of a control group of people who try to lose weight in other ways. After eight weeks, the results show that the treatment group lost an average of $\frac{1}{2}$ pound more than the control group. Assuming that it has no dangerous side effects, does this study suggest that the Fast Diet Supplement is a good treatment for people wanting to lose weight?

Solution Compared to the average person's body weight, the difference of $\frac{1}{2}$ pound hardly matters at all. Thus, while the statistics in this case may be interesting, they don't seem to have much practical significance.

Now try Exercises 23–26.

SUMMARY Eight Guidelines for Evaluating a Statistical Study

1. Identify the goal of the study, the population considered, and the type of study.
2. Consider the source, particularly with regard to whether the researchers may be biased.
3. Look for bias that may prevent the sample from being representative of the population.
4. Look for problems in defining or measuring the variables of interest, which can make it difficult to interpret results.
5. Watch out for confounding variables that can invalidate the conclusions of a study.
6. Consider the setting and the wording of questions in any survey, looking for anything that might tend to produce inaccurate or dishonest responses.
7. Check that results are presented fairly in graphs and concluding statements, since both researchers and media often create misleading graphics or jump to conclusions that the results do not support.
8. Stand back and consider the conclusions. Did the study achieve its goals? Do the conclusions make sense? Do the results have any practical significance?

QUICK QUIZ

Choose the best answer to each of the following questions. Explain your reasoning with one or more complete sentences.

1. You read about an issue that was the subject of an observational study when clearly it should have been studied with a double-blind experiment. The results from the observational study are therefore
   a. still valid, but a little less reliable.
   b. valid, but only if you first correct for the fact that the wrong type of study was done.
   c. essentially meaningless.
2. A study conducted by the oil company Exxon Mobil shows that there was no lasting damage from a large oil spill in Alaska. This conclusion
   a. is definitely invalid, because the study was biased.
   b. may be correct, but the potential for bias means that you should look very closely at how the conclusion was reached.
   c. could be correct if it falls within the confidence interval of the study.
3. Consider a study designed to learn about the social networks of all college freshmen, in which researchers randomly interviewed students living in on-campus dormitories. The way this sample was chosen means the study will suffer from
   a. selection bias.
   b. participation bias.
   c. confounding variables.
4. The show *American Idol* selects winners based on votes cast by anyone who wants to vote. This means that the winner
   a. is the person most Americans want to win.
   b. may or may not be the person most Americans want to win, because the voting is subject to participation bias.
   c. may or may not be the person most Americans want to win, because the voting should have been double-blind.
5. Consider an experiment in which you measure the weights of 6-year-olds. The variable of interest in this study is
   a. the size of the sample.
   b. the weights of 6-year-olds.
   c. the ages of the children under study.
6. Consider a survey in which 1000 people are asked "How often do you go to the dentist?" The variable of interest in this study is
   a. the number of visits to the dentist.
   b. the 1000-person size of the sample.
   c. the integers 0 through 5.
7. Imagine that a survey of randomly selected people finds that people who used sunscreen were *more* likely to have been sunburned in the past year. Which explanation for this result seems most likely?
   a. Sunscreen is useless.
   b. The people in the study all used sunscreen that had passed its expiration date.
   c. People who use sunscreen are more likely to spend time in the sun.
8. You want to know whether people prefer Smith or Jones for mayor, and you are considering two possible ways to word the question. Wording X is "Do you prefer Smith or Jones for mayor?" Wording Y is "Do you prefer Jones or Smith for mayor?" (That is, the names are reversed in the two wordings.) The best approach is to
   a. use Wording X for everyone.
   b. use the same wording for everyone—it doesn't matter whether it is Wording X or Wording Y.
   c. use Wording X for half the people and Wording Y for the other half.
9. A *self-selected survey* is one in which
   a. the people being surveyed decide which question to answer.
   b. people decide for themselves whether to be part of the survey.
   c. the people who design the survey are also the survey participants.
10. If a statistical study is carefully conducted in every possible way, then
    a. its results must be correct.
    b. we can have confidence in its results, but it is still possible that they are not correct.
    c. we say that the study is perfectly biased.

Exercises 5B

REVIEW QUESTIONS

1. Briefly describe each of the eight guidelines for evaluating statistical studies. Give an example to which each guideline applies.
2. Describe and contrast selection bias and participation bias in sampling. Give an example of each.
3. What do we mean by variables of interest in a study?
4. What are confounding variables, and what problems can they cause?

DOES IT MAKE SENSE?

Decide whether each of the following statements makes sense (or is clearly true) or does not make sense (or is clearly false). Explain your reasoning.

5. The TV survey got more than 1 million phone-in responses, so it is clearly more valid than the survey by the professional pollsters, which involved interviews with only a few hundred people.

6. The survey of religious beliefs suffered from selection bias because the questionnaires were handed out only at Catholic churches.
7. My experiment proved beyond a doubt that vitamin C can reduce the severity of colds, because I controlled the experiment carefully for every possible confounding variable.
8. Everyone who jogs for exercise should try the new training regimen, because careful studies suggest it can increase your speed by 1%.

BASIC SKILLS AND CONCEPTS

9–20: Should You Believe This Study? Based solely on the information given, do you have reason to question the results of the following hypothetical studies? Explain your reasoning.

9. A study of the academic preparation of middle-school mathematics teachers used as data the teachers' SAT mathematics scores.
10. An experimental, double-blind study investigates whether people who eat more fast food are more likely to feel tired throughout the day.
11. A study by the liberal Center for American Progress is designed to assess a new Republican tax cut plan.
12. A study financed by a major pharmaceutical company is intended to determine whether its new cholesterol drug is more effective than similar drugs of competing companies.
13. A TV talk show host asks the TV audience, "Do you support new national mileage standards for automobiles?" and asks people to vote by telephone at a toll-free number.
14. A state Democratic Party polls 2000 of its members to determine whether its candidate for the U.S. Senate is likely to win against the Republican candidate.
15. Researchers design five survey questions to determine whether Norwegian citizens are happier than American citizens.
16. A government study is designed to find, based on people who had their tax returns audited, the percentage of taxpayers who understate their income.
17. In a study designed to determine whether people who wear helmets while riding a bicycle have fewer accidents, researchers tracked 500 riders with helmets for one month.
18. A study seeks to learn about obesity among children. The researchers monitor the eating and exercise habits of the children in the study, carefully recording everything they eat and all their activity.
19. Sociologists studying domestic violence circulate a questionnaire asking each respondent if she or he has ever abused a spouse or partner.
20. To gauge public opinion on whether there should be a constitutional amendment to ban flag burning, a survey asked people, "Do you support the American flag?"

21–26: Should You Believe This Claim? Based solely on the information given about the following hypothetical studies, decide whether you would believe the stated claim. Justify your conclusion.

21. A research group that tracks tuition rates at colleges and universities compares the tuition at a small college today and 10 years ago and claims that tuition has increased 150% during that period.
22. A new diet program claims that 200 randomly selected participants lost an average of 24.3 pounds in six weeks and that the program works for anyone with enough discipline.
23. Citing a higher incidence of cell-phone-related accidents among teens, the governor's office claims that banning the use of hand-held cell phones among drivers under 20 years of age will save lives.
24. In a new national poll by ABC News, the BBC, ARD German TV, and the Japanese broadcaster NHK, 55% of Iraqis say things in their own lives are going well, up from 39% six months ago. The number of people who expect conditions to improve nationally in the year ahead has doubled to 46%.
25. A study (in the *Canadian Medical Association Journal*) of 20 nations discovered that Germany has the most mean annual visits to a doctor (8.5), while Finland has the fewest (3.2).
26. According to a *New York Times*/CBS News poll, 60% of baseball fans are bothered by steroid use by players, and 44% say Yankees third baseman Alex Rodriguez should not be allowed in the Hall of Fame.

FURTHER APPLICATIONS

27–34: Bias. Identify at least one potential source of bias in the following studies. Explain why the bias would or would not affect your view of the study.

27. From a poll of people who recently bought cold medicine at all stores of a large drugstore chain, investigators concluded that the mean time between colds for all Americans is 5.6 months.
28. Based on a survey of 2718 people, the National Opinion Research Center concluded that 32% of Americans *always* make a special effort to sort and recycle glass, cans, plastic, or papers. Twenty-four percent of Americans *often* make such an effort.
29. An exit poll designed to predict the winner of a local election uses interviews with everyone who votes between 7:00 and 7:30 a.m.
30. An exit poll designed to predict the winner of a national election uses interviews with randomly selected voters in New York.
31. In order to determine the opinions of people in the 18- to 24-year age group on controlling illegal immigration, researchers survey a random sample of 1000 National Guard members in this age group.
32. A college mails survey forms to all current seniors, asking for the students' choice of their all-time best and worst professors. Students are asked to return the survey in the campus mail.
33. Planned Parenthood members are surveyed to determine whether American adults prefer abstinence, counseling and education, or morning-after pills for high school students.
34. A Fox News poll of 900 registered voters discovered that 55% of Americans are either extremely or very concerned about the safety of the food they eat, and an additional 30% are somewhat concerned. Lower-income households are the most concerned about the safety of their food.

35. **It's All in the Wording.** Princeton Survey Research Associates did a study for *Newsweek* magazine illustrating the effects of wording in a survey. Two questions were asked:
   - Do you personally believe that abortion is wrong?
   - Whatever your own personal view of abortion, do you favor or oppose a woman in this country having the choice to have an abortion with the advice of her doctor?

   To the first question, 57% of the respondents replied yes, and 36% responded no. In response to the second question, 69% of the respondents favored allowing women to have the choice, and 24% opposed allowing women to have the choice. Discuss why the two questions produced seemingly contradictory results. How could the results of the questions be used selectively by various groups?

36. **Tax or Spend?** A Gallup poll asked the following two questions:
   - Do you favor a tax cut or "increased spending on other government programs"? *Result:* 75% favored a tax cut.
   - Do you favor a tax cut or "spending to fund new retirement savings accounts, as well as increased spending on education, defense, Medicare and other programs"? *Result:* 60% were in favor of the spending.

   Discuss why the two questions produced seemingly contradictory results. How could the results of the questions be used selectively by various groups?

37–42: **Stat-Bytes.** Much like sound bytes of news stories, statistical studies are often reduced to one- or two-sentence stat-bytes. For the following stat-bytes taken from various news sources, discuss what crucial information is missing and what more you would want to know before acting on the study.

37. *USA Today* reports that over 60% of adults avoid visits to the dentist because of fear.
38. A Fox News poll reveals that 77% of Americans say "Merry Christmas" rather than "Happy Holidays."
39. *USA Today* reports that two-thirds of adults say that cell phone use during a dinner for two at a nice restaurant is unacceptable.
40. Only 2% of the estates of Americans who died in the past year paid estate taxes, while 60% of Americans favor repealing estate taxes.
41. According to *USA Today*, 26% of Americans rate potatoes their favorite vegetable, making it the most popular vegetable.
42. Thirty percent of newborns in India would qualify for intensive care if they were born in the United States.

43–45: **Accurate Headlines?** Consider the following headlines, each followed by a brief summary of a study. Discuss whether the headline accurately represents the study.

43. Headline: "Drugs shown in 98 percent of movies"

    Story summary: A "government study" claims that drug use, drinking, or smoking was depicted in 98% of the top movie rentals (Associated Press).

44. Headline: "Sex more important than jobs"

    Story summary: A survey found that 82% of 500 people interviewed by phone ranked a satisfying sex life as important or very important, while 79% ranked job satisfaction as important or very important (Associated Press).

45. Headline: "Grape juice may fight disease"

    Story summary: A study of 15 people, partially funded by Welch Foods, found that grape juice helps to expand blood vessels and increase the levels of HDL cholesterol. Both constricted blood vessels and low HDL levels are risk factors for heart disease (*Milwaukee Journal Sentinel*).

46. **Exercise and Dementia.** A recent study in the *Annals of Internal Medicine* was summarized by the Associated Press, in part, as follows:

    > *The study followed 1740 people aged 65 and older who showed no signs of dementia at the outset. The participants' health was evaluated every two years for six years. Out of the original pool, 1185 were later found to be free of dementia, 77 percent of whom reported exercising three or more times a week; 158 people showed signs of dementia, only 67 percent of whom said they exercised that much. The rest either died or withdrew from the study.*

    a. How many people completed the study?

    b. Fill in the following two-way table (with numbers of individuals), using the figures given in the above passage:

	Exercise	No Exercise	Total
Dementia			
No dementia			
Total			

    c. Draw a Venn diagram with two overlapping circles to illustrate the data.

WEB PROJECTS

47. **Polling Organization.** Go to the Web site for a major professional polling organization. Study results from a recent poll, and evaluate the poll according to the guidelines in this section.
48. **Harper's Index.** Go to the Web site for the Harper's Index and study a few of the recently quoted statistics. Be sure to select the option on the page that allows you to see the sources for the statistics. Choose three statistics that you find particularly interesting, and discuss whether, in accord with the guidelines given in this section, you believe them.

IN YOUR WORLD

49. **Applying the Guidelines.** Find a recent news report about a statistical study on a topic that you find interesting. Write a short critique of the study, in which you apply each of the eight guidelines given in this section. (Some of the guidelines may not apply to the particular study you are analyzing. In that case, explain why the guideline is not applicable.)
50. **Believable Results.** Find a recent news report about a statistical study whose results you believe are meaningful and important. In one page or less, summarize the study and explain why you find it believable.

51. **Unbelievable Results.** Find a recent news report about a statistical study whose results you *don't* believe are meaningful or important. In one page or less, summarize the study and why you don't believe its claims.

52. **Legal Experts.** Find a news report concerning a major ongoing trial. Find out whether any of the "expert witnesses" are being paid by either side. Based on what you learn, describe whether you think the experts are giving biased testimony.

53. **Biased Questioning?** Find a recent news report of responses to a single question in an opinion poll. State the exact words of the question and the results of the poll. Analyze the question and the reported results for potential biases. At the end of your analysis, state whether you believe the results, and defend your opinion.

UNIT 5C Statistical Tables and Graphs

Whether you look at a newspaper, a corporate annual report, or a government study, you are almost sure to see tables and graphs of statistical data. Some of these tables and graphs are simple; others can be quite complex. Some make it easy to understand the data; others may be confusing or even misleading. In this unit, we'll investigate some of the basic principles behind tables and graphs, preparing for more complex graphics in Unit 5D.

Frequency Tables

A teacher makes the following list of the grades she gave to her 25 students on an essay:

A C C B C D C C F D C C C B B A B D B A A B F C B

TABLE 5.1

Grade	Frequency
A	4
B	7
C	9
D	3
F	2
Total	25

This list contains all the raw data, but it isn't easy to read. A better way to display these data is with a **frequency table**—a table showing the number of times, or **frequency**, that each grade appears (Table 5.1). The five possible grades are called the **categories** for the table.

There are two common variations on the idea of frequency. The **relative frequency** for a category expresses its frequency as a fraction or percentage of the total. For example, 4 of the 25 students received A grades, so the relative frequency for A grades is 4/25, or 16%. The total relative frequency must always be 1, or 100%. However, because of rounding, you may sometimes find that the relative frequencies in a table or chart add up to slightly more or less than 100%.

The **cumulative frequency** is the number of responses in a particular category and all preceding categories. For example, the cumulative frequency for grades of C and above is 20, because 20 students received grades of either A, B, or C.

DEFINITION

A basic **frequency table** has two columns:

- The first column lists all the **categories** of data.
- The second column lists the **frequency** of each category, which is the number of times each category appears in the data set.

Additional columns may include **relative frequency** (frequency expressed as a fraction or percentage of the total) or **cumulative frequency** (total of frequencies for the given category and all previous categories).

Example 1 Relative and Cumulative Frequency

Add to Table 5.1 columns showing the relative and cumulative frequencies.

Solution Table 5.2 shows the new columns and calculations.

TABLE 5.2

Grade	Frequency	Relative Frequency	Cumulative Frequency
A	4	$4/25 = 16\%$	4
B	7	$7/25 = 28\%$	$7 + 4 = 11$
C	9	$9/25 = 36\%$	$9 + 7 + 4 = 20$
D	3	$3/25 = 12\%$	$3 + 9 + 7 + 4 = 23$
F	2	$2/25 = 8\%$	$2 + 3 + 9 + 7 + 4 = 25$
Total	25	$1 = 100\%$	25

Now try Exercises 15–16.

Time Out to Think

Briefly explain why the total relative frequency should always be 1, or 100%.

Data Types

Essay grades represent subjective ratings, not actual measurements or counts. We say that the grade categories are **qualitative**, because they represent *qualities* such as bad or good. In contrast, scores on a multiple-choice exam are **quantitative**, because they

USING TECHNOLOGY

Frequency Tables in Excel

Excel is easy to use for statistical tables and calculations. The following steps show how you can create the frequency table for Example 1; the screenshot on the left shows the Excel table with the formulas, and the one on the right shows the results of the formulas.

1. Create columns for the grade and frequency data, which you must type in manually; the screenshots show these data in columns B and C. At the bottom of column C, use the SUM function to compute the total frequency in cell C8.
2. Compute the relative frequency (column D) by dividing each frequency in column C by the total frequency from cell C8. You can enter the formula for the first row (=C3/$C$8) and then use the "fill down" editing option to put the correct formulas in the remaining rows. Note: When using the "fill down" option, you must include the dollar signs in front of C and 8 to make the reference to cell C8 an "absolute cell reference." Without these dollar signs, the "fill down" option would make the cell reference shift down (becoming C9, C10, etc.) in each row, which would be incorrect in this case.
3. Cumulative frequency (column E) is the total of all the frequencies up to a given category. The first row shows "=C3" because cell C3 contains the frequency for A grades. The next row (=E3+C4) starts with the value in the prior row (cell E3) and adds the frequency for B grades (cell C4). The pattern continues for the remaining rows, which you can fill with the "fill down" option.

◇	A	B	C	D	E
1					
2		Grade	Frequency	Relative Frequency	Cumulative Frequency
3		A	4	=C3/$C$8	=C3
4		B	7	=C4/$C$8	=E3+C4
5		C	9	=C5/$C$8	=E4+C5
6		D	3	=C6/$C$8	=E5+C6
7		F	2	=C7/$C$8	=E6+C7
8		Total	=SUM(C3:C7)	=SUM(D3:D7)	=C8

◇	A	B	C	D	E
1					
2		Grade	Frequency	Relative Frequency	Cumulative Frequency
3		A	4	16%	4
4		B	7	28%	11
5		C	9	36%	20
6		D	3	12%	23
7		F	2	8%	25
8		Total	25	100%	25

represent an actual count (or measurement) of the number of correct answers. As we'll see shortly, distinguishing between qualitative and quantitative data can be useful in creating tables or graphs.

> **DATA TYPES**
>
> **Qualitative data** describe *qualities* or categories.
> **Quantitative data** represent counts or measurements.

Example 2 Data Types

Classify each of the following types of data as either qualitative or quantitative.

a. Brand names of shoes in a consumer survey
b. Heights of students
c. Audience ratings of a film on a scale of 1 to 5, where 5 means excellent

Solution
a. Brand names are nonnumerical categories, so they are qualitative data.
b. Heights are measurements, so they are quantitative data.
c. Although the film rating categories involve numbers, the numbers represent subjective opinions about a film, not counts or measurements. Thus, they are qualitative data, despite being stated as numbers. **Now try Exercises 17–24.**

Time Out to Think

Give another example in which numbers are used to represent qualitative data rather than quantitative data.

Binning Data

When we deal with quantitative data categories, it's often useful to group, or *bin*, the data into categories that cover a range of possible values. For example, in a table of income levels, it might be useful to create bins of \$0 to \$20,000, \$20,001 to \$40,000, and so on. In this case, the frequency of each bin is simply the number of people with incomes in that bin.

Example 3 Binned Exam Scores

Consider the following set of 20 scores from a 100-point exam:

76 80 78 76 94 75 98 77 84 88 81 72 91 72 74 86 79 88 72 75

Determine appropriate bins and make a frequency table. Include columns for relative and cumulative frequency, and interpret the cumulative frequency for this case.

Solution The scores range from 72 to 98. One way to group the data is with 5-point bins. The first bin represents scores from 95 to 99, the second bin represents scores from 90 to 94, and so on. Note that there is no overlap between bins. We then count the frequency (the number of scores) in each bin. For example, only 1 score is in bin 95 to 99 (the high score of 98) and 2 scores are in bin 90 to 94 (the scores of 91 and 94). Table 5.3 shows the complete frequency table. In this case, we interpret the cumulative frequency of any bin to be the total number of scores in *or above* that bin. For example, the cumulative frequency of 6 for the bin 85 to 89 means that 6 scores are either between 85 and 89 or higher than 89.

TABLE 5.3 Frequency Table for Binned Exam Scores

Scores	Frequency	Relative Frequency	Cumulative Frequency
95 to 99	1	0.05 = 5%	1
90 to 94	2	0.10 = 10%	3
85 to 89	3	0.15 = 15%	6
80 to 84	3	0.15 = 15%	9
75 to 79	7	0.35 = 35%	16
70 to 74	4	0.20 = 20%	20
Total	20	1.00 = 100%	20

Now try Exercises 25–26.

Bar Graphs and Pie Charts

Bar graphs and pie charts are commonly used to show data when the categories are qualitative. You are probably familiar with both, but let's review the basic ideas.

Consider the essay grade data in Table 5.1. A bar graph would show each category with a bar whose length corresponded to its frequency. If you make a bar graph by hand (as opposed to with a computer), you should measure the bar lengths carefully to make sure they correctly correspond to the frequencies. In Figure 5.3, for example, the vertical axis is marked with frequencies $\frac{1}{2}$ centimeter apart. The bar for A grades is 2 centimeters long, because the frequency of A grades is 4. Note that the left side of the bar graph in Figure 5.3 is marked with frequency, while the right side is marked with relative frequency. As you can see, it's equally easy to display frequency or relative frequency (or both) with a bar graph.

In contrast, pie charts are used primarily for relative frequencies, because the total pie must always represent the total relative frequency of 100%. The size of each wedge is proportional to the relative frequency of the category it represents. Figure 5.4 shows a pie chart for the essay grade data. To make comparisons easier, relative frequencies are often written on pie chart wedges.

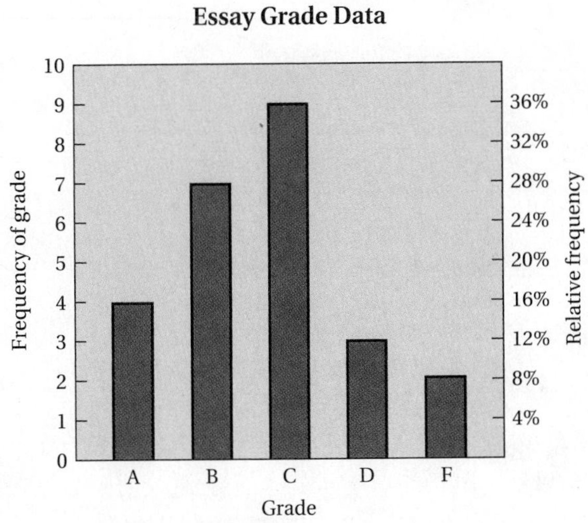

FIGURE 5.3 Bar graph for the essay grade data in Table 5.1.

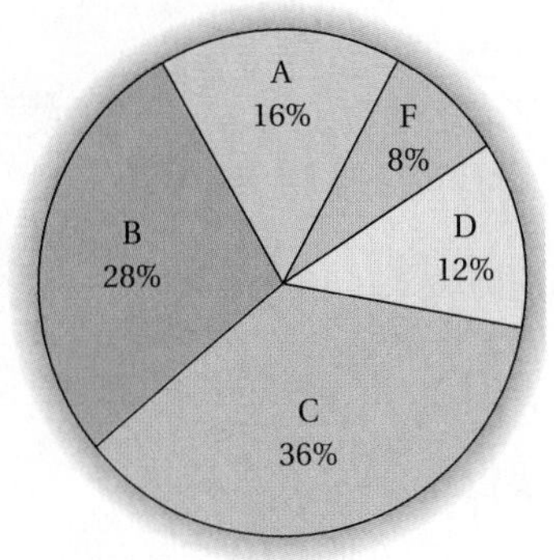

FIGURE 5.4 Pie chart for the essay grade data in Table 5.1.

USING TECHNOLOGY

Bar Graphs and Pie Charts in Excel

Excel can make many types of statistical graphs. Let's start by making a bar graph for the grade data in Table 5.1. The basic process requires the following steps, though the details vary significantly with different versions of Excel.

1. Beginning with the frequency table created in the Using Technology box on p. 321, select the grade letters (column B) and the frequencies (column C).
2. Choose the type of chart you want from the Insert menu; here, we choose a 2-D "column" chart, which is Excel's name for a bar graph. The screen shot below shows the process and the resulting graph created in Excel 2007 for Windows. The process is similar with other versions of Excel.
3. You can customize the labels on the bar graph. The procedure differs for different versions of Excel, but in most versions a right-click will allow you to change the axes and other labels; some versions also offer dialog boxes for changing the labels.

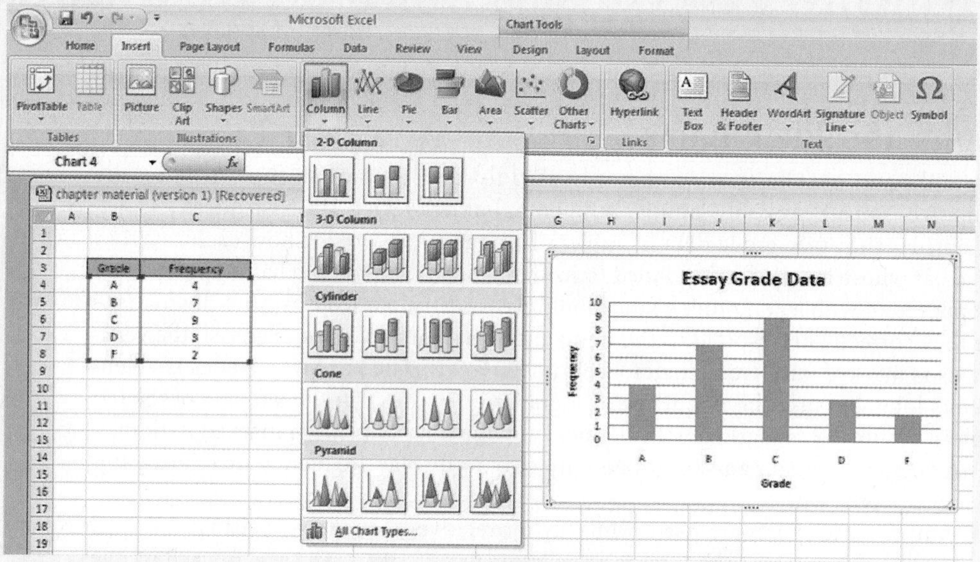

Making a pie chart is similar, except for a couple of things:

- For a pie chart, you will probably want to select the relative frequencies rather than the frequencies (though both will work); it may be helpful to cut and paste these data so that they are next to the letter grades.
- Choose a pie chart rather than a column chart from the Insert menu.
- The labeling process is different from that for bar graphs, as are the options for colors and other decorative features. The screen shot below shows some of the options available in Excel 2007 for Windows; other versions of Excel have similar tools.

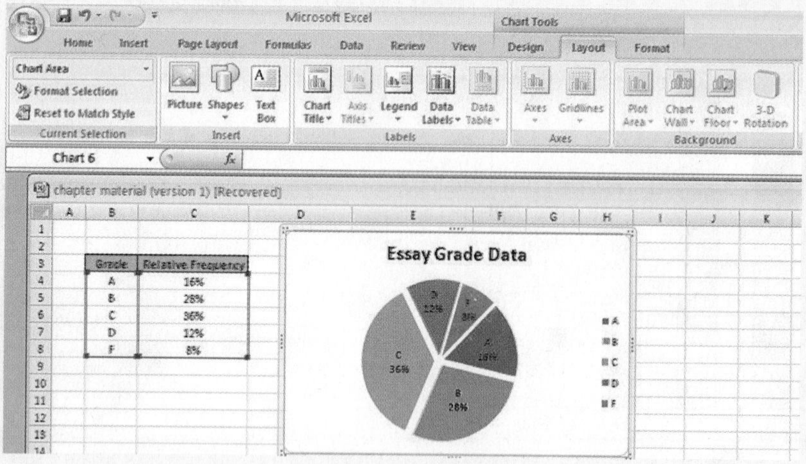

Because the various versions of Excel offer so many options, you should experiment with the different features to learn about the charting possibilities available in Excel.

Nowadays, most people make graphs with the aid of computers that measure bar lengths or wedge sizes automatically. However, you must still specify any labels or axis marks you want on a graph. This labeling is extremely important: Without proper labels, a graph is meaningless. The following summary lists the important labels for graphs. Of course, not all labels are necessary in all cases. For example, pie charts do not require a vertical or horizontal scale. Notice how these rules were applied in Figure 5.3.

IMPORTANT LABELS FOR GRAPHS

Title/caption: The graph should have a title or caption (or both) that explains what is being shown and, if applicable, lists the source of the data.

Vertical scale and title: Numbers along the vertical axis should clearly indicate the scale. The numbers should line up with the tick marks—the marks along the axis that precisely locate the numerical values. Include a label that describes the variable shown on the vertical axis.

Horizontal scale and title: The categories should be clearly indicated along the horizontal axis. (Tick marks may not be necessary for qualitative data, but should be included for quantitative data.) Include a label that describes the variable shown on the horizontal axis.

Legend: If multiple data sets are displayed on a single graph, include a legend or key to identify the individual data sets.

Example 4 Carbon Dioxide Emissions

Carbon dioxide is released into the atmosphere primarily by the combustion of fossil fuels (oil, coal, natural gas). Table 5.4 lists the eight countries that emit the most carbon dioxide each year. Make bar graphs for the total emissions and the emissions per person. Put the bars in descending order of size.

TABLE 5.4 The World's Eight Leading Emitters of Carbon Dioxide

Country	Total Carbon Dioxide Emissions (millions of metric tons of carbon)	Per Person Carbon Dioxide Emissions (metric tons of carbon)
China	1802	1.2
United States	1586	5.3
Russia	432	2.9
India	430	0.4
Japan	337	2.6
Germany	210	2.6
Canada	145	4.6
United Kingdom	145	2.5

Source: U.S. Department of Energy, based on estimated 2007 emissions.

BY THE WAY

China's emergence as the world's leading emitter of carbon dioxide is quite recent. By U.S. Department of Energy estimates, the United States was the leading emitter until 2005, and as recently as 1990 the United States emitted nearly twice as much total carbon dioxide as China. It is likely that China's per person emissions will continue to catch up to those of more developed countries, in which case its total emissions will continue to grow rapidly.

Solution The categories are the countries. Because country names are qualitative data, a bar graph is appropriate.

The values for total carbon dioxide emissions go from 145 to 1802 (millions of tons), so a range of 0 to 2000 makes a good choice for the vertical scale. Each bar's height corresponds to its data value, and we label the category (country) under the bar.

Historical Note

A bar graph with the bars in descending order is often called a *Pareto chart,* after Italian economist Vilfredo Pareto (1848–1923).

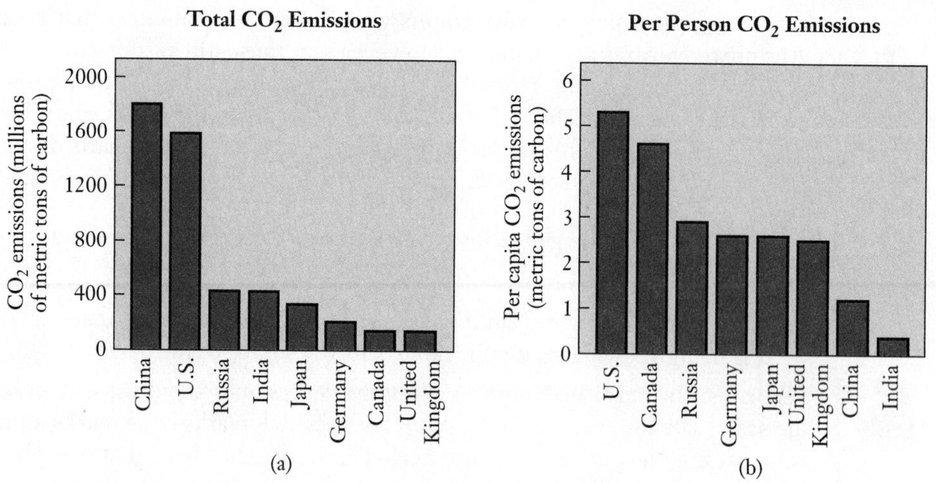

FIGURE 5.5 Bar graphs for (a) total carbon dioxide emissions by country and (b) per person carbon dioxide emissions by country.

Figure 5.5a shows the bar graph for total emissions, with bars in order of decreasing height.

The data values for per person emissions range from 0.4 to 5.3 (tons), so a range of 0 to 6 will work for this vertical scale. Figure 5.5b shows the bar graph, again with bars placed in order of descending height. **Now try Exercises 27–28.**

Time Out to Think

Note that the two bar graphs in Figure 5.5 do not show the countries in the same order. Why not? What can we learn by comparing the two graphs? Explain.

Example 5 Simple Pie Chart

Among the registered voters in Rochester County, 25% are Democrats, 25% are Republicans, and 50% are Independents. Make a pie chart showing the breakdown of party affiliations in Rochester County.

Solution The wedge sizes should correspond to the relative frequencies. Thus, the wedges for Republicans and Democrats each occupy one-fourth of the pie, while the wedge for Independents occupies the remaining half of the pie (Figure 5.6). Note the importance of clear labeling.

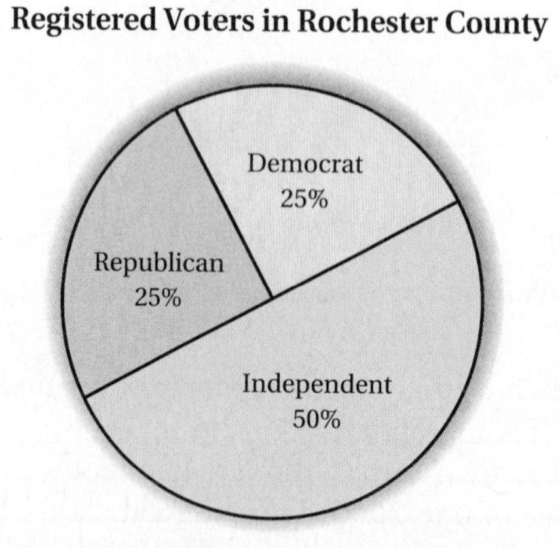

FIGURE 5.6 Party affiliations of registered voters in Rochester County. **Now try Exercises 29–30.**

Example 6 Student Majors

Figure 5.7 is a pie chart showing planned major areas for first-year college students. Make a bar graph showing the same data, with the bars in order of decreasing size. What are the three most popular major areas? Comment on the relative ease with which this question can be answered with the pie chart and the bar graph.

Solution Figure 5.8 shows the bar graph for the data. Note that, because we have only relative frequency data from the pie chart, we can show only relative frequencies on the bar graph. This bar graph makes it immediately obvious that the three most popular major areas are business (16.7%), arts and humanities (12.1%), and professional (11.6%). ("Professional" includes fields with professional licensing, such as architecture, nursing, and pharmacy.) In contrast, it takes a fair amount of study of the pie chart before we can easily list the three most popular major areas.

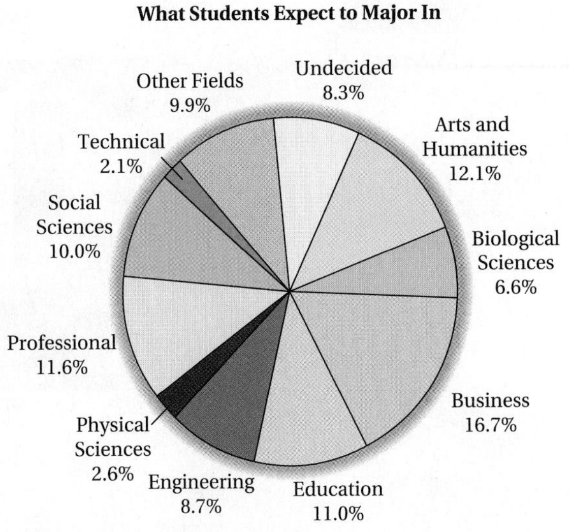

FIGURE 5.7 Planned major areas for first-year college students.
Source: The Chronicle of Higher Education.

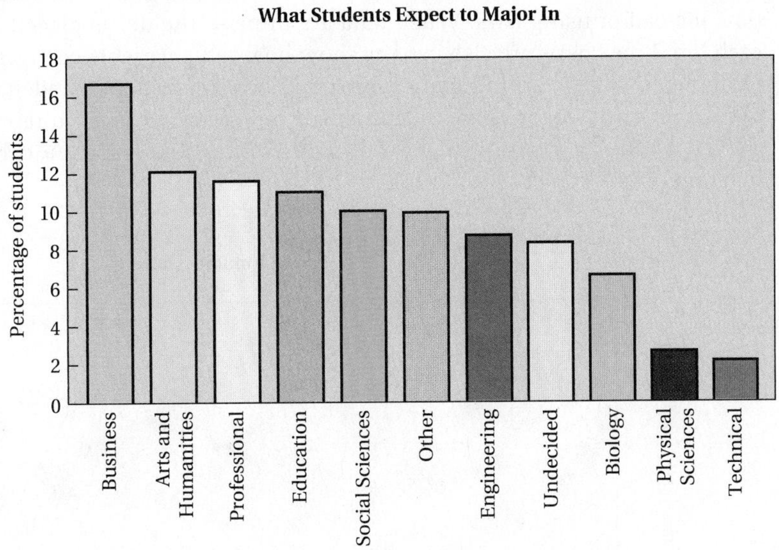

FIGURE 5.8 Bar graph for the data in Figure 5.7.

Now try Exercises 31–32.

Time Out to Think

Example 6 discussed an advantage of a bar graph over a pie chart for showing the data concerning major areas. Do you think the pie chart has any advantages over the bar graph? If so, what?

Histograms and Line Charts

For quantitative data categories, the two most common types of graphics are *histograms* and *line charts*. Figure 5.9(a) shows a histogram for the binned exam data of Table 5.3. Figure 5.9(b) shows a line chart for the same data.

A **histogram** is essentially a bar graph in which the data categories are quantitative. The bars on a histogram must follow the natural order of the numerical categories. In addition, the widths of histogram bars have a specific meaning. For example, the width of each bar in Figure 5.9a represents 5 points on the exam. Because there are no gaps between the categories, the bars on a histogram touch each other.

Take Note

Different books define the terms *histogram* and *bar graph* differently. In this book, a bar graph is any graph that uses bars, and histograms are bar graphs used for quantitative data categories.

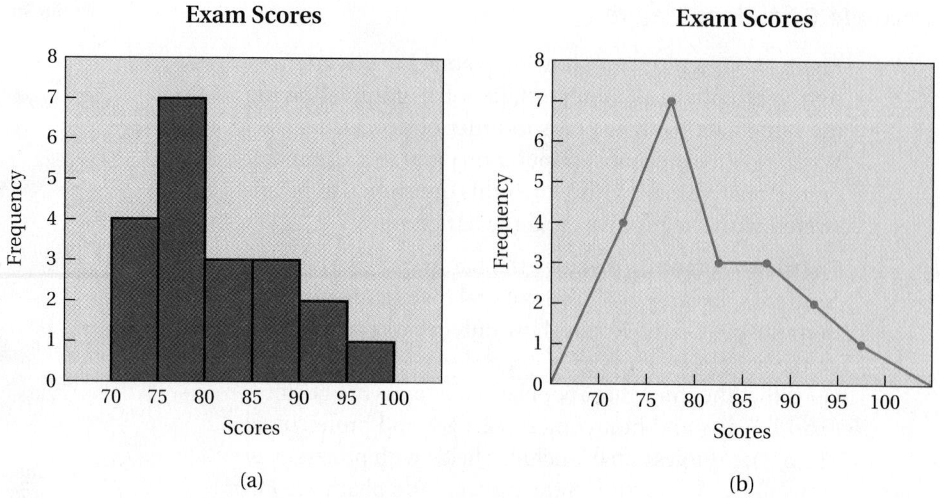

FIGURE 5.9 (a) Histogram for the data in Table 5.3. (b) Line chart for the same data.

A **line chart** serves the same basic purpose as a histogram, but connects a series of dots instead of using bars. When data are binned, the dot is placed at the center of each bin. Line charts are also used to show how some variable changes with time. For example, the line chart in Figure 5.10 shows how the U.S. homicide rate has changed with time. The categories are time intervals; in this case, each bin represents a year in the data. Line charts with time on the horizontal axis are often called **time-series diagrams**.

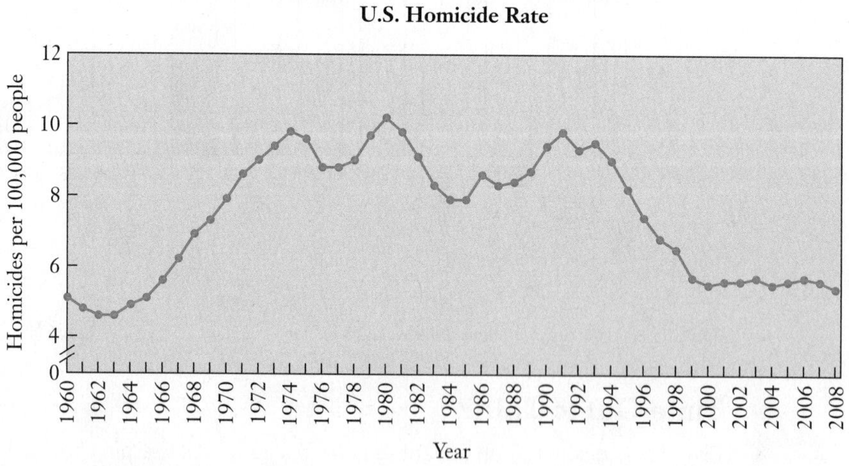

FIGURE 5.10 U.S. homicide rate per 100,000 people.
Source: FBI Uniform Crime Reports.

DEFINITIONS

A **histogram** is a bar graph for quantitative data categories. The bars have a natural order and the bar widths have specific meaning.

A **line chart** shows the data value for each category as a dot, and the dots are connected with lines. For each dot, the horizontal position is the *center* of the bin it represents and the vertical position is the data value for the bin.

A **time-series diagram** is a line chart in which the horizontal axis represents time.

Example 7 Oscar-Winning Actresses

Table 5.5 shows the ages (at the time when they won the award) of all Academy Award–winning actresses through 2008. Make a histogram and a line chart to display these data. Discuss the results.

Solution The fact that the categories are 10-year bins makes the data quantitative, so a histogram is appropriate. Figure 5.11a shows the histogram. The bars touch one another because there are no gaps between the categories.

Figure 5.11b shows the same data as a line chart. The histogram is also included to show how it relates to the line chart. In looking at these data, we see that actresses are most likely to win Oscars when they are fairly young.

TABLE 5.5 Ages of Academy Award–Winning Actresses, 1927–2008

Age	Number of Actresses
20–29	28
30–39	34
40–49	12
50–59	1
60–69	5
70–79	1
80–89	1

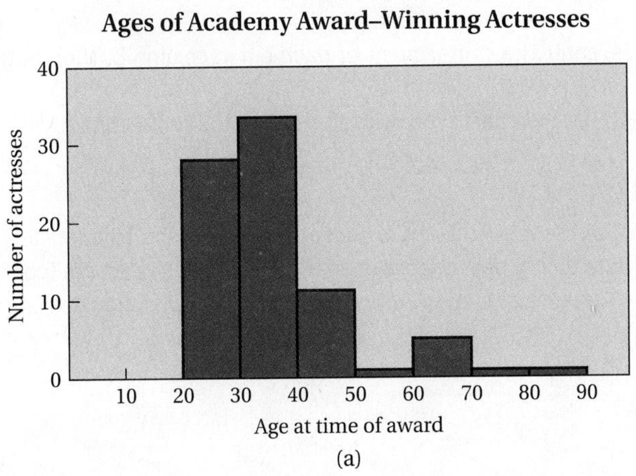

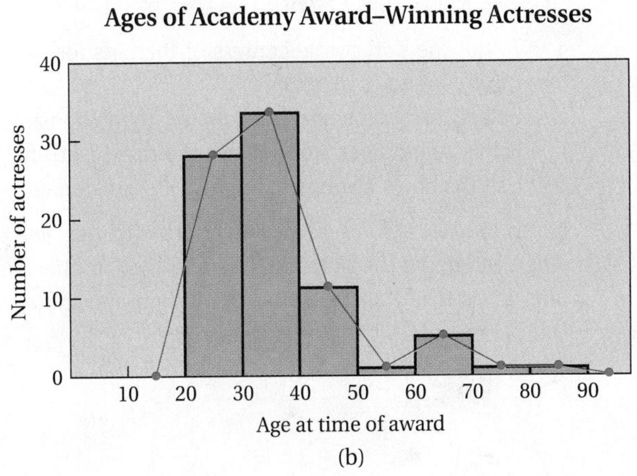

FIGURE 5.11 Histogram for ages of Academy Award–winning actresses through 2008. (b) Line chart for the same data, with histogram overlaid for comparison.

Now try Exercises 33–34.

Example 8 Reading a Time-Series Diagram

Figure 5.12 shows a time-series line chart of stock, bond, and gold prices over a 12-week period. Suppose that, on July 7, you invested \$100 in a stock fund that tracks the S&P 500, \$100 in a bond fund that follows the Treasury Bond Index, and \$100 in gold. If you sold all three funds on August 4, how much did you gain or lose?

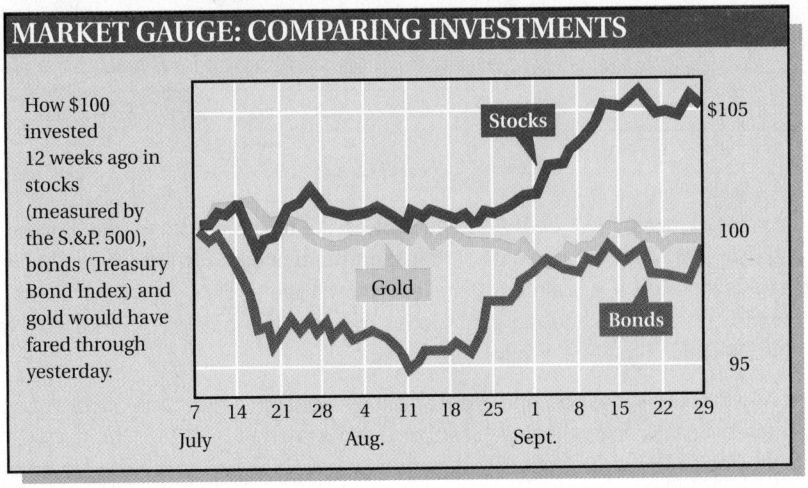

FIGURE 5.12

Historical Note

Gold was once considered to be a solid investment and an important part of any investment portfolio. However, gold prices have languished in recent decades. In 2009, gold reached record high prices of more than \$1000 per ounce, though these were still well short of its inflation-adjusted high of more than \$2200 per ounce in 1980.

Solution The graph shows that the $100 in the stock fund would have been worth about $101 on August 4. The $100 bond investment would have declined in value to about $96. The gold investment would have held its initial value of $100. On August 4, your complete portfolio would have been worth $101 + $96 + $100 = $297. You would have lost $3 on your total investment of $300. **Now try Exercises 35–36.**

USING TECHNOLOGY

Line Charts and Histograms in Excel

Line charts are easy to create in Excel. The screen shot below shows the process for the binned data from Example 3 (p. 322). Follow these steps:

1. To get the dots in the centers of the bins for the scores, enter the center point of each bin in column B. Then put the frequencies in column C.
2. Select the scores and frequencies, then choose "scatter" as the chart type, with the option for connecting points with straight lines. You will get the graph shown.
3. Use the chart options to improve design, labels, and more.

Note: You can also create a line chart with the "line" chart option in Excel. In that case, select *only* the frequencies when you begin the graphing process; then, in the source data dialog box, choose "series" and select the scores (column B) as the "X values." The resulting graph should look the same as that created with the "scatter" option, except the data points will not have dots.

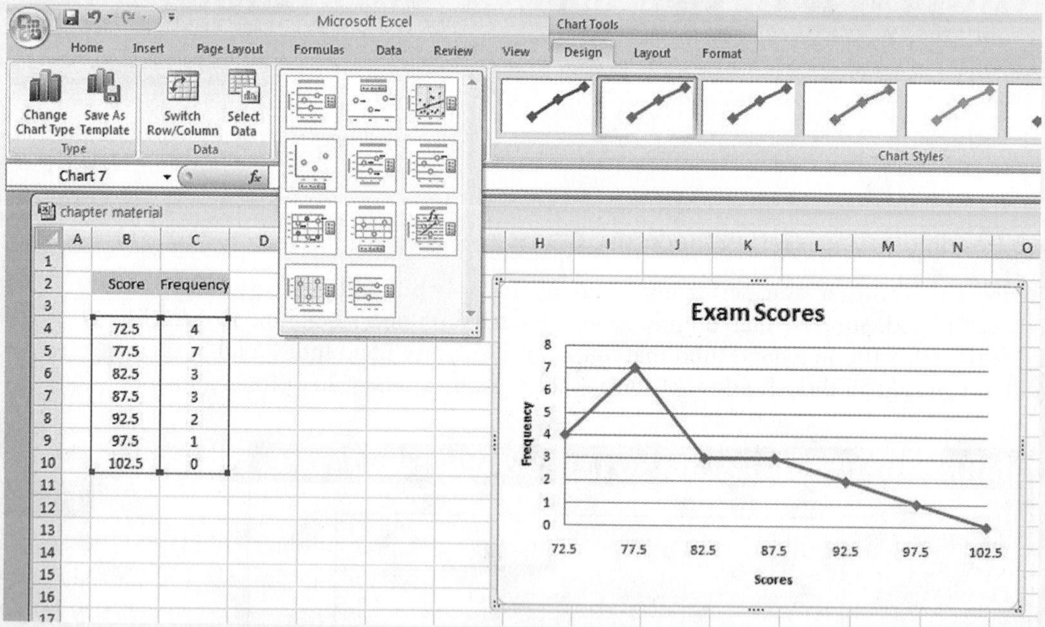

Histograms require a more complex process in Excel. The screen shot on the next page shows the process for the data from Example 3; in this case, we start with the raw data rather than the binned data. Before you begin, make sure that Excel's "Analysis Toolpak" is installed. If it is already installed, you will see a "Data Analysis..." option on the Tools menu or Data ribbon. Otherwise, install it by choosing the "Add-Ins" option. (The location of this option varies in different versions of Excel; use the Help menu to find it easily.)

1. Create one column (column A) with the data values, and another column (column C) with the *upper values* of the bins to be used (rather than the bin center points that we used for the line chart).
2. Select "Data Analysis" from the Tools menu or Data ribbon, then select "Histogram" from the choices offered. The Histogram dialog box will appear, as shown in the screen shot.

3. Select the data (column A) as the "input range" and the bin upper values (column C) as the "bin range." Check the "chart output" box. Excel generates the Bin and Frequency data (columns E and F) and the histogram, as shown. (You can also check "Cumulative Percentage" if you want a column and a graph for the cumulative frequency.)
4. Notice that the bars on the histogram are separated from each other. You can close the gap by right-clicking on any bar, selecting "Format Data Series . . .," and setting the gap width to zero. The histogram should then look like the ones in this book, except that the bars will be labeled in their centers by their upper values.

Note: Once you have created a histogram, you can turn it into a line chart simply by right-clicking on the graph and selecting the "chart type" option from the Insert menu, then choosing the "line" chart option. Again, the graph will differ from those in this book because it will show the dots at the upper bounds of the bins, rather than in their centers.

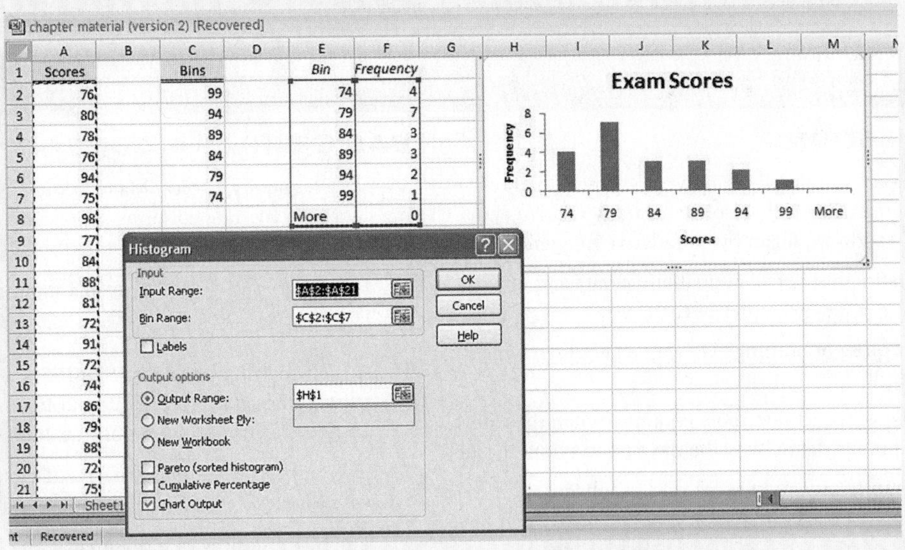

QUICK QUIZ

Choose the best answer to each of the following questions. Explain your reasoning with one or more complete sentences.

1. In a class of 100 students, 25 students received a grade of B. What was the *relative* frequency of a B grade?

   a. 25 b. 0.25

   c. It cannot be calculated with the information given.

2. For the class described in question 1, what was the *cumulative* frequency of a grade of B or above?

   a. 25 b. 0.25

   c. It cannot be calculated with the information given.

3. Which of the following is an example of *qualitative* data?

   a. waist sizes in inches b. ratings of restaurants

   c. meal costs at restaurants

4. The *sizes* of the wedges in a pie chart tell you

   a. the number of categories in the pie chart.

   b. the frequencies of the categories in the pie chart.

   c. the relative frequencies of the categories in the pie chart.

5. You have a table listing ten tourist attractions and their annual numbers of visitors. Which type of display would be most appropriate for these data?

   a. a bar graph

   b. a pie chart

   c. a line chart

6. Where should you put the names of the ten tourist attractions when you make your display of the data described in question 5?

   a. They should be in the title of the display.

   b. They should be in alphabetical order along the vertical axis.

   c. They should be listed along the horizontal axis.

7. You have a list of the GPAs of 100 college graduates, precise to the nearest 0.001. You want to make a frequency table for these data. A good first step would be to

   a. group all the data into bins 0.2 of a grade point wide.

   b. draw a pie chart for the 100 individual GPAs.

   c. count how many people have identical GPAs.

8. You have a list of the average gasoline price for each month during the past year. Which type of display would be most appropriate for these data?

   a. a bar graph   b. a pie chart   c. a line chart

9. A *histogram* is

   a. a graph that shows how some quantity has changed through history.

   b. a graph that shows cumulative frequencies.

   c. a bar chart for quantitative data.

10. You have a histogram and you want to convert it into a line chart. A good first step would be to

    a. make a list of all the categories in alphabetical order.

    b. place a dot at the top of each bar, in the center of the bar.

    c. calculate all the relative frequencies that you can read from the histogram.

Exercises 5C

REVIEW QUESTIONS

1. What is a frequency table? Explain what we mean by the categories and frequencies. What do we mean by relative frequency? What do we mean by cumulative frequency?
2. What is the distinction between qualitative data and quantitative data? Give a few examples of each.
3. What is the purpose of binning? Give an example in which binning is useful.
4. What two types of graphs are most common when the categories are qualitative data? Describe the construction of each.
5. Describe the importance of labeling on a graph, and briefly discuss the kinds of labels that should be included on graphs.
6. What two types of graphs are most common when the categories are quantitative data? Describe the construction of each.

DOES IT MAKE SENSE?

Decide whether each of the following statements makes sense (or is clearly true) or does not make sense (or is clearly false). Explain your reasoning.

7. I made a frequency table with two columns, one labeled *State* and one labeled *State Capitol*.
8. The relative frequency of B grades in our class was 0.3.
9. Your bar graph must be wrong, because your bars are wider than the ones shown on the teacher's answer key.
10. Your bar graph must be wrong, because it shows different frequencies than the ones shown on the teacher's answer key.
11. Your pie chart must be wrong, because you have the 45% frequency wedge near the upper left and the answer key shows it near the lower right.
12. Your pie chart must be wrong, because when I added the percentages on your wedges, they totaled 124%.
13. I was unable to make a bar chart, because the data categories were qualitative rather than quantitative.
14. I rearranged the bars on my histogram so that the tallest bar would come first.

BASIC SKILLS & CONCEPTS

15–16: Frequency Tables. Make frequency tables for the following data sets. Include columns for relative frequency and cumulative frequency.

15. Final grades of 20 students in a math class:

    A A   B B B B B   C C C C C C C C   D D D   F F

16. A Web site that reviews recent movies lists 5 five-star films (the highest rating), 10 four-star films, 20 three-star films, 15 two-star films, and 5 one-star films.

17–24: Qualitative vs. Quantitative. Determine whether the following variables are qualitative or quantitative.

17. The birth months of individuals
18. The responses on a questionnaire: 0 = strongly disagree, . . ., 5 = strongly agree
19. The yes/no responses on a ballot initiative to the question "Do you support an increase in the sales tax?"
20. The amount of rainfall in each month of a year in Chattanooga, Tennessee
21. The flavors of ice cream sold in a shop
22. The breeds of 120 purebred dogs
23. The annual salaries of major league baseball players
24. The gold medal count of each team in the 2010 Olympics

25–26: Binned Frequency Tables. Use the given bin sizes to make a frequency table for the following data set:

89 67 78 75 64 70 83 95 69 84
77 88 98 90 92 68 86 79 60 96

Include columns for relative frequency and cumulative frequency.

25. Use 5-point bins (95 to 99, 90 to 94, etc.).
26. Use 10-point bins (90 to 99, 80 to 89, etc.).
27. **Largest States.** Make a bar graph of the populations of the five most populous states (shown on the next page for 2008), with the bars in descending order.

State	Population
California	36.6 million
Texas	23.9 million
New York	19.3 million
Florida	18.3 million
Illinois	12.9 million

28. **Meat Producers.** Make a bar graph of beef production of the five largest beef-producing nations in the world (data below), with the bars in descending order.

Country	Amount of Beef (millions of metric tons)
U.S.	12.0
Brazil	7.9
China	7.6
Argentina	2.8
India	2.8

29–30: **Pie Charts.** Construct pie charts for the following data sets. The first step is to compute a percentage for each category in the data set.

29. The annual sales (in millions of dollars) of the leading chocolate brands are shown in the table.

Company	Sales ($ millions)
M&Ms	253
Hershey's	186
Hershey's Kisses	114
Dove	112
All others	1377

30. The five leading tourist destinations (in millions of visitors) are shown in the table.

Country	Visitors (millions)
France	81.9
Spain	59.2
U.S.	56.0
China	54.7
Italy	43.7

31. **Government Income.** The pie chart in Figure 4.12 on p. 284 shows the makeup of federal government receipts. Make a bar graph for these data.

32. **Government Spending.** The pie chart in Figure 4.13 on p. 284 shows the makeup of federal government spending. Make a bar graph for these data.

33. **Oscar-Winning Actors.** The following data show ages of Academy Award–winning actors from 1985 to 2008. Make a frequency table for these data using bins of 20–29, 30–39, and so on. Then draw a histogram to display the binned data.

36	62	43	51	32	42	54	52	37	38	32	45
60	46	40	36	47	29	43	37	38	45	50	48

34. **Oscar Winners.** In words, contrast the graphs in Example 7 (for actresses) with the one you drew in Exercise 33. Do actors appear to be more likely to win Oscars when they are younger, older, or neither? Do you think these graphs indicate any difference in how movie makers treat male and female performers? Defend your opinion.

35. **Homicide Rates.** Study Figure 5.10. Write one to two paragraphs summarizing how the homicide rate has changed with time since 1960.

36. **Death Rates.** Figure 5.13 shows overall death rates in the United States during the 20th century. Note that the spike in 1919 was due to a worldwide epidemic of influenza. Write a few sentences summarizing the overall trend, describing how much the death rate changed during the century, and putting the 1919 spike into context in terms of its impact on the population.

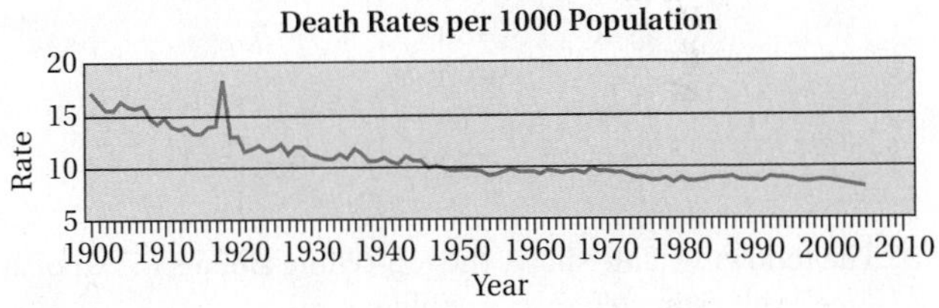

FIGURE 5.13 *Source:* National Center for Health Statistics.

FURTHER APPLICATIONS

37–45: **Statistical Graphs.** Consider the following data sets.

a. State whether the variables are qualitative or quantitative.

b. Draw a bar graph or a pie chart if the data are qualitative. Draw a histogram or a line chart if the data are quantitative.

c. Write a paragraph discussing interesting features of the data revealed by your display.

37. The following frequency table categorizes Nobel Prize winners in literature from 1990 through 2005 by their age at the time they received the award.

Age	Number of Winners
<58	1
58–59	2
60–61	1
62–63	3
64–65	0
66–67	1
68–69	3
70–71	1
72–73	2
74–75	2
76–77	2
>77	1

38. The following table shows the amount spent, in billions of dollars, by the leading U.S. advertisers in 2007.

Advertiser	Spending ($ billions)
Procter and Gamble	5.2
AT&T	3.2
Verizon	3.0
General Motors	3.0
Time Warner	3.0
Ford Motor Company	2.5

39. The following table shows the number of bachelor's degrees (in thousands) conferred on men and women in U.S. colleges and universities over the past 50 years.

Year	Men	Women
1960	260	140
1970	460	335
1980	480	475
1990	490	530
2000	510	710
2010	590	860

40. The following table shows the top-selling albums (CDs) of all time, with estimated sales in millions.

Title, Artist	Sales (millions)
Greatest Hits, Eagles	29.0
Thriller, Michael Jackson	27.0
Led Zeppelin IV, Led Zeppelin	23.0
The Wall, Pink Floyd	23.0
Back in Black, AC/DC	22.0
Greatest Hits, Billy Joel	21.0
Double Live, Garth Brooks	21.0

41. The following table shows the number of daily newspapers (morning and evening) in the United States between 1950 and 2007.

Year	Number of Newspapers
1950	1772
1960	1763
1970	1748
1980	1745
1990	1611
2000	1480
2007	1422

42. The following table gives the percentages of total energy produced in the United States from various sources.

Energy Source	Percentage of Total Energy
Coal	32.2%
Natural gas	31.0%
Crude oil	16.4%
Nuclear power	11.7%
Renewable	8.7%

Source: U.S. Department of Energy.

43. The following table gives the stated religions of first-year college students. (Note: The "other religions" category consists of religions that were stated by less than 1% of the students in the sample.)

Religion	Percent of Sample
Baptist	11.6
Catholic	30.5
Episcopal	1.7
Jewish	2.8
Lutheran	5.8
Methodist	6.4
Mormon	1.5
Presbyterian	4.0
United Church of Christ	1.5
Other religions	19.3
No religion	14.9

Source: UCLA Higher Education Research Institute.

44. The following table gives the rates of violent crimes (rape, robbery, assault, theft) by age of victim. Rates have units of crimes per 1000 people aged 12 or older.

Age Group	Crime Rate
12–15	51.6
16–19	53.0
20–24	43.3
25–34	26.4
35–49	18.5
50–64	10.3
>65	2.0

Source: Bureau of Justice Statistics.

45. The following table gives average family size in the United States since 1940.

Year	Family Size	Year	Family Size
1940	3.76	1980	3.29
1950	3.54	1985	3.23
1960	3.67	1990	3.17
1965	3.70	1995	3.19
1970	3.58	2000	3.17
1975	3.42	2007	3.19

Source: U.S. Bureau of Census.

46. **Alcohol-Related Motor Vehicle Fatalities.** Figure 5.14 shows the number of motor vehicle fatalities in the United States in which alcohol was involved for each year from 1982 to 2007.

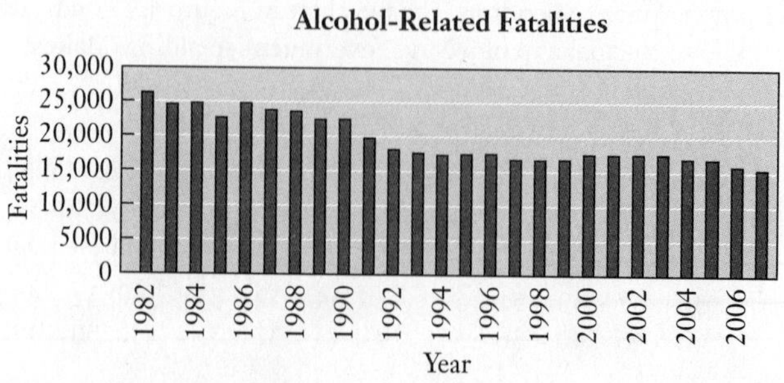

FIGURE 5.14 *Source:* National Highway Traffic Safety Administration.

a. How many alcohol-related fatalities were there in 1982? in 2007? Comment on the overall trend over this period.

b. What is the percent change in alcohol-related fatalities over this period?

c. The total numbers of automobile fatalities in 1982 and 2007 were 43,945 and 41,059, respectively. What percentage of all fatalities in these two years involved alcohol?

d. In view of your answer to part c, can you offer explanations for the trend in these data? Explain.

47. **Ages of Presidents.** The following table gives the order of the presidents of the United States and the ages at which they first took office.

a. Find a creative way to display these data.

b. Which presidents could have said that they were the *youngest* president (or the same age in years as the youngest) at the time they took office?

c. Which presidents could have said that they were the *oldest* president (or the same age in years as the oldest) at the time they took office?

d. Write a paragraph describing significant features of the data.

Order	1	2	3	4	5	6	7	8	9	10	11
Age	57	61	57	57	58	57	61	54	68	51	49
Order	12	13	14	15	16	17	18	19	20	21	22
Age	64	50	48	65	52	56	46	54	49	50	47
Order	23	24	25	26	27	28	29	30	31	32	33
Age	55	55	54	42	51	56	55	51	54	51	60
Order	34	35	36	37	38	39	40	41	42	43	44
Age	62	43	55	56	61	52	69	64	46	54	47

WEB PROJECTS

48. **CO_2 Emissions.** Look for updated data on international carbon dioxide emissions at the Web site for the *International Energy Annual*, published by the U.S. Energy Information Administration (EIA). Create an updated or expanded version of Figure 5.5. Discuss any new features of your updated graphs.

49. **Energy Table.** Explore some of the many energy tables at the U.S. Energy Information Administration (EIA) Web site. Choose a table that you find interesting, and make a graph of its data. You may choose any of the graph types discussed in this section. Explain how you made your graph, and briefly discuss what can be learned from it.

50. **Statistical Abstract.** Go to the Web site for the *Statistical Abstract of the United States*. Explore the selection of "frequently requested tables." Choose one table of interest to you, and make a graph of its data. You may choose any of the graph types discussed in this section. Explain how you made your graph, and briefly discuss what can be learned from it.

IN YOUR WORLD

51. **Frequency Tables.** Find a recent news article that includes some type of frequency table. Briefly describe the table and how it adds to the news report. Do you think the table was constructed in the best possible way for the article? If so, why? If not, what would you have done differently?

52. **Bar Graph.** Find a recent news article that includes a bar graph with qualitative data categories. Briefly explain what the graph shows, and discuss whether it helps make the point of the news article.

53. **Pie Chart.** Find a recent news article that includes a pie chart. Briefly discuss the effectiveness of the pie chart. For example, would it be better if the data were displayed in a bar graph rather than a pie chart? Could the pie chart be improved in other ways?

54. **Histogram.** Find a recent news article that includes a histogram. Briefly explain what the histogram shows, and discuss whether it helps make the point of the news article. Are the labels clear? Is the histogram a time-series diagram? Explain.

55. **Line Chart.** Find a recent news article that includes a line chart. Briefly explain what the line chart shows, and discuss whether it helps make the point of the news article. Are the labels clear? Is the line chart a time-series diagram? Explain.

TECHNOLOGY EXERCISES

56. **Making a Frequency Table.** The following vehicle counts were collected during a tour of a student parking lot.

Category of Car	Frequency
American cars	30
Japanese cars	25
English cars	5
Other European cars	12
Motorcycles	8

a. Use Excel to make a frequency table for these data that includes both the relative frequencies and the cumulative frequencies.

b. What is the sum of the frequencies?

c. What is the sum of the relative frequencies?

d. What is the sum of the cumulative frequencies?

57. **Making a Bar Graph.** Use Excel to make a bar graph of the data in Exercise 56.

58. **Making a Pie Chart.** Use Excel to make a pie chart of the data in Exercise 56.

59. **Making a Line Chart.** Consider the following data on the production of tobacco in the United States between 2000 and 2007.

Year	Tobacco Produced (million lb)
2000	1053
2001	991
2002	871
2003	803
2004	882
2005	645
2006	727
2007	779

Make a line chart that displays these data.

60. **Making a Histogram.** Make a histogram for the data in Exercise 59.

UNIT 5D Graphics in the Media

Now that we've discussed basic types of statistical graphs, we are ready to explore some of the fancier graphics that appear daily in the news. We will also discuss several cautions to keep in mind when interpreting media graphics.

Graphics Beyond the Basics

Many graphical displays of data go beyond the basic types discussed in Unit 5C. Here, we explore a few of the types that are most common in the news media.

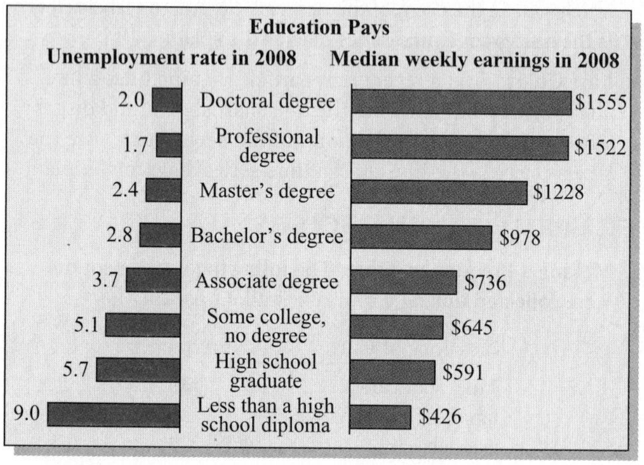

FIGURE 5.15 Income and employment.
Source: Bureau of Labor Statistics.

Multiple Bar Graphs

A **multiple bar graph** is a simple extension of a regular bar graph. It has two or more sets of bars that allow comparison between two or more data sets. All the data sets must involve the same categories so that they can be displayed on the same graph. For example, Figure 5.15 is a multiple bar graph showing how education affects personal employment and income. The categories are levels of education. The two sets of bars represent two different measures of how education affects employment: the unemployment rate and weekly earnings. Note that, in this case, one set of bars is shown to the left and the other to the right. In other cases, a different display strategy might be more appropriate. You should always consider alternative display strategies to make sure that the key message in your data comes across clearly.

Example 1 Education and Employment

Examine Figure 5.15. What is its major message? Why are the two sets of bars shown separately rather than, say, next to each other?

Solution The main message is actually highlighted by the title of the figure: "Education Pays." The data show clearly that the greater your level of education, the less likely you are to be unemployed and the more you are likely to earn. The bars are shown separately because the two scales are different: The unemployment rate is measured in percent and income is measured in dollars. Therefore, if the bars were shown next to each other, two different axis scales would be needed. While such double scaling is sometimes used, in this case the strategy of displaying the bars separately makes the main message easier to see and understand. **Now try Exercises 13–14.**

Stack Plots

Another common type of graph, called a **stack plot**, shows different data sets in a vertical stack. Stack plots usually use either stacked bars or stacked line graphs. Figure 5.16 shows a stack plot using stacked bars. Notice that each bar is divided into sections, and the meaning of each section is listed in the key. For example, the first bar shows that the total budget for the average commuter student at a two-year public college is \$14,054, and the light blue segment in that bar shows that this average student spends \$7341 on room and board.

Figure 5.17 uses a stack plot with stacked lines to show trends in death rates (deaths per 100,000 people) for four diseases since 1900. Each disease has its own color-coded region, or wedge; note the importance of the legend. The *thickness* of a wedge at a particular time tells you its value at that time: When a wedge is thick it has a large value, and when it is thin it has a small value.

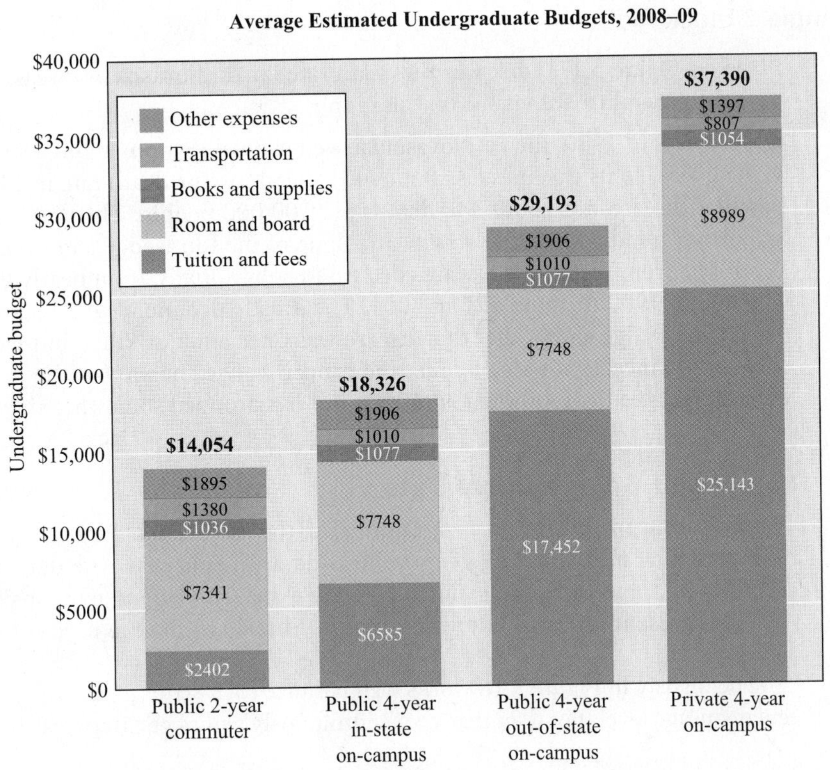

FIGURE 5.16 This stack plot uses stacked bars to show the breakdown by category (tuition and fees, room and board, books and supplies, transportation, other) of average student budgets at different types of institutions.
Source: The College Board, "Trends in College Pricing."

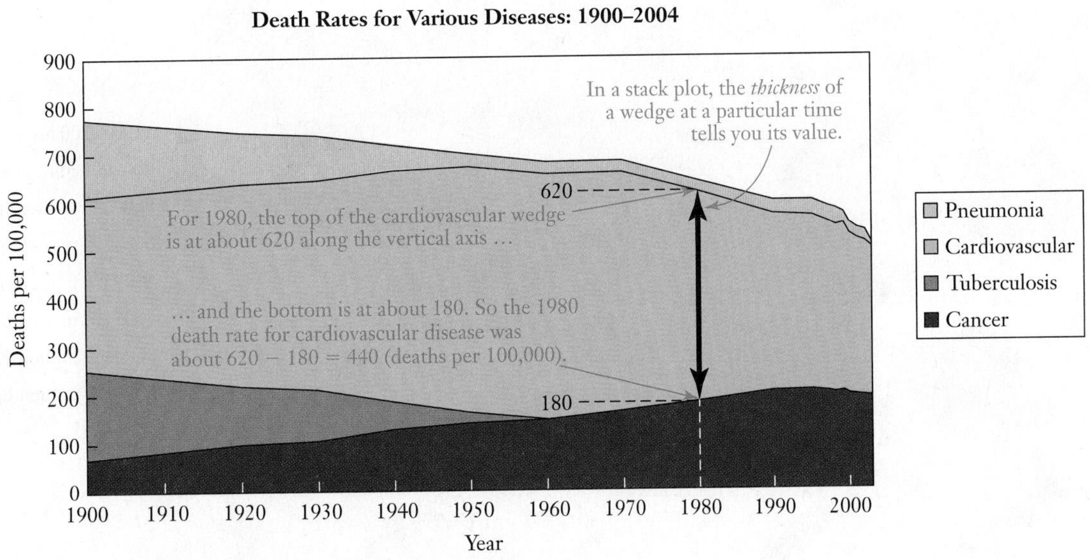

FIGURE 5.17 A stack plot showing trends in death rates from four diseases.
Source: Centers for Disease Control and Prevention.

Example 2 Stack Plot

Based on Figure 5.17, what was the death rate for cardiovascular disease in 1980? Discuss the general trends visible on this graph.

Solution For 1980, the cardiovascular wedge extends from about 180 to 620 on the vertical axis, so its thickness is about 440. Therefore, the death rate in 1980 for cardiovascular disease was about 440 deaths per 100,000 people. The graph shows several important trends. First, the downward slope of the top wedge shows that the overall death rate from these four diseases decreased substantially, from nearly 800 deaths per 100,000 in 1900 to about 525 in 2004. The drastic decline in the thickness of the tuberculosis wedge shows that this disease was once a major killer, but has been nearly wiped out since 1950. Meanwhile, the cancer wedge shows that the death rate from cancer rose steadily until the mid-1990s, but has dropped somewhat since then.

Now try Exercises 15–18.

BY THE WAY

Since the mid-1980s, there has been a small but noticeable resurgence of tuberculosis in the United States. Part of the resurgence is due to new strains of the disease that resist most common drug treatments.

Graphs of Geographical Data

We are often interested in geographical patterns in data. Figure 5.18 shows one common way of displaying geographical data. In this case, the data on per capita (per person) energy use are shown state by state. The legend explains that different colors represent different energy use levels. Similar colors are used for similar usage levels.

The display in Figure 5.18 works well because each state is associated with a unique energy usage level. For data that vary continuously across geographical areas, a **contour**

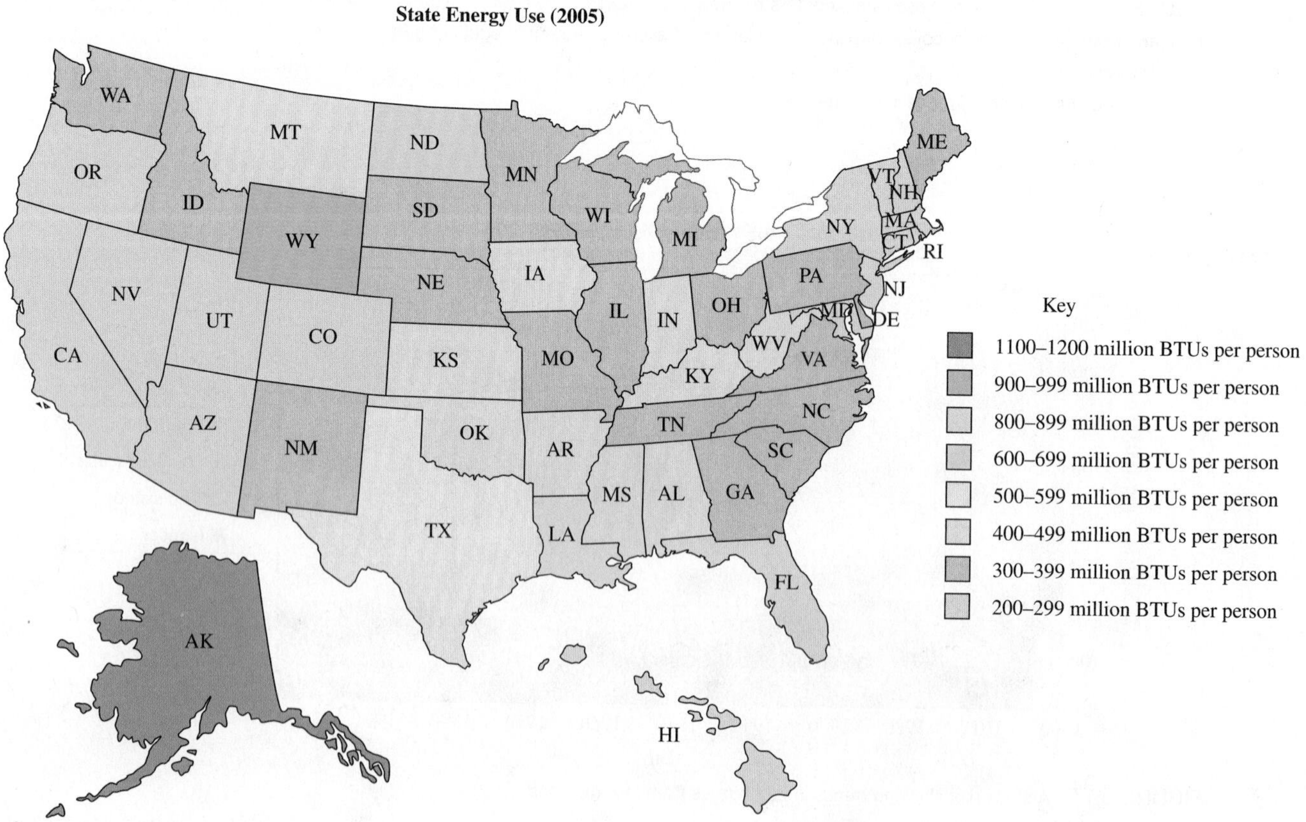

FIGURE 5.18 Geographical data can be displayed with a color-coded map.
Source: U.S. Energy Information Administration.

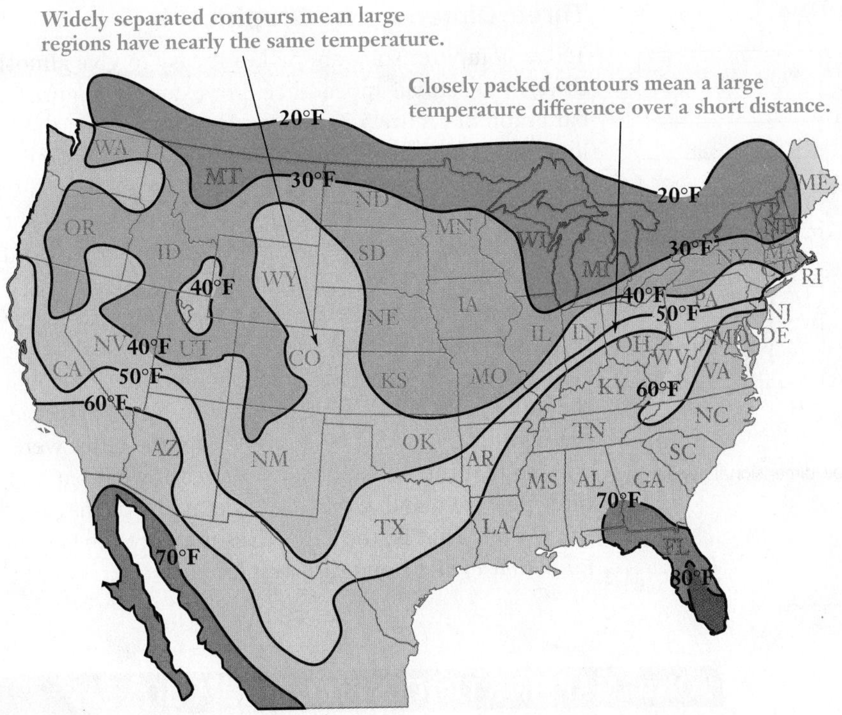

FIGURE 5.19 A contour map of temperature.

map is more convenient. Figure 5.19 shows a contour map of temperature over the United States at a particular time. Each of the *contours* connects locations with the same temperature. For example, the temperature is 50°F everywhere along the contour labeled 50° and 60°F everywhere along the contour labeled 60°F. Between these two contours, the temperature is between 50°F and 60°F. Note that in regions where contours are tightly spaced, there are greater temperature changes. For example, the closely packed contours in the northeast indicate that the temperature varies substantially over small distances. To make the graph easier to read, the regions between adjacent contours are color-coded.

Example 3 Interpreting Geographical Data

Study Figures 5.18 and 5.19, using them to answer the following questions.

a. Which state has the highest per capita energy usage?
b. Were there any temperatures above 80°F in the United States on the date shown in Figure 5.19? If so, where?

> The greatest value of a picture is when it forces us to notice what we never expected to see.
>
> –John Tukey

Solution

a. Alaska is the only state with energy usage in the highest category, which is colored blue and represents energy use between 1100 and 1200 million BTUs per person.
b. The 80° contour passes through southern Florida, so the parts of Florida south of this contour had a high temperature above80°. **Now try Exercises 19–20.**

Time Out to Think

Look for a weather map in today's news. How are the temperature contours shown? Interpret the temperature data.

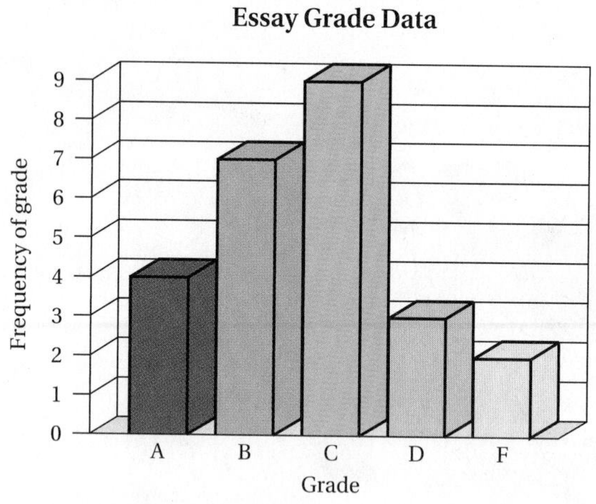

FIGURE 5.20 This graph has a three-dimensional appearance, but shows only two-dimensional data.

Three-Dimensional Graphics

Today, computer software makes it easy to give almost any graph a three-dimensional appearance. For example, Figure 5.20 shows the bar graph of Figure 5.3, but "dressed up" with a three-dimensional look. It may look nice, but the three-dimensional effects are purely cosmetic. They don't provide any information that wasn't already in the two-dimensional graph in Figure 5.3. As this example shows, many "three-dimensional" graphics really only make two-dimensional data look a little fancier.

In contrast, each of the three axes in Figure 5.21 carries distinct information, making it a true three-dimensional graph. Researchers studying migration patterns of a bird species (the bobolink) counted the number of birds flying over seven New York cities throughout the night. As shown on the inset map, the cities were aligned east-west so that the researchers would learn what parts of the state the birds flew over, and at what times of night, as they headed south for the winter. That is, the three axes measure the variables *number of birds, time of night,* and *east-west location.*

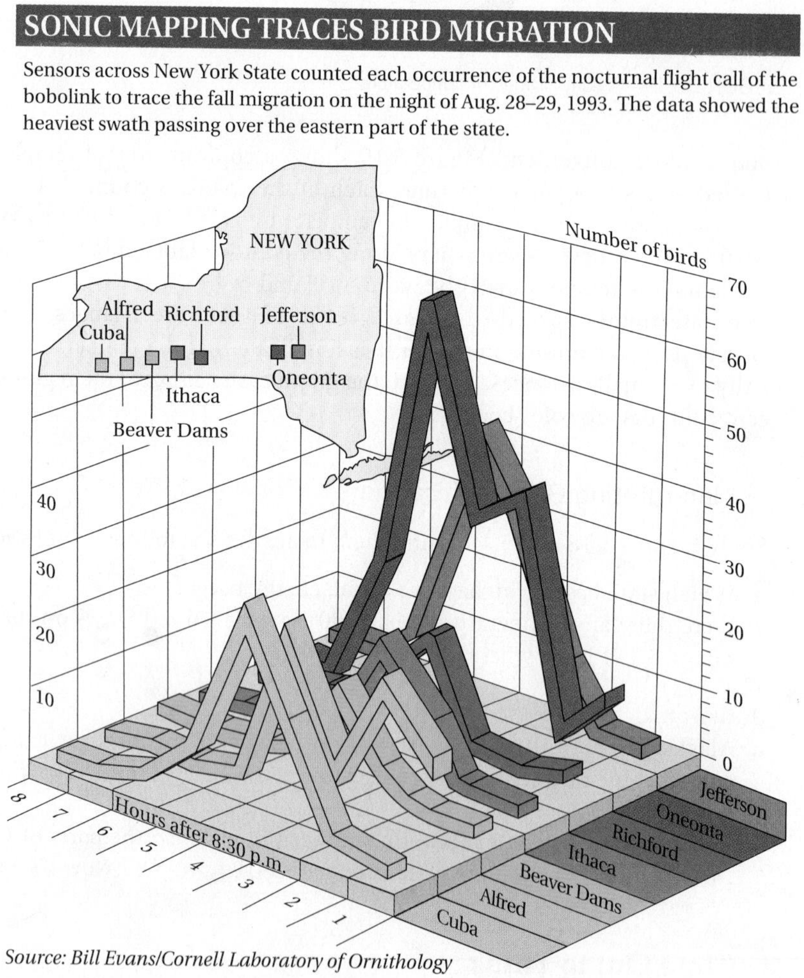

FIGURE 5.21 This graph shows true three-dimensional data.
Source: New York Times.

Example 4 Three-Dimensional Bird Migration

Based on Figure 5.21, at about what time was the largest number of birds flying over the east-west line marked by the seven cities? Over what part of New York did most of the birds fly? Approximately how many birds passed over Oneonta around 12:00 midnight?

Solution The number of birds detected in all the cities peaked between 3 and 5 hours after 8:30 p.m., or between about 11:30 p.m. and 1:30 a.m. More birds flew over the two easternmost cities of Oneonta and Jefferson than over cities farther west. Thus, most of the birds were flying over the eastern part of the state. To answer the specific question about Oneonta, note that 12:00 midnight is the midpoint of time category 4. On the graph, this time aligns with the dip between peaks on the line at Oneonta. Looking across to the *number of birds* axis, we see that about 30 birds were flying over Oneonta at that time. **Now try Exercises 21–22.**

Combination Graphics

All of the graphic types we have studied so far are common and fairly easy to create. But the media today are often filled with many varieties of even more complex graphics. For example, Figure 5.22 shows a graphic concerning the participation of women in the summer Olympics. This single graphic combines a line chart, many pie charts, and numerical data. It is certainly a case of a picture being worth far more than a thousand words.

Example 5 Olympic Women

Describe three trends shown in Figure 5.22.

Solution The line chart shows that the total number of women competing in the summer Olympics has risen fairly steadily, especially since the 1960s, reaching nearly 5000 in the 2008 games. The pie charts show that the percentage of women among all competitors has also increased, reaching 42% in the 2008 games. The bold red numbers at the bottom show that the number of events for women has also increased dramatically, reaching 138 in the 2008 games. **Now try Exercises 23–24.**

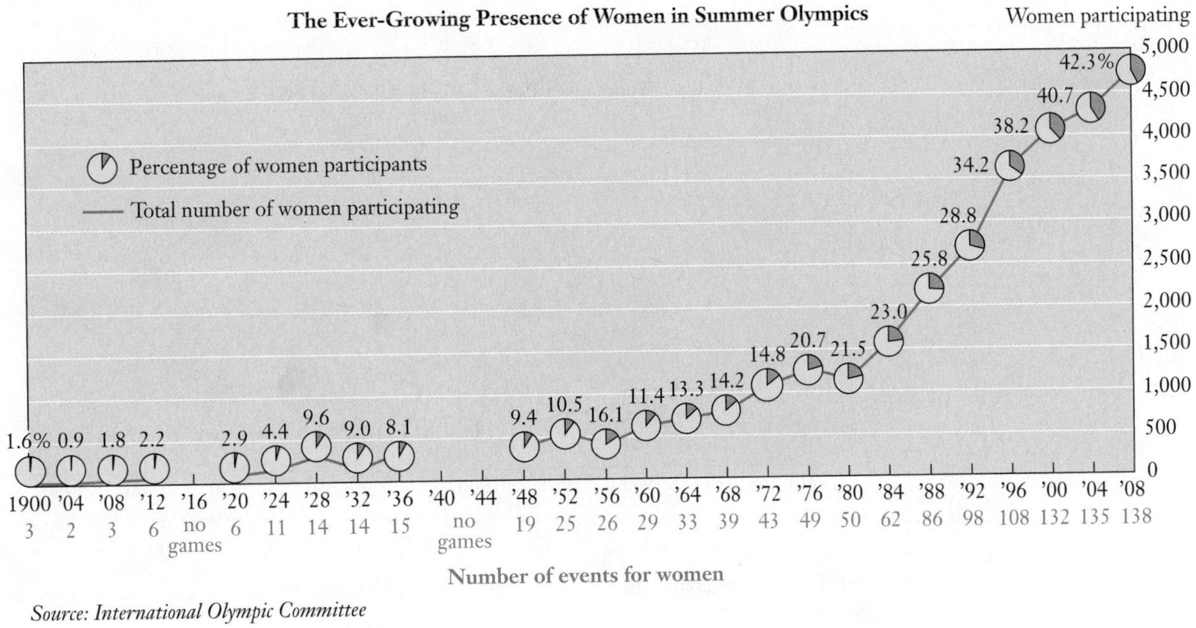

FIGURE 5.22 *Source:* Adapted from *The New York Times.*

Time Out to Think

Do you think the upward trend of the pie charts in Figure 5.22 will continue over the next few Olympic games? Why or why not?

A Few Cautions about Graphics

As we have seen, graphics can offer clear and meaningful summaries of statistical data. However, even well-made graphics can be misleading if we are not careful in interpreting them, and poorly made graphics are almost always misleading. Moreover, some people use graphics in deliberately misleading ways. Here, we discuss a few of the more common ways in which graphics can lead us astray.

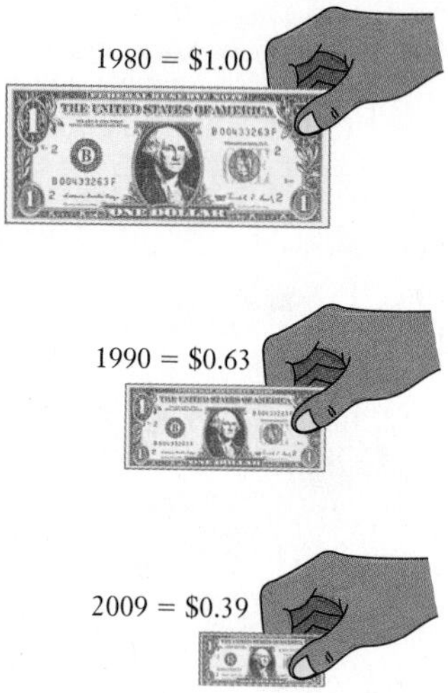

FIGURE 5.23 The lengths of the dollars are proportional to their spending power, but our eyes are drawn to the areas, which decline more than the lengths.

Perceptual Distortions

Many graphics are drawn in a way that distorts our perception of them. Figure 5.23 shows one of the most common types of distortion. The dollar-shaped bars are used to represent the declining value of the dollar over time. The *lengths* of the bars represent the data, but our eyes tend to focus on the *areas* of the bars. For example, the bottom bar is supposed to show that a dollar in 2009 was worth only 39% as much as a dollar in 1980. Its length is indeed 39% that of the top bar, but its area is much smaller in comparison (about 15% of the area of the top bar). This gives the perception that the value of the dollar shrank even more than it really did. **Now try Exercises 25–26.**

Watch the Scales

Figure 5.24a shows the percentage of college students since 1910 who were women. At first glance, it appears that this percentage grew by a huge margin after about 1950. But the vertical axis scale does not begin at zero and does not end at 100%. The increase is still substantial but looks far less dramatic if we redraw the graph with the vertical axis covering the full range of 0 to 100% (Figure 5.24b). From a mathematical point of view, leaving out the zero point on a scale is perfectly honest and can make it easier to see small-scale trends in the data. Nevertheless, as this example shows, it can be visually deceptive if you don't study the scale carefully. **Now try Exercises 27–28.**

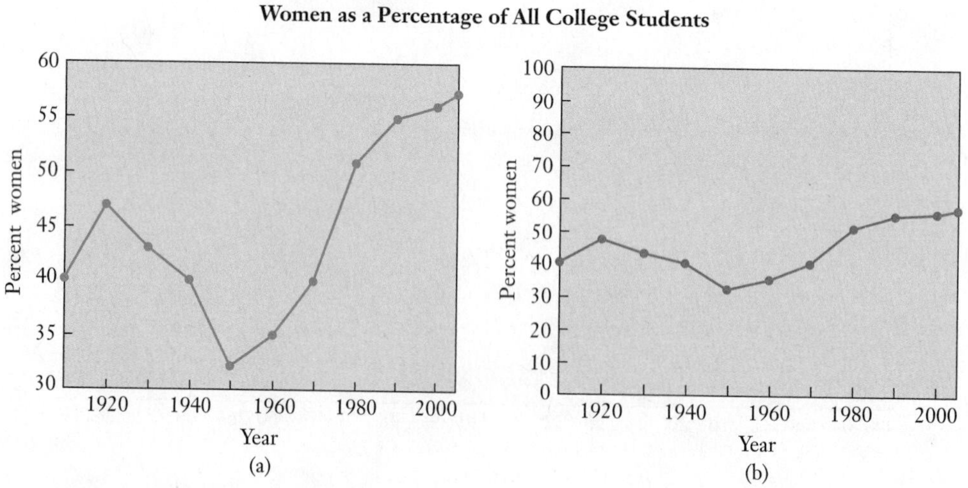

FIGURE 5.24 Both graphs show the same data, but they look very different because their vertical scales have different ranges.

Source: National Center for Education Statistics and Bureau of Labor Statistics.

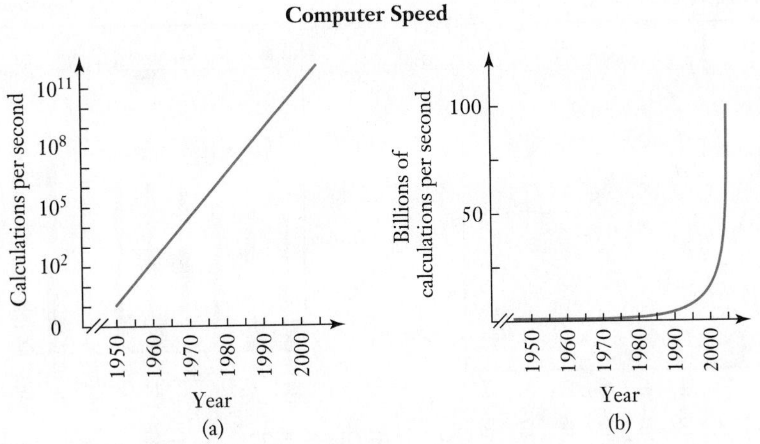

FIGURE 5.25 Both graphs show the same data, but the one on the left uses an exponential scale.

Sometimes the scale may not be deceptive, but still requires care to avoid misinterpretation. Consider Figure 5.25a, which shows how the speeds of the fastest computers have increased with time. At first glance, it appears that speeds have been increasing linearly. For example, it might look as if the speed increased by the same amount from 1990 to 2000 as it did from 1950 to 1960. However, if we look closely, we see that each tick mark on the vertical scale represents a *tenfold* increase in speed. Now we see that computer speed grew from about 1 to 100 calculations per second between 1950 and 1960, and from about 100 million to 10 billion calculations per second between 1990 and 2005. This type of scale is called an *exponential scale* (or *logarithmic scale*), because each unit corresponds to a power of 10. In general, exponential scales are useful for displaying data that vary over a huge range of values. You can see this usefulness by looking at Figure 5.25b, where the computer data have been recast with an ordinary scale. Because the speeds have grown so rapidly, the ordinary scale makes it impossible to see any detail in the early years shown on the graph. **Now try Exercise 29.**

BY THE WAY

In 1965, Intel founder Gordon E. Moore predicted that advances in technology would allow computer chips to double in power roughly every two years. This idea is now called *Moore's law,* and it has held fairly true ever since Moore first stated it.

Time Out to Think

Based on Figure 5.25a, can you predict the speed of the fastest computers in 2015? Could you make the same prediction with Figure 5.25b? Explain.

Percentage Change Graphs

Is college getting more or less expensive? A quick look at Figure 5.26 might give the impression that the cost for private colleges has been holding fairly steady while the cost for public colleges fell steeply after 2004.

But look more closely and you'll see that this is not the case at all. The vertical axis in Figure 5.26 represents the *percentage increase* in costs. A flat graph means only that costs increased by the same percentage each year, not that costs held steady. Similarly, the drop in the graph for public colleges means only that the cost *rose by smaller amounts* in recent years.

In fact, actual costs (not adjusted for inflation) for both public and private colleges have risen substantially with time, as shown in Figure 5.27. Moreover, because the rate of inflation (as measured by the Consumer Price Index; see Unit 3D) has been less than the rate of increase in college costs, the *real cost* of public colleges has steadily risen. Graphs that show percentage change are very common, particularly with economic data. Although they are perfectly honest, you can be misled unless you interpret them with great care.

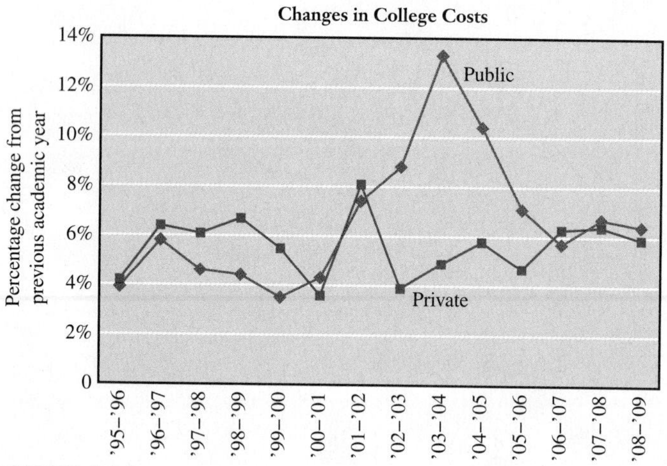

FIGURE 5.26 This graph shows the *rate of increase* with time in tuition and fees at four-year public and private colleges.
Source: The College Board.

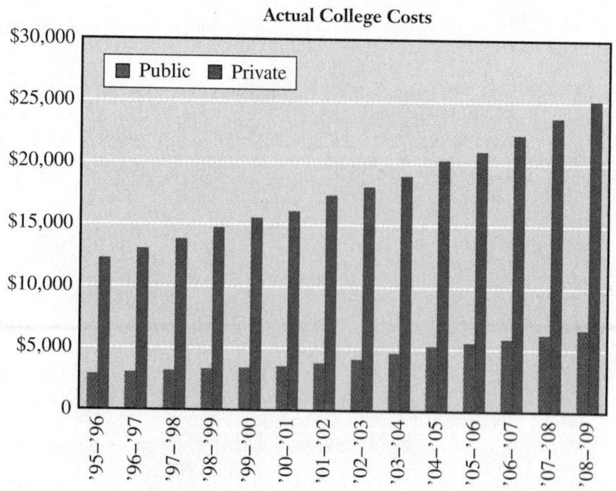

FIGURE 5.27 This graph shows the change with time in the *actual cost* (not adjusted for inflation) of tuition and fees at four-year public and private colleges. You can use the rise in these costs to calculate the percentage increases shown in Figure 5.26.
Source: The College Board.

Now try Exercise 30.

Pictographs

Pictographs are graphs embellished with additional artwork. The artwork may make the graph more appealing, but it can also distract or mislead. Figure 5.28 is a pictograph showing the rise in world population from 1804 to 2054 (numbers for future years are based on United Nations projections). The lengths of the bars correspond correctly to world population for the different years listed. However, the artistic embellishments of this graph are deceptive in several ways. For example, your eye may be drawn to the figures of people lining the globe. Because this line of people rises from the left side of the pictograph to the center and then falls, it might give the impression that future world population will be declining. In fact, the line of people is purely decorative and carries no information.

Perhaps the most serious problem with this pictograph is that it makes it appear that world population has been rising linearly. However, notice that the time intervals on the horizontal axis are not uniform in size. For example, the interval between the bars for 1 billion and 2 billion people is 123 years (from 1804 to 1927), but the interval between the bars for 5 billion and 6 billion people is only 12 years (from 1987 to 1999).

Pictographs are very common, but as this example shows, you have to study them carefully to extract the essential information and not be distracted by the cosmetic effects.

BY THE WAY

If world population were to continue to double at the same rate as it did in the late 20th century, it would reach 34 billion by 2100 and 192 billion by 2200. By about 2650, human population would be so large that it would not fit on the Earth, even if everyone stood elbow-to-elbow everywhere.

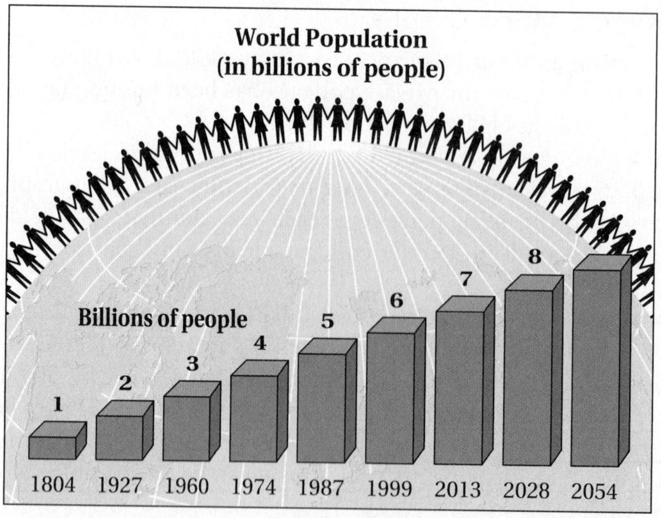

FIGURE 5.28 *Source:* Data from United Nations Population Division, World Population Prospects

Now try Exercises 31–32.

QUICK QUIZ

Choose the best answer to each of the following questions. Explain your reasoning with one or more complete sentences.

1. Consider Figure 5.16. Notice that the red segment of the second bar from the left starts higher up than the red segment of the first bar (at far left). This fact tells us that

   a. books and supplies cost more at public 4-year institutions than at public 2-year institutions.

   b. room and board cost more at public 4-year institutions than at public 2-year institutions.

   c. the sum of tuition and fees, plus room and board, is greater at public 4-year institutions than at public 2-year institutions.

2. Consider Figure 5.17. According to this graph, the approximate death rate from tuberculosis in 1950 was

   a. 2 per 100,000. b. 20 per 100,000. c. 200 per 100,000.

3. Consider Figure 5.18. According to this graph, what is per capita energy use in Oregon (OR)?

   a. between 200 and 299 million BTUs

   b. between 300 and 399 million BTUs

   c. more than 400 million BTUs

4. Consider the Figure 5.19. According to this map, the temperature in Iowa (IA) was

   a. 30°F. b. 40°F. c. between 30°F and 40°F.

5. Consider the tan regions in Figure 5.19, such as the region including northern Texas and eastern Colorado. What can you say about temperatures within those tan regions?

   a. They were 40°F.

   b. They were higher than 40°F but lower than 50°F.

   c. They could have been anything above 40°F.

6. Suppose you are given a contour map showing elevation (altitude) for the state of Vermont. The region with the most closely spaced contours represents

   a. the highest altitude.

   b. the lowest altitude.

   c. the steepest terrain.

7. Consider Figure 5.22. Approximately how many women participated in the 1948 Olympics?

   a. 19 b. 9.4 c. 450

8. Consider Figure 5.24a. The way the graph is drawn

   a. makes the graph completely invalid.

   b. makes the changes from one decade to the next appear larger than they really were.

   c. makes it more difficult to see the upward and downward trends that have occurred over time.

9. Consider Figure 5.25a. Moving one tick mark up the vertical axis represents an increase in computer speed of

   a. 1 billion calculations per second.

   b. a factor of 2.

   c. a factor of 10.

10. Consider Figure 5.26. In years where the graph slopes downward with time,

    a. college costs decreased.

    b. the cost of college rose, but by a lower percentage than in previous years.

    c. the cost of college rose, but the new cost represented a lower proportion of the average person's income.

Exercises 5D

REVIEW QUESTIONS

1. Briefly describe the construction and use of multiple bar graphs and stack plots.
2. What are geographical data? Briefly describe at least two ways to display geographical data. Be sure to explain the meaning of contours on a contour map.
3. What are three-dimensional graphics? Explain the difference between graphics that only appear three-dimensional and those that show truly three-dimensional data.
4. Describe how perceptual distortions can arise in graphics and how they can be misleading.
5. How can graphics be misleading when the scales do not go all the way to zero? Why are such graphics sometimes useful?
6. What is an exponential scale? When is an exponential scale useful?
7. Explain how a graph that shows percentage change can show descending bars (or a descending line) even when the variable of interest is increasing.
8. What is a pictograph? How can a pictograph enhance a graph? How can it make a graph misleading?

DOES IT MAKE SENSE?

Decide whether each of the following statements makes sense (or is clearly true) or does not make sense (or is clearly false). Explain your reasoning.

9. My bar chart contains more information than yours, because I made my bars three-dimensional.
10. I used an exponential scale because the data values for my categories ranged from 7 to 450,000.
11. There's been only a very slight rise in our stock price over the past few months, but I wanted to make it look dramatic so

I started the vertical scale from the lowest price rather than from zero.

12. A graph showing the yearly rate of increase in the number of computer users has a slight downward trend, even though the actual number of users is rising.

BASIC SKILLS & CONCEPTS

13. **Net Grain Production.** Net grain production is the difference between the amount of grain a country produces and the amount of grain its citizens consume. It is positive if the country produces more than it consumes, and negative if the country consumes more than it produces. Figure 5.29 shows the net grain production of four countries in 1990 and projected for 2030.

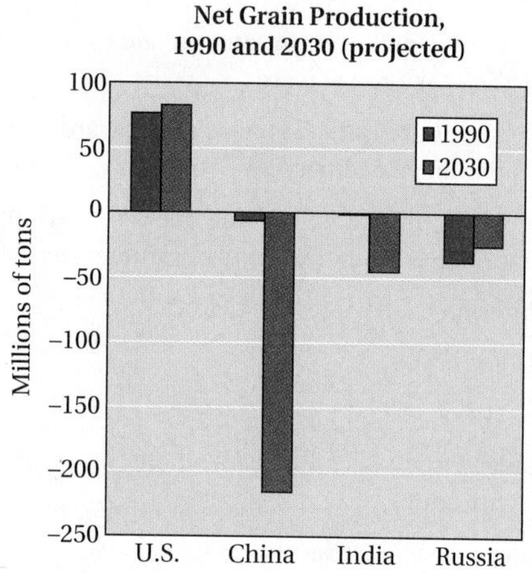

FIGURE 5.29

a. Which of the four countries had to import grain to meet its needs in 1990?

b. Which of the four countries are expected to need to import grain to meet needs in 2030?

c. Given that India and China are the world's two most populous countries, what does this graph tell you about how world agriculture will have to change between now and 2030?

14. **Education and Earnings.** Examine Figure 5.15, which shows the unemployment rate and the median weekly earnings for eight different levels of education.

a. Briefly describe how earnings vary with educational attainment.

b. Briefly describe how unemployment varies with educational attainment.

c. What is the percentage increase in weekly earnings when a professional degree is compared to a bachelor's degree?

d. How much more likely is a high school dropout to be unemployed than a worker with a bachelor's degree?

e. On average, people spend about 45 years in the work force before retiring. Based on the data in Figure 5.15, how much more would the average college graduate (bachelor's degree) earn during these 45 years than the average high school graduate?

15. **Stack Plot.** Answer the following based on Figure 5.17.

a. State whether the death rate for each of the four diseases individually decreased or increased between 1900 and 2004.

b. When was the death rate due to cardiovascular diseases the greatest, and what was the rate?

c. What was the death rate due to cancer in 2000?

d. Based on the trends in the graph, speculate on which of these four diseases will be responsible for the most deaths in 2050. Explain.

16. **College Costs Stack Plot.** Answer the following questions based on Figure 5.16.

a. Which cost category varies the most among the different types of institutions? by how much?

b. Which cost category varies the least among the different types of institutions? Can you explain why this category varies so little?

c. The general trend is for everything to cost more as you go from left to right across the different types of institutions, but one category is an exception and actually shows declines from left to right. Which category? Can you explain why?

17. **College Degrees.** Figure 5.30 shows the numbers of college degrees awarded to men and women over time.

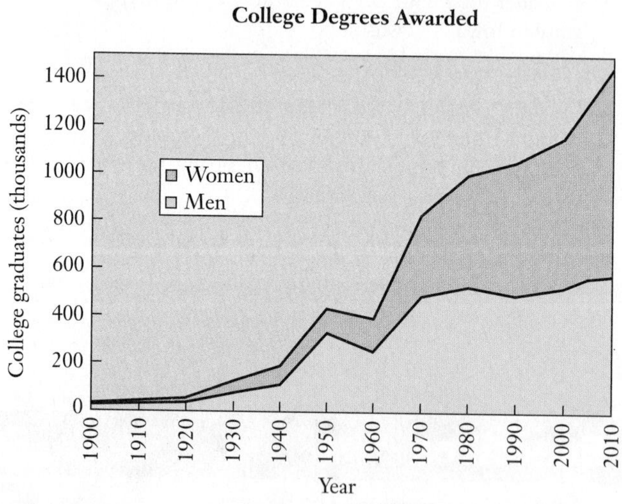

FIGURE 5.30

a. Estimate the numbers of college degrees awarded to men and to women (separately) in 1930 and in 2010.

b. Did men or women earn more degrees in 1980? Did men or women earn more degrees in 2010?

c. During what decade did the *total* number of degrees awarded increase the most?

d. Compare the *total* numbers of degrees awarded in 1950 and 2010.

e. Do you think the stack plot is an effective way to display these data? Briefly discuss other ways that might have been used instead.

18. **Federal Spending.** Figure 5.31 shows the major spending categories of the federal budget over the last 50 years. (*Payments to*

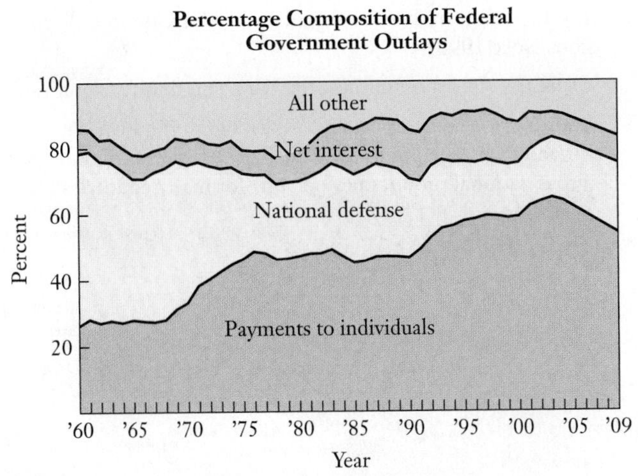

FIGURE 5.31 *Source:* Office of Management and Budget.

individuals includes Social Security and Medicare; *net interest* represents interest payments on the national debt; *all other* represents non-defense discretionary spending.)

Interpret the stack plot and discuss some of the trends it reveals.

a. Find the percentage of the budget that went to net interest in 1990, 1995, and 2005.

b. Find the percentage of the budget that went to defense in 1960, 1980, and 2005.

c. Find the percentage of the budget that went to payments to individuals in 1980, 2000, and 2005.

19. **School Segregation.** One way of measuring segregation is to determine the likelihood that a black student will have white classmates. A *New York Times* study found that, by this measure, segregation increased significantly in the 1990s. Figure 5.32 shows the probability, by county, that a black student had white classmates during the 1997–1998 academic year. Do there appear to be any significant regional differences? Can you pick out any differences between urban and rural areas? Discuss possible explanations for a few of the trends that you see in the figure.

20. **Contour Maps.** Consider the contour map in Figure 5.33, which has six points marked on it. Assume that points A and B correspond to summits, and that the contour lines have 40-foot intervals.

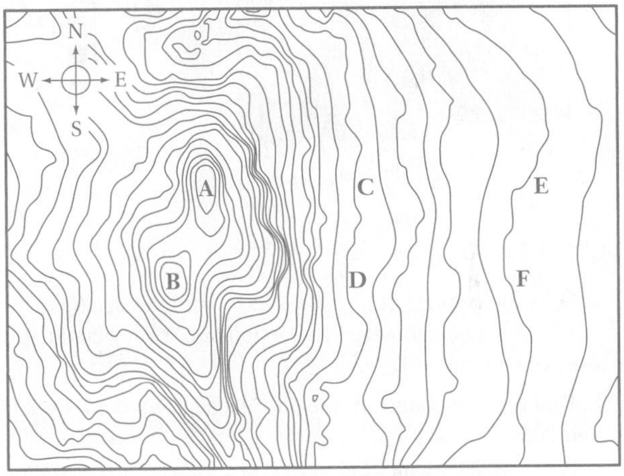

FIGURE 5.33

a. If you walk from A to C, do you walk uphill or downhill?

b. Does your elevation change more in walking from B to D or from D to F?

c. If you walk directly from E to F, does your elevation increase, decrease, or remain the same?

d. What is your net elevation change if you walk from A to C to D to A?

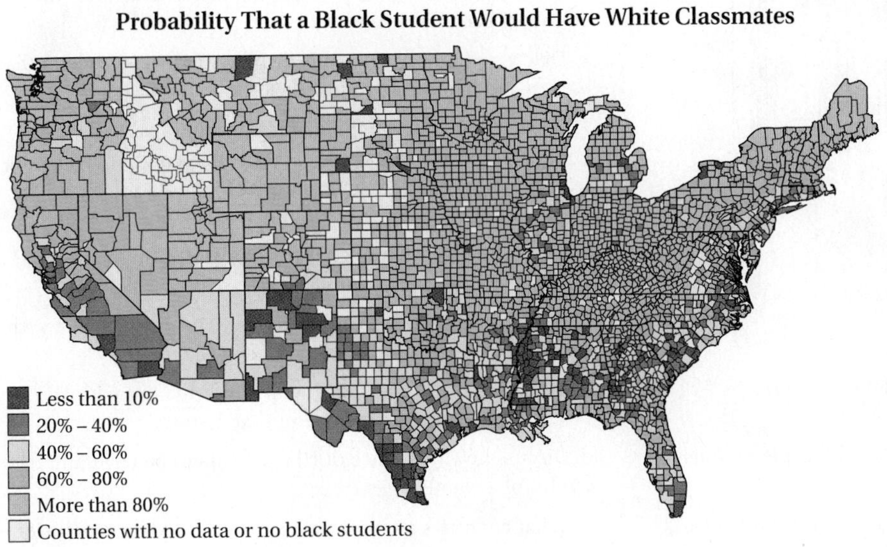

FIGURE 5.32 *Source: New York Times,* April 2, 2000.

21. **U.S. Age Distribution: 3D Plot.** Figure 5.34 shows projections of the age distribution of the U.S. population from 2010 through 2050. Use this graph to answer the following questions.

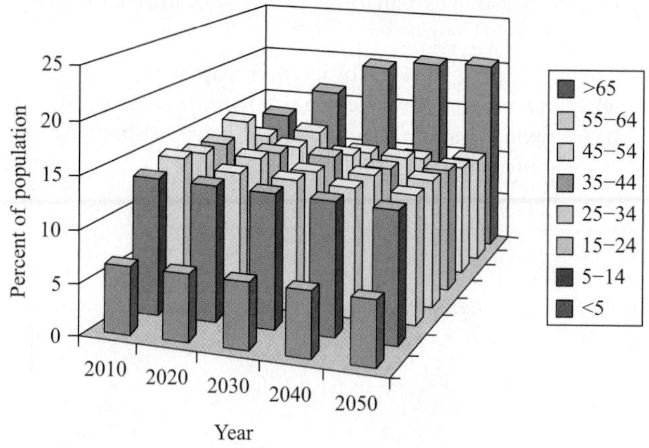

FIGURE 5.34

a. What percentage of the population was over age 65 in 2010? What percentage of the population is projected to be over age 65 in 2050?

b. Describe the change in the 45–54 age group between 2010 and 2050.

c. Does the under-25 segment of the population increase or decrease in size between 2010 and 2050?

d. In what year did (will) 45- to 54-year-olds comprise the largest percentage of the population?

e. Discuss any significant trends that you see in the data.

22. **CO_2 Emitters.** Figure 5.35 shows the carbon dioxide output (in terms of the total weight of the gas) of the world's leading emitters over the past 20 years. (Values for 2005 and 2010 were still estimates at the time this graph was created.)

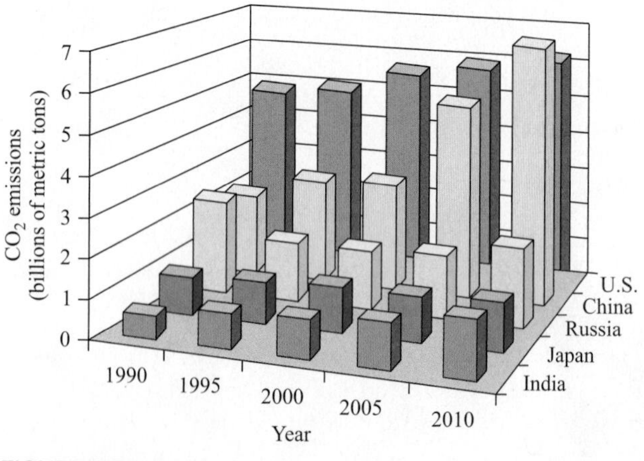

FIGURE 5.35 *Source:* U.S. Department of Energy.

a. By approximately what percentage did U.S. emissions increase between 1990 and 2010?

b. By approximately what percentage did Chinese emissions increase between 1990 and 2010?

c. Based on these estimates, approximately when did China overtake the United States as the leading emitter?

d. Which country has *not* seen a steady increase in CO_2 emissions since 1990?

e. Discuss one aspect of these data that you think is significant.

23. **Happiness Graph.** Consider the display in Figure 5.36, which relates a happiness index to economic strength (gross national product per person) for many countries.

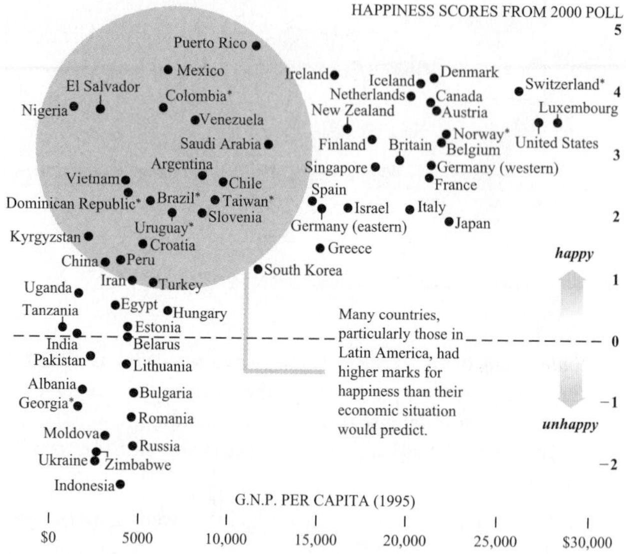

*Poll results for these countries were from 1995.

Source: Ronald Inglehart, "Human Beliefs and Values: A Cross-Cultural Sourcebook Based on the 1999–2002 Values Surveys"

FIGURE 5.36 *Source: New York Times.*

a. What kind of variable is the happiness index (qualitative or quantitative)? What does zero on the happiness scale mean?

b. Are there any countries with a low happiness index despite good economic strength?

c. Characterize geographically the countries with high happiness and high economic strength.

d. The display suggests that certain countries are anomalous; that is, they run counter to expectations. Characterize these countries geographically.

e. Discuss whether or not this display supports the claim that wealth and happiness go together.

24. **HIV Distribution.** Figure 5.37 displays the wealth of various countries (per capita income) and the percentage of adults infected with HIV in the same countries. The size of the bubble is proportional to the actual number of HIV-infected adults.

a. How is the location of countries indicated on the display? On what continent is Benin located?

b. Approximately how many people in South Africa live with HIV? What is the per capita income in that country?

c. Approximately how many people in India live with HIV? What is the per capita income in that country?

d. Discuss how incidence of HIV appears to be related to the wealth of a country.

e. What countries are notable exceptions to your conclusion in part d?

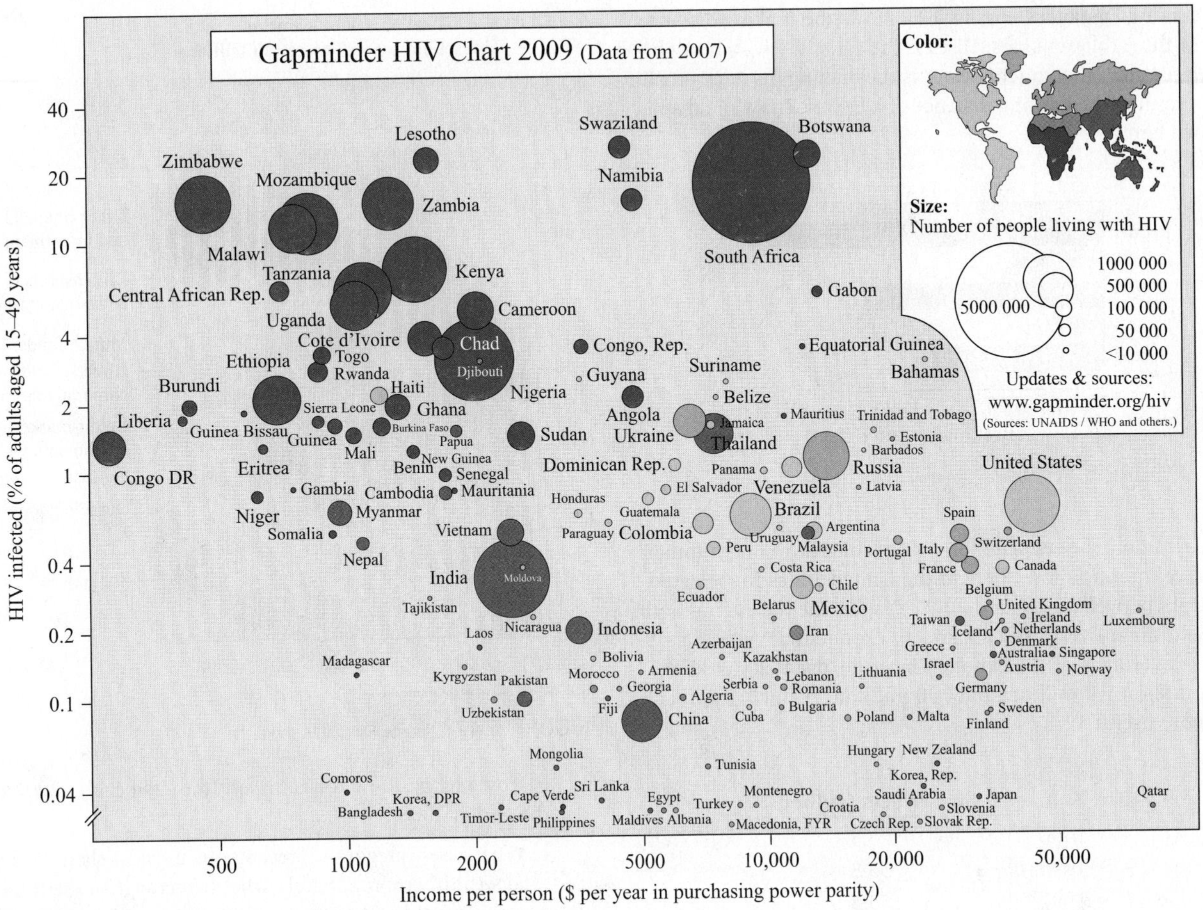

FIGURE 5.37 *Source:* Gapminder, http://www.gapminder.org/.

25. **Volume Distortion.** Figure 5.38 uses television sets to represent the numbers of homes with cable in 1980 and 2008. Note that the heights of the TVs represent the numbers of homes. Briefly explain how the graph creates a perceptual distortion that exaggerates the true change in the number of homes with cable.

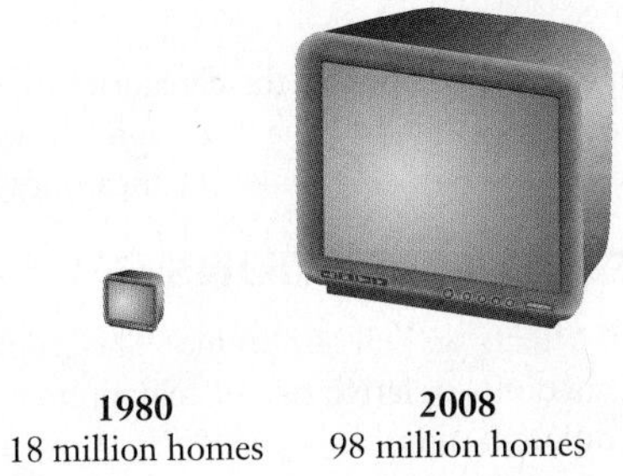

FIGURE 5.38

26. **Three-Dimensional Pies.** The pie charts in Figure 5.39 represent the percentage of Americans in three age categories in 1990 and 2050 (projected). Briefly explain how the three-dimensional effects create a perceptual distortion in this case. Why would flat pies (without the three-dimensional effects) give a more accurate representation of the data?

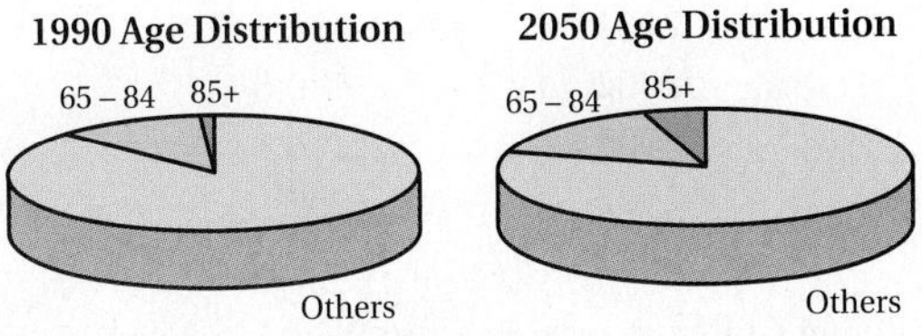

FIGURE 5.39 *Source:* U.S. Census Bureau.

27. **Comparing Earnings.** Figure 5.40 compares the average weekly earnings of men and women. Identify any misleading aspects of the display. Draw the display in a fairer way.

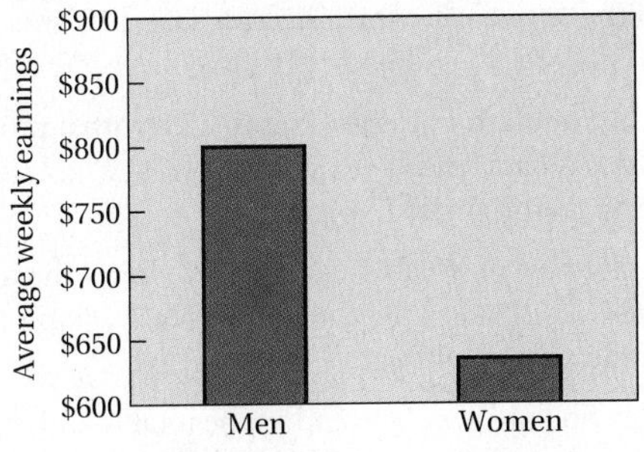

FIGURE 5.40 *Source:* U.S. Census Bureau.

28. **Braking Distances.** Figure 5.41 shows the braking distance for three different cars. Discuss the ways in which it might be deceptive. How much greater is the braking distance of a Lincoln than the braking distance of a Lexus? Draw the display in a fairer way.

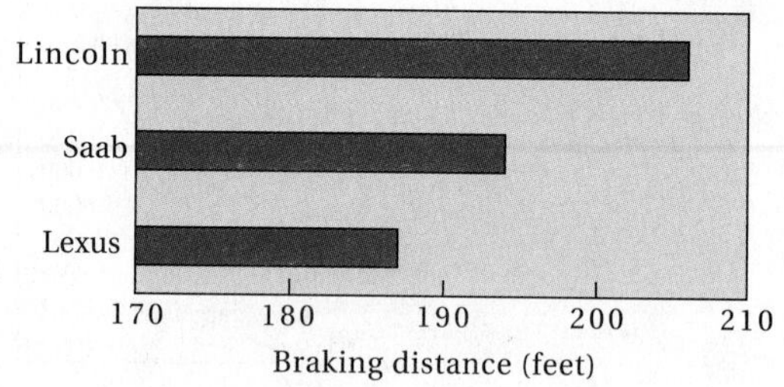

FIGURE 5.41 *Source: Car and Driver.*

29. **Cell Phone Users.** The following table shows the number of cell phone subscribers in the United States for selected years between 1990 and 2007. Display the data using both an ordinary vertical scale and an exponential vertical scale. (*Hint:* For the exponential scale, use tick marks at 1 million, 10 million, and 100 milllion.) Which graph is more useful? Why?

Year	Subscribers (millions)
1990	5.3
1995	33.8
1997	55.3
1998	69.2
1999	86.0
2000	109.5
2001	128.3
2002	140.8
2003	158.7
2007	255

30. **Rising College Costs.** Refer to Figures 5.26 and 5.27 to answer the following questions.

a. In what academic year did public college costs rise by the largest percentage? What was the percentage increase?

b. In the same year (as part a), what was the percentage increase in private college costs?

c. In the same year, which had the larger increase in actual cost (in dollars): public or private colleges? Explain.

31. **World Population.** Recast Figure 5.28 with a proper horizontal axis. What trends are clear in your new graph that are not clear in the original? Explain.

32. **U.S. Sources of Wealth.** Figure 5.42 shows the total wealth of the United States, by category. Use this graph to answer the following questions.

a. Describe the general trend in the total wealth of households in the United States from 2003 to 2008.

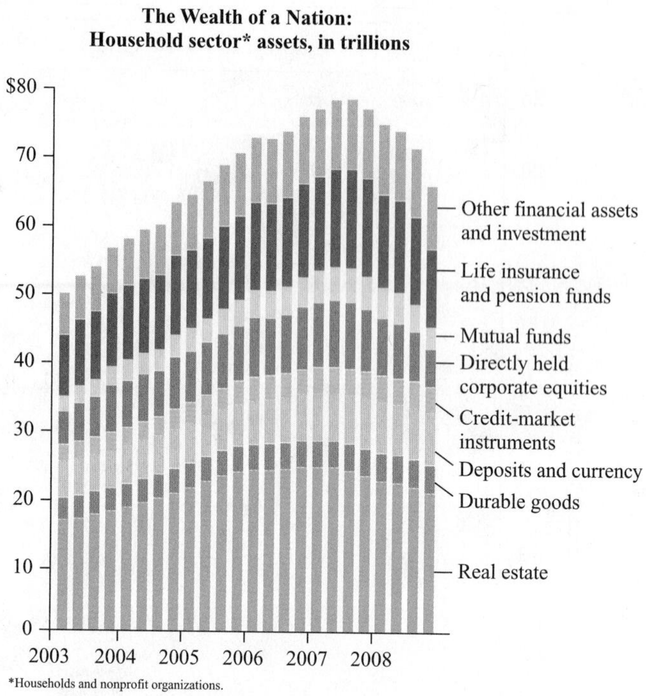

FIGURE 5.42 *Source:* Federal Reserve.

b. How much did total wealth fall from its peak in 2007 to the end of 2008?

c. What asset category represents the greatest share of the total wealth? Approximately what percentage of the total wealth does this category make up, as of the beginning of 2009?

d. The category "directly held corporate equities" represents investments in the stock market. How did the value of stock investments change between mid-2007 and the end of 2008?

e. Based on what has happened to the economy since the beginning of 2009, how do you think total wealth has changed since that time? What category (or categories) would you expect to have changed the most? Explain your reasoning.

f. The meanings of some of the categories might be somewhat mysterious. What might have been done differently, either visually or with words, to make the meanings more clear?

FURTHER APPLICATIONS

33. **Seasonal Effects on Schizophrenia?** The graph in Figure 5.43 shows data on the relative risk of schizophrenia among people born in different months.

a. Note that the scale of the vertical axis does not include zero. Sketch the same risk curve using an axis that includes zero. Comment on the effect of this change.

b. Each value of the relative risk is shown with a dot at its most likely value and with an "error bar" indicating the range in which the data value probably lies. The study concludes that "the risk was also significantly associated with the season of birth." Given the size of the error bars, does this claim appear justified? (Is it possible to draw a flat line that passes through all of the error bars?)

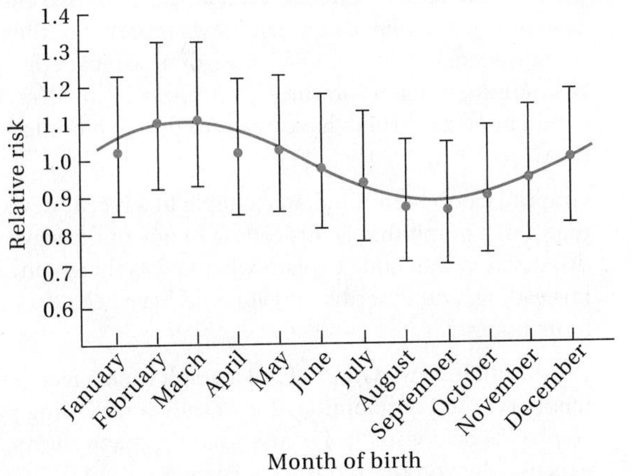

FIGURE 5.43 *Source: New England Journal of Medicine.*

34–38: Creating Graphics. Make a graphical display of the following data sets, choosing any type of display that you feel is appropriate. Explain your choice of display and discuss any interesting features in the data.

34. The following table shows the percentages, for 1970 and 2007, of men and women in various age categories who were never married.

Women	1970	2007	Men	1970	2007
20–24	35.8	75.3	20–24	54.7	86.7
25–29	10.5	43.1	25–29	19.1	57.4
30–34	6.2	24.0	30–34	9.4	33.4
35–39	5.4	16.7	35–39	7.2	23.3
40–44	4.9	13.1	40–44	6.3	18.5

Source: U.S. Census Bureau.

35. The following table gives the percentage of the U.S. population that was foreign born between 1920 and 2006.

Year	Percentage
1920	13.2
1930	11.6
1940	8.8
1950	6.9
1960	5.4
1970	4.7
1980	6.2
1990	8.0
2000	10.4
2006	12.1

Source: U.S. Census Bureau.

36. The following table gives the total number of automobile fatalities and the number of fatalities in which alcohol was involved for 1982 to 2007. All figures are in thousands of deaths.

Year	Total	Alcohol
1982	43,945	26,173
1984	44,257	24,762
1986	46,087	25,017
1988	47,087	23,833
1990	44,599	22,587
1992	39,250	18,290
1994	40,716	17,308
1996	42,065	17,749
1998	41,501	16,673
2000	41,945	17,380
2002	42,815	17,419
2004	42,643	16,919
2006	42,708	15,829
2007	41,059	15,387

Source: National Highway Traffic Safety Administration.

37. The following table gives the number of daily newspapers and their total circulation (in millions) for selected years since 1920.

Year	Number of Daily Newspapers	Circulation (millions)
1920	2042	27.8
1930	1942	39.6
1940	1878	41.1
1950	1772	53.9
1960	1763	58.8
1970	1748	62.1
1980	1747	62.2
1990	1611	62.3
2000	1485	56.1
2006	1437	52.3

Source: Newspaper Association of America.

38. The following table summarizes deaths due to firearms in different nations in a recent year.

Country	Total	Homicides	Suicides	Fatal Accidents
U.S.	35,563	15,835	18,503	1225
Germany	1197	168	1004	25
Canada	1189	176	975	38
Australia	536	96	420	20
Spain	396	76	219	101
U.K.	277	72	193	12
Sweden	200	27	169	4
Vietnam	131	85	16	30
Japan	93	34	49	10

Source: Coalition to Stop Gun Violence.

WEB PROJECTS

39. **Weather Maps.** Many Web sites display contour maps with current weather data. For example, you can use the Yahoo Weather site to generate many different contour weather maps. Generate at least two contour weather maps and discuss what they show.

40. **Cancer Cure.** As shown in Figure 5.17, cancer is one of the leading causes of death today. Nevertheless, scientists have made great progress in treating many forms of cancer. Go to the American Cancer Society Web site and investigate research into cancer cures. Read about one or two recent studies, and write a short report on what you learn. Be sure to include graphics in your report.

IN YOUR WORLD

41. **News Graphics.** Find a recent news report that shows a multiple bar graph or stack plot. Comment on the effectiveness of the display. Could another display have been used to depict the same data?

42. **Geographical Data.** Find an example of a graph of geographical data in a recent news report. Comment on the effectiveness of the display. Could another display have been used to depict the same data?

43. **Three-Dimensional Effects.** Find an example of a three-dimensional display in a recent news report. Are the data three-dimensional or are the three-dimensional effects cosmetic? Comment on the effectiveness of the display. Could another display have been used to depict the same data?

44. **Graphic Confusion.** Find an example in a recent news report of a graph that is misleading in one of the ways discussed in this unit. Explain what makes the graph misleading, and describe how it could have been drawn more honestly.

45. **Outstanding News Graph.** Find a graph from a recent news report that, in your opinion, does a truly outstanding job of displaying data visually. Discuss what the graph shows, and explain why you think it is so outstanding.

UNIT 5E Correlation and Causality

A major goal of many statistical studies is to determine whether one factor *causes* another. For example, does smoking cause lung cancer? In this unit, we will discuss how statistics can be used to search for *correlations* that might suggest a cause-and-effect relationship. Then we'll explore the more difficult task of establishing causality.

Seeking Correlation

> Smoking is one of the leading causes of statistics.
>
> —Fletcher Knebel

What does it mean when we say that smoking *causes* lung cancer? It certainly does *not* mean that you'll get lung cancer if you smoke a single cigarette. It does not even mean that you'll definitely get lung cancer if you smoke heavily for many years, since some heavy smokers do not get lung cancer. Rather, it is a *statistical* statement meaning that you are *much more likely* to get lung cancer if you smoke than if you don't smoke.

Let's try to understand how researchers learned that smoking causes lung cancer. Before they could investigate *cause*, researchers first needed to establish correlations between smoking and cancer. The process of establishing correlations began with observations. The early observations were informal. Doctors noticed that smokers made up a surprisingly high proportion of their patients with lung cancer. This suggestion of a linkage led to carefully conducted studies in which researchers compared lung cancer rates among smokers and nonsmokers. These studies showed clearly that heavier smokers were more likely to get lung cancer. In more formal terms, we say that there is a correlation between the variables *amount of smoking* and *incidence of lung cancer*. A correlation is a special type of relationship between variables, in which a rise or fall in one goes along with a corresponding rise or fall in the other.

DEFINITION

A correlation exists between two variables when higher values of one variable consistently go with higher values of another or when higher values of one variable consistently go with lower values of another.

Here are a few other examples of correlations:

- There is a correlation between the variables *height* and *weight* for people. That is, taller people tend to weigh more than shorter people.
- There is a correlation between the variables *demand for apples* and *price of apples*. That is, demand tends to decrease as prices increase.
- There is a correlation between *practice time* and *skill* among piano players. That is, those who practice more tend to be more skilled.

Establishing a correlation between two variables does *not* mean that a change in one variable *causes* a change in the other. Finding the correlation between smoking and lung cancer did not by itself prove that smoking causes lung cancer. We could imagine, for example, that some gene predisposes a person both to smoking and to lung cancer. Nevertheless, identifying the correlation was the crucial first step in learning that smoking causes lung cancer.

BY THE WAY

Smoking is linked to many serious diseases besides lung cancer, including heart disease and emphysema. Smoking is also linked with less lethal health conditions such as premature skin wrinkling and sexual impotence.

Time Out to Think

Suppose there really were a gene that made people prone to both smoking and lung cancer. Explain why we would still find a strong correlation between smoking and lung cancer in that case, but would not be able to say that smoking caused lung cancer.

Scatter Diagrams

Table 5.6 shows the production cost and gross receipts (total revenue from ticket sales) for the 15 biggest-budget science fiction and fantasy movies of all time (through mid-2009). Movie executives presumably hope there is a favorable correlation between the production budget and the receipts. That is, they hope that spending more to produce a movie will result in higher box office receipts. But is there such a correlation? We can look for a correlation by making a **scatter diagram** showing the relationship between the variables *production cost* and *gross receipts*.

TABLE 5.6 Biggest-Budget Science Fiction and Fantasy Movies

Movie	Production Cost (millions of dollars)	U.S. Gross Receipts (millions of dollars)
Spider-Man 3 (2007)	258	337
King Kong (2005)	207	218
The Golden Compass (2007)	205	70
Superman Returns (2006)	204	200
Spider-Man 2 (2004)	200	373
The Chronicles of Narnia: Prince Caspian (2008)	200	142
Iron Man (2008)	186	318
Terminator Salvation (2009)	185	125
Indiana Jones and the Kingdom of the Crystal Skull (2008)	185	317
The Dark Knight (2008)	185	533
Chronicles of Narnia: The Lion, the Witch and the Wardrobe (2005)	180	292
WALL-E (2008)	180	223
The Mummy: Tomb of the Dragon Emperor (2008)	175	102
Waterworld (1995)	175	88
Van Helsing (2004)	170	120

Note: Gross receipts are for United States only; worldwide receipts are often substantially higher. These figures are not adjusted for inflation.

DEFINITION

A **scatter diagram** is a graph in which each point represents the values of two variables.

The following procedure describes how we make the scatter diagram, which is shown in Figure 5.44:

1. We assign one variable to each axis, and we label each axis with values that comfortably fit the data. Here, we assign *production cost* to the horizontal axis and *gross receipts* to the vertical axis. We choose a range of \$150 to \$300 million for the production cost axis and \$0 to \$550 million for the gross receipts axis.
2. For each movie in Table 5.6, we plot a *single point* at the horizontal position corresponding to its production cost and the vertical position corresponding to its gross receipts. For example, the point for the movie *Prince Caspian* goes at a position of \$200 million on the horizontal axis and \$142 million on the vertical axis. The dashed lines on Figure 5.44 show how we locate this point.
3. (Optional) If we wish, we can label data points, as is done for selected points in Figure 5.44.

Take Note

We often have some reason to think that one variable depends at least in part on the other. In the case of Figure 5.44, we might guess that gross receipts should depend on the production cost. We therefore call production cost the *explanatory variable* and gross receipts the *response variable,* because the production cost might help explain the gross receipts. The explanatory variable is usually plotted on the horizontal axis and the response variable on the vertical axis.

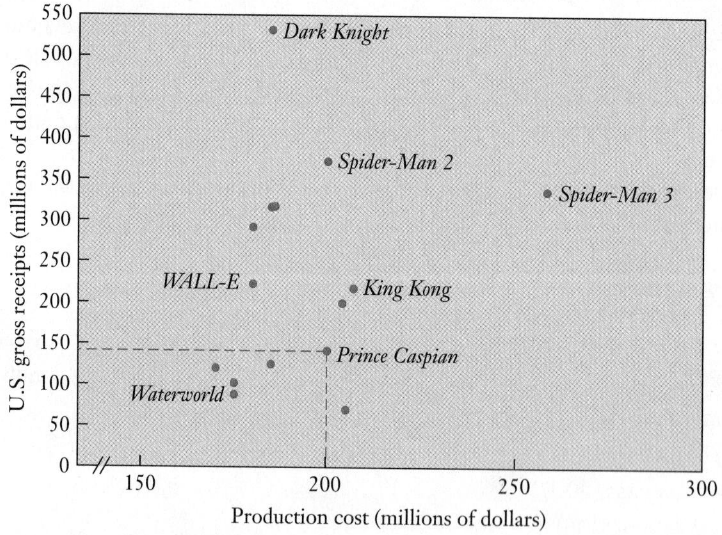

FIGURE 5.44 Scatter diagram for the data in Table 5.6.

Time Out to Think

By studying Table 5.6, associate each of the unlabeled data points in Figure 5.44 with a particular movie.

Types of Correlation

Look carefully at the scatter diagram for movies in Figure 5.44. The dots seem to be scattered about with no apparent pattern. In other words, at least for these big-budget movies, there appears to be little or no correlation between the amount of money spent producing the movie and the amount of money it earned in gross receipts.

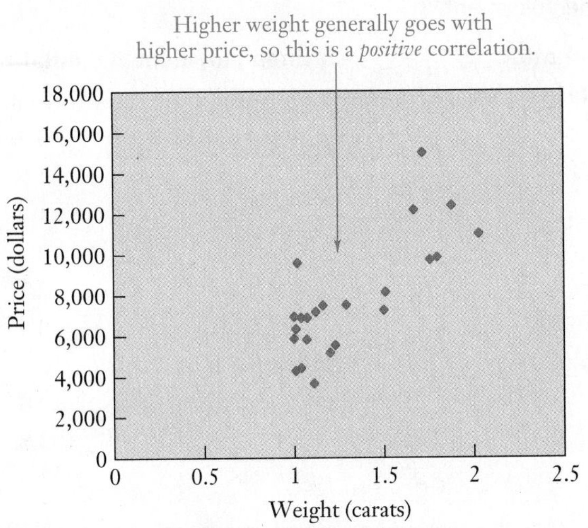

FIGURE 5.45 A scatter diagram for diamond weights and prices.

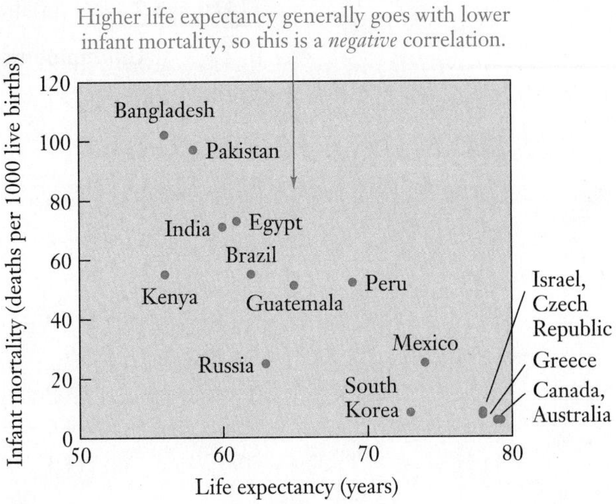

FIGURE 5.46 A scatter diagram for life expectancy and infant mortality.

Now consider the scatter diagram in Figure 5.45, which shows the weights (in carats) and retail prices of 23 diamonds. Here, the dots show a clear upward trend, indicating that larger diamonds generally cost more. The correlation is not perfect. For example, the heaviest diamond is not the most expensive. But the overall trend seems fairly clear. Because the prices tend to increase with the weights, we say that Figure 5.45 shows a **positive correlation.**

In contrast, Figure 5.46 shows a scatter diagram for the variables *life expectancy* and *infant mortality* in 16 countries. We again see a clear trend, but this time it is a **negative correlation:** Countries with *higher* life expectancy tend to have *lower* infant mortality.

Besides stating whether a correlation exists, we can also discuss its strength. The more closely the data follow the general trend, the stronger is the correlation.

BY THE WAY

In statistics, the *correlation coefficient* provides a quantitative measure of the strength of a correlation. It is defined to be 1 for a perfect (meaning all data points lie on a single straight line) positive correlation, −1 for a perfect negative correlation, and 0 for no correlation.

RELATIONSHIPS BETWEEN TWO DATA VARIABLES

No correlation: There is no apparent relationship between the two variables.

Positive correlation: Both variables tend to increase (or decrease) together.

Negative correlation: The two variables tend to change in opposite directions, with one increasing while the other decreases.

Strength of a correlation: The more closely two variables follow the general trend, the stronger the correlation (which may be either positive or negative). In a perfect correlation, all data points lie on a straight line.

Example 1 Inflation and Unemployment

Prior to the 1990s, most economists assumed that the unemployment rate and the inflation rate were negatively correlated. That is, when unemployment goes down, inflation goes up, and vice versa. Table 5.7 shows unemployment and inflation data for the period 1990–2006. Make a scatter diagram for these data. Based on your diagram, does it appear that the data support the historical claim of a link between the unemployment and inflation rates?

TABLE 5.7 U.S. Inflation and Unemployment

Year	Unemployment Rate (%)	Inflation Rate (%)	Year	Unemployment Rate (%)	Inflation Rate (%)
1990	5.6	5.4	2000	4.0	3.4
1991	6.8	4.2	2001	4.2	1.8
1992	7.5	3.0	2002	5.8	1.6
1993	6.9	3.0	2003	6.0	2.3
1994	6.1	2.6	2004	5.5	2.7
1995	5.6	2.8	2005	5.1	3.4
1996	5.4	3.0	2006	4.6	3.3
1997	4.9	2.3	2007	4.6	2.8
1998	4.6	2.3	2008	5.8	3.8
1999	4.3	2.2	2009	8.5	3.6

Source: U.S. Bureau of Labor Statistics; 2009 data through April of that year.

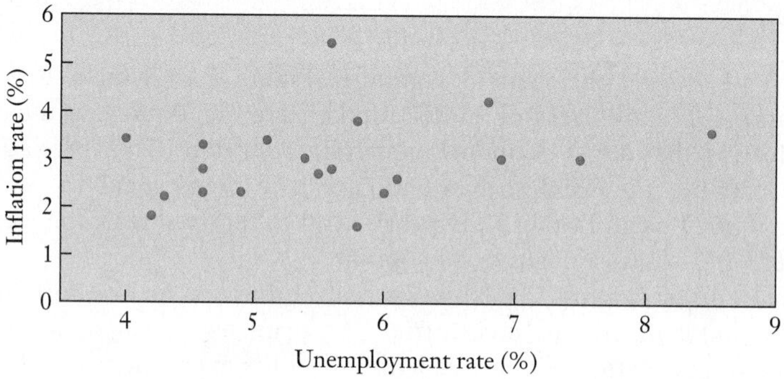

FIGURE 5.47 Scatter diagram for the data in Table 5.7.

Solution We make the scatter diagram by plotting the variable *unemployment rate* on the horizontal axis and the variable *inflation rate* on the vertical axis. To make the graph easy to read, we use values ranging from 3.5% to 9% for the unemployment rate and from 0 to 6% for the inflation rate. Figure 5.47 shows the result. To the eye, there does not appear to be any obvious correlation between the two variables. (A calculation confirms that there is no appreciable correlation.) These data do *not* support the historical claim of a negative correlation between the unemployment and inflation rates. **Now try Exercises 13–14.**

Example 2 Accuracy of Weather Forecasts

The scatter diagrams in Figure 5.48 show two weeks of data comparing the actual high temperature for the day with the same-day forecast (left diagram) and the three-day forecast (right diagram). Discuss the types of correlation on each diagram.

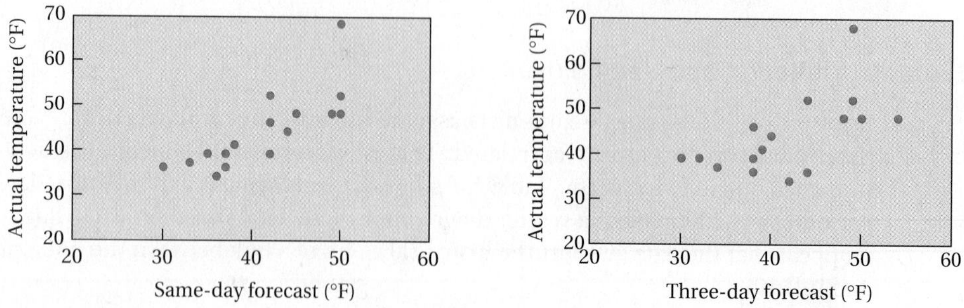

FIGURE 5.48 Comparison of actual high temperatures with same-day and three-day forecasts.

Solution Both scatter diagrams show a general trend in which higher predicted temperatures mean higher actual temperatures. That is, both show positive correlations. However, the points in the left diagram lie more nearly on a straight line, indicating a stronger correlation than in the right diagram. This makes sense, because we expect weather forecasts to be more accurate on the same day than three days in advance.

Now try Exercises 15–16.

Possible Explanations for a Correlation

We began by stating that correlations can help us search for cause-and-effect relationships. But we've already seen that causality is not the only possible explanation for a correlation. For example, the predicted temperatures on the horizontal axis of Figure 5.48 certainly do not *cause* the actual temperatures on the vertical axis. The box on the next page summarizes three possible explanations for a correlation.

USING TECHNOLOGY

Scatter Diagrams in Excel

Excel makes it easy to generate scatter diagrams; the screen shot below shows the process for the data from Example 1.

1. Enter the data, which are shown in columns B (year), C (unemployment rate), and D (inflation rate).
2. Select the columns for the two variables on the scatter diagram—in this case, columns C and D.
3. Choose "Scatter" from the "chart" section of the Insert menu or Data ribbon to make the diagram. You can then use "chart options" (which comes up with a right-click in the graph) to customize the appearance.

Note: Excel also offers the option "Add Trendline," which draws a best-fit line to the data (be sure to choose the "linear" option) and displays a value called R^2, which is the square of the correlation coefficient. Or, you can calculate the correlation coefficient directly with the built-in function CORREL. Values close to -1 indicate a strong negative correlation; values close to $+1$ indicate a strong positive correlation; and values near 0 indicate a weak or no correlation.

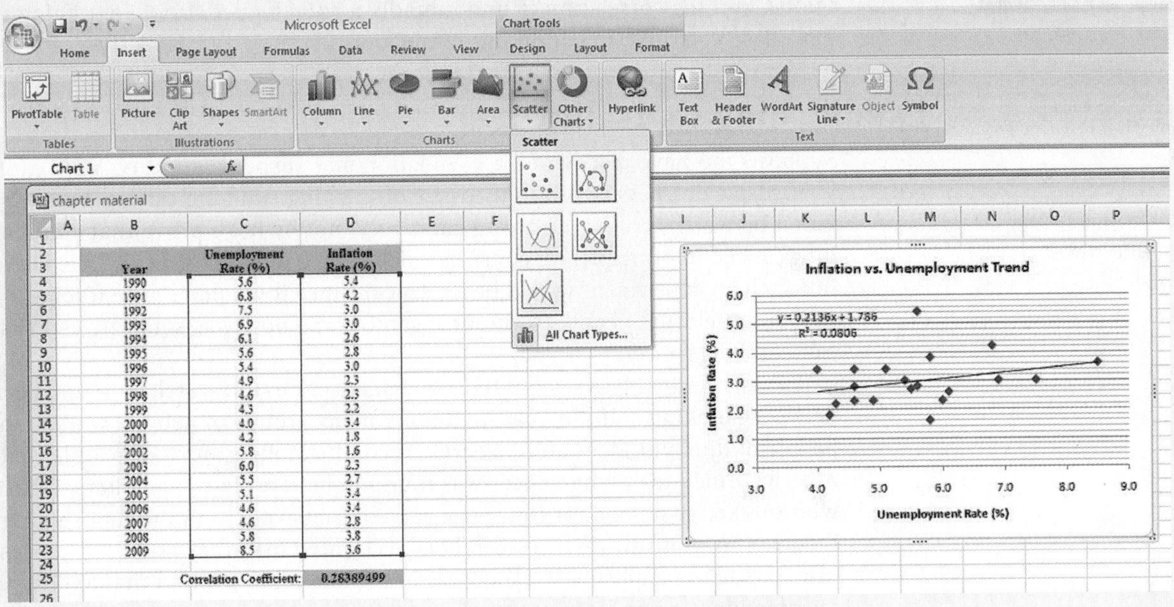

POSSIBLE EXPLANATIONS FOR A CORRELATION

1. The correlation may be a *coincidence.*
2. Both variables might be directly influenced by some *common underlying cause.*
3. One of the correlated variables may actually be a *cause* of the other. Note that, even in this case, we may have identified only one of several causes.

Example 3 Explanation for a Correlation

Consider the correlation between infant mortality and life expectancy in Figure 5.46. Which of the three possible explanations for a correlation applies? Explain.

Solution The negative correlation between infant mortality and life expectancy is probably an example of common underlying cause. Both variables respond to an underlying variable that we might call *quality of health care.* In countries where health care is better in general, infant mortality is lower and life expectancy is higher.

Now try Exercises 17–18.

BY THE WAY

The Super Bowl Indicator went into a slump after Super Bowl 32, correctly predicting the stock market's direction in 5 of the next 10 years—exactly the fraction that would be expected by pure chance.

Example 4 How to Get Rich in the Stock Market (Maybe)

Every financial advisor has a strategy for predicting the direction of the stock market. Most focus on fundamental economic data, such as interest rates and corporate profits. But an alternative strategy relies on a remarkable correlation between the Super Bowl winner in January and the direction of the stock market for the rest of the year: The stock market tends to rise when a team from the old, pre-1970 NFL wins the Super Bowl, and tends to fall otherwise. This correlation successfully matched 28 of the first 32 Super Bowls to the stock market. Suppose that the Super Bowl just ended and the winner was the Detroit Lions, an old NFL team. Should you invest all your spare cash (and maybe even some that you borrow) in the stock market?

Solution Based on the reported correlation, you might be tempted to invest, since the old-NFL winner suggests a rising stock market over the rest of the year. However, this investment would make sense only if you believed that the Super Bowl result actually *causes* the stock market to move in a particular direction. This belief is clearly preposterous, and the correlation is undoubtedly a coincidence. If you are going to invest, don't base your investment on this correlation.

Now try Exercises 19–24.

Establishing Causality

The truth is rarely pure and never simple.

—Oscar Wilde

Suppose you have discovered a correlation and suspect causality. How can you test your suspicion? Let's return to the issue of smoking and lung cancer. The strong correlation between smoking and lung cancer did not by itself prove that smoking causes lung cancer. In principle, we could have looked for proof with a controlled experiment. But such an experiment would be unethical, since it would require forcing a group of randomly selected people to smoke cigarettes. So how was smoking established as a cause of lung cancer?

The answer involves several lines of evidence. First, researchers found correlations between smoking and lung cancer among many groups of people: women, men, and people of different races and cultures. Second, among groups of people that seemed otherwise identical, lung cancer was found to be rarer in nonsmokers. Third, people who smoked more and for longer periods of time were found to have higher rates of lung cancer. Fourth, when researchers accounted for other potential causes of lung cancer (such as exposure to radon gas or asbestos), they found that almost all the remaining lung cancer cases occurred among smokers.

These four lines of evidence made a strong case, but still did not rule out the possibility that some other factor, such as genetics, predisposes people both to smoking and to lung cancer. However, two additional lines of evidence made this possibility highly unlikely. One line of evidence came from animal experiments. In controlled experiments, animals were divided into randomly chosen treatment and control groups. The experiments still found a correlation between inhalation of cigarette smoke and lung cancer, which seems to rule out a genetic factor, at least in the animals. The final line of evidence came from biologists studying cell cultures (that is, small samples of human lung tissue). The biologists discovered the basic process by which ingredients in cigarette smoke can create cancer-causing mutations. This process does not appear to depend in any way on specific genetic factors, making it all but certain that lung cancer is caused by smoking and not by any preexisting genetic factor.

The following box summarizes these ideas about establishing causality. Generally speaking, the case for causality is stronger when more of these guidelines are met.

BY THE WAY

The first four guidelines for establishing causality are called *Mill's methods,* after the English philosopher and economist John Stuart Mill (1806–1873). Mill was a leading scholar of his time and an early advocate of women's right to vote.

GUIDELINES FOR ESTABLISHING CAUSALITY

To investigate whether a suspected cause actually causes an effect:

1. Look for situations in which the effect is correlated with the suspected cause even while other factors vary.
2. Among groups that differ only in the presence or absence of the suspected cause, check that the effect is similarly present or absent.
3. Look for evidence that larger amounts of the suspected cause produce larger amounts of the effect.
4. If the effect might be produced by other potential causes (besides the suspected cause), make sure that the effect still remains after accounting for these other potential causes.
5. If possible, test the suspected cause with an experiment. If the experiment cannot be performed with humans for ethical reasons, consider doing the experiment with animals, cell cultures, or computer models.
6. Try to determine the physical mechanism by which the suspected cause produces the effect.

Time Out to Think

There's a great deal of controversy concerning whether animal experiments are ethical. What is your opinion of animal experiments? Defend your opinion.

BY THE WAY

Based on these studies, the government now recommends that child car seats *never* be used on the front seat, and that children under age 12 sit in the back seat if possible.

Case Study Air Bags and Children

By the mid-1990s, passenger-side air bags had become commonplace in cars. Statistical studies showed that the air bags saved many lives in moderate- to high-speed collisions. But a disturbing pattern also appeared. In at least some cases, young children, especially infants and toddlers in child car seats, were killed by air bags in low-speed collisions.

At first, many safety advocates found it difficult to believe that air bags could be the cause of the deaths. But the observational evidence became stronger, meeting the first four guidelines for establishing causality. For example, the greater risk to infants in child car seats fit Guideline 3, because it indicated that being closer to the air bags increased the risk of death. (A child car seat sits on top of the built-in seat, thereby putting a child closer to the air bags than the child would be otherwise.)

To seal the case, safety experts undertook experiments using dummies. They found that children, because of their small size, often sit where they could be easily hurt by the explosive opening of an air bag. The experiments also showed that an air bag could impact a child car seat hard enough to cause death, thereby revealing the physical mechanism by which the deaths occurred.

BY THE WAY

Carbon dioxide and other greenhouse gases are present naturally in Earth's atmosphere, which is a good thing. Without them, Earth's average temperature would be a frigid −10°F; with them, the global average temperature is about 59°F. From this perspective, the problem with global warming is that human input of carbon dioxide and other greenhouse gases into our atmosphere is rapidly causing our planet to have too much of a good thing.

Case Study What Is Causing Global Warming?

Statistical measurements show that the *global average temperature*—the average temperature everywhere on Earth's surface—has risen about 1.5°F in the past century, with more than half of this warming occurring in just the past 30 years. But what is causing this so-called **global warming?**

Scientists have for decades suspected that the temperature rise is tied to an increase in the atmospheric concentration of carbon dioxide and other *greenhouse gases.* Comparative studies of Earth and other planets, particularly Venus and Mars, show that the greenhouse gas concentration is the single most important factor in determining a planet's average temperature. It is even more important than distance from the Sun. For example, Venus, which is about 30% closer than Earth to the Sun, would be only about 45°F warmer than Earth if it had an Earth-like atmosphere. But because Venus has a thick atmosphere made almost entirely of carbon dioxide, its actual surface temperature is about 880°F—hot enough to melt lead. The reason greenhouse gases cause warming is that they slow the escape of heat from a planet's surface, thereby raising the surface temperature.

In other words, the physical mechanism by which greenhouse gases cause warming is well understood (satisfying Guideline 6 on our list), and there is no doubt that a large rise in carbon dioxide concentration would *eventually* cause Earth to become much warmer. Nevertheless, as you've surely heard, some people have questioned whether the current period of global warming really is due to humans or whether it might be due to natural variations in the carbon dioxide concentration or other natural factors.

BY THE WAY

Interestingly, careful study of data from Earth's past indicates that the temperature increase tends to precede (or "lead") the rise in the CO_2 concentration rather than to follow (or "lag") it—which at one time made some scientists doubt the causal relationship. However, further study showed that this response is due to a positive feedback process: A rising temperature leads to a natural release of more CO_2 into the atmosphere, which makes the temperature rise even more, which leads to more release, and so on.

In an attempt to answer these questions, the United States and other nations have devoted billions of dollars over the past two decades to an unprecedented effort to understand Earth's climate. We still have much more to learn, but the research to date makes a strong case for human input of greenhouse gases as the cause of global warming. Two lines of evidence make the case particularly strong.

The first line of evidence comes from careful measurements of past and present carbon dioxide concentrations in Earth's atmosphere. Figure 5.49 shows the data. Notice that past changes in the carbon dioxide concentration correlate clearly with temperature changes, as we should expect if there is a causal relationship between greenhouse gas concentration and temperature. Moreover, while the past data show that the carbon dioxide concentration varies naturally, it also shows that the recent rise is much greater than any natural increase during the past several hundred thousand years. Human activity is the only viable explanation for the huge recent increase in carbon dioxide concentration.

The second line of evidence comes from experiments. We cannot perform controlled experiments with our entire planet, but we can run experiments with *computer models* that simulate the way Earth's climate works. Earth's climate is incredibly complex, and many uncertainties remain in attempts to model the climate on computers. However, today's models are the result of decades of work and refinement. Each time a model of the past failed to match real data, scientists sought to understand the missing (or incorrect) ingredients in the model and then tried again with improved models. Today's models are not perfect, but they match real climate data quite well, giving scientists confidence that the models have predictive value.

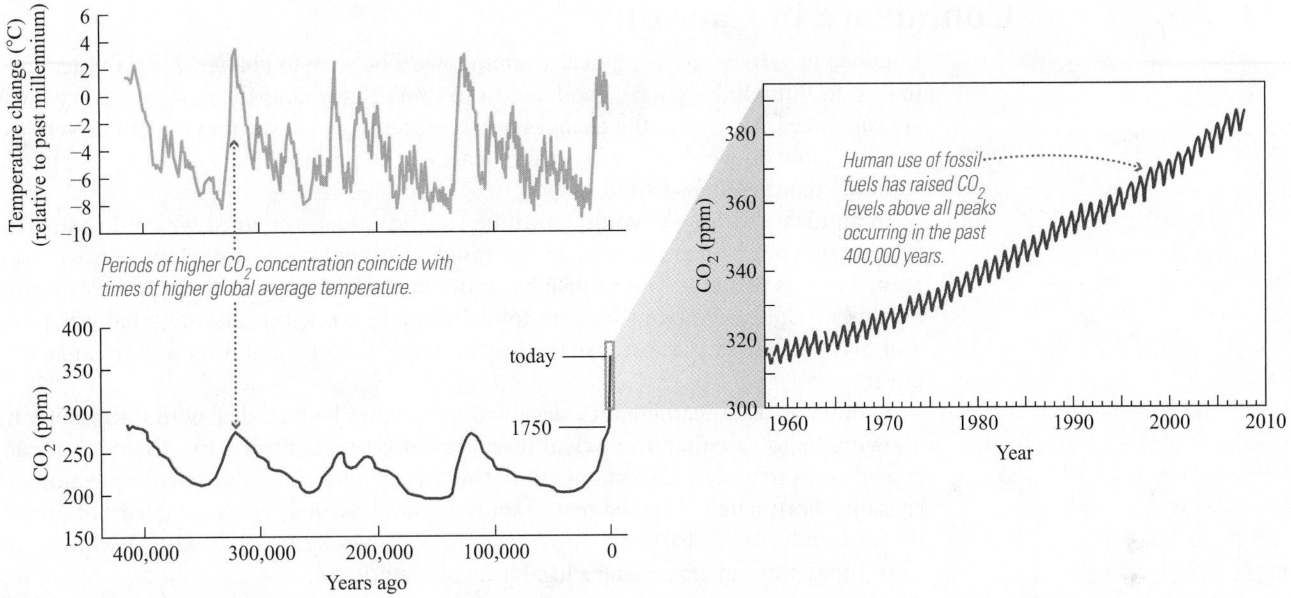

FIGURE 5.49 The atmospheric concentration of carbon dioxide and global average temperature over the past 400,000 years. The recent CO_2 data (right) represent direct measurements (at Mauna Loa, Hawaii); the past data come from studies of air bubbles trapped in Antarctic ice. The concentration is measured in parts per million (ppm).

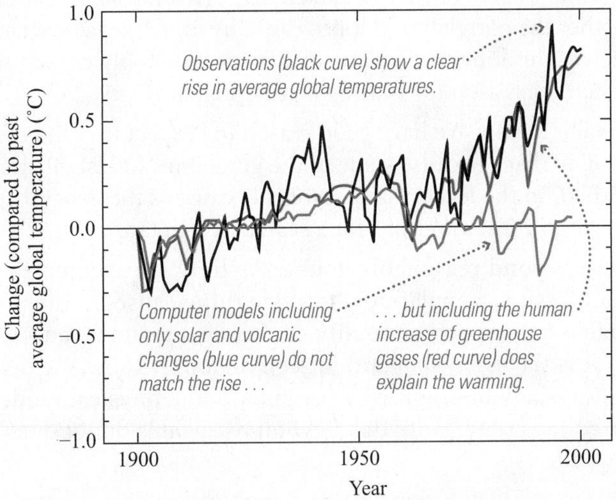

FIGURE 5.50 This graph compares observed temperature changes with models that include only natural factors (blue) and models that also include a human contribution to the greenhouse gas concentration (red). Only the latter gives good agreement with observations (black).

Figure 5.50 compares model data and real data, both for models that include only natural factors and models that also add a human factor. Only the models that include a human contribution agree with the real data, a fact that strongly indicates that human activity is the cause of global warming.

Time Out to Think

Check the idea that human activity causes global warming against each of the six guidelines for establishing causality.

Confidence in Causality

If human activity is *causing* global warming, we'd be wise to change our activities so as to stop it. But while we have good reason to think that this is the case, not everyone is yet convinced. Moreover, the changes needed to slow global warming might be very expensive. How do we decide when we've reached the point where something like global warming requires steps to address it?

In an ideal world, we would continue to study the issue until we could establish for certain that human activity is the cause of global warming. However, we have seen that it is difficult to establish causality and often impossible to *prove* causality beyond all doubt. We are therefore forced to make decisions about global warming, and many other important issues, despite remaining uncertainty about cause and effect.

In other areas of mathematics, accepted techniques help us deal with uncertainty by allowing us to calculate numerical measures of possible errors. But there are no accepted ways to assign such numbers to the uncertainty that comes with questions of causality. Fortunately, another area of study has dealt with practical problems of causality for hundreds of years: our legal system. You may be familiar with the following three broad ways of expressing a legal level of confidence.

BROAD LEVELS OF CONFIDENCE IN CAUSALITY

Possible cause: We have discovered a correlation, but cannot yet determine whether the correlation implies causality. In the legal system, possible cause (such as thinking that a particular suspect possibly caused a particular crime) is often the reason for starting an investigation.

Probable cause: We have good reason to suspect that the correlation involves cause, perhaps because some of the guidelines for establishing causality are satisfied. In the legal system, probable cause is the general standard for getting a judge to grant a warrant for a search or wiretap.

Cause beyond reasonable doubt: We have found a physical model that is so successful in explaining how one thing causes another that it seems unreasonable to doubt the causality. In the legal system, cause beyond reasonable doubt is the usual standard for conviction. It generally demands that the prosecution show how and why (essentially the physical model) the suspect committed the crime. Note that beyond *reasonable* doubt does *not* mean beyond *all* doubt.

While these broad levels remain fairly vague, they give us at least some common language for discussing confidence in causality. If you study law, you will learn much more about the subtleties of interpreting these terms. However, because statistics has little to say about them, we will not discuss them much further in this book.

Time Out to Think

Given what you know about global warming, do you think that human activity is a possible cause, probable cause, or cause beyond reasonable doubt? Defend your opinion. Based on your level of confidence in the causality, how would you recommend setting policies with regard to global warming?

BY THE WAY

For criminal trials, the Supreme Court endorsed this guidance from Justice Ginsburg: "Proof beyond a reasonable doubt is proof that leaves you firmly convinced of the defendant's guilt. There are very few things in this world that we know with absolute certainty, and in criminal cases the law does not require proof that overcomes every possible doubt. If, based on your consideration of the evidence, you are firmly convinced that the defendant is guilty of the crime charged, you must find him guilty. If on the other hand, you think there is a real possibility that he is not guilty, you must give him the benefit of the doubt and find him not guilty."

QUICK QUIZ

Choose the best answer to each of the following questions. Explain your reasoning with one or more complete sentences.

1. If X is correlated with Y,

   a. X causes Y.

   b. increasing values of X go with increasing values of Y.

   c. increasing values of X go with either increasing or decreasing values of Y.

2. Consider Figure 5.46. According to this diagram, life expectancy in Russia is about

   a. 22 years. b. 63 years. c. 58 years.

3. If the points on a scatter diagram fall on a nearly straight line sloping upward, the two variables have

   a. a strong positive correlation.

   b. a weak negative correlation. c. no correlation.

4. If the points on a scatter diagram fall into a broad swath that slopes downward, the two variables have

   a. a strong positive correlation.

   b. a weak negative correlation. c. no correlation.

5. When can you rule out the possibility that changes to variable X *cause* changes to variable Y?

   a. when there is no correlation between X and Y

   b. when there is a negative correlation between X and Y

   c. when a scatter diagram of the two variables shows points lying in a straight line

6. What type of correlation would you expect between wages and the unemployment rate?

   a. none

   b. positive: higher wages would go with higher unemployment

   c. negative: higher wages would go with lower unemployment

7. You have found a higher rate of birth defects among babies born to women exposed to second-hand smoke. To support a claim that the second-hand smoke caused the birth defects, what else should you expect to find?

   a. evidence that higher rates of defects are correlated with exposure to greater amounts of smoke

   b. evidence that these types of birth defects occur only in babies whose mothers were exposed to smoke, and never to any other babies

   c. evidence that the types of birth defects in these babies are more debilitating than other types of birth defects

8. Consider Figure 5.49. According to this graph, how does the CO_2 concentration today compare to the highest CO_2 concentrations during the 400,000 years before humans began industry?

   a. The values are about the same.

   b. Today's value is about 10% higher.

   c. Today's value is about 30% higher.

9. Based on the trend shown in Figure 5.49, predict the CO_2 concentration in the year 2040.

   a. 390 ppm

   b. 420 ppm

   c. 600 ppm

10. A finding by a jury that a person is guilty "beyond reasonable doubt" is supposed to mean that

    a. the person is definitely guilty.

    b. all 12 members of the jury believed that there was more than a 50% chance that the person was guilty.

    c. any reasonable person would conclude that the evidence was sufficient to establish guilt.

Exercises 5E

REVIEW QUESTIONS

1. What is a correlation? Give three examples of pairs of variables that are correlated.
2. What is a scatter diagram, and how is one made? How can we use a scatter diagram to look for a correlation?
3. Define and distinguish among positive correlation, negative correlation, and no correlation. How do we determine the strength of a correlation?
4. Describe the three general categories of explanation for a correlation. Give an example of each.
5. Briefly describe each of the six guidelines presented in this unit for establishing causality. Give an example of the application of each guideline.
6. Briefly describe three levels of confidence in causality and how they can be useful when we do not have absolute proof of causality.

DOES IT MAKE SENSE?

Decide whether each of the following statements makes sense (or is clearly true) or does not make sense (or is clearly false). Explain your reasoning.

7. There is a strong negative correlation between the price of tickets and the number of tickets sold. This suggests that if we want to sell a lot of tickets, we should lower the price.
8. There is a strong positive correlation between the amount of time spent studying and grades in mathematics classes.

This suggests that if you want to get a good grade, you should spend more time studying.

9. I found a nearly perfect positive correlation between variable A and variable B, and therefore was able to conclude that an increase in variable A causes an increase in variable B.
10. I found a nearly perfect negative correlation between variable C and variable D, and therefore was able to conclude that an increase in variable C causes a decrease in variable D.
11. I had originally suspected that an increase in variable E would cause a decrease in variable F, but I no longer believe this because I found no correlation between the two variables.
12. I agree that we should require kids to wear bicycle helmets if helmets really lower injury rates, but it makes no sense to start this requirement until we have absolute proof that helmets cause the lower injury rate.

BASIC SKILLS & CONCEPTS

13–16: Interpreting Scatter Diagrams. Consider the following scatter diagrams.

a. State whether the diagram shows a positive correlation, a negative correlation, or no correlation. If there is a positive or negative correlation, is it strong or weak?

b. Summarize any conclusions that you can draw from the diagram.

13.

2010 Model Cars

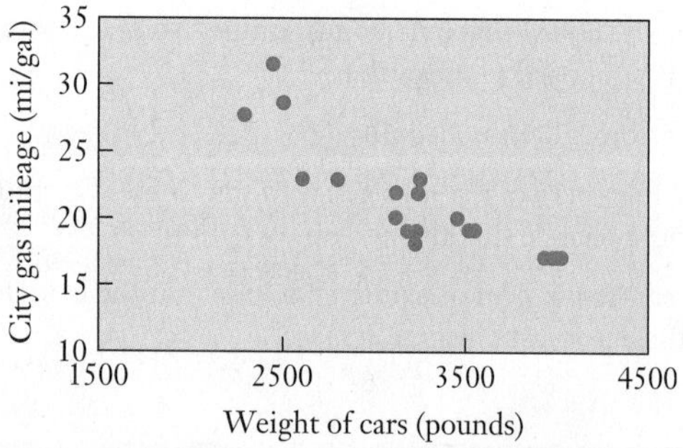

14.

U.S. Presidential Elections, 1964–2008

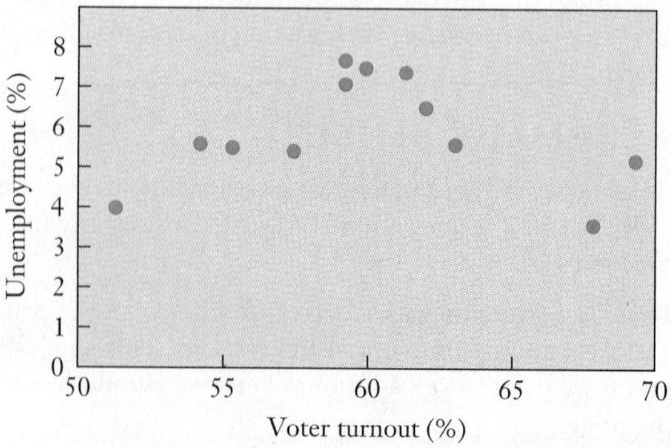

15.

Charitable Giving (11 states) as Percentage of Adjusted Gross Income (AGI)

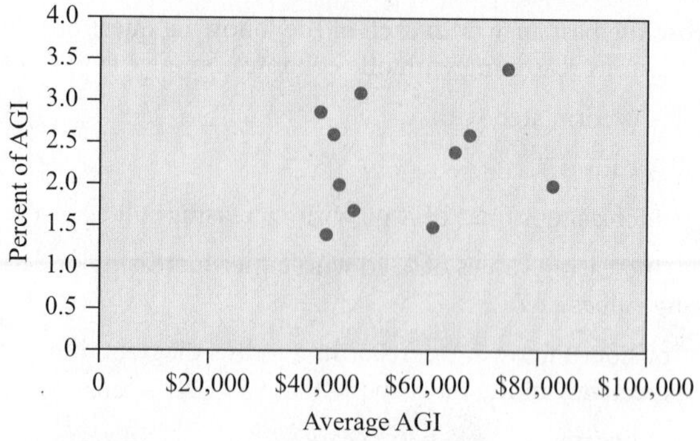

16.

U.S. Farms 1950–2005

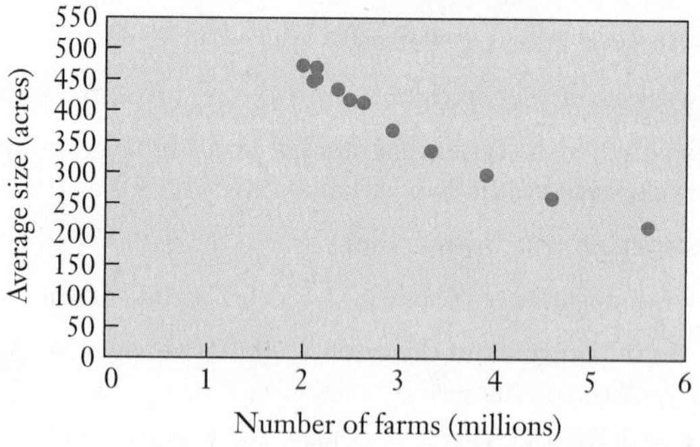

17–24: Types of Correlation. For the following pairs of variables, state the units that might be used to measure each variable. Then state whether you believe that the two variables are correlated. If you believe they are correlated, state whether the correlation is positive or negative. Explain your reasoning.

17. Latitude north of the equator and average high temperature in June
18. Height of person and how frequently he or she attends religious services
19. Age of person and time spent on social networking sites
20. Altitude on a mountain hike and air pressure
21. The year in which a state joined the Union and the area of the state
22. Weight of a person and shoe size
23. Fertility rate of women and life expectancy in a country
24. Average property tax in a school district and average salary of high school teachers

FURTHER APPLICATIONS

25–30: Making Scatter Diagrams. Consider the following data sets.

a. Make a scatter diagram for the data.

b. State whether the two variables appear to be correlated, and if so, state whether the correlation is positive, negative, strong, or weak.

c. Suggest a reason for the correlation or lack of correlation. If you suspect causality, discuss what further evidence you need to establish it.

25. The table below gives the per capita gross national product and the per capita expenditure on defense for eight developed countries. Gross domestic product (GDP) is a measure of the total economic output of a country in monetary terms. Per capita GDP is the GDP averaged over every person in the country.

Country	Per Capita GDP ($)	Per Capita Defense ($)
Australia	36,300	947
France	33,200	807
Germany	34,200	524
Israel	25,800	1331
Japan	33,600	342
Norway	53,000	1241
United Kingdom	35,100	1001
United States	45,800	1974

26. The following table gives number of home runs and batting average for baseball's Most Valuable Players, 1998–2008 (NL = National League and AL = American League).

Player	Home Runs	Batting Average
Sammy Sosa (1998 NL)	66	.308
Juan Gonzalez (1998 AL)	45	.318
Chipper Jones (1999 NL)	45	.319
Ivan Rodriguez (1999 AL)	35	.332
Jeff Kent (2000 NL)	33	.334
Jason Giambi (2000 AL)	43	.333
Barry Bonds (2001 NL)	73	.328
Ichiro Suzuki (2001 AL)	8	.350
Barry Bonds (2002 NL)	46	.370
Miguel Tejada (2002 AL)	34	.308
Barry Bonds (2003 NL)	45	.341
Alex Rodriguez (2003 AL)	47	.298
Barry Bonds (2004 NL)	45	.362
Vladimir Guerrero (2004 AL)	39	.337
Albert Pujols (2005 NL)	41	.330
Alex Rodriguez (2005 AL)	48	.321
Ryan Howard (2006 NL)	58	.313
Justin Morneau (2006 AL)	34	.321
Jimmy Rollins (2007 NL)	30	.296
Alex Rodriguez (2007 AL)	54	.314
Albert Pujols (2008 NL)	37	.357
Dustin Pedroia (2008 AL)	17	.326

27. The following table gives per capita personal income and percent of the population below the poverty level for ten states in 2008.

State	Per Capita Personal Income ($)	Percent of Population Below Poverty Level
California	41,571	12.5
Colorado	41,042	9.8
Illinois	40,322	10.3
Iowa	35,023	9.6
Minnesota	41,034	8.7
Montana	32,458	13.2
Nevada	40,480	9.6
New Hampshire	41,512	5.6
Utah	31,189	9.4
West Virginia	29,537	15.0

28. The following table gives the average hours of television watched in households in five categories of annual income. (*Hint:* For the first and last categories of the household income data, place the dot at the position corresponding to \$25,000 and \$65,000, respectively. For other categories, place the dot at the center of each bin.)

Household Income	Weekly TV Hours
Less than \$30,000	56.3
\$30,000–\$40,000	51.0
\$40,000–\$50,000	50.5
\$50,000–\$60,000	49.7
More than \$60,000	48.7

Source: Nielsen Media Research.

29. The following table gives the average teacher salary and the expenditure on public education per pupil for ten states in 2007.

State	Average Teacher Salary ($)	Per Pupil Expenditure ($)
Alabama	43,389	7672
Alaska	54,658	10,392
Arizona	45,941	5696
Connecticut	60,822	13,005
Massachusetts	58,624	13,294
North Dakota	38,822	8228
Oregon	50,911	8989
Texas	44,899	8048
Utah	40,566	5551
Wyoming	50,692	13,328

30. The following table gives the literacy rate and the infant mortality rate (per 1000 births) for ten countries.

Country	Literacy Rate (%)	Infant Mortality Rate (per 1000 births)
Afghanistan	28	152
Austria	98	4
Burundi	59	60
Colombia	93	19
Ethiopia	43	81
Germany	99	4
Liberia	58	138
New Zealand	99	5
Turkey	87	26
United States	99	6

31–36: Correlation and Causality. Consider the following statements about a correlation. In each case, state the correlation clearly (for example, there is a positive correlation between variable A and variable B). Then state whether the correlation is most likely due to coincidence, a common underlying cause, or a direct cause. Explain your answer.

31. In a large resort city, the crime rate increased as the number of taxi cabs increased.

32. Over the past three decades, the number of miles of freeways in Los Angeles has grown, and traffic congestion has worsened.

33. When gasoline prices rise, sales of sport utility vehicles decline.

34. Sales of ice cream increase whenever the sales of swimming suits increase.

35. Automobile gas mileage decreases with tire pressure.

36. Over a period of twenty years, the number of ministers and priests in a city increased, as did attendance at movies.

37. **Identifying Causes: Headaches.** You are trying to identify the cause of late-afternoon headaches that plague you several days each week. For each of the following tests and observations, explain which of the six guidelines for establishing causality you used and what you concluded.

- The headaches occur only on days when you go to work.
- If you stop drinking Coke at lunch on days when you go to work, the headaches persist.
- In the summer, the headaches occur less frequently if you open the windows of your office slightly. They occur even less often if you open the windows of your office fully.

Having made all these observations, what reasonable conclusion can you reach about the cause of the headaches?

38. **Smoking and Lung Cancer.** There is a strong correlation between tobacco smoking and incidence of lung cancer, and most physicians believe that tobacco smoking causes lung cancer. Yet, not everyone who smokes gets lung cancer. Briefly describe how smoking could cause cancer when not all smokers get cancer.

39. **Longevity of Orchestra Conductors.** A famous study in *Forum on Medicine* (1978) concluded that the mean lifetime of conductors of major orchestras was 73.4 years, about 5 years longer than that of all American males at the time. The author claimed that a life of music *causes* a longer life. Evaluate the claim of causality and propose other explanations for the longer life expectancy of conductors.

40. **High-Voltage Power Lines.** Suppose that people living near a particular high-voltage power line have a higher incidence of cancer than people living farther from the power line. Can you conclude that the high-voltage power line is the cause of the elevated cancer rate? If not, what other explanations might there be for it? What other types of research would you like to see before you conclude that high-voltage power lines cause cancer?

41. **Soccer and Birthdays.** A recent study revealed that the best soccer players in the world tend to have birthdays in the earlier months of the year. Is this a coincidence or can you find a plausible explanation?

WEB PROJECTS

42. **Success in the NFL.** Use the Web to find last season's NFL team statistics. Make a table showing the following for each team: number of wins, average yards gained on offense per game, and average yards allowed on defense per game. Make scatter diagrams to explore the correlations between offense and wins and between defense and wins. Discuss your findings. Do you think that there are other team statistics that would yield stronger correlations with the number of wins?

43. **Statistical Abstract.** Explore the "frequently requested tables" at the Web site for the *Statistical Abstract of the United States*. Choose data that are of interest to you and explore at least two correlations. Briefly discuss what you learn from the correlations.

44. **Air Bags and Children.** Starting with the Web site of the National Highway Traffic Safety Administration, research the latest studies on the safety of air bags, especially with regard to children. Write a short report summarizing your findings and offering recommendations for improving child safety in cars.

45. **Global Warming.** Use the Web to find recent information about global warming and its potential consequences. Discuss the evidence linking human activity to global warming. In light of your findings, suggest how we should deal with the issue of global warming.

46. **Tobacco Lawsuits.** Tobacco companies have been the subject of many lawsuits relating to the dangers of smoking. Research one recent lawsuit. What were the plaintiffs trying to prove? What statistical evidence did they use? How well do you think they established causality? Did they win? Summarize your findings in one to two pages.

IN YOUR WORLD

47. **Correlations in the News.** Find a recent news report that describes some type of correlation. Describe the correlation. Does the article give any sense of the strength of the correlation? Does it suggest that the correlation reflects any underlying causality? Briefly discuss whether you believe the implications the article makes with respect to the correlation.

48. **Causation in the News.** Find a recent news report in which a statistical study has led to a conclusion of causation. Describe the study and the claimed causation. Do you think the claim of causation is legitimate? Explain.

49. **Legal Causation.** Find a news report concerning an ongoing legal case, either civil or criminal, in which establishing causality is important to the outcome. Briefly describe the issue of causation in the case and how the ability to establish or refute causality will influence the outcome of the case.

TECHNOLOGY EXERCISE

50. **Making a Scatter Diagram.** Consider the following data on violent crime rates (measured in violent crimes reported per 100,000 people in the population) and state expenditures per pupil in the public schools in ten different states.

State	Violent Crime Rate	Per Pupil Expenditure
California	523	8834
Connecticut	256	13,005
Florida	723	8493
Maine	118	12,063
Mississippi	291	6866
New Jersey	329	14,675
Ohio	343	10,563
Tennessee	753	7255
Utah	235	5551
Wisconsin	291	10,432

a. Make a scatter diagram of the data.

b. Do the variables in the data set appear to be correlated? Express the correlation in words.

c. Make a trend line for the scatter diagram.

d. Find the correlation coefficient.

CHAPTER 5 Summary

UNIT	KEY TERMS	KEY IDEAS AND SKILLS
5A	statistics *is* a science *are* data population, sample population parameters, sample statistics bias observational study case-control study experiment placebo, placebo effect blinding single-blind double-blind margin of error confidence interval	**Understand and interpret** the five basic steps in a statistical study. **Understand** the importance of a representative sample. **Be familiar** with four common sampling methods: simple random sampling systematic sampling convenience sampling stratified sampling **Distinguish between** observational studies and experiments; also recognize observational case-control studies. **Understand** the placebo effect and the importance of blinding in experiments. **Find** a confidence interval from a margin of error: from (sample statistic − margin of error) to (sample statistic + margin of error)
5B	selection bias participation bias variable (in a statistical study)	**Understand and apply** eight guidelines for evaluating a statistical study.
5C	frequency table categories frequency relative frequency cumulative frequency data types qualitative quantitative bar chart pie chart histogram line chart time-series diagram	**Interpret and create** frequency tables. **Interpret and create** bar graphs and pie charts. **Interpret and create** histograms and line charts.
5D	multiple bar graph stack plot geographical data contour map	**Interpret** multiple bar graphs, stack plots, contour maps, and other media graphs. **Distinguish between** true three-dimensional data and graphs that have a three-dimensional look for cosmetic reasons only. **Be aware of** common cautions about graphs.
5E	correlation cause scatter diagram	**Distinguish between** correlation and causality. **Create and interpret** scatter diagrams and use them to identify correlations: positive, negative, or no correlation strength of correlation **Know** three possible explanations for a correlation: coincidence common underlying cause true cause **Understand and apply** six guidelines for establishing causality.

6

Some people hate the very name of statistics, but I find them full of beauty and interest. Whenever they are not brutalised, but delicately handled by the higher methods, and are warily interpreted, their power of dealing with complicated phenomena is extraordinary.

—Sir Francis Galton (1822–1911)

Putting Statistics to Work

UNIT 6A

Characterizing Data: We often describe data by their average and their distribution. We investigate such descriptions and discover the multiple meanings of "average."

UNIT 6B

Measures of Variation: We discuss common measures of the variation, or spread, in a data set: the range, the five-number summary, and the standard deviation.

UNIT 6C

The Normal Distribution: The normal distribution is the formal name for the famous bell-shaped curve. We study the characteristics of the normal distribution and learn why it is so important.

UNIT 6D

Statistical Inference: The heart of most statistical studies lies with *inferring* a conclusion about a population from results for a sample. We explore three important ideas about inference: statistical significance, the margin of error, and hypothesis testing.

In Chapter 5, we explored statistics as they are presented in the news: reports on major statistical studies, opinion polls, graphics, and attempts to establish cause and effect. Now, we are ready to do some actual statistical calculations. With the tools in this chapter, you will have a strong introduction to the powerful science of statistics.

ACTIVITY Bankrupting the Auto Companies

Use this activity to gain a sense of the kinds of problems this chapter will enable you to study. Try working through it before you begin the chapter, then return to it after you've learned the chapter material.

For decades, the "Big Three" American auto companies—General Motors, Chrysler, and Ford—were the world's largest and most profitable automakers. But their market share gradually eroded, and in 2009 both Chrysler and General Motors declared bankruptcy. What caused the precipitous fall of the U.S. automakers? The answer is complex and subject to great debate, but politically people have tended to divide into two camps. Conservatives tend to blame the fall on the United Auto Workers Union, claiming that the union's wage and benefit demands made labor costs so high that the companies could not compete with Japanese automakers (such as Toyota, Honda, and Nissan), whose workers are not unionized. Liberals tend to blame management, claiming that poor business decisions—rather than high labor costs—caused the decline. Not surprisingly, both sides wield statistics to make their arguments.

The bar chart below shows some of the key data, on which both sides agree. Working in small groups, discuss the following questions, which will show you some of the statistical ideas that we will discuss in this chapter.

Average Hourly Cost of Factory Workers in the United States

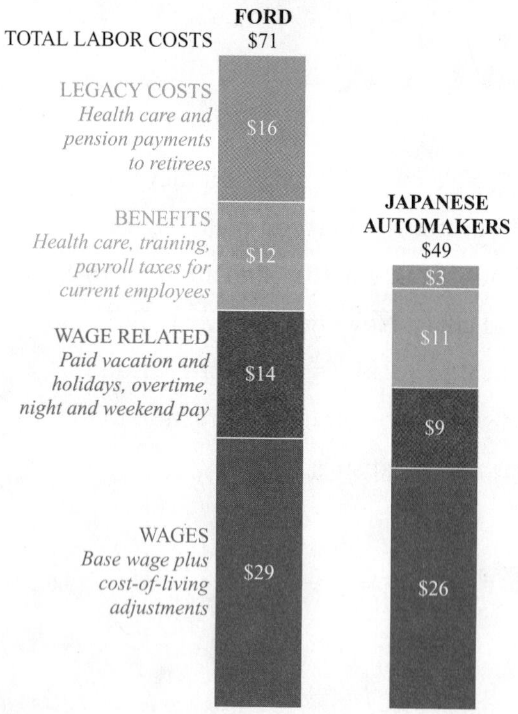

This bar graph compares labor costs for factories in the United States operated by Ford and by Japanese automakers (Toyota, Honda, and Nissan). Ford's workers are unionized; the others are not.

Source: Ford; adapted from *The New York Times.*

1. Based on the data in the bar chart, many news reports claimed that the unionized autoworkers at the Big Three earned over $20/hour more than their nonunion counterparts working for Japanese automakers. Notice that "legacy costs" are payments that go to retirees, not current workers, so the actual *compensation* paid to current workers includes only the categories for wages, wage-related expenses, and benefits. How does the compensation of the union and nonunion autoworkers compare? Do you think the news media were biased when they reported a $20/hour difference? Are they biased in the fact that they generally did *not* mention that unionized autoworker compensation is considerably higher than the approximately $30/hour average for workers across all industries in the United States? What do *you* think would be a fair report on how union and nonunion autoworker compensation compares?
2. As a percentage of total labor costs, how do the legacy costs of U.S. and Japanese automakers compare? The U.S. companies have these high legacy costs primarily because they have far more retirees, a result of having been in business in the United States for a much longer time. (More generous retirement benefits also play a role in the legacy cost difference.) This fact led some people to suggest that the government "level the playing field" by subsidizing the retiree expenses, while others suggested that the difficult financial situation was a problem of the union's own making and that the retirees should accept lower benefits. Do some research on the current situation with regard to the legacy costs. For example, has the government provided any subsidy for the retirement benefits, or have retirees lost some of their benefits? Comment on whether you think the current situation is sustainable and fair. If you think it is not, what would *you* change?
3. Auto company data indicate that the higher wages of the unionized U.S. automakers add an average of about $800 to the cost of every car or small truck they produce. How does this compare to the price of a new car? Do you think that an

$800 reduction in the price of cars from U.S. automakers would have a significant impact on their sales? An interesting fact to consider: As of 2008, the average price of a car from the "Big Three" was about $2500 less than the price of a comparable car from one of the Japanese automakers, yet the Japanese automakers were still gaining market share at the expense of the U.S. automakers.

4. What is the current status of the Big Three automakers? What are their prospects for the future? For one of these companies, find and use as many statistics as you can to make the case either that the company is on the road to recovery or that it still faces a very difficult future. If you were the CEO of this company, what would *you* try to do to ensure its long-term survival?

UNIT 6A Characterizing Data

Frequency tables and graphs (see Units 5C and 5D) show us how data are distributed over various categories. More formally, we say that a table or graph gives the **distribution** of a data set. For example, a distribution of essay grades shows how many students received grades of A, B, C, D, and F. In this case, the categories are the grades.

> **DEFINITION**
>
> The **distribution** of a variable (or data set) describes the values taken on by the variable and the frequency (or relative frequency) of these values.

In many cases, however, we are less interested in the complete distribution than in a few descriptive terms that summarize it. In this unit, we'll study how we can characterize a data distribution by its center, or average, and by its shape.

What Is Average?

The term *average* comes up frequently in the news, but you may be surprised to learn that it does not always have the same meaning. Let's begin by studying three common ways of characterizing the center of a data distribution, all of which are sometimes called the "average."

Mean, Median, and Mode

Table 6.1 shows the number of movies (original and sequels or prequels) in each of five popular science fiction series.

What is the average number of films in these series? One way to answer this question is to compute the **mean**. We find the mean by dividing the total number of movies by five (because there are five series):

$$\text{mean} = \frac{4 + 3 + 6 + 11 + 6}{5} = \frac{30}{5} = 6.0$$

TABLE 6.1 Five Science Fiction Movie Series

Title	Number of Movies in Series (as of 2009)
Alien	4
Back to the Future	3
Planet of the Apes	6
Star Trek	11
Star Wars	6

In other words, these five series have a mean of 6.0 movies. More generally, we find the mean of any data set by summing all the data values and then dividing by the number of data values. The mean is what most people think of as the average. In essence, it represents the balance point for a data distribution, as shown in Figure 6.1.

We could also describe the average number of films in these five series by computing the **median**, or middle value, of the

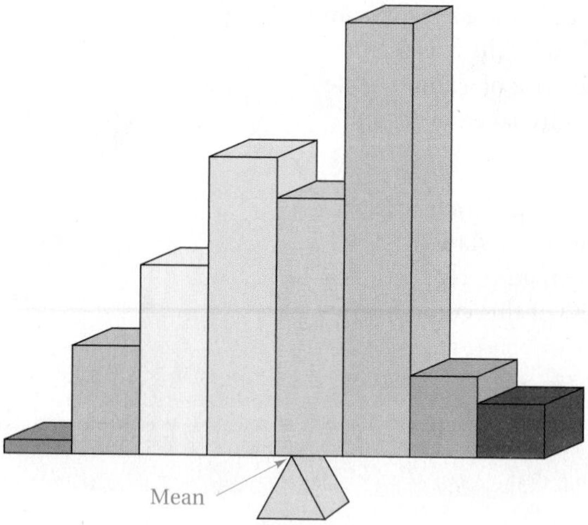

FIGURE 6.1 A histogram made from blocks would balance at the position of its mean.

data set. To find a median, we arrange the data values in ascending (or descending) order, repeating data values that appear more than once. If the number of values is odd, there is exactly one value in the middle of the list, and this value is the median. If the number of values is even, there are two values in the middle of the list, and the median is the number that lies halfway between them. Putting the data in Table 6.1 in ascending order gives the list

$$3, 4, 6, 6, 11$$

The median number of movies is 6 because 6 is the middle number in the list.

Another value sometimes used as a measure of average is the **mode**, which is the most common value (or group of values) in a data set. In the case of the movies, the mode is 6 because this value occurs twice in the data set, while the other values occur once. A data set may have one mode, more than one mode, or no mode. Sometimes the mode refers to a group of closely spaced values rather than a single value.

MEASURES OF CENTER IN A DISTRIBUTION

The **mean** is what we most commonly call the average value. It is defined as follows:

$$\text{mean} = \frac{\text{sum of all values}}{\text{total number of values}}$$

The **median** is the middle value in the sorted data set (or halfway between the two middle values if the number of values is even).

The **mode** is the most common value (or group of values) in a distribution.

USING TECHNOLOGY

Mean, Median, Mode in Excel

Excel provides the built-in function AVERAGE for calculating a mean, and functions for calculating MEDIAN and MODE. The screen shot below shows the use of these functions for the data from Example 1; column B shows the functions and column C shows the results. Note that the results agree with those calculated in Example 1.

◇	A	B	C
1	Data	1.09	
2		1.29	
3		1.29	
4		1.35	
5		1.39	
6		1.49	
7		1.59	
8		1.79	
9	Mean	=AVERAGE(B1:B8)	1.41
10	Median	=MEDIAN(B1:B8)	1.37
11	Mode	=MODE(B1:B8)	1.29
12			

Example 1 Price Data

Eight grocery stores sell the PR energy bar for the following prices:

$1.09 $1.29 $1.29 $1.35 $1.39 $1.49 $1.59 $1.79

Find the mean, median, and mode for these prices.

Solution The mean price is $1.41:

$$\text{mean} = \frac{\begin{pmatrix} \$1.09 + \$1.29 + \$1.29 + \$1.35 \\ + \$1.39 + \$1.49 + \$1.59 + \$1.79 \end{pmatrix}}{8} = \$1.41$$

To find the median, we first sort the data in ascending order:

$$\underbrace{\$1.09 \quad \$1.29 \quad \$1.29}_{\text{3 values below}} \quad \underbrace{\$1.35 \quad \$1.39}_{\text{2 middle values}} \quad \underbrace{\$1.49 \quad \$1.59 \quad \$1.79}_{\text{3 values below}}$$

Because there are eight prices (an even number), there are two values in the middle of the list: $1.35 and $1.39. Therefore, the median lies halfway between these two values, which we calculate by adding them and dividing by 2:

$$\text{median} = \frac{\$1.35 + \$1.39}{2} = \$1.37$$

The mode is $1.29, because this is the only price that occurs more than once.

Now try Exercises 13–18.

FRAZZ reprinted by permission of United Feature Syndlcate, Inc.

Effects of Outliers

To explore the differences among the mean, median, and mode, imagine that the five graduating seniors on a college basketball team receive the following first-year contract offers to play in the National Basketball Association (zero indicates that the player did not receive a contract offer):

$$\$0 \quad \$0 \quad \$0 \quad \$0 \quad \$3{,}500{,}000$$

The mean contract offer is

$$\text{mean} = \frac{\$0 + \$0 + \$0 + \$0 + \$3{,}500{,}000}{5} = \$700{,}000$$

Is it therefore fair to say that the *average* contract offer was $700,000?

Not really. The problem is that the single player receiving the large offer makes the mean much larger than it would be otherwise. In fact, if we ignore this one player and look only at the other four, the mean contract offer is zero! Because this one value of $3,500,000 is so extreme compared to the others, we call it an **outlier** (or *outlying value*). As our example shows, an outlier can pull the mean significantly upward (or downward), thereby making the mean unrepresentative of the data set as a whole.

> **DEFINITION**
>
> An **outlier** is a data value that is much higher or much lower than almost all other values.

While the outlier pulls the mean contract offer upward, it has no effect on the median contract offer, which remains zero for the five players. In fact, the value of an outlier never has an effect on the median, because outliers don't lie in the middle of a data set. Outliers do not affect the mode either.

Time Out to Think

Is it fair to use the median as the *average* contract offer for the five players? Why or why not?

BY THE WAY

A survey once found that geography majors at the University of North Carolina had a far higher mean starting salary than geography majors from other schools. The reason for the high mean turned out to be a single outlier—the basketball superstar and geography major named Michael Jordan.

Example 2 Mistake?

A track coach wants to determine an appropriate heart rate for her athletes during their workouts. She chooses five of her best runners and asks them to wear heart rate monitors during a workout. In the middle of the workout, she reads the following heart rates for the five athletes: 130, 135, 140, 145, 325. Which is a better measure of the average in this case: the mean or the median? Why?

Solution Four of the five values are fairly close together and seem reasonable for mid-workout heart rates. The high value of 325 is an outlier. This outlier seems likely to be a mistake (perhaps caused by a faulty heart monitor), because anyone with such a high heart rate should be in cardiac arrest. If the coach uses the mean as the average, she will be including this outlier—which means she will be including any mistake made when it was recorded. If she uses the median as the average, she'll have a more reasonable value, because the median won't be affected by the outlier. **Now try Exercises 19–20.**

Confusion About "Average"

The different meanings of "average" can lead to confusion. Sometimes this confusion arises because we are not told whether the "average" is the mean or the median, and other times because we are not given enough information about how the average was computed. The following two examples illustrate such situations.

Example 3 Wage Dispute

Figures won't lie, but liars will figure.

—Charles H. Grosvenor

A newspaper surveys wages for assembly workers in regional high-tech companies and reports an average of \$22 per hour. The workers at one large firm immediately request a pay raise, claiming that they work as hard as employees at other companies but their average wage is only \$19. The management rejects their request, telling them that they are *overpaid* because their average wage, in fact, is \$23. Can both sides be right? Explain.

Solution Both sides can be right if they are using different definitions of average. In this case, the workers may be using the median while management uses the mean. For example, imagine that there are only five workers at the firm and their wages are \$19, \$19, \$19, \$19, and \$39. The median of these five wages is \$19 (as the workers claimed), but the mean is \$23 (as management claimed). **Now try Exercises 21–22.**

Example 4 Which Mean?

All 100 first-year students at a small college take three courses in the Core Studies Program. The first two courses are taught in large lectures, with all 100 students in a single class. The third course is taught in ten classes of 10 students each. Students and administrators get into an argument about whether classes are too large. The students claim that the mean size of their Core Studies classes is 70. The administrators claim that the mean class size is only 25 students. Can both sides be right? Explain.

Solution Both sides are right, but they are using different means. The students have calculated the mean size of the classes in which each student is personally enrolled. Each student is taking two classes with enrollments of 100 each and one class with an enrollment of 10, so the mean size of each student's classes is

$$\frac{\text{total enrollment in student's classes}}{\text{number of classes student is taking}} = \frac{100 + 100 + 10}{3} = 70$$

The administrators have calculated the mean enrollment in all classes. There are two classes with 100 students each and ten classes with 10 students each, making a total enrollment of 300 students in 12 classes. The mean enrollment per class is

$$\frac{\text{total enrollment}}{\text{number of classes}} = \frac{300}{12} = 25$$

The two claims about the mean are both correct, but very different, because the students and administrators used different means. The students calculated the mean *class size per student*, while the administrators calculated the mean number of *students per class*. **Now try Exercises 23–26.**

Time Out to Think

In Example 4, could the administrators redistribute faculty assignments so that all classes had 25 students each? How? Discuss the advantages and disadvantages of such a change.

Shapes of Distributions

We next turn our attention to describing the overall shape of a distribution. We can *see* the complete shape of a distribution on a graph. In essence, our goal is to describe the general shape in words. Although such descriptions carry less information than a table or graph, they are still useful. We will focus on three characteristics of a distribution: its number of peaks, its symmetry or skewness, and its variation.

Number of Peaks

Because we are interested primarily in the *general* shapes of distributions, it's often easier to work with smooth curves than actual data. Figure 6.2 shows three examples of this idea, two in which the actual distributions are shown as histograms and one in which the actual distribution is shown as a line chart. The smooth curves approximate the actual distributions, but do not show all of their details.

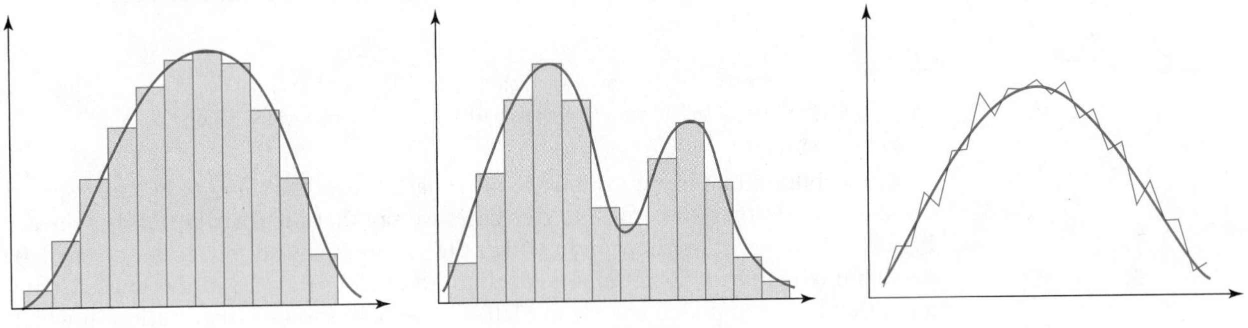

(a) (b) (c)

FIGURE 6.2 The smooth curves approximate the actual shapes of the distributions. Note that (a) and (c) are single-peaked (or unimodal), while (b) is double-peaked (or bimodal).

The first way we might characterize the shape is by its number of peaks. The distributions in Figure 6.2a and Figure 6.2c are single-peaked (or *unimodal*). Note that the peak represents the mode of each distribution. The distribution in Figure 6.2b has two peaks, so we say that it is double-peaked (or *bimodal*). Other distributions may have no peaks (in which case they are called *uniform distributions*) or more than two peaks.

Example 5 Number of Peaks

How many peaks would you expect for each of the following distributions? Why?

a. Heights of all women at a college
b. Heights of all students at a college
c. The numbers of people with particular last digits (0 through 9) in their Social Security numbers

Solution

a. The distribution of heights of women is single-peaked because many women are at or near the mean height, with fewer and fewer women at heights much taller or shorter than the mean.

b. The distribution of heights of all students (men and women) will likely have two peaks, one corresponding to the mode of men's heights and one corresponding to the mode of women's heights.
c. The last digits of Social Security numbers are essentially random, so the frequencies of the different digits (0 through 9) should be nearly equal. That is, about 10% of all Social Security numbers end in 0, 10% end in 1, and so on. The result is a uniform distribution with no peak.

Now try Exercises 27–34, part a.

Symmetry or Skewness

A second way to describe shape is in terms of symmetry or skewness. A distribution is **symmetric** if its left half is a mirror image of its right half. The distributions in Figure 6.3 are all symmetric.

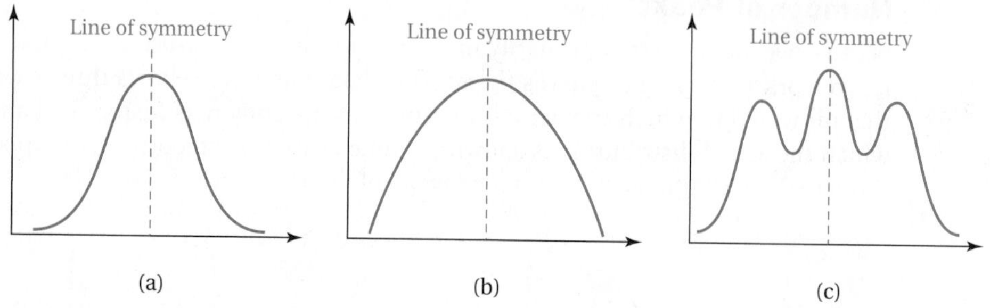

FIGURE 6.3 These distributions are all symmetric because their left halves are mirror images of their right halves. Note that (a) and (b) are single-peaked while (c) is triple-peaked (or trimodal).

A distribution that is not symmetric must have values that tend to be more spread out on one side than the other. In this case, we say that the distribution is **skewed**. Figure 6.4a shows a distribution in which the values are more spread out on the left, making it **left-skewed.** Sometimes it is helpful to think of such a distribution as having a tail that has been pulled toward the left. Figure 6.4b shows a distribution in which the values are more spread out on the right, making it **right-skewed**. It looks as if it has a tail pulled toward the right.

Figure 6.4 also shows how skewness affects the relative positions of the mean, median, and mode. By definition, the mode is the peak in a single-peaked distribution. In a left-skewed distribution, the tail pulls the mean and median to the left of the mode. Moreover, the low values in the data set tend to make the mean less than the median. Similarly, a right-skewed distribution pulls the mean and median to the right—that is, to values greater than the mode. In such cases, the large values in the data set tend to make the mean greater than the median. When the distribution is symmetric and single-peaked, both the mean and the median are equal to the mode.

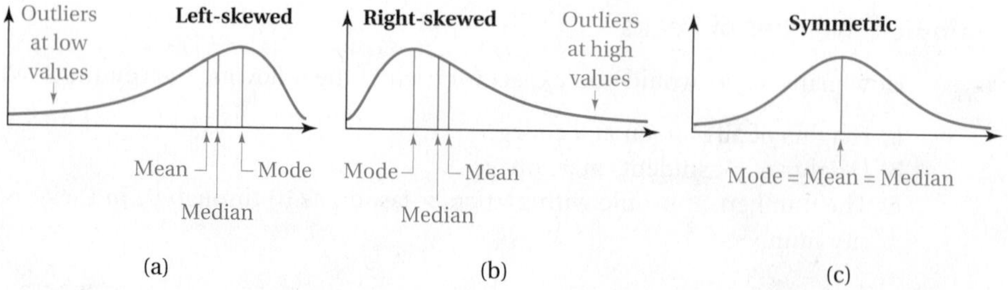

FIGURE 6.4 (a) Skewed to the left (left-skewed): The mean and median are less than the mode. (b) Skewed to the right (right-skewed): The mean and median are greater than the mode. (c) Symmetric distribution: The mean, median, and mode are the same.

SYMMETRY AND SKEWNESS

A distribution is **symmetric** if its left half is a mirror image of its right half.

A distribution is **left-skewed** if its values are more spread out on the left side.

A distribution is **right-skewed** if its values are more spread out on the right side.

Time Out to Think

In a skewed distribution, the median is a better measure of the center of the distribution than the mean. Why do you think this is true?

Example 6 Skewness

For each of the following situations, state whether you expect the distribution to be symmetric, left-skewed, or right-skewed. Explain.

a. Heights of a sample of 100 women
b. Family income in the United States
c. Speeds of cars on a road where a visible patrol car is using radar to detect speeders

Solution

a. The distribution of heights of women is symmetric, because roughly equal numbers of women are shorter and taller than the mean and extremes of height are rare on either side of the mean.
b. The distribution of family income is right-skewed. Most families are middle-class, so the mode of this distribution is a middle-class income (somewhere around \$50,000 in the United States). But a few very high-income families pull the mean to a considerably higher value, stretching the distribution to the right (high-income) side.
c. Drivers usually slow down when they are aware of a patrol car looking for speeders. Few if any drivers will be exceeding the speed limit, but some drivers tend to slow to well below the speed limit. The distribution of speeds will be left-skewed, with a mode near the speed limit but a few cars going well below the speed limit.

Now try Exercises 27–34, part b.

BY THE WAY

Speed kills. On average in the United States, someone is killed in an auto accident about every 12 minutes. About one-third of these fatalities involve a speeding driver.

Time Out to Think

In ordinary English, the term *skewed* is often used to mean that something is distorted or depicted in an unfair way. How is this use of *skew* related to its meaning in statistics?

Variation

A third way to describe a distribution is by its **variation**, which is a measure of how much the data values are spread out. A distribution in which most data values are clustered together has a low variation. As shown in Figure 6.5a, such a distribution has

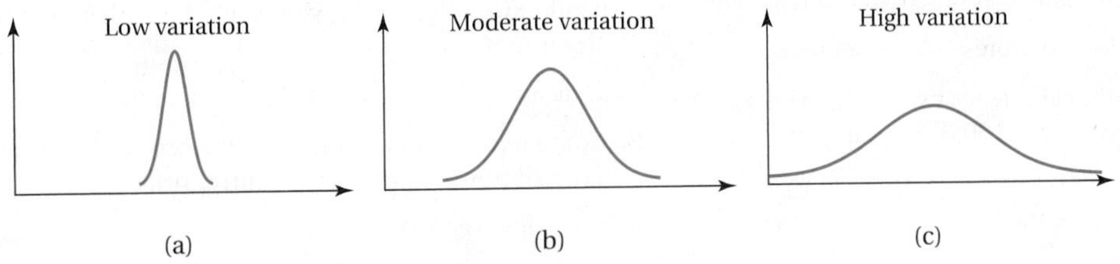

FIGURE 6.5 From left to right, these three distributions have increasing variation.

a fairly sharp peak. The variation is higher when the data are distributed more widely around the center, which makes the peak broader. Figure 6.5b shows a distribution with moderate variation and Figure 6.5c shows a distribution with high variation. We'll discuss methods for quantitatively describing variation in Unit 6B.

DEFINITION

Variation describes how widely data values are spread out about the center of a distribution.

Example 7 Variation in Marathon Times

How would you expect the variation to differ between times in the Olympic marathon and times in the New York marathon? Explain.

Solution The Olympic marathon invites only elite runners, whose times are likely to be clustered relatively near world record times. The New York marathon allows runners of all abilities, whose times are spread over a very wide range (from near the world record to many hours). Therefore, the variation among the times should be greater in the New York marathon than in the Olympic marathon.

Now try Exercises 27–34, part c.

QUICK QUIZ

Choose the best answer to each of the following questions. Explain your reasoning with one or more complete sentences.

1. You want to find the *mean* weight of the apples in a barrel. What do you need to do?

   a. Lay the apples out in order of increasing weight and find the weight of the apple in the middle.

   b. Find the total weight of all the apples and divide by the number of apples.

   c. Divide the number of apples in the barrel by the weight of the barrel.

2. On a math exam, one student scores 79 while 25 students score below 79 and 25 students score above 79. The score of 79 therefore represents the

   a. mean. b. median. c. mode.

3. One hundred students take a chemistry exam. All but two of the students score between 50 and 80 points, but one student gets a 31 and one student gets a 98. The scores of 31 and 98 represent

   a. mean scores. b. skewed scores. c. outliers.

4. Twenty students take a political science exam. Eighteen score between 70 and 75, and two score 100. What can you conclude?

   a. The mean is higher than the median.

   b. The median is higher than the mean.

   c. The median is higher than the mode.

5. A survey asks students at your school to state how many sodas they drink per week. The results show a mean of 12 sodas per week and a median of 8 sodas per week. What can you conclude?

   a. Something must have been done wrong in computing the mean and median.

   b. Most students drink between 8 and 12 sodas per week.

   c. At least one student drinks more than 16 sodas per week.

6. Among professional actors, a small number of superstars earn much more money than most other actors. A distribution of actor salaries is therefore

   a. symmetric.

   b. left-skewed, with outliers at low values.

   c. right-skewed, with outliers at high values.

7. The distribution of wages at the company you work for is right-skewed, with outliers at high values. Assuming you would like a high wage, you would hope that your wage was closer to the

   a. mean. b. median. c. mode.

8. Compared to a distribution with a broad central peak, a distribution with a sharp central peak

   a. has low variation.

   b. has high variation.

   c. is symmetric.

9. Consider the time it takes to drive from an outlying suburb to downtown. At which time would you expect the driving time to have the highest variation?

   a. at 3:00 in the morning   b. at 7:00 Sunday morning

   c. during rush hour

10. The mayor of a town is considering a run for governor. She conducts a poll asking registered voters to rate their likelihood of voting for her on a scale of 1 to 5, where 1 means "definitely would not vote for her" and 5 means "definitely would vote for her." The most encouraging result would be

    a. low median, high variation.

    b. high median, low variation.

    c. high median, high variation.

Exercises 6A

REVIEW QUESTIONS

1. Define and distinguish among mean, median, and mode.
2. What are outliers? Describe the effects of outliers on the mean, median, and mode.
3. Briefly describe at least two possible sources of confusion about the "average."
4. Give simple examples of a single-peaked distribution and a double-peaked distribution.
5. What do we mean when we say that a distribution is symmetric? Give simple examples of a symmetric distribution, a left-skewed distribution, and a right-skewed distribution.
6. What do we mean by the variation of a distribution? Give simple examples of distributions with different amounts of variation.

DOES IT MAKE SENSE?

Decide whether each of the following statements makes sense (or is clearly true) or does not make sense (or is clearly false). Explain your reasoning.

7. In my data set of 10 exam scores, the mean turned out to be the score of the person with the third highest grade. No two people got the same score.
8. In my data set of 10 exam scores, the median turned out to be the score of the person with the third highest grade. No two people got the same score.
9. I made a distribution of 15 apartment rents in my neighborhood. One apartment had a much higher rent than all of the others, and this outlier caused the mean rent to be higher than the median rent.
10. If management and employees use the same data and do the calculations properly, they will always agree on the average wage.
11. The distribution of grades was left-skewed, but the mean, median, and mode were all the same.
12. There's much more variation in the ages of the general population than in the ages of students in my college extension course, but both turn out to have the same mean.

BASIC SKILLS & CONCEPTS

13–18: Mean, Median, and Mode. Compute the mean, median, and mode of the following data sets.

13. Weights (in grams) of copper-nickel quarters made after 1965:

    5.67 5.72 5.63 5.70 5.73 5.64

14. Body temperature (in degrees Farenheit) of randomly selected normal and healthy adults:

    98.6 98.6 98.0 98.0 99.0
    98.4 98.4 98.4 98.4 98.6

15. Total points scored in the games of an NBA (basketball) playoff series:

    201 195 232 176 189 215 200

16. Golf scores from a recent WPGA tournament:

    69 70 70 71 73 73 75 76 76 78
    80 81 81 82 83 84 85 86 87 88

17. Rainfall amounts (in inches) for six consecutive months in a particular city:

    2.5 0.8 1.3 1.2 0.4 0.9

18. Weights (in grams) of randomly selected M&M plain candies:

    0.957 0.912 0.842 0.925 0.939 0.886
    0.914 0.913 0.958 0.947 0.920

19. **Outlier Coke.** Cans of Coca-Cola vary slightly in weight. Here are the measured weights of seven cans, in pounds:

    0.8161 0.8194 0.8165 0.8176
    0.7901 0.8143 0.8126

    Find the mean and median of these weights. Which, if any, of these weights would you consider to be an outlier? What are the mean and median weights if the outlier is excluded?

20. **Margin of Victory.** The data set below gives the margin of victory in the NFL Superbowl games for 2002–2009.

    3 12 11 3 3 27 3 27

    a. Find the mean and median margin of victory.

    b. Identify the outliers in the set. If you eliminate the outliers on the high side, what are the new mean and median?

21–26: Appropriate Average. State, with an explanation, whether the mean, median, or mode gives the best description of the following averages.

21. The average household income in Missouri
22. The average age at first marriage for men in America
23. The average number of times that people change jobs during their careers
24. The average number of pieces of lost luggage per flight from an airline company's perspective.
25. The average weight of potatoes in a 10-pound bag

26. The average waiting time in the lines for a drive-up window at a bank

27–34: **Describing Distributions.** Consider the following distributions.

a. How many peaks would you expect for the distribution? Explain.

b. Would you expect the distribution to be symmetric, left-skewed, or right-skewed? Explain.

c. Would you expect the variation of the distribution to be small, moderate, or large? Explain.

27. The exam scores for 100 students when 40 students got an F, 25 students got a D, and 20 students got a C
28. The weights of all people who use an ice rink that is open to figure skaters in the morning and to hockey players in the afternoon
29. The weights of all athletes on a college track team (men and women combined)
30. The numbers of people whose telephone numbers end in 0, 1, 2, 3, 4, 5, 6, 7, 8, and 9 (the data set has 10 values)
31. The monthly sales of snow shovels over a one-year period at a store in Buffalo, New York
32. The weights of cars at a dealership at which about half of the inventory consists of compact cars and half of the inventory consists of sport utility vehicles
33. The prices of 32-ounce containers of 20 different brands of laundry detergent
34. The ages of patrons who visit an amusement park

FURTHER APPLICATIONS

35–37: **Smooth Distributions.** Through each histogram, draw a smooth curve that captures its important features. Then classify the distribution according to its number of peaks, symmetry or skewness, and variation.

35. Times between 300 eruptions of Old Faithful geyser in Yellowstone National Park, shown in Figure 6.6

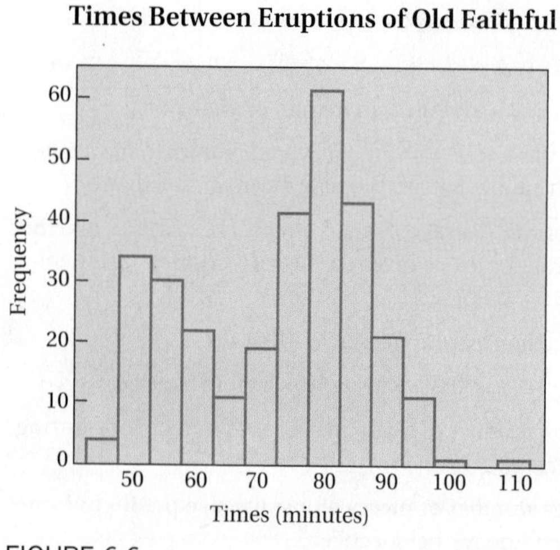

FIGURE 6.6 *Source:* Hand et al., *Handbook of Small Data Sets,* 1994.

36. Time until failure for a sample of 108 computer chips that failed, shown in Figure 6.7

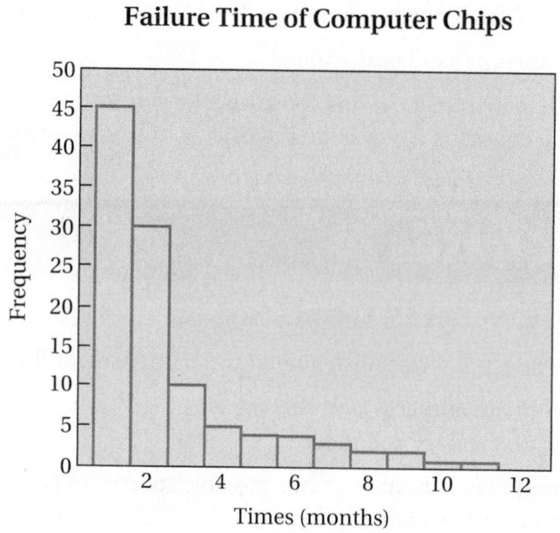

FIGURE 6.7 *Source:* Hand et al., *Handbook of Small Data Sets,* 1994.

37. Weights of a sample of 391 rugby players, shown in Figure 6.8

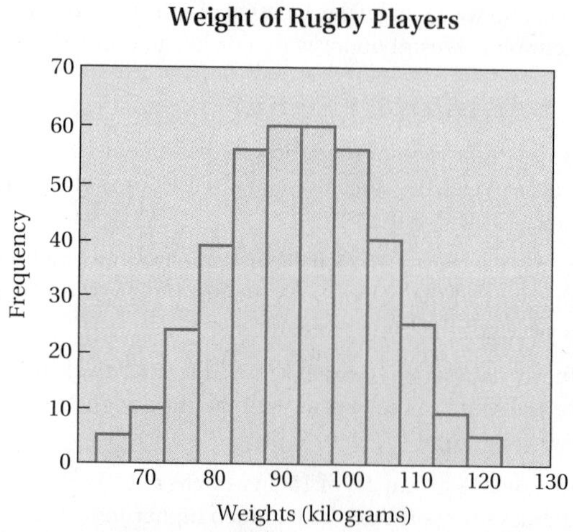

FIGURE 6.8 *Source:* Hand et al., *Handbook of Small Data Sets,* 1994.

38. **LOTTO Numbers.** Figure 6.9 shows the distribution of numbers (1 through 42) from 5964 drawings of balls in the Colorado LOTTO.

    a. Does it make sense to describe the symmetry of this distribution? Explain.

    b. Does it make sense to describe the number of peaks of this distribution? Explain.

    c. If you made the distribution of numbers for another 6000 drawings, would it look the same as Figure 6.9? Explain.

    d. If you made the distribution of numbers for 1,000,000 drawings, what would you expect the distribution to look like?

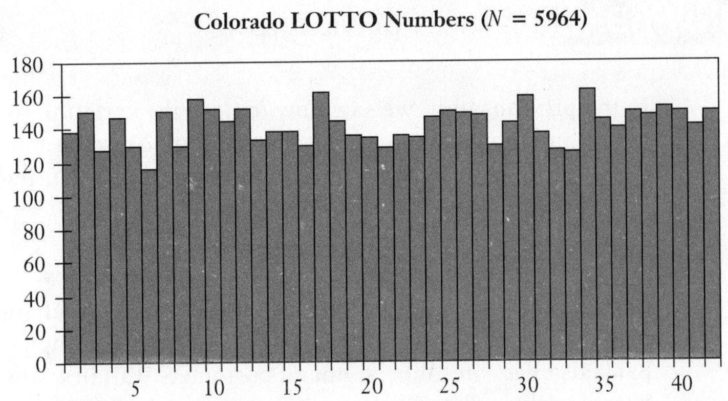

FIGURE 6.9

39. **Family Income.** Suppose you study family income in a random sample of 300 families. You find that the mean family income is \$55,000; the median is \$45,000; and the highest and lowest incomes are \$250,000 and \$2400, respectively.

    a. Draw a rough sketch of the income distribution, with clearly labeled axes. Describe the distribution as symmetric, left-skewed, or right-skewed.

    b. How many families in the sample earned less than \$45,000? Explain how you know.

    c. Based on the given information, can you determine how many families earned more than \$55,000? Why or why not?

40. **Airline Delays.** Suppose you are a scheduler for a major airline, analyzing a distribution of flight delays (departures) during one day at an airport. The distribution of delay times has the following properties: The mean delay is 10 minutes, the median delay is 6 minutes, the mode of the distribution is 0 minutes, and the maximum delay is 25 minutes.

    a. Draw a rough sketch of the distribution with clearly labeled axes. Is the distribution skewed (and if so, which way) or symmetric?

    b. What percentage of flights were delayed less than 6 minutes?

    c. What percentage of flights were delayed more than 6 minutes?

    d. Discuss the pros and cons of using the mean and the median to present the average flight delay of your airline to the public.

WEB PROJECTS

41. **Salary Data.** Many Web sites offer data on salaries in different careers. Find salary data for a career you are considering. What are the mean and median salaries for this career? How do these salaries compare to those of other careers that interest you?

42. **New York Marathon.** The Web site for the New York marathon gives frequency data for finish times in the most recent marathon. Study the data, make a rough sketch of the distribution, and describe the shape of the distribution in words.

43. **Tax Statistics.** The IRS Web site provides statistics collected from tax returns on income, refunds, and much more. Choose a set of statistics from this Web site and study the distribution. Describe the distribution in words, and discuss anything you learn that is relevant to national tax policies.

44. **Education Statistics.** Visit the Web site of the National Center for Education Statistics and view the most recent copy of the *Digest of Educational Statistics*. Choose one of the many tables or graphs in the report that display a distribution. Describe the variables that are presented, discuss the effectiveness of the presentation, and interpret the results.

IN YOUR WORLD

45. **Averages in the News.** Find three recent news reports that refer to some type of average. In each case, explain whether the average is a mean, a median, or some other type of average.

46. **Daily Averages.** Cite three examples of averages that you deal with in your own life (such as grade point average or batting average). In each case, explain whether the average is a mean, a median, or some other type of average. Briefly describe how the average is useful to you.

47. **Distributions in the News.** Find three recent examples in the news of distributions shown as histograms or line charts. Over each distribution, draw a smooth curve that captures its general features. Then classify the distribution according to its number of peaks, symmetry or skewness, and variation.

TECHNOLOGY EXERCISES

48. **Comparing Averages.** The following data sets give the weights of the starting players on two basketball teams.

    A: {160, 155, 125, 115, 115}   B: {145, 140, 135, 125, 110}

    a. Use a calculator or Excel to compute the mean, median, and mode of the data sets.

    b. Does the coach of team A have a claim to the heavier team? Explain.

    c. Does the coach of team B have a claim to the heavier team? Explain.

    d. Is the mean weight of the two teams combined equal to the mean of the two mean weights found for the teams individually?

    e. Is the median weight of the two teams *combined* equal to the median of the two median weights found for the teams individually?

UNIT 6B Measures of Variation

In the previous unit, we saw how to describe variation in a qualitative sense. But the idea of variation is so important that we should also be able to describe it quantitatively. In this unit, we'll study several common ways of measuring variation.

Why Variation Matters

BY THE WAY

In 1997, doctors told 25-year-old Lance Armstrong that, according to the averages, he had less than a 50–50 chance of surviving his testicular cancer, which had already spread to his brain. He not only survived, but went on to win the Tour de France (bicycle race) a record seven consecutive times. His story shows that, on a personal level, variation can be much more important than any average.

Imagine customers waiting in line for tellers at two different banks. Customers at Big Bank can enter any one of three different lines leading to three different tellers. Best Bank also has three tellers, but all customers wait in a single line and are called to the next available teller. The following values are waiting times, in minutes, for eleven customers at each bank. The times are arranged in ascending order.

Big Bank (three lines):	4.1	5.2	5.6	6.2	6.7	7.2	7.7	7.7	8.5	9.3	11.0
Best Bank (one line):	6.6	6.7	6.7	6.9	7.1	7.2	7.3	7.4	7.7	7.8	7.8

You'll probably find more unhappy customers at Big Bank than at Best Bank, but it's *not* because the average wait is any longer. In fact, you can verify that the mean and median waiting times are 7.2 minutes at both banks. The difference in customer satisfaction comes from the *variation* in waiting times at the two banks. The waiting times at Big Bank vary over a fairly wide range, so a few customers have long waits and are likely to become annoyed. In contrast, the variation of the waiting times at Best Bank is small, so all customers feel they are being treated roughly equally. The histograms in Figure 6.10 show the differences in variation visually.

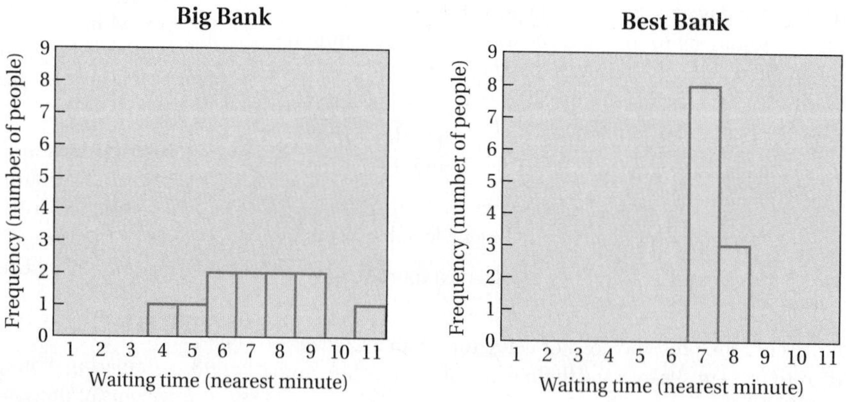

FIGURE 6.10 Histograms for the waiting times at Big Bank and Best Bank, shown with data binned to the nearest minute.

Time Out to Think

Explain *why* Big Bank, with three separate lines, should have a greater variation in waiting times than Best Bank. Then consider several places where you commonly wait in lines, such as the grocery store, a bank, a concert ticket outlet, or a fast food restaurant. Does each place use a single customer line or multiple lines? If the place uses multiple lines, do you think a single line would be better? Explain.

Now try Exercises 13–14.

Range

The simplest way to describe the variation of a data set is to compute its **range**, defined as the difference between the highest (maximum) and lowest (minimum) values. For example, the waiting times for Big Bank vary from 4.1 to 11.0 minutes, so the range is $11.0 - 4.1 = 6.9$ minutes. The waiting times for Best Bank vary from 6.6 to 7.8 minutes, so the range is $7.8 - 6.6 = 1.2$ minutes. The range is much larger for Big Bank, reflecting its greater variation.

> **DEFINITION**
>
> The **range** of a data set is the difference between its highest and lowest data values:
>
> $$\text{range} = \text{highest value (max)} - \text{lowest value (min)}$$

Although the range is easy to compute and can be useful, it occasionally can be misleading, as the next example shows.

Example 1 Misleading Range

Consider the following two sets of quiz scores for nine students. Which set has the greater range? Would you also say that the scores in this set are more varied?

Quiz 1:	1	10	10	10	10	10	10	10	10
Quiz 2:	2	3	4	5	6	7	8	9	10

Solution The range for Quiz 1 is $10 - 1 = 9$ points, which is greater than the range for Quiz 2 of $10 - 2 = 8$ points. However, aside from a single low score (an outlier), Quiz 1 has no variation at all because every other student got a 10. In contrast, no two students got the same score on Quiz 2, and the scores are spread throughout the list of possible scores. The scores on Quiz 2 are more varied even though Quiz 1 has the greater range.

Now try Exercises 15–18, part a.

Quartiles and the Five-Number Summary

A better way to describe variation is to consider a few intermediate data values in addition to the high and low values. A common way involves looking at the quartiles, or values that divide the data distribution into quarters. The following list repeats the waiting times at the two banks, with the **quartiles** shown in bold. Note that the middle quartile, which divides the data set in half, is simply the median.

			lower quartile ↓			median ↓			upper quartile ↓		
Big Bank:	4.1	5.2	**5.6**	6.2	6.7	**7.2**	7.7	7.7	**8.5**	9.3	11.0
Best Bank:	6.6	6.7	**6.7**	6.9	7.1	**7.2**	7.3	7.4	**7.7**	7.8	7.8

> **DEFINITIONS**
>
> The **lower quartile** (or *first quartile*) divides the lowest fourth of a data set from the upper three-fourths. It is the median of the data values in the *lower half* of a data set.
>
> The **middle quartile** (or *second quartile*) is the overall median.
>
> The **upper quartile** (or *third quartile*) divides the lowest three-fourths of a data set from the upper fourth. It is the median of the data values in the *upper half* of a data set.

Take Note

Statisticians do not universally agree on the precise methods for calculating quartiles, and different procedures can result in slightly different values.

DILBERT reprinted by permission of United Feature Syndicate, Inc.

Once we know the quartiles, we can describe a data set with a **five-number summary** consisting of the lowest value, the lower quartile, the median, the upper quartile, and the highest value. For the waiting times at the two banks, the five-number summaries are

Big Bank:		*Best Bank:*	
low	= 4.1	low	= 6.6
lower quartile	= 5.6	lower quartile	= 6.7
median	= 7.2	median	= 7.2
upper quartile	= 8.5	upper quartile	= 7.7
high	= 11.0	high	= 7.8

We can display the five-number summary with a **boxplot** (sometimes called a *box-and-whisker plot*). Using a number line for reference, we enclose the values from the lower to the upper quartile in a box. We then draw a line through the box at the median and add two "whiskers" extending from the box to the lowest and highest values. Figure 6.11 shows boxplots for the bank waiting times. Both the box and the whiskers are broader for Big Bank than for Best Bank, indicating that the waiting times have greater variation at Big Bank.

Historical Note

The boxplot was invented by American statistician John Tukey, widely regarded as one of the most accomplished statisticians of the 20th century. Tukey invented many powerful statistical methods and was a proponent of a thriving area of statistics called exploratory data analysis (EDA). Tukey died in July 2000 at the age of 85.

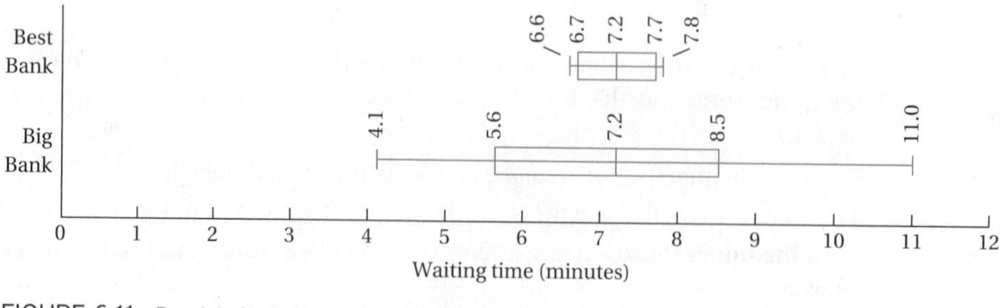

FIGURE 6.11 Boxplots for the waiting times at Big Bank and Best Bank.

THE FIVE-NUMBER SUMMARY

The **five-number summary** for a data set consists of the following five numbers:

low value *lower quartile* *median* *upper quartile* *high value*

A **boxplot** shows the five-number summary visually, with a rectangular box enclosing the lower and upper quartiles, a line marking the median, and whiskers extending to the low and high values.

Example 2 Race Times

Consider the following two sets of twenty 100-meter running times (in seconds):

Set 1:

9.92	9.97	9.99	10.01	10.06	10.07	10.08	10.10	10.13	10.13
10.14	10.15	10.17	10.17	10.18	10.21	10.24	10.26	10.31	10.38

Set 2:

9.89	9.90	9.98	10.05	10.35	10.41	10.54	10.76	10.93	10.98
11.05	11.21	11.30	11.46	11.55	11.76	11.81	11.85	11.87	12.00

Compare the variation in the two data sets with five-number summaries and boxplots.

Solution Each set has 20 data points, so the median lies halfway between the 10th and 11th times. The lower quartile is the median of the *lower half* of the times, which lies halfway between the 5th and 6th times. The upper quartile is the median of the *upper half* of the times, which lies halfway between the 15th and 16th times. You should confirm that the five-number summaries are as follows.

First Set of Times:	*Second Set of Times:*
low = 9.92	low = 9.89
lower quartile = 10.065	lower quartile = 10.38
median = 10.135	median = 11.015
upper quartile = 10.195	upper quartile = 11.655
high = 10.38	high = 12.00

Figure 6.12 shows the corresponding boxplots on the same scale, clearly illustrating the greater variation in the second set of times.

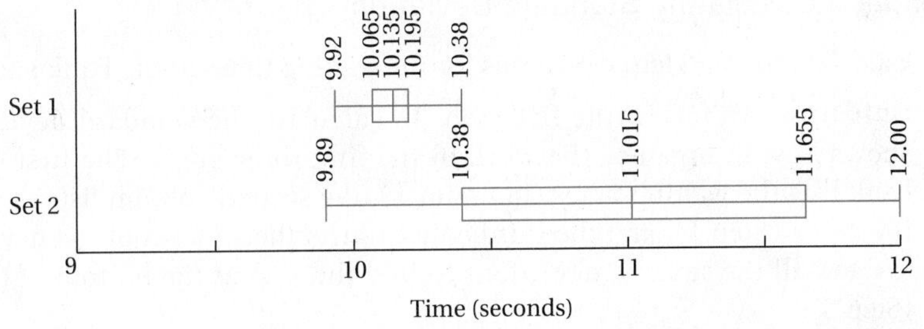

FIGURE 6.12

Now try Exercises 15–18, part b.

Standard Deviation

The five-number summary characterizes variation well, but statisticians often prefer to describe variation with a single number. The single number most commonly used to describe variation is called the **standard deviation**.

The standard deviation is a measure of how far data values are spread around the mean of a data set. To calculate a standard deviation, we first find the mean and then find how much each data value "deviates" from the mean. Consider our earlier data sets, in which the mean waiting time was 7.2 minutes for both Big Bank and Best Bank. A waiting time of 8.2 minutes has a **deviation** from the mean of 8.2 minutes − 7.2 minutes = 1.0 minute, because it is 1.0 minute greater than the mean. A waiting time of 5.2 minutes has a deviation from the mean of 5.2 minutes − 7.2 minutes = −2.0 minutes (*negative* 2 minutes), because it is 2.0 minutes *less* than the mean.

In essence, the standard deviation is a measure of the average of all the deviations from the mean. However, for technical reasons, this average is not a simple mean. Instead, it is computed as described in the box below.

Take Note

The standard deviation formula given here, in which we divide the sum of the squared deviations by the total number of data values *minus* 1, is technically valid only for data from *samples.* When dealing with populations, we do not subtract 1. In this book, we will use only the sample formulas.

CALCULATING THE STANDARD DEVIATION

Step 1. Compute the mean of the data set. Then find the deviation from the mean for every data value by subtracting the mean from the data value. That is, for every data value:

$$\text{deviation from mean} = \text{data value} - \text{mean}$$

Step 2. Find the squares (second power) of all the deviations from the mean.

Step 3. Add all the squares of the deviations from the mean.

Step 4. Divide this sum by the total number of data values *minus* 1.

Step 5. The standard deviation is the square root of this quotient.

All of these steps are included in the standard deviation formula:

$$\text{standard deviation} = \sqrt{\frac{\text{sum of (deviations from the mean)}^2}{\text{total number of data values} - 1}}$$

USING TECHNOLOGY

Standard Deviation in Excel

The built-in Excel function STDEV automates the calculation of standard deviation so that all you have to do is enter the data and then use the function. The screen shot below shows the process for the Big Bank data, with the functions shown in column B and the results in column C. Note that the results agree with those found for Big Bank in Example 3.

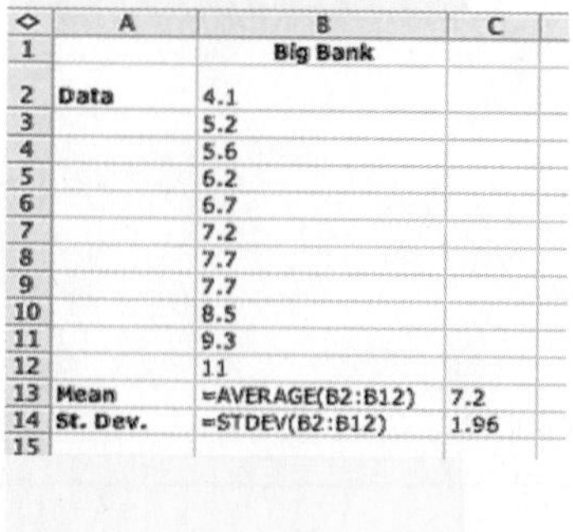

◇	A	B	C
1		Big Bank	
2	Data	4.1	
3		5.2	
4		5.6	
5		6.2	
6		6.7	
7		7.2	
8		7.7	
9		7.7	
10		8.5	
11		9.3	
12		11	
13	Mean	=AVERAGE(B2:B12)	7.2
14	St. Dev.	=STDEV(B2:B12)	1.96
15			

Although the standard deviation formula may look complex, it is easy to use for small data sets. Note that, because we square the deviations in Step 3 and take the square root in Step 5, the units of the standard deviation are the same as the units of the data values. For example, if the data values have units of minutes, the standard deviation also has units of minutes. (Also note that the result of Step 4, which is the square of the standard deviation, is called the *variance.*)

Example 3 Calculating Standard Deviation

Calculate the standard deviations for the waiting times at Big Bank and Best Bank.

Solution We follow the five steps to calculate the standard deviations. Table 6.2 shows how to organize the work in the first three steps. The first column for each bank lists the waiting times (in minutes), the second column lists the deviations from the mean (Step 1), and the third column lists the squares of the deviations (Step 2). We add all the squared deviations to find the sum at the bottom of the third column (Step 3).

For Step 4, we divide the sums from Step 3 by the total number of data values *minus* 1. Because there are 11 data values, we divide by 10:

$$\textit{Big Bank:} \quad \frac{38.46}{10} = 3.846$$

$$\textit{Best Bank:} \quad \frac{1.98}{10} = 0.198$$

TABLE 6.2 Calculating Standard Deviation

BIG BANK			BEST BANK		
Time	**Deviation (Time − Mean)**	**(Deviation)²**	**Time**	**Deviation (Time − Mean)**	**(Deviation)²**
4.1	$4.1 - 7.2 = -3.1$	$(-3.1)^2 = 9.61$	6.6	$6.6 - 7.2 = -0.6$	$(-0.6)^2 = 0.36$
5.2	$5.2 - 7.2 = -2.0$	$(-2.0)^2 = 4.00$	6.7	$6.7 - 7.2 = -0.5$	$(-0.5)^2 = 0.25$
5.6	$5.6 - 7.2 = -1.6$	$(-1.6)^2 = 2.56$	6.7	$6.7 - 7.2 = -0.5$	$(-0.5)^2 = 0.25$
6.2	$6.2 - 7.2 = -1.0$	$(-1.0)^2 = 1.00$	6.9	$6.9 - 7.2 = -0.3$	$(-0.3)^2 = 0.09$
6.7	$6.7 - 7.2 = -0.5$	$(-0.5)^2 = 0.25$	7.1	$7.1 - 7.2 = -0.1$	$(-0.1)^2 = 0.01$
7.2	$7.2 - 7.2 = 0.0$	$(0.0)^2 = 0.0$	7.2	$7.2 - 7.2 = 0.0$	$(0.0)^2 = 0.0$
7.7	$7.7 - 7.2 = 0.5$	$(0.5)^2 = 0.25$	7.3	$7.3 - 7.2 = 0.1$	$(0.1)^2 = 0.01$
7.7	$7.7 - 7.2 = 0.5$	$(0.5)^2 = 0.25$	7.4	$7.4 - 7.2 = 0.2$	$(0.2)^2 = 0.04$
8.5	$8.5 - 7.2 = 1.3$	$(1.3)^2 = 1.69$	7.7	$7.7 - 7.2 = 0.5$	$(0.5)^2 = 0.25$
9.3	$9.3 - 7.2 = 2.1$	$(2.1)^2 = 4.41$	7.8	$7.8 - 7.2 = 0.6$	$(0.6)^2 = 0.36$
11.0	$11.0 - 7.2 = 3.8$	$(3.8)^2 = 14.44$	7.8	$7.8 - 7.2 = 0.6$	$(0.6)^2 = 0.36$
Mean = 7.2		Sum = 38.46	Mean = 7.2		Sum = 1.98

Finally, Step 5 tells us that the standard deviation is the square root of the numbers from Step 4:

Big Bank: standard deviation $= \sqrt{3.846} \approx 1.96$ minutes

Best Bank: standard deviation $= \sqrt{0.198} \approx 0.44$ minute

We conclude that the standard deviation of the waiting times is 1.96 minutes at Big Bank and 0.44 minute at Best Bank. As expected, the standard deviation is larger for the bank with the greater variation in waiting times. **Now try Exercises 15–18, part c.**

Time Out to Think

Look closely at the individual deviations in Table 6.2 in Example 3. Do the standard deviations for the two data sets seem like reasonable "averages" for the deviations? Explain.

Interpreting the Standard Deviation

A good way to develop a deeper understanding of the standard deviation is to consider an approximation called the **range rule of thumb**, summarized in the following box.

THE RANGE RULE OF THUMB

The standard deviation is *approximately* related to the range of a data set by the **range rule of thumb:**

$$\text{standard deviation} \approx \frac{\text{range}}{4}$$

If we know the range of a data set (range = high − low), we can use this rule to estimate the standard deviation. Alternatively, if we know the standard deviation for a data set, we estimate the low and high values as follows:

$$\text{low value} \approx \text{mean} - 2 \times \text{standard deviation}$$
$$\text{high value} \approx \text{mean} + 2 \times \text{standard deviation}$$

BY THE WAY

Another way of interpreting the standard deviation uses a mathematical rule called *Chebyshev's theorem*. It states that, for any data set, at least 75% of all data values lie within 2 standard deviations of the mean, and at least 89% of all data values lie within 3 standard deviations of the mean.

The range rule of thumb works reasonably well for data sets in which values are distributed fairly evenly. It does not work well when the high or low values are extreme outliers. You must use judgment in deciding whether the range rule of thumb is applicable in a particular case.

Example 4 Using the Range Rule of Thumb

Use the range rule of thumb to estimate the standard deviations for the waiting times at Big Bank and Best Bank. Compare the estimates to the actual standard deviations found in Example 3.

Solution The waiting times for Big Bank vary from 4.1 to 11.0 minutes, which means a range of $11.0 - 4.1 = 6.9$ minutes. The waiting times for Best Bank vary from 6.6 to 7.8 minutes, for a range of $7.8 - 6.6 = 1.2$ minutes. The range rule of thumb gives the following estimates for the standard deviations:

$$\textit{Big Bank:}\quad \text{standard deviation} \approx \frac{6.9}{4} \approx 1.7$$

$$\textit{Best Bank:}\quad \text{standard deviation} \approx \frac{1.2}{4} = 0.3$$

The actual standard deviations calculated in Example 3 are 1.96 and 0.44, respectively. For these two cases, the estimates from the range rule of thumb slightly underestimate the actual standard deviations. Nevertheless, the estimates put us in the right ballpark, showing that the rule is useful. **Now try Exercises 15–18, part d.**

BY THE WAY

Technologies such as catalytic converters have helped reduce the amounts of many pollutants emitted by cars (per mile driven), but increasing gas mileage is the only way to reduce the carbon dioxide emissions implicated in global warming. This is a major reason why auto manufacturers are developing high-mileage "hybrid" vehicles and zero-emission vehicles that run on electricity or fuel cells.

Example 5 Estimating a Range

Studies of the gas mileage of a Prius under varying driving conditions show that it gets a mean of 45 miles per gallon with a standard deviation of 4 miles per gallon. Estimate the minimum and maximum gas mileage that you can expect under ordinary driving conditions.

Solution From the range rule of thumb, the low and high values for gas mileage are approximately

$$\begin{aligned} \text{low value} &\approx \text{mean} - 2 \times \text{standard deviation} \\ &= 45 - (2 \times 4) \\ &= 37 \\ \text{high value} &\approx \text{mean} + 2 \times \text{standard deviation} \\ &= 45 + (2 \times 4) \\ &= 53 \end{aligned}$$

The range of gas mileage for the car is roughly from a minimum of 37 miles per gallon to a maximum of 53 miles per gallon. **Now try Exercises 15–18, part e.**

QUICK QUIZ

Choose the best answer to each of the following questions. Explain your reasoning with one or more complete sentences.

1. The lowest score on an exam was 62, the median score was 75, and the high score was 96. The range was
   a. 34. b. 62. c. 75.

2. Which of the following is *not* part of a five-number summary?
   a. the low value
   b. the median
   c. the mean

3. The lower quartile for wages at a coffee shop is \$8.25, and the upper quartile is \$10.75. What can you conclude?

   a. Half the workers earn between \$8.25 and \$10.75.

   b. The median is \$9.50.

   c. The range is \$2.50.

4. Is it possible for a distribution to have a mean that is higher than its upper quartile?

   a. Yes; this is always the case.

   b. Yes, but only if there are outliers at high values.

   c. No.

5. Suppose you are given the mean and just one data value from a distribution. What can you calculate?

   a. the range

   b. the deviation for the single data value

   c. the standard deviation

6. The standard deviation is best described as a measure of

   a. the average values in a data set.

   b. the spread of the data values around the mean.

   c. the range of the data values.

7. What type of data distribution has a *negative* standard deviation?

   a. distribution in which most of the values are negative numbers

   b. distribution in which most of the values lie below the mean

   c. none—the standard deviation cannot be negative

8. In any distribution, it is always true that

   a. the range is at least as large as the standard deviation.

   b. the standard deviation is at least as large as the range.

   c. the range is always at least twice the mean.

9. Which data set would you expect to have the highest standard deviation?

   a. heights (lengths) of newborn infants

   b. heights of all elementary school children

   c. heights of first-grade boys

10. Professors Smith, Jones, and Garcia all got the same mean grade of 2.7 (a B−) on their student evaluations last semester. The standard deviations were 0.2 for Smith, 0.5 for Jones, and 1.1 for Garcia. Which professor received a very high grade from the most students?

    a. Smith b. Jones c. Garcia

Exercises 6B

REVIEW QUESTIONS

1. Consider two grocery stores at which the mean time in line is the same but the variation is different. At which store would you expect the customers to have more complaints about the waiting time? Explain.

2. Describe how we define and calculate the range of a distribution.

3. What are the quartiles of a distribution? How do we find them?

4. Define the five-number summary, and explain how to depict it visually with a boxplot.

5. Describe the process of calculating a standard deviation. Give a simple example of its calculation (such as calculating the standard deviation of the numbers 2, 3, 4, 4, and 6). What is the standard deviation if all of the sample values are the same?

6. Briefly describe the use of the range rule of thumb for interpreting the standard deviation. What are its limitations?

DOES IT MAKE SENSE?

Decide whether each of the following statements makes sense (or is clearly true) or does not make sense (or is clearly false). Explain your reasoning.

7. Both exams had the same range, so they must have had the same median.

8. The highest exam score was in the upper quartile of the distribution.

9. For the 30 students who took the test, the high score was 80, the median was 74, and the low score was 40.

10. I examined the data carefully, and the range was greater than the standard deviation.

11. The standard deviation for the heights of a group of 5-year-old children is smaller than the standard deviation for the heights of a group of children who range in age from 3 to 15.

12. The mean gas mileage of the compact cars we tested was 34 miles per gallon, with a standard deviation of 5 gallons.

BASIC SKILLS & CONCEPTS

13. **Big Bank Verification.** Find the mean and median for the waiting times at Big Bank given in the beginning of this unit. Show your work clearly, and verify that both are 7.2 minutes.

14. **Best Bank Verification.** Find the mean and median for the waiting times at Best Bank given in the beginning of this unit. Show your work clearly, and verify that both are 7.2 minutes.

15–18: Comparing Variations. Consider the following data sets.

a. Find the mean, median, and range for each of the two data sets.

b. Give the five-number summary and draw a boxplot for each of the two data sets.

c. Find the standard deviation for each of the two data sets.

d. Apply the range rule of thumb to estimate the standard deviation of each of the two data sets. How well does the rule work in each case? Briefly discuss why it does or does not work well.

e. Based on all your results, compare and discuss the two data sets in terms of their center and variation.

15. The table below gives the cost of living index for six East Coast cities and six West Coast cities (using the ACCRA index, where 100 represents the average cost of living for all participating cities with a population of over 1.5 million).

East Coast Cities		West Coast Cities	
Atlanta	98.2	Los Angeles	155.8
Baltimore	108.7	Portland	113.2
Boston	135.4	San Diego	144.8
Miami	111.5	San Francisco	182.4
New York City	216.0	San Jose	156.0
Washington, DC	140.0	Seattle	122.7

16. The table below gives the average state and local taxes paid by a family of four with an income of $75,000 in ten (east and west) coast cities and ten noncoastal cities.

East/West Coast Cities		Noncoastal Cities	
Atlanta	8261	Albuquerque	6369
Baltimore	8923	Cheyenne	2899
Boston	7875	Columbus, OH	7434
Los Angeles	7488	Denver	5535
New York City	10,490	Detroit	8257
Portland	7789	Kansas City	6805
Providence	9729	Louisville	7954
Seattle	4876	Oklahoma City	6593
Virgina Beach	6411	Salt Lake City	7153
Washington, DC	7594	Wichita	5683

Source: District of Columbia Government.

17. Researchers at the Pennsylvania State University conducted experiments with popular trees in which one group of trees was given fertilizer and irrigation while the other group was given no treatment. The weight in kilograms of trees in the two groups are as follows:

No treatment:	0.15	0.02	0.16	0.37	0.22
Treatment:	2.03	0.27	0.92	1.07	2.38

18. The following data sets give the approximate lengths of Beethoven's nine symphonies and Mahler's nine symphonies (in minutes).

Beethoven:	28	36	50	33	30	40	38	26	68
Mahler:	52	85	94	50	72	72	80	90	80

FURTHER APPLICATIONS

19–25: Understanding Variation. The following exercises give four data sets consisting of seven numbers.

a. Make a histogram for each set.

b. Give the five-number summary and draw a boxplot for each set.

c. Compute the standard deviation for each set.

d. Based on your results, briefly explain how the standard deviation provides a useful single-number summary of the variation in these data sets.

19. The following sets of numbers all have a mean of 9:

$$\{9, 9, 9, 9, 9, 9, 9\}, \{8, 8, 9, 9, 9, 10, 10\},$$
$$\{8, 8, 8, 9, 10, 10, 10\}, \{6, 6, 6, 9, 12, 12, 12\}$$

20. The following sets of numbers all have a mean of 6:

$$\{6, 6, 6, 6, 6, 6, 6\}, \{5, 5, 6, 6, 6, 7, 7\},$$
$$\{5, 5, 5, 6, 7, 7, 7\}, \{3, 3, 3, 6, 9, 9, 9\}$$

21. **Pizza Deliveries.** After recording the pizza delivery times for two different pizza shops, you conclude that one pizza shop has a mean delivery time of 45 minutes with a standard deviation of 3 minutes. The other shop has a mean delivery time of 42 minutes with a standard deviation of 20 minutes. Interpret these figures. If you liked the pizzas from both shops equally well, which one would you order from? Why?

22. **Airline Arrival Times.** Two airlines have data on the arrival times of their flights. An arrival time of +2 minutes means the flight arrived 2 minutes early. An arrival time of −5 minutes means the flight arrived 5 minutes late. Skyview Airlines has a mean arrival time of 0.5 minute with a standard deviation of 9.6 minutes. SkyHigh Airlines has a mean arrival time of −2.5 minutes with a standard deviation of 4.0 minutes. Explain the meaning of these figures and why they would affect your choice of airlines.

23. **Portfolio Standard Deviation.** The book *Investments* by Zvi Bodie, Alex Kane, and Alan Marcus claims that the returns for investment portfolios with a single stock have a standard deviation of 0.55, while the returns for portfolios with 32 stocks have a standard deviation of 0.325. Explain how the standard deviation measures the risk in these two types of portfolios.

24. **Defect Rates.** Two factories each produce 1000 computer chips per day. In Factory A, the number of defective chips per day is 3 with a standard deviation of 2.5. In Factory B, the number of defective chips per day is 4 with a standard deviation of 0.5. Use these figures to either defend or discredit the claim that Factory A has a more reliable manufacturing process.

25. **Batting Standard Deviation.** For the last 100 years, the mean batting average in the major leagues has remained fairly constant at about .260. However, the standard deviation of batting averages has decreased from about .049 in the 1870s to .031 at present. What does this tell us about the batting averages of players? Based on these facts, would you expect batting averages above .350 to be more or less common today than in the past? Explain.

WEB PROJECTS

26. **Web Data Sets.** Go to any Web site that gives data sets, such as the Census Bureau, the U.S. Energy Information Administration, or the Statistical Abstract of the United States. Choose three data sets that you find interesting. In each case, describe the data distribution and discuss the variation in the distribution. How is the variation important in understanding the data?

IN YOUR WORLD

27. **Ranges in the News.** Find two examples of data distributions in recent news reports; they may be given either as tables or as graphs. In each case, state the range of the distribution and explain its meaning in the context of the news report.

28. **Summarizing a News Data Set.** Find an example of a data distribution given in the form of a table in a recent news report. Make a five-number summary and a boxplot for the distribution.

29. **Range Rule in the News.** For each of the two data distributions you found in Exercise 27 above, estimate the standard deviation by applying the range rule of thumb. Discuss whether you think the estimate is valid in each case.

TECHNOLOGY EXERCISES

30. **Computing Standard Deviation.** The following data set gives the time intervals in minutes between eruptions of Old Faithful geyser in Yellowstone National Park.

98 92 95 87 96 90 65 92 95 93 98 94

a. Use a calculator or Excel to compute the mean, median, and standard deviation of the data.

b. Suppose Old Faithful missed the second eruption in the set above, giving the following new data set:

190 95 87 96 90 65 92 95 93 98 94

How does this change affect the mean and standard deviation computed in part a?

c. Suppose the next data point in the data set in part a equals the mean of the data set. Does this new data point change the mean, median, or standard deviation of the original data set?

UNIT 6C The Normal Distribution

A special and very common type of distribution is represented by a *bell-shaped curve*; it is formally called a **normal distribution**. The normal distribution arises in many circumstances, and describes many data sets concerning human characteristics. For example, distributions of men's or women's heights and weights tend to be normal, as do distributions of scores on standardized tests.

All normal distributions have the same characteristic bell shape, but they can differ from one another in two ways. First, they may differ in the location of their central peaks. Because a normal distribution is symmetric, the peak represents the mean, median, and mode of the data set. Second, they can differ in their variation, or the spread of data values around the peak. Figure 6.13 shows two normal distributions. Both have the same mean of 75, but distribution (a) has a lower peak and greater variation.

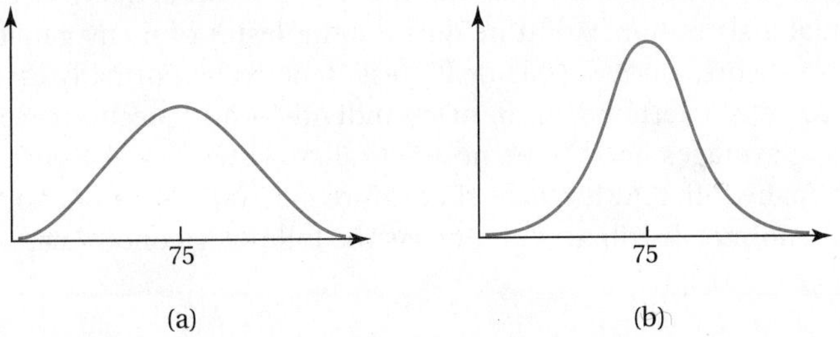

FIGURE 6.13 Both distributions are normal and have the same mean of 75, but distribution (a) has a lower peak and greater variation (a larger standard deviation).

DEFINITION

The **normal distribution** is a symmetric, bell-shaped distribution with a single peak. Its peak corresponds to the mean, median, and mode of the distribution.

Historical Note

Using data taken from French and Scottish soldiers, the Belgian social scientist Adolphe Quetelet realized in the 1830s that human characteristics such as height and chest circumference are normally distributed. This observation led him to coin the term "the average man."

Example 1 The Normal Shape

Figure 6.14a shows a famous data set of the chest sizes of 5738 Scottish militiamen collected in about 1846. Figure 6.14b shows the distribution of the population densities of the 50 states. Which distribution appears to be normal? Explain.

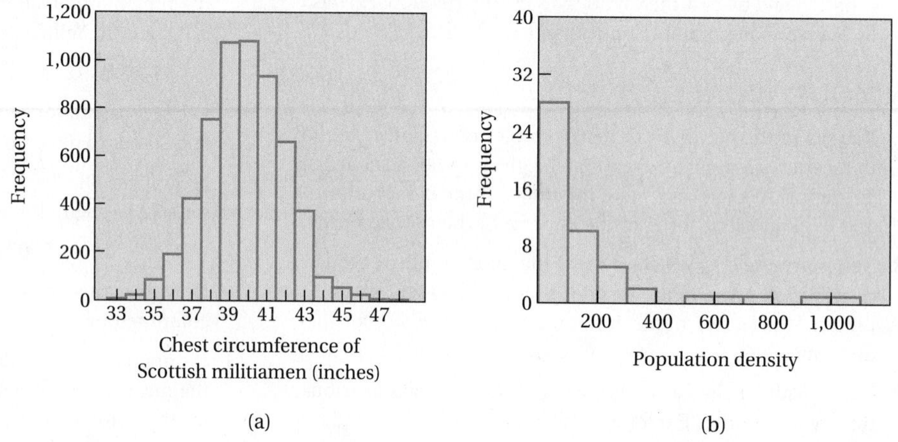

FIGURE 6.14

Solution The distribution of chest sizes in Figure 6.14a is nearly symmetric with a mean between 39 and 40 inches. Values far from the mean are less common, giving it the bell shape of a normal distribution. The distribution in Figure 6.14b shows that most states have low population densities, but a few have much higher densities. This fact makes the distribution right-skewed, so it is not a normal distribution. **Now try Exercises 11–12.**

What Is Normal?

We can better appreciate the importance of the normal distribution if we understand why it is so common. The bell shape tells us why the normal distribution fits human characteristics such as height: Most men or women have heights clustered near the mean height (for their sex), so a data set of heights has a peak at the mean height. But as we consider heights increasingly far from the mean on either side, we find fewer and fewer people. This "tailing off" of heights far from the mean produces the two tails of the normal distribution.

On a deeper level, any quantity that is the result of *many* factors is likely to follow a normal distribution. Adult heights are the result of many genetic and environmental factors. Scores on SAT tests or IQ tests tend to be normally distributed because each test score is determined from many individual test questions. Sports statistics, such as batting averages, tend to be normally distributed because they involve many people with many different levels of skill. More generally, we can expect a data set to have a nearly normal distribution if it meets the following conditions.

CONDITIONS FOR A NORMAL DISTRIBUTION

A data set that satisfies the following four criteria is likely to have a nearly normal distribution:

1. Most data values are clustered near the mean, giving the distribution a well-defined single peak.
2. Data values are spread evenly around the mean, making the distribution symmetric.
3. Larger deviations from the mean become increasingly rare, producing the tapering tails of the distribution.
4. Individual data values result from a combination of many different factors, such as genetic and environmental factors.

Example 2 Is It a Normal Distribution?

Which of the following variables would you expect to have a normal or nearly normal distribution?

a. Scores on a very easy test
b. Shoe sizes of a random sample of adult women

Solution

a. Tests have a maximum score (100%) that limits the size of the data values. If a test is easy, the mean will be high and many scores will be near the maximum. The fewer lower scores can be spread out well below the mean. We therefore expect the distribution of scores to be left-skewed and not normal.
b. Shoe size is a human trait determined by many genetic and environmental factors. We expect women's shoe sizes to cluster near a mean and become less common farther from the mean. Therefore, we expect shoe sizes to have a normal distribution.

Now try Exercises 13–18.

The Standard Deviation in Normal Distributions

Because all normal distributions have the same bell shape, we can characterize the variation of any normal distribution with just a single number: the standard deviation. Recall from Unit 6B that, for any distribution, the standard deviation gives a measure of the spread of data values around the mean. For a normal distribution, the standard deviation gives a very precise description of the variation, based on a simple rule often called the **68-95-99.7 rule**.

THE 68-95-99.7 RULE FOR A NORMAL DISTRIBUTION

- About 68% (more precisely, 68.3%), or just over two-thirds, of the data points fall within 1 standard deviation of the mean.
- About 95% (more precisely, 95.4%) of the data points fall within 2 standard deviations of the mean.
- About 99.7% of the data points fall within 3 standard deviations of the mean.

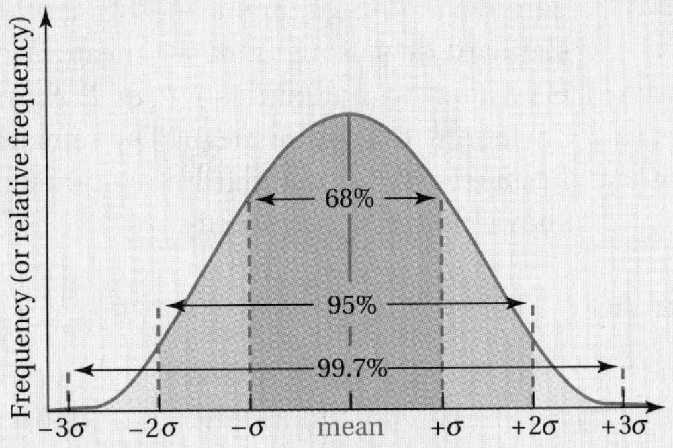

FIGURE 6.15 The 68-95-99.7 rule for a normal distribution.

Figure 6.15 shows the 68-95-99.7 rule graphically. The horizontal axis is marked with the position of the mean and the positions corresponding to 1, 2, and 3 standard deviations above and below the mean. The standard deviation is abbreviated by the Greek letter σ (*sigma*). The vertical axis may represent the frequency or relative frequency of data values.

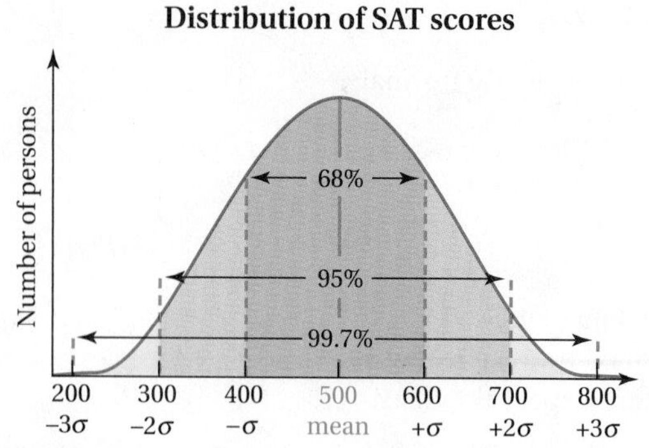

FIGURE 6.16 The distribution of SAT scores.

Example 3 SAT Scores

Each test that makes up the SAT is designed so that its scores are normally distributed with a mean of 500 and a standard deviation of 100. Interpret this statement according to the 68-95-99.7 rule.

Solution From the 68-95-99.7 rule, about 68% of students have scores within 1 standard deviation (100 points) of the mean of 500 points; that is, about 68% of the students score between 400 and 600. About 95% of the students score within 2 standard deviations (200 points) of the mean, or between 300 and 700. About 99.7% of the students score within 3 standard deviations (300 points) of the mean, or between 200 and 800. Figure 6.16 illustrates this interpretation graphically. Note that the horizontal axis shows both actual scores and the distance from the mean in standard deviations. **Now try Exercise 19.**

Example 4 Detecting Counterfeits

Vending machines can be adjusted to reject coins above and below certain weights. The weights of legal U.S. quarters are normally distributed with a mean of 5.67 grams and a standard deviation of 0.0700 gram. If a vending machine is adjusted to reject quarters that weigh more than 5.81 grams and less than 5.53 grams, what percentage of legal quarters will be rejected by the machine?

Solution A weight of 5.81 is 0.14 gram, or 2 standard deviations, above the mean. A weight of 5.53 is 0.14 gram, or 2 standard deviations, below the mean. Thus, the machine accepts quarters that are within 2 standard deviations of the mean. Conversely, the machine rejects quarters that are more than 2 standard deviations from the mean. By the 68-95-99.7 rule, about 95% of legal quarters will be accepted and about 5% of legal quarters will be rejected. **Now try Exercise 20.**

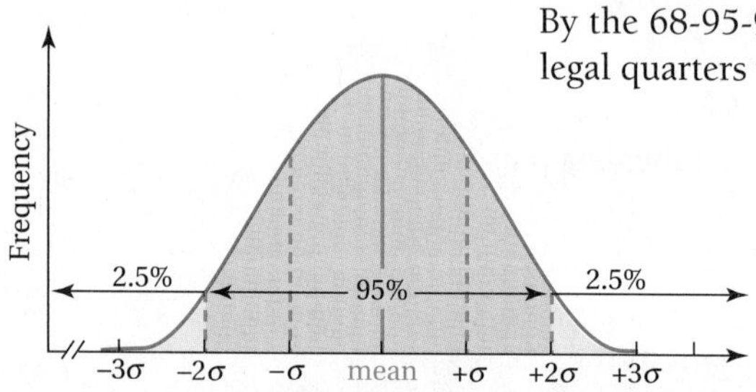

FIGURE 6.17 Because 95% of the data values lie within 2 standard deviations of the mean, 5% must lie farther than 2 standard deviations from the mean. Of this 5%, half (or 2.5%) lie more than 2 standard deviations below the mean and half lie more than 2 standard deviations above the mean.

Applying the 68-95-99.7 Rule

We can use the 68-95-99.7 rule to answer many questions about the frequencies (or relative frequencies) of data values in a normal distribution. For example, suppose we want to know the percentage of values that lie *more* than 2 standard deviations above the mean. The 68-95-99.7 rule tells us that 95% of the data values lie *within* 2 standard deviations of the mean, so 5% of the data values lie *more than* 2 standard deviations from the mean. Because the normal distribution is symmetric, half of this 5%, or 2.5%, must lie more than 2 standard deviations below the mean. The remaining 2.5% of data values must lie more than 2 standard deviations above the mean. Figure 6.17 shows this idea graphically.

Example 5 Normal Auto Prices

A survey finds that the prices paid for two-year-old Ford Fusion cars are normally distributed with a mean of $10,500 and a standard deviation of $500. Consider a sample of 10,000 people who bought two-year-old Ford Fusions.

a. How many people paid between $10,000 and $11,000?
b. How many paid less than $10,000?
c. How many paid more than $12,000?

Solution

a. Given the mean of $10,500 and standard deviation of $500, prices between $10,000 and $11,000 are within 1 standard deviation of the mean. From the 68-95-99.7 rule, about 68% of the 10,000 car buyers, or 6800 people, paid prices in this range.

b. The remaining 32%, or 3200 people, paid prices more than 1 standard deviation from the mean, or outside the \$10,000 to \$11,000 range. Half of these people, or 1600 people, paid prices below \$10,000 (while the other half paid prices above \$11,000).

c. A price of \$12,000 is \$1500 above the mean of \$10,500. Because the standard deviation is \$500, this price is 3 standard deviations above the mean. From the 68-95-99.7 rule, about 99.7% of the car buyers paid prices *within* 3 standard deviations of the mean, leaving 0.3% paying either more or less. Half of the 0.3%, or 0.15%, paid a price *more than* 3 standard deviations above the mean. Out of 10,000 people, 0.15% represents 15 people. That is, approximately 15 people paid more than \$12,000.

Now try Exercises 21–24.

Standard Scores

The 68-95-99.7 rule applies to data values that are exactly 1, 2, or 3 standard deviations from the mean. For other cases, we can generalize this rule if we know precisely how many standard deviations from the mean a particular data value lies. The number of standard deviations a data value lies above or below the mean is called its **standard score** (or *z-score*), which is often abbreviated by the letter z. For example:

- The standard score of the mean is $z = 0$, because it is 0 standard deviations from the mean.
- The standard score of a data value 1.5 standard deviations above the mean is $z = 1.5$.
- The standard score of a data value 2.4 standard deviations below the mean is $z = -2.4$.

The following box explains the computation of standard scores.

> **COMPUTING STANDARD SCORES**
>
> The number of standard deviations a data value lies above or below the mean is called its **standard score** (or *z-score*), defined by
>
> $$z = \text{standard score} = \frac{\text{data value} - \text{mean}}{\text{standard deviation}}$$
>
> The standard score is positive for data values above the mean and negative for data values below the mean.

USING TECHNOLOGY

Standard Scores in Excel

Excel has a built-in function STANDARDIZE that returns the standard score for any data value, given the mean and standard deviation of the distribution. Enter the data in the form "=STANDARDIZE(data value, mean, standard deviation)." The screen shot below shows this function with a table for the data value, mean, and standard deviation from Example 6; the function references the cells (B1, B2, B3) containing those data. Column C shows the results.

	A	B	C
1	data value	95	
2	mean	100	
3	standard deviation	16	
4	standard score	=STANDARDIZE(B1,B2,B3)	-0.3125

Example 6 Standard IQ Scores

The Stanford-Binet IQ test is designed so that scores are normally distributed with a mean of 100 and a standard deviation of 16. Find the standard scores for IQ scores of 95 and 125.

Solution The standard score for an IQ of 95 is

$$z = \frac{\text{data value} - \text{mean}}{\text{standard deviation}} = \frac{95 - 100}{16} = -0.31$$

That is, an IQ of 95 lies 0.31 standard deviation *below* the mean.

The standard score for an IQ of 125 is

$$z = \frac{\text{data value} - \text{mean}}{\text{standard deviation}} = \frac{125 - 100}{16} = 1.56$$

That is, an IQ of 125 lies 1.56 standard deviations *above* the mean.

Now try Exercises 25–28.

BY THE WAY

By comparing IQ tests and questions that have stayed the same over the years, Dr. James Flynn discovered a startling fact: Raw scores on IQ tests (before they are set to a mean of 100) rose steadily during the 20th century, so that someone scoring an "intellectually deficient" IQ of 70 today would have rated an "intellectually superior" IQ of 130 a century ago. It seems unlikely that people today are really so much smarter than their parents and grandparents, but no one has yet found a clear explanation for Flynn's discovery.

Standard Scores and Percentiles

Once we know the standard score of a data value, the properties of the normal distribution allow us to find its **percentile** in the distribution. You are probably familiar with the idea of percentiles. For example, if you scored in the 45th percentile on the SAT, 45% of the SAT scores were lower than yours.

PERCENTILES

The ***n*th percentile** of a data set is the smallest value in the set with the property that *n*% of the data values are *less than or equal to* it. A data value that lies between two percentiles is said to lie *in* the lower percentile.

Time Out to Think

Is it possible for someone to score above the 100th percentile on a standardized test? Why or why not?

A *standard score table*, such as Table 6.3, allows us to find percentiles from standard scores. For each of many standard scores in a normal distribution, the table gives the percentage of values in the distribution *less than or equal to* that value. For example, Table 6.3 shows that 55.96% of the values in a normal distribution have a standard score less than or equal to 0.15. In other words, a data value with a standard score of 0.15 lies in the 55th percentile.

TABLE 6.3 Standard Scores and Percentiles

z-score	Percentile	*z*-score	Percentile	*z*-score	Percentile	*z*-score	Percentile
−3.5	0.02	−1.0	15.87	0.0	50.00	1.1	86.43
−3.0	0.13	−0.95	17.11	0.05	51.99	1.2	88.49
−2.9	0.19	−0.90	18.41	0.10	53.98	1.3	90.32
−2.8	0.26	−0.85	19.77	0.15	55.96	1.4	91.92
−2.7	0.35	−0.80	21.19	0.20	57.93	1.5	93.32
−2.6	0.47	−0.75	22.66	0.25	59.87	1.6	94.52
−2.5	0.62	−0.70	24.20	0.30	61.79	1.7	95.54
−2.4	0.82	−0.65	25.78	0.35	63.68	1.8	96.41
−2.3	1.07	−0.60	27.43	0.40	65.54	1.9	97.13
−2.2	1.39	−0.55	29.12	0.45	67.36	2.0	97.72
−2.1	1.79	−0.50	30.85	0.50	69.15	2.1	98.21
−2.0	2.28	−0.45	32.64	0.55	70.88	2.2	98.61
−1.9	2.87	−0.40	34.46	0.60	72.57	2.3	98.93
−1.8	3.59	−0.35	36.32	0.65	74.22	2.4	99.18
−1.7	4.46	−0.30	38.21	0.70	75.80	2.5	99.38
−1.6	5.48	−0.25	40.13	0.75	77.34	2.6	99.53
−1.5	6.68	−0.20	42.07	0.80	78.81	2.7	99.65
−1.4	8.08	−0.15	44.04	0.85	80.23	2.8	99.74
−1.3	9.68	−0.10	46.02	0.90	81.59	2.9	99.81
−1.2	11.51	−0.05	48.01	0.95	82.89	3.0	99.87
−1.1	13.57	0.0	50.00	1.0	84.13	3.5	99.98

As Table 6.3 shows, we sometimes use fractions of percentiles instead of whole percentiles. For example, because 55.96% of the values in a normal distribution have a standard score less than 0.15, we might say that this standard score lies in the 55th percentile, the 55.9th percentile, or the 55.96th percentile, depending on how much precision we desire.

Example 7 Cholesterol Levels

Cholesterol levels in men 18 to 24 years of age are normally distributed with a mean of 178 and a standard deviation of 41.

a. In what percentile is a man with a cholesterol level of 190?
b. What cholesterol level corresponds to the 90th percentile, the level at which treatment may be necessary?

Solution

a. The standard score for a cholesterol level of 190 is

$$z = \frac{\text{data value} - \text{mean}}{\text{standard deviation}} = \frac{190 - 178}{41} \approx 0.29$$

Table 6.3 shows that a standard score of 0.29 corresponds to about the 61st percentile.

b. Table 6.3 shows that 90.32% of all data values have a standard score less than 1.3. That is, the 90th percentile is about 1.3 standard deviations above the mean. The standard deviation is 41, so 1.3 standard deviations is $1.3 \times 41 = 53.3$. Adding this value to the mean, we find that the 90th percentile begins at about $178 + 53 = 231$. A person with a cholesterol level above 231 may need treatment.

Now try Exercises 29–30.

Example 8 Women in the Army

The heights of American women aged 18 to 24 are normally distributed with a mean of 65 inches and a standard deviation of 2.5 inches. In order to serve in the U.S. Army, women must be between 58 inches and 80 inches tall. What percentage of women are ineligible to serve based on their height?

Solution The standard scores for the army's minimum and maximum heights of 58 inches and 80 inches are

For 58 inches: $$z = \frac{\text{data value} - \text{mean}}{\text{standard deviation}} = \frac{58 - 65}{2.5} = -2.8$$

For 80 inches: $$z = \frac{\text{data value} - \text{mean}}{\text{standard deviation}} = \frac{80 - 65}{2.5} = 6.0$$

Table 6.3 shows that a standard score of -2.8 corresponds to the 0.26 percentile. A standard score of 6.0 does not appear in the table, which means it is above the 99.98th percentile (since that is the highest percentile shown in the table). Therefore, 0.26% of all women are too short to serve in the army and fewer than 0.02% of all women are too tall to serve in the army. Altogether, this means that less than about 0.28% of women, or about one out of every 400 women, are ineligible to serve in the army based on their height.

Now try Exercises 31–32.

Time Out to Think

Note that the army standards reject a larger percentage of short women than tall women. Why do you think this is the case? Is it fair?

USING TECHNOLOGY

Normal Distribution Percentiles in Excel

With the built-in function NORMDIST, Excel can save you the work of using a table like Table 6.3. To find a data value's percentile in a normal distribution, enter data in the form "=NORMDIST (data value, mean, standard deviation, TRUE)"; the fourth input (TRUE) is necessary to get a percentile result. The screen shot below shows the calculation of the standard score and percentile for the data in Example 7a. Column C shows the results; note that the percentile is returned as a fraction, so you need to multiply by 100 to convert to a percentage.

◇	A	B	C
1	data value	190	
2	mean	178	
3	standard deviation	41	
4	standard score	=STANDARDIZE(B1,B2,B3)	0.29
5	percentile	=NORMDIST(B1,B2,B3,TRUE)	0.615

QUICK QUIZ

Choose the best answer to each of the following questions. Explain your reasoning with one or more complete sentences.

1. Graphs of normal distributions
   a. always look exactly the same.
   b. always have the same characteristic bell shape.
   c. can have any shape as long as they have a sharp central peak.
2. In a normal distribution, the mean
   a. is equal to the median.
   b. is greater than the median.
   c. can be greater or less than the median.
3. In a normal distribution, data values farther from the mean are
   a. less common than data values close to the mean.
   b. more common than data values close to the mean.
   c. equally as common as data values close to the mean.
4. Consider wages at a fast-food restaurant where most of the workers earn the minimum wage. Would you expect the wages of all workers at this restaurant to have a normal distribution?
   a. Yes, because wage distributions are always normal.
   b. No, because the minimum wage is not enough money to live on.
   c. No, because the fact that no one earns less than the minimum wage means the distribution cannot be symmetric.
5. In a normal distribution, about 2/3 of the data values fall within
   a. 1 standard deviation of the mean.
   b. 2 standard deviations of the mean.
   c. 3 standard deviations of the mean.
6. Suppose a car driven under different conditions gets a mean gas mileage of 40 miles per gallon with a standard deviation of 3 miles per gallon. If you drive this car many times, your mileage on 99.7% of the trips will be between
   a. 37 and 43 miles per gallon.
   b. 40 and 43 miles per gallon.
   c. 31 and 49 miles per gallon.
7. Consider again the car described in Exercise 6. On about what percentage of the trips will your gas mileage be above 43 miles per gallon?
   a. 16%
   b. 2.5%
   c. 68%
8. Consider an exam with a normal distribution of scores with a mean of 75 and a standard deviation of 6. If you get an 84 on the exam, your *standard score* (z-score) is
   a. 84.
   b. 9.
   c. 1.5.
9. An acquaintance tells you that his IQ is in the 102nd percentile. You can conclude that
   a. he is smarter than 102% of all people.
   b. he is smarter than 2% of all people.
   c. he doesn't understand percentiles.
10. The height of a particular 7-year-old girl has a standard score of −0.60 among the heights of all 7-year-old girls. From Table 6.3, you know that
    a. she is 0.6 inch shorter than average for her age.
    b. she is taller than about 27% of all 7-year-old girls.
    c. she is shorter than about 27% of all 7-year-old girls.

Exercises 6C

REVIEW QUESTIONS

1. What is a normal distribution? Briefly describe the conditions that make a normal distribution. Give an example of a data set that is likely to have a normal distribution, and explain why.
2. What is the 68-95-99.7 rule for normal distributions? Explain how it can be used to answer questions about frequencies of data values in a normal distribution.
3. What is a standard score? How do you find the standard score for a particular data value?
4. What is a percentile? Describe how Table 6.3 allows you to relate standard scores and percentiles.

DOES IT MAKE SENSE?

Decide whether each of the following statements makes sense (or is clearly true) or does not make sense (or is clearly false). Explain your reasoning.

5. The heights of male basketball players at Kentucky College are normally distributed with a mean of 6 feet 3 inches and a standard deviation of 3 inches.
6. The weights of babies born at Belmont Hospital are normally distributed with a mean of 6.8 pounds and a standard deviation of 1.2 pounds.

7. The weights of babies born at Belmont Hospital are normally distributed with a mean of 6.8 pounds and a standard deviation of 7 pounds.
8. On yesterday's mathematics exam, the standard score was 75.
9. My professor graded the final on a curve, and she gave a grade of A to anyone who had a standard score of 2 or more.
10. Jack is in the 50th percentile for height, so he is of median height.

BASIC SKILLS & CONCEPTS

11–12: Normal Shape. Consider the following sets of three distributions, all of which are drawn to the same scale. Identify the two distributions that are normal. Of the two normal distributions, which one has the larger variation?

11.

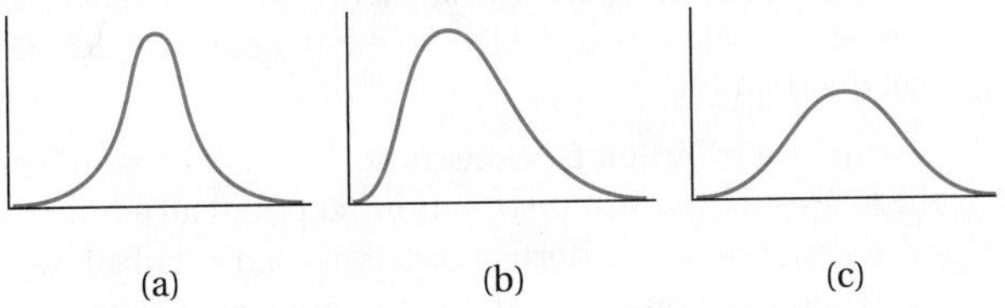

12.

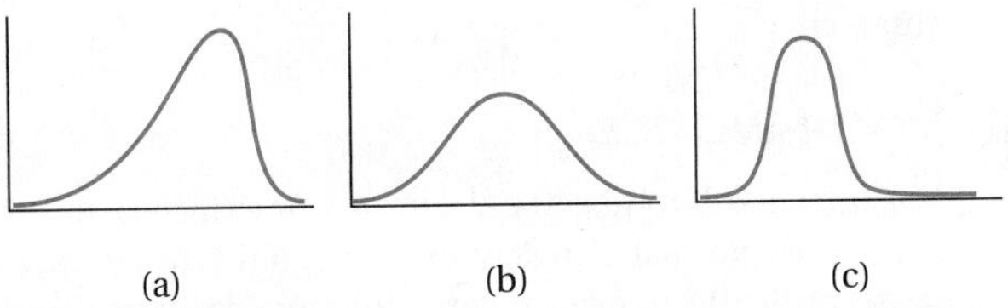

13–18: Normal Distributions. State, with an explanation, whether you would expect the following data sets to be normally distributed.

13. The delay in departure of trains from a station (note that trains, buses, and airplanes cannot leave early)
14. The weights of lawn fertilizer bags labeled "40 pounds"
15. The distances between the bull's-eye of a target and 100 darts thrown by an expert
16. The distances of tee shots hit with the same club by a professional golfer during a four-day tournament
17. Scores on an easy statistics exam
18. The times of runners at the Olympic marathon
19. **The 68-95-99.7 Rule.** A set of test scores is normally distributed with a mean of 100 and a standard deviation of 20. Use the 68-95-99.7 rule to find the percentage of scores in each of the following categories.
    a. less than 100 b. less than 120
    c. less than 140 d. less than 60
    e. greater than 60 f. greater than 160
    g. greater than 80 h. between 60 and 140
20. **The 68-95-99.7 Rule.** The resting heart rates for a sample of individuals are normally distributed with a mean of 70 and a standard deviation of 15. Use the 68-95-99.7 rule to find the percentage of heart rates in each of the following categories.
    a. less than 55 b. less than 40
    c. less than 85 d. less than 100
    e. greater than 85 f. greater than 55
    g. greater than 40 h. between 55 and 85

21–28: Standard Scores. The scores on a psychology exam were normally distributed with a mean of 67 and a standard deviation of 8.

21. About what percentage of scores were above 59?
22. About what percentage of scores were below 83?
23. A failing grade on the exam was anything 2 or more standard deviations below the mean. What was the cutoff for a failing score? Approximately what percentage of the students failed?
24. If 500 students took the exam, approximately how many students scored below 75?
25. What is the standard score for an exam score of 67?
26. What is the standard score for an exam score of 59?
27. What is the standard score for an exam score of 55?
28. What is the standard score for an exam score of 88?

29–30: Standard Scores and Percentiles. Use Table 6.3 to find the standard score and percentile of the following data values.

29. a. A data value 1 standard deviation above the mean
    b. A data value 0.5 standard deviation above the mean
    c. A data value 1.5 standard deviations below the mean
30. a. A data value 0.5 standard deviation below the mean
    b. A data value 2 standard deviations below the mean
    c. A data value 1.2 standard deviations above the mean

31–32: Percentiles. Use Table 6.3 to find the approximate standard score of the following data values. Then state the approximate number of standard deviations that the value lies above or below the mean.

31. a. A data value in the 20th percentile
    b. A data value in the 80th percentile
    c. A data value in the 63rd percentile
32. a. A data value in the 10th percentile
    b. A data value in the 35th percentile
    c. A data value in the 88th percentile

FURTHER APPLICATIONS

33–36: Pregnancy Length. Actual lengths of pregnancy terms are nearly normally distributed about a mean pregnancy length (of about 38 to 39 weeks) with a standard deviation of 15 days.

33. About what percentage of births would be expected to occur within 15 days of the mean pregnancy length?
34. About what percentage of births would be expected to occur within 1 month of the mean pregnancy length?
35. About what percentage of births would be expected to occur more than 15 days after the mean pregnancy length?

36. About what percentage of births would be expected to occur more than 30 days after the mean pregnancy length? (*Note:* In practice, doctors will induce labor before this time, because of potential danger to the baby.)

37. **Heights.** According to data from the National Health Survey, the heights of all adult American women are normally distributed with a mean of 63.6 inches and a standard deviation of 2.5 inches. Give the standard score and approximate percentile for women with each of the following heights.

    a. 66 inches

    b. 62 inches

    c. 61.5 inches

    d. 64.7 inches

38. **Body Mass Index (BMI).** The body mass indices of American men between ages 30 and 50 are normally distributed with a mean of 26.2 and a standard deviation of 4.7.

    a. Determine the standard score and percentile of a BMI of 22.

    b. Determine the standard score and percentile of a BMI of 28.

    c. Several health organizations have declared that men with a BMI of 25 or greater are overweight and that men with a BMI of 30 or greater are obese. What percentage of American men are overweight? obese?

39. **Is It Likely?** Suppose you read that the average height of a class of 45 eighth-graders is 55 inches with a standard deviation of 40 inches. Is this likely? Explain.

40. **Is It Likely?** The exam scores in your statistics course have a mean of 70 and a standard deviation of 50. Is this likely? Explain

41–47: **GRE Scores.** Scores on the verbal Graduate Record Exam (GRE) have a mean of 462 and a standard deviation of 119. Scores on the quantitative GRE have a mean of 584 and a standard deviation of 151. Assume the scores are normally distributed.

41. Suppose a graduate school requires (among other qualifications) that applicants score at or above the 90th percentile on both exams. What verbal and quantitative scores are required?

42. What percentage of students taking the verbal exam score above 600?

43. What percentage of students taking the quantitative exam score above 600?

44. Suppose you score 700 on the quantitative exam. Approximately what score would you need on the verbal exam to be in the same percentile?

45. A perfect score on either exam is 800. What percentage of students score 800 on the quantitative exam?

46. A perfect score on either exam is 800. What percentage of students score 800 on the verbal exam?

47. What percentage of students score below 400 on each exam?

WEB PROJECTS

48. **SAT Scores.** The College Board Web site gives the distribution of scores for the verbal and mathematics SAT (in 50-point bins). Collect these data and make a histogram for each test. Discuss the truth of the claim that SAT scores are normally distributed.

49. **Data and Story Library.** Visit the Data and Story Library Web site, and find one example (of many) of a normal distribution. Write a short description of the variable under consideration, details of the distribution, and an explanation of why you expect this variable to have an approximately normal distribution.

50. **Normal Distribution Demonstration.** Do a Web search on the keywords "normal distribution" and find an animated demonstration of the normal distribution. Describe how the demonstration works and the useful features that you observed.

IN YOUR WORLD

51. **Normal Distributions.** Many data sets described in the news have nearly normal distributions, though the article may not say so explicitly. In news reports, find two data sets that you suspect have nearly normal distributions. Explain your reasoning.

52. **Non-Normal Distributions.** In news reports, find two data sets that you suspect *do not* have nearly normal distributions. Explain your reasoning.

USING TECHNOLOGY

53. **Heights of American Men.** The heights of American adult men are normally distributed with a mean of 69.7 inches and a standard deviation of 2.7 inches. Use a calculator or Excel to answer the following questions.

    a. What are the standard score and percentile of a height of 72 inches?

    b. What are the standard score and percentile of a height of 65 inches?

    c. What percentage of the American adult male population is taller than 6'4"?

    d. What percentage of the American adult male population is shorter than 5'4"?

    e. Assume that the American population consists of 115 million adult men. Approximately how many men are at least as tall as the basketball player Kobe Bryant, who is 6'7" tall?

UNIT 6D Statistical Inference

The ideas we have discussed so far in this chapter apply to describing actual data collected from a sample. However, as discussed in Unit 5A, the goal of most statistical studies is to learn something about an entire population. The heart of most statistical studies therefore lies with *inferring* a conclusion about a population from results for a sample.

The process of statistical inference can be complex, but many of the ideas are fairly easy to understand. In this unit, we explore three important ideas: *statistical significance*, the *margin of error* (already introduced in Unit 5A), and *hypothesis testing*. Although we will not work with these ideas in great detail, understanding them is important for interpreting statistical studies in the news.

Statistical Significance

Suppose you are trying to test whether a coin is fair—that is, whether it is equally likely to land heads or tails. You toss the coin 100 times, finding 52 heads and 48 tails. Should you conclude that the coin is unfair? No. While you should expect to see *roughly* 50 heads and 50 tails in every 100 tosses, you should also expect some variation from one sample of 100 tosses to another. A small deviation from a perfect 50–50 split between heads and tails does not necessarily mean that the coin is unfair, because we expect small deviations to occur *by chance*.

Now suppose you toss the coin 100 times and get 20 heads and 80 tails. It's difficult to attribute such a large deviation from 50–50 to chance. So while it is *possible* that you observed a very rare set of 100 tosses, it's more likely that the coin is unfair. When the difference between what is observed and what is expected is too great to be explained by chance alone, we say the difference is **statistically significant.**

> **DEFINITION**
>
> A set of measurements or observations in a statistical study is said to be **statistically significant** if it is unlikely to have occurred by chance.

Example 1 Significant Events?

Are the following events statistically significant? Explain.

a. The major league baseball team with the worst win-loss record defeats the team with the best record.
b. In terms of the global average temperature, five of the years between 1990 and 1999 were the five hottest years in the 20th century.

Solution

a. We expect a team with a poor win-loss record to lose most of its games. However, we also expect it to win occasionally, even against the team with the best record. This event is not statistically significant.
b. By chance alone, any particular year in a century would have a 5 in 100, or 1 in 20, chance of being one of the five hottest years. Having five of those years come in the same decade is unlikely to have occurred by chance alone. This event is statistically significant and suggests that the world is warming up. **Now try Exercises 15–18.**

From Sample to Population

We can now apply the idea of statistical significance to making an inference from a sample to a population. Suppose that in a poll of 1000 randomly selected people, 51% support the President. A week later, in another poll with a different random sample of 1000 people, only 49% support the President. Should we conclude that the opinions of all Americans changed during the one week between the polls?

You can probably guess that the answer is no. Because each poll involved a *sample* of only 1000 people, we shouldn't expect its result to be an *exact* match for the entire population of Americans. Because the two polls found only slightly different percentages (51% versus 49%), it's quite possible that the real percentage of Americans supporting the President did not change at all.

In terms of statistical significance, the change in the poll results from 51% to 49% is *not* statistically significant. Therefore, we should not infer any real change in the population based on these polls. In contrast, if the poll results had fallen from 70% one week to 30% the next, we would conclude that the change *was* statistically significant and that the opinions of Americans really did change in just one week.

Example 2 Statistical Significance in Experiments

A researcher conducts a double-blind experiment that tests whether a new herbal formula is effective in preventing colds. During a three-month period, the 100 randomly selected people in a treatment group take the herbal formula while the 100 randomly selected people in a control group take a placebo. The results show that 30% of the people in the treatment group get colds, compared to 32% of the people in the control group. Can we conclude that the herbal formula is effective in preventing colds?

Solution The difference between 30% getting colds in the treatment group and 32% getting colds in the control group seems small enough to be the result of chance alone. The difference is not statistically significant, and we should not conclude that the treatment made any difference at all. **Now try Exercises 19–20.**

Quantifying Statistical Significance

In Example 2, it's fairly obvious that the difference between 30% colds in the treatment group and 32% colds in the control group is not statistically significant. But suppose the findings are less obvious. For example, suppose 22% of the people in the treatment group had colds compared to 34% of the people in the control group. Is this difference enough to be statistically significant?

To answer this question, we need a quantitative definition for statistical significance. Quantitatively, statistical significance is defined as follows.

QUANTIFYING STATISTICAL SIGNIFICANCE

- If the probability of an observed difference occurring by chance is 1 in 20 (0.05) or less, the difference is statistically significant *at the 0.05 level.*
- If the probability of an observed difference occurring by chance is 1 in 100 (0.01) or less, the difference is statistically significant *at the 0.01 level.*

Take Note

The method used to calculate the statistical significance for this example involves something called the *chi-square statistic,* which you will study if you take a course in statistics.

For the case of 22% colds in the treatment group and 34% in the control group, the difference turns out to be significant at the 0.05 level, but not at the 0.01 level. This means that if the treatment had no effect at all, we could still expect to see these results in roughly 1 out of 20 similar experiments *just by chance alone.* You can probably see that some caution is in order when working with statistical significance. While significance at the 0.05 level gives at least some evidence that the treatment works, it is by no means conclusive.

Time Out to Think

Suppose an experiment finds that people taking a new herbal remedy get fewer colds than people taking a placebo. The results are statistically significant at the 0.01 level. Has the experiment proven that the herbal remedy works? Explain.

Example 3 Polio Vaccine Significance

In 1954, a large experiment was conducted to test the effectiveness of a new vaccine for polio created by Dr. Jonas Salk (1914–1995). The experiment involved a sample of 400,000 children chosen from the population of all children in the United States. Half of these 400,000 children received an injection of the Salk vaccine. The other half received an injection of a placebo containing only salt water. Among the children receiving the Salk vaccine, only 33 contracted polio. There were 115 cases of polio among the children who did not get the Salk vaccine. The probability of this difference between the groups occurring by chance turns out to be much less than 0.01. Describe the implications of this result.

Solution We say that the results of the polio vaccine test are statistically significant at much less than the 0.01 level. That is, the probability that the difference in the control and treatment groups occurred by chance is less than 1 in 100. Therefore, we can be confident that the vaccine really was responsible for the fewer cases of polio in the treatment group. As a result of this conclusion, the vaccine was immediately put into wide use. **Now try Exercises 21–24.**

BY THE WAY

If you had been a parent in the 1940s or 1950s, polio would have been one of your greatest fears. Each year during this long polio epidemic, thousands of young children were paralyzed by the disease. Today, thanks to the polio vaccine, the disease is rare. A global effort to vaccinate children against polio, begun at the urging of the World Health Organization, seeks to eradicate polio entirely within the next few years.

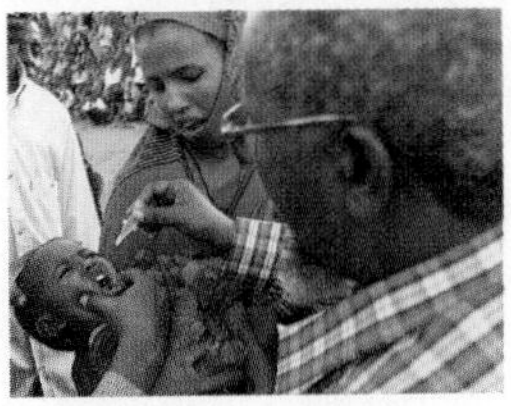

Margin of Error and Confidence Intervals

Suppose an opinion poll finds that 74% of Americans are happy with their home life, with a margin of error of 3 percentage points. Recall that the margin of error (see Unit 5A) defines an interval in which the *population parameter*—in this case, the percentage of Americans who are happy with their home life—is likely to fall. Therefore, the true percentage of all Americans who are happy with their home life is likely to be within 3 percentage points of 74%, or between 71% and 77%. Now we are ready to explore in more detail what we mean by an interval in which the population parameter is "likely" to fall.

Imagine that you conduct a survey of *all* 400 students at a small high school. Each Y (for yes) or N (for no) below is one student's answer to the question "Are you satisfied with the education you are receiving?"

YNYYNYNNYNYYNNNYYYYNYNYNYYYNYYNYYNNNYYYNYNYNYNYYYY
YYNYYNYYNNNYYYNYNYNYNYYYYYNYYNYNYNYYNNNYYYYNYNYNYN
YYYYNYNYNYYNYYNYYNNNYYYNYNYNYNYYYYYNYYNYNNYNYYNNNN
NYYYNYNYNYNYYYYYNYYNYNNYNYYNNNYYYYNYNYNYYYNYYNYYNY
YNYNNYNYYNNNYYYNNNYYYNYNYNYNYYYYYYNYNYNYYYNYYNYYNY
YYNYYNYYYYNNNYYYNNNYYYNYNYNYYNYNNYNYNYNYNYYYYYYNYN
YNYYYYYYNYNYNYYNYNNYNYYNNNYYYNNNYYYNYNNYYYNYYNYYYN
YYNYNYNYYYNYYNYNNYNYYNNNYYYNNNYYYNYNYNYNYYYNYYNYYY

If you counted carefully, you would find that 240 of the 400 responses, or 60%, are Y. Because this survey involved the complete population of students at the school, the proportion of students who are satisfied with their education, 60%, is a *population parameter*.

Now suppose that, as in most surveys, it's impractical to question every individual in the population. So instead of asking all 400 students, you choose a random sample of only 25 students. The responses of this sample are

YNYYNYYNYNYYNYYYNNYYYNNYY

Counting carefully, you find that 16 of the 25 responses, or 64%, are Y. As we should expect, this sample statistic is *not* exactly equal to the true population parameter of 60%.

Take Note

In this discussion, we deal with percentages, or *proportions*. In other situations (such as test scores or height measurements), we may be interested in a *mean* rather than a proportion. The general ideas are the same, but the specific details and formulas are different for means and proportions.

Moreover, because the sample was chosen randomly, we should expect to get a different result if we choose a different sample of 25 students. For example, suppose another sample produces the following responses:

YYNNNYYNYYYNNYNYYNYNYNYYN

This time, 14 of the 25 responses, or 56%, are Y.

Now, imagine that you could repeat the process of drawing a random sample of 25 students hundreds or thousands of times. Because the true proportion of Y responses in the population is 60%, most of the samples would have a proportion of Ys that is close to 60%. Samples with proportions far from 60% would be relatively rare, and samples with proportions higher than 60% would occur about as often as samples with proportions lower than 60%. If you look back at Unit 6C, you'll see that we have just described three of the four conditions for a *normal distribution*.

In fact, a mathematical theorem, called the *central limit theorem*, states that the distribution of proportions from many samples of the same size is approximately a normal distribution. The theorem also says that the mean of this distribution is the true proportion for the entire population. Figure 6.18 shows this distribution. It is called a **sampling distribution** because it consists of proportions from many individual samples.

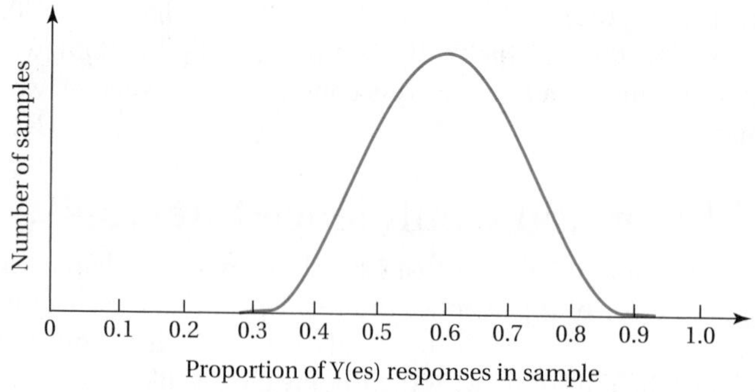

FIGURE 6.18 Suppose a true population proportion is 0.6, or 60%. If you record the proportions you find in hundreds or thousands of individual samples of the same size, the resulting distribution approximates a normal distribution. The mean of this distribution is the population proportion of 0.6.

The central limit theorem tells us not only that the sampling distribution is approximately normal with the true population proportion as its mean, but also that its standard deviation is approximately $1/(2\sqrt{n})$, where n is the size of the samples. Two standard deviations is twice this value, or $1/\sqrt{n}$. From the 68-95-99.7 rule (see Unit 6C), about 95% of all possible samples should have proportions within 2 standard deviations, or $1/\sqrt{n}$, of the true population proportion. Therefore, if we take just a single sample, there is a 95% chance that its sample proportion falls within $1/\sqrt{n}$ of the true population proportion. In other words, if we add and subtract $1/\sqrt{n}$ from the sample result, we can be 95% confident that this **confidence interval** contains the true population proportion. We define $1/\sqrt{n}$ to be the **margin of error** for 95% confidence. Note that the margin of error decreases as the sample size increases.

Take Note

The precise formula for the margin of error is

$$E = 1.96\sqrt{\frac{\hat{p}(1-\hat{p})}{n}},$$

where $\hat{p}$ is the proportion found for the sample. This formula requires $n\hat{p} \geq 5$ and $n(1-\hat{p}) \geq 5$, conditions that are usually met in practice.

MARGIN OF ERROR AND CONFIDENCE INTERVAL

Suppose you draw a single sample of size n from a large population and measure its *sample proportion*. The **margin of error** for 95% confidence is

$$\text{margin of error} \approx \frac{1}{\sqrt{n}}$$

The 95% **confidence interval** is found by subtracting and adding the margin of error from the sample proportion. You can be 95% confident that the true population proportion lies within this interval. The margin of error decreases as the sample size increases.

Example 4 Poll Margins

Find the margin of error and 95% confidence interval for the following surveys.

a. A survey of 500 people finds that 52% plan to vote for Smith for governor.
b. A survey of 1500 people finds that 87% support stricter penalties for child abuse.

Solution

a. The proportion measured for the sample is 52%, or 0.52. For a poll of $n = 500$ people, the margin of error is approximately

$$\frac{1}{\sqrt{n}} = \frac{1}{\sqrt{500}} \approx 0.045$$

Adding and subtracting 0.045, or 4.5%, from the sample proportion of 52% produces a 95% confidence interval from 47.5% to 56.5%. We can be 95% confident that the true proportion of people who plan to vote for Smith lies in this interval.

b. The proportion measured for the sample is 87%, or 0.87. For a poll of $n = 1500$ people, the margin of error is approximately

$$\frac{1}{\sqrt{n}} = \frac{1}{\sqrt{1500}} \approx 0.026$$

Adding and subtracting 0.026, or 2.6%, from the sample proportion of 87% produces a 95% confidence interval from 84.4% to 89.6%. We can be 95% confident that the true proportion of people who support the stricter penalties lies in this interval.

Now try Exercises 25–28.

Example 5 Unemployment Rate

Suppose the Bureau of Labor Statistics finds 3420 unemployed people in a sample of $n = 60{,}000$ people. Estimate the population unemployment rate and give a 95% confidence interval.

Solution The sample proportion is the unemployment rate for the sample:

$$\frac{3420}{60{,}000} = 0.057$$

This proportion is likely to be close to the true population unemployment rate. The margin of error is approximately

$$\frac{1}{\sqrt{60{,}000}} \approx 0.004$$

We add and subtract the margin of error of 0.004 from the sample proportion of 0.057, yielding a 95% confidence interval from 0.053 to 0.061, or 5.3% to 6.1%. We can be 95% confident that the interval from 5.3% to 6.1% contains the true unemployment rate for the population.

Now try Exercises 29–32.

BY THE WAY

The actual margin of error for the unemployment survey is smaller than that found here because the Labor Department surveys 60,000 *households,* which contain more than 60,000 people.

Time Out to Think

Note that the margin of error is generally defined for a 95% confidence interval, as opposed to some higher level of confidence such as 99% or 99.99%. Do you think this level of confidence is enough for most surveys? Can you think of cases in which it is *not* enough?

Hypothesis Testing

Advertisers make claims about their products. Schools make claims about the quality of education they offer. Lawyers make claims about a suspect's guilt or innocence. Medical diagnoses are claims about the presence or absence of disease. Pharmaceutical companies make claims about the effectiveness of their drugs. But how do we know whether any of these claims are true? Statistics offers an answer, through a powerful set of techniques for testing the validity of claims. The techniques go by the name of **hypothesis testing**, and they play a fundamental role in almost every aspect of modern life.

BY THE WAY

The Gender Choice product consisted of printed instructions and a thermometer. It was based on the idea that the gender of a baby could be determined through careful timing of conception. There was no evidence that the product actually worked, and it is no longer available.

Let's look at an example that illustrates the basic ideas behind hypothesis testing. A company once claimed that its product, called Gender Choice, could increase a woman's chances of giving birth to a baby girl. The company actually claimed that the chance of a baby girl could be increased "up to 80%," but let's focus simply on the claim that the chance of having a baby girl is greater than the expected 50%. How could you test whether this claim is true?

One way would be to study a random sample of, say, 100 babies born to women who used the Gender Choice product. If the product does *not* work, we would expect about half of these babies to be girls. If it does work, we would expect significantly more than half of the babies to be girls.

First, we need to define a few terms used in hypothesis testing as they relate to the Gender Choice study. Notice that the study compares the actual proportion of baby girls in the sample to the proportion expected if the product does not work. This means we are dealing with two claims, or *hypotheses*, about the product:

- The **null hypothesis** is the claim that Gender Choice does *not* work and the proportion of baby girls is 50%.
- The **alternative hypothesis** is the claim that Gender Choice does work and the proportion of girls is greater than 50%.

More generally, the null hypothesis should make a specific claim about the value of a population parameter (generally either a population mean or a population proportion). In this case, the null hypothesis makes the specific claim that the proportion of baby girls (the population parameter) equals 50%, as expected under normal conditions.

NULL AND ALTERNATIVE HYPOTHESES

The **null hypothesis** claims a specific value for a population parameter. (It is often the value expected in the case of no special effect.) It takes the form

$$\text{null hypothesis: population parameter} = \text{claimed value}$$

The **alternative hypothesis** is the claim that is accepted if the null hypothesis is rejected.

BY THE WAY

The word *null* comes from the Latin *nullus*, meaning "nothing." A null hypothesis often states that there is no special effect or difference. The null hypothesis is often denoted by H_0 (pronounced "H-naught"). The alternative hypothesis is often denoted by H_a.

Example 6 Formulating Hypotheses

The manufacturer of a new car model advertises that the car averages 38 miles per gallon on the highway. A consumer group says that this claim is overstated and that the actual average (mean) is less than 38 miles per gallon. State the null and alternative hypotheses for a hypothesis test.

Solution The null hypothesis must make a specific claim about the value of a population parameter, which in this case is the average (mean) gas mileage of all cars of this model. That is, the null hypothesis is the manufacturer's claim of 38 miles per gallon on the highway. The alternative hypothesis is the consumer group's claim that the actual highway gas mileage is less than 38 miles per gallon. In summary:

null hypothesis: mean gas mileage = 38 miles per gallon

alternative hypothesis: mean gas mileage < 38 miles per gallon

Now try Exercises 33–38, part a.

Outcomes of a Hypothesis Test

In conducting a hypothesis test, we assume that the null hypothesis is true until proven otherwise. There are two possible outcomes to any hypothesis test.

TWO POSSIBLE OUTCOMES OF A HYPOTHESIS TEST

- Rejecting the null hypothesis, in which case we have evidence that supports the alternative hypothesis.
- Not rejecting the null hypothesis, in which case we lack sufficient evidence to support the alternative hypothesis.

We cannot prove conclusively that a null hypothesis is *true*, which is why "accepting the null hypothesis" is not listed as a possible outcome. At best, we can only find statistical evidence that the null hypothesis is *false*, in which case we can safely reject it.

Time Out to Think

Our legal principles maintain that criminal suspects are innocent until proven guilty. At the end of a criminal trial, juries can render only two possible verdicts: guilty or not guilty. Putting these ideas into the language of hypothesis testing, state the null hypothesis for a criminal trial. How do the two possible verdicts correspond to the two possible outcomes of a hypothesis test?

Example 7 Gender Choice Outcomes

Describe the two possible outcomes of a hypothesis test concerning the Gender Choice product.

Solution Recall that the null hypothesis states that the proportion of girl babies is the expected 50%, while the alternative hypothesis states that it is greater than 50%. There are two possible outcomes:

1. We can reject the null hypothesis and accept the alternative hypothesis. In this case, we conclude that the percentage of girl babies is greater than 50% and that the product actually works.
2. We can decide not to reject the null hypothesis. This means we have no grounds for doubting the null hypothesis, but it does *not* prove that the null hypothesis is true. For Gender Choice, it means that, while we lack evidence that the product works, we have not proven that it does *not* work. **Now try Exercises 33–38, part b.**

The Null Hypothesis: To Reject or Not to Reject

Suppose you study a sample of 100 babies born to women using the Gender Choice product and find that 64 of the babies are girls. How do you decide whether this constitutes evidence for rejecting the null hypothesis? The answer comes down to probabilities and statistical significance.

According to the null hypothesis, the true proportion of baby girls among the population of Gender Choice users is 50%. However, even if the null hypothesis is true, it is still possible that a single sample of 100 babies could contain 64 girls *by chance alone*. Using statistical methods that we will not cover here, it is possible to calculate that the probability of obtaining a sample with at least 64 girls by chance is about 3 in 1000. Now, recall that statistical significance at the 0.01 level requires that the probability of an event occurring by chance be less than 1 in 100. Because 3 in 1000 (0.003) is less than 1 in 100 (0.01), observing 64 baby girls is statistically significant at the 0.01 level. Because of this high level of statistical significance, we have good reason to reject the null hypothesis. This, in turn, means that we have strong support for the alternative hypothesis that Gender Choice works.

HYPOTHESIS TEST DECISIONS

We decide the outcome of a hypothesis test by comparing the actual sample result (mean or proportion) to the result expected if the null hypothesis is true.

- If the chance of a sample result at least as extreme as the observed result is less than 1 in 100 (or 0.01), the test is significant at the 0.01 level. The test offers strong evidence for rejecting the null hypothesis (and accepting the alternative hypothesis).
- If the chance of a sample result at least as extreme as the observed result is less than 1 in 20 (or 0.05), the test is significant at the 0.05 level. The test offers moderate evidence for rejecting the null hypothesis.
- If the chance of a sample result at least as extreme as the observed result is greater than 1 in 20, the test is not significant. The test does not provide sufficient grounds for rejecting the null hypothesis.

Example 8 Birth Weight Significance

A county health official believes that the mean birth weight of male babies at a local hospital is greater than the national average of 3.39 kilograms. A random sample of 145 male babies born at that hospital has a mean birth weight of 3.61 kilograms. Assuming that the mean birth weight of all male babies born at the hospital is the national average of 3.39 kilograms, a calculation shows that the probability of selecting a sample with a mean birth weight of at least 3.61 kilograms is 0.032. Formulate the null and alternative hypotheses. Then discuss whether the sample provides evidence for rejecting or not rejecting the null hypothesis.

Take Note

In statistics, the actual probability of obtaining a particular sample result (under the assumption that the null hypothesis is true) is called a *p*-value. The *p*-value for the sample in Example 8 is the given probability of 0.032.

Solution The null hypothesis is the claim that the mean birth weight of all male babies born at this hospital is the national average of 3.39 kilograms. The alternative hypothesis is the claim of the health official—that the hospital mean is higher than the national average.

null hypothesis:	mean birth weight $=$ 3.39 kilograms
alternative hypothesis:	mean birth weight $>$ 3.39 kilograms

Under the assumption that the null hypothesis is true, the chance of observing a sample with a mean of at least 3.61 kilograms is 0.032. This is less than 0.05 but greater than 0.01, so the result is statistically significant at the 0.05 level but not at the 0.01 level. Statistical significance at the 0.05 level provides moderate evidence for rejecting the null hypothesis, in which case the county official's claim would be supported.

Now try Exercises 39–44.

QUICK QUIZ

Choose the best answer to each of the following questions. Explain your reasoning with one or more complete sentences.

1. Assume that the national divorce rate is 30% (meaning that 30% of marriages end in divorce). In which community is the difference from this national rate statistically significant?

   a. Smallville, where the divorce rate is 26%

   b. Bigville, where the divorce rate is 34%

   c. Midville, where the divorce rate is 60%

2. Researchers are testing a new cancer treatment. To determine whether the treatment offers a statistically significant improvement in survival rates, the researchers must

   a. give the treatment to at least 1000 people.

   b. compare the survival rate of the new treatment to that of other treatments or no treatment.

   c. determine the physiological mechanism through which the new treatment works.

3. Working with equal sample sizes researchers compared three new cold remedies to a placebo. Which remedy is most likely to be most effective?

   a. the one that gave results statistically significant at the 0.01 level

   b. the one that gave results statistically significant at the 0.05 level

   c. the one that gave results that were not statistically significant

4. Researchers conduct 20 experiments to test the effectiveness of a new weight loss pill compared to the effectiveness of a placebo. For 19 of the 20 experiments, the results are not statistically significant. However, one of the experiments shows that the pill works better than the placebo with statistical significance at the 0.05 level. A fair report of the results for all 20 experiments together would say that

   a. the treatment works effectively about 5% of the time.

   b. we can have 95% confidence that the treatment works for at least some people.

   c. there is no evidence that the treatment works.

5. A poll finds that 65% of the people surveyed approve of the President's handling of the economy, with a margin of error (for 95% confidence) of 3%. The 95% confidence interval for this poll is

   a. 62% to 65%.

   b. 62% to 68%.

   c. 63.5% to 66.5%.

6. Suppose you repeated the poll described in Exercise 5 hundreds of times, each time with a different sample of the population. Which of the following best describes what you would find?

   a. In 95% of the polls, the result would show that 65% of the people interviewed approve of the President's handling of the economy.

   b. In 95% of the polls, the result would show that between 62% and 68% of the people interviewed approve of the President's handling of the economy.

   c. In 95% of the polls, the result would be within 3% of the true proportion of the population that approves of the President's handling of the economy.

7. Consider a survey with a margin of error of 4%. If you want to reduce the margin of error to 2%, you should repeat the survey with

   a. half as many people.

   b. twice as many people.

   c. four times as many people.

8. You want to test your hypothesis that local gas stations are charging much more than the national average price for gasoline. A good *null hypothesis* for this test would be

   a. local gas prices equal the national average gas price.

   b. local gas prices are higher than the national average gas price.

   c. local gas prices show much more variation than national gas prices.

9. You carry out a test of the hypothesis described in Exercise 8. If the results show that you *cannot* reject the null hypothesis, then

   a. local gas prices are actually the same as the national average.

   b. local gas prices are actually below the national average.

   c. you cannot be sure that local prices are the same as the national average, but there is insufficient evidence for a claim that local gas prices are above the national average.

10. Suppose you again carry out a test of the hypothesis described in Exercise 8, but this time your results show that prices are above the national average, and by an amount that you might find by chance in only 1 out of 100 similar tests. A good description of this result would be that

    a. you've proven that local gas prices are above the national average.

    b. you've found a result that is statistically significant at the 0.01 level.

    c. there's a 99% chance that local prices are at least 1% above the national average.

Exercises 6D

REVIEW QUESTIONS

1. What is statistical inference? Why is it important?
2. Describe the meaning of statistical significance. What does it mean for a result to be statistically significant at the 0.05 level? at the 0.01 level?
3. How does the idea of statistical significance apply to the question of whether results from a sample can be generalized to conclusions about a population? Explain.
4. Explain why you should usually expect that a proportion found in a single sample will be close to, but not exactly, the true proportion in a population.
5. Briefly describe the use of the formula for margin of error. Give an example in which you interpret the margin of error in terms of 95% confidence.
6. What is the purpose of a hypothesis test? How do we formulate the null and alternative hypotheses for a test?
7. What are the two possible conclusions of a hypothesis test? Explain, and also explain why accepting the null hypothesis is *not* a possible outcome.
8. Briefly discuss how the idea of statistical significance helps us decide whether to reject or not reject a null hypothesis.

DOES IT MAKE SENSE?

Decide whether each of the following statements makes sense (or is clearly true) or does not make sense (or is clearly false). Explain your reasoning.

9. The study found that more people were cured by the new drug than by the old drug, but the result was not statistically significant.
10. There can no longer be any doubt that our product, the Magic Diet Pill, really works. We financed a study in which the pill led to more weight loss than a placebo, with results significant at the 0.05 level.
11. Both agencies conducted their surveys carefully, both asked the same question and found about the same proportion of "yes" responses, and both interviewed the same number of people. However, the margin of error was smaller for Agency A's survey than for Agency B's survey.
12. If you want to reduce the margin of error in your pre-election survey, you should use a larger sample.
13. We began the trial with the null hypothesis stating that the toxic waste dump had no effect on disease rates among the residents nearby. The alternative hypothesis therefore stated that the toxic waste dump did have an effect on disease rates among the residents nearby.
14. We began the trial with the null hypothesis stating that the toxic waste dump had no effect on the residents nearby, and our trial proved this hypothesis to be true.

BASIC SKILLS & CONCEPTS

15–20: Subjective Significance. For each of the following events, state whether you think the difference between what occurred and what you would expect by chance is statistically significant.

15. In 60 rolls of a standard six-sided die, you get 2 sixes.
16. In 100 tosses of a fair coin, you get 48 heads.
17. An airline with a 95% on-time departure rate has 11 out of 200 flights with late departures.
18. A basketball player with a 92% free-throw percentage misses 18 free throws in a row.
19. Ten winners of the Power Ball lottery in a row bought their tickets at the same 7–11 store.
20. Of the 45 students in your mathematics class, 42 have the same birthday.
21. **Human Body Temperature.** A study by University of Maryland researchers measured the body temperatures of 106 individuals. The mean for the sample was 98.20°F. The accepted value for human body temperature is 98.60°F. If we assume that the mean body temperature is actually 98.60°F, the probability of getting a sample with a mean of 98.20°F or less turns out to be less than 1 in 1 million. Is this result significant at the 0.05 level? at the 0.01 level? Would it be reasonable to conclude that the accepted value for human body temperature is wrong? Explain.
22. **Seat Belts and Children.** In a study of children injured in automobile crashes (*American Journal of Public Health*, Vol. 82, No. 3), those wearing seat belts had a mean stay of 0.83 day in an intensive care unit. Those not wearing seat belts had a mean stay of 1.39 days. The probability of this difference in means occurring by chance turns out to be less than 1 in 10,000. Is this result significant at the 0.05 level? at the 0.01 level? Would it be reasonable to conclude that seat belts reduce the severity of injuries? Explain.
23. **SAT Preparation.** A study of 75 students who took an SAT preparation course (*American Education Research Journal*, Vol. 19, No. 3) concluded that the mean improvement on the SAT was 0.6 point. If we assume that the preparation course has no effect, the probability of getting a mean improvement of 0.6 point by chance is 0.08, or 8 in 100. Discuss whether this preparation course results in statistically significant improvement.
24. **Weight by Age.** A National Health Survey determined that the mean weight of a sample of 804 men aged 25 to 34 was 176 pounds, while the mean weight of a sample of 1657 men aged 65 to 74 was 164 pounds. The difference is significant at the 0.01 level. Interpret this result.

25–32: Margin of Error. Find the margin of error and the 95% confidence interval for the following studies. Briefly interpret the 95% confidence interval.

25. According to a Gallup poll of 1012 people, about one-third (32%) of Americans keep a dog for protection.

26. A recent survey of 65,000 households by the U.S. Department of Labor reported an unemployment rate of 8.9%.
27. A 2009 poll of 540 people aged 12–17, conducted by ICR of Media, Pennsylvania, concluded that 64% of American teenagers support the current legal drinking age of 21.
28. A 2009 study by the Pew Forum on Religion and Public Life, based on surveys of 1110 people, concluded that 59% of Americans oppose legalizing gay marriage.
29. A CBS News poll of 1003 American adults concluded that 48% of Americans feel that people with strong religious convictions face discrimination in this country.
30. A Yankelovich survey of 2818 Americans, conducted in 14 U.S. cities, concluded that while 73% of Americans know that health experts recommend drinking eight or more eight-ounce servings of water each day, 51% fall short of that goal.

31. A 2009 CBS poll of 1100 parents concluded that 41% of all parents believe that the future for the next generation will be worse.
32. A CBS/*New York Times* poll of 1229 adults concluded that 28% of all American adults did not have very much trust and confidence in the news media, while 15% had "a great deal" of trust and confidence.

33–38: Formulating Hypotheses. Consider the following claims related to statistical studies.

a. State the null and alternative hypotheses for a hypothesis test.

b. Describe the two possible outcomes of the test, using the context of the given situation.

33. The governor claims that the percentage of adults over 25 who have graduated from high school is greater than 85%, the national average.
34. The Food and Drug Administration claims that the amount of vitamin C in tablets produced by a company is less than the advertised 500 milligrams.
35. The head of the state school board claims that the mean teacher salary in her state is above the national average of $47,750.
36. The director of public works for a small town claims that the mean water usage among households exceeds 1675 gallons per month, the level required for the water supply to last through the year.
37. An external review team claims that the percentage of underrepresented students in the incoming freshman class is less than the target of 20%.
38. A chemical company wishes to defend its claim that the levels of pollution downstream from its plant are less than the minimum level specified by the Environmental Protection Agency.

39–44: Hypothesis Tests. The following exercises describe the results of a hypothesis test in terms of the probability of obtaining a particular sample. In each case, use the given context to formulate the null and alternative hypotheses. Then discuss whether the sample provides evidence for rejecting or not rejecting the null hypothesis.

39. The owner of a car rental company claims that the mean annual mileage for the population of all cars in his fleet is more than 11,725 miles (which is the mean annual mileage for all cars in the United States). A random sample of $n = 225$ cars from his fleet has a mean annual mileage of 12,000 miles. Assuming that the mean annual mileage for all cars in his fleet is 11,725 miles, the probability of selecting a random sample with a mean annual mileage of 12,000 miles or more is 0.01.
40. A Senate candidate claims that a majority of voters support her. A poll of 400 voters finds that the proportion of voters who support the candidate is 0.51 (51%). Assuming that the proportion of people in the population who support her is $p = 0.5$, the probability of selecting a sample in which the proportion is 0.51 or more is 0.345.
41. A hospital administrator finds that the mean hospital stay for a sample of 81 women after childbirth is 2.3 days. She claims that the mean stay at her hospital is greater than the national average of 2.1 days. Assuming that the average at her hospital is the same as the national average, the probability of observing a sample with a mean of 2.3 days or more is 0.17.

42. Each baseball in a random sample of 40 new balls is dropped onto a concrete surface and the bounce height is recorded. The heights have a mean of 92.67 inches (based on data from *USA Today*). A statistically literate manager claims that the mean bounce height for all baseballs is 90.10 inches and the probability of observing a sample mean of 92.67 is 0.035.

43. A marketing company claims that the mean household income of HDTV owners across the population is greater than \$50,000. A random sample of 1700 households with HDTVs shows that the mean household income is \$51,182. Assuming that the true mean is \$50,000, the probability of selecting a sample with a mean income of \$51,182 or more is 0.007.

44. A Roper poll used a sample of 100 randomly selected car owners. Within the sample, the mean time for ownership of a single car was 7.01 years. Assuming that the actual mean ownership time is 7.5 years, the probability of selecting a sample with a mean time of ownership of 7.01 or less is 0.10.

FURTHER APPLICATIONS

45. **Nielsen Ratings.** Nielsen ratings are based on televisions in 5000 households; Nielsen estimates that 13,000 people live in these households. Suppose Nielsen reports that *American Idol* had 65% of the TV audience. Interpret this result with a 95% confidence interval, based on a sample size of 13,000 people.

46. **Male Birth Weight.** The mean birth weight of male babies born to 121 mothers taking a vitamin supplement is 3.67 kilograms (based on New York Department of Health data). The national average birth weight of male babies is 3.39 kilograms. Discuss the significance of the sample observation given that the probability of observing such a sample is estimated to be 0.0015.

47. **Better Margin of Error.** Suppose you want to decrease the margin of error by a factor of 2—for example, from 4% to 2%. By what factor must you increase the sample size? Explain.

48. **Better Margin of Error.** Suppose you want to decrease the margin of error by a factor of 10—for example, from 1% to 0.1%. By what factor must you increase the sample size? Explain.

49. **Gallup Description.** The Gallup Organization includes the following explanation after its summary of opinion polls. Are the figures in the explanation (sample size and margin of error) consistent? Comment on the provision that is made about "error and bias."

    The results reported here are based on telephone interviews with a randomly selected national sample of 1,019 adults, 18 years and older. For results based on the whole sample, one can say with 95 percent confidence that the maximum error attributable to sampling and other random effects is plus or minus 3 percentage points. In addition to sampling error, question wording and practical difficulties in conducting surveys can introduce error or bias into the findings of public opinion polls.

WEB PROJECTS

50. **Vital Significance.** Visit a Web site that has vital statistics, which generally concern birth and death rates. Choose a question that interests you, such as whether there are significant differences in the numbers of births at different times of year or whether there are differences in the infant mortality rates between selected states. Collect the relevant data and determine subjectively whether you think the observed differences are significant. Discuss any implications of your findings.

51. **Recent Polls.** Visit the Web sites of polling organizations and gather the results of a particular poll. Describe the details of the actual polling procedure. Interpret the results in terms of a 95% confidence interval. What conclusions can you draw? Explain.

52. **Genetically Modified Foods.** Use the Web to learn about current studies of whether genetically modified foods are safe for human consumption and for the environment. Choose a study that interests you. Describe how it is an example of a hypothesis test, and discuss its results and conclusions.

IN YOUR WORLD

53. **Statistical Significance.** Find a recent news report in which the idea of statistical significance is used. Write a one-page summary of the study and the result that is considered to be statistically significant. Be sure to discuss whether you believe the result and why.

54. **Significant Experiment?** Find a recent news story about a statistical study that used an experiment to determine whether some new treatment was effective. Based on the available information, briefly discuss what you can conclude about the statistical significance of the results. Given this significance (or lack of), do you think the new treatment is useful? Explain.

55. **Margin of Error.** Find three recent surveys that quote a result as a proportion (or percentage) along with a margin of error. Based on the sample size in each case, calculate the margin of error with the formula given in this unit. Does your calculation agree with the stated margin of error? Explain.

56. **Confidence Intervals.** Find three recent surveys that quote a result as a proportion (or percentage) along with a margin of error. Interpret each result in terms of a 95% confidence interval.

57. **Hypothesis Testing.** Find a news report describing a statistical study that involved a hypothesis test. (News reports rarely state explicitly that a hypothesis test was used, but you should be able to decide from the context whether a hypothesis test was involved.) State the null and alternative hypotheses for the study, and describe how a conclusion was reached.

CHAPTER 6 Summary

UNIT	KEY TERMS	KEY IDEAS AND SKILLS
6A	distribution mean median mode outlier symmetric distribution skewed (left or right) distribution variation	**Measures of center in a distribution:** $\text{Mean} = \dfrac{\text{sum of all values}}{\text{total number of values}}$ Median is the middle value. Mode is the most common value. **Understand** effects of outliers. **Be aware of** potential confusion with the term average. **Characterize** the shape of a distribution by number of peaks symmetric, left-skewed, or right-skewed variation
6B	range quartiles five-number summary boxplot standard deviation	**Understand and calculate** measures of variation: $\text{range} = \text{highest value} - \text{lowest value}$ five-number summary (low value, lower quartile, median, upper quartile, high value) $\text{standard deviation} = \sqrt{\dfrac{\text{sum of (deviations from the mean)}^2}{\text{total number of data values} - 1}}$ **Interpret** standard deviation with the range rule of thumb.
6C	normal distribution 68-95-99.7 rule standard score percentile	**Describe** a normal distribution and conditions under which it can be expected. **Understand and apply** the 68–95–99.7 rule for normal distributions. **Use** a standard score table for normal distributions.
6D	statistical significance sampling distribution confidence interval margin of error hypothesis test null hypothesis alternative hypothesis	**Understand** the concept of statistical significance, including significance at the 0.05 level significance at the 0.01 level **Understand** how a margin of error arises from a sampling distribution. **Understand and conduct** a basic hypothesis test and make decisions based on the test.

UNIT 7A

Fundamentals of Probability: We examine basic concepts of probability and three ways to determine probabilities: theoretically, empirically, and subjectively.

UNIT 7B

Combining Probabilities: Using basic rules for adding and multiplying probabilities, we can calculate probabilities for more complex and interesting events.

UNIT 7C

The Law of Large Numbers: We cannot predict a single coin toss, but the law of large numbers allows us to make surprisingly accurate statements about thousands of coin tosses. We study this idea and its application to lotteries, insurance, and more.

UNIT 7D

Assessing Risk: Probability comes into play whenever we deal with risk. We explore how to describe risk in connection with travel, diseases, and life expectancy.

UNIT 7E

Counting and Probability: We study permutations and combinations and apply them to probability and to exploring coincidences.

7

You can take it as understood
That your luck changes only if it's good.

—Ogden Nash, *Roulette Us Be Gay*

Probability: Living with the Odds

Probability is involved in virtually every decision we make. Sometimes the role of probability is clear, as in deciding whether to buy a lottery ticket or whether to plan a picnic based on the probability of rain. In other cases, probability guides decisions on a deeper level. For example, you might choose a particular college because you believe that it is most likely to meet your personal needs. In this chapter, we will look at just how practical and powerful probability can be in our everyday lives.

ACTIVITY Lotteries

Use this activity to gain a sense of the kinds of problems this chapter will enable you to study. Try working through it before you begin the chapter, then return to it after you've learned the chapter material.

Lotteries are big business and a major revenue source for many governments. By 2009, all but seven states in the United States had some type of lottery, generating a national total of more than $52 billion in sales. About one-third of that money ($17 billion) ends up as state revenue, with the rest going to prizes and expenses. Lotteries present many lessons in probability, and lottery statistics can fuel great debate over whether lotteries are an appropriate way for governments to generate revenue. Working individually or in groups, consider the following questions.

1. Based on the data above and the U.S. population of approximately 300 million, how much does the average American spend on the lottery each year?
2. Surveys indicate that fewer than half of all Americans play the lottery in any given year. What is the average spending per lottery player? Does this result surprise you, or is it consistent with what you would expect based on the spending of your friends or family members who play the lottery?
3. Does your state have a lottery? If so, look up the various games available and the probabilities of winning different prizes. If not, look up the Multi-State Powerball game. Consider the fact that lottery operators have spent millions of dollars researching how to encourage people to play the lottery as much as possible. Discuss how this research is being applied in the selection of the games and probabilities for your state (or Powerball).
4. Find advertisements for your state lottery (or Powerball). Do the advertisements give a fair assessment of the probabilities you found in question 3? Do they seem deceptive in any way? Explain.
5. Past studies of gambling have suggested that while people in nearly all income groups are almost equally likely to play the lottery, lower income people tend to play more. Search for statistics concerning the percentage of income spent on the lottery by people in different income groups. Is it fair to say, as critics allege, that lotteries are a form of regressive taxation? Defend your opinion.
6. Based on your answers above and any additional data you can find, discuss the various moral dimensions of lotteries. For example: Are there moral issues related to government sponsorship of gambling? For governments that need more revenue, are lotteries better than higher taxes? Are lotteries unfair to the poor or uneducated?

UNIT 7A Fundamentals of Probability

Probability plays such a huge role in our lives that it is essential to understand how it works. In this unit, we'll discuss fundamental concepts required for probability calculations.

Let's begin by considering a toss of two coins. Figure 7.1 shows that there are four different ways the coins could fall. We say that each of these four ways is a different **outcome** of the coin toss. The outcomes are the most basic possible results of the coin toss. But suppose we are interested only in the number of heads. Because the two middle outcomes in Figure 7.1 each have 1 head, we say that these two outcomes represent the same **event**. That is, an event describes one or more possible outcomes that all have

FIGURE 7.1 The four possible outcomes for a toss of two coins. The two middle outcomes both represent the same event of 1 head.

the same property of interest—in this case, the same number of heads. Figure 7.1 shows that there are four possible outcomes for the two-coin toss, but only three possible events: 0 heads, 1 head, and 2 heads.

DEFINITIONS

Outcomes are the most basic possible results of observations or experiments.

An **event** consists of one or more outcomes that share a property of interest.

Mathematically, we express probabilities with numbers between 0 and 1. For example, the probability of a coin landing on heads is one-half, or 0.5. If an event is impossible, such as the event of meeting a married bachelor, we assign it a probability of 0. At the other extreme, an event that is certain to occur has a probability of 1. The probability of the Sun rising tomorrow is essentially 1. We use the notation $P(\text{event})$ to mean the probability of an event. We often denote events by letters or symbols. For example, using H to represent the event of heads on a coin toss, we write $P(\text{H}) = 0.5$.

The false ideas prevalent among all classes of the community respecting chance and luck illustrate the truth that common consent argues almost of necessity of error.

—Richard Proctor, *Chance and Luck* (1887 textbook)

EXPRESSING PROBABILITY

The probability of an event, expressed as $P(\text{event})$, is always between 0 and 1 (inclusive). A probability of 0 means the event is impossible and a probability of 1 means the event is certain.

Time Out to Think

Consider families of three children. List the different outcomes (birth orders) that result in the *event* of two boys and one girl.

With these basic definitions and notation, we are ready to discuss the three basic techniques for finding probabilities. They go by the names *theoretical method, empirical method*, and *subjective method*. We'll explore each in turn.

Theoretical Probabilities

When we say that the probability of heads on a coin toss is 1/2, we are *assuming* that the coin is fair, so it is equally likely to land heads or tails. In essence, the probability is based on a *theory* of how the coin behaves, so we say that the probability of 1/2 comes from the **theoretical method.**

As another example, consider rolling a single die. Because there are six equally likely outcomes (Figure 7.2), the theoretical probability for each outcome is 1/6. For example, the theoretical probability of rolling a 3 is 1/6. As long as all outcomes are equally likely, we can use the following procedure to calculate theoretical probabilities.

Take Note

Except when stated otherwise, we assume that dice are fair, six-sided cubes with face values of 1 through 6.

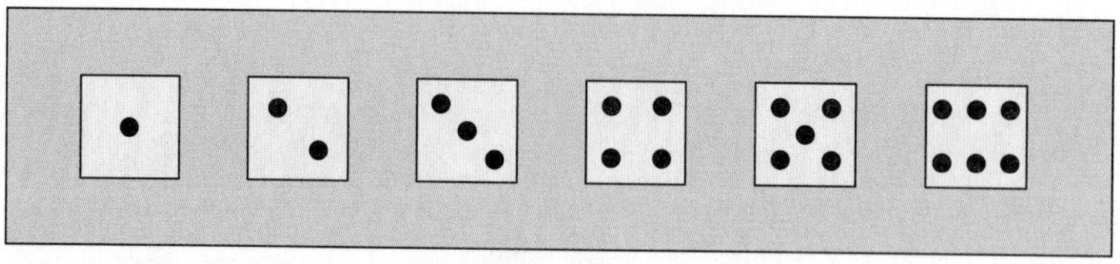

FIGURE 7.2 The six possible outcomes for a roll of one die.

BY THE WAY

Theoretical methods are also called *a priori* methods. The words *a priori* are Latin for "before the fact" or "before experience."

THEORETICAL METHOD FOR EQUALLY LIKELY OUTCOMES

Step 1: Count the total number of possible outcomes.

Step 2: Among all the possible outcomes, count the number of ways the event of interest, A, can occur.

Step 3: Determine the probability, $P(A)$, from

$$P(A) = \frac{\text{number of ways } A \text{ can occur}}{\text{total number of outcomes}}$$

Example 1 Playing Card Probabilities

Figure 7.3 shows the 52 playing cards in a standard deck. There are four *suits*, known as hearts, spades, diamonds, and clubs. Each suit has cards for the numbers 2 through 10 plus a jack, queen, king, and ace (for a total of 13 cards in each suit). Notice that hearts and diamonds are red, while spades and clubs are black. If you draw one card from a standard deck, what is the probability that it is a spade?

Solution Each of the 52 cards is equally likely to be drawn, so we can apply the three-step theoretical method.

Step 1: Each card represents a possible outcome, so there are 52 possible outcomes.

Step 2: The event of interest is drawing a spade, and there are 13 spades in the deck.

Step 3: The probability that a randomly drawn card is a spade is

$$P(\text{spade}) = \frac{\text{number of outcomes that are spades}}{\text{total number of possible outcomes}} = \frac{13}{52} = \frac{1}{4}$$

Now try Exercises 21–28.

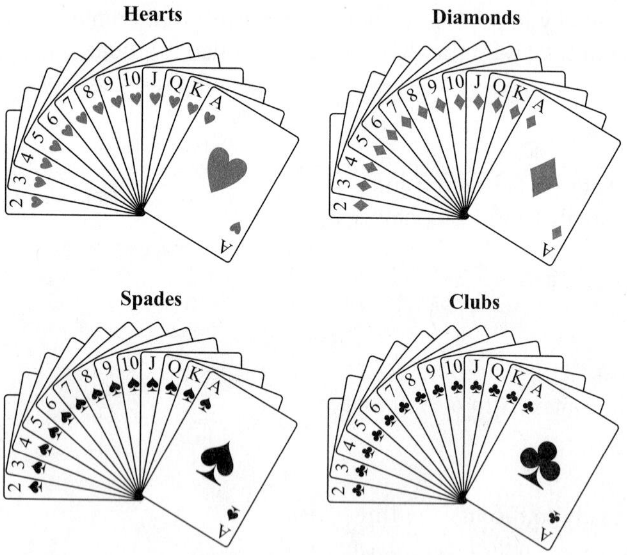

FIGURE 7.3 Playing cards in a standard 52-card deck.

Example 2 Guessing Birthdays

You select a person at random from a large conference group. What is the probability that the person has a birthday in July? Assume 365 days in a year.

Solution If we assume that births are equally likely to occur on any day of the year, then we can use the three-step theoretical method.

Step 1: Each possible birthday represents an outcome, so there are 365 possible outcomes.

Step 2: July has 31 days, so 31 of the 365 total outcomes represent the event of a July birthday.

Step 3: The probability that a randomly selected person has a July birthday is

$$P(\text{July birthday}) = \frac{31}{365} \approx 0.085$$

which is slightly more than 1 in 12. **Now try Exercises 29–32.**

Time Out to Think

Continuing Example 2, find the probability of selecting a person with a July 4 birthday.

BY THE WAY

In fact, births are not evenly distributed over the twelve months. Even when the different lengths of months are accounted for, the lowest birth rate is in January and the highest rates are in June and July.

Example 3 Two Boys and a Girl

What is the probability that a family with three children has two boys and one girl? Assume boys and girls are equally likely.

Solution We apply the theoretical method for equally likely outcomes.

Step 1: There are two possible outcomes for each birth: boy (B) or girl (G). For a family with three children, the total number of possible outcomes (birth orders) is $2 \times 2 \times 2 = 8$ (see the Brief Review on p. 420). The eight possible outcomes are the birth orders BBB, BBG, BGB, BGG, GBB, GBG, GGB, and GGG.

Step 2: Of these eight possible outcomes, three have two boys and one girl: BBG, BGB, and GBB.

Step 3: The probability that a family with three children has two boys and one girl is

$$P(2\text{ boys}) = \frac{3}{8} = 0.375$$

In words, the probability that a family with three children has two boys and one girl is 3/8, or 0.375. **Now try Exercises 33–38.**

Empirical Probabilities

Suppose that, from historical and geological records, we discover that a river has risen above flood level 9 times in the past 1000 years. We might reasonably claim that the probability of such a flood in any given year is about 9 in 1000, or 0.009. This probability is not based on any theoretical ideas. Instead, it is based on observations. When we determine a probability based on observations or experiments, we use the **empirical method**. Because we could also say that the relative frequency of years with floods is 9 in 1000, the empirical method is sometimes called the *relative frequency method*.

Besides being useful when there is no theoretical basis for finding a probability, the empirical method is useful for checking the validity of theoretical probabilities. For example, suppose you toss a coin 100 times and get 75 heads. In this case, the empirical probability for heads is 75/100, or 0.75, which is significantly higher than the theoretical probability of 0.5 for a fair coin. You therefore have reason to suspect that the coin is unfair.

He that leaves nothing to chance will do few things ill, but will do very few things.

—George Savile Halifax

BY THE WAY

The term "100-year flood" is often used to describe a flood of a magnitude that occurs only once every 100 years, on average. Because this is a probability, it is possible (though rare) to have 100-year floods in two or more consecutive years.

Example 4 500-Year Flood

Geological records indicate that a river has crested above a particular high flood level just four times in the past 2000 years. What is the empirical probability that the river will crest above this flood level next year?

Solution Based on the observation of 4 floods in 2000 years, the empirical probability is

$$\frac{4}{2000} = \frac{1}{500} = 0.002$$

The empirical probability of a flood next year is 1 in 500, or 0.002. Because a flood of this magnitude occurs on average once every 500 years, it could be called a "500-year flood." **Now try Exercises 39–40.**

Example 5 Empirical Coin Tossing

If you are interested only in the number of heads in coin tosses, then the possible events when tossing two coins are 0 heads, 1 head, and 2 heads (see Figure 7.1). Suppose you repeat a two-coin toss 100 times and your results are as follows:

- 0 heads occurs 22 times.
- 1 head occurs 51 times.
- 2 heads occurs 27 times.

A Brief Review The Multiplication Principle

Let's review an important method for counting outcomes. Suppose we toss two coins and want to count the total number of possible outcomes. Individually, each coin has two possible outcomes: heads (H) and tails (T). Together, the two coins have $2 \times 2 = 4$ possible outcomes: HH, HT, TH, and TT (see Figure 7.1).

We can extend this thinking to additional coins. For example, if we toss three coins, the total number of possible outcomes is $2 \times 2 \times 2 = 8$, as shown in Figure 7.4. We can generalize these examples with the following rule, often called the **multiplication principle.**

The Multiplication Principle

Suppose there are M possible outcomes for one process and N possible outcomes for a second process. The total number of possible outcomes for the two processes combined is $M \times N$. This idea extends to any number of processes. For example, if a third process has R possible outcomes, the total number of possible outcomes for the three processes combined is $M \times N \times R$.

Example: How many outcomes are possible when you roll two dice?
Solution: A single die has six possible outcomes: the numbers 1 through 6 (see Figure 7.2). A second die also has six possible outcomes. The total number of possible outcomes for two dice is $6 \times 6 = 36$.

Example: A restaurant menu offers two choices for an appetizer, five choices for a main course, and three choices for a dessert. How many different three-course (appetizer, main course, dessert) meals are possible?
Solution: There are two possible outcomes when selecting an appetizer, five possible outcomes when selecting a main course, and three possible outcomes when selecting dessert. The total number of possible outcomes is $2 \times 5 \times 3 = 30$; that is, 30 different three-course meals are possible.

Example: A college offers 12 natural science classes, 15 social science classes, 10 English classes, and 8 fine arts classes. You must take one class from each category to meet your core requirements. How many possible ways are there to meet the core requirements?
Solution: Each selection of a course from a category represents a distinct process. We therefore find the total number of ways to meet the requirements by multiplying the number of choices in each category: $12 \times 15 \times 10 \times 8 = 14{,}400$. There are 14,400 different ways to choose your courses to meet the requirements.

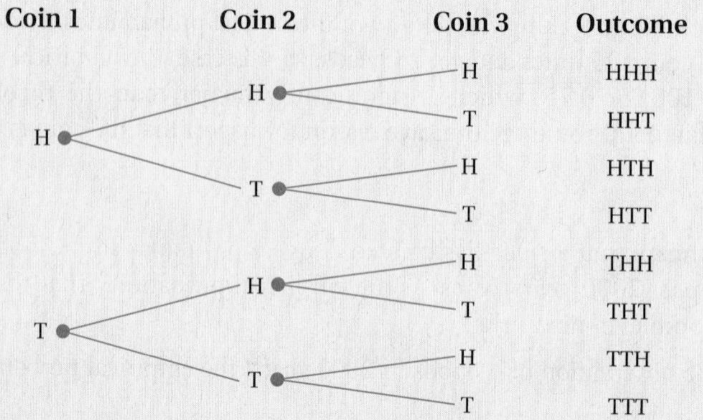

FIGURE 7.4 The first column shows the two possible outcomes for the first coin. Each of these two outcomes branches into two possible outcomes for the second coin (second column). Each of these four outcomes branches into two possible outcomes for the third coin (third column). The last column shows the eight possible outcomes.

Now try Exercises 13–20.

Compare the empirical probabilities to the theoretical probabilities. Do you have reason to suspect that the coins are unfair?

Solution Let's begin by finding the theoretical probabilities for two tossed coins. Figure 7.1 shows that there are four possible outcomes for the two coins. Only 1 of these 4 outcomes has 0 heads, so the theoretical probability for the event of 0 heads is $1/4$, or 0.25. Similarly, only 1 of the 4 outcomes has 2 heads, so the theoretical probability for the event of 2 heads is also 0.25. Finally, 2 of the 4 outcomes have 1 head, so this event has a probability of $2/4$, or 0.5.

We find the empirical probabilities by dividing the number of times each event occurred by the total of 100 tosses. The event of 0 heads occurred 22 times, so its empirical probability is $22/100$, or 0.22. Similarly, the empirical probabilities for the events of 1 head and 2 heads are 0.51 and 0.27, respectively. Because each empirical probability is quite close to the theoretical probability, we have no reason to suspect that the coins are unfair. **Now try Exercises 41–44.**

Historical Note

As early as 3600 B.C.E., rounded bones called *astragali* were used much like dice for games of chance in the Middle East. Our familiar cubical dice appeared about 2000 B.C.E. in Egypt and in China. Playing cards were invented in China in the 10th century and brought to Europe in the 14th century.

Time Out to Think

How does the conclusion of Example 5 resemble the idea of a *hypothesis test*, discussed in Unit 6D?

Subjective Probabilities

The third method for determining probabilities is to make a **subjective estimate** using experience or intuition. For example, you could make a subjective estimate of the probability that a friend will be married in the next year. Weather forecasts are often subjective probabilities based on the experience of the forecaster combined with current weather data. There is not much we can say mathematically about subjective probabilities because their validity depends on personal experience and judgment.

THREE TYPES OF PROBABILITY

A **theoretical probability** is based on a model in which all outcomes are equally likely. It is determined by dividing the number of ways an event can occur by the total number of possible outcomes.

An **empirical probability** is based on observations or experiments. It is the relative frequency of the event of interest.

A **subjective probability** is an estimate based on experience or intuition.

BY THE WAY

Another approach to finding probabilities, called the *Monte Carlo method*, uses computer simulations. This technique essentially finds empirical probabilities, but the experiments are simulations in a computer rather than actual experiments in a lab.

Example 6 Which Type of Probability?

Identify the method that resulted in the following statements.

a. I'm 100% certain that you'll be happy with this car.
b. Based on data from the Department of Transportation, the chance of dying in an automobile accident during a one-year period is 1 in 7000.
c. The chance of rolling a 7 with a twelve-sided die is $1/12$.

Solution

a. This is a subjective probability based on the opinion of the speaker.
b. This is an empirical probability because it is based on observations recorded in the data set.
c. This is a theoretical probability because it is based on a model of a fair twelve-sided die that is equally likely to land on any of its twelve sides. **Now try Exercises 45–46.**

Probability of an Event *Not* Occurring

Suppose we are interested in the probability that a particular event or outcome does *not* occur. For example, suppose we want to know the probability that a 4 does *not* appear on one roll of a die. We can start by finding the probability of getting a 4. There are 6 possible outcomes for the roll of the die (the numbers 1 through 6), so the probability of rolling a 4 is $P(4) = 1/6$. Note that it is certain (which means that the probability is 1) that either we roll a 4 or we do not roll a 4. We can write this fact as

$$P(4) + P(\text{not } 4) = 1$$

It then follows that the probability that a 4 does *not* occur is

$$P(\text{not } 4) = 1 - P(4) = 1 - \frac{1}{6} = \frac{5}{6}$$

This answer makes sense because there are five possible events besides 4 (rolls of 1, 2, 3, 5, and 6). We can generalize this observation for any event.

> **PROBABILITY OF AN EVENT *NOT* OCCURRING**
>
> Suppose the probability of an event A is $P(A)$. Then the probability that event A does *not* occur is $1 - P(A)$.

Example 7 Not Two Boys

What is the probability that a randomly chosen family with three children does *not* have two boys and one girl? Assume boys and girls are equally likely.

Solution In Example 3, we found that the probability of two boys and one girl in a family with three children is 3/8, or 0.375. Therefore, the probability that a family with three children does *not* have two boys and one girl is $1 - 3/8 = 5/8$, or 0.625.

Now try Exercises 47–54.

Probability Distributions

TABLE 7.1 Tossing Two Coins

Event	Probability
2 heads, 0 tails	0.25
1 head, 1 tail	0.50
0 heads, 2 tails	0.25
Total	1

Consider again the possible outcomes and events for tossing two coins (see Figure 7.1). There are four possible outcomes, each with a probability of 1/4. If we are interested only in the total number of heads, two of the four outcomes—the outcomes HT and TH—represent the same event of 1 head. Therefore, the event of 1 head has a probability of 2/4, or 1/2. Table 7.1 summarizes the probabilities of the three possible events of 0 head, 1 head, and 2 heads. This table is a **probability distribution**, which displays the probability for *every possible event*. The sum of all the probabilities must be 1, because it is certain that one of the events will occur when two coins are tossed.

> **MAKING A PROBABILITY DISTRIBUTION**
>
> A **probability distribution** represents the probabilities of all possible events. To make a table of a probability distribution:
>
> **Step 1:** List all possible *outcomes*. Use a table or figure if it is helpful.
> **Step 2:** Identify outcomes that represent the same *event*. Find the probability of each event (using the theoretical method).
> **Step 3:** Make a table in which one column lists each event and another column lists each probability. The sum of all the probabilities must be 1.

Example 8 Tossing Three Coins

Make a table of the probability distribution for the number of heads that occur when three coins are tossed simultaneously.

Solution We apply the three-step process.

Step 1: The diagram in Figure 7.4 (in the Brief Review on p. 420) shows the eight possible outcomes when three coins are tossed. Each outcome is equally likely and has a probability of 1/8.

Step 2: Several of the outcomes represent the same event. For example, the outcomes HTT, THT, and TTH all represent the event of 1 head and 2 tails. This event therefore has a probability of 3/8. Similarly, the outcomes HHT, HTH, and THH all represent the event of 2 heads and 1 tail. This event also has a probability of 3/8.

Step 3: There are four possible events: 0 heads, 1 head, 2 heads, and 3 heads. We have their probabilities from steps 1 and 2. Table 7.2 shows the complete probability distribution.

Now try Exercise 55.

TABLE 7.2 Tossing Three Coins

Result	Probability
3 heads, 0 tails	1/8
2 heads, 1 tail	3/8
1 head, 2 tails	3/8
0 heads, 3 tails	1/8
Total	1

Time Out to Think

When four coins are tossed, how many different outcomes are there? If you record the number of heads, how many different events are possible?

Example 9 Two Dice Distribution

Make a probability distribution for the sum of the dice when two dice are rolled. What is the most probable sum?

Solution Because there are six ways for each die to land, there are $6 \times 6 = 36$ outcomes of rolling two dice. We can enumerate all 36 outcomes by making a table in which we list one die along the rows and one die along the columns. Each of the 36 outcomes is equally likely, so each has a probability of 1/36. For each outcome, the table also shows the sum of the numbers on the two dice.

	1	2	3	4	5	6
1	$1 + 1 = 2$	$1 + 2 = 3$	$1 + 3 = 4$	$1 + 4 = 5$	$1 + 5 = 6$	$1 + 6 = 7$
2	$2 + 1 = 3$	$2 + 2 = 4$	$2 + 3 = 5$	$2 + 4 = 6$	$2 + 5 = 7$	$2 + 6 = 8$
3	$3 + 1 = 4$	$3 + 2 = 5$	$3 + 3 = 6$	$3 + 4 = 7$	$3 + 5 = 8$	$3 + 6 = 9$
4	$4 + 1 = 5$	$4 + 2 = 6$	$4 + 3 = 7$	$4 + 4 = 8$	$4 + 5 = 9$	$4 + 6 = 10$
5	$5 + 1 = 6$	$5 + 2 = 7$	$5 + 3 = 8$	$5 + 4 = 9$	$5 + 5 = 10$	$5 + 6 = 11$
6	$6 + 1 = 7$	$6 + 2 = 8$	$6 + 3 = 9$	$6 + 4 = 10$	$6 + 5 = 11$	$6 + 6 = 12$

The possible *events* are the sums from 2 to 12. We find the probability of each event by counting all the outcomes for each sum and then dividing the number of outcomes by 36. For example, the five highlighted outcomes in the table have a sum of 8, so the probability of a sum of 8 is 5/36. Table 7.3 shows the complete probability distribution. The most likely event is a sum of 7, which has a probability of 6/36, or 1/6.

TABLE 7.3 Probability Distribution for the Sum of Two Dice

Event (Sum)	2	3	4	5	6	7	8	9	10	11	12	Total
Probability	1/36	2/36	3/36	4/36	5/36	6/36	5/36	4/36	3/36	2/36	1/36	1

Now try Exercise 56.

Stating the Odds

You've probably noticed that there are several ways to express the idea of *probability*. For example, saying that the *chance* of getting heads on a coin toss is 1/2 is equivalent to saying that the *probability* is 1/2. Another common term for probability is **odds**, but strictly speaking the two terms have different meanings. Odds are often stated as the *ratio* of the probability that a particular event will occur to the probability that it will not occur.

> **DEFINITION**
>
> The **odds for** an event A are
>
> $$\text{odds for event } A = \frac{P(A)}{P(\text{not } A)}$$
>
> The **odds against** an event A are
>
> $$\text{odds against event } A = \frac{P(\text{not } A)}{P(A)}$$
>
> Note: In gambling, the term **odds on** generally means the *odds against*.

Although odds are defined as fractions, we usually state them by reducing the fraction to simplest terms and reading it as a ratio. For example, the probability of rolling a 4 on a single die is 1/6 and the probability of *not* rolling a 4 is 5/6. Therefore, the *odds for* rolling a 4 are

$$\frac{P(4)}{P(\text{not } 4)} = \frac{1/6}{5/6} = \frac{1}{5}$$

We usually state these *odds for* rolling a 4 as *1 to 5*. Taking the reciprocal, we can say the *odds against* rolling a 4 are *5 to 1*.

In gambling, the "odds against" (or "odds on") usually expresses how much you can gain with a win for each dollar you bet. For example, suppose the odds on a particular horse at a horse race are 3 to 1. Then for each \$1 you bet on this horse, you will gain \$3 if the horse wins. If you place a \$2 bet and the horse wins, you will gain $3 \times \$2 = \$6$. (You will also receive back the money you bet, so when you collect on your \$2 bet you will receive the \$6 gain plus your original \$2, for a total of \$8.) Of course, as with any form of gambling, you are more likely to lose than to win.

BY THE WAY

What's a blue moon? Many people now say that a blue moon is the second full moon in a calendar month. But the editors of *Sky and Telescope* discovered that this definition came from a mistake in a 1946 issue of their magazine. No one knows the original definition of blue moon, but the phrase "once in a blue moon" has come to mean an extremely low probability of occurrence.

Example 10 Two-Coin Odds

What are the odds for getting two heads in tossing two coins? What are the odds against it?

Solution As we found earlier, the probability of getting two heads in tossing two coins is 1/4. That is, $P(2 \text{ heads}) = 1/4$. The probability of not getting two heads in tossing two coins is $P(\text{not } 2 \text{ heads}) = 1 - 1/4 = 3/4$. Thus, the odds for getting two heads are

$$\frac{P(2 \text{ heads})}{P(\text{not } 2 \text{ heads})} = \frac{1/4}{3/4} = \frac{1}{3}$$

The odds for getting two heads in two coin tosses are 1 to 3. We take the reciprocal of the *odds for* to find the *odds against*. Thus, the odds against getting two heads in tossing two coins are 3 to 1. **Now try Exercises 57–60.**

Example 11 Horse Race Payoff

At a horse race, the odds on Blue Moon are given as 7 to 2. If you bet \$10 and Blue Moon wins, how much will you gain?

Solution The 7 to 2 odds mean that, for each \$2 you bet on Blue Moon, you gain \$7 if you win. A \$10 bet is equivalent to five \$2 bets, so you gain $5 \times \$7 = \$35$. You also get your \$10 back, so you will receive \$45 when you collect on your winning ticket.

Now try Exercises 61–62.

QUICK QUIZ

Choose the best answer to each of the following questions. Explain your reasoning with one or more complete sentences.

1. Suppose you toss one coin three times in a row and get heads, tails, heads (HTH). If you are interested in the number of heads that appear, which one of the following sets of three tosses has a different outcome but corresponds to the same event as the first set of tosses?

   a. THT b. HHT c. HHH

2. During the course of the basketball season, Shawna made 67 out of 100 free throws. When we say that her probability of making a free throw during the playoffs is 0.67, what type of probability are we stating?

   a. a theoretical probability

   b. an empirical probability

   c. a subjective probability

3. A box contains 20 chocolates, but only 2 of them are the dark chocolate that you like. When we say that the probability of drawing one of the dark chocolates at random is 0.1, what type of probability are we stating?

   a. a theoretical probability

   b. an empirical probability

   c. a subjective probability

4. Suppose the probability of winning a big prize in the lottery is X. What is the probability of *not* winning?

   a. Y b. $P(X)$ c. $1 - X$

5. When you toss one coin, the probability that you'll get heads is 1/2. Assuming the coin is fair, this means that

   a. if you toss two coins, you'll get 1 head and 1 tail.

   b. if you toss 100 coins, you'll get 50 heads and 50 tails.

   c. if you toss 1000 coins, there's no way to predict the precise number of heads you'll get, though it will probably be close to 500.

6. On a roll of two dice, Serena bets that the sum will be 5, and Mackenzie bets that the sum will be 8. Who has a higher probability of winning? (*Hint:* See Table 7.3.)

   a. Serena b. Mackenzie

   c. Both have an equal probability of winning.

7. Suppose you toss four 6-sided dice. How many *outcomes* are possible?

   a. 6 b. $4 \times 4 \times 4 \times 4 \times 4 \times 4$

   c. $6 \times 6 \times 6 \times 6$

8. Suppose you toss four 6-sided dice. How many different sums are possible?

   a. 11 b. 21 c. $6 \times 6 \times 6 \times 6$

9. You are playing 5-card poker with a deck of 52 cards. If you could make a probability distribution showing the individual probabilities of all possible hands, the sum of all the individual probabilities would be

   a. 1. b. 5. c. 52.

10. The odds on (or odds against) TripleTreat winning the Kentucky Derby are 3 to 1. This means that whoever set the odds thinks that TripleTreat's probability of winning is

    a. 1 in 4. b. 1 in 3. c. 3 in 4.

Exercises 7A

REVIEW QUESTIONS

1. Distinguish between an outcome and an event in probability. Give an example in which the same event can occur through two or more outcomes.

2. Explain the notation $P(\text{event})$. Why must the probability always be between 0 and 1 (inclusive)?

3. Briefly describe the differences among theoretical, empirical, and subjective techniques for finding probabilities. Give an example of each.

4. How is the probability of an event *not* occurring related to the probability that it *does* occur? Why?

5. What is a probability distribution? Explain how to make a table of a probability distribution.
6. Explain the common usage of the term *odds* and its usage in gambling.

DOES IT MAKE SENSE?

Decide whether each of the following statements makes sense (or is clearly true) or does not make sense (or is clearly false). Explain your reasoning.

7. When I toss four coins, there are four different outcomes that all represent the event of one head and three tails.
8. The probability that my sister will get into the college of her choice is 3.7.
9. I estimate that the probability of my getting married in the next 3 years is 0.7.
10. Because either there is life on Mars or there is not, the probability of life on Mars is 0.5.
11. The probability that Jonas will win the race is 0.6 and the probability that he will not win is 0.5.
12. Based on data showing that we've had snow on Christmas in 27 of the past 100 years, the probability of snow this year is 0.27.

BASIC SKILLS & CONCEPTS

13–20: Review of the Multiplication Principle. Use the skills covered in the Brief Review on p. 420 to answer the following questions.

13. How many different choices of car do you have if a particular model comes in 15 colors and three styles (sedan, station wagon, or hatchback)?
14. A local ski sale features nine types of skis, eight types of bindings, and twelve types of boots. How many different ski/binding/boot packages are available?
15. A restaurant has a special menu that features three choices of soup, six choices of entree, and five choices of dessert. How many different three-course meals could you order?
16. Three districts each elect one representative to the County Commission. There are two candidates in District 1, three candidates in District 2, and four candidates in District 3. How many different Commissions are possible?
17. The local paint store offers 28 basic colors, each of which can be combined with four different textures. How many different paint combinations are available?
18. You are required to take five courses, one each in humanities, sociology, science, math, and music. You have a choice of four humanities courses, three sociology courses, five science courses, two math courses, and three music courses. How many different sets of five courses are possible?
19. In designing your new home entertainment center, you have a choice of seven different flat-screen TVs, nine different DVD players, and eleven different speaker sets. How many different systems could you design?
20. The car model you are considering comes with or without air conditioning, with or without a sun roof, with or without a CD player, and in eight stock colors. How many different versions of the car are available?

21–38: Theoretical Probabilities. Use the theoretical method to determine the probability of the given outcomes and events. State any assumptions that you make.

21. Drawing a queen from a standard deck of cards
22. Drawing a black card (club or spade) from a standard deck of cards
23. Rolling a single die and getting a 1 or 2
24. Rolling two dice and getting a sum of 4
25. Drawing a royalty card (jack, queen, king) from a standard deck of cards
26. Rolling a single die and getting an even number
27. Drawing an ace of hearts or an ace of diamonds from a standard deck of cards
28. Rolling two dice and getting the same number on both dice
29. Randomly meeting someone with a phone number that ends in a 1 or 2
30. Randomly meeting someone born on a Sunday
31. Randomly meeting someone born between 2:00 p.m. and 3:00 p.m.
32. Randomly meeting someone born in April or October (assume 365 days in a year)
33. Randomly selecting a two-child family with one boy and one girl
34. Randomly selecting a three-child family with exactly two girl children
35. Randomly selecting a three-child family with three girls
36. Randomly selecting a pair of white socks from a drawer that holds five pairs of black socks, nine pairs of blue socks, and eight pairs of white socks
37. Randomly meeting someone whose address ends in the same digit as yours
38. Waiting longer than 15 minutes when you arrive randomly at a bus stop at which the bus arrives promptly on the hour and on the half hour

39–44: Empirical Probabilities. Use the empirical method to estimate the following probabilities.

39. After recording the forecasts of your local weatherman for 30 days, you conclude that he gave a correct forecast 18 times. What is the probability that his next forecast will be correct?
40. What is the probability of a 200-year flood this year?
41. Halfway through the season, a basketball player has hit 72% of her free throws. What is the probability that her next free throw will be successful?
42. You count 42 heads when you toss a coin 100 times. If you don't know whether the coin is fair, what is the probability that the next toss will be a tail?

43. A doctor diagnosed pneumonia in 250 patients and 225 of them actually had pneumonia. What is the probability that the next patient diagnosed with pneumonia will actually have pneumonia?

44. What is the probability that a baseball player with a .300 batting average will get a hit at his next at-bat?

45–46: **Subjective Probability.** State your estimate of the subjective probability, and explain how you arrived at your estimate.

45. The probability that you'll graduate from college within the next four years

46. The probability that you'll get an A on the final exam in this course

47–54: **Event *Not* Occurring.** Determine the probability of the following events. State any assumptions that you use.

47. What is the probability of not rolling a 2 with a fair die?

48. What is the probability of not tossing three tails with three fair coins?

49. What is the probability that an 75% free-throw shooter will miss his next free throw?

50. What is the probability that the next person you meet was not born in July? (Assume 365 days in a year.)

51. What is the probability of not rolling a sum of 7 with two fair dice?

52. What is the probability of a sunny day after a forecast of a 30% chance of rain?

53. What is the probability of not having a 100-year flood this year?

54. What is the probability of randomly meeting someone not born in May or June? (Assume 365 days in a year.)

55–56: **Probability Distributions.** Make a probability distribution for the given set of events.

55. The number of heads when four fair coins are tossed

56. The sums that appear when two fair four-sided dice (tetrahedrons) are tossed

57–60: **Odds.** Use the definition given in the text to find both the *odds for* and the *odds against* the following events.

57. Rolling a fair die and getting a 1 or a 2

58. Flipping two fair coins and getting two tails

59. Rolling a fair die and getting a 5 or a 6

60. Flipping two fair coins and getting a head and a tail

61–62: **Gambling Odds.** Use the definition of odds in betting to find the following odds.

61. The odds on (against) your bet are 3 to 4. If you bet $20 and win, how much will you gain?

62. The odds on (against) your bet are 5 to 4. If you bet $20 and win, how much will you gain?

FURTHER APPLICATIONS

63. **Gender Politics.** The following table gives the gender and political party of the 100 delegates at a political convention. Suppose you encounter a delegate at random.

	Women	Men
Republicans	21	28
Democrats	25	16
Independents	6	4

a. What is the probability that you meet a woman?

b. What is the probability that you meet an Independent?

c. What is the probability that you do not meet a Democrat?

d. What is the probability that you meet a female Republican?

e. What is the probability that you meet someone who is not a male Democrat?

64. **Senior Citizens.** In 2010, there were 40 million people over 65 years of age out of a U.S. population of 310 million. By 2050, it is estimated that there will be 82 million people over 65 years of age out of a U.S. population of 439 million. Would your chances of meeting a person over 65 at random be greater in 2010 or 2050? Explain.

65. **Fair Coins?** You toss three coins 1000 times; the following table shows the results. Compute the empirical probability for each event. Compare the empirical probabilities to the theoretical probabilities for three tossed coins. Do you have reason to believe the coins are unfair? Explain.

Result	Number of Occurrences
0 heads	260
1 head	495
2 heads	245
3 heads	0
Total	1000

66. **Marriage Age.** The following table gives percentages of all married women and men who were married for the first time in each age category. What is the probability that a randomly encountered married woman was married, for the first time, between the ages of 35 and 44? Make a probability distribution for ages of first marriage for men and women.

Age at First Marriage	Women (%)	Men (%)
Under 20	16.6	6.6
20–24	40.8	36.0
25–29	27.2	34.3
30–34	10.1	14.8
35–44	4.5	7.1
45–64	0.7	1.1
65 and over	0.1	0.1

67. **Deceptive Odds.** Suppose event *A* has a 0.99 probability of occurring and event *B* has a 0.96 probability of occurring—both high probabilities. Compute the odds for event *A* and the odds for event *B*. Comment on the relative difference between the odds for the two events compared to the relative difference between the probabilities. How are the odds deceptive in this case?

68. **Project: Thumb Tack Probabilities.** Find a standard thumb tack and practice tossing it onto a flat surface. Notice that there are two different outcomes: The tack can land with its point facing down or with its point facing up.

a. Toss the tack 50 times and record the outcomes.

b. Give the empirical probabilities of the two outcomes based on these results.

c. If possible, ask several other people to repeat the process. How well do your probabilities agree?

69. **Project: Three-Coin Experiment.** Toss three coins (at once) 50 times and record the outcomes in terms of the number of heads. Based on your observations, give the empirical probability of each result. Do the empirical results agree with the theoretical probabilities? Explain.

WEB PROJECTS

70. **Blood Groups.** The four major blood groups are designated A, B, AB, and O. Within each group there are two Rh types: positive and negative. Find data on the relative frequency of blood groups, including the Rh types. Make a table showing the probability of meeting someone in each of the eight blood groups.

71. **Accidents.** Find data that give the empirical probabilities of various types of accidents (such as being killed by lightning, by a shark bite, or by a falling airplane part). Are the empirical probabilities consistent with your intuition?

IN YOUR WORLD

72. **Probability in the News.** Find a news article or research report that makes use of a probability. Interpret the probability and discuss whether it is theoretical, empirical, or subjective.

73. **Probability in Your Life.** Describe a recent instance from your own life when you used probability to make a decision. What type of probability did you use? How did it help you make the decision?

74. **Gambling Odds.** Find an advertisement for a gambling establishment or lottery in which the term *odds* is used, and interpret its meaning.

UNIT 7B Combining Probabilities

In 1654, a French con man known as the Chevalier de Mère (his given name was Antoine Gombaud) bet other gamblers even money that he could roll at least one 6 in four rolls of a standard six-sided die. The Chevalier made quite a profit on this bet, despite having calculated his chance of winning incorrectly!

Because the probability of rolling a 6 on one roll of a die is 1/6, the Chevalier falsely reasoned that his chances would be four times as great on four rolls, or $4/6 = 0.67$. In fact, the chance of rolling a 6 within four tries is only 0.52 (as we will show shortly). Nevertheless, because a probability of 0.52 means winning more often than losing, the Chevalier profited over the long run.

As gamblers caught on to this "con game," they were no longer willing to play. The Chevalier therefore proposed a new game in which he rolled *two* dice and bet that he could throw a *double-6* within 24 rolls. He knew that, on any single roll of the two dice, the probability of a double-6 is 1/36 (see Unit 7A, Example 9). He then used his faulty reasoning to guess that, if he rolled the pair of dice 24 times, his odds of rolling at least one double-6 would be $24/36 = 0.67$.

To his dismay, the Chevalier began losing money. To understand his losses, he turned to the mathematician Blaise Pascal, who, in turn, began a correspondence about probability with the mathematician Pierre de Fermat. Pascal and Fermat quickly recognized the error in the Chevalier's reasoning and developed methods for properly combining probabilities. In this unit, we will study some of these methods.

Historical Note

Blaise Pascal was a precocious Parisian who made fundamental contributions to mathematics and physics. He was deeply religious and his work *Pensées* is an important treatise of western philosophy. Pascal died at the age of 39. Pierre de Fermat was a lawyer, but his passion was mathematics. He spent his life corresponding with mathematicians and preoccupied with difficult problems. One of his most famous claims, known as *Fermat's last theorem*, was proved only recently.

Time Out to Think

The Chevalier multiplied the single-roll probability of 1/6 by 4 rolls to get his guess that he had a 4/6 chance of rolling a 6 within 4 rolls. Based on this reasoning, what would he have guessed for the probability of rolling a 6 within 6 rolls? How does this show the error in his reasoning?

And Probabilities

Suppose you toss two dice and want to know the probability that *both* will come up 4. One way to find the probability is to use the theoretical method from Unit 7A. Because a double-4 is one of 36 possible outcomes for two dice, its probability is 1/36.

Alternatively, we can consider the two dice individually. For each die, the probability of a 4 is 1/6. Rolling a double-4 means rolling a 4 on the first die *and* a 4 on the second die. We find the probability of a double-4 by multiplying the two individual probabilities:

$$P(\text{double } 4) = P(4) \times P(4) = \frac{1}{6} \times \frac{1}{6} = \frac{1}{36}$$

By either method, the probability of rolling a double-4 is 1/36. In general, we call the probability of event *A and* event *B* occurring an ***and* probability** (or *joint probability*).

The advantage of the multiplication technique is that it can easily be extended to other situations involving two or more events. For example, we can use it to find the probability of getting ten heads in a row on a coin toss or of having a baby *and* getting a pay raise in the same year. However, we must distinguish between events that are *independent* and events that are *dependent* upon each other. Let's investigate each case.

Independent Events

The repeated roll of a single die produces **independent events** because the outcome of one roll does not affect other rolls. Similarly, coin tosses are independent events because one coin toss does not affect others. For independent events, we calculate the *and* probability by multiplication.

AND PROBABILITY: INDEPENDENT EVENTS

Two events are **independent** if the outcome of one does not affect the probability of the other event. Consider two independent events *A* and *B* with individual probabilities $P(A)$ and $P(B)$. The probability that *A* and *B* occur together is

$$P(A \text{ and } B) = P(A) \times P(B)$$

This principle can be extended to any number of independent events. For example, the *and* probability of three independent events *A*, *B*, and *C* is

$$P(A \text{ and } B \text{ and } C) = P(A) \times P(B) \times P(C)$$

BY THE WAY

Whether events are independent is not always obvious. Consider a set of basketball free throws by a single player. Some people argue that the probability of a basket is the same for each free throw. Others suggest that the psychological impact of success or failure on one free throw affects the player's chances of making the next one. Despite many statistical studies of basketball free throws, no one has clearly established which view is correct.

Example 1 Consecutive Floods

Find the probability that a 100-year flood (a flood with a 0.01 probability of striking in a given year) will strike a city in two consecutive years. Assume that a flood in one year does not affect the likelihood of a flood in the next year.

Solution We are told to assume that floods in different years are independent events. Therefore, we find the probability of floods in two consecutive years by multiplying the probability for each individual year:

$$P(2 \text{ consecutive flood years}) = \underbrace{P(\text{flood})}_{\text{year 1}} \times \underbrace{P(\text{flood})}_{\text{year 2}} = 0.01 \times 0.01 = 0.0001$$

The probability of a 100-year flood in two consecutive years is 1 in 10,000. While events with such low probability can certainly occur, remember that this calculation *assumes* that the chance of a flood is 0.01 in any year. If a 100-year flood were to occur in two consecutive years, we might wonder whether the 0.01 probability of a single flood was correct.

Now try Exercises 11–12.

Example 2 Three Coins

Suppose you toss three coins. What is the probability of getting three tails?

Solution Because coin tosses are independent, we multiply the probability of tails on each individual coin:

$$P(3 \text{ tails}) = \underbrace{P(\text{tails})}_{\text{coin 1}} \times \underbrace{P(\text{tails})}_{\text{coin 2}} \times \underbrace{P(\text{tails})}_{\text{coin 3}} = \frac{1}{2} \times \frac{1}{2} \times \frac{1}{2} = \frac{1}{8}$$

The probability of three tails on three tossed coins is 1/8. **Now try Exercises 13–14**

Dependent Events

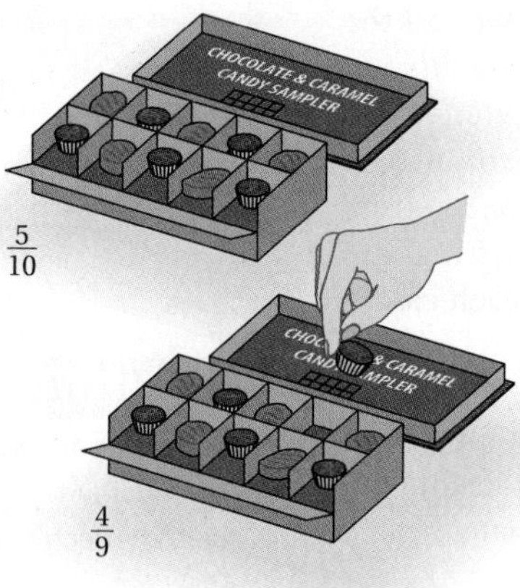

Suppose you draw candy randomly from a box that initially contains five chocolates and five caramels. Clearly, the probability of getting a chocolate on your first try is 5/10, or 1/2. Now, suppose you get a chocolate on the first try and eat it. What is the probability of getting another chocolate on your second draw?

Because you've already eaten one chocolate, the box now contains only nine pieces of candy, of which four are chocolate. Thus, the probability of getting a chocolate on the second try is 4 out of 9, or 4/9. This is *not* the same as the 1/2 probability on the first draw. Because the outcome of the first event affects the probability of the second event, we say that the events are **dependent events**.

Calculating the probability for dependent events still involves multiplying the individual probabilities, but we must take into account how prior events affect subsequent events. In the case of the candy box, we find the probability of getting two chocolates in a row by multiplying the 1/2 probability on the first draw by the 4/9 probability on the second draw:

$$P(2 \text{ chocolates}) = \underbrace{P(\text{chocolate})}_{\text{first draw}} \times \underbrace{P(\text{chocolate})}_{\text{second draw}} = \frac{1}{2} \times \frac{4}{9} = \frac{2}{9}$$

The probability of drawing two chocolates in a row is 2/9. We can generalize this example to any set of dependent events.

Time Out to Think

Suppose that instead of eating the first candy you draw, you put it back in the box. Without doing any calculations, compare the probability of drawing two chocolates in a row when you replace the candy in the box to the probability of drawing two chocolates in a row when you eat the first candy. Which probability is larger and why?

Take Note

$P(B \text{ given } A)$ is called a *conditional probability*. Some books denote it as $P(B|A)$.

***AND* PROBABILITY: DEPENDENT EVENTS**

Two events are **dependent** if the outcome of one event affects the probability of the other event. The probability that dependent events *A* and *B* occur together is

$$P(A \text{ and } B) = P(A) \times P(B \text{ given } A)$$

where $P(B \text{ given } A)$ means "the probability of event *B* given the occurrence of event *A*." This principle can be extended to any number of dependent events. For example, the *and* probability of three dependent events *A*, *B*, and *C* is

$$P(A \text{ and } B \text{ and } C) = P(A) \times P(B \text{ given } A) \times P(C \text{ given } A \text{ and } B)$$

Example 3 Bingo

The game of Bingo involves drawing labeled buttons from a bin at random, without replacement. There are 75 buttons, 15 for each of the letters B, I, N, G, and O. What is the probability of drawing two B buttons in the first two selections?

Solution Bingo involves dependent events because removing a button changes the contents of the bin. The probability of drawing a B on the first draw is 15/75. If this occurs, the bin has 74 buttons remaining, of which 14 are the letter B. Therefore, the probability of drawing a B button on the second draw is 14/74. The probability of drawing two B buttons in the first two selections is

$$P(B \text{ and } B) = \underbrace{P(B)}_{\text{first draw}} \times \underbrace{P(B)}_{\text{second draw}} = \frac{15}{75} \times \frac{14}{74} \approx 0.0378$$

The probability of drawing the letter B on the first two selections is 0.0378, or just under 4 in 100. **Now try Exercises 15–16.**

Example 4 Jury Selection

A three-person jury must be selected at random from a pool of 12 people that has 6 men and 6 women. What is the probability of selecting an all-male jury?

Solution Because there are 6 men in the pool of 12 people, the probability that the first juror is male is 6/12. If the first juror is male, the remaining pool has 5 men among 11 people. Therefore, the probability that the second juror is also male is 5/11. If both the first two jurors are male, the pool is left with 4 men among 10 people, making the probability of a third male juror 4/10. The combined probability is

$$P(3 \text{ men}) = \underbrace{P(\text{man})}_{\text{juror 1}} \times \underbrace{P(\text{man given male juror 1})}_{\text{juror 2}} \times \underbrace{P(\text{man given male jurors 1 and 2})}_{\text{juror 3}}$$

$$= \frac{6}{12} \times \frac{5}{11} \times \frac{4}{10} = \frac{120}{1320} \approx 0.091$$

The probability of selecting an all-male jury is roughly 0.09, or 9%. **Now try Exercises 17–26.**

BY THE WAY

In the late 1960s, the famed baby doctor Benjamin Spock was convicted by an all-male jury of encouraging draft resistance during the Vietnam War. His defense argued that a jury with women would have been more sympathetic.

Either/Or Probabilities

Suppose we want to know the probability that *either* of two events occurs, rather than the probability that both events occur. In that case, we are looking for an ***either/or* probability**, such as the probability that either a #2 bus or a #9 bus will be the next to arrive at your stop. As with *and* probabilities, there are two cases to consider; we call them *overlapping* and *non-overlapping* events.

Non-Overlapping Events

A coin can land either heads *or* tails, but it can't land on both heads *and* tails at the same time. When two events cannot occur at the same time, they are said to be **non-overlapping** (or *mutually exclusive*). If we make a Venn diagram (see Unit 1C) in which the circles represent different events, non-overlapping events are those for which there is no overlap between the circles. For example, the circles for heads and tails in a coin toss do not overlap because a coin cannot land both heads and tails at the same time (Figure 7.5). We can calculate *either/or* probabilities for non-overlapping events with the following rule.

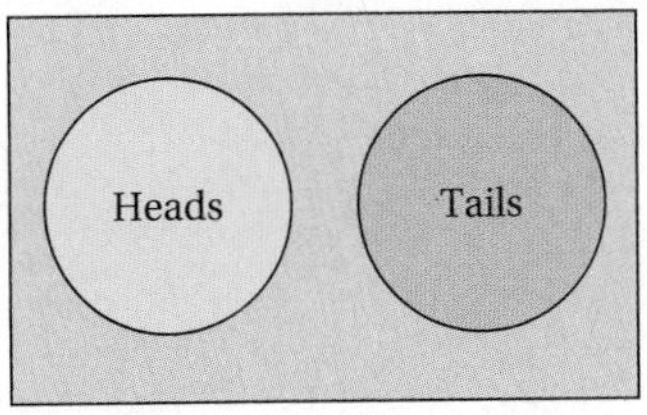

FIGURE 7.5 Venn diagram for non-overlapping events.

EITHER/OR PROBABILITY: NON-OVERLAPPING EVENTS

Two events are **non-overlapping** if they cannot occur together. If A and B are non-overlapping events, the probability that either A or B occurs is

$$P(A \text{ or } B) = P(A) + P(B)$$

This principle can be extended to any number of non-overlapping events. For example, the probability that either event A, event B, or event C occurs is

$$P(A \text{ or } B \text{ or } C) = P(A) + P(B) + P(C)$$

Example 5 Either/Or Dice

Suppose you roll a single die. What is the probability of rolling either a 2 or a 3?

Solution The outcomes 2 and 3 are non-overlapping because a single die can land only one way. Each probability is 1/6 (because there are 6 ways for the die to land), so the combined probability is

$$P(2 \text{ or } 3) = P(2) + P(3) = \frac{1}{6} + \frac{1}{6} = \frac{2}{6}$$

The probability of rolling either a 2 or a 3 is 2/6, or 1/3. **Now try Exercises 27–28.**

Overlapping Events

Suppose you have a standard deck of 52 cards and want to know the probability of drawing either a queen or a club. Because there are 4 queens in the deck, the probability of drawing a queen is 4/52. Similarly, because there are 13 clubs in the deck, the probability of drawing a club is 13/52. The sum of the two probabilities is

$$\frac{4}{52} + \frac{13}{52} = \frac{17}{52}$$

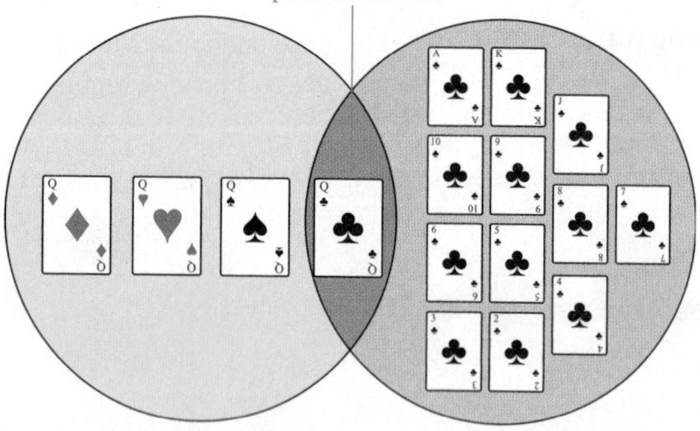

FIGURE 7.6 Venn diagram for overlapping events. One circle represents queens in a deck of cards and the other represents clubs. The overlap region contains the queen of clubs, which belongs to both circles.

However, this is *not* the probability of drawing a queen *or* a club. The Venn diagram in Figure 7.6 shows why. One circle represents the 4 queens in the deck and the other represents the 13 clubs in the deck. The circles overlap because one card—the queen of clubs—is both a queen *and* a club. That is, the events of drawing a queen and drawing a club are **overlapping events** because both can occur together. If we simply add the individual probabilities, as above, the queen of clubs gets counted twice (once as a queen and once as a club). We can correct the calculation by subtracting the double-counted probability of drawing the queen of clubs, which is 1/52 (because the queen of clubs is just 1 of the 52 cards in the deck). This gives us

$$\begin{aligned} P(\text{queen or club}) &= P(\text{queen}) + P(\text{club}) - P(\text{queen and club}) \\ &= \frac{4}{52} + \frac{13}{52} - \frac{1}{52} = \frac{16}{52} \end{aligned}$$

The probability of drawing a queen or a club is 16/52. You can also see this result from the Venn diagram, which shows 16 cards (out of 52 total) that are either a queen or a club (or both).

> ***EITHER/OR* PROBABILITY: OVERLAPPING EVENTS**
>
> Two events are **overlapping** if they *can* occur together. If A and B are overlapping events, the probability that either A or B occurs is
>
> $$P(A \text{ or } B) = P(A) + P(B) - P(A \text{ and } B)$$

The principal means for ascertaining truth—induction and analogy—are based on probabilities; so that the entire system of human knowledge is connected with the theory of probability.

—Pierre Simon, Marquis de Laplace (1819)

Example 6 Democrats and Women

You select one person at random from a room with eight people: two Democratic men, two Republican men, two Democratic women, and two Republican women. What is the probability that you will select *either* a woman or a Democrat?

Solution The probability of selecting a Democrat is 1/2, because half of the people in the room are Democrats. Similarly, half of the people are women, so the probability of selecting a woman is also 1/2. We cannot simply add these probabilities, because two of the eight people in the room are both Democrats and women. The probability of choosing one of these two people is 2/8, or 1/4. Thus, the probability of selecting either a woman or a Democrat is

$$\begin{aligned} P(\text{woman or Democrat}) &= P(\text{woman}) + P(\text{Democrat}) - P(\text{woman and Democrat}) \\ &= \frac{1}{2} + \frac{1}{2} - \frac{1}{4} = \frac{3}{4} \end{aligned}$$

The probability that you will select either a woman or a Democrat is 3/4, or 0.75.

Now try Exercises 29–38.

The *At Least Once* Rule

Suppose you toss a coin four times. What is the probability of getting *at least one* head? There are four different ways to get at least one head: by getting 1 head, 2 heads, 3 heads, or 4 heads. Thus, one way to solve this problem is to add the individual probabilities:

$$P(\text{at least one H in 4 tosses}) = P(1\text{ H}) + P(2\text{ H}) + P(3\text{ H}) + P(4\text{ H})$$

To complete this calculation, we'd need to make a probability distribution that showed the probability for each of the four ways of getting at least one head.

Fortunately, there is an easier way. Because you either *do* or *do not* get at least one head in the four coin tosses, the sum of these two probabilities is 1:

$$P(\text{at least one H in 4 tosses}) + P(\text{no heads in 4 tosses}) = 1$$

(Getting "no heads" means *not* getting at least one head.) Subtracting the probability of no heads from both sides, we find

$$P(\text{at least one H in 4 tosses}) = 1 - P(\text{no heads in 4 tosses})$$

It's easy to find the probability of no heads. The probability of not getting heads on one coin toss is $P(\text{not H}) = 1/2$, so the probability of no heads in four tosses is

$$\begin{aligned} P(\text{no H in 4 tosses}) &= \underbrace{P(\text{not H})}_{\text{toss 1}} \times \underbrace{P(\text{not H})}_{\text{toss 2}} \times \underbrace{P(\text{not H})}_{\text{toss 3}} \times \underbrace{P(\text{not H})}_{\text{toss 4}} \\ &= [P(\text{not H})]^4 \end{aligned}$$

The last step follows because $P(\text{not H})$ is the same for all four tosses. By substituting $P(\text{not H}) = 1/2$, we find that the probability of at least one head in 4 coin tosses is

$$\begin{aligned} P(\text{at least one H in 4 tosses}) &= 1 - P(\text{no H in 4 tosses}) \\ &= 1 - [P(\text{not H})]^4 \\ &= 1 - \left[\frac{1}{2}\right]^4 = 1 - \frac{1}{16} = \frac{15}{16} \end{aligned}$$

We can generalize this example to any question of the form "What is the probability of *at least one* particular event in a series of independent trials?"

THE *AT LEAST ONCE* RULE (FOR INDEPENDENT EVENTS)

Suppose the probability of an event A occurring in one trial is $P(A)$. If all trials are independent, the probability that event A occurs *at least once* in n trials is

$$\begin{aligned} P(\text{at least one event } A \text{ in } n \text{ trials}) &= 1 - P(\text{no events } A \text{ in } n \text{ trials}) \\ &= 1 - [P(\text{not } A \text{ in one trial})]^n \end{aligned}$$

Example 7 100-Year Flood

What is the probability that a region will experience at least one 100-year flood (a flood that has a 0.01 chance of occurring in any given year) during the next 100 years? Assume that 100-year floods in consecutive years are independent events.

Solution Because there's a 0.01 probability of a flood in any one year, there is a 0.99 chance that a flood will *not* occur in any one year. The *at least once* rule gives us the probability of at least one flood in 100 years:

$$\begin{aligned} P(\text{at least one flood in 100 years}) &= 1 - [P(\text{no flood in one year})]^{100} \\ &= 1 - [0.99]^{100} \approx 0.634 \end{aligned}$$

There is a 0.634, or almost 2 out of 3, chance that a 100-year flood will occur at least once in the next 100 years.

Now try Exercises 39–44.

Time Out to Think

Suppose a region has not experienced a 100-year flood in 100 years. Should you be surprised? Would this fact give you reason to suspect that 100-year floods don't really occur in this region?

Example 8 Lottery Chances

You purchase 10 lottery tickets, for which the probability of winning some prize on a single ticket is 1 in 10. What is the probability that you will have at least one winning ticket among the 10 tickets?

Lottery: a tax on people who are bad at math.

—Message circulated on the Internet

Solution Because the probability of winning with any one ticket is 0.1, the probability of not winning with one ticket is 0.9. Therefore, the probability of winning at least once with ten tickets is

$$\begin{aligned} P(\text{at least one winner in 10 tickets}) &= 1 - [P(\text{not winning on one ticket})]^{10} \\ &= 1 - [0.9]^{10} \approx 0.651 \end{aligned}$$

The probability of at least one winning ticket among 10 is 0.651. This also means that the probability of all ten tickets being losers is $1 - 0.651 = 0.349$. In other words, you stand a better than 1 in 3 chance of losing on all ten tickets that you buy.

Now try Exercises 45–50.

Return to the Chevalier

We are now ready to return to the story of the Chevalier de Mère. Recall that, in his first game, he bet that he could get at least one 6 in four rolls of a die. We can use the *at least once* rule to calculate his probability of winning. The probability of a 6 on any single roll is 1/6, so the probability of *not* 6 is 5/6. Thus, the probability of getting at least one 6 in four rolls is

$$\begin{aligned} P(\text{at least one 6 in 4 rolls}) &= 1 - [P(\text{not 6 on one roll})]^4 \\ &= 1 - \left[\frac{5}{6}\right]^4 \approx 0.518 \end{aligned}$$

The Chevalier's probability of winning in the first game was 0.518. Although this is considerably lower than the 4/6 (0.667) probability he had guessed, it is still better than even odds. He was likely to come out ahead if he played the game many times.

In his second game, he bet that he could roll a double-6 within 24 tries. The probability of a double-6 on any single roll is 1/36, so the probability of not getting a double-6 on a single roll is 35/36. Therefore, the probability of getting at least one double-6 in 24 rolls is

$$\begin{aligned} P(\text{at least one double-6 in 24 rolls}) &= 1 - [P(\text{not double-6 on one roll})]^{24} \\ &= 1 - \left[\frac{35}{36}\right]^{24} \approx 0.491 \end{aligned}$$

The Chevalier's probability of winning in his second game was 0.491, which is slightly less than even odds. Therefore, he was likely to lose more games than he won.

Time Out to Think

Comment on how the difference between a 52% and a 49% chance of winning can be the difference between rags and riches in gambling. How can casinos exploit this idea?

QUICK QUIZ

Choose the best answer to each of the following questions. Explain your reasoning with one or more complete sentences.

1. The probability of rolling two dice and getting a double-1 (making a sum of 2, or "snake eyes") is 1 in 36. Suppose you roll two dice *twice*. Which statement is *not* true?

   a. The probability of getting a double-1 is 1/36 for each individual roll.

   b. The probability of getting a double-1 both times is $1/36 \times 1/36$.

   c. The probability of getting a double-1 on at least one of the two rolls is 2/36.

2. The rule $P(A \text{ and } B) = P(A) \times P(B)$ holds

   a. in all cases.

   b. only if it is possible for both *A* and *B* to occur together (simultaneously).

   c. only if an outcome of *A* on one trial does not affect the probability of an outcome of *B* on the next.

3. Each of the following states a probability for two events. In which case are the events *dependent?*

   a. the probability of an Olympic diver scoring 8 or above on two consecutive dives

   b. the probability of choosing two pink roses from a vase with 25 roses

   c. the probability of finding two people in your class with a birth date of February 29

4. A box of candy contains five dark chocolates and five white chocolates. If you pick randomly and eat each candy after choosing it, what is the probability of choosing three dark chocolates in a row?

   a. $1/2 \times 1/2 \times 1/2$ b. $5/10 \times 4/10 \times 3/10$

   c. $1/2 \times 4/9 \times 3/8$

5. The events of being born on a Wednesday and being born in July are

   a. independent. b. mutually exclusive.

   c. overlapping.

6. You roll two dice. Based on the probabilities shown in Table 7.3, which of the following has a probability *greater* than 0.5?

   a. rolling a sum of 2 or 3 or 4 or 5

   b. rolling a sum of 2 or 3 or 4 or 10 or 11 or 12

   c. rolling a sum of 5 or 6 or 7 or 8

7. You roll two dice twice. Based on the probabilities shown in Table 7.3, what is the probability that you'll get a sum of 3 on the first roll and a sum of 4 on the second roll?

   a. $2/36 \times 3/36$

   b. $2/36 + 3/36$

   c. $(2/36 \times 3/36)^2$

8. You toss two coins ten times, and you want to know the probability of getting two heads at least once in the ten trials. To get the answer in the easiest possible way, what is the first thing you should calculate?

   a. the probability of getting two heads exactly once during the ten trials

   b. the probability of *not* getting two heads in a single trial

   c. the probability of getting two heads on both of the first two trials

9. You purchase 25 lottery tickets for which the probability of winning some prize on a single ticket is 1 in 100. Your probability of having at least one winner among your 25 tickets is

   a. 25 in 100.

   b. 0.25^{10}.

   c. $1 - (0.99)^{25}$.

10. One in 100 tennis balls produced at a factory is defective. If you randomly select five tennis balls, what is the probability that at least one will be defective?

    a. 5×0.01^5 b. 0.99^5 c. $1 - 0.99^5$

Exercises 7B

REVIEW QUESTIONS

1. How did the gambling habits of the Chevalier de Mère help launch the mathematical study of probability?

2. Give an example in which we would be interested in an *and* probability. How do we determine whether the events are independent or dependent? Give examples of each case, and explain how we calculate the probabilities.

3. Give an example in which we would be interested in an *either/or* probability. How do we determine whether the events are overlapping or non-overlapping? Give examples of each case, and explain how we calculate the probabilities.

4. What is the *at least once* rule? Explain how the *at least once* rule can be used to find the correct probabilities in the games of the Chevalier de Mère.

DOES IT MAKE SENSE?

Decide whether each of the following statements makes sense (or is clearly true) or does not make sense (or is clearly false). Explain your reasoning.

5. The probability of getting heads *and* tails when you toss a coin is 0, but the probability of getting heads *or* tails is 1.

6. If you toss a coin and get heads three times in a row, you're due to get tails on the next toss.

7. The probability of drawing an ace or a spade from a deck of cards is the same as the probability of drawing the ace of spades.

8. I can't believe you chose the lottery numbers 1-2-3-4-5-6. Getting six numbers in a row is much less likely than getting other random numbers.

9. My chance of getting a 5 on the roll of one die is 1/6, so my chance of getting at least one 5 when I roll three dice is 3/6.

10. To find the probability that at least one of my 25 lottery tickets is a winner, I calculated the probability that none of my tickets is a winner and subtracted it from 1.

BASIC SKILLS & CONCEPTS

11–26: ***And* Probabilities.** Determine whether the following events are independent or dependent. Then find the probability of the event.

11. The next four births at a hospital all being girls

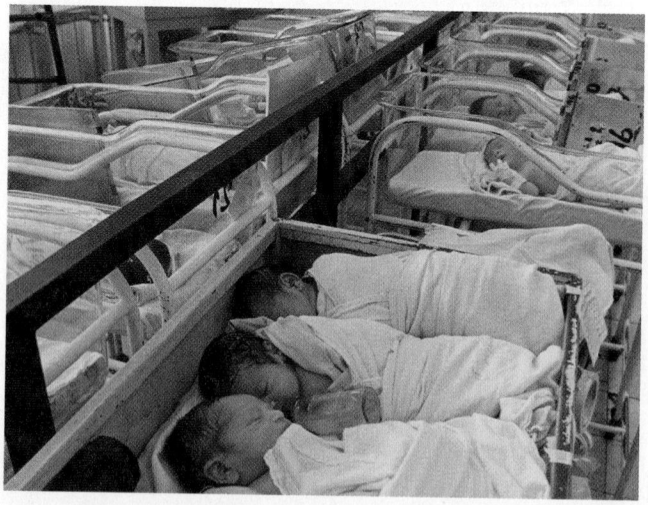

12. Discovering that your three best friends all have a birthday in April

13. Rolling two 2s followed by one 6 on three tosses of a fair die

14. Drawing three queens in a row from a standard deck of cards when the drawn card is returned to the deck each time

15. Drawing three queens in a row from a standard deck of cards when the drawn card is not returned to the deck each time
16. Drawing three hearts in a row from a regular deck of cards when the drawn card is not returned to the deck each time
17. Rolling four fair dice and getting an even number on all four dice
18. Rolling four fair dice and getting four 6s
19. Drawing three spades in a row from a regular deck of cards when the drawn card is returned to the deck each time
20. Being dealt four red cards off the top of a regular deck of well-shuffled cards
21. Purchasing four winning lottery tickets in a row when each ticket has a 1 in 10 chance of being a winner
22. Randomly selecting a three-person committee consisting entirely of Americans from a pool of 12 British people and 18 Americans
23. Selecting all women for a seven-person jury from a pool of 15 men and 15 women
24. Selecting three fully charged batteries in a row from a large batch in which 5% of the batteries are dead
25. Randomly meeting three international students in a row on a campus where 1 in 12 students is an international student
26. Four rainy days in a row when the forecast calls for a "20% chance of rain" each day

27–38: ***Either/Or* Probabilities.** Determine whether the following events are overlapping or non-overlapping. Then find the probability of the event.

27. Drawing either a red 6 or a black 8 on one draw from a regular deck of cards
28. Getting a sum of either 6 or 8 on a roll of two dice
29. Drawing either a jack or a spade from a regular deck of cards
30. Drawing either a face card (jack, queen, or king) or a diamond from a regular deck of cards
31. Getting a sum of either 10, 11, or 12 on a roll of two dice
32. Drawing either a jack or a king from a regular deck of cards
33. Rolling a 2 or a red number on a die on which the even numbers are red and the odd numbers are black
34. Rolling a 3 or a red number on a die on which the even numbers are red and the odd numbers are black
35. Randomly meeting either a woman or a Republican in a group composed of 20 Democratic men, 40 Republican men, 60 Democratic women, and 80 Republican women
36. Randomly meeting either a man or an American in a group composed of 20 English women, 15 English men, 10 American women, and 5 American men
37. Randomly selecting a three-child family with either one or two boy children
38. Randomly selecting a girl or a non–soccer player from a sixth-grade class of 12 boys, 7 of whom play soccer, and 15 girls, 10 of whom play soccer

39–50: ***At Least Once* Problems.** Use the *at least once* rule to find the probabilities of the following events.

39. Getting at least one 6 in four rolls of a single die
40. Getting at least one 1 in eight rolls of a single die
41. Getting at least one 3 when rolling three fair dice
42. Getting at least one head when tossing six fair coins
43. Drawing at least one king when you draw a card from a standard deck 8 times (replacing the card each time you draw, so there are always 52 cards in the deck)
44. Drawing at least one king when you draw a card from a standard deck 20 times (replacing the card each time you draw, so there are always 52 cards in the deck)
45. Getting rain at least once in six days if the probability of rain on each single day is 0.2
46. Getting high winds at least once in 20 days if the probability of high winds on each single day is 0.1
47. Meeting at least one person with flu in 12 random encounters on campus when the infection rate is 4% (4 in 100 people have flu)
48. Meeting at least one left-handed person in eight random encounters on campus when the incidence rate is 11% (11 in 100 people are left-handed)
49. Getting at least one parking ticket in five occasions when you do not pay the parking meter, when the chances of getting a ticket when not paying are 0.3
50. Getting at least one false test for strep throat in five trials when the false report probability is 0.025

FURTHER APPLICATIONS

51. **Probability and Court.** The data in the following table show the outcomes of guilty and not-guilty pleas in 1028 criminal court cases.

	Guilty Plea	Not-Guilty Plea
Sent to prison	392	58
Not sent to prison	564	14

Source: Brereton and Casper, *Law and Society Review*, Vol. 16, No. 7.

a. What is the probability that a randomly selected defendant either pled guilty or was sent to prison?

b. What is the probability that a randomly selected defendant either pled not guilty or was not sent to prison?

52. **Testing a Drug.** A new cold medication was tested by giving 120 people the drug and 100 people a placebo. A control group consisted of 120 people who were given no treatment. The number of people in each group who showed improvement is shown in the table below.

	Cold Drug	Placebo	Control	Total
Improvement	70	55	40	165
No improvement	50	45	80	175
Total	120	100	120	340

a. What is the probability that a randomly selected person in the study either was given the placebo or was in the control group?

b. What is the probability that a randomly selected person either was given the drug or improved?

c. What is the probability that a randomly selected person was given the drug and improved?

d. What is the probability that a randomly selected person who improved was given the drug?

e. What is the probability that a randomly selected person who was given the drug improved?

f. Based on these data, does the drug appear to be effective? Explain.

53. **Polling Calls.** A telephone pollster has a list of names and telephone numbers for 45 voters, 20 of whom are listed as registered Democrats and 25 of whom are listed as registered Republicans. Calls are made in random order. Suppose you want to find the probability that the first two calls are to Republicans.

a. Are these independent or dependent events? Explain.

b. If you treat them as dependent events, what is the probability that the first two calls are to Republicans?

c. If you treat them as independent events, what is the probability that the first two calls are to Republicans?

d. Compare the results of parts b and c.

54. **Dominant and Recessive Genes.** Many traits are controlled by a dominant gene, **A**, and a recessive gene, **a**. A child gets two genes, one from each parent. Suppose a child's parents each have the gene combination **Aa**; that is, each parent is equally likely to pass either the **A** or the **a** gene to the child. Make a table showing the probability distribution for the child's possible gene combinations, which are **AA**, **Aa**, and **aa**. If the combinations **AA** and **Aa** both result in the same dominant trait (say, brown hair) and **aa** results in the recessive trait (say, blond hair), what is the probability that a child will have the dominant trait? What is the probability that the child will have the recessive trait?

55. **Better Bet for the Chevalier.** Suppose that the Chevalier de Mère had bet that he could roll a double-6 in 25 rolls, rather than 24. In that case, what would have been his probability of winning? Had he made this bet, would he still have lost over time? Explain.

56. **Lottery Odds.** The probability of a $2 winner in a particular state lottery is 1 in 10, the probability of a $5 winner is 1 in 50, and the probability of a $10 winner is 1 in 500.

a. What is the probability of getting either a $2, $5, or $10 winner? Compare to the probability of getting only a $2 winner.

b. If you buy 50 lottery tickets, what is the probability that you will get at least one $5 winner?

c. If you buy 500 lottery tickets, what is the probability that you will get at least one $10 winner?

57. **Miami Hurricanes.** Studies of the Florida Everglades show that, historically, the Miami region is hit by a hurricane about every 20 years.

a. Based on the historical record, what is the empirical probability that Miami will be hit by a hurricane next year?

b. What is the probability that Miami will be hit by hurricanes in two consecutive years?

c. What is the probability that Miami will be hit by at least one hurricane in the next 10 years?

58. **Sexually Transmitted Infections.** It is estimated that by age 24, one in three sexually active people will have a sexually transmitted infection (STI). Assume that 20% of the sexually active students on a particular campus have an STI.

a. If a student has ten sexual partners over a period of time, what is the probability that at least one of these partners is infected with an STI?

b. If a student has 20 different sexual partners over a period of time, what is the probability that at least one partner is infected with an STI?

WEB PROJECTS

59. **Lottery Chances.** Find a lottery Web site and study the probabilities of winning. Based on your findings, what is the probability of winning at least once if you play ten times? Explain any assumptions you make.

60. **HIV Probabilities.** Research the empirical probabilities of HIV among various groups in the population (for example, groups based on ethnicity, nationality, or sexual orientation). Based on your findings, discuss the relative dangers of sexual promiscuity within various populations.

IN YOUR WORLD

61. **Combined Probability in the News.** Find a recent news report in which two or more probabilities were combined in some way. Describe how and why they were combined.

62. **Combined Probability in Your Life.** Cite a recent situation or decision in your life that involved an *and* probability or an *either/or* probability. How did the probability affect the situation or decision?

UNIT 7C The Law of Large Numbers

If you toss a coin once, you cannot predict exactly how it will land; you can only state that the probability of a head is 0.5. If you toss the coin 100 times, you still cannot predict precisely how many heads will occur. However, you can reasonably expect to get heads *close to* 50% of the time. If you toss the coin 1000 times, you can expect the proportion of heads to be even closer to 50%. In general, the more times you toss the coin, the closer the percentage of heads will be to exactly 50%. While individual events may be unpredictable, large collections of events should show some pattern or regularity. This principle is called the **law of large numbers** (or the *law of averages*).

> **THE LAW OF LARGE NUMBERS**
>
> The **law of large numbers** applies to a process for which the probability of an event A is $P(A)$ and the results of repeated trials are independent. It states: *If the process is repeated over many trials, the proportion of the trials in which event A occurs will be close to the probability P(A). The larger the number of trials, the closer the proportion should be to P(A).*

We can illustrate the law of large numbers with a die rolling experiment. The probability of a 1 on a single roll is $P(1) = 1/6 \approx 0.167$. To avoid the tedium of rolling the die many times, we can use a computer to *simulate* random rolls of the die. Figure 7.7 shows a computer simulation of rolling a single die 5000 times. The horizontal axis gives the number of rolls, and the height of the curve gives the proportion of 1s. Although the curve bounces around when the number of rolls is small, the proportion of 1s approaches the probability 0.167, in agreement with the law of large numbers.

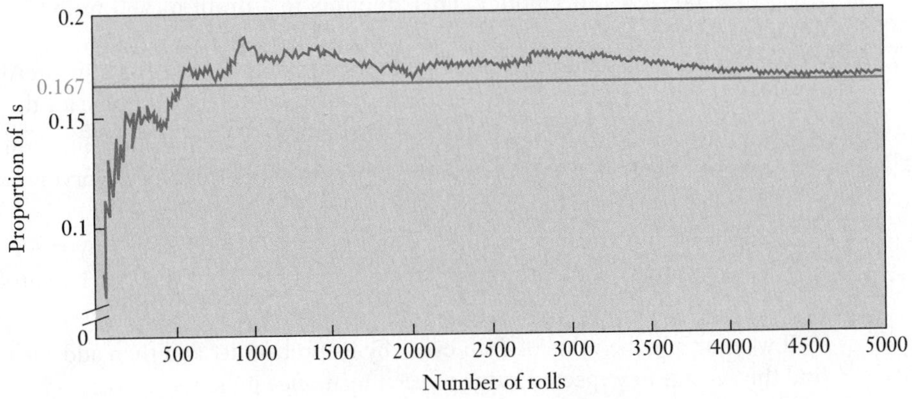

FIGURE 7.7 Results of computer simulation of rolling a die. As the number of rolls grows large, the proportion of 1s gets close to the probability of getting a 1 on a single roll, which is approximately 0.167.

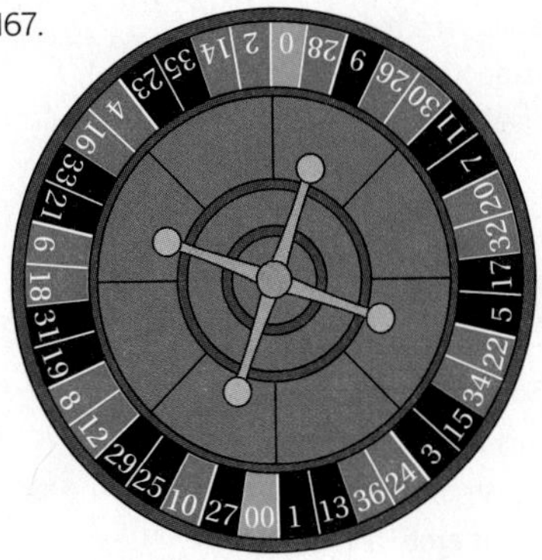

Example 1 Roulette

A roulette wheel has 38 numbers: 18 are black, 18 are red, and the numbers 0 and 00 are green.

a. What is the probability of getting a red number on any spin?

b. If patrons in a casino spin the wheel 100,000 times, how many times should you expect a red number?

Solution

a. There are 18 red numbers among 38 total, so the probability of red on a single spin is $18/38 \approx 0.474$.

Historical Note

The modern insurance industry's roots lie in statistical tables of birth and death data compiled by John Graunt in London in the 1660s. Those tables were further improved by Edmund Halley (the discoverer of Halley's Comet), and they led to a thriving insurance industry in London. In 1687, Edward Lloyd opened a coffee house in London that specialized in insuring almost all risks, including maritime travel and trade. Lloyd's of London remains a major insurer today.

b. The law of large numbers tells us that as the game is played more and more times, the proportion of times that the wheel comes up red should get closer to 0.474. Thus, in 100,000 tries, the wheel should come up red close to 47.4% of the time, or about 47,400 times.

Now try Exercises 13–14.

Expected Value

Suppose the InsureAll Company sells a special type of insurance that pays you \$100,000 in the event that you quit your job because of serious illness. Based on data from past claims, the empirical probability that a policyholder will make a claim for loss of job is 1 in 500. Should the insurance company expect to earn a profit if it sells the policies for \$250 each?

If InsureAll sells only a few policies, we cannot predict the profit or loss. For example, selling 100 policies for \$250 each generates revenue of $100 \times \$250 = \$25{,}000$. If none of the 100 policyholders files a claim, InsureAll makes a tidy profit. But if even one policyholder makes a \$100,000 claim, InsureAll faces a huge loss.

However, if InsureAll sells a large number of policies, the law of large numbers tells us that the proportion of policies for which claims must be paid should be very close to the 1 in 500 probability for a single policy. For example, if InsureAll sells 1 million policies, it should expect that the number of policyholders making the \$100,000 claim will be close to

$$\underbrace{1{,}000{,}000}_{\text{number of policies}} \times \underbrace{\frac{1}{500}}_{\substack{\text{probability of}\\ \$100{,}000\text{ claim}}} = 2000$$

Take Note

There is an alternative way to calculate expected value. In the insurance example, we could define Event 1 as a policy with no claim and Event 2 as a policy on which the company pays a \$100,000 claim. Event 1 has a value to the company of \$250 (the sales price of a policy) and a probability of 499/500. Event 2 has a value to the company of \$250 (the policy price) *minus* the \$100,000 paid out with a claim, or −\$99,750, and a probability of 1/500. Notice that this method still gives the same expected value of \$50:

$$\left(\$250 \times \frac{499}{500}\right) + \left(-\$99{,}750 \times \frac{1}{500}\right) = \$50$$

Some statisticians prefer this alternative method because the sum of the event probabilities is 1.

Paying these 2000 claims will cost

$$2000 \times \$100{,}000 = \$200 \text{ million}$$

This cost of \$200 million represents an *average* of \$200 for each of the 1 million policies. If the policies sell for \$250 each, InsureAll should expect to earn an average of $\$250 - \$200 = \$50$ per policy. This amounts to a profit of \$50 million on sales of 1 million policies.

We can find this same answer with a more formal procedure. The InsureAll example involves two distinct events, each with a particular *probability* and *value* for the company:

1. In the event that a person buys a policy, the value to the company is the \$250 price of the policy. The probability of this event is 1 because everyone who buys a policy pays the \$250.
2. In the event that a person files a claim, the value to the company is −\$100,000. It is negative because the company loses \$100,000 in this case. The probability of this event is 1/500.

If we multiply the value of each event by its probability and then add the results, we find the average or **expected value** of each insurance policy:

$$\text{expected value} = \underbrace{\$250}_{\text{value of policy sale}} \times \underbrace{1}_{\substack{\text{probability of}\\ \text{earning } \$250 \text{ on sale}}} + \underbrace{(-\$100{,}000)}_{\substack{\text{value of}\\ \text{claim}}} \times \underbrace{\frac{1}{500}}_{\substack{\text{probability of}\\ \text{paying claim}}}$$

$$= \$250 - \$200 = \$50$$

This expected profit of \$50 per policy is the same answer we found earlier. Keep in mind that this value is expected only if InsureAll sells enough policies for the law of large numbers to come into play.

Time Out to Think

Should InsureAll expect to see a profit of \$50 on each individual policy? Should it expect a profit of \$50,000 on 1000 policies? Explain.

EXPECTED VALUE

Consider two events, each with its own value and probability. The **expected value** is

$$\text{expected value} = \begin{pmatrix}\text{event 1}\\ \text{value}\end{pmatrix} \times \begin{pmatrix}\text{event 1}\\ \text{probability}\end{pmatrix} + \begin{pmatrix}\text{event 2}\\ \text{value}\end{pmatrix} \times \begin{pmatrix}\text{event 2}\\ \text{probability}\end{pmatrix}$$

This formula can be extended to any number of events by including more terms in the sum.

Historical Note

The French mathematician and philosopher Blaise Pascal used expected value to argue for believing in God. He used p to represent the probability that God exists, and then assigned values for the consequences of believing and not believing in God. He claimed that the consequence of not believing in God in the case that God actually exists is infinitely bad (negative), which led him to conclude that no matter how small p might be, the expected value of believing in God is positive and the expected value of not believing in God is infinitely negative. Of course, other philosophers have disputed Pascal's analysis.

Example 2 Lottery Expectations

Suppose that \$1 lottery tickets have the following probabilities: 1 in 5 to win a free ticket (worth \$1), 1 in 100 to win \$5, 1 in 100,000 to win \$1000, and 1 in 10 million to win \$1 million. What is the expected value of a lottery ticket? Discuss the implications. (Note: Winners do *not* get back the \$1 they spend on the ticket.)

Solution The easiest way to proceed is to make a table of all the relevant events with their values and probabilities. We are calculating the expected value of a lottery ticket to *you*, so the ticket price has a negative value (it costs you money) while the values of winnings are positive.

Event	Value	Probability	Value × Probability
Ticket purchase	−\$1	1	$-\$1 \times 1 = -\$1$
Win free ticket	\$1	$\frac{1}{5}$	$\$1 \times \frac{1}{5} = \$0.20$
Win \$5	\$5	$\frac{1}{100}$	$\$5 \times \frac{1}{100} = \$0.05$
Win \$1000	\$1000	$\frac{1}{100{,}000}$	$\$1000 \times \frac{1}{100{,}000} = \$0.01$
Win \$1 million	\$1,000,000	$\frac{1}{10{,}000{,}000}$	$\$1{,}000{,}000 \times \frac{1}{10{,}000{,}000} = \$0.10$
			Sum: −\$0.64

The expected value is the sum of all the products *value* × *probability*, which the table shows to be −\$0.64. Therefore, averaged over many tickets, you should expect to lose 64¢ for each \$1 lottery ticket that you buy. If you buy, say, 1000 tickets, you should expect to *lose* about 1000 × \$0.64 = \$640. **Now try Exercises 15–18.**

Time Out to Think

Many states use lotteries to finance worthy causes such as parks, recreation, and education. Lotteries also tend to keep state taxes at lower levels. On the other hand, research shows that lotteries are played primarily by people with low incomes. Do you think lotteries are good social policy? Do you think lotteries are good economic policy?

DILBERT reprinted by permission of United Feature Syndicate, Inc.

BY THE WAY

As of 2009, the highest price ever paid at auction for a painting was $135 million for Gustav Klimt's 1907 portrait *Adele Bloch-Bauer I.*

Example 3 Art Auction

You are at an art auction, trying to decide whether to bid $50,000 for a particular painting. You believe that you have a 1/2 probability of reselling the painting to a client in New York for $70,000 and a 1/4 probability of reselling the painting to a client in San Francisco for $80,000. Otherwise, you will have to keep the painting—an option that has benefits, but not monetary ones. What is the expected value of a $50,000 bid?

Solution There are three relevant events to consider:

- With probability 1, you will pay $50,000 to buy the painting. This option represents a monetary loss to you, so it has a negative value.
- With probability 1/2, you will sell the painting for $70,000. This option is a gain, so it has a positive value.
- With probability 1/4, you will sell the painting for $80,000. This option is also a gain, so it has a positive value.

Therefore, the expected value of a $50,000 bid is

$$\begin{aligned}\text{expected value} &= \begin{pmatrix}\text{value of}\\ \text{event 1}\end{pmatrix} \times \begin{pmatrix}\text{prob of}\\ \text{event 1}\end{pmatrix} + \begin{pmatrix}\text{value of}\\ \text{event 2}\end{pmatrix} \times \begin{pmatrix}\text{prob of}\\ \text{event 2}\end{pmatrix}\\ &\quad + \begin{pmatrix}\text{value of}\\ \text{event 3}\end{pmatrix} \times \begin{pmatrix}\text{prob of}\\ \text{event 3}\end{pmatrix}\\ &= (-\$50{,}000 \times 1) + \left(\$70{,}000 \times \frac{1}{2}\right) + \left(\$80{,}000 \times \frac{1}{4}\right)\\ &= -\$50{,}000 + \$35{,}000 + \$20{,}000 = \$5000\end{aligned}$$

With a $50,000 bid, you could expect to gain $5000 by the purchase. It's important to remember that expected value refers to expected gain or loss over *many* such purchases. If this is your only purchase, it might be better to reconsider or to assign a high value to admiring the painting in your own house! **Now try Exercises 19–22.**

The Gambler's Fallacy

Consider a simple game involving a coin toss: You win $1 if the coin lands heads and you lose $1 if it lands tails. Now, suppose you toss the coin 100 times and get 45 heads and 55 tails, putting you $10 in the hole. Are you "due" for a streak of better luck?

You probably recognize that the answer is *no*. Each coin toss is independent of previous tosses, so your past bad luck has no bearing on your future chances. However, many gamblers—especially compulsive gamblers—guess just the opposite. They believe that when their luck has been bad, it's due for a change. This mistaken belief is often called the **gambler's fallacy** (or the *gambler's ruin*).

The value of our expectations always signifies something in the middle between the best we can hope for and the worst we can fear.

—Jacob Bernoulli, 17th-century mathematician

DEFINITION

The **gambler's fallacy** is the mistaken belief that a streak of bad luck makes a person "due" for a streak of good luck.

Time Out to Think

A farmer knows that at this time of year in his part of the country, the probability of rain on a given day is 0.5. It hasn't rained in 10 days and he needs to decide whether to start irrigating. Is he justified in postponing irrigation because he is due for a rainy day? Explain.

One reason people succumb to the gambler's fallacy is a misunderstanding of the law of large numbers. In our coin toss game, the law of large numbers tells us that the proportion of heads tends to be closer to 50% for larger numbers of games. But this does *not* mean that you are likely to recover early losses. The following example shows why.

Historical Note

One of the most famous compulsive gamblers in history was the Russian writer Fyodor Dostoyevsky. He played at roulette throughout Europe in the 19th century. He once reported that he "won 10,000 francs at first, . . . but I got carried away and dropped half my winnings." His experience with gambling formed the basis of his work *The Gambler.*

Example 4 Continued Losses

You are playing the coin toss game, in which you win \$1 for heads and lose \$1 for tails. After 100 tosses, you are \$10 in the hole because you have 45 heads and 55 tails. You continue playing until you've tossed the coin 1000 times, at which point you've gotten 480 heads and 520 tails. Does the result agree with what we expect from the law of large numbers? Have you gained back any of your losses? Explain.

Solution The proportion of heads in your first 100 tosses was 45%. After 1000 tosses, the proportion of heads has increased to 480 out of 1000, or 48%. This agrees with the law of large numbers, because the proportion grew closer to 50%. However, you've now won \$480 for the 480 heads while losing \$520 for the 520 tails, for a net loss of \$40. In other words, your losses have actually *increased* from \$10 to \$40, despite the fact that the proportion of heads grew closer to 50%. **Now try Exercises 23–25.**

Streaks

Another common misunderstanding that contributes to the gambler's fallacy involves expectations about streaks. Suppose you toss a coin six times and see the outcomes HHHHHH (all heads). Then you toss it six more times and see the outcomes HTTHTH. Most people would say that the latter outcome is "natural" while the streak of all heads is surprising. However, both outcomes are equally likely. In fact, all possible sets of six outcomes are equally likely: The probability of any *single* particular outcome is 1/2, so all sets of six particular outcomes have the same probability of $(1/2)^6 = 1/64$.

Example 5 Hot Hand at the Craps Table

The popular casino game of craps involves rolling dice. Suppose you are playing craps and suddenly find yourself with a "hot hand": You roll a winner on ten consecutive bets. Is your hand really "hot"? Should you increase your bet because you are on a hot streak? Assume that you are making bets with a 0.486 probability of winning on a single play (the best odds available in craps).

Solution First, let's consider the chance of winning ten times in a row. With a probability of 0.486 on a single play, the chance of ten straight wins is

$$(0.486)^{10} \approx 0.000735$$

Your streak of ten straight wins has a probability of only about 7 in 10,000, which might make you think that your hand really is "hot." However, look around the casino. If it is a large casino, several hundred people may be playing at the craps tables, and there may be *tens of thousands* of individual rolls each night. It is almost inevitable that someone will have a "hot streak" of ten straight wins. Indeed, even longer hot streaks are likely during any given night. Your apparent "hot hand" is a mere coincidence and your probability of winning on your next bet is still only 0.486. Increasing your bet based on a mere coincidence would be foolish. **Now try Exercises 26–28.**

Luck is a mighty queer thing. All you know about it for certain is that it's bound to change.

—Bret Harte, *The Outcasts of Poker Flat*

The House Edge

A casino makes money because games are set up so that the expected earnings of patrons are negative (that is, losses). Because the casino earns whatever patrons lose, the casino's earnings are positive. The amount that the casino, or *house*, can expect to earn per dollar bet is called the **house edge**. That is, the house edge is the expected value *to the casino* of a particular bet.

The house edge varies from game to game. It tends to be greatest in games where big winnings are possible, such as slot machines. It tends to be least in games where strategy can improve your odds, such as blackjack. But the house edge is always present, and gamblers who believe they can beat the house regularly are sadly succumbing to the gambler's fallacy.

Example 6 The House Edge in Roulette

The game of roulette is usually set up so that betting on red is a 1 to 1 bet. That is, you win the same amount of money as you bet if red comes up. Betting on a single number is a 35 to 1 bet. That is, you win 35 times as much as you bet if your number comes up. What is the house edge in each of these two cases? If patrons wager \$1 million on such bets, how much should the casino expect to earn?

Solution For each case, the house edge is the casino's expected earnings on the bet. The probability of red is 18/38 (see Example 1), so the probability of not red is 20/38. Let's call the *value* of red for the casino −\$1, indicating that the casino pays the amount of the patron's bet when red comes up. The value of not red for the casino is \$1, because it wins the patron's bet if red does not come up. The house edge when patrons bet on red is

$$\Big(\underbrace{\$1}_{\text{value to casino of not red}} \times \underbrace{\frac{20}{38}}_{\text{probability of not red}}\Big) + \Big(\underbrace{-\$1}_{\text{value to casino of red}} \times \underbrace{\frac{18}{38}}_{\text{probability of red}}\Big) \approx \$0.053$$

That is, the casino can expect to gain \$0.053 per dollar gambled. If patrons bet \$1 million on red, the casino can expect to earn about \$1 million × 0.053 = \$53,000.

The probability of winning a bet on a single number is 1/38 because there are 38 numbers on the roulette wheel. The 35 to 1 payoff offered by the casino on this bet means the casino pays the patron 35 times the amount of the bet, so its value to the casino is −\$35. The probability that the bet does not win is 37/38. The casino gains the patron's bet in this case, so its value is \$1. The house edge when patrons bet on a single number is

$$\Big(\underbrace{\$1}_{\text{value to casino of not hitting the number}} \times \underbrace{\frac{37}{38}}_{\text{probability of not hitting the number}}\Big) + \Big(\underbrace{-\$35}_{\text{value to casino of hitting the number}} \times \underbrace{\frac{1}{38}}_{\text{probability of hitting the number}}\Big) \approx \$0.053$$

This is the same house edge as for the red bet. Again, if patrons bet \$1 million on single numbers, the house can expect to win \$53,000. **Now try Exercises 29–30.**

Time Out to Think

Given the house edge, is it possible for a casino to lose money on its gambling results alone? Explain.

QUICK QUIZ

Choose the best answer to each of the following questions. Explain your reasoning with one or more complete sentences.

1. Suppose that the probability of a hurricane striking Florida in any single year is 1 in 10, and that this probability has been the same for the past 1000 years. Which of the following is implied by the law of large numbers?

   a. If no hurricanes have hit Florida in the past 10 years, then the probability of a hurricane hitting next year is greater than 0.1.

   b. Florida has been hit by close to (but not necessarily exactly) 100 hurricanes in the past 1000 years.

   c. Florida has been hit by exactly 100 hurricanes in the past 1000 years.

2. Consider a lottery with 100 million tickets in which each ticket has a unique number. Each ticket sold for \$1, and one ticket is drawn for a single prize of \$75 million (and no other prizes). The expected value of a single ticket is

   a. \$1. b. \$75. c. −\$0.25.

3. Consider the lottery described in Exercise 2. If you were to spend \$1 million to purchase 1 million lottery tickets, the most likely result would be that

   a. you would be the lottery winner.

   b. you would win back \$750,000 of your \$1 million.

   c. you would lose your entire \$1 million.

4. You are betting on a game in which each bet has an expected value of −\$0.33. This means that

   a. you will win 33 cents every time you play.

   b. you will lose 33 cents every time you play.

   c. if you play the game many times, on average you will have lost about 33 cents per game.

5. An insurance company knows that the average cost to build a home in a new California subdivision is \$100,000, and that in any particular year there is a 1 in 50 chance of a wildfire destroying all the homes in the subdivision. Based on these data and assuming the insurance company wants a positive expected value when it sells policies, what is the minimum that the company must charge for fire insurance policies in this subdivision?

   a. \$50 per year b. \$2000 per year

   c. \$100,000 per year

6. You know a shortcut to work that uses side streets instead of the freeway. Most of the time, the shortcut takes 5 minutes off the driving time by freeway. However, about once in every ten trips, an accident blocks traffic on the shortcut, with the result that the trip takes 20 minutes longer than it would by freeway. In terms of the amount of time the shortcut saves, what is the expected value of the shortcut?

   a. (5 minutes × 0.9) + (−20 minutes × 0.1)

   b. (5 minutes × 0.1) + (−25 minutes × 0.1)

   c. 5 minutes

7. Cameron is betting on a game in which the probability of winning is 1 in 5. He's lost five games in a row, so he decides to double his bet on the sixth game. This strategy shows

   a. good logic, since he's due for a win.

   b. good logic, because he's more likely to win when the bet is larger.

   c. poor logic, as he has an 80% chance of losing the double bet.

8. Cameron is betting on a game in which the probability of winning is 1 in 5. He's *won* five games in a row, so he decides to double his bet on the sixth game. This strategy shows

   a. good logic, since he's having a good day and will probably win again.

   b. poor logic, because on such a good day he should bet much more.

   c. poor logic, as he has an 80% chance of losing the double bet.

9. A \$1 slot machine at a casino is set so that it returns 97% of all the money put into it in the form of winnings, with most of the winnings in the form of huge but low-probability jackpots. What is your probability of winning when you put \$1 in this slot machine?

   a. 0.03 b. 0.97

   c. It cannot be calculated from the given data, but it is certainly quite low.

10. Consider the slot machine described in Exercise 9. Which statement is *true* if patrons have deposited \$10 million into this slot machine?

    a. 97% of the patrons have been winners.

    b. 3% of the patrons have been winners.

    c. The casino's profit has been close to \$300,000.

Exercises 7C

REVIEW QUESTIONS

1. Explain the meaning of the law of large numbers. Does this law say anything about what will happen in a single observation or experiment? Why or why not?
2. In 10 tosses of a fair coin, should you be surprised to see 6 heads? In 1000 tosses of a fair coin, should you be surprised to see 600 heads? Explain in terms of the law of large numbers.
3. What is an expected value, and how is it computed? Should we always expect to get the expected value? Why or why not?
4. What is the gambler's fallacy? Give an example.

5. Explain why the probability is the same for any particular set of ten coin toss outcomes. How does this idea affect our thinking about streaks?

6. What is the house edge in gambling? Explain how it virtually guarantees that a casino will win more money than it loses.

DOES IT MAKE SENSE?

Decide whether each of the following statements makes sense (or is clearly true) or does not make sense (or is clearly false). Explain your reasoning.

7. The expected value to me of each raffle ticket I purchased is −$0.85.

8. The expected value of each insurance policy our company sells is $150, so if we sell 10 more policies our profits will increase by $1500.

9. If you toss a coin four times, it's much more likely to land in the order HTHT than HHHH. (H stands for heads and T for tails.)

10. I haven't won in my last 25 pulls on the slot machine, so I'm due to win on the next pull.

11. I haven't won in my last 25 pulls on the slot machine, so I must be having a bad day and I'm sure to lose if I play again.

12. I've lost $750 so far today on roulette. I'm going to play a little longer so that I can reduce my losses to $500.

BASIC SKILLS & CONCEPTS

13. **Understanding the Law of Large Numbers.** Suppose you toss a fair coin 10,000 times. Should you expect to get exactly 5000 heads? Why or why not? What does the law of large numbers tell you about the results you are likely to get?

14. **Speedy Driver.** Suppose a person who has a habit of driving fast has never had a traffic citation. What does it mean to say that "the law of averages [large numbers] will catch up with him"? Is it true? Explain.

15–18: Expected Value in Games. Find the expected value (to you) of the described game. Would you expect to win or lose money in 1 game? in 100 games? Explain.

15. You are given 5 to 1 odds against tossing three heads with three coins, meaning you win $5 if you succeed and you lose $1 if you fail.

16. You are given 9 to 1 odds against tossing three heads with three coins, meaning you win $9 if you succeed and you lose $1 if you fail.

17. You are given 2 to 1 odds against rolling two even numbers with the roll of two fair dice, meaning you win $2 if you succeed and you lose $1 if you fail.

18. You are given 8 to 1 odds against rolling a double number (for example, two 1s or two 2s) with the roll of two fair dice, meaning you win $8 if you succeed and you lose $1 if you fail.

19–20: Insurance Claims. Find the expected value (to the company) per policy sold. If the company sells 10,000 policies, what is the expected profit or loss? Explain.

19. An insurance policy sells for $900. Based on past data, an average of 1 in 50 policyholders will file a $10,000 claim, an average of 1 in 100 policyholders will file a $25,000 claim, and an average of 1 in 250 policyholders will file a $60,000 claim.

20. An insurance policy sells for $500. Based on past data, an average of 1 in 50 policyholders will file a $5000 claim, an average of 1 in 100 policyholders will file a $10,000 claim, and an average of 1 in 200 policyholders will file a $30,000 claim.

21. **Expected Wait.** Suppose you arrive at a bus stop randomly, so all arrival times are equally likely. The bus arrives regularly every 30 minutes without delay (say, on the hour and on the half hour). What is the expected value of your waiting time? Explain.

22. **Expected Wait.** A bus arrives at a bus stop at noon, 12:20, and 1:00. You arrive at the bus stop at random times between noon and 1:00 every day, so all arrival times are equally likely.

a. What is the probability that you will arrive at the bus stop between noon and 12:20? What is your mean waiting time in that case? (Exercise 21 may be helpful.)

b. What is the probability that you will arrive at the bus stop between 12:20 and 1:00? What is your mean waiting time in that case?

c. Overall, what is your expected waiting time for the bus?

d. Would your expected waiting time be longer or shorter if the bus arrived at equally spaced intervals (say, noon, 12:30, 1:00)? Explain.

23. **Gambler's Fallacy and Coins.** Suppose you play a coin toss game in which you win $1 if a head appears and lose $1 if a tail appears. In the first 100 coin tosses, heads comes up 46 times and tails comes up 54 times.

a. What percentage of times has heads come up in the first 100 tosses? What is your net gain or loss at this point?

b. Suppose you toss the coin 200 more times (a total of 300 tosses), and at that point heads has come up 47% of the time. Is this increase in the percentage of heads consistent with the law of large numbers? Explain. What is your net gain or loss at this point?

c. How many heads would you need in the next 100 tosses in order to break even after 400 tosses? Is this likely to occur?

d. Suppose that, still behind after 400 tosses, you decide to keep playing because you are "due" for a winning streak. Explain how this belief would illustrate the gambler's fallacy.

24. **Gambler's Fallacy and Dice.** Suppose you roll a die with the following rules: You win $1 if the die comes up with an even number and you lose $1 if it comes up odd.

a. Suppose you get 45 even numbers in your first 100 rolls. How much money have you won or lost?

b. On the second 100 rolls, your luck improves and you roll 47 even numbers. How much money have you won or lost over 200 rolls?

c. Your luck continues to improve, and you roll 148 even numbers in your next 300 rolls. How much money have you won or lost over your total of 500 rolls?

d. How many even numbers would you have to roll in the next 100 rolls to break even? Is this likely? Explain.

e. What were the percentages of even numbers after 100, 200, and 500 rolls? Explain how this illustrates the law of large numbers, even while your losses increased.

25. **Can You Catch Up?** Suppose you toss a fair coin 100 times, getting 42 heads and 58 tails, which is 16 more tails than heads.

a. Explain why, on your next toss, the *difference* between the numbers of heads and tails is as likely to grow to 17 as it is to shrink to 15.

b. Extend your explanation from part a to explain why, if you toss the coin 1000 more times, the final difference between the numbers of heads and tails is as likely to be larger than 16 as it is to be smaller than 16.

c. Suppose you are betting on heads with each coin toss. After the first 100 tosses, you are well on the losing side. Explain why, if you continue to bet, you will most likely remain on the losing side. How is this answer related to the gambler's fallacy?

26. **Lottery Draw.** Consider a lottery game in which six balls are drawn randomly from a set of balls numbered 1 through 42. One week, the winning combination consists of balls numbered 21, 4, 17, 33, 40, and 9. The next week, the winning balls are numbered 1, 2, 3, 4, 5, and 6. Is the second winning set more or less likely than or just as likely as the first? Explain.

27. **Coin Streak.** You toss a coin 1000 times and record the results. You then look through your results and find that at one point you got heads ten times in a row. What is the probability of getting heads ten times in ten tosses? Should you be surprised to find this "streak" in your set of 1000 tosses? Explain.

28. **Hot Batter.** You play softball and have a batting average of .333, meaning you average 1 hit in every 3 times at bat. During your 25-game season, you have one game in which you get a hit all three times you bat. Do you think you were "hot" that day, or was it just luck? Explain your reasoning.

29. **House Edge in Blackjack.** In a large casino, the house wins on its blackjack tables with a probability of 50.7%. All bets at blackjack are 1 to 1: If you win, you gain the amount you bet; if you lose, you lose the amount you bet.

a. If you bet $1 on each hand, what is the expected value to you of a single game? What is the house edge?

b. If you played 100 games of blackjack in an evening, betting $1 on each hand, how much should you expect to win or lose? Explain.

c. If you played 100 games of blackjack in an evening, betting $5 on each hand, how much should you expect to win or lose? Explain.

d. If patrons bet $1,000,000 on blackjack in one evening, how much should the casino expect to earn? Explain.

30. **Profitable Casino.** Averaged over all games and all bets being played, the house edge of a particular casino is 0.06, or 6¢ per dollar gambled. If a total of $100 million is wagered in the casino over the course of a year, what is the casino's total profit? Explain.

FURTHER APPLICATIONS

31–32: Powerball. The table below gives recent prizes and probabilities of winning (on a single $1 ticket) for the Multi-State Powerball lottery. Find the expected value of the winnings for a single lottery ticket, given the following grand prizes. Then state how much you can expect to win or lose if you spend $365 per year on the lottery. Briefly discuss your results.

Prize	Probability
Grand Prize	1 in 195,249,054
$200,000	1 in 5,138,133
$10,000	1 in 723,145
$100	1 in 19,030
$100	1 in 13,644
$7	1 in 359
$7	1 in 787
$4	1 in 23
$3	1 in 62

31. The grand prize is $30 million.

32. The grand prize is $10 million.

33–34: Mega Millions. The table below gives recent prizes and probabilities of winning (on a single $1 ticket) for the Mega Millions lottery. Find the expected value of the winnings for a single lottery ticket, given the following jackpots. Then state how much you can expect to win or lose if you spend $365 per year on the lottery. Briefly discuss your results.

Prize	Probability
Jackpot	1 in 175,711,536
$250,000	1 in 3,904,701
$10,000	1 in 689,065
$150	1 in 15,313
$150	1 in 13,781
$10	1 in 844
$7	1 in 306
$3	1 in 141
$2	1 in 75

33. The jackpot is $5 million.

34. The jackpot is $20 million.

35. **Extra Points in Football.** Football teams have the option of trying to score either 1 or 2 extra points after a touchdown. They can get 1 point by kicking the ball through the goal posts or 2 points by running or passing the ball across the goal line. In the NFL in 2008, 1-point kicks were successful 96% of the time, while 2-point attempts were successful only 49% of the time. In either case, failure means zero points. Calculate the expected values of the 1-point and 2-point attempts (separately). Based on these expected values, which option makes more sense in most cases? Explain.

36. **Roulette.** When you bet $5 on the number 7 in roulette at a typical casino, you have a 37/38 probability of losing $5 and a 1/38 probability of making a net gain of $175 (after paying your bet). If you bet $5 on an odd number, the probability of losing $5 is 20/38 and the probability of a net gain of $5 is 18/38.

    a. What is the expected value of betting $5 on the number 7?

    b. What is the expected value of betting $5 on an odd number?

    c. Which is the best option: bet on 7, bet on an odd number, or don't bet?

37. **Household Size.** It is estimated that 57% of Americans live in households with 1 or 2 people, 32% live in households with 3 or 4 people, and 11% live in households with 5 or more people. Using 1.5 for the expected number of people in households with 1 or 2 people, 3.5 for households with 3 or 4 people, and 6 for households of 5 or more people, find the expected number of people in an American household. How is this related to the mean household size?

38. **Psychology of Expected Values.** In 1953, French economist Maurice Allais studied how people assess risk. Here are two survey questions that he used:

    Decision 1

    Option A: 100% chance of gaining $1,000,000

    Option B: 10% chance of gaining $2,500,000; 89% chance of gaining $1,000,000; and 1% chance of gaining nothing

    Decision 2

    Option A: 11% chance of gaining $1,000,000 and 89% chance of gaining nothing

    Option B: 10% chance of gaining $2,500,000 and 90% chance of gaining nothing

    Allais discovered that for decision 1, most people chose option A, while for decision 2, most people chose option B.

    a. For each decision, find the expected value of each option.

    b. Are the responses given in the surveys consistent with the expected values?

    c. Give a possible explanation for the responses in Allais's surveys.

WEB PROJECTS

39. **Lotteries.** Go to the Web site for all U.S. lotteries and study the summary of state and multi-state lottery odds and prizes. Pick five lotteries and determine the expected value for winnings in each case. Discuss your results.

40. **The Morality of Gambling.** Republican Senator Richard Lugar attacked state-supported lotteries and the trend toward increasing legalization of gambling, saying "the spread of gambling is a measure of the moral erosion taking place in our country. . . . It says that if you play enough, you can hit the jackpot and be freed from the discipline of self-support through a job or the long commitment to ongoing education." Do a Web search on "gambling and morality" to find other opinions on this issue. Write a short summary of your findings and your own opinion, which you should defend clearly.

IN YOUR WORLD

41. **Law of Large Numbers.** Describe a news story in which the law of large numbers is mentioned. Is the term used in an accurate way? Explain.

42. **Personal Law of Large Numbers.** Describe a situation in which you personally have made use of the law of large numbers, either correctly or incorrectly. Why did you use the law of large numbers in this situation? Was it helpful?

43. **The Gambler's Fallacy.** Describe a situation in which you or someone you know has fallen victim to the gambler's fallacy. How should the situation have been dealt with?

UNIT 7D Assessing Risk

A smooth-talking but honest salesman comes to you, offering a new product:

> *I can't reveal the details yet, but you will love this product! It will improve your life in more ways than you can count. Its only downside is that it will eventually kill everyone who uses it. Will you buy one?*

Not likely! After all, could any product be so great that you would die for it? A few weeks later, the salesman shows up again:

> *No one was buying, so we've made some improvements. Your chance of being killed by the product is now only 1 in 10. Ready to buy?*

Despite the improvement, most people still would send the salesman home and wait for his inevitable return:

> *Okay, this time we've really perfected it. We've made it so safe that it would take 20 years for it to kill as many people as live in San Francisco. And it can be yours for a mere $20,000.*

You may be surprised to realize that, if you are like most Americans, you'll jump at this offer. The product is, after all, the automobile. It does indeed improve our lives in many ways, and $20,000 is a fairly typical price. And, given that roughly 40,000 Americans are killed in auto accidents each year, it kills the equivalent of the population of San Francisco (roughly 800,000) in about 20 years.

As this example shows, we continually make tradeoffs between benefits and risks. In this unit, we'll see how ideas of probability can help us quantify risk, thereby allowing us to make informed decisions about such tradeoffs.

The cost of living is going up and the chance of living is going down.

—Flip Wilson, comedian

BY THE WAY

Roughly 110 people die in automobile accidents per day in the United States, or 1 every 13 minutes. Automobile accidents are the leading cause of death in all age groups between 6 and 27. Vehicle occupants account for 85% of automobile fatalities, while pedestrians and cyclists account for 15%

Risk and Travel

Are you safer in a small car or a sport utility vehicle? Are cars today safer than those 30 years ago? If you need to travel across country, are you safer flying or driving? To answer these and many similar questions, we must quantify the risk involved in travel. We can then make decisions appropriate for our own personal circumstances.

Travel risk is often expressed in terms of an **accident rate** or **death rate**. For example, suppose an annual accident rate is 750 accidents per 100,000 people. This means that, within a group of 100,000 people, on average 750 will have an accident over the period of a year. The statement also gives an empirical probability: It says that the probability of a person being involved in an accident is 750 in 100,000, or 0.0075.

However, caution is needed in working with accident and death rates. For example, travel risks are sometimes stated *per 100,000 people*, as above, but other times they are stated *per trip* or *per mile*. If we use death rates *per trip* to compare the risks of flying and driving, we neglect the fact that airplane trips are typically much longer than automobile trips. Similarly, if we use accident rates *per person*, we neglect the fact that most automobile accidents involve only minor injuries.

Example 1 Is Driving Getting Safer?

Figure 7.8 shows the number of automobile fatalities and the total number of miles driven (among all Americans) per year from 1970 to 2008. In terms of *death rate per mile driven*, compare 1970 (approximately 52,600 deaths and 1.1 trillion miles driven) with 2008 (approximately 37,300 deaths and 2.9 trillion miles driven). Comment on how the risk of driving has changed.

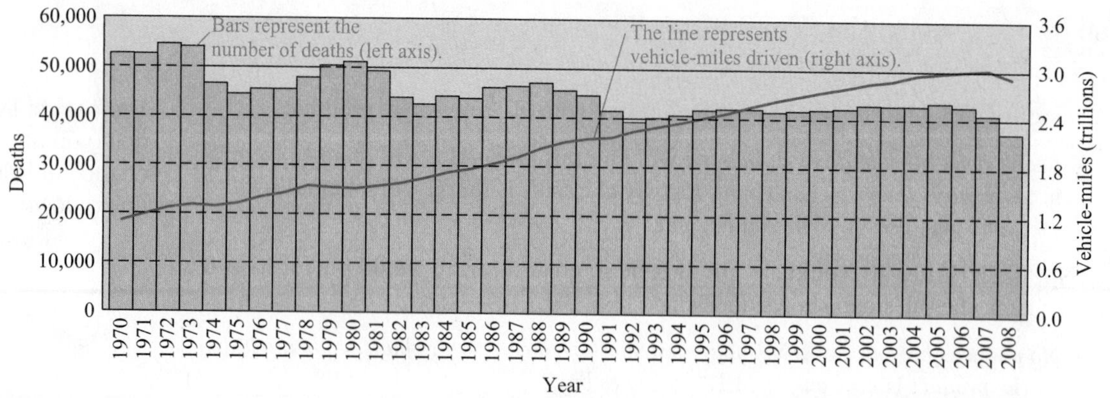

FIGURE 7.8 This graph shows the annual number of deaths (bars) and the annual number of vehicle-miles driven (line) in the United States from 1970 to 2008.
Source: National Transportation Safety Board.

Solution We start by comparing the approximate death rates per mile for 1970 and 2008:

1970: $\dfrac{52{,}600 \text{ deaths}}{1.1 \times 10^{12} \text{miles}} \approx 4.8 \times 10^{-8} \text{ death per mile}$

2008: $\dfrac{37{,}300 \text{ deaths}}{2.9 \times 10^{12} \text{ miles}} \approx 1.3 \times 10^{-8} \text{ death per mile}$

Note that, because $10^8 = 100$ million, 4.8×10^{-8} death per mile is equivalent to 4.8 deaths per 100 million miles. We conclude that, over 38 years, the death rate per 100 million miles dropped from 4.8 to 1.3. By this measure, driving became much safer over the period. Most researchers believe the improvements resulted from better automobile design and from safety features, such as shoulder belts and air bags, that are much more common today. **Now try Exercises 9–12.**

Example 2 Which Is Safer: Flying or Driving?

For the period 1989–2008, the average (mean) number of deaths in commercial airplane accidents in the United States was roughly 60 per year. (The actual number varied significantly from year to year.) As of 2008, airplane passengers in the United States traveled a total of about 8 billion miles per year. Use these numbers to calculate the death rate per mile of air travel. Compare the risk of flying to the risk of driving.

Solution Assuming 60 deaths and 8 billion miles in an average year, the risk of air travel is

$$\frac{60 \text{ deaths}}{8 \times 10^9 \text{ miles}} \approx 0.75 \times 10^{-8} \text{ death per mile}$$

This risk of about 0.75 death per 100 million miles is a little more than half the risk of 1.3 deaths per 100 million miles for driving. Note that, because the average air trip covers a considerably longer distance than the average driving trip, the risk *per trip* is higher for air travel, although the risk *per mile* is lower. **Now try Exercises 13–14.**

Time Out to Think

What other measures might be used to compare the risks of driving and flying? Is there a measure of risk for which flying would appear safer than driving? Overall, do you think it is fair to say that flying is safer than driving?

TABLE 7.4 Leading Causes of Death in the United States (2006)

Cause	Deaths	Cause	Deaths
Heart disease	631,636	Diabetes	72,449
Cancer	559,888	Alzheimer's disease	72,432
Stroke	137,199	Pneumonia/Influenza	56,326
Pulmonary diseases	124,583	Kidney disease	45,344
Accidents	121,599	Septicemia (blood poisoning)	34,234

Source: Centers for Disease Control and Prevention

Vital Statistics

Data concerning births and deaths of citizens, often called *vital statistics*, are important to understanding risk-benefit tradeoffs. For example, insurance companies use vital statistics to assess risks and set rates. Health professionals study vital statistics to assess medical progress and decide where research resources should be concentrated. Demographers use birth and death rates to predict future population trends.

One important set of vital statistics, shown in Table 7.4, concerns causes of death. A more complete table would categorize data by age, sex, and race. In addition, vital statistics are often expressed in terms of deaths per person or per 100,000 people, which makes it easier to compare the rates for different years and for different states or countries.

BY THE WAY

For college-age students, alcohol consumption presents one of the most serious health risks. According to a report from the National Institutes of Health, each year drinking contributes to 1400 deaths among college students (many of these through car crashes in which alcohol was a factor), as well as 500,000 injuries and 70,000 cases of sexual assault.

Example 3 Interpreting Vital Statistics

Assuming a U.S. population of 300 million, find and compare risks per person and per 100,000 people for pneumonia/influenza and cancer.

Solution We find the risk per person by dividing the number of deaths by the total population of 300 million:

$$\textit{Pneumonia/Influenza:} \quad \frac{56{,}326 \text{ deaths}}{300{,}000{,}000 \text{ people}} \approx 0.00019 \text{ death per person}$$

$$\textit{Cancer:} \quad \frac{559{,}888 \text{ deaths}}{300{,}000{,}000 \text{ people}} \approx 0.0019 \text{ death per person}$$

We can convert these numbers to deaths per 100,000 people by multiplying the per person rates by 100,000. We find that the pneumonia/influenza death rate is about 19 per 100,000 people, while the cancer death rate is about 190 per 100,000 people. These numbers can be interpreted as empirical probabilities, so we conclude that the probability of death by cancer is about 10 times that of death by pneumonia/influenza.

Now try Exercises 15–20.

Time Out to Think

Table 7.4 suggests that the probability of death by stroke is higher than the probability of death by accident, but these data include all age groups. How do you think the risks of stroke and accident would differ between young people and old people? Explain.

Life Expectancy

One of the most commonly cited vital statistics is *life expectancy*, which is often used to compare overall health at different times or in different countries. However, the idea of life expectancy is surprisingly subtle, so let's investigate it. Figure 7.9a shows the overall U.S. death rate, in deaths per 1000 people, for different age groups. We see an elevated risk of death near birth, after which the death rate drops to very low levels. At about 15 years of age, the death rate begins a gradual rise.

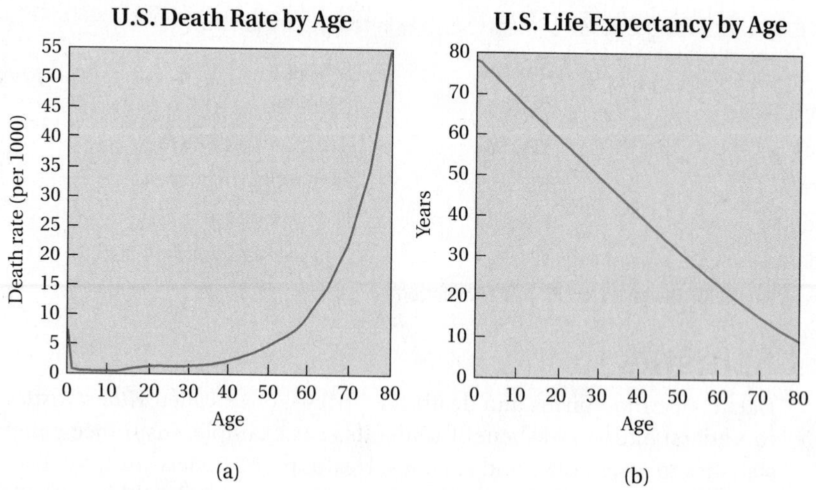

FIGURE 7.9 (a) The overall U.S. death rate (deaths per 1000 people) for different ages. (b) Life expectancy for different ages.
Source: U.S. National Center for Health Statistics (2006 data, released 2009)

Figure 7.9b shows the **life expectancy** of Americans of different ages, defined as the number of years a person of a given age can expect to live on average. As we would expect, life expectancy is higher for younger people because, on average, they have longer left to live. At birth, the life expectancy of Americans today is about 78 years (75.2 years for men and 80.4 years for women).

BY THE WAY

Life expectancies vary widely around the world, from lows below 40 years in some sub-Saharan countries in Africa to highs above 80 years in several European and Asian countries. As of 2008, the United States ranked 30th in life expectancy.

DEFINITION

Life expectancy is the number of years a person with a given age today can expect to live on average.

The subtlety in interpreting life expectancy comes from changes in medical science and public health. Life expectancies are calculated by studying *current* death rates. For example, when we say that the life expectancy of infants born today is 78 years, we mean that the average baby will live to age 78 *if there are no future changes* in medical science or public health. That is, while life expectancy provides a useful measure of current overall health, it should not be considered a *prediction* of future life spans.

In fact, because of advances in both medical science and public health, life expectancies increased significantly during the past century. Figure 7.10 shows that U.S. life expectancy at birth rose approximately 30 years during the 20th century. If this trend continues in this century, today's infants are likely to live much longer than 78 years on average. On the other hand, declining public health can lead to falling life expectancies. For example, war-torn nations often experience precipitous drops in life expectancy as public health deteriorates.

The reports of my death are greatly exaggerated.

—Mark Twain, from London, in cable to the Associated Press

Time Out to Think

Using Figure 7.10, compare the life expectancies of men and women. Briefly discuss these differences. Do they have any implications for social policy? for insurance rates? Explain.

Incidentally, the change in life expectancy shown in Figure 7.10 is truly remarkable: In less than 100 years, life expectancy increased by about 60%. There may be no better single measure of the changes that science and technology have brought to society.

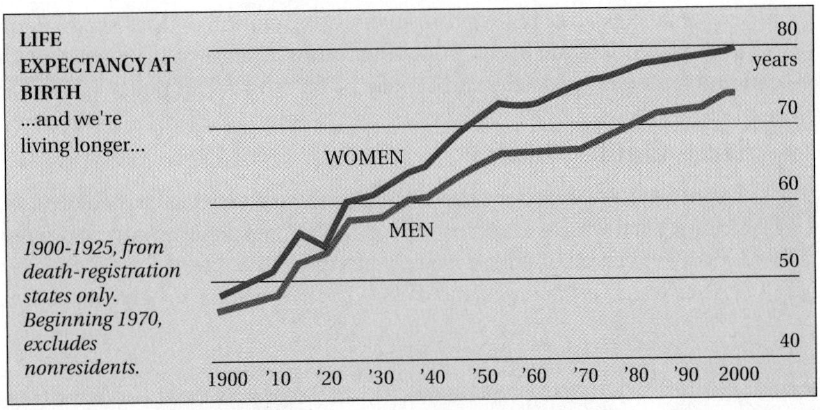

FIGURE 7.10 Changes in U.S. life expectancy during the 20th century.
Source: New York Times and National Center for Health Science Statistics.

Example 4 Life Expectancies

Using Figure 7.9b, find the life expectancies of a 20-year-old person and a 60-year-old person. Are the numbers consistent? Explain.

Solution The graph shows that the life expectancy at age 20 is about 59 years and at age 60 is about 23 years. This means that an average 20-year-old can expect to live about 59 more years, to age 79. An average 60-year-old can expect to live about 23 more years, to age 83.

It might at first seem strange that 60-year-olds have a longer average life span than 20-year-olds (83 years versus 79 years). But remember that life expectancies are based on current data. If there were no changes in medicine or public health, a 60-year-old would have a greater probability of reaching age 83 than a 20-year-old simply because he or she has already made it to age 60. However, if medicine and public health continue to improve, today's 20-year-olds may live to older ages than today's 60-year-olds.

Now try Exercises 21–26.

Case Study Life Expectancy and Social Security

As discussed in Unit 4F, Social Security benefits are paid from a combination of taxes collected from today's wage earners (representing most of the "FICA" taxes taken from your paycheck) and the so-called Social Security Trust Fund. Because of the changing age makeup of the U.S. population, the number of retirees collecting Social Security benefits is expected to become much larger in the future, while the number of wage earners paying Social Security taxes is expected to remain relatively constant. One of the biggest challenges to the future of Social Security is finding a way to make sure there is enough money to pay benefits for future retirees.

Current projections show that, without significant changes, the Social Security program will be unable to pay full benefits after about 2037. Social Security officials have proposed several different ways to solve this problem, including changes in the amounts of benefits paid, increases in the Social Security tax rate, changes in the retirement age, and partially or fully privatizing the Social Security program. Each of these proposals faces political obstacles. But, in addition, all of these proposals are based on assumptions about future life expectancy. Without corresponding changes in retirement age, longer lifespans mean more years of Social Security benefits.

More specifically, recent proposals by Social Security officials have assumed that life expectancy at birth will rise only slightly during this century. For example, the Social Security projections assume that American women will not reach a life expectancy of 82 years until 2033—but women in France have *already* achieved this life expectancy. Does it really seem likely that it will take until 2033 for the United States to achieve the life expectancies already found in many other nations? If, as seems more likely, Social Security projections are underestimating future changes in life expectancy, then the financial problems facing Social Security may be far worse than policy makers are banking on.

Time Out to Think

Suppose that life expectancy advances the same amount in this century as it did in the 20th century. What will life expectancy be by 2100? How would that affect programs like Social Security? What other effects would you expect it to have on society? Overall, do you think large increases in life expectancy will be good or bad for society? Defend your opinion.

QUICK QUIZ

Choose the best answer to each of the following questions. Explain your reasoning with one or more complete sentences.

1. If the number of car accidents goes down while the total number of miles driven goes up, the accident rate per mile driven

   a. goes down.

   b. goes up.

   c. stays the same.

2. Based on the trends shown in Figure 7.8, years during which the number of deaths from automobiles held steady are also years in which

   a. the death rate per mile went down.

   b. the death rate per mile held steady.

   c. the number of miles driven held steady.

3. Based on the trends shown in Figure 7.8, how has the safety of driving changed over the past 40 years?

   a. During the 1970s and 1980s, the death rate per mile went up and down, but more recently it has held steady.

   b. The death rate per mile has generally fallen with time.

   c. The death rate per mile has gone up and down, with no overall trend.

4. You are told the number of deaths due to AIDS in Africa in a given year. To calculate the death rate per person, what else do you need to know?

   a. the number of people infected with AIDS

   b. the amount of time the victims had the disease

   c. the population of Africa

5. Based on Table 7.4 and a U.S. population of 300 million, the death rate from accidents *per 100,000 people* is

   a. 121,599.

   b. $\frac{121{,}599}{300 \text{ million}}$.

   c. $\frac{121{,}599}{300 \text{ million}} \times 100{,}000$.

6. Based on Figure 7.9, besides the elderly, the group facing the greatest risk of death is

   a. infants.

   b. teenagers.

   c. men in their mid-30s.

7. Which statement about life expectancy is true?

   a. Everyone in the United States has the same life expectancy.

   b. Your life expectancy tells you how long you personally should expect to live.

   c. Your life expectancy will decline as you get older.

8. The life expectancy at birth of an American girl today is about 80 years. Does this mean that we should expect girls born today to live an average of 80 years?

   a. Yes; that's what we mean by life expectancy.

   b. No, because their life expectancies will get lower as they get older.

   c. No, because this life expectancy assumes no change in medical science or public health, both of which are almost certain to change.

9. Based on Figure 7.10, which statement is *not* true?

   a. Americans today live, on average, more than 50% longer than Americans in 1900.

   b. The life expectancies of men are rapidly catching up with the life expectancies of women.

   c. If the increase in life expectancy during 2000–2050 is the same as during 1950–2000, the life expectancy of men will reach about 85 by 2050.

10. How does an increasing life expectancy affect Social Security as it is currently structured?

    a. It means that the total amount of money paid to Social Security beneficiaries will be much higher than it would be otherwise.

    b. It pushes the year at which Social Security first runs a deficit further into the future.

    c. It has no effect, since budget planners have already taken into account the likelihood that life expectancies will increase dramatically.

Exercises 7D

REVIEW QUESTIONS

1. Briefly explain why quantifying risk is important to decision making.
2. Give an example of a rate used to measure risk in travel. Why are rates more useful than total numbers of deaths or accidents in measuring risk? How are such rates similar to probabilities?
3. What are vital statistics? How are they usually described? Give a few examples.
4. Explain the meaning of the term *life expectancy*. How does life expectancy change with age? How is it affected by changes in the overall health of a population?

DOES IT MAKE SENSE?

Decide whether each of the following statements makes sense (or is clearly true) or does not make sense (or is clearly false). Explain your reasoning.

5. No one can succeed in selling a product that will kill thousands of people per year.
6. Fewer people are killed in motorcycle accidents than in automobile accidents, so motorcycles must be safer than cars.
7. Your life expectancy is the major factor in determining how long you live.
8. A 60-year-old has a shorter life expectancy than a 20-year-old.

BASIC SKILLS & CONCEPTS

9–12: Automobile Safety. Use the table to answer the following questions.

Year	U.S. Population (millions)	Traffic Fatalities	Licensed Drivers (millions)	Vehicle-Miles (trillions)
1987	242	46,390	162	1.9
2000	281	41,821	185	2.7
2004	294	42,646	198	2.9
2007	300	41,059	206	3.0
2008	304	37,313	208	2.9

9. Express the 2008 fatality rate in deaths per 100 million vehicle-miles traveled.
10. Express the 2008 fatality rate in deaths per 100,000 population.
11. Express the 2008 fatality rate in deaths per 100,000 licensed drivers.
12. Use three different fatality rates (deaths per 100,000 people, deaths per 100,000 drivers, and deaths per 100 million vehicle-miles) to compare the risk of automobile travel in 1987 and 2008. Discuss your conclusions in detail.
13. **Airline Safety.** In 2008 there were 3 fatalities and 28 accidents in commercial aviation among major (not commuter) airlines over 19.3 million flight hours, 7.8 billion miles flown, and 10.8 million departures. Compute the accident and fatality rates in units of deaths or accidents per 100,000 flight hours, per 1 billion miles flown, and per 100,000 departures.
14. **General Aviation Safety.** In 2008 there were 495 deaths and 1559 accidents in general aviation (personal, corporate, instructional) over 21.9 million flight hours. Compute the accident and fatality rates in units of accidents or deaths per 100,000 flight hours. Discuss and compare the safety of commercial aviation (see Exercise 13) and general aviation.

15–20: Causes of Death. Use Table 7.4 and assume a U.S. population of 304 million.

15. What is the empirical probability of death by diabetes during a single year? How much greater is the risk of death by diabetes than the risk of death by septicemia?
16. How much greater is the risk of death by accident than the risk of death by kidney disease?
17. What is the death rate due to Alzheimer's disease in deaths per 100,000 of the population?
18. What is the death rate due to heart disease in deaths per 100,000 of the population?
19. If you lived in a typical city of 500,000, how many people would you expect to die of a stroke in a year?
20. If you lived in a typical city of 500,000, how many people would you expect to die of pulmonary disease in a year?

21–26: Mortality Rates. Use the graphs in Figure 7.9 to answer the following questions.

21. Estimate the death rate for 60- to 65-year-olds. Assuming that there were about 13.4 million 60- to 65-year-olds, how many people in this bracket could be expected to die in a year?
22. Approximately what is the death rate for 25- to 35-year-olds? If the population in this age category is 42 million, how many 25- to 35-year-olds can be expected to die in a year?
23. To what age could the average 40-year-old expect to live?
24. At what average age will today's 80-year-olds die? Assume no changes to life expectancies over the next 20 years.
25. Suppose that a life insurance company insures 1 million 50-year-old people in a given year. (Assume a death rate of 5 per 1000 people.) The cost of the premium is \$200 per year, and the death benefit is \$50,000. What is the expected profit or loss for the insurance company?
26. Suppose that a life insurance company insures 5000 40-year-old people in a given year. (Assume a death rate of 3 per 1000 people.) The cost of the premium is \$200 per year, and the death benefit is \$50,000. How much can the company expect to gain (or lose) in a year?

FURTHER APPLICATIONS

27. **High/Low U.S. Birth Rates.** The highest and lowest birth *rates* in the United States in 2006 were in Utah and Vermont, respectively. Utah reported 53,504 births for the year with a population of about 2.6 million people. Vermont reported 6511 births with a population of about 620,000 people. Use these data to answer the following questions.

    a. How many people were born each day of the year in Utah?

    b. How many people were born each day of the year in Vermont?

    c. What was the birth rate in Utah in births per 100,000 people?

    d. What was the birth rate in Vermont in births per 100,000 people?

28. **High/Low U.S. Death Rates.** In 2006, the highest and lowest death rates in the United States were in West Virginia and Colorado, respectively. West Virginia reported 20,676 deaths with a population of about 1.81 million. Colorado reported 29,519 deaths with a population of 4.75 million.

    a. Compute the death rates in West Virginia and Colorado in deaths per 100,000 people.

    b. How many people die each day in West Virginia?

    c. The death rate in West Virginia is almost double the death rate in Colorado. Does this mean that twice as many people died in 2006 in West Virginia as in Colorado? Explain.

29. **U.S. Birth and Death Rates.** In 2008 the U.S. population was about 304 million. The overall birth rate was 14.3 births per 1000, and the overall death rate was 8.0 deaths per 1000.

    a. Approximately how many births were there in the United States?

    b. About how many deaths were there in the United States?

    c. Based on births and deaths alone (i.e., not counting immigration), about how much did the U.S. population rise during 2008?

    d. Suppose that during 2008 the U.S. population actually increased by 3.5 million. Based on this fact and your results from part c, estimate how many people immigrated to the United States. What proportion of the overall population growth was due to immigration?

30. **Sex Ratios.** Figure 7.11 shows the ratio of men to women in various age categories from 1920 to 2000. Discuss the patterns and trends that you see in this figure, and offer explanations in terms of mortality and life expectancy.

31. **Multiple Births.** Each year there are approximately 4.3 million births in the United States, of which 133,000 are twin births (that is, $2 \times 133{,}000$ babies), 6118 are triplet births, and 355 are quadruplet births. Assume that births of five or more babies in one delivery are negligible in number.

    a. If you are an expectant mother, what is the approximate probability that you will give birth to more than one baby? Assume that multiple births are randomly distributed in the population.

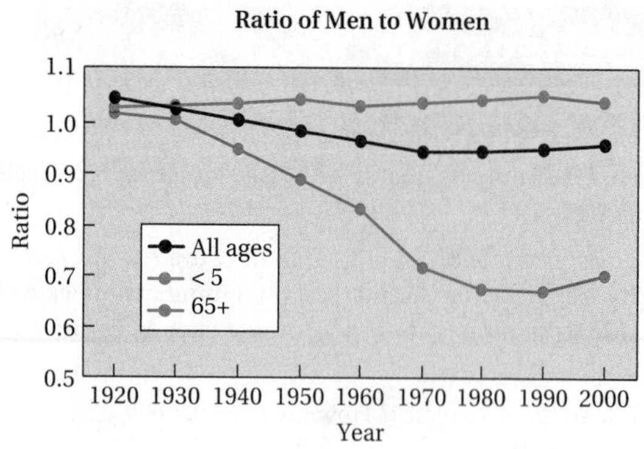

FIGURE 7.11

    b. What is the approximate probability that a randomly selected newborn is a twin? (Remember that there are two babies for each twin birth.)

    c. What is the approximate probability that a randomly selected newborn is a twin, a triplet, *or* a quadruplet?

WEB PROJECTS

32. **Cancer vs. Heart Disease.** Heart disease and cancer are the two leading causes of death in this country. Based on mortality data for the last ten years available from the Centers for Disease Control and Prevention, make a case either for or against the claim that cancer will soon overtake heart disease as the leading cause of death.

33. **Travel Safety.** The Bureau of Transportation Statistics collects safety data for many forms of travel (for example, train and bus). Visit the Web site and do a comparative study of the safety of automobiles and another form of transportation. Write a short report summarizing your conclusions.

34. **Life Expectancy.** Find more information about how life expectancies are determined. Use several of the life expectancy calculators that are available on the Web. Do they seem to give accurate or realistic results? Write a short summary of your findings.

IN YOUR WORLD

35. **Travel Safety.** Find a recent news report discussing some aspect of travel safety (such as risk of accidents in automobiles or airplanes, the efficacy of child car seats, or the effects of driving while talking on a cell phone). Summarize any statistics given about risks, and give your overall opinion regarding the safety issue under discussion.

36. **Vital Statistics.** Find a recent news report that gives new data about any aspect of vital statistics. Summarize the report and the statistics, and discuss any personal or social implications of the new data.

37. **Life Expectancies.** Find a recent news report that discusses life expectancies in any context. Summarize the report, and discuss the social implications of the given life expectancy data.

UNIT 7E Counting and Probability

As we have seen, computing theoretical probabilities requires counting outcomes. In previous units, we considered problems in which the counting was straightforward or the multiplication principle could be used (see the Brief Review on p. 420). Here, we'll discuss counting tools that enable us to solve a much wider range of probability problems and to explore the nature of coincidences.

Arrangements with Repetition

Suppose that license plates in your state can display seven numerals (Figure 7.12). How many different 7-number license plates are possible? There are 10 possibilities (the numerals 0 through 9) for the first position and the same 10 possibilities for the second position, so there are $10 \times 10 = 100$ possibilities for the first two positions combined. Similarly, because there are also 10 possibilities for the third position, there are $10 \times 10 \times 10 = 1000$ possibilities for the first three positions. For all seven positions, each with 10 possibilities, the total number of possibilities is

$$10 \times 10 \times 10 \times 10 \times 10 \times 10 \times 10 = 10^7$$

This system allows for 10 million different license plates.

The license plate problem involves making selections from a *single* group of choices—in this case, the numerals 0–9. However, the same numerals may be selected over and over again. This type of counting problem, in which we repeatedly select from the same group of choices, is called **arrangements with repetition.**

FIGURE 7.12 For each of the seven positions on the license plate, there are ten choices, resulting in 10^7 possible license plates.

> **ARRANGEMENTS WITH REPETITION**
>
> If we make r selections from a group of n choices, a total of $\underbrace{n \times n \times \cdots \times n}_{r \text{ times}} = n^r$ different arrangements are possible.

Example 1 Arrangements with Repetition

a. How many seven-symbol license plates are possible if both numerals *and* letters can be used in any order?

b. How many six-character passwords can be made by combining lowercase letters, uppercase letters, numerals, and the characters @, \$, and &?

Solution

a. With 10 numerals and 26 letters in the alphabet, there are 36 choices for each of the seven symbols. We are therefore selecting $r = 7$ symbols with $n = 36$ choices for each symbol, so the number of seven-symbol license plates is

$$n^r = 36^7 = 78{,}364{,}164{,}096$$

There are more than 78 billion possible seven-symbol license plates.

b. Each password character can be selected from the set of 26 lowercase letters, 26 uppercase letters, 10 numerals, and the three symbols @, \$, and &, making a total of 65 characters to choose from. For six-character passwords, we select $r = 6$ symbols with $n = 65$ choices for each character. The total number of possible passwords is

$$n^r = 65^6 = 75{,}418{,}890{,}625$$

More than 75 billion passwords are possible with these choices.

Now try Exercises 23–24.

Time Out to Think

Compare the numbers of possibilities in Example 1 to the human population. Will a state using seven-symbol license plates ever run out of possibilities? Do you think a six-symbol password is secure against hackers?

Permutations and Combinations

Suppose you coach a team of four swimmers. How many different ways can you put together a four-person relay team?

You can choose any of the four swimmers for the first leg. Once you've chosen the first swimmer, you have three swimmers left to choose from for the second leg. Therefore, the number of possible choices for the first two legs combined is $4 \times 3 = 12$. You then have two swimmers to choose from for the third leg, and you will have only one choice left for the last leg. The total number of possible arrangements for the relay is

$$4 \times 3 \times 2 \times 1 = 24$$

BY THE WAY

The word *permute* (root of *permutation*) comes from a Latin term meaning "to change throughout."

Figure 7.13 shows all 24 possible relay orders with a tree diagram in which the four swimmers are labeled A, B, C, and D. The first row shows the four possibilities for the first leg. The second row shows the three possible second-leg choices for each of the first-leg choices. The third row shows each of the prior possibilities branching into two possibilities for the third leg, and the fourth row shows the single remaining choice for the last leg in each case. Counting across the bottom row, we see the total of 24 possibilities. Each of the 24 different relay orders is called a **permutation** of the four letters A, B, C, and D.

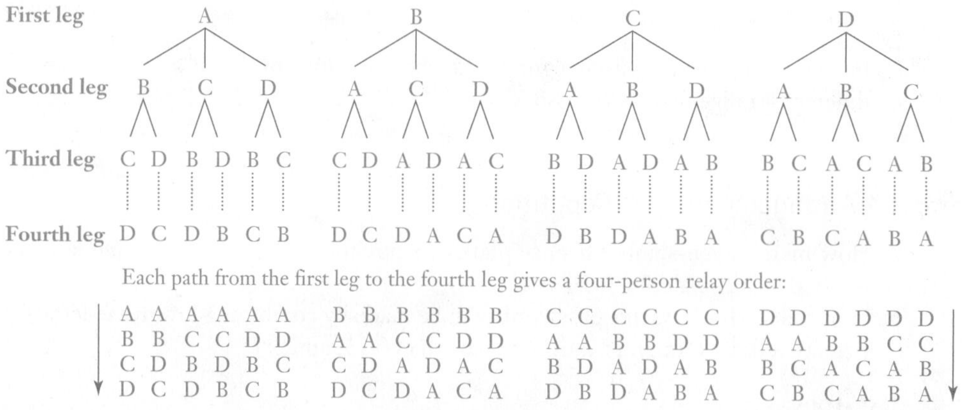

FIGURE 7.13 Tree diagram for the relay possibilities with four swimmers A, B, C, and D. There are four choices for the first leg. Each possible choice for the first leg leads to three remaining choices for the second leg. After the swimmers have been chosen for the first two legs, two choices remain for the third leg. Once the first three legs have been chosen, only one swimmer remains for the fourth leg.

PERMUTATIONS

Mathematically, we are dealing with **permutations** whenever all selections come from a single group of items, no item may be selected more than once, and the *order of arrangement matters* (for example, ABCD is considered to be different from DCBA). The total number of permutations possible with a group of n items is $n!$, where $n! = n \times (n-1) \times \cdots \times 2 \times 1$ is read "n factorial."

A Brief Review Factorials

Products of the form $4 \times 3 \times 2 \times 1$ come up so frequently in counting problems that they have a special name. Whenever a positive integer n is multiplied by all the preceding positive integers, the result is called **n factorial** and is denoted $n!$ (the exclamation mark is read as "factorial"). For example:

$$1! = 1$$
$$2! = 2 \times 1 = 2$$
$$3! = 3 \times 2 \times 1 = 6$$
$$4! = 4 \times 3 \times 2 \times 1 = 24$$
$$5! = 5 \times 4 \times 3 \times 2 \times 1 = 120$$

In general,

$$n! = n \times (n-1) \times (n-2) \times \cdots \times 2 \times 1$$

Note that $n!$ grows rapidly with n. For example, $20! \approx 2.4 \times 10^{18}$, $40! \approx 8.2 \times 10^{47}$, and $60! \approx 8.3 \times 10^{81}$. In fact, factorials quickly become so large that many calculators cannot handle them above $n = 69$ (if the calculator limit is 10^{100}). Note also that, by definition, $0! = 1$.

Example: Calculate each of the following *without* using the factorial key on your calculator.

a. $\dfrac{6!}{4!}$ b. $\dfrac{25!}{22!}$ c. $\dfrac{200!}{199!}$

Solution:

a. We can write out the entire calculation, but it is easier if we simplify it by canceling like terms in the numerator and denominator:

$$\frac{6!}{4!} = \frac{6 \times 5 \times \cancel{4} \times \cancel{3} \times \cancel{2} \times \cancel{1}}{\cancel{4} \times \cancel{3} \times \cancel{2} \times \cancel{1}} = \frac{6 \times 5 \times \cancel{4!}}{\cancel{4!}}$$
$$= 6 \times 5 = 30$$

b. This calculation is easier if we recognize that $25! = 25 \times 24 \times 23 \times 22!$, giving us

$$\frac{25!}{22!} = \frac{25 \times 24 \times 23 \times \cancel{22!}}{\cancel{22!}} = 25 \times 24 \times 23 = 13{,}800$$

c. If you tried 200! on your calculator, you would probably get an error because it is too large for most calculators to handle. But this calculation is easy if we recognize that $200! = 200 \times 199!$, so

$$\frac{200!}{199!} = \frac{200 \times \cancel{199!}}{\cancel{199!}} = 200$$

Now try Exercises 11–22.

Example 2 Class Schedules

A middle school principal needs to schedule six different classes—algebra, English, history, Spanish, science, and gym—in six different time periods. How many different class schedules are possible?

Solution This is a case of permutations because all selections come from the same group of classes, each class is scheduled only once, and the order of the classes matters (because a schedule that begins with Spanish is different from one that begins with gym). The principal may choose any of the six classes for the first period, leaving five choices for the second period. After the first two periods are filled, there are four choices left for the third period. Similarly, there are three choices for the fourth period, two choices for the fifth period, and only one choice for the sixth period. Altogether, the number of possible schedules is

$$6! = 6 \times 5 \times 4 \times 3 \times 2 \times 1 = 720$$

The principal can schedule the six classes in 720 different ways. **Now try Exercise 25.**

USING TECHNOLOGY

Factorials

Many calculators have a special key for factorials, usually labeled $n!$ For example, to calculate $6!\,(=720)$, press (6) ($n!$) (=). Excel has a built-in function FACT for factorials, as shown in the screen shot below.

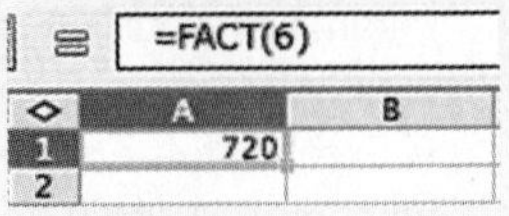

The Permutations Formula

Suppose you coach a team of ten swimmers, from which you must put together a four-person relay team. How many possibilities do you have in this case?

This time, you have ten swimmers from which to choose for the first leg of the relay. Once you make the first choice, you have nine swimmers from which to choose for the

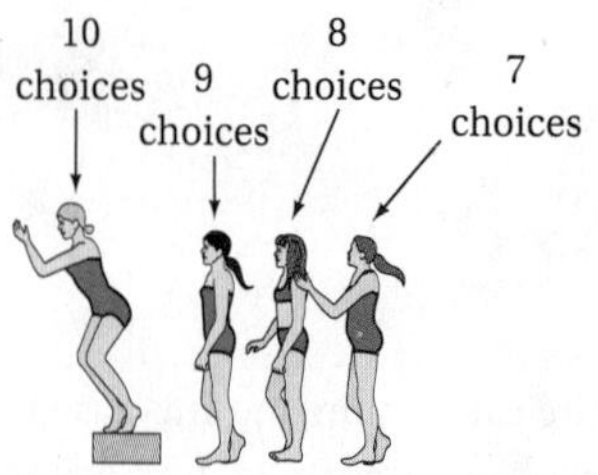

FIGURE 7.14 With ten swimmers from which to choose a four-person relay team, you have ten choices for the first position, nine for the second position, eight for the third position, and seven for the fourth position. This results in $10 \times 9 \times 8 \times 7 = 5040$ possible relay teams.

second leg, then eight choices for the third leg, and seven choices for the fourth leg (Figure 7.14). The total number of relay possibilities is

$$10 \times 9 \times 8 \times 7 = 5040$$

Each of the 5040 relays represents a different *permutation* because each relay swimmer is selected from the same group of ten swimmers, no swimmer can swim more than once, and the order of the swimmers in the relay is important. However, in this case the relays make use of only four of the total of ten swimmers. Therefore, the number of possible relays made from "ten swimmers selected four at a time" is 5040.

We can find a general formula for permutations by writing the product $10 \times 9 \times 8 \times 7$ in a slightly different way:

$$10 \times 9 \times 8 \times 7 = \frac{10 \times 9 \times 8 \times 7 \times \cancel{6!}}{\cancel{6!}} = \frac{10!}{(10-4)!}$$

Note that, in the final formula on the right,

- the number 10 in the numerator is the number of swimmers from which the coach may choose the four relay participants, and
- the number $10 - 4 = 6$ in the denominator is the number of swimmers who do *not* swim in the relay.

Permutations have their own special notation: We read ${}_{10}P_4$ as "the number of permutations of ten items selected four at a time." Using this compact notation, we have

$${}_{10}P_4 = \frac{10!}{(10-4)!} = 5040$$

Generalizing, we have a formula for calculating the number of permutations.

THE PERMUTATIONS FORMULA

If we make r selections from a group of n items, the number of permutations is

$${}_nP_r = \frac{n!}{(n-r)!} = \underbrace{n \times (n-1) \times (n-2) \times \cdots \times (n-r+1)}_{r \text{ factors here}}$$

where ${}_nP_r$ is read as "the number of permutations of n items taken r at a time."

USING TECHNOLOGY

Permutations

Many calculators have a special key for permutations, usually labeled ${}_nP_r$. For example, to find the number of permutations of $n = 10$ items taken $r = 4$ at a time, press (10) (${}_nP_r$) (4) (=). In Excel, use the built-in function PERMUT, as shown in the screen shot below.

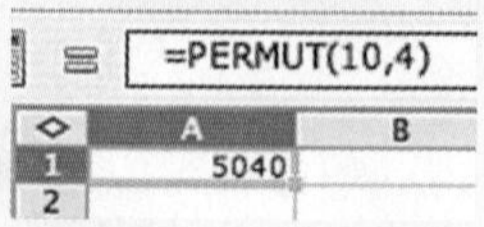

Example 3 Leadership Election

A city has 12 candidates running for three leadership positions. The top vote-getter will become the mayor, the second vote-getter will become the deputy mayor, and the third vote-getter will become the treasurer. How many outcomes are possible for the three leadership positions?

Solution The voters choose $r = 3$ leaders from a group of $n = 12$ candidates. The order in which leaders are chosen matters because each of the three leadership positions is different. Therefore, we are looking for the number of permutations of 12 candidates taken 3 at a time:

$${}_{12}P_3 = \frac{12!}{(12-3)!} = \frac{12!}{9!} = \frac{12 \times 11 \times 10 \times \cancel{9!}}{\cancel{9!}} = 12 \times 11 \times 10 = 1320$$

There are 1320 possible outcomes for the three leadership positions.

Now try Exercise 26.

Example 4 Batting Orders

How many ways can the manager of a baseball team form a (9-player) batting order from a roster of 15 players?

Solution The manager forms a batting order by selecting $r = 9$ players from the roster of $n = 15$ players. Therefore, the number of possible batting orders is the number of permutations of 15 players taken 9 at a time:

$$\begin{aligned} {}_{15}P_9 &= \frac{15!}{(15-9)!} = \frac{15!}{6!} \\ &= 15 \times 14 \times 13 \times 12 \times 11 \times 10 \times 9 \times 8 \times 7 = 1{,}816{,}214{,}400 \end{aligned}$$

Nearly 2 *billion* batting orders are possible for a baseball team with a roster of 15 players!

Now try Exercise 27.

Time Out to Think

Major league baseball teams carry a roster of 25 players.Without actually calculating, describe how the calculation of the number of possible batting orders would be different for a major league team than for the team in Example 4.

Combinations

Suppose that the five members of a city council decide they need a three-person committee to study the impact of a new shopping center. The council members are Ursula, Vern, Wendy, Yolanda, and Zeke (U, V, W, Y, and Z, for short). How many committees could be formed from the five council members?

First, note that this problem is *not* a permutation problem because we are interested only in the makeup of the committee, *not* the order in which the names are listed. For example, if we were dealing with permutations, we would consider ZWU to be different from WZU. In this case, however, both arrangements are equivalent because they both represent the same committee (with members Zeke, Wendy, and Ursula). Problems of this type are called **combinations** problems.

A committee is a group of important individuals who singly can do nothing, but who together can agree that nothing can be done.

—Fred Allen, comedian

One way to count the possible committees is to list them all. Going in alphabetical order, we begin by listing all three-person committees that include Ursula:

UVW UVY UVZ UWY UWZ UYZ

Next, we list the committees that include Vern but not Ursula:

VWY VWZ VYZ

This leaves only one committee that includes neither Ursula nor Vern:

WYZ

We've found a total of ten three-person committees that can be made from the five council members.

This method of listing all the possible committees works, but it can become quite tedious when the numbers are large. Fortunately, we can get the same answer with an alternative strategy. First, we find the number of *permutations* of the $n = 5$ council members selected $r = 3$ at a time:

$${}_5P_3 = \frac{5!}{(5-3)!} = \frac{5!}{2!} = 5 \times 4 \times 3 = 60$$

That is, there are 60 possible permutations when we choose three people from a group of five. However, because order matters for permutations but does not matter for committees, the number of permutations is an *overcount* of the actual number of different committees. More specifically, any three-person committee can be listed in 3! = 3 × 2 × 1 = 6 different orders. For example, the committee consisting of Zeke, Yolanda, and Wendy has six different permutations:

ZYW ZWY YZW YWZ WZY WYZ

Because each three-person committee is counted 3! = 6 times by the permutations formula, this formula gives us six times the actual number of committees. We must therefore divide the number of permutations by 3! to find the number of committees:

$$\frac{{}_5P_3}{3!} = \frac{60}{3!} = \frac{60}{3 \times 2 \times 1} = 10$$

This is the same result we obtained by listing the three-person committees. The permutations part of the equation is ${}_nP_r$, where $n = 5$ and $r = 3$. We then divided this term by $r! = 3!$ to correct for the overcounting. Generalizing, the formula for combinations is the permutations formula divided by $r!$.

USING TECHNOLOGY

Combinations

Many calculators have a special key for combinations, usually labeled ${}_nC_r$. For example, to find the number of combinations of $n = 10$ items taken $r = 4$ at a time, press (10) (${}_nC_r$) (4) (=). In Excel, use the built-in function COMBIN, as shown in the screen shot below.

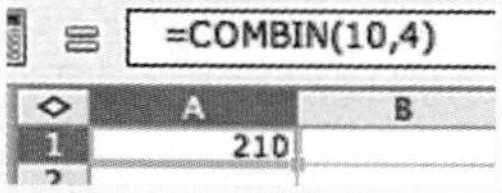

COMBINATIONS

Combinations occur whenever all selections come from a single group of items, no item may be selected more than once, and the order of arrangement does *not* matter (for example, ABCD is considered to be the same as DCBA). If we make r selections from a group of n items, the number of possible combinations is

$${}_nC_r = \frac{{}_nP_r}{r!} = \frac{n!}{(n-r)! \times r!}$$

where ${}_nC_r$ is read as "the number of combinations of n items taken r at a time."

Example 5 Ice Cream Combinations

Suppose that you select 3 different flavors of ice cream in a shop that carries 12 flavors. How many flavor combinations are possible?

Solution We are looking for the number of combinations of $n = 12$ flavors selected $r = 3$ at a time. From the combinations formula, the number of flavor combinations is

$${}_{12}C_3 = \frac{12!}{(12-3)! \times 3!} = \frac{12!}{9! \times 3!} = \frac{12 \times 11 \times 10 \times \cancel{9!}}{\cancel{9!} \times 3!} = \frac{12 \times 11 \times 10}{3 \times 2 \times 1}$$
$$= \frac{1320}{6} = 220$$

There are 220 different three-flavor combinations possible from the 12 flavors.

Now try Exercise 28.

Example 6 Poker Hands

How many different five-card poker hands can be dealt from a standard deck of 52 cards? What is the probability of one particular hand, such as a *royal flush* of hearts (a hand consisting of the ace, king, queen, jack, and 10 of hearts)?

Solution This is a combinations problem, because the order of the cards in a hand does not matter. The number of combinations of $n = 52$ cards drawn $r = 5$ at a time is

$${}_{52}C_5 = \frac{52!}{(52-5)! \times 5!} = \frac{52!}{47! \times 5!} = \frac{52 \times 51 \times 50 \times 49 \times 48 \times \cancel{47!}}{\cancel{47!} \times 5 \times 4 \times 3 \times 2 \times 1} = 2{,}598{,}960$$

More than 2.5 million hands are possible in five-card poker. Any particular hand, such as the royal flush of hearts, has a probability of about 1 in 2.6 million.

Now try Exercise 29.

Time Out to Think

Consider the following unimpressive poker hand: 5 of clubs, 7 of hearts, 3 of diamonds, 2 of spades, 9 of hearts. How does the probability of this hand, which has no value in poker, compare to the probability of a royal flush of spades, which is the highest-value hand in poker? Explain.

Historical Note

New Hampshire began the first legalized lottery in the United States in 1964. Since then, most states have adopted lotteries as a source of revenue. Many states also participate in multi-state lottery games (such as the Powerball game or Mega Millions). Lotteries have existed in various forms and places for centuries, including the Roman Empire (1st century) and Italy in the Middle Ages.

Example 7 (Not) Winning the Lottery

Suppose you play a lottery in which the winner is chosen by drawing 6 balls at random from a drum containing 52 numbered balls (numbered 1 through 52). What is the probability that your 6 numbers will match the 6 winning numbers?

Solution The order in which the balls are drawn does not matter, so finding the total number of possible outcomes is a combinations problem. The number of combinations for $n = 52$ balls selected $r = 6$ at a time is

$$_{52}C_6 = \frac{52!}{(52-6)! \times 6!} = \frac{52!}{46! \times 6!} = 20{,}358{,}520$$

There are more than 20 million possible combinations of 6 numbers, so the chance that your 6 numbers will match the 6 winning numbers is less than 1 in 20 million.

Now try Exercises 30–40.

Probability and Coincidence

Probability has important applications to the idea of coincidences. For example, only a few of the many millions of people who play lotteries win multimillion-dollar prizes each year. Because any particular person's probability of winning is so low, winners often attribute their fortune to "good luck" or to some special "system" they used in choosing lottery numbers. However, *someone* was bound to win, and the particular winners actually won by mere coincidence. Said differently, it is virtually certain that *someone* will win a big lottery prize during the next year. Yet the probability that *you* will win the big prize is exceedingly small.

COINCIDENCES ARE BOUND TO HAPPEN

Although a *particular* outcome may be highly unlikely, *some* similar outcome may be extremely likely or even certain to occur. In general, this means that coincidences will inevitably be experienced by someone, even if these coincidences have a low probability for any particular person.

BY THE WAY

Studies show that most people playing lotteries vastly overestimate their chances of winning. Here's one good way to think about it: Imagine playing a lottery with 1 million players and 1 winner. Because 999,999 out of the 1 million players will not win, there is a 99.9999% chance that the following statement will be true: "Someone will win, but it will *not* be you."

Coincidences come in many different forms. You may be surprised to find that two people at your dinner party have the same birthday or that a friend's mother met your mother on a trip to China. You might flip a coin and get heads ten times in a row or have a dream that seems to predict an event that later occurs. It is tempting to chalk these cases up to something more mysterious than mere coincidence. But the laws of probability dictate that many coincidences are bound to happen, even though the particular form of a coincidence is unpredictable. The following example about birthday coincidences demonstrates one of the more surprising aspects of this idea.

Example 8 Birthday Coincidence

Suppose there are 25 students in your class.

a. What is the probability that at least one person in the class has the same birthday as you? (Assume 365 days in a year.)

b. What is the probability that *some* pair of students in the class of 25 shares the *same* birthday? Compare this result to the result from part a.

Solution

a. This is an *at least once* question (see Unit 7B). We begin by recognizing that, with 365 days in a year, the probability that any particular student has your birthday is 1/365. Therefore, the probability that a particular student does not have your birthday is 364/365. From the *at least once* rule, the probability that at least one of the 24 other students has your birthday is

$$\begin{aligned} P(\text{at least one with your birthday}) &= 1 - [P(\text{not your birthday})]^{24} \\ &= 1 - \left[\frac{364}{365}\right]^{24} \\ &= 1 - 0.936 = 0.064 \end{aligned}$$

The probability that at least one other student shares your birthday is only 0.064, which is about 1 in 16.

b. This question differs from the question in part a because the pair sharing the same birthday does not have to include you; it can be *any* pair of two students. But this is still an *at least once* question, because we are looking for the probability of a shared birthday among at least one pair of students. We can therefore find the answer as follows:

$$P(\text{at least one pair of shared birthdays}) = 1 - P(\text{no shared birthdays})$$

The easiest way to find the probability of no shared birthdays is by calculating the probability that all 25 students have *different* birthdays. We begin by considering just two students from the class. The first student has a birthday on 1 of the 365 days of the year, so the probability that the second student has a different birthday is 364/365. Now consider a third student. If the first two students have different birthdays, then 2 of the 365 days are already "taken." Therefore, the probability that the third student's birthday falls on a third different day is 363/365, since 363 days are not yet "taken" for birthdays. Putting the probabilities together, we find that the chance that the first three students all have different birthdays is

$$\underbrace{\frac{364}{365}}_{\text{probability that first two students have different birthdays}} \times \underbrace{\frac{363}{365}}_{\text{probability that third student also has different birthday}}$$

Similarly, if the first three students all have different birthdays, the probability that a fourth student has a different birthday from any of the first three is 362/365. And so on. Finally, if the first 24 students all have different birthdays, then 24 of the 365 days are "taken," leaving 365 − 24 = 341 possible different birthdays for the 25th student. Overall, the probability that all 25 students have different birthdays is

$$\frac{364}{365} \times \frac{363}{365} \times \cdots \times \frac{341}{365} = \frac{364 \times 363 \times \cdots \times 341}{365^{24}}$$

Although we could write the product in the numerator more compactly as 364!/340!, the factorials are too large for most calculators to handle. Therefore, the better way to proceed is by computing the numerator and denominator separately. The result is

$$\frac{364 \times 363 \times \cdots \times 341}{365^{24}} \approx \frac{1.348 \times 10^{61}}{3.126 \times 10^{61}} \approx 0.431$$

This is the probability that there are *no* shared birthdays among the 25 students in the class. Therefore, the probability that there is at least one pair of shared birthdays is

$$\begin{aligned} P(\text{at least one pair of shared birthdays}) &= 1 - P(\text{no shared birthdays}) \\ &\approx 1 - 0.431 = 0.569 \end{aligned}$$

There's a 0.569 probability (about 57%) that at least two of the 25 students have the same birthday! Most people are very surprised at how much higher this probability is than the 0.064 probability that at least one of the students shares *your* birthday, but it illustrates the fact that *some* coincidence is far more likely than a *particular* coincidence. **Now try Exercises 41–42.**

QUICK QUIZ

Choose the best answer to each of the following questions. Explain your reasoning with one or more complete sentences.

1. You are asked to create a 4-character password, and each character may be any of the 26 letters of the alphabet or the 10 numerals 0 through 9. How many different passwords are possible?

   a. 36 b. 36^4 c. $26^4 + 10^4$

2. A waitress has three different entrees for the three people sitting at a table, but has forgotten which person ordered which entree. How many possible ways are there for her to serve the entrees?

   a. 3 b. 3^3 c. 6

3. A teacher has 28 students, and 5 of them will be chosen to participate in a play that has 5 distinct characters. Which of the following questions requires calculating *permutations* to solve?

   a. How many different sets of 5 children can be selected for the play?

   b. How many different choices are possible for each role in the play?

   c. Once the 5 children have been chosen, how many different ways can their roles be arranged?

4. For the permutations question in Exercise 3, the correct statement of the required calculation is

   a. ${}_{28}P_5$. b. ${}_5P_5$. c. ${}_5P_{28}$.

5. A soccer coach who has 15 children on her team will be playing 7 children at a time, each at a distinct position. Which number is *largest?*

   a. the number of combinations of 7 children that can be chosen from the 15

   b. the number of permutations of the 7 positions that are possible with the 15 children

   c. the number of different ways of arranging the 7 children playing at any one time among the 7 positions

6. One term in the denominator of the combinations formula is $(n - r)!$. Suppose you are trying to determine the number of different possible 4-person teams that can be put together from a group of 9 people. Then the term $(n - r)!$ means

   a. $4 \times 3 \times 2 \times 1$. b. $9 \times 8 \times 7 \times 6 \times 5$.

   c. $5 \times 4 \times 3 \times 2 \times 1$.

7. Overall, the number of different 4-person teams (order does not matter) that can be put together from a group of 9 people is

   a. 9!. b. $9 \times 8 \times 7 \times 6$. c. $\frac{9 \times 8 \times 7 \times 6}{4 \times 3 \times 2 \times 1}$.

8. One person in a stadium filled with 100,000 people is chosen at random to win a free pair of airline tickets. The probability that *someone* will win the tickets

   a. is 1 in 100,000. b. is 1.

   c. depends on the cost of the plane tickets.

9. One person in a stadium filled with 100,000 people is chosen at random to win a free pair of airline tickets. What is the probability that it will *not* be you?

   a. 1 in 100,000 b. 0.99 c. 0.99999

10. There are 365 possible birthdays in a year. In a class of 25 students, the chance of finding 2 students with the same birthday is

   a. 25/365. b. $2 \times 25/365$. c. greater than 0.5.

Exercises 7E

REVIEW QUESTIONS

1. What are arrangements with repetition? Give an example of a situation in which the n^r formula gives the number of possible arrangements.
2. What do we mean by *permutations*? Explain the meaning of each of the terms in the permutations formula. Give an example of its use.
3. What do we mean by *combinations*? Explain the meaning of each of the terms in the combinations formula. Give an example of its use.
4. Explain what we mean when we say that *some* outcome is much more likely than a particular outcome. How does this idea affect our perception of coincidences?

DOES IT MAKE SENSE?

Decide whether each of the following statements makes sense (or is clearly true) or does not make sense (or is clearly false). Explain your reasoning.

5. I used the permutations formula to determine how many possible relay orders we could make with the 10 girls on our swim team.
6. I used the combinations formula to determine how many different five-card poker hands are possible.
7. The number of different possible batting orders for 9 players on a 25-person baseball team is so large that there's no hope of trying them all out.
8. It must be my lucky day, because the five-card poker hand I got had only about a 1 in 2.5 million chance of being dealt to me.
9. The probability that two people in a randomly selected group will have the same last name is much higher than the probability that someone will have the same last name as I do.
10. Someone wins the lottery every week, so I figure that if I keep playing eventually I will be the one who wins.

BASIC SKILLS & CONCEPTS

11–22: Review of Factorials. Use the skills covered in the Brief Review on p. 459 to evaluate the following quantities *without* using the factorial key on your calculator (you may use the multiplication key). Show your work.

11. $6!$ 12. $12!$ 13. $\frac{5!}{3!}$

14. $\frac{10!}{8!}$ 15. $\frac{12!}{4!\,3!}$ 16. $\frac{9!}{4!\,2!}$

17. $\frac{11!}{3!(11-3)!}$ 18. $\frac{30!}{29!}$ 19. $\frac{8!}{3!(8-3)!}$

20. $\frac{30!}{28!}$ 21. $\frac{6!\,8!}{4!\,5!}$ 22. $\frac{15!}{2!\,13!}$

23–40: Counting Methods. Answer the following questions using the appropriate counting technique, which may be either arrangements with repetition, permutations, or combinations. Be sure to explain why this counting technique applies to the problem.

23. How many different nine-digit zip codes can be formed?
24. How many different five-character passwords can be formed from the lowercase letters of the alphabet?
25. How many different five-character passwords can be formed from the lowercase letters of the alphabet if repetition is not allowed?
26. A city council with nine members must elect a four-person executive committee consisting of a mayor, deputy mayor, secretary, and treasurer. How many executive committees are possible?
27. How many ways can the nine performances at a piano recital be ordered?
28. A city council with nine members must appoint a three-person subcommittee. How many subcommittees are possible?
29. Suppose you have 20 CDs from which you choose 6 CDs to put in the CD player in your car. If you are not particular about the order, how many 6-CD sets are possible?
30. How many 6-person lineups can be formed from a 15-player volleyball roster, assuming every player can be assigned to any position?
31. How many different birth orders with respect to gender are possible in a family with five children? (For example, BBBGG and BGBGG are different orders.)
32. How many different 5-card hands can be dealt from a 52-card deck?
33. How many license plates can be made of the form *XX–YYYYY*, where *X* is a letter of the alphabet and *Y* is a numeral 0–9?
34. How many different groups of six balls can be drawn from a barrel containing balls numbered 1–36?
35. How many different telephone numbers of the form *aaa-bbb-cccc* can be formed if the area code *aaa* cannot contain 0 and the prefix *bbb* cannot contain 9?
36. How many anagrams (rearrangements) of the letters ILOVEMATH can you make?

37. How many different three-letter "words" can be formed from the genetic alphabet ACGT?

38. The debate club has 15 members, but only 5 can compete at the next meet. How many 5-person teams are possible?

39. A recording engineer wants to make a CD with 12 songs. In how many different ways can the CD be made?

40. A dog shelter is giving away 15 different dogs, but you have room for only 4 of them. How many different dog families could you have?

41–42: Birthday Coincidences. Suppose you are part of a group of people at a dinner party. For the situations given, find the probability that at least one of the other guests has *your* birthday and the probability that *some* pair of guests shares the same birthday. Discuss your results. (Assume 365 days in a year.)

41. You are one of 12 people at the party.

42. You are one of 20 people at the party.

FURTHER APPLICATIONS

43. **Ice Cream Shop.** Josh and John's Ice Cream Shop offers 20 different flavors of ice cream and 8 different toppings. Answer the following questions by using the appropriate counting technique (multiplication principle, arrangements with repetitions, permutations, or combinations). Explain why you chose the particular counting technique.

a. How many different sundaes can you create using one of the ice cream flavors and one of the toppings?

b. How many different triple cones can you create from the 20 flavors if the same flavor may be used more than once? Assume that you specify which flavor goes on the bottom, middle, and top.

c. Using the 20 flavors, how many different triple cones can you create with 3 *different* flavors if you specify which flavor goes on the bottom, middle, and top?

d. Using the 20 flavors, how many different triple cones can you create with 3 *different* flavors if you don't care about the order of the flavors on the cone?

44. **Telephone Numbers.** A ten-digit phone number in the United States consists of a three-digit area code followed by a three-digit *exchange* followed by a four-digit number.

a. The first digit of the area code cannot be 0 or 1. The first digit of the exchange cannot be 0 or 1. How many different ten-digit phone numbers can be formed? Can a city with 2 million telephone numbers be served by a single area code? Explain.

b. How many exchanges are needed to serve a city of 80,000 people? Explain.

45. **Pizza Hype.** Luigi's Pizza Parlor advertises 56 different three-topping pizzas. How many individual toppings does Luigi actually use? Ramona's Pizzeria advertises 36 different two-topping pizzas. How many toppings does Ramona actually use? (*Hint:* In these problems, you are given the total number of combinations, and you must find the number of toppings that are used.)

46. **ZIP Codes.** The U.S. Postal Service uses both five-digit and nine-digit ZIP codes.

a. How many five-digit ZIP codes are available to the U.S. Postal Service?

b. For a U.S. population of 300 million people, what is the average number of people per five-digit ZIP code if all possible ZIP codes are used? Explain.

c. How many nine-digit ZIP codes are available to the U.S. Postal Service? Could everyone in the United States have his or her own personal nine-digit ZIP code? Explain.

47–54: Counting and Probability. Find the probability of the given event.

47. Choosing six numbers that match six randomly selected balls when the balls are numbered 1 through 36

48. Choosing five numbers that match five randomly selected balls when the balls are numbered 1 through 42

49. Being dealt 5 cards from a standard 52-card deck, and the cards are a 10, jack, queen, king, and ace, all of the same suit

50. Guessing the top three winners (in order) from a group of ten finalists in a soccer tournament

51. Guessing the top three winners (in any order) from a group of 15 finalists in a spelling bee

52. Randomly selecting 3 Ohio students from a group of 16 students, 7 of whom are from Ohio

53. Being dealt 5 cards from a standard 52-card deck and getting four of a kind (for example, four aces)

54. Being in the first half of the program when you are one of ten performers whose order of performance is randomly selected

55. **Hot Streaks.** Suppose that 2000 people are all playing a game for which the chance of winning is 48%.

a. Assuming everyone plays exactly five games, what is the probability of one person winning five games in a row? On average, how many of the 2000 people could be expected to have a "hot streak" of five games?

b. Assuming everyone plays exactly ten games, what is the probability of one person winning ten games in a row? On average, how many of the 2000 people could be expected to have a "hot streak" of ten games?

56. **Joe DiMaggio's Record.** One of the longest-standing records in sports is the 56-game hitting streak (in baseball) of Joe DiMaggio. Assume that a player on a long "hot streak" is batting .400, which is about the best that anyone ever hits over a period of 50 or more games. (A batting average of .400 means the batter gets a hit 40% of the time. Typically, only a handful of players each year hit that well for a period as long as 56 games.)

a. What is the probability that a player batting .400 will get at least one hit in four at-bats?

b. Use the result in part a to calculate the probability of a .400 hitter getting a hit in one stretch of 56 consecutive games, assuming four at-bats per game.

c. Suppose that, instead of batting .400, a player has a more ordinary average of .300. In that case, what is the probability of the player getting a hit in one stretch of 56 consecutive games, assuming four at-bats per game?

d. Considering the results in parts b and c and the fact that baseball has been played for about 100 years, are you surprised that *someone* set a record of hitting in 56 consecutive games? Explain clearly.

57. **Coin Streaks.** Toss a coin 100 times and record your results (heads or tails) in order. What was your longest streak of consecutive heads or tails? Calculate the probability of this streak by itself. For example, if your longest streak was four heads, what is the probability of four heads in four tosses? Should you be surprised that you got such a streak? Explain.

WEB PROJECT

58. **The "Monty Hall" Problem.** A famous controversy about a probability question erupted over an item in the "Ask Marilyn" column in *Parade* magazine, written by Marilyn Vos Savant. The problem her column addressed was loosely based on a TV game show called *Let's Make a Deal*, hosted by Monty Hall, and hence is known as the Monty Hall Problem. Here's the question:

> *Suppose that you're on a game show and you're given the choice of three doors: Behind one door is a car; behind the other two doors are goats. You pick a door, say No. 1, and the host, who knows what's behind the doors, opens another door, say No. 3, which has a goat. He then says to you, "Do you want to change your pick to door No. 2?" Is it to your advantage to switch your choice?*

Marilyn answered that the probability of winning was higher if the contestant switched. This answer generated a huge number of letters, including a few from mathematicians, claiming that she was wrong. Marilyn answered with the following logic. When you first pick door No. 1, the chance that you picked the one with the car is 1/3. The probability that you chose a door with a goat is 2/3. When the host opens door No. 3 to reveal a goat, it does not change the 1/3 probability that you picked the right door in the first place. Thus, as only one other door remains, the probability that it contains the car is 2/3. Visit a few of the many Web sites devoted to the Monty Hall Problem to gain some understanding of its subtleties. Do you agree with Marilyn's logic? If so, try to explain it in your own words. If not, present an alternative approach.

IN YOUR WORLD

59. **Lottery Chances.** Find an article or advertisement about a lottery in which choosing a winner involves combinations. Calculate the probability of winning. Does your calculation agree with the advertised probability? Explain.

60. **Amazing Coincidence.** Discuss a seemingly amazing coincidence that you've read about or experienced yourself. Based on ideas of probability, decide whether the coincidence was bound to happen to someone. Was it really as amazing as it seemed? Explain.

TECHNOLOGY EXERCISES

61. **Comparing Factorials to Powers.**

a. Use Excel to complete the following table.

n	$n!$	10^n
1		
2		
3		
4		
5		
6		
7		
8		
9		
10		

b. Your table should show that $10! < 10^{10}$. Extend the table (which is easily done by dragging the three columns down) to determine the smallest integer n such that $n! > 10^n$.

62. **Computing Lottery Probabilities.**

a. Use Excel to compute the number of ways in which 5 lottery balls can be selected from a pool of 44 balls. What is the probability of winning such a lottery (by matching all five numbers)?

b. Use Excel to compute the number of ways in which 6 lottery balls can be selected from a pool of 40 balls. What is the probability of winning such a lottery (by matching all six numbers)?

c. Which lottery offers a better chance of winning?

63. **Poker Probability.** It can be shown that if you are dealt five cards from a standard shuffled deck of cards, the probability of being dealt a full house (three cards of one kind and two cards of another kind, such as 99933) is

$$\frac{{}_{13}C_1 \times {}_4C_3 \times {}_{12}C_1 \times {}_4C_2}{{}_{52}C_5}.$$

Use Excel to evaluate this probability.

CHAPTER 7 Summary

UNIT	KEY TERMS	KEY IDEAS AND SKILLS
7A	outcome event theoretical probability empirical probability subjective probability probability distribution odds	**Distinguish among** theoretical, empirical, and subjective probabilities. **Determine** theoretical probabilities: $P(A) = \dfrac{\text{number of ways } A \text{ can occur}}{\text{total number of outcomes}}$ **Make** a probability distribution.
7B	*and* probability independent events dependent events *either/or* probability non-overlapping events overlapping events	***And* probability, independent events:** $P(A \text{ and } B) = P(A) \times P(B)$ ***And* probability, dependent events:** $P(A \text{ and } B) = P(A) \times P(B \text{ given } A)$ ***Either/or* probability, non-overlapping events:** $P(A \text{ or } B) = P(A) + P(B)$ ***Either/or* probability, overlapping events:** $P(A \text{ or } B) = P(A) + P(B) - P(A \text{ and } B)$ ***At least once* rule:** $P(\text{at least one event } A \text{ in } n \text{ trials}) = 1 - P(\text{no events } A \text{ in } n \text{ trials})$ $= 1 - [P(\text{not } A \text{ in one trial})]^n$
7C	law of large numbers expected value gambler's fallacy house edge	**Understand and apply** the law of large numbers. **Calculate and interpret** expected values: $\text{expected value} = \left(\begin{array}{c}\text{event 1}\\\text{value}\end{array}\right) \times \left(\begin{array}{c}\text{event 1}\\\text{probability}\end{array}\right) + \left(\begin{array}{c}\text{event 2}\\\text{value}\end{array}\right) \times \left(\begin{array}{c}\text{event 2}\\\text{probability}\end{array}\right)$
7D	accident rate death rate life expectancy	**Measure** risk in terms of accident or death rates. **Understand and interpret** vital statistics and life expectancy.
7E	arrangements with repetition permutations combinations	**Arrangements with repetition:** For r selections from a group of n choices, the number of arrangements is n^r. **Permutations:** For r selections from a group of n items, ${}_nP_r = \dfrac{n!}{(n-r)!}$ **Combinations:** For r selections from a group of n items, ${}_nC_r = \dfrac{{}_nP_r}{r!} = \dfrac{n!}{(n-r)! \times r!}$ **Coincidences are bound to happen**—understand why and the implications for probability.

UNIT 8A

Growth: Linear versus Exponential: We contrast the two basic forms of growth: *linear growth* by the same absolute amount in any time period and *exponential growth* by the same relative amount in any time period. We also explore the remarkable effects of the repeated doublings that characterize exponential growth.

UNIT 8B

Doubling Time and Half-Life: Exponential growth is characterized by a constant *doubling time,* while exponential decay is characterized by a constant *half-life*. We explore both ideas and some of their many applications.

UNIT 8C

Real Population Growth: Real population growth is neither strictly linear nor strictly exponential. We study both the reasons for and the limits to population growth, which have important implications for the future of the human race.

UNIT 8D

Logarithmic Scales: Earthquakes, Sounds, and Acids: We study the meaning and use of three important *logarithmic scales:* the magnitude scale for earthquakes, the decibel scale for sound, and the pH scale for acidity.

8

The greatest shortcoming of the human race is (its) inability to understand the exponential function.

—Albert A. Bartlett,
Professor of Physics,
University of Colorado

Exponential Astonishment

World population is currently growing by some 75 million people per year—enough to fill an entire new United States in only four years. A growing population means new challenges for our species, which we can meet only if we understand this growth. In this chapter, we will investigate the mathematical laws of growth—specifically, exponential growth. We will focus on what we call *exponential astonishment:* the intuition-defying reality of exponential growth. Although we will emphasize population growth, we will also study many other important topics, including the decay of waste from nuclear power plants, the depletion of natural resources, and the environmental effects of acid rain.

ACTIVITY Towers of Hanoi

Use this activity to gain a sense of the kinds of problems this chapter will enable you to study. Try working through it before you begin the chapter, then return to it after you've learned the chapter material.

The game called *Towers of Hanoi* consists of three pegs and a set of disks of varying sizes. Each disk has a hole in its center so that it can be moved from peg to peg. The game begins with all the disks stacked on one peg in order of decreasing size (see photo). The object of the game is to move the entire stack of disks to a different peg, following two rules:

Rule 1. Only one disk can be moved at a time.
Rule 2. A larger disk can never be placed on top of a smaller disk.

You can easily find or make a version of the Towers of Hanoi game; many Web sites have online simulations of the game, or you can make your own version by cutting disks out of cardboard. Play the game with seven disks, looking for the most efficient strategy for moving the disks. Once you have found the best strategy, answer the following questions.

1. You can view the game as a series of goals. The first goal is to end up with 1 disk on another peg, the second goal is to end up with 2 disks on another peg, and so on, until all the disks are on another peg. The first goal requires only one move: taking the smallest (top) disk and moving it to a different peg. The second goal then requires two more moves: first moving the second-smallest disk to the empty peg and then putting the smallest disk on top of it. Complete the following table as you continue the game.

Goal	Moves Required for This Step	Total Moves in Game So Far
1 disk on another peg	1	1
2 disks on another peg	2	$1 + 2 = 3$
3 disks on another peg		
4 disks on another peg		
5 disks on another peg		
6 disks on another peg		
7 disks on another peg		

2. Look at the patterns in the table. Find general formulas for the second and third columns after n steps. Confirm that your formulas give the correct results for all the entries in the table. (*Hint:* If you are using the most efficient strategy, both formulas will involve powers of 2, with n appearing in the exponent.)

3. Use the formula for the total moves in the game (column 3) to predict the total number of moves required to complete the game with 10 disks (rather than 7).

4. The game is related to a legend claiming that, at the beginning of the world, the Brahma put three large diamond needles on a brass slab in the Great Temple, and placed 64 disks of solid gold on one needle; the disks were arranged in order of decreasing size, just like the disks in the Towers of Hanoi game. Working in shifts, day and night, the temple priests moved the golden disks according to the two rules of the game. How many total moves are required to move the entire set of 64 disks to another needle?

5. The legend holds that upon completion of the task of moving all 64 disks, the temple will crumble and the world will come to an end. Assume that the priests

can move very fast, so they move one disk each second. Based on your answer to question 4, how many years will it take to move the entire stack of 64 disks? If the legend is true, do we have anything to worry about right now? (Useful data: Scientists estimate the current age of the universe to be about 14 billion years.)

6. The way in which the number of moves required for each step increases is an example of exponential growth—the topic of this chapter. Briefly comment on what this game illustrates about the nature of exponential growth.

UNIT 8A Growth: Linear versus Exponential

Imagine two communities, Straightown and Powertown, each with an initial population of 10,000 people (Figure 8.1). Straightown grows at a constant rate of 500 people per year, so its population reaches 10,500 after 1 year, 11,000 after 2 years, 11,500 after 3 years, and so on. Powertown grows at a constant rate of 5 *percent* per year. Because 5% of 10,000 is 500, Powertown's population also reaches 10,500 after 1 year. In the second year, however, Powertown's population increases by 5% of 10,500, which is 525, to 11,025. In the third year, Powertown's population increases by 5% of 11,025, or by 551 people. Figure 8.1 contrasts the populations of the two towns over a 45-year period. Note that Powertown's population rises ever more steeply and quickly outpaces Straightown's.

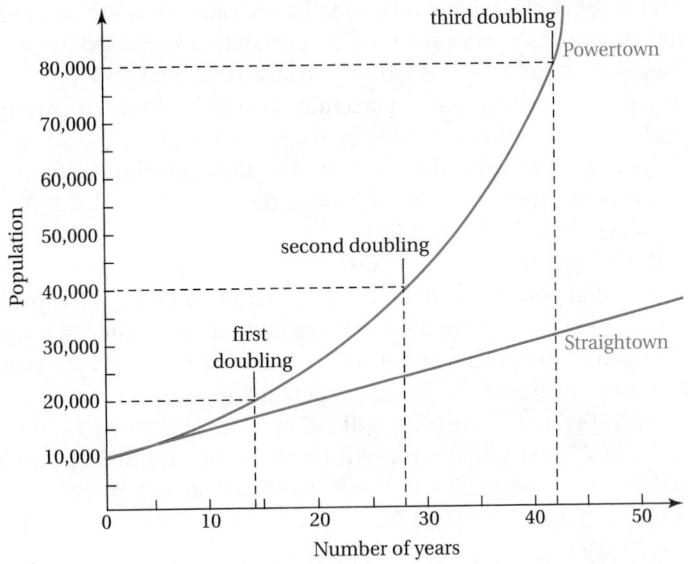

FIGURE 8.1 Straightown grows linearly, while Powertown grows exponentially.

Straightown and Powertown illustrate two fundamentally different types of growth. Straightown grows by the same *absolute* amount—500 people—each year, which is characteristic of **linear growth.** In contrast, Powertown grows by the same *relative* amount—5%—each year, which is characteristic of **exponential growth.**

> **TWO BASIC GROWTH PATTERNS**
>
> **Linear growth** occurs when a quantity grows by the same *absolute* amount in each unit of time.
>
> **Exponential growth** occurs when a quantity grows by the same *relative* amount—that is, by the same *percentage*—in each unit of time.

The terms *linear* and *exponential* can also be applied to quantities that decrease with time. For example, *exponential decay* occurs when a quantity decreases by the same relative amount in each unit of time. In the rest of this unit, we will explore the surprising properties of exponential growth.

Example 1 Linear or Exponential?

In each of the following situations, state whether the growth (or decay) is linear or exponential, and answer the associated questions.

a. The number of students at Wilson High School has increased by 50 in each of the past four years. If the student population was 750 four years ago, what is it today?
b. The price of milk has been rising 3% per year. If the price of a gallon of milk was $4 a year ago, what is it now?
c. Tax law allows you to depreciate the value of your equipment by $200 per year. If you purchased the equipment three years ago for $1000, what is its depreciated value today?
d. The memory capacity of state-of-the-art computer hard drives is doubling approximately every two years. If a company's top-of-the-line drive holds 2.5 terabytes today, what will it hold in six years?
e. The price of high-definition TV sets has been falling by about 25% per year. If the price is $1000 today, what can you expect it to be in two years?

Solution

a. The number of students increased by the same absolute amount each year, so this is *linear growth*. Because the student population increased by 50 students per year, in four years it grew by $4 \times 50 = 200$ students, from 750 to 950.
b. The price rises by the same percent each year, so this is *exponential growth*. If the price was $4 a year ago, it increased by $0.03 \times \$4 = \$0.12$, making the price $4.12.
c. The equipment value decreases by the same absolute amount each year, so this is *linear decay*. In three years, the value decreases by $3 \times \$200 = \$600$, so the value decreases from $1000 to $400.
d. A doubling is the same as a 100% increase, so the two-year doubling time represents *exponential growth*. With a doubling every two years, the capacity will double three times in six years: from 2.5 terabytes to 5 terabytes after two years, from 5 to 10 terabytes after four years, and from 10 to 20 terabytes after six years.
e. The price decreases by the same percentage each year, so this is *exponential decay*. From $1000 today, the price will fall by 25%, or $0.25 \times \$1000 = \$250$, in one year. Therefore, next year's price will be $750. The following year, the price will again fall by 25%, or $0.25 \times \$750 = \$187.50$, so the price after two years will be $\$750 - \$187.50 = \$562.50$.

Now try Exercises 9–16.

The Impact of Doublings

Look again at the graph of Powertown's population in Figure 8.1. After about 14 years, the original population has doubled to 20,000. In the next 14 years, it doubles again to 40,000. It then doubles again, to 80,000, 14 years after that. This type of repeated *doubling*, in which each doubling occurs in the same amount of time, is a hallmark of exponential growth.

The time it takes for each doubling depends on the rate of the exponential growth. In Unit 8B, we'll see how the doubling time depends on the percentage growth rate. Here, we'll explore three parables that show how doublings make exponential growth so very different from linear growth.

Parable 1: From Hero to Headless in 64 Easy Steps

Legend has it that, when chess was invented in ancient times, a king was so enchanted that he said to the inventor, "Name your reward."

"If you please, king, put one grain of wheat on the first square of my chessboard," said the inventor. "Then, place two grains on the second square, four grains on the third square, eight grains on the fourth square, and so on." The king gladly agreed, thinking the man a fool for asking for a few grains of wheat when he could have had gold or jewels. But let's see how it adds up for the 64 squares on a chessboard.

Table 8.1 shows the calculations. Each square gets twice as many grains as the previous square, so the number of grains on any square is a power of 2. The third column shows the total number of grains up to each point, and the last column gives a simple formula for the total number of grains.

TABLE 8.1

Square	Grains on This Square	Total Grains Thus Far	Formula for Total Grains
1	$1 = 2^0$	1	$2^1 - 1$
2	$2 = 2^1$	$1 + 2 = 3$	$2^2 - 1$
3	$4 = 2^2$	$3 + 4 = 7$	$2^3 - 1$
4	$8 = 2^3$	$7 + 8 = 15$	$2^4 - 1$
5	$16 = 2^4$	$15 + 16 = 31$	$2^5 - 1$
⋮	⋮	⋮	⋮
64	2^{63}		$2^{64} - 1$

From the pattern in the last column, we see that the grand total for all 64 squares is $2^{64} - 1$ grains. How much wheat is this? With a calculator, you can confirm that $2^{64} = 1.8 \times 10^{19}$, or about 18 *billion billion*. Not only would it be difficult to fit so many grains on a chessboard, but this number happens to be larger than the total number of grains of wheat harvested in all human history. The king never finished paying the inventor and, according to legend, instead had him beheaded. **Now try Exercises 17–20.**

Parable 2: The Magic Penny

One lucky day, you meet a leprechaun who promises to give you fantastic wealth, but hands you only a penny before disappearing. You head home and place the penny under your pillow. The next morning, to your surprise, you find two pennies under your pillow. The following morning, you find four pennies, and the fourth morning, eight pennies. Apparently, the leprechaun gave you a *magic* penny: While you sleep, each magic penny turns into *two* magic pennies. Table 8.2 shows your growing wealth. Note that "day 0" is the day you met the leprechaun. Generalizing from the first four rows of the table, the amount under your pillow after t days is

$$\$0.01 \times 2^t$$

We can use this formula to figure out how long it will be until you have fantastic wealth. After $t = 9$ days, you'll have $\$0.01 \times 2^9 = \$5.12$, which is barely enough to buy lunch. But by the end of a month, or $t = 30$ days, you'll have $\$0.01 \times 2^{30} = \$10{,}737{,}418.24$. That is, you'll be a millionaire within a month, and you'll need a much larger pillow! In fact, if your magic pennies keep doubling, by the end of just 51 days you'll have $\$0.01 \times 2^{51} \approx \$22.5$ trillion, which is more than enough to pay off the national debt of the United States. **Now try Exercises 21–24.**

TABLE 8.2

Day	Amount Under Pillow
0	$\$0.01 \times 2^0 = \$0.01$
1	$\$0.01 \times 2^1 = \$0.02$
2	$\$0.01 \times 2^2 = \$0.04$
3	$\$0.01 \times 2^3 = \$0.08$
4	$\$0.01 \times 2^4 = \$0.16$
⋮	⋮
t	$\$0.01 \times 2^t$

Parable 3: Bacteria in a Bottle

For our third parable, we turn to a story with relevance to the future of the human race. Suppose you place a single bacterium in a bottle at 11:00 a.m. It grows and at

11:01 divides into two bacteria. These two bacteria each grow and at 11:02 divide into four bacteria, which grow and at 11:03 divide into eight bacteria, and so on.

Now, suppose the bacteria continue to double every minute, and the bottle is full at 12:00. You may already realize that the number of bacteria at this point must be 2^{60} (because they doubled every minute for 60 minutes), but the important fact is that we have a bacterial disaster on our hands: Because the bacteria have filled the bottle, the entire bacterial colony is doomed. Let's examine this tragedy in greater detail, by asking a few questions about the demise of the colony.

BY THE WAY

The bacteria in a bottle parable was developed by Professor Albert A. Bartlett, University of Colorado, who has given more than 1670 lectures on the lessons of exponential growth around the country over the past 40 years.

- *Question 1:* If the tragedy occurred because the bottle was full at 12:00, when was the bottle *half*-full?

  Answer: Because it took one hour to fill the bottle, many people guess that it was half-full after a half-hour, or at 11:30. However, because the bacteria double in number every minute, they must also have doubled during the last minute, which means the bottle went from being half-full to full during the final minute. That is, the bottle was half-full at 11:59, just 1 minute before the disaster.

- *Question 2:* Imagine that *you* are a mathematically sophisticated bacterium, and at 11:56 you recognize the impending disaster. You immediately jump on your soapbox and warn that unless your fellow bacteria slow their growth dramatically, the end is just 4 minutes away. Will anyone believe you?

  Answer: You've done your mathematics correctly; the bottle will indeed be full in just 4 minutes. But how will it appear to others who have not done the calculations? As we've already seen, the bottle will be half-full at 11:59. Continuing to work backward through the doublings each minute, we find that it will be $\frac{1}{4}$ full at 11:58, $\frac{1}{8}$ full at 11:57, and $\frac{1}{16}$ full at 11:56. Therefore, if your fellow bacteria look around the bottle at 11:56, they'll see that only $\frac{1}{16}$ of the bottle has been used. In other words, the amount of unused space is *15 times* the amount of used space. You are asking them to believe that, in just the next 4 minutes, they'll fill 15 times as much space as they did in their entire 56-minute history. Unless they do the mathematics for themselves, they are unlikely to take your warnings seriously. Figure 8.2 shows the situation graphically. Note that the bottle remains nearly empty for most of the 60 minutes, but the continued doublings fill it rapidly in the final 4 minutes.

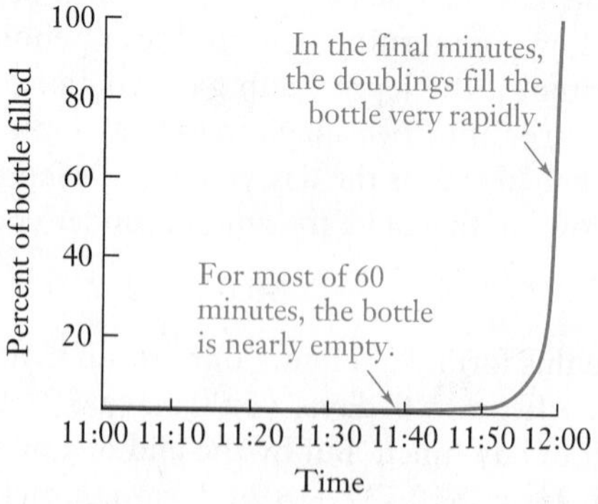

FIGURE 8.2 The population of the bacteria in the bottle

- *Question 3:* It's 11:59 and, with the bottle half-full, your fellow bacteria are finally taking your warnings seriously. They quickly start a space program, sending little bacterial spaceships out into the lab in search of new bottles. Thankfully, they discover three more bottles (making a total of four, including the one already occupied). Working quickly, they initiate a mass migration by packing bacteria onto spaceships and sending them to the new bottles. They successfully distribute the population evenly among the four bottles, just in time to avert the disaster. Given that they now have four bottles rather than just one, how much time have they gained for their civilization?

Answer: Because it took one hour to fill one bottle, you might guess that it would take four hours to fill four bottles. But remember that the bacterial population continues to *double* each minute. If there are enough bacteria to fill one bottle at 12:00, there will be enough to fill two bottles by 12:01 and four bottles by 12:02. The discovery of three new bottles gives them only 2 additional minutes.

Facts do not cease to exist because they are ignored.

—Aldous Huxley

- *Question 4:* Suppose the bacteria continue their space program, constantly looking for more bottles. Is there any hope that further discoveries will allow the colony to continue its exponential growth?

  Answer: Let's do some calculations. After n minutes, the bacterial population is 2^n. For example, it is $2^0 = 1$ when the first bacterium starts the colony at 11:00, $2^1 = 2$ at 11:01, $2^2 = 4$ at 11:02, and so on. There are 2^{60} bacteria when the first bottle fills at 12:00, and 2^{62} bacteria when four bottles are full at 12:02. Suppose that, somehow, the bacteria managed to keep doubling every minute until 1:00. By that time, the number of bacteria would be 2^{120}, because it has been 120 minutes since the colony began. Now, we must figure out how much space they'd require for this population.

  The smallest bacteria measure approximately 10^{-7} m (0.1 micrometer) across. If we assume that the bacteria are roughly cube-shaped, the volume of a single bacterium is

$$(10^{-7}\text{ m})^3 = 10^{-21}\text{ m}^3$$

  Therefore, the colony of 2^{120} bacteria would occupy a total volume of

$$2^{120} \times 10^{-21}\text{ m}^3 \approx 1.3 \times 10^{15}\text{ m}^3$$

  With this volume, the bacteria would cover the entire surface of the Earth in a layer more than 2 meters deep! (See Exercise 27 to calculate this result for yourself.)

  In fact, if the doublings continued for just $5\frac{1}{2}$ hours, the volume of bacteria would exceed the volume of the entire universe (see Exercise 28). Needless to say, this cannot happen. The exponential growth of the colony cannot possibly continue for long, no matter what technological advances might be imagined. **Now try Exercises 25–28.**

Time Out to Think

Some people have suggested that we could find room for an exponentially growing human population by colonizing other planets in our solar system. Is this possible?

Doubling Lessons

The three parables reveal at least two key lessons about the repeated doublings that arise with exponential growth. First, if you look back at Table 8.1, you'll notice that the number of grains on each square is nearly equal to the total number of grains on all previous squares combined. For example, the 16 grains on the fifth square are 1 more than the total of 15 grains on the first four squares combined.

Second, all three parables show quantities growing to impossible proportions. We cannot possibly fit all the wheat harvested in world history on a chessboard; $22 trillion worth of pennies won't fit under your pillow, and it is far more than the number of pennies ever produced; and a colony of bacteria can't possibly fill the universe.

KEY FACTS ABOUT EXPONENTIAL GROWTH

- Exponential growth leads to repeated doublings. With each doubling, the amount of increase is approximately equal to the *sum* of all preceding doublings.
- Exponential growth cannot continue indefinitely. After only a relatively small number of doublings, exponentially growing quantities reach impossible proportions.

QUICK QUIZ

Choose the best answer to each of the following questions. Explain your reasoning with one or more complete sentences.

1. A town's population increases in one year from 100,000 to 110,000. If the population is growing *linearly*, at a steady rate, then at the end of a second year it will be

   a. 110,000. b. 120,000. c. 121,000.

2. A town's population increases in one year from 100,000 to 110,000. If the population is growing *exponentially* at a steady rate, then at the end of a second year it will be

   a. 110,000. b. 120,000. c. 121,000.

3. The balance owed on your credit card doubles from $1000 to $2000 in 6 months. If your balance is growing *exponentially*, how much longer will it be until it reaches $4000?

   a. 6 months b. 12 months c. 18 months

4. The number of songs in your iPod has risen from 200 to 400 in 3 months. If the number of songs is increasing *linearly*, how much longer will it be until you have 800 songs?

   a. 3 months

   b. 6 months

   c. $1\frac{1}{2}$ months

5. Which of the following is an example of *exponential decay?*

   a. The population of a rural community is falling by 100 people per year.

   b. The price of gasoline is falling by $0.02 per week.

   c. Government support for education is falling 1% per year.

6. On a chessboard with 64 squares, you place 1 penny on the first square, 2 pennies on the second square, 4 pennies on the third square, and so on. If you could follow this pattern to fill the entire board, about how much money would you need in total?

   a. about $1.28 b. about $500,000

   c. about 10,000 times as much as the current U.S. federal debt

7. At 11:00 you place a single bacterium in a bottle, and at 11:01 it divides into 2 bacteria, which at 11:02 divide into 4 bacteria, and so on. How many bacterial will be in the bottle at 11:30?

   a. 2×30 b. 2^{30} c. 2×10^{30}

8. Consider the bacterial population described in Exercise 7. How many more bacteria are in the bottle at 11:31 than at 11:30?

   a. 30 b. 2^{30} c. 2^{31}

9. Consider the bacterial population described in Exercise 7. If the bacteria occupy a volume of 1 cubic meter at 12:02 and continue their exponential growth, when will they occupy a volume of 2 cubic meters?

   a. 12:03 b. 12:04 c. 1:02

10. Which of the following is *not* true of any exponentially growing population?

    a. With every doubling, the population increase is nearly equal to the total increase from all previous doublings.

    b. The steady growth makes it easy to see any impending crisis long before the crisis becomes severe.

    c. The exponential growth must eventually stop.

Exercises 8A

REVIEW QUESTIONS

1. Describe the basic differences between linear growth and exponential growth.
2. Briefly explain how repeated doublings characterize exponential growth. Describe the impact of doublings, using the chessboard or magic penny parable.
3. Briefly summarize the story of the bacteria in the bottle. Be sure to explain the answers to the four questions asked in the text, and describe why the answers are surprising.
4. Explain the meaning of the two key facts about exponential growth given at the end of this unit. Then create your own example of exponential growth and describe the influence and impact of repeated doubling.

DOES IT MAKE SENSE?

Decide whether each of the following statements makes sense (or is clearly true) or does not make sense (or is clearly false). Explain your reasoning.

5. Money in a bank account earning compound interest at an annual percentage rate of 3% is an example of exponential growth.
6. Suppose you had a magic bank account in which your balance doubled each day. If you started with just \$1, you'd be a millionaire in less than a month.
7. A small town that grows exponentially can become a large city in just a few decades.
8. Human population has been growing exponentially for a few centuries, and we can expect this trend to continue forever in the future.

BASIC SKILLS & CONCEPTS

9–16: **Linear or Exponential?** State whether the growth (or decay) is linear or exponential, and answer the associated question.

9. The population of MeadowView is increasing at a rate of 325 people per year. If the population is 2500 today, what will it be in four years?
10. The population of Winesburg is increasing at a rate of 3% per year. If the population is 75,000 today, what will it be in three years?
11. During the 1999 episode of hyperinflation in Brazil, the price of food increased at a rate of 30% per month. If your food bill was R\$100 one month during this period, what was it three months later? (R\$ is the symbol for the *real*, Brazil's unit of currency.)
12. The price of a gallon of gasoline is increasing by 3¢ per week. If the price is \$3.10 per gallon today, what will it be in ten weeks?
13. The price of computer memory is decreasing at a rate of 14% per year. If a memory chip costs \$50 today, what will it cost in three years?
14. The value of your car is decreasing by 10% per year. If the car is worth \$12,000 today, what will it be worth in two years?
15. The value of your house is increasing by \$2000 per year. If it is worth \$100,000 today, what will it be worth in five years?
16. The value of your house is decreasing by 7% per year. If it is worth \$250,000 today, what will it be worth in three years?

17–20: **Chessboard Parable.** Use the chessboard parable presented in the text. Assume that each grain of wheat weighs 1/7000 pound.

17. How many grains of wheat should be placed on square 16 of the chessboard? Find the total number of grains and their total weight (in pounds) at this point.
18. How many grains of wheat should be placed on square 32 of the chessboard? Find the total number of grains and their total weight (in pounds) at this point.
19. What is the total weight of all the wheat when the chessboard is full?
20. According to the U.S. Department of Agriculture, the current world harvest of all wheat, rice, and corn is less than 2 billion tons per year. How does this total compare to the weight of the wheat on the chessboard? (*Hint*: 1 ton = 2000 pounds.)

21–24: **Magic Penny Parable.** Use the magic penny parable presented in the text.

21. How much money would you have after 22 days?
22. Suppose that you stacked the pennies after 22 days. How high would the stack rise, in kilometers? (*Hint*: Find a few pennies and a ruler.)
23. How many days would elapse before you had a total of over \$1 billion? (*Hint*: Proceed by trial and error.)
24. Suppose that you could keep making a single stack of the pennies. After how many days would the stack be long enough to reach the nearest star (beyond the Sun), which is about 4.3 light-years (4.0×10^{13} km) away? (*Hint*: Proceed by trial and error.)

25–26: **Bacteria in a Bottle Parable.** Use the bacteria parable presented in the text.

25. How many bacteria are in the bottle at 11:50? What fraction of the bottle is full at that time?
26. How many bacteria are in the bottle at 11:15? What fraction of the bottle is full at that time?
27. **Knee-Deep in Bacteria.** The total surface area of Earth is about 5.1×10^{14} m^2. Assume that the bacteria continued their doublings for two hours (as discussed in the text), at which point they were distributed uniformly over Earth's surface. How deep would the bacterial layer be? Would it be knee-deep, more than knee-deep, or less than knee-deep? (*Hint*: Remember that a volume divided by an area gives a depth.)
28. **Bacterial Universe.** Suppose the bacteria in the parable continued to double their population every minute. How long would it take until their volume exceeded the total volume of the observable universe, which is about 10^{79} m^3? (*Hint*: Proceed by trial and error.)

FURTHER APPLICATIONS

29. **Human Doubling.** Human population in the year 2000 was about 6 billion. Suppose this population increases exponentially with a doubling time of 50 years.

a. Extend the following table, showing the population at 50-year intervals under this scenario, until you reach the year 3000. Use scientific notation, as shown.

Year	Population
2000	6×10^9
2050	$12 \times 10^9 = 1.2 \times 10^{10}$
2100	$24 \times 10^9 = 2.4 \times 10^{10}$
⋮	⋮

b. The total surface area of Earth is about 5.1×10^{14} m^2. Assuming that people could occupy all this area (in reality, most of it is ocean), approximately when would people be so crowded that every person would have only 1 m^2 of space?

c. Suppose that, when we take into account the area needed to grow food and to find other resources, each person actually requires about 10^4 m^2 of area to survive. About when would we reach this limit?

d. Suppose that we learn to colonize other planets and moons in our solar system. The total surface area of the worlds in our solar system that could potentially be colonized (not counting gas planets such as Jupiter) is roughly five times the surface area of Earth. Under the assumptions of part c, could humanity fit in our solar system in the year 3000? Explain.

30. **Doubling Time vs. Initial Amount.**

a. Would you rather start with one penny ($0.01) and double your wealth every day or start with one dime ($0.10) and double your wealth every five days (assuming you want to get rich)? Explain.

b. Would you rather start with one penny ($0.01) and double your wealth every day or start with $1000 and double your wealth every two days (assuming you want to get rich in the long run)? Explain.

c. Which is more important in determining how fast exponential growth occurs: the doubling time or the initial amount? Explain.

WEB PROJECTS

31. **Computing Power.** Choose an aspect of computing power (such as processor speed or memory chip capacity) and investigate its growth. Has the growth been exponential? How much longer is the exponential growth likely to continue? Explain.

32. **Web Growth.** Investigate the growth of the Web itself, in terms of both number of users and number of Web pages. Has the growth been linear or exponential? How do you think the growth will change in the future? Explain.

IN YOUR WORLD

33. **Linear Growth.** Identify at least two news stories that describe a quantity undergoing linear growth or decay. Describe the growth or decay process.

34. **Exponential Growth.** Identify at least two news stories that describe a quantity undergoing exponential growth or decay. Describe the growth or decay process.

UNIT 8B Doubling Time and Half-Life

Exponential growth leads to repeated doublings and exponential decay leads to repeated *halvings*. However, in most cases of exponential growth or decay, we are given the rate of growth or decay—usually as a percentage—rather than the time required for doubling or halving. In this unit, we'll convert between growth (or decay) rates and doubling (or halving) times.

Doubling Time

The time required for each doubling in exponential growth is called the **doubling time**. For example, the doubling time for the magic penny (see Unit 8A) was one day, because your wealth doubled each day. The doubling time for the bacteria in the bottle was one minute.

Given the doubling time, we can easily calculate the value of a quantity at any time. Consider an initial population of 10,000 that grows with a doubling time of 10 years:

- In 10 years, or one doubling time, the population increases by a factor of 2, to a new population of $2 \times 10{,}000 = 20{,}000$.
- In 20 years, or two doubling times, the population increases by a factor of $2^2 = 4$, to a new population of $4 \times 10{,}000 = 40{,}000$.
- In 30 years, or three doubling times, the population increases by a factor of $2^3 = 8$, to a new population of $8 \times 10{,}000 = 80{,}000$.

We can generalize this idea by letting t be the amount of time that has passed and T_{double} be the doubling time. Note that after $t = 30$ years with a doubling time of $T_{double} = 10$ years, there have been $t/T_{double} = 30/10 = 3$ doublings. Generalizing, we find that the number of doublings after a time t is t/T_{double}. That is, the size of the population after time t is the initial population times $2^{t/T_{double}}$.

CALCULATIONS WITH THE DOUBLING TIME

After a time t, an exponentially growing quantity with a doubling time of T_{double} increases in size by a factor of $2^{t/T_{double}}$. The new value of the growing quantity is related to its initial value (at $t = 0$) by

$$\text{new value} = \text{initial value} \times 2^{t/T_{double}}$$

Time Out to Think

Consider an initial population of 10,000 that grows with a doubling time of 10 years. Confirm that the above formula gives a population of 80,000 after 30 years, as we found earlier. What does the formula predict for the population after 50 years?

Example 1 Doubling with Compound Interest

Compound interest (Unit 4B) produces exponential growth because an interest-bearing account grows by the same percentage each year. Suppose your bank account has a doubling time of 13 years. By what factor does your balance increase in 50 years?

Solution The doubling time is $T_{double} = 13$ years, so after $t = 50$ years your balance increases by a factor of

$$2^{t/T_{double}} = 2^{50\,yr/13\,yr} = 2^{3.8462} \approx 14.382$$

For example, if you start with a balance of \$1000, in 50 years it will grow to \$1000 × 14.382 = \$14,382. **Now try Exercises 25–32.**

Example 2 World Population Growth

World population doubled from 3 billion in 1960 to 6 billion in 2000. Suppose that world population continued to grow (from 2000 on) with a doubling time of 40 years. What would the population be in 2030? in 2200?

Solution The doubling time is $T_{double} = 40$ years. If we let $t = 0$ represent 2000, the year 2030 is $t = 30$ years later. If the 2000 population of 6 billion is used as the initial value, the population in 2030 would be

$$\begin{aligned} \text{new value} &= \text{initial value} \times 2^{t/T_{double}} \\ &= 6 \text{ billion} \times 2^{30\,yr/40\,yr} \\ &= 6 \text{ billion} \times 2^{0.75} \approx 10.1 \text{ billion} \end{aligned}$$

By 2200, which is $t = 200$ years after 2000, the population would reach

$$\begin{aligned} \text{new value} &= \text{initial value} \times 2^{t/T_{double}} \\ &= 6 \text{ billion} \times 2^{200\,yr/40\,yr} \\ &= 6 \text{ billion} \times 2^{5} = 192 \text{ billion} \end{aligned}$$

If world population continued to grow at the same rate it did between 1960 and 2000, it would reach 10 billion by 2030 and 192 billion by 2200.

Now try Exercises 33–34.

Time Out to Think

Do you think that it's really possible for the human population on Earth to reach 192 billion? Why or why not?

DILBERT reprinted by permission of United Feature Syndicate, Inc.

The Approximate Doubling Time Formula

Consider an ecological study of a prairie dog community. The community contains 100 prairie dogs when the study begins, and researchers soon determine that the population is increasing at a rate of 10% per month. That is, each month the population grows to 110% of, or 1.1 times, its previous value (see the "*of* versus *more than*" rule in Unit 3A). Table 8.3 tracks the population growth (rounded to the nearest whole number).

TABLE 8.3 Growth of a Prairie Dog Community

Month	Population	Month	Population
0	100	8	$(1.1)^8 \times 100 = 214$
1	$(1.1)^1 \times 100 = 110$	9	$(1.1)^9 \times 100 = 236$
2	$(1.1)^2 \times 100 = 121$	10	$(1.1)^{10} \times 100 = 259$
3	$(1.1)^3 \times 100 = 133$	11	$(1.1)^{11} \times 100 = 285$
4	$(1.1)^4 \times 100 = 146$	12	$(1.1)^{12} \times 100 = 314$
5	$(1.1)^5 \times 100 = 161$	13	$(1.1)^{13} \times 100 = 345$
6	$(1.1)^6 \times 100 = 177$	14	$(1.1)^{14} \times 100 = 380$
7	$(1.1)^7 \times 100 = 195$	15	$(1.1)^{15} \times 100 = 418$

Note that the population nearly doubles (to 195) after 7 months, then nearly doubles again (to 380) after 14 months. This roughly seven-month doubling time is related to the 10% growth rate as follows:

$$\text{doubling time} \approx \frac{70}{\text{percentage growth rate}} = \frac{70}{10/\text{mo}} = 7\text{ mo}$$

This formula, in which the doubling time is approximately 70 divided by the percentage growth rate, works whenever the growth rate is relatively small (less than about 15%). It is often called the **rule of 70**.

APPROXIMATE DOUBLING TIME FORMULA (RULE OF 70)

For a quantity growing exponentially at a rate of P% per time period, the doubling time is *approximately*

$$T_{\text{double}} \approx \frac{70}{P}$$

This approximation works best for small growth rates and breaks down for growth rates over about 15%.

Example 3 Population Doubling Time

World population was about 6.0 billion in 2000 and was growing at a rate of about 1.4% per year. What is the approximate doubling time at this growth rate? If this growth rate were to continue, what would world population be in 2030? Compare to the result in Example 2.

Solution We can use the approximate doubling time formula because the growth rate is much less than 15%. The percentage growth rate of 1.4% per year means we set $P = 1.4/\text{yr}$:

$$T_{\text{double}} \approx \frac{70}{P} = \frac{70}{1.4/\text{yr}} = 50 \text{ yr}$$

The doubling time is approximately 50 years. The year 2030 is $t = 30$ years after 2000, so the population in 2030 would be

$$\begin{aligned} \text{new value} &= \text{initial value} \times 2^{t/T_{\text{double}}} \\ &= 6.0 \text{ billion} \times 2^{30\,\text{yr}/50\,\text{yr}} \\ &= 6.0 \text{ billion} \times 2^{0.6} \approx 9.1 \text{ billion} \end{aligned}$$

At a 1.4 % growth rate, world population would be about 9 billion in 2030. This is a billion fewer people than predicted in Example 2, in which the doubling time was assumed to be 40 years rather than 50 years. **Now try Exercises 35–36.**

Example 4 Solving the Doubling Time Formula

World population doubled in the 40 years from 1960 to 2000. What was the average percentage growth rate during this period? Contrast this growth rate with the 2000 growth rate of 1.4% per year.

Solution We can answer the question by solving the approximate doubling time formula for P. We multiply both sides of the formula by P and divide both sides by T_{double}. You should confirm that this gives the following result:

$$P \approx \frac{70}{T_{\text{double}}}$$

Substituting $T_{\text{double}} = 40$ years, we find

$$P \approx \frac{70}{T_{\text{double}}} = \frac{70}{40 \text{ yr}} = 1.75/\text{yr}$$

The average population growth rate between 1960 and 2000 was about $P\% = 1.75\%$ per year. This is 0.35 percentage point higher than the 2000 growth rate of 1.4% per year. **Now try Exercises 37–40.**

Exponential Decay and Half-Life

Exponential *decay* occurs whenever a quantity *decreases* by the same percentage in every fixed time period (for example, by 20% every year). In that case, the value of the quantity repeatedly decreases to half its value, with each halving occurring in a time called the **half-life.**

You may have heard half-lives described for radioactive materials such as uranium or plutonium. For example, radioactive plutonium-239 (Pu-239) has a half-life of about 24,000 years. To understand the meaning of the half-life, suppose that 100 pounds of Pu-239 is deposited at a nuclear waste site. The plutonium gradually decays into other substances as follows:

- In 24,000 years, or one half-life, the amount of Pu-239 declines to 1/2 its original value, or to $(1/2) \times 100$ pounds $= 50$ pounds.

BY THE WAY

Plutonium-239 is the chemical element plutonium in a form (or *isotope*) with atomic weight 239. Atomic weight is the total number of protons and neutrons in the nucleus. Because all plutonium nuclei have 94 protons, Pu-239 nuclei have $239 - 94 = 145$ neutrons.

Historical Note

The atomic bomb that devastated Nagasaki during World War II generated its destructive power by fission of plutonium-239. (The Hiroshima bomb used uranium-235.)

- In 48,000 years, or two half-lives, the amount of Pu-239 declines to $(1/2)^2 = 1/4$ its original value, or to $(1/4) \times 100$ pounds $= 25$ pounds.
- In 72,000 years, or three half-lives, the amount of Pu-239 declines to $(1/2)^3 = 1/8$ its original value, or to $(1/8) \times 100$ pounds $= 12.5$ pounds.

We can generalize this idea much as we did earlier for the doubling time. A single halving reduces a quantity by a factor of $1/2$, two halvings reduce it by a factor of $(1/2)^2$, and three halvings reduce it by a factor of $(1/2)^3$. If we let t be the amount of time that has passed and T_{half} be the half-life, then the number of halvings after a time t is t/T_{half}. That is, the quantity after time t is the original quantity times this factor of $(1/2)^{t/T_{\text{half}}}$.

CALCULATIONS WITH THE HALF-LIFE

After a time t, an exponentially decaying quantity with a half-life of T_{half} decreases in size by a factor of $(1/2)^{t/T_{\text{half}}}$. The new value of the decaying quantity is related to its initial value (at $t = 0$) by

$$\text{new value} = \text{initial value} \times \left(\frac{1}{2}\right)^{t/T_{\text{half}}}$$

BY THE WAY

Ordinary carbon is carbon-12, which is stable (not radioactive). Carbon-14 is produced in the Earth's atmosphere by high-energy particles coming from the Sun. It mixes with ordinary carbon and therefore becomes incorporated into living tissue through respiration (breathing).

Example 5 Carbon-14 Decay

Radioactive carbon-14 has a half-life of about 5700 years. It collects in organisms only while they are alive. Once they are dead, it only decays. What fraction of the carbon-14 in an animal bone still remains 1000 years after the animal has died?

Solution The half-life is $T_{\text{half}} = 5700$ years, so the fraction of the initial amount remaining after $t = 1000$ years is

$$\left(\frac{1}{2}\right)^{t/T_{\text{half}}} = \left(\frac{1}{2}\right)^{1000\,\text{yr}/5700\,\text{yr}} \approx 0.885$$

For example, if the bone originally contained 1 kilogram of carbon-14, the amount remaining after 1000 years is approximately 0.885 kilogram. We can use this idea to determine the age of bones found at archaeological sites, as we'll discuss in Unit 9C.

Now try Exercises 41–44.

Example 6 Plutonium After 100,000 Years

Suppose that 100 pounds of Pu-239 is deposited at a nuclear waste site. How much of it will still be present in 100,000 years?

Solution The half-life of Pu-239 is $T_{\text{half}} = 24{,}000$ years. Given an initial amount of 100 pounds, the amount remaining after $t = 100{,}000$ years is

$$\text{new value} = \text{initial value} \times \left(\frac{1}{2}\right)^{t/T_{\text{half}}} = 100\text{ lb} \times \left(\frac{1}{2}\right)^{100{,}000\,\text{yr}/24{,}000\,\text{yr}} \approx 5.6\text{ lb}$$

About 5.6 pounds of the original 100 pounds of Pu-239 will still be present in 100,000 years.

Now try Exercises 45–48.

Time Out to Think

Plutonium, which is not found naturally on the Earth, is made in nuclear reactors for use both as fuel for nuclear power plants and for nuclear weapons. Based on its half-life, explain why the safe disposal of Pu-239 poses a significant challenge.

The Approximate Half-Life Formula

The approximate doubling time formula (the rule of 70) found earlier works equally well for exponential decay if we replace the doubling time with the half-life and the percentage growth rate with the percentage decay rate.

APPROXIMATE HALF-LIFE FORMULA

For a quantity decaying exponentially at a rate of $P\%$ per time period, the half-life is *approximately*

$$T_{\text{half}} \approx \frac{70}{P}$$

This approximation works best for small decay rates and breaks down for decay rates over about 15%.

Take Note

Some books treat P as negative for exponential decay, in which case the half-life is defined as $70/|P|$, where $|P|$ is the absolute value of P.

Example 7 Devaluation of Currency

Suppose that inflation causes the value of the Russian ruble to fall at a rate of 12% per year (relative to the dollar). At this rate, approximately how long does it take for the ruble to lose half its value?

Solution We can use the approximate half-life formula because the decay rate is less than 15%. The 12% decay rate means we set $P = 12/\text{yr}$:

$$T_{\text{half}} \approx \frac{70}{P} = \frac{70}{12/\text{yr}} \approx 5.8 \text{ yr}$$

The half-life is a little less than six years, meaning that the ruble loses half its value (against the dollar) in six years.

Now try Exercises 49–52.

Exact Formulas for Doubling Time and Half-Life

The approximate doubling time and half-life formulas are useful because they are easy to remember. However, for more precise work or for cases of larger rates where the approximate formulas break down, we need the exact formulas, given below. In Unit 9C, we will see how they are derived. These formulas use the **fractional growth rate**, defined as $r = P/100$, with r positive for growth and negative for decay. For example, if the percentage growth rate is 5% per year, the fractional growth rate is $r = 0.05$ per year. For a 5% *decay* rate per year, the fractional growth rate is $r = -0.05$ per year.

EXACT DOUBLING TIME AND HALF-LIFE FORMULAS

For an exponentially growing quantity with a fractional growth rate r, the doubling time is

$$T_{\text{double}} = \frac{\log_{10} 2}{\log_{10}(1 + r)}$$

For an exponentially decaying quantity, we use a *negative* value for r (for example, if the decay rate is $P = 5\%$ per year, we set $r = -0.05$ per year). The half-life is

$$T_{\text{half}} = -\frac{\log_{10} 2}{\log_{10}(1 + r)}$$

Note that *the units of time used for T and r must be the same.* For example, if the fractional growth rate is 0.05 per *month*, then the doubling time will also be measured in months. Also note that the formulas ensure that both T_{double} and T_{half} have positive values.

Example 8 Large Growth Rate

A population of rats is growing at a rate of 80% per month. Find the exact doubling time for this growth rate and compare it to the doubling time found with the approximate doubling time formula.

Solution The growth rate of 80% per month means $P = 80/\text{mo}$ or $r = 0.8/\text{mo}$. The doubling time is

$$T_{\text{double}} = \frac{\log_{10} 2}{\log_{10}(1 + 0.8)} = \frac{0.301\,030}{\log_{10}(1.8)} = \frac{0.301\,030}{0.255\,273} \approx 1.18 \text{ mo}$$

A Brief Review Logarithms

A **logarithm** (or **log**, for short) is a power or exponent. In this book, we will focus on base 10 logs, also called **common logs**, which are defined as follows:

$\log_{10} x$ *is the power to which 10 must be raised to obtain x.*

You may find it easier to remember the meaning with a less technical definition:

$\log_{10} x$ means "10 to what power equals x?"

For example:

$$\begin{aligned} \log_{10} 1000 &= 3 & &\text{because } 10^3 = 1000 \\ \log_{10} 10{,}000{,}000 &= 7 & &\text{because } 10^7 = 10{,}000{,}000 \\ \log_{10} 1 &= 0 & &\text{because } 10^0 = 1 \\ \log_{10} 0.1 &= -1 & &\text{because } 10^{-1} = 0.1 \\ \log_{10} 30 &\approx 1.477 & &\text{because } 10^{1.477} \approx 30 \end{aligned}$$

Four important rules follow directly from the definition of a logarithm.

1. Taking the logarithm of a power of 10 gives the power. That is,

$$\log_{10} 10^x = x$$

2. Raising 10 to a power that is the logarithm of a number gives back the number. That is,

$$10^{\log_{10} x} = x \qquad (x > 0)$$

3. Because powers of 10 are multiplied by adding their exponents, we have the *addition rule* for logarithms:

$$\log_{10} xy = \log_{10} x + \log_{10} y \qquad (x > 0 \text{ and } y > 0)$$

4. We can "bring down" an exponent within a logarithm by applying the *power rule* for logarithms:

$$\log_{10} a^x = x \times \log_{10} a \qquad (a > 0)$$

Most calculators have a key to compute $\log_{10}$ of any positive number. You should find this key on your calculator and use it to verify that $\log_{10} 1000 = 3$ and $\log_{10} 2 \approx 0.301\,030$.

Example: Given that $\log_{10} 2 \approx 0.301\,030$, find each of the following:

a. $\log_{10} 8$

b. $10^{\log_{10} 2}$

c. $\log_{10} 200$

Solution:

a. We notice that $8 = 2^3$. Therefore, from Rule 4,

$$\begin{aligned} \log_{10} 8 &= \log_{10} 2^3 \\ &= 3 \times \log_{10} 2 \approx 3 \times 0.301\,030 = 0.903\,09 \end{aligned}$$

b. From Rule 2,

$$10^{\log_{10} 2} = 2$$

c. We notice that $200 = 2 \times 100 = 2 \times 10^2$. Therefore, from Rule 3,

$$\log_{10} 200 = \log_{10}(2 \times 10^2) = \log_{10} 2 + \log_{10} 10^2$$

From Rule 1, we know that $\log_{10} 10^2 = 2$, so

$$\begin{aligned} \log_{10} 200 &= \log_{10}(2 \times 10^2) = \log_{10} 2 + \log_{10} 10^2 \\ &\approx 0.301\,030 + 2 = 2.301\,030 \end{aligned}$$

Example: Someone tells you that $\log_{10} 600 = 5.778$. Should you believe it?

Solution: Because 600 is between 100 and 1000, $\log_{10} 600$ must be between $\log_{10} 100$ and $\log_{10} 1000$. From Rule 1, we find that $\log_{10} 100 = \log_{10} 10^2 = 2$ and $\log_{10} 1000 = \log_{10} 10^3 = 3$. Therefore, $\log_{10} 600$ must be between 2 and 3, so the claimed answer of 5.778 must be wrong.

Now try Exercises 13–24.

The doubling time is almost 1.2 months. Note that this answer makes sense: With the population growing by 80% in a month, we expect it to take a little over a month to grow by 100% (which is a doubling). In contrast, the approximate doubling time formula predicts a doubling time of $70/P = 70/80 = 0.875$ month, which is less than one month. We see that the approximate formula does not work well for large growth rates.

Now try Exercises 53–54.

USING TECHNOLOGY

Logarithms

Most calculators have a key for computing common (base 10) logarithms, usually labeled *log*. Note, however, that some calculators use log to mean the natural (base e) logarithm; you can check by testing that your calculator correctly returns $\log_{10} 10 = 1$.

In Excel, use the built-in function LOG10, as shown in the screen shot below. (You can also use the LOG function, which can be used for any base but uses base 10 by default.)

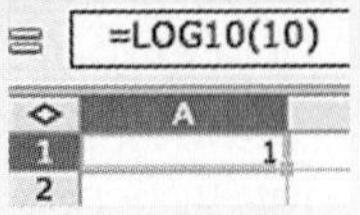

Example 10 Ruble Revisited

Suppose the Russian ruble is falling in value against the dollar at 12% per year. Using the exact half-life formula, determine how long it takes the ruble to lose half its value. Compare your answer to the approximate answer found in Example 7.

Solution The percentage decay rate is $P = 12\%/\text{yr}$. Because this is a rate of *decay*, we set the fractional growth rate to $r = -0.12/\text{yr}$. The half-life is

$$T_{\text{half}} = -\frac{\log_{10} 2}{\log_{10}(1 - 0.12)} = \frac{0.301030}{-0.055517} \approx 5.42 \text{ yr}$$

The ruble loses half its value against the dollar in about 5.42 years. This result is about 0.4 year less than the 5.8 years obtained with the approximate formula. We see that the approximate formula is reasonably accurate for the 12% rate.

Now try Exercises 55–56.

QUICK QUIZ

Choose the best answer to each of the following questions. Explain your reasoning with one or more complete sentences.

1. Suppose an investment rises consistently so that its value doubles every 7 years. By what factor will its value rise in 30 years?

   a. $2^{30/7}$ b. $2^{30} - 2^7$ c. 7×2^{30}

2. Suppose your salary is increasing at a rate of 2.5% per year. Then your salary will double in approximately

   a. 2.5 years. b. $\frac{70}{2.5}$ years. c. $\frac{2.5}{70}$ years.

3. Which of the following is *not* a good approximation of a doubling time?

   a. Inflation running at 35% per year will cause prices to double in about 2 years.

   b. A town growing at 2% per year will double its population in about 35 years.

   c. A bank account balance growing at 7% per year will double in about 10 years.

4. A town's population doubles in 15 years. Its percentage growth rate is approximately

   a. 15% per year. b. $\frac{70}{15}$% per year. c. $\frac{15}{70}$% per year.

5. Radioactive tritium (hydrogen-3) has a half-life of about 12 years, which means that if you start with 1 kg of tritium, 0.5 kg will decay during the first 12 years. How much will decay during the next 12 years?

   a. $\frac{12}{0.5}$ kg b. 0.5 kg c. 0.25 kg

6. Radioactive uranium-235 has a half-life of about 700 million years. Suppose a rock is 2.8 billion years old. What fraction of the rock's original uranium-235 still remains?

   a. $\frac{1}{2}$ b. $\frac{1}{16}$ c. $\frac{1}{700}$

7. The population of an endangered species is falling at a rate of 7% per year. Approximately how long will it take the population to drop by half?

   a. 7 years b. 10 years c. 17 years

8. $\log_{10} 10^8 =$

   a. 100,000,000 b. 108 c. 8

9. A rural population is falling at a rate of 20% per decade. If you wish to calculate its exact half-life, you should set the fractional growth rate per decade to

a. $r = 20$.

b. $r = 0.2$.

c. $r = -0.2$.

10. A new company's revenues are growing 15% per year. The doubling time for its revenues is

a. $\frac{\log_{10} 2}{\log_{10} 1.15}$ years.
b. $\frac{\log_{10} 2}{\log_{10} 0.85}$ years.

c. $\frac{\log_{10}(1 + 0.15)}{\log_{10} 2}$ years.

Exercises 8B

REVIEW QUESTIONS

1. What is a doubling time? Suppose a population has a doubling time of 25 years. By what factor will it grow in 25 years? in 50 years? in 100 years?

2. Given a doubling time, explain how you calculate the value of an exponentially growing quantity at any time *t*.

3. State the approximate doubling time formula and the conditions under which it works well. Give an example.

4. What is a half-life? Suppose a radioactive substance has a half-life of 1000 years. What fraction will be left after 1000 years? after 2000 years? after 4000 years?

5. Given a half-life, explain how you calculate the value of an exponentially decaying quantity at any time *t*.

6. State the approximate half-life formula and the conditions under which it works well. Give an example.

7. Briefly describe exact doubling time and half-life formulas. Explain all their terms.

8. Give an example in which it is important to use the exact doubling time or half-life formula, rather than the approximate formula. Explain why the approximate formula does not work well in this case.

DOES IT MAKE SENSE?

Decide whether each of the following statements makes sense (or is clearly true) or does not make sense (or is clearly false). Explain your reasoning.

9. Our town is growing with a doubling time of 25 years, so its population will triple in 50 years.

10. Our town is growing at a rate of 7% per year, so it will double in population about every 10 years.

11. A toxic chemical decays with a half-life of 10 years, so half of it will be gone 10 years from now and all the rest will be gone 20 years from now.

12. The half-life of plutonium-239 is about 24,000 years, so we can expect some of the plutonium produced in recent decades to still be around 100,000 years from now.

BASIC SKILLS & CONCEPTS

13–24: Logarithms. Refer to the Brief Review on p. 486. Determine whether each statement is true or false *without* doing any calculations. Explain your reasoning.

13. $10^{0.928}$ is between 1 and 10.

14. $10^{3.334}$ is between 500 and 1000.

15. $10^{-5.2}$ is between $-100{,}000$ and $-1{,}000{,}000$.

16. $10^{-2.67}$ is between 0.001 and 0.01.

17. $\log_{10} \pi$ is between 3 and 4.

18. $\log_{10} 96$ is between 3 and 4.

19. $\log_{10} 1{,}600{,}000$ is between 16 and 17.

20. $\log_{10}(8 \times 10^9)$ is between 9 and 10.

21. $\log_{10}\left(\frac{1}{4}\right)$ is between -1 and 0.

22. $\log_{10} 0.00045$ is between 5 and 6.

23. Using the approximation $\log_{10} 2 = 0.301$, find each of the following *without* a calculator.

a. $\log_{10} 8$ b. $\log_{10} 2000$ c. $\log_{10} 0.5$
d. $\log_{10} 64$ e. $\log_{10} 1/8$ f. $\log_{10} 0.2$

24. Using the approximation $\log_{10} 5 = 0.699$, find each of the following *without* a calculator.

a. $\log_{10} 50$ b. $\log_{10} 5000$ c. $\log_{10} 0.05$
d. $\log_{10} 25$ e. $\log_{10} 0.20$ f. $\log_{10} 0.04$

25–32: Doubling Time. Each exercise gives a doubling time for an exponentially growing quantity. Answer the questions that follow.

25. The doubling time of a population of fruit flies is 8 hours. By what factor does the population increase in 24 hours? in 1 week?

26. The doubling time of a bank account balance is 20 years. By what factor does it grow in 40 years? in 100 years?

27. The doubling time of a city's population is 17 years. How long does it take for the population to quadruple?

28. Prices are rising with a doubling time of 2 months. By what factor do prices increase in a year?

29. The initial population of a town is 10,000, and it grows with a doubling time of 10 years. What will the population be in 12 years? in 24 years?

30. The initial population of a town is 10,000, and it grows with a doubling time of 8 years. What will the population be in 12 years? in 24 years?

31. The number of cells in a tumor doubles every 2.5 months. If the tumor begins as a single cell, how many cells will there be after 2 years? after 4 years?

32. The number of cells in a tumor doubles every 6 months. If the tumor begins with a single cell, how many cells will there be after 6 years? after 10 years?

33–34: World Population. In 2009 world population was 6.8 billion. Use the given doubling time to predict the population in 2019, 2059, and 2109.

33. Assume a doubling time of 45 years.

34. Assume a doubling time of 60 years.

35. **Rabbits.** A community of rabbits begins with an initial population of 100 and grows 7% per month. Make a table, similar to Table 8.3, that shows the population for each of the next 15 months. Based on the table, find the doubling time of the population and briefly discuss how well the approximate doubling time formula works for this case.

36. **Mice.** A community of mice begins with an initial population of 1000 and grows 20% per month. Make a table, similar to Table 8.3, that shows the population for each of the next 15 months. Based on the table, find the doubling time of the population and briefly discuss how well the approximate doubling time formula works for this case.

37–40: Doubling Time Formula. Use the approximate doubling time formula (rule of 70). Discuss whether the formula is valid for the case described.

37. The Consumer Price Index is increasing at a rate of 4% per year. What is its doubling time? By what factor will prices increase in 3 years?

38. A city's population is growing at a rate of 3.5% per year. What is its doubling time? By what factor will the population increase in 50 years?

39. Prices are rising at a rate of 0.3% per month. What is their doubling time? By what factor will prices increase in 1 year? in 8 years?

40. Oil consumption is increasing at a rate of 2.2% per year. What is its doubling time? By what factor will oil consumption increase in a decade?

41–48: Half-Life. Each exercise gives a half-life for an exponentially decaying quantity. Answer the questions that follow.

41. The half-life of a radioactive substance is 50 years. If you start with some amount of this substance, what fraction will remain in 100 years? in 200 years?

42. The half-life of a radioactive substance is 400 years. If you start with some amount of this substance, what fraction will remain in 120 years? in 2500 years?

43. The half-life of a drug in the bloodstream is 18 hours. What fraction of the original drug dose remains in 24 hours? in 48 hours?

44. The half-life of a drug in the bloodstream is 4 hours. What fraction of the original drug dose remains in 24 hours? in 48 hours?

45. The current population of a threatened animal species is 1 million, but it is declining with a half-life of 20 years. How many animals will be left in 30 years? in 70 years?

46. The current population of a threatened animal species is 1 million, but it is declining with a half-life of 25 years. How many animals will be left in 20 years? in 40 years?

47. Cobalt-56 has a half-life of 77 days. If you start with 1 kilogram of cobalt-56, how much will remain after 150 days? after 300 days?

48. Radium-226 is a metal with a half-life of 1600 years. If you start with 1 kilogram of radium-226, how much will remain after 1000 years? after 10,000 years?

49–52: Half-Life Formula. Use the approximate half-life formula. Discuss whether the formula is valid for the case described.

49. Urban encroachment is causing the area of a forest to decline at a rate of 7% per year. What is the half-life of the forest? What fraction of the forest will remain in 30 years?

50. A clean-up project is reducing the concentration of a pollutant in the water supply, with a 3.5% decrease per week. What is the half-life of the concentration of the pollutant? What fraction of the original amount of the pollutant will remain when the project ends after 1 year (52 weeks)?

51. Poaching is causing a population of elephants to decline by 8% per year. What is the half-life for the population? If there are 10,000 elephants today, how many will remain in 50 years?

52. The production of a gold mine is declining by 6% per year. What is the half-life for the production decline? If its current annual production is 5000 kilograms, what will its production be in 15 years?

53–56: Exact Formulas. Compare the doubling times found with the approximate and exact doubling time formulas. Then use the exact doubling time formula to answer the given question.

53. Inflation is causing prices to rise at a rate of 12% per year. For an item that costs $500 today, what will the price be in 4 years?

54. Hyperinflation is driving up prices at a rate of 80% per month. For an item that costs $1000 today, what will the price be in 1 year?

55. A nation of 100 million people is growing at a rate of 4% per year. What will its population be in 30 years?

56. A family of 100 termites invades your house and grows at a rate of 20% per week. How many termites will be in your house after 1 year (52 weeks)?

FURTHER APPLICATIONS

57. **Plutonium on Earth.** Scientists believe that Earth once had naturally existing plutonium-239. Suppose Earth had 10 trillion tons of Pu-239 when it formed. Given plutonium's half-life of 24,000 years and Earth's current age of 4.6 billion years, how much would remain today? Use your answer to explain why plutonium is not found naturally on Earth today.

58. **Nuclear Weapons.** Thermonuclear weapons use tritium for their nuclear reactions. Tritium is a radioactive form of hydrogen (containing 1 proton and 2 neutrons) with a half-life of about 12 years. Suppose a nuclear weapon contains 1 kilogram of tritium. How much will remain in 50 years? Use your answer to explain why thermonuclear weapons require regular maintenance.

WEB PROJECTS

59. **National Growth Rates.** Find growth rates, doubling times, and population projections tabulated for different countries. Select several countries from several continents and record relevant growth data. Comment on whether the doubling times and growth rates are consistent. Discuss how these data are used to make population projections.

60. **World Population Growth.** The Web site for the U.S. Census Bureau contains a wealth of data on world population. Visit this site and gather data on world population growth over the last 50 years. Estimate the population growth rate over each decade. Compute the associated doubling times. Write a two-paragraph statement on the trends that you observe.

IN YOUR WORLD

61. **Doubling Time.** Find a news story that gives an exponential growth rate. Find the approximate doubling time from the growth rate and discuss the implications of the growth.

62. **Radioactive Half-Life.** Find a news story that discusses some type of radioactive material. If it is not given, look up the half-life of the material. Discuss the implications for disposal of the material.

TECHNOLOGY EXERCISES

63. **Logarithms I.** Use a calculator or Excel to find each of the logarithms in Exercise 23. Give answers to 6 decimal places.

64. **Logarithms II.** Use a calculator or Excel to find each of the logarithms in Exercise 24. Give answers to 6 decimal places.

UNIT 8C Real Population Growth

Perhaps the most important application of exponential growth concerns human population. From the time of the earliest humans more than 2 million years ago until about 10,000 years ago, human population probably never exceeded 10 million. The advent of agriculture brought about more rapid population growth. Human population reached 250 million by C.E. 1 and continued growing slowly to about 500 million by 1650.

Exponential growth set in with the Industrial Revolution. Our rapidly developing ability to grow food and exploit natural resources allowed us to build more homes for more people. Meanwhile, improvements in medicine and health science lowered death rates dramatically. In fact, world population began growing at a rate exceeding that of steady exponential growth, in which the doubling time would have remained constant. Population doubled from 500 million to 1 billion in the 150 years from 1650 to 1800. It then doubled again, to 2 billion, by 1922, only about 120 years. The next doubling, to 4 billion, was complete by 1974, a doubling time of only 52 years. World population is estimated to have reached 6 billion during 1999, and 6.8 billion in 2009. Figure 8.3 shows the estimated human population over the past 12,000 years.

To put current world population growth in perspective, consider the following facts:

- Every four years, the world adds as many people as the total population of the United States.

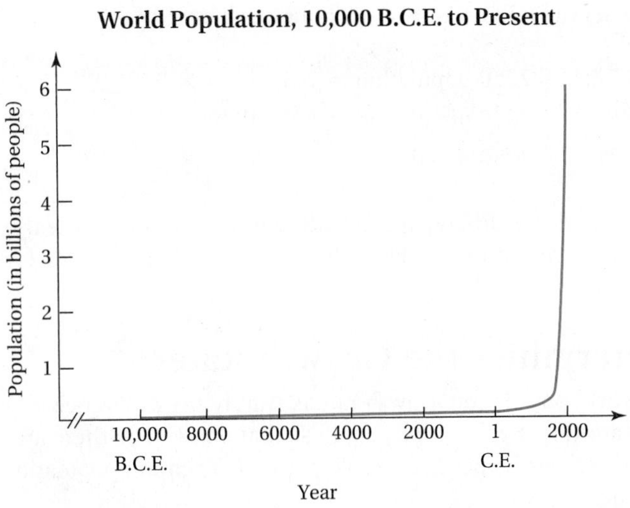

FIGURE 8.3 World population.

- Each month, world population increases by the equivalent of the population of Switzerland.
- While you study during the next hour and a half, world population will increase by about 10,000 people.

Projections of future population growth have large uncertainties. Nevertheless, current trends suggest that world population will reach 7 billion by about 2012 and 8 billion by 2025. Even in the United States, where population is growing more slowly than the world average, the population is expected to increase by *100 million* people within the next 50 years. Fortunately, while the absolute increase in population remains huge, these numbers indicate that the growth rate is declining. This fact makes many researchers suspect that the growth rate will continue its downward trend, thereby preventing a population catastrophe.

BY THE WAY

Most of the projected population growth (9 out of 10 people) will take place in the developing regions. By 2030, more than 1 billion people are expected to be added to Asia alone, and India is expected to overtake China as the most populous nation.

Example 1 Varying Growth Rate

The average annual growth rate for world population since 1650 has been about 0.7%. However, the annual rate has varied significantly. It peaked at about 2.1% during the 1960s and is currently (as of 2009) about 1.2%. Find the approximate doubling time for each of these growth rates. Use each to predict world population in 2050, based on a 2009 population of 6.8 billion.

Solution Using the approximate doubling time formula (Unit 8B), we find the doubling times for the three rates:

$$\text{For 0.7\%:}\quad T_{\text{double}} \approx \frac{70}{P} = \frac{70}{0.7/\text{yr}} = 100 \text{ yr}$$

$$\text{For 2.1\%:}\quad T_{\text{double}} \approx \frac{70}{P} = \frac{70}{2.1/\text{yr}} = 33 \text{ yr}$$

$$\text{For 1.2\%:}\quad T_{\text{double}} \approx \frac{70}{P} = \frac{70}{1.2/\text{yr}} = 58 \text{ yr}$$

To predict world population in 2050, we use the formula

$$\text{new value} = \text{initial value} \times 2^{t/T_{\text{double}}}$$

BY THE WAY

For individual countries, the growth rate depends on immigration and emigration as well as on birth and death rates. In the United States, immigration comprises about half the overall growth rate. Of course, immigration and emigration do not affect *world* population, since no one is moving to or from the Earth.

We set the initial value to 6.8 billion and note that 2050 is $t = 41$ years after 2009:

For 0.7%: $2050 \text{ population} = 6.8 \text{ billion} \times 2^{41\text{yr}/100\text{yr}} \approx 9.0 \text{ billion}$

For 2.1%: $2050 \text{ population} = 6.8 \text{ billion} \times 2^{41\text{yr}/33\text{yr}} \approx 16.1 \text{ billion}$

For 1.2%: $2050 \text{ population} = 6.8 \text{ billion} \times 2^{41\text{yr}/58\text{yr}} \approx 11.1 \text{ billion}$

Notice the large differences for different growth rates. Clearly, decisions we make to affect the growth rate today will have major implications for human population in the future. **Now try Exercises 13–16.**

What Determines the Growth Rate?

The world population growth rate is simply the difference between the birth rate and the death rate. For example, suppose that on average there are 8.5 births per 100 people and 6.5 deaths per 100 people per year. Then the population growth rate is

$$\frac{8.5}{100} - \frac{6.5}{100} = \frac{2}{100} = 0.02 = 2\%$$

OVERALL GROWTH RATE

The world population growth rate is the difference between the birth rate and the death rate:

$$\text{growth rate} = \text{birth rate} - \text{death rate}$$

Interestingly, birth rates dropped rapidly throughout the world during the past 60 years—the same period that has seen the largest population growth in history. Indeed, worldwide birth rates have never been lower than they are today. Today's rapid population growth comes from the fact that death rates have fallen even more dramatically.

Example 2 Birth and Death Rates

BY THE WAY

By 2009, the world birth rate had fallen to about 2.0 per 100 people and the death rate had fallen to about 0.8 per 100 people.

In 1950, the world birth rate was 3.7 births per 100 people and the world death rate was 2.0 deaths per 100 people. By 1975, the birth rate had fallen to 2.8 births per 100 people and the death rate to 1.1 deaths per 100 people. Contrast the growth rates in 1950 and 1975.

Solution In 1950, the overall growth rate was

$$\frac{3.7}{100} - \frac{2.0}{100} = \frac{1.7}{100} = 1.7\%$$

In 1975, the overall growth rate was

$$\frac{2.8}{100} - \frac{1.1}{100} = \frac{1.7}{100} = 1.7\%$$

Despite a dramatic fall in birth rates during the 25-year period, the growth rate remained unchanged because death rates fell equally dramatically. **Now try Exercises 17–20.**

Time Out to Think

Suppose that medical science finds a way to extend human lifespans significantly. How would this affect the population growth rate?

Carrying Capacity and Real Growth Models

As we saw in Unit 8A, exponential growth cannot continue indefinitely. Indeed, human population cannot continue to grow much longer at its current rate, because we'd be elbow to elbow over the entire Earth in just a few centuries. Theoretical models of population growth therefore assume that human population is ultimately limited by the **carrying capacity** of Earth—the number of people that Earth can support.

> **DEFINITION**
>
> For any particular species in a given environment, the **carrying capacity** is the maximum sustainable population. That is, it is the largest population the environment can support for extended periods of time.

Two important models for populations approaching the carrying capacity are (1) a gradual leveling off, known as *logistic growth*, and (2) a rapid increase followed by a rapid decrease, known as *overshoot and collapse*. Let's investigate each model.

Logistic Growth

A **logistic growth** model assumes that population growth gradually slows as the population approaches the carrying capacity. For example, if the carrying capacity is 12 billion people, a logistic model assumes that population growth will slow as this number is approached. The growth rate falls to zero as the carrying capacity is approached, allowing the population to remain steady at that level thereafter.

> **LOGISTIC GROWTH**
>
> When the population is small relative to the carrying capacity, **logistic growth** is exponential with a fractional growth rate close to the base growth rate r. As the population approaches the carrying capacity, the logistic growth rate approaches zero. The logistic growth rate at any particular time depends on the population at that time, the carrying capacity, and the base growth rate r:
>
> $$\text{logistic growth rate} = r \times \left(1 - \frac{\text{population}}{\text{carrying capacity}}\right)$$

Figure 8.4 contrasts logistic and exponential growth for the same base growth rate r. In the exponential case, the growth rate stays equal to r at all times. In the logistic case, the growth rate starts out equal to r, so the logistic curve and the exponential curve

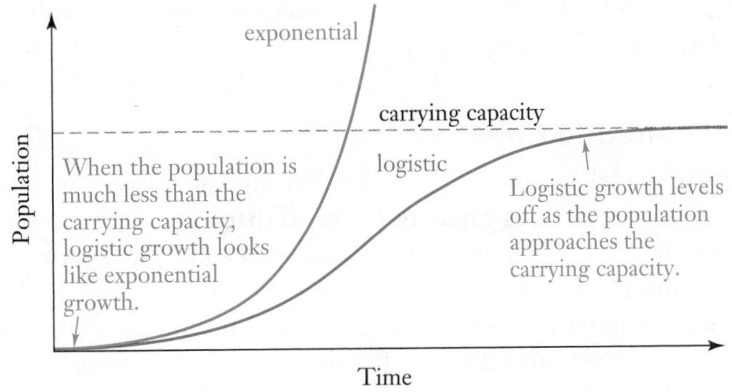

FIGURE 8.4 This graph contrasts exponential growth with logistic growth for the same base growth rate r.

look the same at early times. As time progresses, the logistic growth rate becomes ever smaller than r, and it finally reaches zero as the population levels out at the carrying capacity.

Example 3 Are We Growing Logistically?

Assume that the Earth's carrying capacity is 12 billion people. Given that the population growth rate peaked in the 1960s at about 2.1%, when the population was about 3 billion, is it reasonable to assume that human population has been following a logistic growth pattern since the 1960s? Is it reasonable to assume that population has been growing logistically throughout the past century? Explain.

Solution We need to compare the 2009 growth rate of about 1.2% (see Example 1) to the growth rate predicted by a logistic model. First, we must use the 1960s data to find the base growth rate r in the logistic model. You should confirm that solving the logistic growth rate formula for r gives

$$r = \frac{\text{growth rate}}{\left(1 - \frac{\text{population}}{\text{carrying capacity}}\right)}$$

Substituting the 1960s growth rate of 2.1% = 0.021 and population of 3 billion, along with a carrying capacity of 12 billion, we find

$$r = \frac{0.021}{\left(1 - \frac{3 \text{ billion}}{12 \text{ billion}}\right)} = \frac{0.021}{(1 - 0.25)} \approx 0.028$$

Now, we use this value of r to predict the growth rate for the 2009 population of about 6.8 billion:

$$\text{growth rate} = 0.028 \times \left(1 - \frac{6.8 \text{ billion}}{12 \text{ billion}}\right) \approx 0.012$$

This logistic model predicts a current growth rate of 1.2%, matching the actual current growth rate of 1.2%. Therefore, it is reasonable to say that human population has been growing logistically since the 1960s. However, human population has not been following logistic growth over longer periods. Logistic growth requires a continually decreasing growth rate, which is inconsistent with the growth rate peaking in the 1960s. In conclusion, it is still too early to know whether the growth rate will continue to decline as population approaches 12 billion or whether we are simply experiencing a temporary change in the exponential growth rate. **Now try Exercises 21–22.**

BY THE WAY

Overshoot and collapse characterizes many predator-prey populations. The population of a predator increases rapidly, causing the prey population to collapse. Once the prey population collapses, the predator population must also collapse because of lack of food. Once the predator population collapses, the prey population can begin to recover—as long as it has not gone extinct.

Overshoot and Collapse

A logistic model assumes that the growth rate automatically adjusts as the population approaches the carrying capacity. However, because of the astonishing rate of exponential growth, real populations often increase beyond the carrying capacity in a relatively short period of time. This phenomenon is called **overshoot**.

When a population overshoots the carrying capacity of its environment, a decrease in the population is inevitable. If the overshoot is substantial, the decrease can be rapid and severe—a phenomenon known as **collapse**. Figure 8.5 contrasts a logistic growth model with overshoot and collapse.

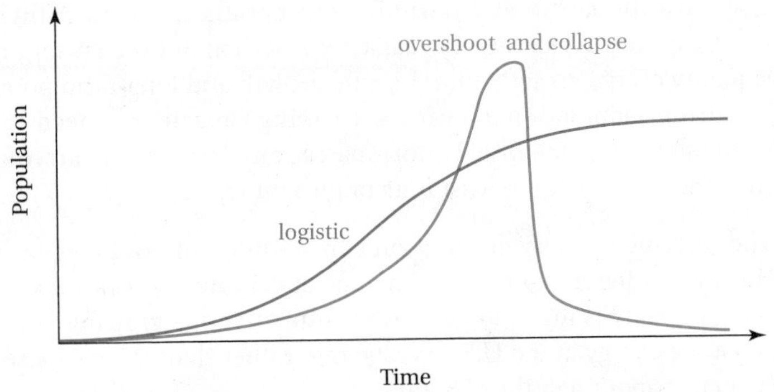

FIGURE 8.5 This graph contrasts logistic growth with overshoot and collapse.

Time Out to Think

The concept of carrying capacity can be applied to any localized environment. Consider the decline of past civilizations such as the ancient Greeks, Romans, Mayans, and Anasazi. Does an overshoot and collapse model describe the fall of any of these or other civilizations? Explain.

What Is the Carrying Capacity?

Given that human population cannot grow exponentially forever, logistic growth is clearly preferable to any kind of overshoot and collapse. Logistic growth means a sustainable future population, while overshoot and collapse might mean the end of our civilization.

PRACTICAL MATTERS

Choosing Our Fate

As the parable of the bacteria in a bottle (Unit 8A) showed, exponential growth cannot continue indefinitely. The exponential growth of human population *will* stop. The only questions are *when* and *how.*

First consider the question of *when*. The highest estimates put the Earth's carrying capacity around 40 billion, which we would reach within about 150 years at recent growth rates. In that case, regardless of other assumptions, population growth must stop or slow considerably within the next 150 years—quite soon on the scale of human history.

As for *how,* there are only two basic ways to slow the growth of a population:

- a decrease in the birth rate or
- an increase in the death rate.

Most people are already choosing the first option, as birth rates now are at historic lows. Indeed, population actually is *decreasing* in a few European nations. Nevertheless, worldwide birth rates still are much higher than death rates, so exponential growth continues.

If a decrease in birth rates doesn't halt the exponential growth, an increase in the death rate will. If population significantly overshoots the carrying capacity by the time this process begins, the increase in the death rate will be dramatic—probably on a scale never before seen. This forecast is not a threat, a warning, or a prophecy of doom. It is simply a law of nature: *Exponential growth always stops.*

As human beings, we can choose to slow our population growth through intelligent and careful decisions. Or, we can choose to do nothing, leaving ourselves to the mercy of natural forces over which we have no more control than we do over hurricanes, tornadoes, earthquakes, or the explosions of distant stars. Either way, it's a choice that each and every one of us must make, and upon which our entire future depends.

The most fundamental question about population growth therefore concerns the carrying capacity. If the carrying capacity is well above the current population, then we have plenty of time to settle into logistic growth and long-term population stability. But if the current population is near the carrying capacity, we need to act quickly to prevent overshoot and collapse. Unfortunately, any estimate of carrying capacity is subject to great uncertainty, for at least four important reasons:

- The carrying capacity depends on consumption of resources such as energy. However, different countries consume at very different rates. For example, the carrying capacity is much lower if we assume that the growing population will consume energy at the U.S. average rate rather than the Japanese average rate (which is about half the U.S. rate).
- The carrying capacity depends on assumptions about the environmental impact of the average person. A larger average impact on the environment means a lower carrying capacity.
- The carrying capacity can change with both human technology and the environment. For example, estimates of carrying capacity typically consider the availability of fresh water. However, if we can develop new sources of energy (such as fusion), nearly unlimited amounts of fresh water may be obtained through the desalinization of seawater. Conversely, global warming might alter the environment and reduce our ability to grow food, thereby lowering the carrying capacity.
- Even if we could account for the many individual factors in the carrying capacity (such as food production, energy, and pollution), the Earth is such a complex system that precisely predicting the carrying capacity may well be impossible. For example, no one can predict whether or how much the loss of rain forest species affects the carrying capacity.

The power of population is indefinitely greater than the power in the Earth to produce subsistence for man.

—Thomas Malthus

The history of attempts to guess the carrying capacity of the Earth is full of missed predictions. Among the most famous was that made by English economist Thomas Malthus (1766–1834). In a 1798 paper entitled *An Essay on the Principle of Population as It Affects the Future Improvement of Society,* Malthus argued that food production would not be able to keep up with the rapidly growing populations of Europe and America. He concluded that mass starvation would soon hit these continents. His prediction did not come true, primarily because advances in technology *did* allow food production to keep pace with population growth.

Time Out to Think

Some people argue that while Malthus's immediate predictions didn't come true, his overall point about a limit to population is still valid. Others cite Malthus as a classic example of underestimating the ingenuity of our species. What do you think? Defend your opinion.

Case Study The Population of Egypt

Over long periods of time, real population growth patterns tend to be quite complex. Sometimes the growth may look exponential, while at other times it may appear logistic or like overshoot and collapse. It may even appear to be some combination of these possibilities all at once.

One of the few cases for which long-term population data are available is that of Egypt. Figure 8.6 shows these data, along with a few historical events that affected

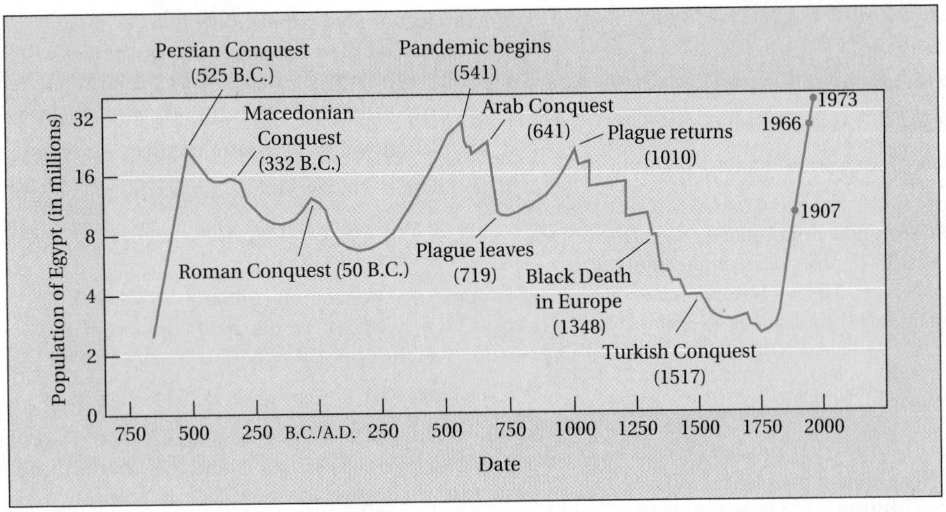

FIGURE 8.6 The historical population of Egypt. Notice that each tick mark on the vertical axis represents a doubling of the population in millions (2, 4, 8, 16, 32).

Source: T. H. Hollingsworth, *Historical Demography* (Ithaca, NY: Cornell University Press, 1969).

BY THE WAY

Current UN projections suggest that world population will level out later in this century at about 9 billion. These projections assume that the fertility rate will decline from the current level of 2.6 children per woman to the "replacement level" of 2.1 children per woman by 2050—an assumption that in turn is based on an assumption of greater availability of and education about contraceptive choices.

the population. (The graph uses an exponential vertical scale, with each tick mark representing a number twice as big as the previous one.) Note the complexity of the pattern. Even with the best mathematical models, it is hard to imagine that scientists in ancient Egypt could have predicted the future population of the region over a period of even a hundred years, let alone several thousand years.

This example offers an important lesson about mathematical models. They are useful for gaining insight into the processes being modeled. However, mathematical models can be used to *predict* future changes only when the processes are relatively simple. For example, it is easy to use mathematical modeling to predict the path of a spaceship because the law of gravity is relatively simple. But the growth of human population is such a complex phenomenon that we have little hope of ever being able to predict it reliably.

QUICK QUIZ

Choose the best answer to each of the following questions. Explain your reasoning with one or more complete sentences.

1. World population is currently rising by about 75 million people per year. About how many people are added to the population each minute?

   a. 5 b. 30 c. 140

2. Based on the data given in the text, world population in 2012 will be about

   a. 5.2 billion.

   b. 7.0 billion.

   c. 8.7 billion.

3. The primary reason for the rapid growth of human population over the past century has been

   a. an increasing birth rate. b. a decreasing death rate.

   c. a combination of an increasing birth rate and a decreasing death rate.

4. The *carrying capacity* of the Earth is defined as

   a. the maximum number of people who could fit elbow-to-elbow on the planet.

   b. the maximum population that could be sustained for a long period of time.

   c. the peak population that would be reached just before a collapse in the population size.

5. Which of the following would cause estimates of Earth's *carrying capacity* to increase?

   a. the discovery of a way to make people live longer

   b. the spread of a disease that killed off many crops

   c. the development of a new, inexpensive, and nonpolluting energy source

6. Recall the bacteria in a bottle example from Unit 8A, in which the number of bacteria in a bottle doubles each minute until the bottle is full and the bacteria all die. The full history of the population of these bacteria, including their death, is an example of

   a. overshoot and collapse.

   b. unending exponential growth.

   c. logistic growth.

7. When researchers project that human population will reach a steady 9 billion later in this century, what type of growth model are they assuming?

   a. overshoot and collapse

   b. exponential

   c. logistic

8. The projection that population will level out at 9 billion people is based on the assumption that birth rates will fall from current levels. Suppose instead that the birth rate returns to what it was in 1950. If the death rate remains steady,

   a. population will grow to far more than 9 billion.

   b. population will level off before reaching 9 billion.

   c. population will still level off at 9 billion, but a little sooner than otherwise expected.

9. Suppose that population continues to grow at the 2009 rate of 1.2% per year. Given the 2009 population of 6.8 billion, when will the population double to about 14 billion?

   a. around 2070 b. around 2215 c. around 2450

10. Which of the following is *not* a requirement if world population is to level out, without an increase in the death rate, later in this century at 9 or 10 billion people?

    a. We must increase food production by close to 50%.

    b. The average woman must give birth to fewer children than she does at present.

    c. We must discover a new source of inexpensive and nonpolluting energy.

Exercises 8C

REVIEW QUESTIONS

1. Based on Figure 8.3, contrast the changes in human population for the 10,000 years preceding C.E. 1 and the 2000 years since. What has happened over the past few centuries?
2. Briefly describe how the overall growth rate is related to birth and death rates.
3. How do today's birth and death rates compare to those in the past? Why is human population growing?
4. What do we mean by carrying capacity? Why is it so difficult to determine the carrying capacity of Earth?
5. What is logistic growth? Why would it be good if human population growth followed a logistic growth pattern in the future?
6. What is overshoot and collapse? Under what conditions does it occur? Why would it be a bad thing for the human race?

DOES IT MAKE SENSE?

Decide whether each of the following statements makes sense (or is clearly true) or does not make sense (or is clearly false). Explain your reasoning.

7. Within the next decade, world population will grow by more than twice the current population of the United States.
8. If birth rates fall more than death rates, the growth rate of world population will fall.
9. The carrying capacity of our planet depends only on our planet's size.
10. Thanks to rapid increases in computing technology, we should be able to pin down the carrying capacity of the Earth to a precise number within just a few years.
11. In the wild, we always expect the population of any animal species to follow a logistic growth pattern.
12. Past history gives us strong reason to believe that human population is following a logistic growth pattern.

BASIC SKILLS & CONCEPTS

13–16: Varying Growth Rates. Starting from a 2009 population of 6.8 billion, use the given growth rate to find the approximate doubling time (use the rule of 70) and to predict world population in 2050.

13. Use the average annual growth rate between 1850 and 1950, which was about 0.9%.
14. Use the average annual growth rate between 1950 and 2000, which was about 1.8%.
15. Use the average annual growth rate between 1970 and 2000, which was about 1.6%.
16. Use the current annual growth rate of the United States, which is about 0.7%.

17–20: Birth and Death Rates. The following table gives the birth and death rates for four countries in three different years.

	Birth Rate (per 1000)			Death Rate (per 1000)		
Country	1985	1995	2007	1985	1995	2007
Czech Rep.	14.5	9.3	9.0	11.8	11.4	10.6
Israel	23.8	21.0	17.7	6.6	6.3	6.2
Sweden	11.8	11.7	10.2	11.3	11.0	10.3
U.S.	15.7	15.1	14.2	8.7	8.8	8.3

For the country given in each exercise, do the following:

a. Find the country's net growth rate due to births and deaths (i.e., neglect immigration) in 1985, 1995, and 2007.

b. Describe in words the general trend in the country's growth rate. Based on this trend, predict how the country's population will change over the next 20 years. Do you think your prediction is reliable? Explain.

17. Czech Republic
18. Israel
19. Sweden
20. United States

21. **Logistic Growth.** Consider a population that begins growing exponentially at a base rate of 4.0% per year and then follows a logistic growth pattern. If the carrying capacity is 60 million, find the actual growth rate when the population is 10 million, 30 million, and 50 million.

22. **Logistic Growth.** Consider a population that begins growing exponentially at a base rate of 6.0% per year and then follows a logistic growth pattern. If the carrying capacity is 80 million, find the actual growth rate when the population is 10 million, 50 million, and 70 million.

FURTHER APPLICATIONS

23–26: **U.S. Population.** Starting from an estimated U.S. population of 305 million in 2009, use the given growth rate to estimate U.S. population in 2059 and 2109. Use the approximate doubling time formula.

23. Use the current U.S. annual growth rate of 0.7%.
24. Use a growth rate of 0.5%.
25. Use a growth rate of 1.0%.
26. Use a growth rate of 0.4%.

27. **Population Growth in Your Lifetime.** Starting from the 6.8 billion population in 2009, assume that world population maintains its current annual growth rate of 1.2%. What will be the world population when you are 50 years old? 80 years old? 100 years old?

28. **Slower Growth.** Repeat Exercise 27, but for a growth rate of 1% rather than 1.2%.

29–32: **World Carrying Capacity.** For the given carrying capacities, use the 1960s peak annual growth rate of 2.1% and population of 3 billion to predict the base growth rate and current growth rate with a logistic model. Assume a current world population of 6.8 billion. How do the predicted growth rates compare to the actual growth rate of about 1.2% per year?

29. Assume the carrying capacity is 8 billion.
30. Assume the carrying capacity is 10 billion.
31. Assume the carrying capacity is 15 billion.
32. Assume the carrying capacity is 20 billion.

33. **Growth Control Mediation.** A city with a 2010 population of 100,000 has a growth control policy that limits the increase in residents to 2% per year. Naturally, this policy causes a great deal of dispute. On one side, some people argue that *growth* costs the city its small-town charm and clean environment. On the other side, some people argue that *growth control* costs the city jobs and drives up housing prices. Finding their work limited by the policy, developers suggest a compromise of raising the allowed growth rate to 5% per year. Contrast the populations of this city in 2020, 2030, and 2070 for 2% annual growth and 5% annual growth. Use the approximate doubling formula. If you were asked to mediate the dispute between growth control advocates and opponents, explain the strategy you would use.

WEB PROJECTS

34. **Population Predictions.** Find population predictions from an organization that studies population, such as the United Nations or the U.S. Census Bureau. Read about how the predictions are made. Write a short summary of the methods used to predict future population. Be sure to discuss the uncertainties in the predictions.

35. **Carrying Capacity.** Find several different opinions concerning the Earth's human population carrying capacity. Based on your research, draw some conclusions about whether overpopulation presents an immediate threat. Write a short essay detailing the results of your research and clearly explaining your conclusions.

36. **U.S. Population Growth.** Research population growth in the United States to determine the relative proportions of the growth resulting from birth rates and from immigration. Then research both the problems and the benefits of the growing U.S. population. Form your own opinions about whether the United States has a population problem. Write an essay covering the results of your research and stating and defending your opinions.

37. **Thomas Malthus.** Find more information about Thomas Malthus and his famous predictions about population. Write a short paper on either his personal biography or his work.

38. **Extinction.** Choose an endangered species and research why it is in decline. Is the decline a case of overshoot and collapse? Is human activity changing the carrying capacity for the species? Write a short summary of your findings.

IN YOUR WORLD

39. **Population Growth.** Find a recent news story that concerns population growth. Does the story consider the long-term effects of the growth? If so, do you agree with the claims? If not, discuss a few possible effects of future growth.

40. **Immigration.** Within the United States, immigration is an important part of the overall population growth. Find a recent story that discusses either the pros or the cons of immigration. Discuss the story and its conclusions.

UNIT 8D Logarithmic Scales: Earthquakes, Sounds, and Acids

You've probably heard the strength of earthquakes described in *magnitudes*, the loudness of sounds described in *decibels*, or the acidity of household cleansers described by *pH*. In all three cases, the measurement scale involves exponential growth, because successive numbers on the scale increase by the same relative amount. For example, a liquid with pH 5 is ten times more acidic than one with pH 6. In this unit, we will explore these three important scales. They are commonly called **logarithmic scales**, which makes sense if you remember that logarithms are powers (see the Brief Review on p. 486).

The Magnitude Scale for Earthquakes

Earthquakes are a fact of life for much of the world's population (Figure 8.7). In the United States, California and Alaska are most prone to earthquakes, although earthquakes can strike almost anywhere. Most earthquakes are so minor that they can hardly be felt, but severe earthquakes can kill tens of thousands of people. Table 8.4 lists the frequencies of earthquakes of various strengths according to standard categories defined by geologists.

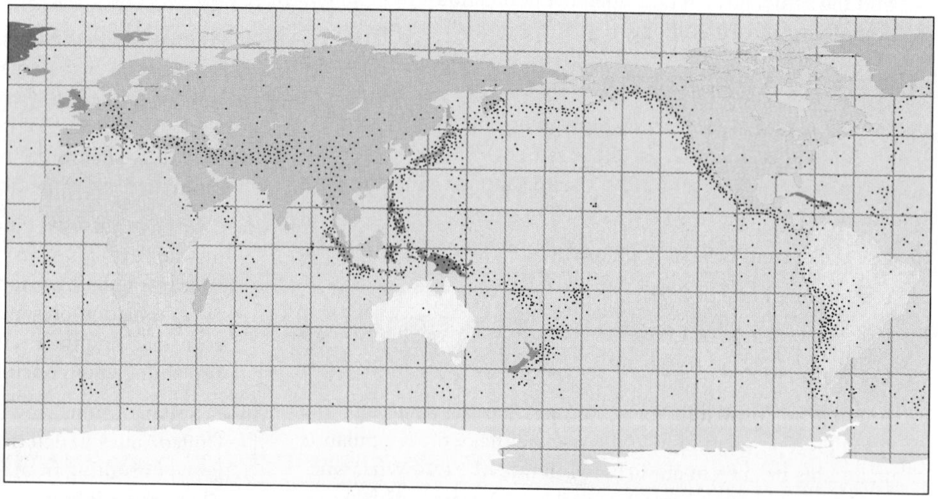

FIGURE 8.7 The distribution of earthquakes around the world. Each dot represents an earthquake. *Source:* From U.S. Geological Survey.

Historical Note

The original magnitude scale was created by Charles Richter in 1935. This *Richter scale* measured the up and down motion of the ground during a quake. Magnitude 0 was defined as the smallest detectable quake, and each increase of 1 magnitude corresponded to a factor of 10 increase in ground motion. Most earthquakes have nearly the same magnitude on the Richter scale and on the modern magnitude scale, but only the latter quantifies the actual energy released by the earthquake.

TABLE 8.4 Earthquake Categories and Their Frequency

Category	Magnitude	Approximate Number per Year (Worldwide Average Since 1900)
Great	8 and up	1
Major	7–8	18
Strong	6–7	120
Moderate	5–6	800
Light	4–5	6000
Minor	3–4	50,000
Very minor	less than 3	magnitude 2–3: 1000 per day magnitude 1–2: 8000 per day

Scientists measure earthquake strength with the earthquake **magnitude scale.** The magnitude is related to the energy released by the earthquake. But each magnitude represents about 32 times as much energy as the previous magnitude. For example, a magnitude 8 earthquake releases 32 times as much energy as a magnitude 7 earthquake. More technically, the magnitude scale is defined as follows.

THE EARTHQUAKE MAGNITUDE SCALE

The magnitude scale for earthquakes is defined so that each magnitude represents about 32 times as much energy as the prior magnitude. More technically, the magnitude, *M*, is related to the released energy, *E*, by the following equivalent formulas:

$$\log_{10}E = 4.4 + 1.5M \quad \text{or} \quad E = (2.5 \times 10^4) \times 10^{1.5M}$$

The energy is measured in joules (see Unit 2B); magnitudes have no units.

Earthquakes of the same magnitude may cause vastly different amounts of damage depending on *how* their energy is released. Every earthquake releases some of its energy into the Earth's interior, where it is fairly harmless, and some along the Earth's surface, where it shakes the ground up and down. A moderate earthquake that releases most of its energy along the surface can do more damage than a strong earthquake that releases most of its energy into the interior.

Deaths from earthquakes generally arise indirectly. Ground shaking can cause buildings to collapse, which is why the worst earthquake disasters tend to occur in regions where people cannot afford the high cost of earthquake-resistant construction. Other earthquake-related disasters occur when the shaking triggers landslides or tsunamis.

Time Out to Think

Surface waves from earthquakes make the ground roll up and down like ripples moving outward on a pond. Given this motion, suggest a few ways that buildings can be designed to withstand earthquakes. Do you think it is possible to make a building that could withstand *any* earthquake? Why or why not?

Example 1 The Meaning of One Magnitude

Using the formula for earthquake magnitudes, calculate precisely how much more energy is released for each 1 magnitude on the earthquake scale.

Solution We must look closely at the formula that gives the energy:

$$E = (2.5 \times 10^4) \times 10^{1.5M}$$

The first term, 2.5×10^4, is a constant number that is the same no matter what value we use for *M*. The magnitude appears only in the second term, $10^{1.5M}$. Each time we raise the magnitude by 1, such as from 5 to 6 or from 7 to 8, the total energy *E* increases by a factor of $10^{1.5}$. Therefore, each successive magnitude represents $10^{1.5} \approx 31.623$ times as much energy as the prior magnitude. This is approximately 32 times as much energy, as stated earlier. **Now try Exercises 9–10.**

Example 2 Comparing Disasters

The 1989 San Francisco earthquake, in which 90 people were killed, had magnitude 7.1. Calculate the energy released, in joules. Compare the energy of this earthquake to that of the 2003 earthquake that destroyed the ancient city of Bam, Iran, which had magnitude 6.3 and killed an estimated 50,000 people.

Solution The energy released by the San Francisco earthquake was

$$E = (2.5 \times 10^4) \times 10^{1.5M} = (2.5 \times 10^4) \times 10^{1.5 \times 7.1} \approx 1.1 \times 10^{15} \text{ joules}$$

The San Francisco earthquake was $7.1 - 6.3 = 0.8$ magnitude greater than the Iran earthquake. It therefore released $10^{1.5 \times 0.8} = 10^{1.2} \approx 16$ times as much energy. Nevertheless, the Iran earthquake killed many more people, because more buildings collapsed.

Now try Exercises 11–14.

Measuring Sounds in Decibels

The **decibel scale** is used to compare the loudness of sounds. It is defined so that a sound of 0 decibels, abbreviated 0 dB, represents the softest sound audible to the human ear. Table 8.5 lists the approximate loudness of some common sounds.

Take Note

In absolute terms, the intensity of the softest audible sound is about 10^{-12} watt per square meter.

TABLE 8.5 Typical Sounds in Decibels

Decibels	Times as Loud as Softest Audible Sound	Example
140	10^{14}	jet at 30 meters
120	10^{12}	strong risk of damage to human ear
100	10^{10}	siren at 30 meters
90	10^{9}	threshold of pain for human ear
80	10^{8}	busy street traffic
60	10^{6}	ordinary conversation
40	10^{4}	background noise in average home
20	10^{2}	whisper
10	10^{1}	rustle of leaves
0	1	softest audible sound
−10	0.1	inaudible sound

Historical Note

A decibel is 1/10 of a *bel*, a unit named for Alexander Graham Bell (1847–1922). Bell's mother was deaf, and his father was a pioneer in teaching speech to the deaf. Bell became a professor of vocal physiology at Boston University and married a deaf pupil. He patented his most famous invention, the telephone, in 1876.

THE DECIBEL SCALE FOR SOUND

The loudness of a sound in decibels is defined by the following equivalent formulas:

$$\text{loudness in dB} = 10 \log_{10}\left(\frac{\text{intensity of the sound}}{\text{intensity of softest audible sound}}\right)$$

or

$$\frac{\text{intensity of the sound}}{\text{intensity of softest audible sound}} = 10^{(\text{loudness in db})/10}$$

Example 3 Computing Decibels

Suppose a sound is 100 times as intense as the softest audible sound. What is its loudness, in decibels?

Solution We are looking for the loudness in decibels, so we use the first form of the decibel scale formula:

$$\text{loudness in dB} = 10 \log_{10}\left(\frac{\text{intensity of the sound}}{\text{intensity of softest audible sound}}\right)$$

The ratio in parentheses is 100, because we are given that the sound is 100 times as intense as the softest audible sound. We find

$$\text{loudness in dB} = 10 \log_{10} 100 = 10 \times 2 = 20 \text{ dB}$$

A sound that is 100 times as intense as the softest possible sound has a loudness of 20 dB, which is equivalent to a whisper (see Table 8.5). **Now try Exercises 15–18.**

Example 4 Sound Comparison

How does the intensity of a 57-dB sound compare to that of a 23-dB sound?

Solution We can compare the loudness of two sounds by working with the second form of the decibel scale formula. You should confirm for yourself that by dividing the intensity of Sound 1 by the intensity of Sound 2, we find

$$\frac{\text{intensity of Sound 1}}{\text{intensity of Sound 2}} = 10^{[(\text{loudness of Sound 1 in dB}) - (\text{loudness of Sound 2 in dB})]/10}$$

Substituting 57 dB for Sound 1 and 23 dB for Sound 2, we have

$$\frac{\text{intensity of Sound 1}}{\text{intensity of Sound 2}} = 10^{[(\text{loudness of Sound 1 in dB}) - (\text{loudness of Sound 2 in dB})]/10}$$

$$= 10^{\frac{57-23}{10}} = 10^{3.4} \approx 2512$$

A sound of 57 dB is about 2500 times as intense as a sound of 23 dB.

Now try Exercises 19–20.

The Inverse Square Law for Sound

You've probably noticed that sounds get weaker with distance. If you sit right in front of the speakers at an outdoor concert, the sound may be almost deafening, while people a mile away may not hear the music at all. It's easy to understand why.

Figure 8.8 shows the idea. The sound from the speaker gets spread over a larger and larger *area* as it moves farther from the speaker. This area increases with the *square* of the distance from the speaker. For example, at 2 meters the sound is spread over an area $2^2 = 4$ times as large as the area at 1 meter, at 3 meters the sound is spread over an area $3^2 = 9$ times as large as the area at 1 meter, and so on. That is, the intensity of the sound weakens with the *square* of the distance.

Because the intensity of sound decreases with the square of the distance, we say that sound follows an **inverse square law**. In other words, the intensity of a sound at a distance d from its source is proportional to $1/d^2$. Many other quantities also follow inverse square laws with distance, including the brightness of a light and the strength of gravity.

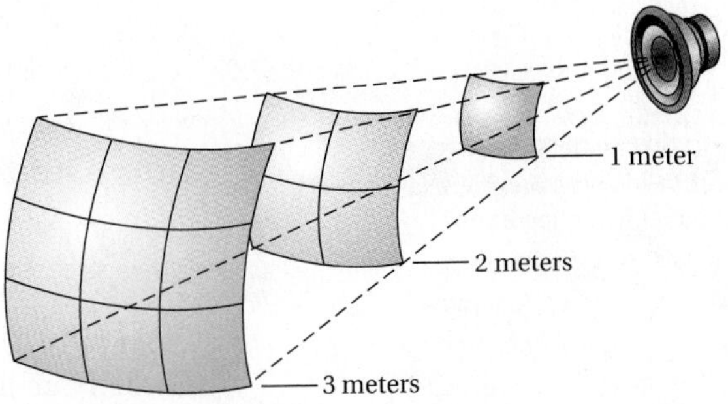

FIGURE 8.8 This figure shows why the intensity of sound decreases with the *square* of the distance from the source. Notice that the area at 2 meters is $2^2 = 4$ times as large as the area at 1 meter, and the area at 3 meters is $3^2 = 9$ times as large.

THE INVERSE SQUARE LAW FOR SOUND

The intensity of sound decreases with the square of the distance from the source, meaning that the intensity is proportional to $1/d^2$. We therefore say that sound follows an **inverse square law** with distance.

Example 5 Sound Advice

How far should you be from a jet to avoid a strong risk of damage to your ear?

Solution Table 8.5 shows that the sound from a jet at a distance of 30 meters is 140 dB, and 120 dB is the level of sound that poses a strong risk of ear damage. The ratio of the intensity of these two sounds is

$$\frac{\text{intensity of 140-dB sound}}{\text{intensity of 120-dB sound}} = \frac{10^{140/10}}{10^{120/10}} = \frac{10^{14}}{10^{12}} = 10^2 = 100$$

The sound of the jet at 30 meters is 100 times as intense as a sound that presents a strong risk of ear damage. To prevent ear damage, you must therefore be far enough from the jet to weaken this sound intensity by at least a factor of 100. Because sound intensity follows an inverse square law with distance, moving 10 times as far away weakens the intensity by a factor of $10^2 = 100$. You should be more than $10 \times 30\text{ m} = 300\text{ m}$ from the jet to be safe. **Now try Exercises 21–24.**

BY THE WAY

What we perceive as sound actually is tiny pressure changes in the air. Sound travels through air as a wave of pressure changes, called a sound wave. When a sound wave strikes the eardrum, its energy causes the eardrum to move in response. The brain analyzes the motions of the eardrum, perceiving sound.

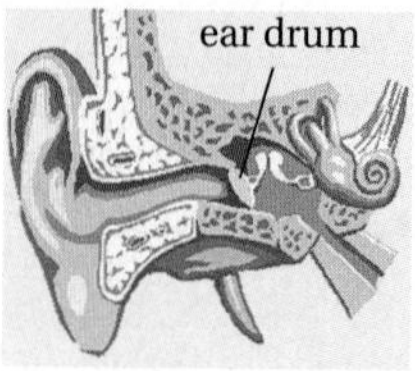

The pH Scale for Acidity

If you check the labels of many household products, including cleansers, drain openers, and shampoo, you will see that they state a quantity called the **pH.** The pH is used by chemists to classify substances as **neutral, acidic,** or **basic** (also called *alkaline*). By definition,

- Pure water is *neutral* and has a pH of 7.
- *Acids* have a pH lower than 7.
- *Bases* have a pH higher than 7.

Table 8.6 gives a few typical pH values.

TABLE 8.6 Typical pH Values

Solution	pH	Solution	pH
lemon juice	2	pure water	7
stomach acid	2–3	baking soda	8.4
vinegar	3	household ammonia	10
drinking water	6.5	drain opener	10–12

Time Out to Think

Check around your house or apartment for labels that state a pH. Are the substances acids or bases?

BY THE WAY

Neutral hydrogen atoms consist of a single, positively charged proton and a single, negatively charged electron. H^+ ions are positive because they are missing the negatively charged electron and hence are simply protons.

Chemically, acidity is related to the concentration of positively charged hydrogen ions, which are hydrogen atoms without their electron. The ions themselves are denoted H^+ for hydrogen with a positive charge. The concentration of hydrogen ions is denoted $[H^+]$ and is usually measured in units of *moles per liter*. A **mole** is *Avogadro's number* of particles, which is about 6×10^{23} particles.

THE PH SCALE

The pH scale is defined by the following equivalent formulas:

$$\text{pH} = -\log_{10}[H^+] \quad \text{or} \quad [H^+] = 10^{-\text{pH}}$$

where $[H^+]$ is the hydrogen ion concentration in moles per liter. Pure water is neutral and has a pH of 7. Acids have a pH lower than 7 and bases have a pH higher than 7.

Example 6 Finding pH

What is the pH of a solution with a hydrogen ion concentration of 10^{-12} mole per liter? Is it an acid or a base?

Solution Using the first version of the pH formula with a hydrogen ion concentration of $[H^+] = 10^{-12}$ mole per liter, we find

$$pH = -\log_{10}[H^+] = -\log_{10}10^{-12} = -(-12) = 12$$

(Recall that $\log_{10}10^x = x$.) A solution with a hydrogen ion concentration of 10^{-12} mole per liter has pH 12. Because this pH is well above 7, the solution is a strong base.

Now try Exercises 25–30.

BY THE WAY

The word *acid* comes from the Latin *acidus*, meaning "sour." Some fruits taste sour because they are acidic. Bases are substances that can neutralize the action of acids. Common antacid tablets (for upset stomachs) are bases and work by neutralizing stomach acid.

Acid Rain

Normal raindrops are mildly acidic, with a pH slightly under 6. However, the burning of fossil fuels releases sulfur or nitrogen that can form sulfuric or nitric acids in the air, and these acids can make raindrops far more acidic than normal, creating the problem known as **acid rain.** Acid rain in the northeastern United States and *acid fog* in the Los Angeles area have been observed with pH as low as 2—the same acidity as pure lemon juice!

Acid rain can kill trees and other plants, doing serious damage to forests. Many forests in the northeastern United States and southeastern Canada have been damaged by acid rain. Acid rain can also "kill" lakes by making the water so acidic that nothing can survive. Thousands of lakes in the northeastern United States and southeastern Canada have suffered this fate. Surprisingly, you can often recognize a dead lake by its exceptionally clear water—clear because it lacks the living organisms that usually make the water murky.

BY THE WAY

Acid rain is caused primarily by emissions from coal-burning power plants and industries. The problem is particularly bad when coal with a high sulfur content is burned. Today, China has the worst acid rain problems in the world, due to heavy use of coal.

Example 7 Acid Rain versus Normal Rain

In terms of hydrogen ion concentration, compare acid rain with a pH of 2 to ordinary rain with a pH of 6.

Solution For acid rain with pH 2, the hydrogen ion concentration is

$$[H^+] = 10^{-pH} = 10^{-2} \text{ mole per liter}$$

For ordinary rain with pH 6, the hydrogen ion concentration is

$$[H^+] = 10^{-pH} = 10^{-6} \text{ mole per liter}$$

Therefore, the hydrogen ion concentration in the acid rain is greater than that in ordinary rain by a factor of

$$\frac{10^{-2}}{10^{-6}} = 10^{-2-(-6)} = 10^4$$

Acid rain is 10,000 times as acidic as ordinary rain.

Now try Exercises 31–32.

QUICK QUIZ

Choose the best answer to each of the following questions. Explain your reasoning with one or more complete sentences.

1. The energy release of a magnitude 7 earthquake is about how many times as great as that of a magnitude 5 earthquake?

   a. 32×32 times as great b. $10^{(7-5)}$ times as great

   c. 7/5 times as great

2. Why do individual earthquakes in less developed countries tend to cause more deaths than those in developed countries?

   a. Less developed countries have earthquakes with higher magnitudes.

   b. Buildings are more likely to collapse in less developed countries.

   c. The population density is higher in less developed countries.

3. What is a 0-decibel sound?

   a. the softest sound that a human ear can hear

   b. a sound with zero intensity

   c. a sound that cannot be stated on the decibel scale

4. A sound of 95 decibels is defined to be

   a. 95 times as loud as the softest audible sound.

   b. $10^{9.5}$ times as loud as the softest audible sound.

   c. 10^{95} times as loud as the softest audible sound.

5. How does the intensity of a 10-decibel sound compare to that of a 0-decibel sound?

   a. It is 10 times as great. b. It is 10^{10} times as great.

   c. It is not possible to compare to a 0-decibel sound.

6. Like sound, gravity follows an inverse square law with distance. This means that if you triple the distance between two objects, the strength of gravity between them

   a. increases by a factor of 3.

   b. decreases by a factor of 3.

   c. decreases by a factor of 9.

7. Which of the following describes the strongest acid?

   a. a pH of 17

   b. a pH of 5

   c. a pH of 1

8. A pH of 0 means that the hydrogen ion concentration is

   a. 0.

   b. 1 mole per liter.

   c. the same as that in pure water.

9. A hydrogen ion concentration of 10^{-5} moles per liter means a pH of

   a. -5.

   b. $\log_{10}5$.

   c. 5.

10. Suppose you wish to revive a lake that has been damaged by acid rain. You should add to the lake something that

    a. increases its pH.

    b. decreases its pH.

    c. changes its pH from positive to negative.

Exercises 8D

REVIEW QUESTIONS

1. What is the magnitude scale for earthquakes? What increase in energy is represented by an increase of 1 magnitude on the earthquake scale?
2. What is the decibel scale? Describe how it is defined.
3. What is pH? What pH values define an acid, a base, and a neutral substance?
4. What is acid rain? Why is it a serious environmental problem?

DOES IT MAKE SENSE?

Decide whether each of the following statements makes sense (or is clearly true) or does not make sense (or is clearly false). Explain your reasoning.

5. An earthquake of magnitude 8 will do twice as much damage as an earthquake of magnitude 4.
6. A 120-dB sound is 20% louder than a 100-dB sound.
7. If I double the amount of water in the cup, I'll also double the pH of the water in the cup.
8. The lake water was crystal clear, so it could not possibly have been affected by acid rain.

BASIC SKILLS & CONCEPTS

9–14: Earthquake Magnitudes. Use the earthquake magnitude scale to answer the questions.

9. How much energy, in joules, is released by an earthquake of magnitude 4?
10. How many times as much energy is released by an earthquake of magnitude 6 as by one of magnitude 4?
11. How much energy, in joules, was released by the December 2004 earthquake in Indonesia that triggered devastating tsunamis (magnitude 9.0)?
12. How much energy, in joules, was released by the 2008 earthquake in Sichuan province, China (magnitude 7.9), which killed at least 68,000 people, including many school children?

13. Compare the energy of a magnitude 6 earthquake to that released by a 1-megaton nuclear bomb (5×10^{15} joules).

14. What magnitude earthquake would release energy equivalent to that of a 1-megaton nuclear bomb (5×10^{15} joules)? Which would be more destructive, the bomb or the earthquake? Why?

15–20: The Decibel Scale. Use the decibel scale to answer the questions.

15. How many times as loud as the softest audible sound is the sound of ordinary conversation?

16. How many times as loud as the softest audible sound is the sound of a siren at 30 meters?

17. What is the loudness, in decibels, of a sound 10 million times as loud as the softest audible sound?

18. What is the loudness, in decibels, of a sound 10 trillion times as loud as the softest audible sound?

19. How much louder (more intense) is a 55-dB sound than a 10-dB sound?

20. Suppose that a sound is 100 times as loud as (more intense than) a whisper. What is its loudness in decibels?

21–24: Inverse Square Law. Use the inverse square law for sound to answer the questions.

21. How many times greater is the intensity of sound from a concert speaker at a distance of 1 meter than the intensity at a distance of 3 meters?

22. How many times greater is the intensity of sound from a concert speaker at a distance of 1 meter than the intensity at a distance of 200 meters?

23. How many times greater is the intensity of sound from a concert speaker at a distance of 10 meters than the intensity at a distance of 50 meters?

24. How many times greater is the intensity of sound from a concert speaker at a distance of 20 meters than the intensity at a distance of 200 meters?

25–32: The pH Scale. Use the pH scale to answer the questions.

25. If the pH of a solution increases by 4 (e.g., from 4 to 8), how much does the hydrogen ion concentration change? Does the change make the solution more acidic or more basic?

26. If the pH of a solution decreases by 3.5 (e.g., from 6.5 to 3), how much does the hydrogen ion concentration change? Does the change make the solution more acidic or more basic?

27. What is the hydrogen ion concentration of a solution with pH 8.5?

28. What is the hydrogen ion concentration of a solution with pH 3.5?

29. What is the pH of a solution with a hydrogen ion concentration of 0.001 mole per liter? Is this solution an acid or a base?

30. What is the pH of a solution with a hydrogen ion concentration of 10^{-12} mole per liter? Is this solution an acid or a base?

31. How many times more acidic is acid rain with a pH of 2 than ordinary rain with a pH of 6?

32. How many times more acidic is acid rain with a pH of 2.5 than ordinary rain with a pH of 6?

FURTHER APPLICATIONS

33–38: Logarithmic Thinking. Briefly describe, in words, the effects you would expect in the situations given.

33. An earthquake of magnitude 2.8 strikes the Los Angeles area.

34. You have your ear against a new speaker when it emits a sound with an intensity of 160 dB.

35. A young child (too young to know better) finds and drinks from an open bottle of drain opener with pH 12.

36. An earthquake of magnitude 8.5 strikes the Tokyo area.

37. Your friend is calling to you from across the street in New York City, with a shout that registers 90 dB. Traffic is heavy, and several emergency vehicles are passing by with sirens.

38. A forest situated a few hundred miles from a coal-burning industrial area is subjected regularly to acid rain, with pH 4, for many years.

39. **Sound and Distance**

a. The decibel level for busy street traffic in Table 8.5 is based on the assumption that you stand very close to the noise source—say, 1 meter from the street. If your house is 100 meters from a busy street, how loud will the street noise be, in decibels?

b. At a distance of 10 meters from the speakers at a concert, the sound level is 135 dB. How far away should you sit to reduce the level to 120 dB?

c. Imagine that you are a spy in a restaurant. The conversation you want to hear is taking place in a booth across the room, about 8 meters away. The people are speaking softly, so they hear each other's voice at about 20 dB (they are sitting about 1 meter apart). How loud is the sound of their voices when it reaches your table? If you have a miniature amplifier in your ear and want to hear their voices at 60 dB, by what factor must you amplify their voices?

40. **Variation in Sound with Distance.** Suppose that a siren is placed 0.1 meter from your ear.

a. How many times as loud as a siren at 30 meters will the sound you hear be?

b. How loud will the siren next to your ear sound, in decibels?

c. How likely is it that this siren will cause damage to your eardrum? Explain.

41. **Toxic Dumping in Acidified Lakes.** Consider a situation in which acid rain has heavily polluted a lake to a level of pH 4. An unscrupulous chemical company dumps some acid into the lake illegally. Assume that the lake contains 100 million gallons of water and that the company dumps 100,000 gallons of acid with pH 2.

a. What is the hydrogen ion concentration, $[H^+]$, of the lake polluted by acid rain alone?

b. Suppose that the unpolluted lake, without acid rain, would have pH 7. If the lake were then polluted by company acid alone (no acid rain), what hydrogen ion concentration, $[H^+]$, and pH would it have?

c. What is the hydrogen ion concentration, $[H^+]$, after the company dumps the acid into the acid rain–polluted lake (pH 4)? What is the new pH of the lake?

d. If the U.S. Environmental Protection Agency can test for changes in pH of only 0.1 or greater, could the company's pollution be detected?

WEB PROJECTS

42. **Earthquakes.** Go to the U.S. Geological Survey Web site and learn more about earthquakes and how they cause damage. Write a short report on some aspect of earthquakes.

43. **Earthquake Disasters.** Find the death tolls for some of the worst earthquake disasters in history. How strongly do the death tolls correlate with the earthquake magnitudes? Discuss the factors that determine the devastation caused by an earthquake.

44. **Acid Rain.** Investigate the problem of acid rain in a region where it has been a particular problem, such as the northeastern United States, southeastern Canada, the Black Forest in Germany, eastern Europe, or China. Write a report on your findings. The report should include a description of the acidity of the rain, the source of the acidity, the damage being caused by the acid rain, and the status of efforts to alleviate this damage.

IN YOUR WORLD

45. **Earthquakes.** Find a recent news story dealing with some aspect of earthquakes, such as their destructive power, attempts to predict them, or ways of building to withstand them. How does the magnitude of an earthquake affect the issue? Explain.

46. **Acid Rain.** Find a recent news story dealing with acid rain. Discuss the source of the rain and its environmental impacts.

CHAPTER 8 Summary

UNIT	KEY TERMS	KEY IDEAS AND SKILLS
8A	linear growth exponential growth doublings	In **linear growth**, a quantity grows by the same *absolute* amount in each unit of time. In **exponential growth**, a quantity grows by the same *relative* amount in each unit of time. **Understand** the impact of doublings and why exponential growth cannot continue indefinitely.
8B	doubling time half-life rule of 70	**Doubling time calculations:** After time t, for an exponentially growing quantity with doubling time T_{double}, $\text{new value} = \text{initial value} \times 2^{t/T_{\text{double}}}$ The **approximate doubling time formula** for a quantity growing exponentially at a rate of P% per time period: $T_{\text{double}} \approx \frac{70}{P}$ The **exact doubling time formula** for a quantity growing exponentially at a fractional rate r: $T_{\text{double}} = \frac{\log_{10} 2}{\log_{10}(1 + r)}$ **Half-life calculations:** After time t, for an exponentially decaying quantity with half-life T_{half}, $\text{new value} = \text{initial value} \times \left(\frac{1}{2}\right)^{t/T_{\text{half}}}$ **The approximate half-life formula** for a quantity decaying exponentially at a rate of P% per time period: $T_{\text{half}} \approx \frac{70}{P}$ **The exact half-life formula** for a quantity decaying exponentially at a fractional rate (r must be negative): $T_{\text{half}} = -\frac{\log_{10} 2}{\log_{10}(1 + r)}$
8C	overall growth rate birth rate death rate carrying capacity logistic growth overshoot and collapse	**Logistic growth:** $\text{logistic growth rate} = r \times \left(1 - \frac{\text{population}}{\text{carrying capacity}}\right)$ **Contrast** exponential growth, logistic growth, and overshoot and collapse. **Understand** factors affecting the carrying capacity.

(*Continues on the next page*)

UNIT	KEY TERMS	KEY IDEAS AND SKILLS
8D	logarithmic scale earthquake magnitude decibel inverse square law pH acid base neutral acid rain	**Earthquake magnitude scale:** $\log_{10} E = 4.4 + 1.5M$ or $E = (2.5 \times 10^4) \times 10^{1.5M}$ **Decibel scale:** $\text{loudness in dB} = 10 \log_{10}\left(\dfrac{\text{intensity of the sound}}{\text{intensity of softest audible sound}}\right)$ or $\dfrac{\text{intensity of the sound}}{\text{intensity of softest audible sound}} = 10^{(\text{loudness in dB})/10}$ **Inverse square law for sound:** The intensity of a sound *decreases* with the *square* of the distance from the source. **pH scale:** $\text{pH} = -\log_{10}[H^+]$ or $[H^+] = 10^{-\text{pH}}$

UNIT 10C

Fractal Geometry: In the past few decades, an entirely new type of geometry has become important both in the arts and in our understanding of nature. We explore a few of the ideas that underlie *fractal geometry*.

10

A work of morality, politics, criticism, perhaps even eloquence will be more elegant, other things being equal, if it is shaped by the hand of geometry.

—Bernard Le Bovier de Fontenelle, 1729

Modeling with Geometry

We live in a three-dimensional world, and much of our understanding of that world is rooted in geometry. Surveying land for a new park, analyzing a satellite photograph of the Earth, navigating a ship at sea, and creating a medical image all rely on ideas that originated with the ancient Greeks. This chapter illustrates how both ancient and modern geometry help us understand the world around us.

UNIT 10C Fractal Geometry

The geometry of the previous two units is classical geometry developed largely by the ancient Greeks. While this geometry still serves us well in many applications, it does not work as well with many forms that arise in nature. In recent decades, a new geometry called **fractal geometry** has emerged. It has proved to be so effective at describing nature that it is now used in art and film to create realistic imagery. Figure 10.43 shows an imaginary landscape generated entirely on a computer using fractal geometry.

FIGURE 10.43 A fractal landscape, generated by Anne Burns.

What Are Fractals?

We can investigate fractals by envisioning measurements made with "rulers" of different lengths, such as 10 meters, 1 meter, 1 millimeter, and so on. Each length laid out by a ruler is called an **element** (of length). Suppose we use a ruler of length 10 meters and find that an object is 50 elements long. Then the total length of the object is $50 \times 10\text{ m} = 500\text{ m}$. More generally, the length of any object is

$$\text{total length} \approx \text{number of elements} \times \text{length of each element}$$

Measuring the Perimeter of Central Park

FIGURE 10.44 The rectangular layout of Central Park.

Imagine that you are asked to measure the perimeter of Central Park in New York City, which was designed in the shape of a rectangle (Figure 10.44). Suppose you start with a 10-meter ruler. Multiplying the number of elements by their 10-meter length gives you a measurement of the park perimeter.

Now, suppose that you use a shorter ruler—say, a 1-meter ruler. Your measurement with the 1-meter ruler will not differ much from that with the 10-meter ruler, because you are simply measuring the straight sides of the park. That is, ten 1-meter rulers will fit along the same straight line as one 10-meter ruler. In fact, the length of the ruler will not significantly affect measurements of the Central Park perimeter (Figure 10.45).

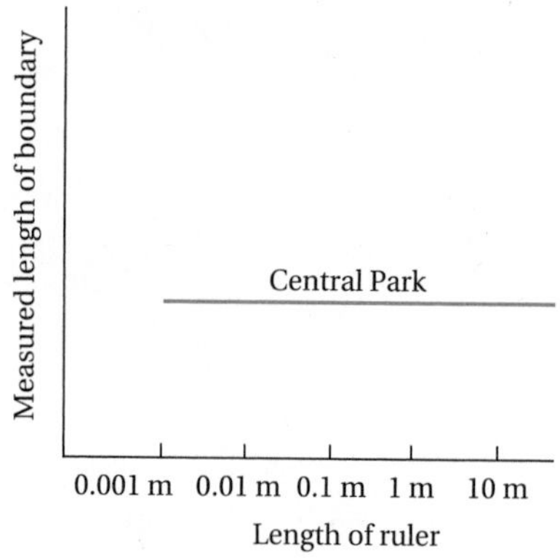

FIGURE 10.45 Ruler length does not affect the measured length of the Central Park perimeter.

Measuring an Island Coastline

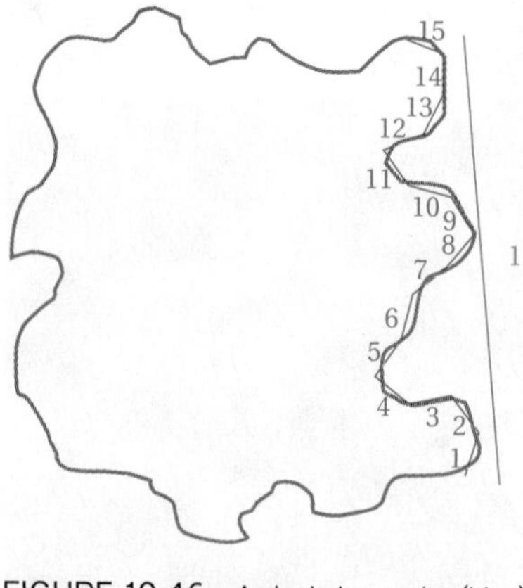

FIGURE 10.46 A single long ruler (blue) cannot measure details that can be measured with shorter rulers (red).

Next, imagine that you are asked to measure the perimeter of an island. To avoid problems with tides and waves, imagine that it is winter and the water around the island is frozen. Your task is to measure the length of the coastline defined by the ice-land boundary.

Suppose you begin by using a 100-meter ruler, laying it end to end around the island. The 100-meter ruler (the single blue line segment in Figure 10.46) will adequately measure large-scale features such as bays and estuaries, but will miss features such as promontories and inlets that are less than 100 meters across. Switching to a 10-meter ruler will allow you to follow many features that were missed by the 100-meter ruler. As a result, you'll measure a *longer* perimeter (the short line segments in Figure 10.46).

The 10-meter ruler is still too long to measure all the features along the coastline, so you'll find an even greater perimeter if you switch to a 1-meter ruler. In fact, as you use shorter and shorter rulers to measure the coastline, you'll get longer and longer estimates of the perimeter because shorter rulers measure new levels of detail. Figure 10.47 shows how the measured length of the coastline grows larger when measured with shorter rulers. We cannot agree on the "true" length of the coastline because, unlike the clearly defined perimeter of Central Park, it depends on the length of the ruler used.

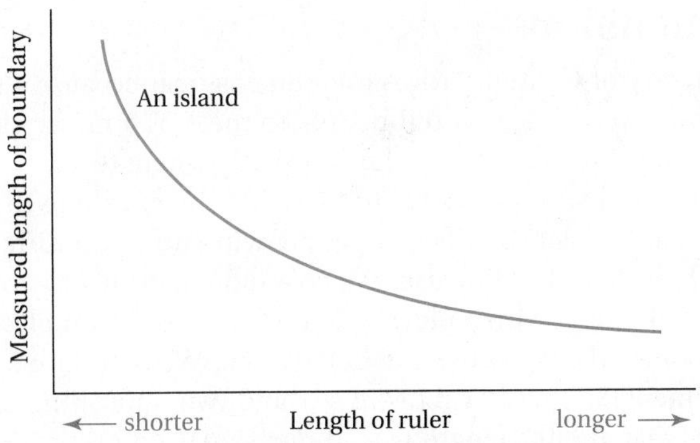

FIGURE 10.47 The measured perimeter of an island gets longer (vertical axis) as the ruler length gets shorter (horizontal axis).

Rectangles and Coastlines Under Magnification

Imagine viewing a piece of the rectangular perimeter of Central Park under a magnifying glass. No new details will appear—it is still a straight-line segment (Figure 10.48a). In contrast, if you view a piece of the coastline under a magnifying glass, you will see details that were not visible without magnification (Figure 10.48b).

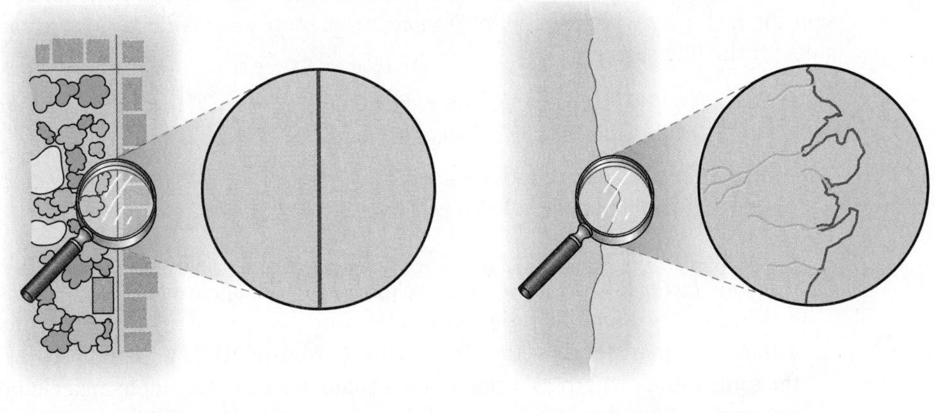

FIGURE 10.48 (a) A segment of a rectangle looks the same under magnification. (b) A segment of coastline reveals new details under magnification.

Objects like the coastline that continually reveal new features at smaller scales are called **fractals**. Many natural objects have fractal structure. For example, coral (Figure 10.49a) and mountain ranges (Figure 10.49b) both reveal more and more features when viewed under greater magnification, and hence are fractals.

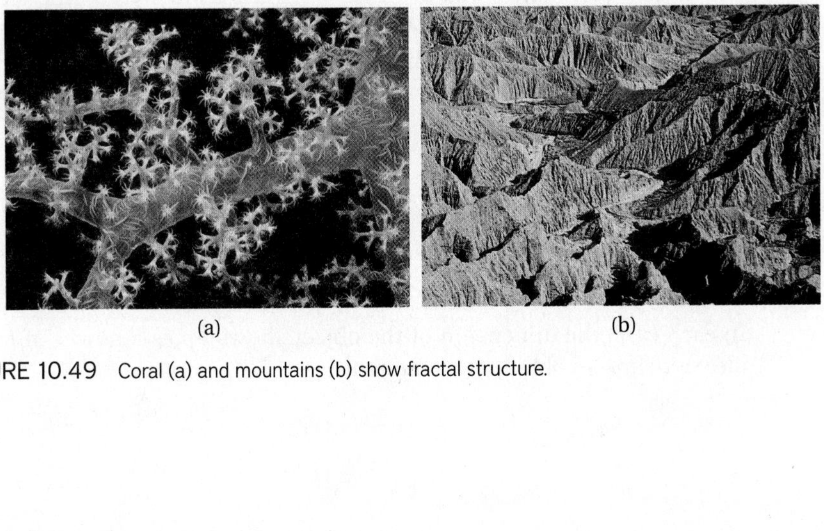

FIGURE 10.49 Coral (a) and mountains (b) show fractal structure.

Fractal Dimension

The boundary of Central Park is one-dimensional because a single number locates any point. For example, if you tell people to meet 375 meters from the park's northwest corner, going clockwise, they'll know exactly where to go.

In contrast, if you tell people to meet 375 meters along the coastline from a particular point on the island, different people will end up in different places depending on the length of the ruler they use. We conclude that the coastline is *not* an ordinary one-dimensional object with a clearly defined length. But it clearly isn't two-dimensional either, because the coast itself is not an area. We therefore say that the coastline has a **fractal dimension** that lies *between* one and two, indicating that the coastline has some properties that are like length (one dimension) and others that are more like area (two dimensions).

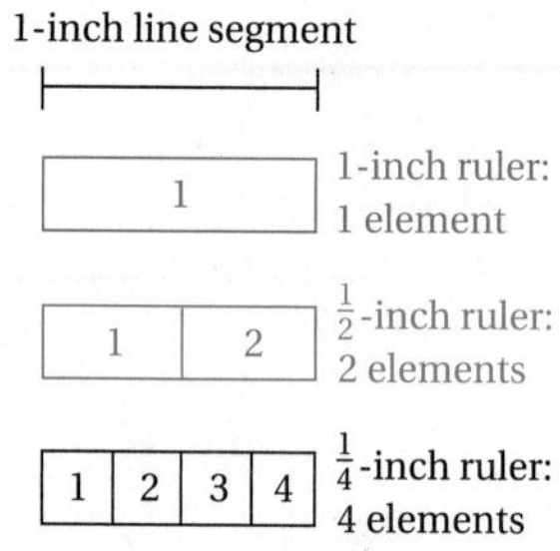

FIGURE 10.50 For a line segment, reducing ruler length by a factor R increases the number of elements by a factor $N = R$.

A New Definition of Dimension

If we measure a 1-inch line segment with a 1-inch ruler, we find *one* 1-inch element (Figure 10.50). Using a ruler that is smaller by a factor of 2, or $\frac{1}{2}$ inch in length, we find *two* elements along the 1-inch line segment. If we choose a ruler that is smaller by a factor of 4, or $\frac{1}{4}$ inch in length, we find *four* elements of length along the 1-inch line segment.

Let's use R to represent the *reduction factor* in the length of the ruler and N to represent the factor by which the *number of elements* increases. We can now restate our results for the line segment:

- Reducing the ruler length by a *reduction factor* $R = 2$ (to $\frac{1}{2}$ inch) leads to an increase in the *number of elements* by a factor $N = 2$.
- Reducing the ruler length by a *reduction factor* $R = 10$ (to $\frac{1}{10}$ inch) leads to an increase in the *number of elements* by a factor $N = 10$.

Generalizing for the line segment, we find that decreasing the ruler length by a *reduction factor* R leads to an increase in the *number of elements* by a factor $N = R$.

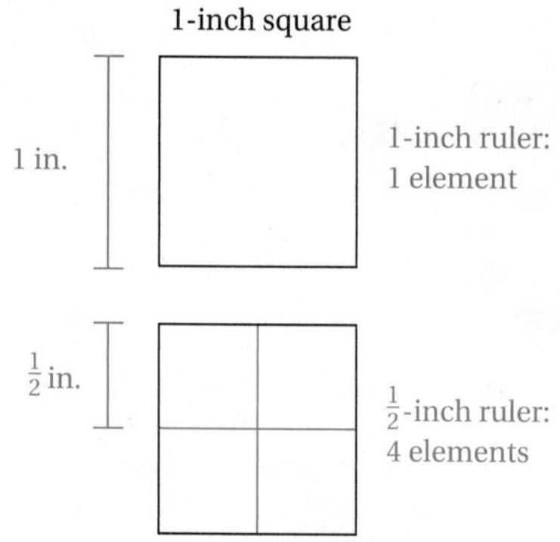

FIGURE 10.51 For a square, reducing ruler length by a factor R increases the number of elements by a factor $N = R^2$.

We can use a similar process to determine the area of a square by counting the number of *area elements* that fit within it (Figure 10.51). Using a ruler that has the same 1-inch length as a side of the square, we can fit a single area element in the square. If we reduce the ruler length by a factor $R = 2$, to $\frac{1}{2}$ inch, we fit $N = 4$ times as many elements in the square. Reducing the ruler length by $R = 4$, to $\frac{1}{4}$ inch, fits $N = 16$ times as many elements in the square. Generalizing for the square, we find that reducing the ruler length by a reduction factor R increases the number of area elements by a factor $N = R^2$.

For a cube, we can count the number of *volume elements* that fit within it (Figure 10.52). A ruler with the same 1-inch length as a side of the cube makes a single volume element that fits in the cube. This time, reducing the ruler length by a factor $R = 2$, to $\frac{1}{2}$ inch, allows us to fit $N = 8$ times as many volume elements in the cube. Reducing the ruler length by $R = 4$, to $\frac{1}{4}$ inch, fits $N = 64$ times as many elements in the cube. Generalizing for the cube, we find that reducing the ruler length by a factor R increases the number of volume elements by a factor $N = R^3$.

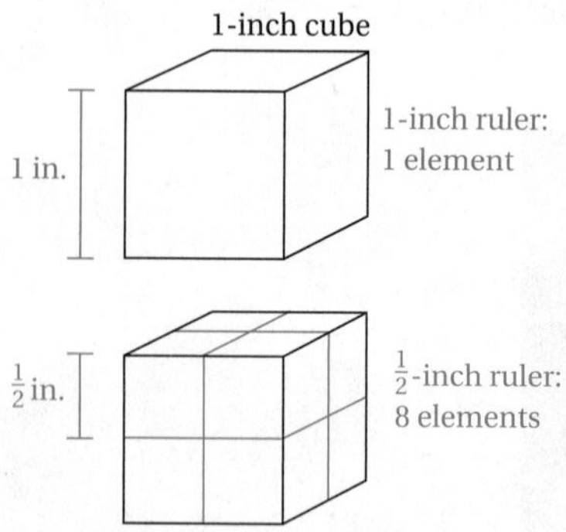

FIGURE 10.52 For a cube, reducing ruler length by a factor R increases the number of elements by a factor $N = R^3$.

Let's summarize our results:

- For a one-dimensional object (such as a line segment), we found $N = R^1$.
- For a two-dimensional object (such as a square), we found $N = R^2$.
- For a three-dimensional object (such as a cube), we found $N = R^3$.

In each case, the dimension of the object shows up as a power of R. We use this idea to define an object's *fractal dimension*.

> **DEFINITION**
>
> The **fractal dimension** of an object is defined as a number D such that
>
> $$N = R^D$$
>
> where N is the factor by which the number of elements increases when we shorten the ruler by a reduction factor R.

Example 1 Finding a Fractal Dimension

In measuring an object, every time you reduce the length of your ruler by a factor of 3, the number of elements increases by a factor of 4. What is the fractal dimension of this object?

Solution Reducing the ruler length by a factor $R = 3$ increases the number of elements by a factor $N = 4$. We are therefore looking for a fractal dimension D such that

$$4 = 3^D$$

We now solve for D as follows.

1. Starting equation: $4 = 3^D$
2. Take the logarithm of both sides: $\log_{10} 4 = \log_{10} 3^D$
3. On the right side, apply the rule that $\log_{10} a^x = x \log_{10} a$: $\log_{10} 4 = D \log_{10} 3$
4. Interchange the left and right sides and divide both sides by $\log_{10} 3$: $D = \dfrac{\log_{10} 4}{\log_{10} 3} \approx 1.2619$

The *fractal dimension* of this object is about 1.2619. **Now try Exercises 15–26.**

The Snowflake Curve

What kind of object could have a fractal dimension like the one we calculated in Example 1? Let's consider a special object called a **snowflake curve**, generated by a process that begins with a straight-line segment. As shown at the bottom of Figure 10.53, we designate the starting line segment L_0, which has a length of 1. We then generate L_1 with the following three steps:

1. Divide the line segment L_0 into three equal pieces.
2. Remove the middle piece.
3. Replace the middle piece with two segments of the same length arranged as two sides of an equilateral triangle.

Note that L_1 consists of four line segments and that each has a length of $\frac{1}{3}$ (because L_0 was divided into three equal pieces).

Next, we repeat the three steps on *each* of the four segments of L_1. The result is L_2, which has 16 line segments, each of length $\frac{1}{9}$.

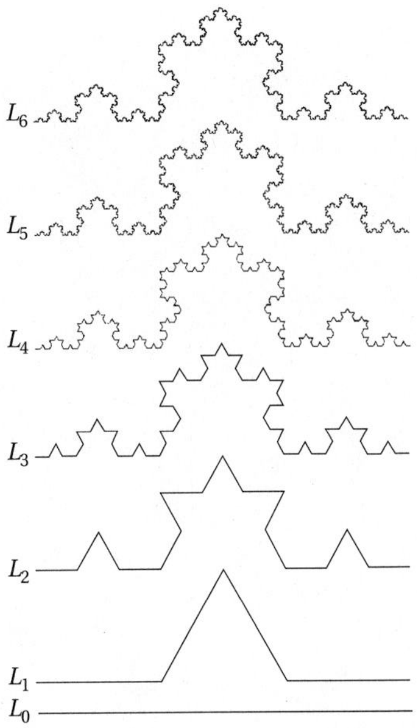

FIGURE 10.53 The generating process for the snowflake curve, from L_0 (bottom) to L_6 (top).

> **Time Out to Think**
>
> Count the segments shown in Figure 10.53 to confirm that L_2 has 16 line segments. Measure to confirm that each is $\frac{1}{9}$ the length of L_0. Why are the segments $\frac{1}{9}$ the length of L_0? How long are the segments of L_3?

BY THE WAY

The snowflake curve is sometimes called a *Koch curve* after Helga von Koch, who first described it in 1906.

Repeating the three-step process on each segment of the current figure generates L_3, L_4, L_5, and so forth. If we could repeat this process an *infinite* number of times, the snowflake curve, denoted L_∞, would be the ultimate result. Any figure that we actually draw, whether L_6 or $L_{1,000,000}$, can only be an approximation to the true snowflake curve.

Now imagine measuring the length of the complete snowflake curve, L_∞. A ruler with a length of 1 would simply lie across the base of the snowflake curve, missing all fine detail and measuring only the straight-line distance between the endpoints. This ruler would yield only one element along the snowflake curve. Reducing the ruler length by a factor $R = 3$, to $\frac{1}{3}$, would make it the same length as each of the four segments of L_1. This ruler would find four elements along the snowflake curve, or $N = 4$ times as many elements as the first ruler. Reducing the ruler length by another factor $R = 3$, to $\frac{1}{9}$, would make it the length of each of the 16 segments of L_2. This new ruler would find 16 elements along the snowflake curve, or $N = 4$ times as many elements as the previous ruler.

In general, every time we reduce the ruler length by another factor $R = 3$, we find $N = 4$ times as many elements. This is exactly the situation described in Example 1, which means that the snowflake curve has fractal dimension $D \approx 1.2619$.

What does it mean to have a fractal dimension of 1.2619? The fact that the fractal dimension is greater than 1 means that the snowflake curve has more "substance" than an ordinary one-dimensional object. In a sense, the snowflake curve begins to fill the part of the plane in which it lies. The closer the fractal dimension of an object is to 1, the more closely it resembles a collection of line segments. The closer the fractal dimension is to 2, the closer it comes to filling a part of a plane.

Example 2 How Long Is a Snowflake Curve?

How much longer is L_1 than L_0? How much longer is L_2 than L_0? Generalize your results, and discuss the length of a complete snowflake curve.

Solution Recall that L_0 has a length of 1. Figure 10.53 shows that L_1 consists of four line segments, each of length $\frac{1}{3}$. Its length is therefore $\frac{4}{3}$ times the length of L_0, or $\frac{4}{3}$:

$$\text{length of } L_1 = \frac{4}{3}$$

L_2 has 16 line segments, each of length $\frac{1}{9}$. Its length is

$$\text{length of } L_2 = \frac{16}{9} = \left(\frac{4}{3}\right)^2$$

Generalizing, we find that

$$\text{length of } L_n = \left(\frac{4}{3}\right)^n$$

Because $\left(\frac{4}{3}\right)^n$ grows without bound as n gets larger, we conclude that the complete snowflake curve, L_∞, must be infinitely long. **Now try Exercise 27.**

The Snowflake Island

The **snowflake island** is a *region* (island) bounded by three snowflake curves. The process of drawing the snowflake island begins with an equilateral triangle (Figure 10.54). Then we convert *each* of the three sides of the triangle into a snowflake curve, L_∞. We cannot draw the complete snowflake island because it would require an infinite number of steps, but Figure 10.54 shows the results where the sides are L_0, L_1, L_2, and L_6.

The snowflake island illustrates some truly extraordinary properties. In Example 2, we found that a single snowflake curve is infinitely long. Therefore, the coastline of the

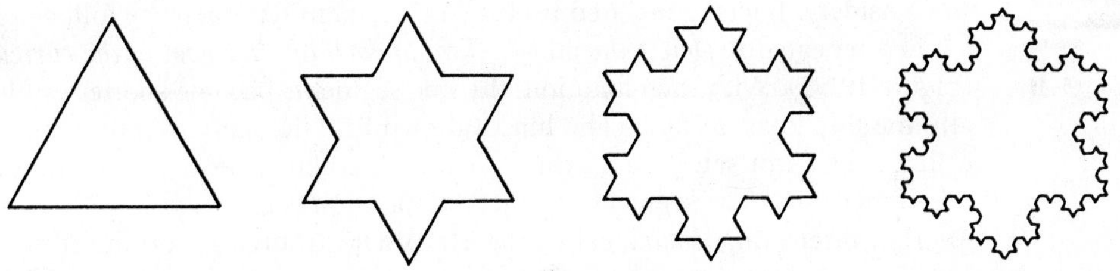

FIGURE 10.54 Left to right, successive approximations to a snowflake island, with sides made from L_0, L_1, L_2, and L_6, respectively.

snowflake island also must be infinitely long, because it is made of three snowflake curves. However, Figure 10.54 shows that the island's area is clearly contained within the bounds of the page. We have the intriguing result that a snowflake island is an object with a *finite area* and an *infinitely long boundary.*

Real Coastlines and Borders

Note that each of the four pieces of L_2 in Figure 10.53 looks exactly like L_1, except smaller. Similarly, L_3 consists of four pieces that each look like L_2. In fact, if we magnify *any* piece of the snowflake curve, L_∞, it will look exactly like one of the earlier curves, $L_0, L_1, L_2, \ldots$, used in its generation. Because the snowflake curve looks similar to itself when examined at different scales, we say that it is a **self-similar fractal**. The snowflake curve's self-similarity is due to repeated application of a simple set of rules.

Natural objects, such as real coastlines, also reveal new details under higher magnification. Unlike a self-similar fractal, a natural object isn't likely to look *exactly* the same when magnified. Nevertheless, if we have data about how measured lengths change with different "ruler" sizes, we can still assign a fractal dimension to a natural object.

The first significant data concerning the fractal dimensions of natural objects were collected by Lewis Fry Richardson in about 1960. Richardson's data represented measurements and estimates of the lengths of various coastlines and international borders measured by "rulers" of varying sizes. His data suggest that most coastlines have a fractal dimension of about $D = 1.25$, which is very close to the fractal dimension of a snowflake curve.

BY THE WAY

Lewis Fry Richardson was an eclectic and eccentric English scientist who proposed computer methods for predicting the weather in 1920—before computers were invented!

Example 3 The Fractal Border of Spain and Portugal

Portugal claims that its international border with Spain is 987 kilometers in length. Spain claims that the border is 1214 kilometers in length. However, the two countries agree on the location of the border. How is this possible?

Solution The border follows a variety of natural objects including rivers and mountain ranges. It is therefore a fractal, with more and more detail revealed on closer and closer examination. Like the snowflake curve, the border will be *longer* if it is measured with a shorter "ruler." It is therefore possible for Spain and Portugal to agree on the border's location but disagree on its length if they measured the border with "rulers" of different length. Spain claims a longer border length, so it must have used a shorter ruler for the measurement. **Now try Exercise 28.**

The Fascinating Variety of Fractals

The process of repeating a rule over and over to generate a self-similar fractal is called **iteration**. Different sets of rules can produce a fascinating variety of self-similar fractals. Let's look at just a few.

FIGURE 10.55 Several steps (top to bottom) in generating the Cantor set.

Consider a fractal generated from a line segment to which the following rule is applied repeatedly: *Delete the middle third of each line segment of the current figure* (Figure 10.55). With each iteration, the line segments become shorter until eventually the line turns to dust. The limit (after infinitely many iterations) is a fractal called the **Cantor set**. Because this ephemeral structure results from diminishing a one-dimensional line segment, its fractal dimension is less than 1.

Another interesting fractal, called the **Sierpinski triangle**, is produced by starting with a solid black equilateral triangle and iterating with the following rule: *For each black triangle in the current figure, connect the midpoints of the sides and remove the resulting inner triangle* (Figure 10.56). In the complete Sierpinski triangle, which would require *infinitely* many iterations to produce, every remaining black triangle would be infinitesimally small. Therefore, the total area of the black regions in the complete Sierpinski triangle is zero. The fractal dimension of the Sierpinski triangle is between 1 and 2. It is less than 2 because "material" has been removed from the initial two-dimensional triangle.

FIGURE 10.56 Several steps (left to right) in generating the Sierpinski triangle.
From THE SCIENCE OF FRACTAL IMAGES, Heinz-Otto Peitgen & Dietmar Saupe, Eds., (c) 1988, Springer-Verlag , N.Y. Reprinted by permission of the author.

FIGURE 10.57 An approximation to a Sierpinski sponge.

A closely related object is the **Sierpinski sponge** (Figure 10.57). It is generated by starting with a solid cube and iterating with this rule: *Divide each cube of the current object into 27 identical subcubes and remove the central subcube and the center cube of each face*. The resulting object has a fractal dimension between 2 and 3. It has less than a full three dimensions because material has been removed from the space occupied by the sponge.

An infinite variety of fractals can be generated by iteration. Some are remarkably beautiful, such as the famous **Mandelbrot set** (Figure 10.58).

All the self-similar fractals we have considered so far are created by repeating the exact same set of rules in each iteration. An alternative approach, called **random iteration**, is to introduce slight random variation in every iteration. The resulting fractals therefore are *not* precisely self-similar, but they are close. Such fractals often appear remarkably realistic. For example, Barnsley's fern (Figure 10.59) is a fractal produced by random iteration, and it looks very much like a real fern.

The fact that fractals so successfully replicate natural forms suggests an intriguing possibility: Perhaps nature produces the many diverse forms that we see around us through simple rules that are applied repeatedly and with a hint of randomness. Because of this observation and because modern computers can test iterative processes, fractal geometry surely will remain an active field of research for decades to come.

FIGURE 10.58 The Mandelbrot set.

FIGURE 10.59 Two views of Barnsley's fern.

QUICK QUIZ

Choose the best answer to each of the following questions. Explain your reasoning with one or more complete sentences.

1. Fractal geometry is useful because
   a. it is the only type of geometry in which fractional answers (rather than only integer answers) are possible.
   b. it can be used to create shapes that look more like naturally existing shapes.
   c. it is the well-tested geometry invented by the ancient Greeks.
2. Suppose you measure the length of a coastline with a ruler that is precise only to the nearest meter, then measure it again with a ruler that is precise to the nearest millimeter. The second measurement will be
   a. larger than the first. b. smaller than the first.
   c. the same as the first.
3. Which of the following has a shape that makes it a fractal?
   a. a perfect square b. a leaf c. a table top
4. Which of the following is a general characteristic of a fractal?
   a. It has an infinite area.
   b. You need a ruler to measure its length.
   c. When you look at it with greater magnification, you see new details.
5. How do fractal dimensions differ from dimensions in Euclidean geometry?
   a. They can be greater than 3.
   b. They can be negative.
   c. They can have fractional values.
6. An island coastline has a fractal dimension
   a. less than 0.
   b. between 0 and 1.
   c. between 1 and 2.
7. Which statement about the fractal object known as a snowflake curve is *not* true?
   a. It is the curve labeled L_6 in Figure 10.53.
   b. It is infinite in length.
   c. It can be laid out within a flat plane.
8. According to fractal geometry, which of the following is *not* possible?
   a. a finite area bounded by an infinitely long curve
   b. a finite area bounded by a finite curve
   c. an infinite area bounded by a finite curve
9. What characterizes a self-similar fractal?
   a. The same pattern repeats under greater magnification.
   b. It can be built entirely from similar triangles.
   c. Its fractal dimension is the same as its ordinary (Euclidean) dimension.
10. Which object represented in this unit has an infinite surface area but a finite volume?
    a. the snowflake island
    b. the Sierpinski sponge
    c. Barnsley's fern

Exercises 10C

REVIEW QUESTIONS

1. What is a fractal? Explain why measuring a fractal with a shorter ruler leads to a longer measurement.
2. Why do fractal dimensions fall in between the ordinary dimensions of 0, 1, 2, and 3?
3. Explain the meaning of the factors R and N used in calculating fractal dimensions.
4. What is the snowflake curve? Explain why we cannot actually draw it, but can only draw partial representations of it.
5. What is the snowflake island? Explain how it can have an infinitely long coastline, yet have a finite area.
6. What do we mean by a self-similar fractal? How is a self-similar fractal, like the snowflake curve, similar to a real coastline? How is it different?
7. Briefly describe what we mean by the process of iteration in generating fractals. Describe the generation of the Cantor set, the Sierpinski triangle, and the Sierpinski sponge. Describe the fractal dimension of each.
8. What is random iteration? Why do objects generated by random iteration make scientists think that fractals are important in understanding nature?

DOES IT MAKE SENSE?

Decide whether each of the following statements makes sense (or is clearly true) or does not make sense (or is clearly false). Explain your reasoning.

9. I can use a yardstick to find the area of my rectangular patio.
10. I can use a yardstick to measure the length of the mountain skyline accurately.
11. The area of the snowflake island is given by its length times its width.
12. The measured length of fractals increases as the ruler length increases.
13. The edge of this leaf has a fractal dimension of 1.34.
14. This entire leaf, riddled with holes, has a fractal dimension of 1.87.

BASIC SKILLS & CONCEPTS

15–26: Ordinary and Fractal Dimensions. Find the dimension of each object, and state whether or not it is a fractal.

15. In measuring the length of the object, when you reduce the length of your ruler by a factor of 2, the number of length elements increases by a factor of 2.
16. In measuring the area of the object, when you reduce the length of your ruler by a factor of 2, the number of area elements increases by a factor of 4.
17. In measuring the volume of the object, when you reduce the length of your ruler by a factor of 2, the number of volume elements increases by a factor of 8.
18. In measuring the length of the object, when you reduce the length of your ruler by a factor of 2, the number of length elements increases by a factor of 3.
19. In measuring the area of the object, when you reduce the length of your ruler by a factor of 2, the number of area elements increases by a factor of 6.
20. In measuring the volume of the object, when you reduce the length of your ruler by a factor of 2, the number of volume elements increases by a factor of 12.
21. In measuring the length of the object, when you reduce the length of your ruler by a factor of 5, the number of length elements increases by a factor of 5.
22. In measuring the area of the object, when you reduce the length of your ruler by a factor of 5, the number of area elements increases by a factor of 25.
23. In measuring the volume of the object, when you reduce the length of your ruler by a factor of 5, the number of volume elements increases by a factor of 125.
24. In measuring the length of the object, when you reduce the length of your ruler by a factor of 5, the number of length elements increases by a factor of 7.
25. In measuring the area of the object, when you reduce the length of your ruler by a factor of 5, the number of area elements increases by a factor of 30.
26. In measuring the volume of the object, when you reduce the length of your ruler by a factor of 5, the number of volume elements increases by a factor of 150.
27. **The Quadric Koch Curve and Quadric Koch Island.** To draw the *quadric Koch curve* (one of many variations of the snowflake curve), one begins with a horizontal line segment and applies the following rule: Divide each line segment into four equal pieces; replace the second piece with three line segments of equal length that make the shape of a square above the original piece; and replace the third piece with three line segments making a square below the original piece. The quadric Koch curve would result from infinite applications of the rule; the first three stages of the construction are shown in Figure 10.60.

    a. Determine the relation between N and R for the quadric Koch curve.

    b. What is the fractal dimension of the quadric Koch curve? Can you draw any conclusions about the length of the quadric Koch curve? Explain.

    c. The *quadric Koch island* is constructed by beginning with a square and then replacing each of the four sides of the square with a quadric Koch curve. Explain why the total area of the quadric Koch island is the same as the area of the original square. How long is the coastline of the quadric Koch island?

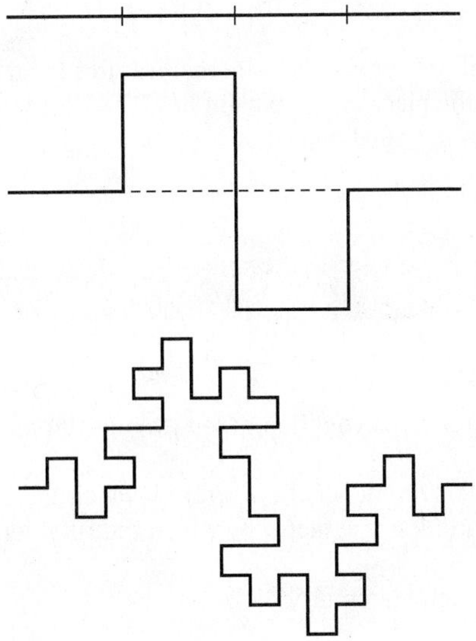

FIGURE 10.60

28. **Fractal Dimension from Measurements.** An ambitious and patient crew of surveyors has used various rulers to measure the length of the coastline of Dragon Island. The following table gives the measured length of the island, L, and the length of the ruler used, r.

r meters	100	10	1	0.1	0.01	0.001
L meters	315	1256	5000	19,905	79,244	315,479

a. Make a second table with the entries $\log_{10} r$ and $\log_{10} L$.

b. Graph these data ($\log_{10} r$, $\log_{10} L$) on a set of axes. Connect the data points.

c. If the graph of the data is close to a straight line, it is an indication that the coastline is a self-similar fractal. Does the coastline of Dragon Island appear to be a self-similar fractal?

d. What is the approximate slope of the line on your graph? Call the slope s. The fractal dimension of the coastline is $D = 1 - s$. What is the fractal dimension of the coastline of Dragon Island?

FURTHER APPLICATIONS

29. **The Cantor Set.** Recall that the Cantor set is formed by starting with a line segment and then successively removing the middle one-third of each segment in the current figure (Figure 10.55). If a ruler the length of the original line segment is used, it detects one element in the Cantor set because it can't "see" details smaller than itself. If the ruler is reduced in size by a factor of $R = 3$, it finds two elements (only solid pieces of line, not holes, are measured). If the ruler is reduced in size by a factor of $R = 9$, how many elements does it find? Based on these results, what is the fractal dimension of the Cantor set? Explain why this number is less than 1.

30. **Ordinary Dimensions for Ordinary Objects.**

a. Suppose you want to measure the length of the sidewalk in front of your house. Describe a thought process by which you can conclude that $N = R$ for the sidewalk and hence that its fractal dimension is the same as its ordinary dimension of 1.

b. Suppose you want to measure the area of your living room floor, which is square-shaped. Describe a thought process by which you can conclude that $N = R^2$ for the living room and hence that its fractal dimension is the same as its ordinary dimension of 2.

c. Suppose you want to measure the volume of a cubical swimming pool. Describe a thought process by which you can conclude that $N = R^3$ for the pool and hence that its fractal dimension is the same as its ordinary dimension of 3.

31. **Fractal Dimensions for Fractal Objects.**

a. Suppose you are measuring the length of the stream frontage along a piece of mountain property. You begin with a 15-meter ruler and find just one element along the length of the stream frontage. When you switch to a 1.5-meter ruler, you are able to trace finer details of the stream edge and you find 20 elements along its length. Switching to a 15-centimeter ruler, you find 400 elements along the stream frontage. Based on these measurements, what is the fractal dimension of the stream frontage?

b. Suppose you are measuring the area of a very unusual square leaf with many holes, perhaps from hungry insects, in a fractal pattern (e.g., similar to the Sierpinski triangle, Figure 10.56). You begin with a 10-centimeter ruler and find that it lies over the entire square, making just one element. When you switch to a 5-centimeter ruler, you are better able to cover areas of leaf while skipping areas of holes and you find 3 area elements. You switch to a 2.5-centimeter ruler and find 9 area elements. Based on these measurements, what is the fractal dimension of the leaf? Explain *why* the fractal dimension is less than 2.

c. Suppose you are measuring the volume of a cube cut from a large rock that contains many cavities forming a fractal pattern. Beginning with a 10-meter ruler, you find just one volume element. Smaller rulers allow you to ignore cavities, gauging only the volume of rock material. With a 5-meter ruler, you find 6 volume elements. With a 2.5-meter ruler, you find 36 volume elements. Based on these measurements, what is the fractal dimension of the rock? Explain why a fractal dimension between 2 and 3 is reasonable. (Ignore the practical difficulties caused by the fact that you cannot see through a rock to find all its holes!)

32. **Fractal Patterns in Nature.** Describe at least five natural objects that exhibit fractal patterns. In each case, explain the structure that makes the pattern a fractal, and estimate its fractal dimension.

33. **Natural Fractals Through Branching.** One way natural objects reveal fractal patterns is by branching. For example, the intricate structure of the human lung, the web of capillaries in a muscle, the branches or roots of a tree, and the successive division of streams in a river delta all involve branching at different spatial scales. Explain why structures formed by branching resemble self-similar fractals. Further, explain why fractal geometry rather than ordinary geometry leads to a greater understanding of such structures.

WEB PROJECTS

34. **Fractal Research.** Locate at least two Web sites devoted to fractals and use them to write a two- to three-page paper on either a specific use of fractals or a technique for generating fractals.

35. **Fractal Art.** Visit a Web site that features fractal art. Choose a specific piece of art, explain how it was generated, and discuss its visual impact.

CHAPTER 10 Summary

UNIT	KEY TERMS	KEY IDEAS AND SKILLS
10C	fractal geometry fractal dimension snowflake curve snowflake island self-similar fractal iteration	**Explain** why different rulers can give different length measurements of natural objects. **Fractal dimension:** $N = R^D$, where N is the factor by which the number of elements increases and R is the factor by which the ruler length is reduced. **Understand** the uses of fractal geometry.

UNIT 11C

Proportion and the Golden Ratio: Proportion is another critical concept in art. We discuss proportion and its implications by exploring the famous golden ratio.

11

(Mathematics) seems to stand for all that is practical, poetry for all that is visionary, but in the kingdom of the imagination you will find them close akin, and they should go together as a precious heritage to every youth.

—Florence Milner, *School Review*, 1898

Mathematics and the Arts

The connections between art and mathematics go deep into history. The ties are most evident in architecture: the Great Pyramids in Egypt, the Eiffel Tower in France, and modern-day skyscrapers all required mathematics in their design. But mathematics has contributed in equally profound ways to music, painting, and sculpture. In this chapter, we explore a few of the many connections between mathematics and the arts.

UNIT 11C Proportion and the Golden Ratio

> The senses delight in things duly proportioned.
>
> —St. Thomas Aquinas (1225–1274)

In Unit 11B, we studied how mathematics enters into art through the ideas of symmetry and perspective. In this unit, we turn our attention to the third major mathematical idea involved with art: proportion.

The importance of proportion was expressed well by the astronomer Johannes Kepler (1571–1630):

> *Geometry has two great treasures: one is the theorem of Pythagoras; the other, the division of a line into extreme and mean ratio. The first we may compare to gold; the second we may name a precious jewel.*

Kepler's statement about *the division of a line into extreme and mean ratio* describes one of the oldest principles of proportion. It dates back to the time of Pythagoras (c. 500 B.C.E.), when scholars asked the following question: How can a line segment be divided into two pieces that have the most appeal and balance?

Although this was a question of beauty, there seemed to be general agreement on the answer. Suppose a line segment is divided into two pieces, as shown in Figure 11.38. We call the length of the long piece L and the length of the short piece 1.

FIGURE 11.38

The Greeks claimed that the most visually pleasing division of the line had the property that the ratio of the length of the long piece to the length of the short piece is the same as the ratio of the length of the entire line segment to the length of the long piece. That is,

$$\frac{L}{1} = \frac{L+1}{L}$$

This statement of proportion can be solved (see Exercise 19) to find that L has a special value, denoted by the Greek letter ϕ (phi, pronounced "fie" or "fee"), which is

$$\phi = \frac{1+\sqrt{5}}{2} = 1.61803\ldots$$

The number ϕ is more commonly called the **golden ratio** (or *golden section*); it is also sometimes called the *divine proportion*. It is an irrational number often approximated as 1.6, or $\frac{8}{5}$. Figure 11.39 shows that, for any line segment divided in two pieces according to the golden ratio, the ratio of the long piece to the short piece is

FIGURE 11.39

$$\frac{x}{y} = \frac{1.61803\ldots}{1} = \phi \approx \frac{8}{5}$$

Example 1 Calculating a Golden Ratio

Suppose the line segment in Figure 11.40 is divided according to the golden ratio. If the length of the longer piece labeled x is 5 centimeters, how long is the entire line segment?

FIGURE 11.40

BY THE WAY

The Greek letter ϕ is the first letter in the Greek spelling of Phydias, the name of a Greek sculptor who may have used the golden ratio in his work.

Solution Because the line segment is divided in the golden ratio, we know that $x/y = \phi$. We solve for y by multiplying both sides by y and dividing both sides by ϕ:

$$\frac{x}{y} = \phi \quad \rightarrow \quad y = \frac{x}{\phi}$$

Substituting $x = 5$ cm and the approximate value 1.6 for ϕ, we find

$$y = \frac{5 \text{ cm}}{\phi} \approx \frac{5 \text{ cm}}{1.6} \approx 3.1 \text{ cm}$$

The entire segment has a length of $x + y$, so its total length is approximately 5 cm + 3.1 cm = 8.1 cm.
Now try Exercises 11–12.

The Golden Ratio in Art History

Although the ancient Greeks struggled with the notion of irrational numbers, they embraced the golden ratio. Consider the *pentagram* (Figure 11.41), which was the seal of the mystical Pythagorean Brotherhood. This five-pointed star inscribed in a circle produces a pentagon at the center. The golden ratio occurs in at least ten different ways in the pentagram. For example, if the length of each side of the pentagon is 1, then the length of each arm of the star is ϕ.

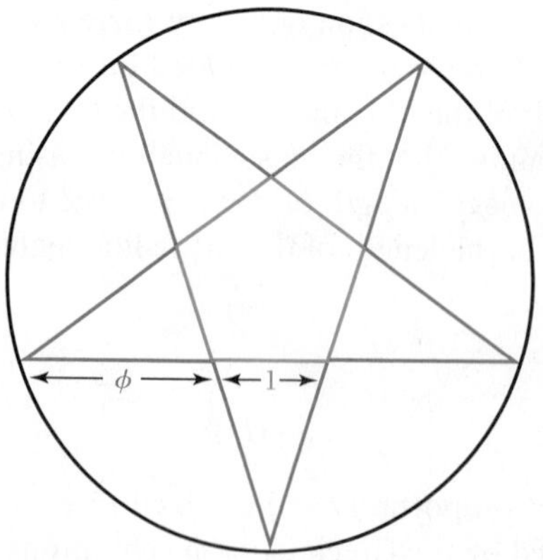

FIGURE 11.41 A pentagram.

Time Out to Think

Using a ruler, find at least one other place in the pentagram of Figure 11.41 where the ratio of the lengths of two line segments is the golden ratio.

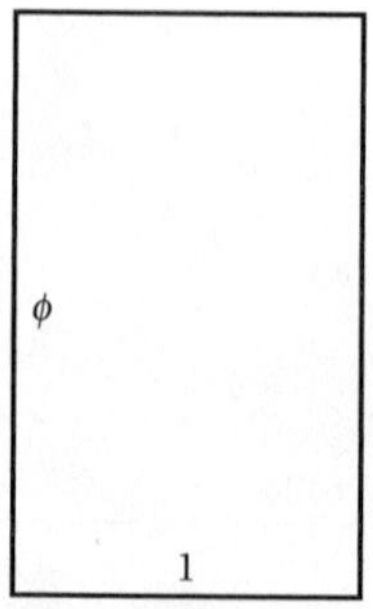

FIGURE 11.42 A golden rectangle—the side lengths have a ratio $\phi \approx \frac{8}{5}$.

From the golden ratio it is a short step to another famous Greek expression of proportion, the **golden rectangle**—a rectangle whose long side is ϕ times as long as its short side. A golden rectangle can be of any size, but its sides must have a ratio of $\phi \approx \frac{8}{5}$. Figure 11.42 shows a golden rectangle.

FIGURE 11.43 The proportions of the Parthenon have been claimed to closely match those of a golden rectangle as shown, though the claim has been disputed.

BY THE WAY

The Parthenon was completed in about 430 B.C.E. as a temple to Athena Parthenos, the Warrior Maiden. It stands on the Acropolis (which means "the uppermost city"), about 500 feet above Athens.

The golden rectangle had both practical and mystical importance to the Greeks. It became a cornerstone of their philosophy of *aesthetics*—the study of beauty. There is considerable speculation about the uses of the golden rectangle in art and architecture in ancient times. For example, it is widely claimed that many of the great monuments of antiquity, such as the Pyramids in Egypt, were designed in accordance with the golden rectangle. And, whether by design or by chance, the proportions of the Parthenon (in Athens, Greece) match those of the golden rectangle very closely (Figure 11.43).

The golden rectangle also appears in many more recent works of art and architecture. The book *De Divina Proportione,* illustrated by Leonardo da Vinci in 1509, is filled with references to and uses of ϕ. Da Vinci's unfinished painting *St. Jerome* (Figure 11.44) appears to place the central figure inside an imaginary golden rectangle. More recently, the French impressionist painter Georges Seurat is said to have used the golden ratio on every canvas. The abstract geometric paintings of the 20th-century Dutch painter Piet Mondrian (Figure 11.45) are filled with golden rectangles.

Today, the golden rectangle appears in many everyday items. Photographs, note cards, cereal boxes, posters, and windows often have proportions close to that of the golden rectangle. But the question remains as to whether the golden rectangle is really more pleasing. In the late 19th century, the German psychologist Gustav Fechner

FIGURE 11.44 *St. Jerome,* by Leonardo da Vinci.

FIGURE 11.45 *Place de la Concorde,* by Piet Mondrian, is filled with golden rectangles.

(1801–1887) studied the question statistically. He showed several rectangles with various length to width ratios to hundreds of people and recorded their choices for the most and least visually pleasing rectangles. The results, given in Table 11.2, show that almost 75% of the participants chose one of the three rectangles with proportions closest to that of the golden rectangle.

BY THE WAY

Despite evidence of the appeal of the golden rectangle and ratio, there are theories to the contrary. A 1992 study by George Markowsky discredits claims that the golden ratio was used in art and architecture, attributing them to coincidence and bad science. He also claims that statistical studies of people's preferences, such as Fechner's research, are not conclusive (see Exercise 26).

TABLE 11.2 Fechner's Data

Length to Width Ratio	Most Pleasing Rectangle (Percentage Response)	Least Pleasing Rectangle (Percentage Response)
1.00	3.0	27.8
1.20	0.2	19.7
1.25	2.0	9.4
1.33	2.5	2.5
1.45	7.7	1.2
1.50	20.6	0.4
$\phi \approx 1.62$	**35.0**	**0.0**
1.75	20.0	0.8
2.00	7.5	2.5
2.50	1.5	35.7

Time Out to Think

Do you think that the golden rectangle is visually more pleasing than other rectangles? Explain.

Example 2 Household Golden Ratios

The following household items were found to have the dimensions shown. Which item comes closest to having the proportions of the golden ratio?

- Standard sheet of paper: 8.5 in. × 11 in.
- 8 × 10 picture frame: 8 in. × 10 in.
- 35-mm slide: 35 mm × 23 mm

Solution The ratio of the sides of a standard sheet of paper is 11/8.5 = 1.29, which is 20% less than the golden ratio. The ratio of the sides of a standard picture frame is 10/8 = 1.25, which is 23% less than the golden ratio. The ratio of the sides of a 35-mm slide is 35/23 = 1.52, which is 6% less than the golden ratio. Of the three objects, the 35-mm slide is closest to being a golden rectangle. **Now try Exercises 13–18.**

The Golden Ratio in Nature

The golden ratio appears to be common in the "artwork" of nature. One striking example is spirals created from golden rectangles. We begin by dividing a golden rectangle to make a square on its left side, as shown in Figure 11.46a. If you measure the sides of the remaining smaller rectangle to the right of the square, you'll see that it is a smaller golden rectangle.

We now repeat this splitting process on the second golden rectangle, this time making the square on the top (instead of the left) of the golden rectangle. This split makes a third, even smaller, golden rectangle. Continuing to split each new golden rectangle in this manner generates the result shown in Figure 11.46b. We then connect opposite corners of all the squares with a smooth curve. The result is a continuous curve called a **logarithmic spiral** (or *equiangular spiral*). This spiral very closely matches the spiral shape of the beautiful chambered nautilus shell (Figure 11.46c).

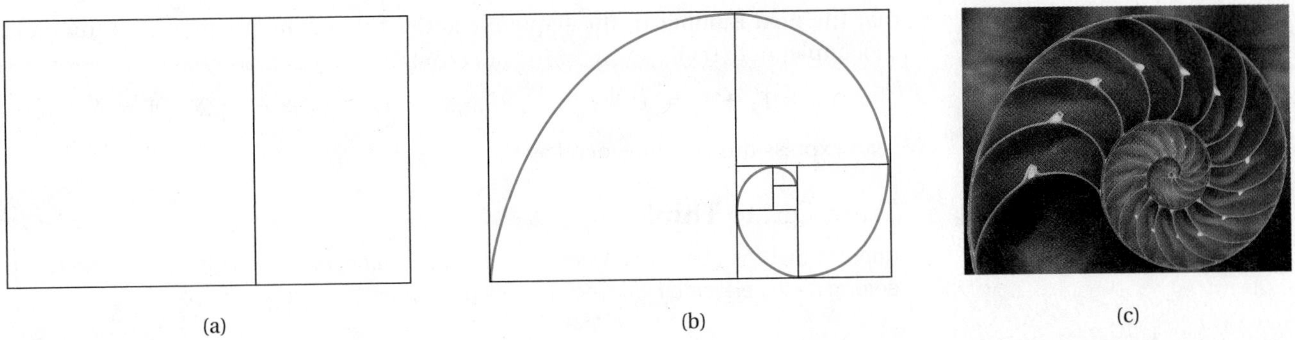

FIGURE 11.46 (a) A logarithmic spiral begins with a golden rectangle that is divided to make a square on the left. (b) The process is repeated in each successive golden rectangle, and a spiral is created by connecting the corners of all the squares. (c) A chambered nautilus shell looks much like a logarithmic spiral.

Another intriguing connection between the golden ratio and nature comes from a problem in population biology, first posed by a mathematician known as Fibonacci in 1202. Fibonacci's problem essentially asked the following question about the reproduction of rabbits.

> *Suppose that a pair of baby rabbits takes one month to mature into adults, then produces a new pair of baby rabbits the following month and each subsequent month. Further suppose that each newly born pair of rabbits matures and gives birth to additional pairs with the same reproductive pattern. If no rabbits die, how many pairs of rabbits are in the population at the beginning of each month?*

Figure 11.47 shows the solution to this problem for the first six months. The number of pairs of rabbits at the beginning of each month forms a sequence that begins 1, 1, 2, 3, 5, 8. Fibonacci found that the numbers in this sequence continue to grow with the following pattern:

$$1, 1, 2, 3, 5, 8, 13, 21, 34, 55, \ldots$$

This sequence of numbers is known as the **Fibonacci sequence.**

If we let F_n denote the nth Fibonacci number, then we have $F_1 = 1$, $F_2 = 1$, $F_3 = 2$, $F_4 = 3$, and so forth. The most basic property of the Fibonacci sequence

BY THE WAY

Fibonacci, also known as Leonardo of Pisa, is credited with popularizing the use of Hindu-Arabic numerals in Europe. His book *Liber Abaci* (*Book of the Abacus*), published in 1202, explained their use and the importance of the number zero.

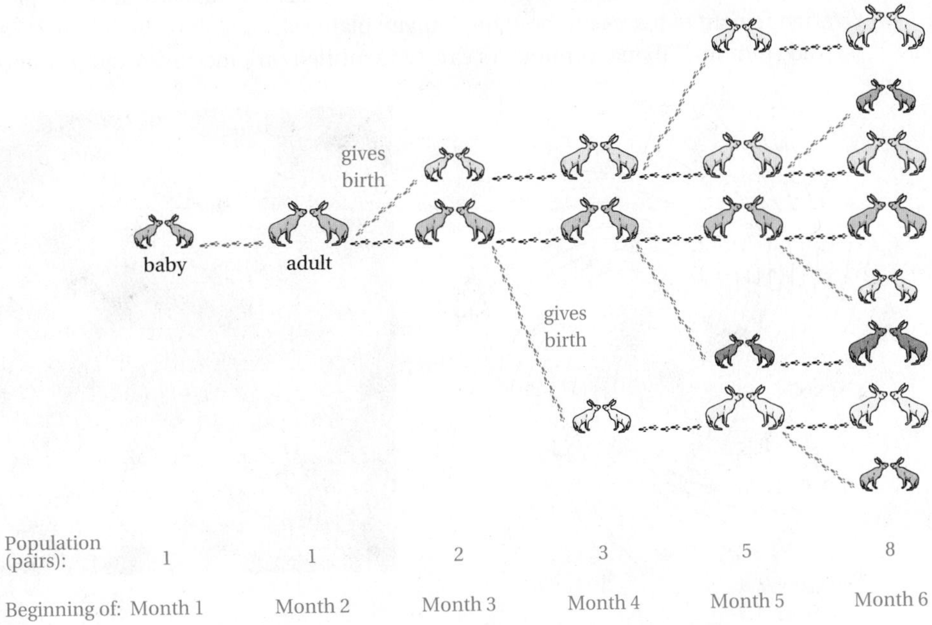

FIGURE 11.47

is that the next number in the sequence is the sum of the previous two numbers. For example, note that

$$F_3 = F_2 + F_1 = 1 + 1 = 2 \quad \text{and} \quad F_4 = F_3 + F_2 = 2 + 1 = 3$$

We can express this rule in general as $F_{n+1} = F_n + F_{n-1}$.

Time Out to Think

Confirm that the above rule works for Fibonacci numbers F_3 through F_{10}. Use the rule to determine the eleventh Fibonacci number (F_{11}).

The connection between the Fibonacci numbers and the golden ratio becomes clear when we compute the ratios of successive Fibonacci numbers, as shown in Table 11.3. Note that, as we go further out in the sequence, the ratios of successive Fibonacci numbers get closer and closer to the golden ratio $\phi = 1.61803\ldots$.

TABLE 11.3 Ratios of Successive Fibonacci Numbers

$F_3/F_2 =$	$2/1 = 2.0$	$F_{11}/F_{10} =$	$89/55 \approx 1.618182$
$F_4/F_3 =$	$3/2 = 1.5$	$F_{12}/F_{11} =$	$144/89 \approx 1.617978$
$F_5/F_4 =$	$5/3 \approx 1.667$	$F_{13}/F_{12} =$	$233/144 \approx 1.618056$
$F_6/F_5 =$	$8/5 = 1.600$	$F_{14}/F_{13} =$	$377/233 \approx 1.618026$
$F_7/F_6 =$	$13/8 = 1.625$	$F_{15}/F_{14} =$	$610/377 \approx 1.618037$
$F_8/F_7 =$	$21/13 \approx 1.6154$	$F_{16}/F_{15} =$	$987/610 \approx 1.618033$
$F_9/F_8 =$	$34/21 \approx 1.61905$	$F_{17}/F_{16} =$	$1597/987 \approx 1.618034$
$F_{10}/F_9 =$	$55/34 \approx 1.61765$	$F_{18}/F_{17} =$	$2584/1597 \approx 1.618034$

There are many examples of the Fibonacci sequence in nature. The heads of sunflowers and daisies consist of a clockwise spiral superimposed on a counterclockwise spiral (both of which are logarithmic spirals), as shown in Figure 11.48. The number of individual florets in each of these intertwined spirals is a Fibonacci number—for example, 21 and 34 or 34 and 55. Biologists have also observed that the number of petals on many common flowers is a Fibonacci number (for example, irises have 3 petals, primroses have 5 petals, ragworts have 13 petals, and daisies have 34 petals). The arrangement of leaves on the stem of many plants also exhibits the Fibonacci sequence. And spiraling Fibonacci numbers can be identified on pine cones and pineapples.

(a) (b)

FIGURE 11.48

QUICK QUIZ

Choose the best answer to each of the following questions. Explain your reasoning with one or more complete sentences.

1. The golden ratio is
   a. exactly 1.6.
   b. a perfect number discovered by Pythagoras.
   c. $\frac{1+\sqrt{5}}{2}$.
2. Which of the following is *not* a characteristic of the golden ratio?
   a. It is an irrational number.
   b. It is between 1 and 2.
   c. It is the fourth number in the Fibonacci sequence.
3. If a one-foot line segment is divided according to the golden ratio, the two pieces
   a. have equal length.
   b. have lengths of roughly 2 inches and 10 inches.
   c. have lengths of roughly 0.4 foot and 0.6 foot.
4. To make a golden rectangle, you should
   a. inscribe a rectangle in a circle.
   b. draw a rectangle so that the ratio of the long side to the short side is the golden ratio.
   c. draw a rectangle so that the ratio of the diagonal to the short side is the golden ratio.
5. Suppose you want a bay window to have the proportions of a golden rectangle. If the window is to be 10 feet high, approximately how wide should it be?
   a. 5 feet
   b. $6\frac{1}{4}$ feet
   c. 12 feet
6. Why did the Greeks tend to build rectangular buildings with the proportions of golden rectangles?
   a. They thought these buildings were the most visually pleasing.
   b. They thought these buildings were structurally stronger.
   c. They thought these buildings could be constructed at the lowest possible cost.
7. Suppose you start with a golden rectangle and cut a square out of it. The remaining piece of the golden rectangle will be
   a. another golden rectangle.
   b. another square.
   c. a logarithmic spiral.
8. The rabbit model of Fibonacci is an example of
   a. a linearly growing population.
   b. an exponentially growing population.
   c. a logistically growing population.
9. The 18th, 19th, and 20th numbers in the Fibonacci sequence are, respectively, 2584, 4181, and 6765. The 21st number is
   a. 2584×4181.
   b. $4181 + 6765$.
   c. 6765×1.6.
10. In what way does the golden ratio appear in the Fibonacci sequence?
    a. It is the ratio between all pairs of successive Fibonacci numbers.
    b. The ratio of successive Fibonacci numbers gets ever closer to the golden ratio as the numbers get higher.
    c. It is the ratio of the last Fibonacci number to the first one.

Exercises 11C

REVIEW QUESTIONS

1. Explain the golden ratio in terms of proportions of line segments.
2. How is a golden rectangle formed?
3. What evidence suggests that the golden ratio and golden rectangle hold particular beauty?
4. What is a logarithmic spiral? How is it formed from a golden rectangle?
5. What is the Fibonacci sequence?
6. What is the connection between the Fibonacci sequence and the golden ratio? Give some examples of the Fibonacci sequence in nature.

DOES IT MAKE SENSE?

Decide whether each of the following statements makes sense (or is clearly true) or does not make sense (or is clearly false). Explain your reasoning.

7. Maria cut her 4-foot walking stick into two 2-foot sticks in keeping with the golden ratio.
8. Dan attributes his love of dominoes to the fact that dominoes are golden rectangles.
9. The circular pattern in the floor is attractive because it exhibits the golden ratio.
10. Each year, Juliet's age is another Fibonacci number.

BASIC SKILLS & CONCEPTS

11. **Golden Ratio.** Draw a line segment 6 inches long. Now subdivide it according to the golden ratio. Verify your work by computing the ratio of the whole segment length to the long segment length and the ratio of the long segment length to the short segment length.

12. **Golden Ratio.** A line is subdivided according to the golden ratio, with the smaller piece having a length of 5 meters. What is the length of the entire line?

13. **Golden Rectangles.** Measure the sides of each rectangle in Figure 11.49, and compute the ratio of the long side to the short side for each rectangle. Which ones are golden rectangles?

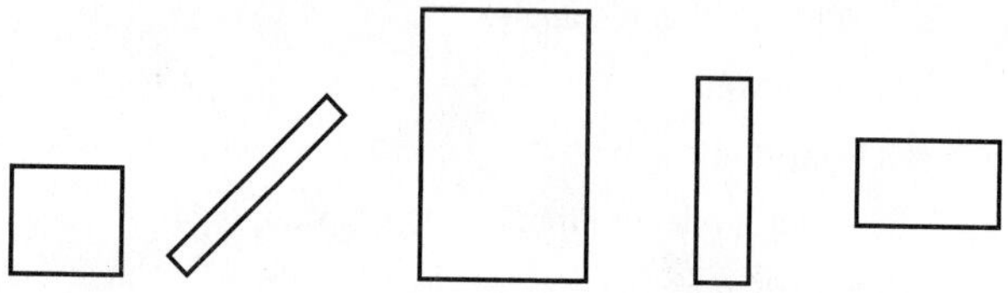

FIGURE 11.49

14–17: **Dimensions of Golden Rectangles.** Consider the following lengths of one side of a golden rectangle. Find the length of the other side. Notice that the other side could be either longer or shorter than the given side. Use the approximation $\phi \approx 1.62$ for your work.

14. 2.7 inches
15. 5.8 meters
16. 12.6 kilometers
17. 0.66 centimeter

18. **Everyday Golden Rectangles.** Find at least three everyday objects with rectangular shapes (for example, billboards, cereal boxes, windows). In each case, measure the side lengths and calculate the ratio. Are any of these objects golden rectangles? Explain.

FURTHER APPLICATIONS

19. **Finding ϕ.** The property that defines the golden ratio is

$$\frac{L}{1} = \frac{L+1}{L}$$

a. Show that, if we multiply both sides by L and rearrange, this equation becomes

$$L^2 - L - 1 = 0$$

Confirm that substituting the value of ϕ for L satisfies this equation.

b. The quadratic formula states that, for any equation of the form $ax^2 + bx + c = 0$, the solutions are given by

$$x = \frac{-b + \sqrt{b^2 - 4ac}}{2a}$$

and

$$x = \frac{-b - \sqrt{b^2 - 4ac}}{2a}$$

Use the quadratic formula to solve for L in the formula for the golden ratio. Show that one of the roots is ϕ.

20. **Properties of ϕ.**

a. Enter $\phi = \left(1 + \sqrt{5}\right)/2$ into your calculator. Show that $1/\phi = \phi - 1$.

b. Now compute ϕ^2. How is this number related to ϕ?

21. **Logarithmic Spirals.** Draw a rectangle that is 10 centimeters on a side. Follow the procedure described in the text for subdividing the rectangle until you can draw a logarithmic spiral. Do all work carefully, and show your measurements with your work.

22. **The Lucas Sequence.** A sequence called the *Lucas sequence* is closely related to the Fibonacci sequence. The Lucas sequence begins with the numbers $L_1 = 1$ and $L_2 = 3$ and then uses the same relation $L_{n+1} = L_n + L_{n-1}$ to generate $L_3, L_4, \ldots$.

a. Generate the first ten Lucas numbers.

b. Compute the ratio of successive Lucas numbers L_2/L_1, L_3/L_2, L_4/L_3, and so on. Can you determine if these ratios approach a single number? What number is it?

23. **Graphing Fechner's Data.** Consider Gustav Fechner's data shown in Table 11.2. Make a histogram that displays the responses for both the most pleasing and the least pleasing rectangle proportions.

24. **The Golden Navel.** An old theory claims that, on average, the ratio of the height of a person to the height of his/her navel is the golden ratio. Collect "navel ratio data" from as many people as possible. Graph the ratios in a histogram, find the average ratio over your entire sample, and discuss the outcome. Do your data support the theory?

25. **Mozart and the Golden Ratio.** In a paper called "The Golden Section and the Piano Sonatas of Mozart" (*Mathematics Magazine*, Vol. 68, No. 4, 1995), John Putz gives the lengths (in measures) of the first part (a) and the second part (b) of the movements of the 19 Mozart piano sonatas. Some of the data are given below.

a = length of first part	b = length of second part
38	62
28	46
56	102
56	88
24	36
77	113
40	69
46	60
15	18
39	63
53	67

a. The ratio of the length of the whole movement to the length of the longer segment is $(a + b)/b$. Add a third column to the table and compute this ratio for the given data.

b. Make a histogram of the ratios that you computed in part a (choosing an appropriate bin size). Comment on how well they are approximated by ϕ.

c. Read the article by John Putz. Do you believe that Mozart composed with the golden ratio in mind?

26. **Debunking the Golden Ratio.** Find the article "Misconceptions about the Golden Ratio" by George Markowsky (*College Mathematics Journal*, Vol. 23, No. 1, 1992). Choose at least one of the misconceptions that Markowsky discusses, summarize it, and then explain whether you find his argument convincing. Discuss your opinion of whether the golden ratio has been consciously used by artists and architects in their work.

WEB PROJECTS

27. **Golden Controversies.** Many Web sites are devoted to the controversy concerning the role of the golden ratio in art. Find a specific argument on one side of this controversy and summarize it in a one- to two-page essay.

28. **Fibonacci Numbers.** Learn more about Fibonacci numbers and possible occurrences of the Fibonacci sequence in nature. Write a short essay about one aspect of Fibonacci numbers that you find interesting.

IN YOUR WORLD

29. **Proportion in Life.** Describe at least three ways in which the use of visual proportion affects your life.

30. **The Golden Ratio.** Find a recent picture of a new building or architectural design. Study the picture and decide whether the golden ratio is involved in any way.

CHAPTER 11 Summary

UNIT	KEY TERMS	KEY IDEAS AND SKILLS
11C	proportion golden ratio golden rectangle Fibonacci sequence	**The golden ratio:** $\phi = \frac{1 + \sqrt{5}}{2} = 1.61803\ldots$ **The Fibonacci sequence:** $1, 1, 2, 3, 5, 8, 13, 21, 34, 55, \ldots$ **Understand** claimed uses of the golden ratio in both art and nature.

CREDITS

Prologue

p. 1: Julie Jacobson/AP Wide World Photos. **p. 2:** From ON THE PULSE OF THE MORNING by Maya Angelou. Used by permission of Random House, Inc.

Chapter 1

p. 13: Monkey Business images/Shutterstock. **p. 14:** Jeffrey Bennett. **p. 16:** Kaspars Grinvalds/Shutterstock. **p. 21:** Jeff Bennett. **p. 22:** © Bettmann/Corbis. **p. 23:** Jastrow/Wikipedia Foundation, Inc. **p. 24:** Corbis RF. **p. 25:** Andrey Volodin/iStockphoto. **p. 43:** Corbis RF. **p. 51:** Terry Healy/iStockphoto. **p. 52:** Figure 9.42, p. 278 from THE COSMIC PERSPECTIVE, 4e, by Jeffrey Bennett, Megan Donahue, Nicholas Schneider and Mark Voit. Copyright © 2007 by Pearson Education, publishing as Addison Wesley. Reprinted by permission of Pearson Education, Inc. **p. 64:** PhotoDisc/Getty Images. **p. 76:** Khuong Hoang/Stockphoto.

Chapter 2

p. 79: pckane/Stockphoto. **p. 80:** Johan Fr Ohman/Wikipedia, The Free Encyclopedia **p. 88:** Corbis RF. **p. 90:** Milous/Stockphoto. **p. 95:** © AP Wide World Photos. **p. 99 (top):** Kmusser/Wikipedia Foundation, Inc. **p. 99 (bottom):** © Corbis. **p. 102:** Getty Images, Inc.–PhotoDisc. **p. 103:** Thinkstock/Jupiter Unlimited. **p. 107:** MADD. **p. 111:** Corbis RF. **p. 113:** Adapted from *How to Solve It* by George Polya. Princeton University Press, 1957. **p. 114** © ScienceCartoonsPlus.com Sidney Harris. **p. 121:** Rob Marmion/Shutterstock.

Chapter 3

p. 127: Getty Images–Digital Vision. **p. 128:** © Beth Anderson. **p. 147:** Corbis RF. **p. 150 (top):** Figure 14.5, p. 482 from THE COSMIC PERSPECTIVE, 4e, by Jeffrey Bennett, Megan Donahue, Nicholas Schneider and Mark Voit. Copyright © 2007 by Pearson Education, publishing as Addison Wesley. Reprinted by permission of Pearson Education, Inc. **p. 150 (bottom):** Corbis RF. **p. 152 (top):** Jeffrey Bennett. **p. 152 (bottom):** Jeff Hester and Paul Scowen (Arizona State University), and NASA. **p. 153:** Shutterstock. **p. 163:** Corbis RF. **p. 166:** Hubble Space Telescope/NASA Headquarters. **p. 168:** Corbis RF. **p. 172:** © Gene Blevins/Corbis. **p. 178:** © CORBIS. All Rights Reserved. **p. 185:** Laurence Gough/Shutterstock. **p. 187:** © CORBIS. All Rights Reserved. **p. 189** (Fig. 3.5): Adapted from the *New York Times*, April 7, 1995. © 1995 The New York Times Company. Used with permission. All Rights Reserved. **p. 194** (Fig. 3.6): From the *New York Times*, June 26, 2003. © 2003 The New York Times. Used with permission. All Rights Reserved.

Chapter 4

p. 197: Thinkstock Royalty Free. **p. 198:** Ryan McVay/Getty Images, Inc.–PhotoDisc–Royalty Free. **p. 202:** Getty Images–Digital Vision. **p. 209:** University College–Oxford. **p. 222:** Getty Images–PhotoDisc–Royalty Free. **p. 233:** © Jon Hrusa/epa/CORBIS. All Rights Reserved. **p. 239:** © AFP/Getty Images, Inc. **p. 242:** Getty Images–PhotoDisc–Royalty Free. **p. 254:** Getty Images–Digital Vision. **p. 256:** R. Gino Santa Maria/Shutterstock. **p. 259:** Robert F. Bukaty/AP Wide World Photos. **p. 265:** © ThinkStock–Royalty Free. **p. 266:** © CORBIS. All Rights Reserved. **p. 270:** Getty Images–PhotoDisc–Royalty Free. **p. 272:** Christopher Halloran/Shutterstock. **p. 273:** © PhotoDisc. **p. 283:** Albert J. Copley/Getty Images, Inc.–PhotoDisc–Royalty Free.

Chapter 5

p. 295: Comstock Complete. **p. 296:** contour99/iStockphoto. **p. 297:** Getty Images–Digital Vision. **p. 301:** CORBIS–New York. **p. 311 (top):** Getty Images–PhotoDisc–Royalty Free. **p. 311 (bottom):** © ScienceCartoonsPlus.com Sidney Harris. **p. 316:** Michael Okoniewski. **pp. 323–327** (Figs. 5.3–5.8): From Bennett/Briggs/Triola, STATISTICAL REASONING FOR EVERYDAY LIFE 2E, © 2003 Pearson Education, Inc., publishing as Pearson Addison Wesley. Reprinted by permission of Pearson Education. **p. 329** (Fig. 5.12): From the *New York Times*, September 30, 1995. © 1995 The New York Times. Used with permission. All Rights Reserved. **p. 340** (Fig. 5.21): From the *New York Times*, October 3, 1995. © 1995 The New York Times. Used with permission. All Rights Reserved. **p. 341** (Fig. 5.22): From the *New York Times*, August 20, 2000. © 2000 The New York Times. Used with permission. All Rights Reserved. **p. 347** (Fig. 5.32): From the *New York Times*, April 4, 2000. © 2000 The New York Times. Used with permission. All Rights Reserved. **p. 351** (Fig. 5.43): From the *New England Journal of Medicine*, 2/25/99. Copyright © 1999 Massachusetts Medical Society. All rights reserved. **p. 358:** © AP Wide World Photos. **p. 359 (top):** CORBIS. All Rights Reserved. **p. 359 (bottom):** © PhotoDisc. **p. 361** (Figs. 5.49–5.50): From THE COSMIC PERSPECTIVE, 4e, by Jeffrey Bennett, Megan Donahue, Nicholas Schneider and Mark Voit. Copyright © 2007 by Pearson Education, publishing as Addison Wesley. Reprinted by permission of Pearson Education, Inc.

Chapter 6

p. 369: Iofoto/Dreamstime LLC–Royalty Free. **p. 373:** William R. Sallaz/PCN Photography. **p. 382:** Karimala/Dreamstime LLC–Royalty Free. **p. 388:** © Adrian Baras/Shutterstock. **p. 390:** MCales/Shutterstock. **p. 396:** PhotoEdit, Inc. **p. 403:** Sayyid Azim/AP Wide World Photos. **p. 406:** © Jeffrey Bennett. **p. 411 (top):** © Jeff Bennett. **p. 411 (bottom):** delihayat/Shutterstock.

Chapter 7

p. 415: Fred K. Smith. **p. 416:** AP Wide World Photos. **p. 419 (top):** Buccina Studios/Getty Images, Inc.–PhotoDisc–Royalty Free. **p. 419 (bottom):** FEMA. **p. 421:** Svantse/Dreamstime LLC–Royalty Free. **p. 424:** Xaoc/Dreamstime LLC–Royalty Free. **p. 429:** Brandon Parry/Shutterstock. **p. 436:** Luis Romero/AP Wide World Photos. **p. 443:** Corbis RF. **p. 446:** Corbis RF. **p. 449:** Ron Hilton/Stockphoto. **p. 462:** Bcubic/Dreamstime LLC–Royalty Free. **p. 467:** © Jeffrey Bennett. **p. 468:** CORBIS–NY.

Chapter 8

p. 471: Rich Lindie/Shutterstock. **p. 472:** www.puzzlemaster.ca. **p. 476:** Albert Allen Bartlett. **p. 484 (top):** National Archives and Records Administration. **p. 484 (bottom):** © Richard A. Cooke/ CORBIS. All Rights Reserved. **p. 489 (left column):** Getty Images–PhotoDisc–Royalty Free. **p. 489 (right column):** James Gritz/Getty Images, Inc.–PhotoDisc–Royalty Free. **p. 491:** Getty Images–PhotoDisc–Royalty Free. **p. 492:** © Morton Beebe/Corbis. **p. 493:** Getty Images–PhotoDisc–Royalty Free. **p. 499:** Justin Horrocks/iStockphoto.com. **p. 501:** USGS/Wikipedia, The Free Encyclopedia. **p. 502:** Photos.com. **p. 505 (top):** Jonelle Weaver/ Getty Images, Inc.–PhotoDisc–Royalty Free. **p. 505 (bottom):** Eric Gevaert/Shutterstock. **p. 507:** Corbis RF. **p. 508:** Corbis RF.

Chapter 9

p. 511: NASA. **p. 514:** Stewart Drolet/iStockphoto.com. **p. 517:** shrimpo1967/Wikipedia, The Free Encyclopedia. **p. 531:** Leong Yoke Shu/Shutterstock. **p. 537:** Getty Images–PhotoDisc–Royalty Free. **p. 544:** Jonathan Blair/CORBIS–NY. **p. 547:** Steve Estvanik/ Dreamstime LLC–Royalty Free.

Chapter 10

p. 551: Caro M. Highsmith, courtesy of the Library of Congress. **p. 552:** NASA Headquarters. **p. 560 (top):** David Buffington/ Getty Images, Inc.–PhotoDisc–Royalty Free. **p. 560 (bottom):** Hisham F. Ibrahim/Getty Images, Inc.–PhotoDisc–Royalty Free. **p. 568:** Dennis DiCicco. **pp. 567–569** (Figs. 10.26–10.28): From THE COSMIC PERSPECTIVE, 4e, by Jeffrey Bennett, Megan Donahue, Nicholas Schneider and Mark Voit. Copyright © 2007 by Pearson Education, publishing as Addison Wesley. Reprinted by permission of Pearson Education, Inc. **p. 571:** Getty Images–PhotoDisc–Royalty Free. **p. 574:** Getty Images–PhotoDisc–Royalty Free. **p. 578:** Getty Images–PhotoDisc–Royalty Free. **p. 581** (Fig. 10.43): Anne Burns. **p. 583** (Fig. 10.49a): Ian Cartwright/ Getty Images, Inc.–PhotoDisc–Royalty Free. **p. 583** (Fig. 10.49b): William Briggs. **p. 585** (Fig. 10.53): From THE SCIENCE OF FRACTAL IMAGES, Heinz-Otto Peitgen & Dietmar Saupe, Eds., © 1988, Springer-Verlag, N.Y. Reprinted with permission. **p. 587** (Fig. 10.54): "4 stages in construction of a snowflake island" from Benoit B. Mandelbrot, THE FRACTAL GEOMETRY OF NATURE, © 1982 by Benoit B. Mandelbrot. New York. W. H. Freeman & Co., page 43. Reprinted by permission of the author. **p. 588** (Fig. 10.56): From THE SCIENCE OF FRACTAL IMAGES, Heinz-Otto Peitgen & Dietmar Saupe, Eds., © 1988, Springer-Verlag, N.Y. Reprinted with permission. **p. 588** (Fig. 10.57): "Menger Sponge" from Benoit B. Mandelbrot, THE FRACTAL GEOMETRY OF NATURE, © 1982 by Benoit B. Mandelbrot. New York. W. H. Freeman & Co., page 45. Reprinted by permission of the author. **p. 589** (Fig. 10.58): © Professor Robert Devaney, Department of Mathematics, Boston University. Reprinted by permission of the author. **p. 589** (Fig. 10.59): Figure 3.10.8(b) from FRACTALS EVERYWHERE, by Michael Barnsley, copyright © 1988 by Academic Press. Reprinted by permission.

Chapter 11

p. 593: © Chad Ehlers/Stock Connection. **p. 595:** © Archivo Iconografico, S.A./Corbis. **p. 596:** © PhotoDisc Blue. **p. 601:** Tatiana Morozova/Shutterstock. **p. 604** (Fig. 11.6): Scala/Art Resource, NY. **p. 604** (Fig. 11.7): © The Granger Collection. **p. 605** (Fig. 11.8): From "Perspective, Jan Vredeman de Vries." Dover Publications, Inc., NY. Reprinted by permission. **p. 605** (Fig. 11.9): © Corbis/ Bettmann. **p. 605** (Fig. 11.10): M. C. Escher's "Belvedere" © 2003 Cordon Art B.V.-Baarn-Holland. All Rights Reserved. **p. 606** (Fig. 11.11): © The Granger Collection. **p. 606** (Fig. 11.12): © John R. Jones; Papilio/Corbis. **p. 608** (Fig. 11.19): © The Granger Collection. **p. 608** (Fig. 11.20): Tate Gallery, London/Art Resource, NY. **p. 608** (Fig. 11.21): Anne Burns, Professor of Mathematics, Long Island University, C. W. Post Campus. **p. 610** (Fig. 11.27): Courtesy of Paul J. Steinhardt, Princeton University. **p. 617** (Fig. 11.43): © Corbis. **p. 617** (Fig. 11.44): Scala/Art Resource, NY. **p. 617** (Fig. 11.45): © 2004 Mondrian/Holtzman Trust/ Artists Rights Society (ARS), New York. **p. 619** (Fig. 11.46c): © PhotoDisc. **p. 620** (Fig. 11.48b): © PhotoDisc.

Chapter 12

p. 625: J. K. Bowers/iStockphoto.com. **p. 628:** © PhotoDisc. **p. 630:** © Bettmann/Corbis. **p. 641:** PhotoDisc. **p. 650 (top):** © Reuters NewMedia Inc./Corbis. **p. 650 (bottom):** Lawrence Jackson/The White House Photo Office. **p. 651:** Bettmann/Corbis. **p. 657:** PhotoDisc. **p. 667** (Fig. 12.4): From the *New York Times*, June 29, 2006. © 2006 The New York Times. Used with permission. All Rights Reserved. **p. 668:** © Bettmann/Corbis.

Answers to Selected Exercises

CHAPTER 1

Unit 1A Quick Quiz

1. a 2. c 3. b 4. a 5. b 6. b 7. b 8. c 9. b 10. a

Unit 1A Exercises

5. Does not make sense
7. Makes sense
9. Does not make sense
11. a. *Premise:* Apple's iPhone outsells all other smart phones. *Conclusion:* It must be the best smart phone on the market.
    b. The fact that many people buy the iPhone does not necessarily mean it is the best smart phone.
13. a. *Premise:* Fifty years of searching has not revealed life on other planets. *Conclusion:* Life in the universe must be confined to Earth.
    b. Failure to find life does not imply that life does not exist.
15. a. *Premise:* He refused to testify by invoking his Fifth Amendment rights. *Conclusion:* He must be guilty.
    b. The conclusion is stated as if it were the only possible conclusion.
17. a. *Premise:* The Senator doesn't have a religious affiliation. *Conclusion:* He can't have the personal values required to represent me.
    b. The conclusion is based on a personal allegation.
19. a. *Premise:* Good grades are needed to get into college, and a college diploma is necessary for a good career. *Conclusion:* Attendance should count in high school grades.
    b. The premise (which is often true) directs attention away from the conclusion.
21. *Premise:* Obesity and video game sales have increased steadily for the last decade. *Conclusion:* Video games are compromising the health of Americans. False cause
23. *Premise:* All the mayors of my home town have been men. *Conclusion:* Men are better qualified for high office than women. Hasty generalization
25. *Premise:* My baby was vaccinated and later developed autism. *Conclusion:* I believe that vaccines cause autism. False cause
27. *Premise:* Shakespeare's plays have been read for many centuries. *Conclusion:* Everyone loves Shakespeare. Circular reasoning
29. *Premise:* After I last gave to a charity, an audit showed that most of the money was used to pay its administrators in the front office. *Conclusion:* I will not give money to the tsunami relief organization. Appeal to ignorance or personal attack
31. *Premise:* The Congressperson is a member of the National Rifle Association. *Conclusion:* I'm sure she will not support a ban on assault rifles. Personal attack or straw man
33. *Premise:* Republicans favor repealing the estate tax, which falls most heavily on the rich. *Conclusion:* Republicans think the rich need to be richer. Straw man
35. *Premise:* My little boy loves dolls and my little girl loves trucks. *Conclusion:* It's not true that little boys are more interested in mechanical toys and girls prefer maternal toys. Appeal to ignorance or hasty generalization

Unit 1B Quick Quiz

1. c 2. a 3. c 4. c 5. c 6. a 7. c 8. a 9. b 10. a

Unit 1B Exercises

7. Does not make sense
9. Makes sense
11. Does not make sense
13. Proposition
15. Not a proposition
17. Not a proposition
19. Asia is not in the northern hemisphere. The statement is true; the negation is false.
21. The Beatles were a German band. The statement is true; the negation is false.
23. Sarah did go to dinner.
25. The Congressman voted in favor of discrimination.
27. Paul appears to support building the new dorm.

29.

q	r	q *and* r
T	T	T
T	F	F
F	T	F
F	F	F

31. Cucumbers are vegetables. Apples are fruit. Both propositions are true, so the conjunction is true.
33. The Mississippi River flows through Louisiana. The Colorado River flows through Arizona. Both propositions are true, so the conjunction is true.
35. Some people are happy. Some people are short. Both propositions are true, so the conjunction is true.

37.

q	r	s	q *and* r *and* s
T	T	T	T
T	T	F	F
T	F	T	F
T	F	F	F
F	T	T	F
F	T	F	F
F	F	T	F
F	F	F	F

39. Exclusive
41. Exclusive
43. Inclusive

45.

r	s	r or s
T	T	T
T	F	T
F	T	T
F	F	F

47.

p	not p	p and (not p)
T	F	F
F	T	F

49.

p	q	r	p or q or r
T	T	T	T
T	T	F	T
T	F	T	T
T	F	F	T
F	T	T	T
F	T	F	T
F	F	T	T
F	F	F	F

51. Oranges are vegetables. Oranges are fruit. The second proposition is true, so the disjunction is true.
53. The Nile River is in Africa. China is in Europe. The first proposition is true, so the disjunction is true.
55. Trees walk. Rocks run. Neither proposition is true, so the disjunction is false.
57. Search on *economic* AND *depression* AND *America*.
59. Search on *politicians* AND (*Ohio* OR *Indiana*) AND *Jones*.

61.

p	r	if p, then r
T	T	T
T	F	F
F	T	T
F	F	T

63. *Hypothesis:* Eagles can fly. *Conclusion:* Eagles are birds. Both propositions are true, and the implication is true.
65. *Hypothesis:* London is in England. *Conclusion:* Chicago is in Bolivia. The hypothesis is true, the conclusion is false, and the implication is false.
67. *Hypothesis:* Pigs can fly. *Conclusion:* Fish can brush their teeth. The hypothesis is false, the conclusion is false, and the implication is true.
69. *Hypothesis:* Butterflies can fly. *Conclusion:* Butterflies are birds. The hypothesis is true, the conclusion is false, and the implication is false.
71. If a creature is a monkey, then it is a mammal.
73. If you are eating, then you are alive.
75. If you are bald, then you are a male.
77. *Converse:* If José owns a Mac, then he owns a computer. *Inverse:* If José does not own a computer, then he does not own a Mac. *Contrapositive:* If José does not own a Mac, then he does not own a computer.
79. *Converse:* If Teresa works in Massachusetts, then she works in Boston. *Inverse:* If Teresa does not work in Boston, then she does not work in Massachusetts. *Contrapositive:* If Teresa does not work in Massachusetts, then she does not work in Boston.
81. *Converse:* If it is warm outside, then the sun is shining. *Inverse:* If the sun is not shining, then it is not warm outside. *Contrapositive:* If it is not warm outside, then the sun is not shining.
83. If you die young, then you are good.
85. If a free society cannot help the many who are poor, then it cannot save the few who are rich.
87. "If Sue lives in Cleveland, then she lives in Ohio" when, in fact, Sue lives in Cincinnati.
89. If Ramon lives in Albuquerque, then he lives in New Mexico.
91. a. Yes b. Yes c. Yes d. Yes e. No f. Yes
93. Believing is sufficient for achieving. Achieving is necessary for believing.
95. Loving until it hurts is sufficient for there being no hurt but only more love. There being no hurt but only more love is necessary for loving until it hurts.

97.

p	q	p and q	not (p and q)	(not p) or (not q)
T	T	T	F	F
T	F	F	T	T
F	T	F	T	T
F	F	F	T	T

The propositions are equivalent.

99.

p	q	p and q	not (p and q)	(not p) and (not q)
T	T	T	F	F
T	F	F	T	F
F	T	F	T	F
F	F	F	T	T

The propositions are not equivalent.

101.

p	q	r	p and q	(p and q) or r	p or r	p or q	(p or r) and (p or q)
T	T	T	T	T	T	T	T
T	T	F	T	T	T	T	T
T	F	T	F	T	T	T	T
T	F	F	F	F	T	T	T
F	T	T	F	T	T	T	T
F	T	F	F	F	F	T	F
F	F	T	F	T	T	F	F
F	F	F	F	F	F	F	F

The propositions are not equivalent.

Unit 1C Quick Quiz

1. b 2. c 3. a 4. b 5. a 6. c 7. a 8. c 9. a 10. c

Unit 1C Exercises

7. Does not make sense
9. Does not make sense
11. Does not make sense
13. Natural
15. Rational
17. Rational
19. Real
21. Rational
23. Real
25. Rational

27. Real
29. {Sunday, Monday, Tuesday, Wednesday, Thursday, Friday, Saturday}
31. {New Mexico, Oklahoma, Arkansas, Louisiana}
33. {36, 49, 64, 81, 100, 121}
35. {3, 9, 15, 21, 27}
37.

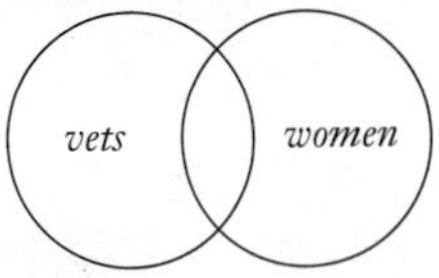

39.

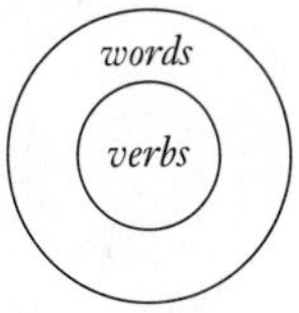

41.

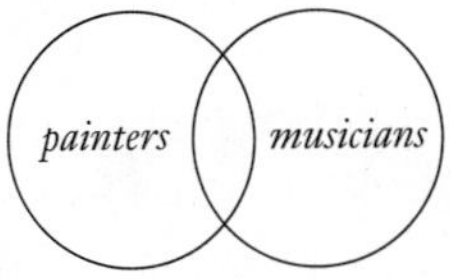

43.

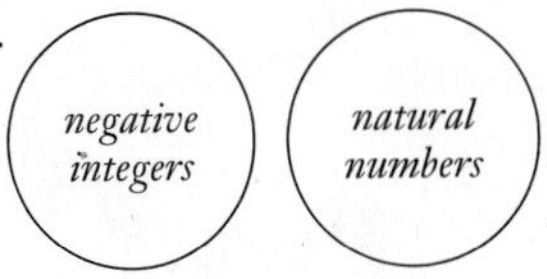

45. *Subject:* widows. *Predicate:* women.

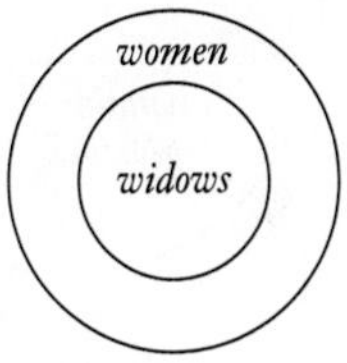

47. All U.S. presidents are people over 30 years old. *Subject:* U.S. presidents. *Predicate:* people over 30.

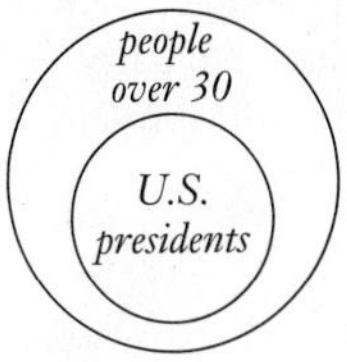

49. No monkeys are gambling animals. *Subject:* monkeys. *Predicate:* gambling animals.

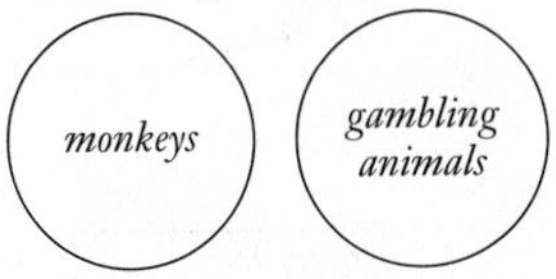

51. All winners are people who smile. *Subject:* winners. *Predicate:* people who smile.

53.

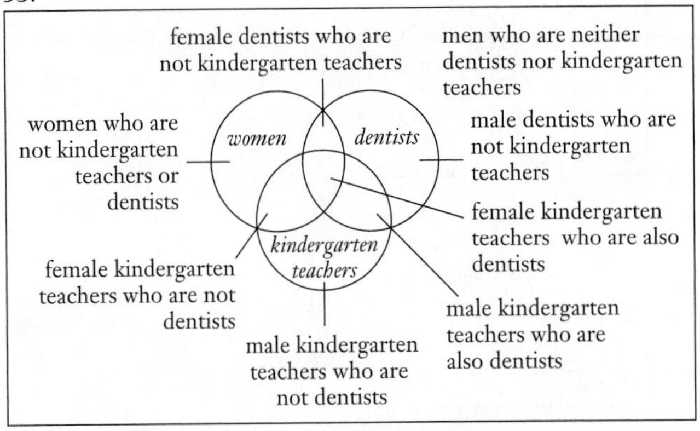

55.

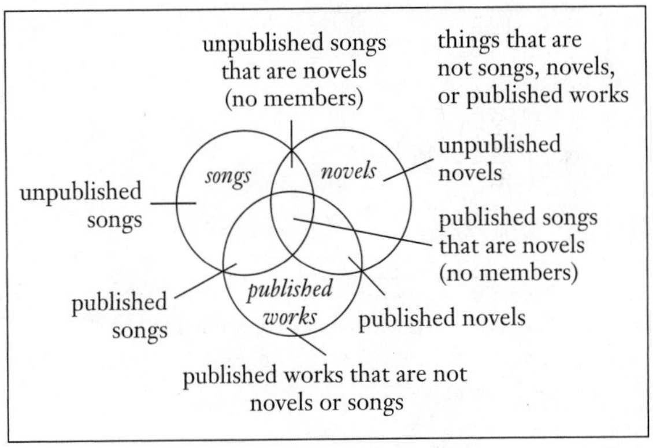

57.

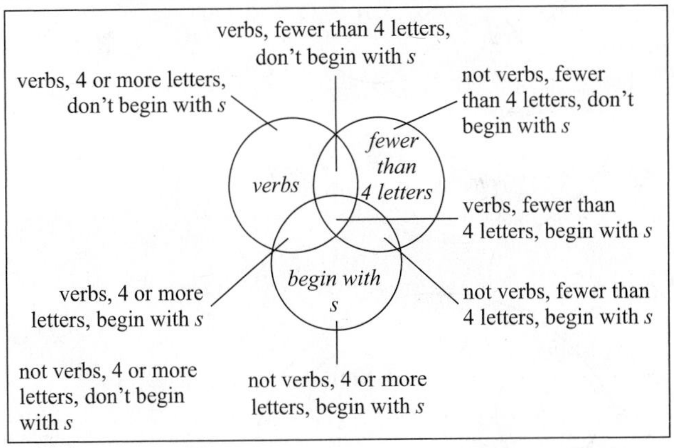

59. a. 31 b. 22 c. 44 d. 81
61. a. 20 b. 22 c. 8 d. 34
63.

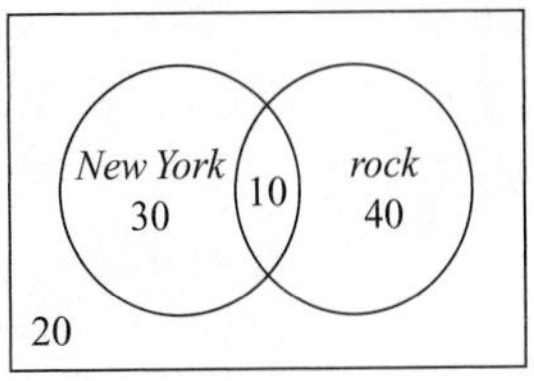

65. 15, 10

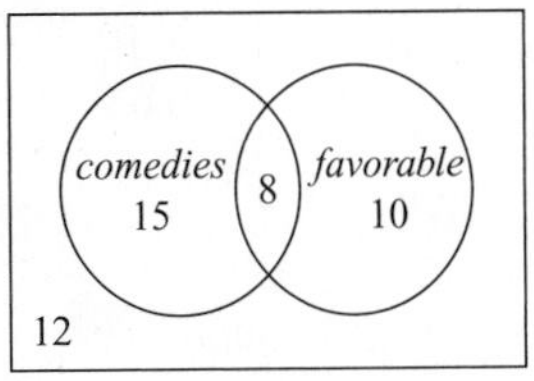

67.

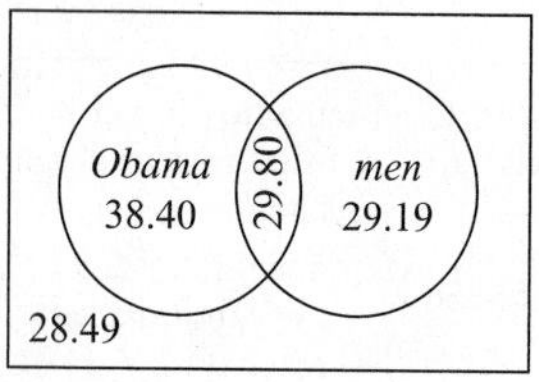

69.

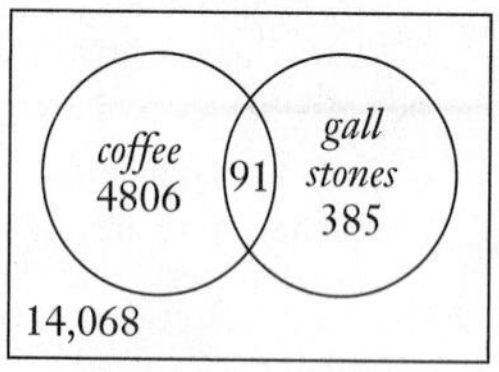

71. a.

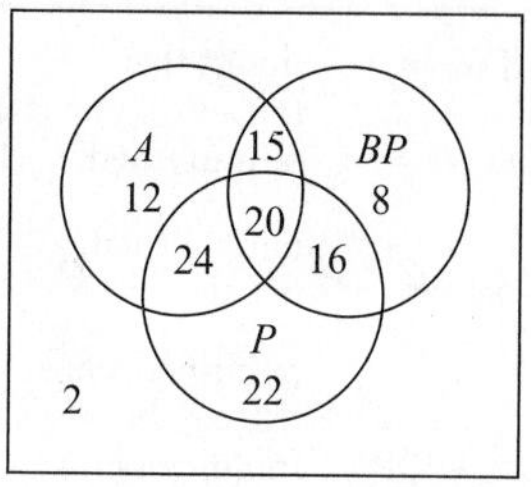

b. 95 c. 23 d. 82 e. 15 f. 117

73.

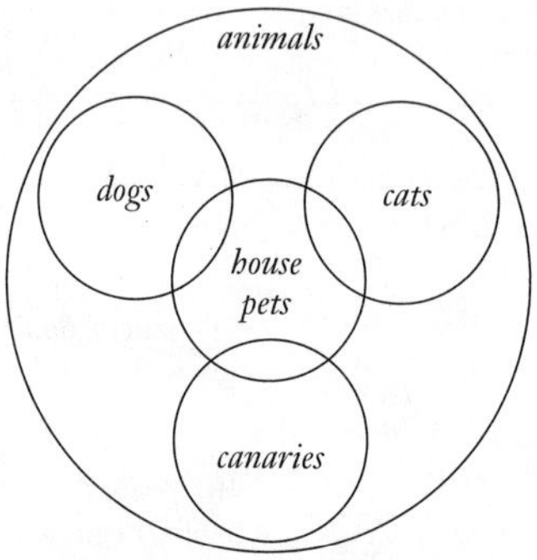

75.

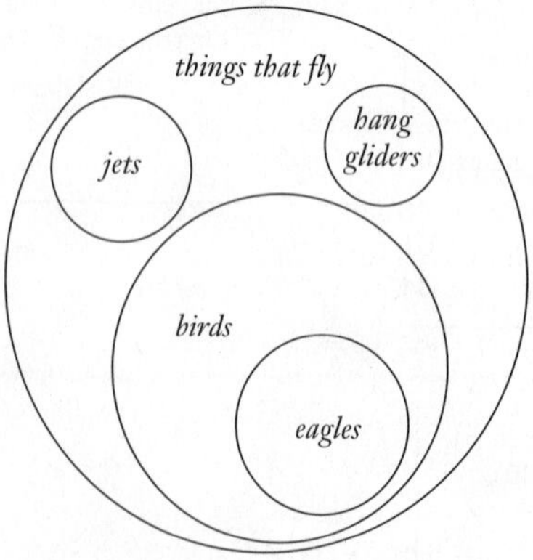

77.

	Vegetarian	Meat/fish	Total
Wine	20	40	60
No wine	45	15	60
Total	65	55	120

79. a. 47% b. Not enough information c. 27%
d. Not enough information e. About 60 million

81. a.

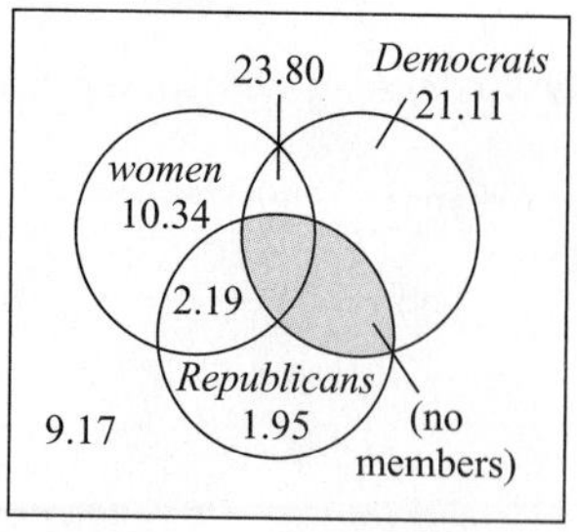

b.

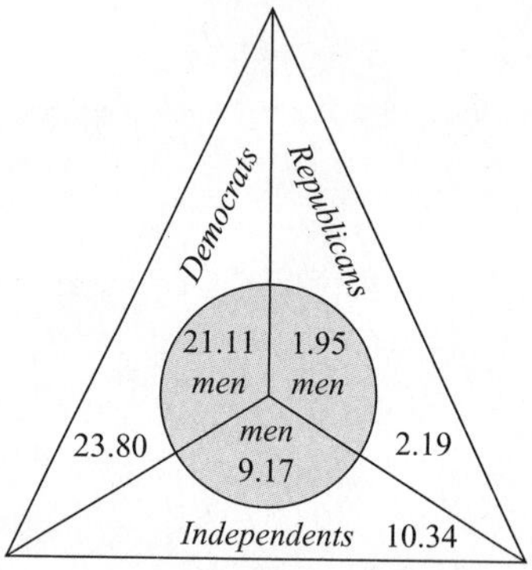

83.

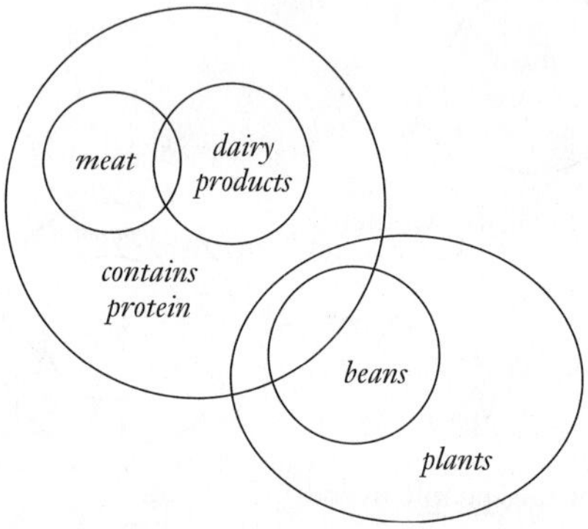

There could not be beans that are dairy products. Meat that is a dairy product is not excluded by premises. No dairy products are plants. There could be plants with protein.

85. a.

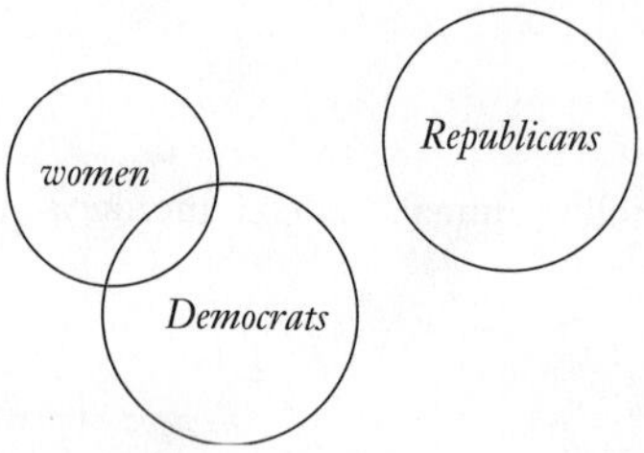

b. Yes. c. Yes.

87. a. 16 options b.

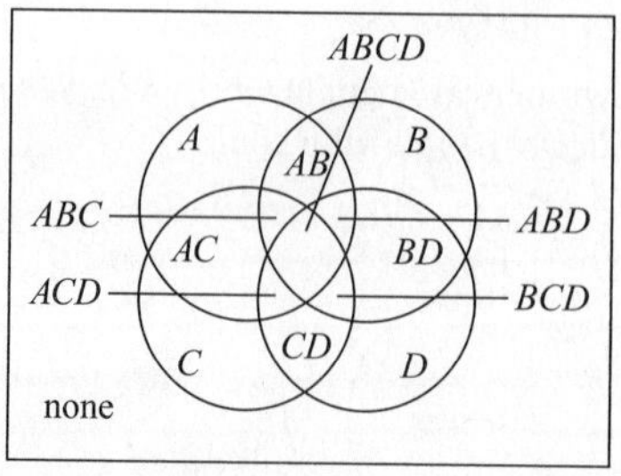

c. There are no regions for A and D only, and for B and C only.
d. 32 options e. 2^N options

Unit 1D Quick Quiz

1. b 2. c 3. c 4. a 5. c 6. b 7. c 8. c 9. b 10. b

Unit 1D Exercises

9. Does not make sense
11. Makes sense
13. Does not make sense
15. Inductive
17. Inductive
19. Inductive
21. Inductive
23. Premises are true; argument is moderately strong; conclusion is true.
25. Premises are true; argument *seems* moderately strong; conclusion is false.
27. Premises are true; argument is moderately strong; conclusion is true.
29. All European countries are countries that use the euro as currency; valid. The first premise is false, so the argument is not sound.

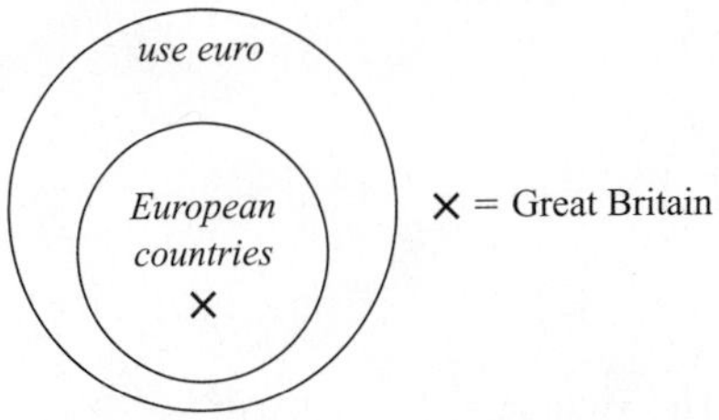

31. All states west of the Mississippi River are not in the eastern time zone; valid. The premises are true, and the argument is sound.

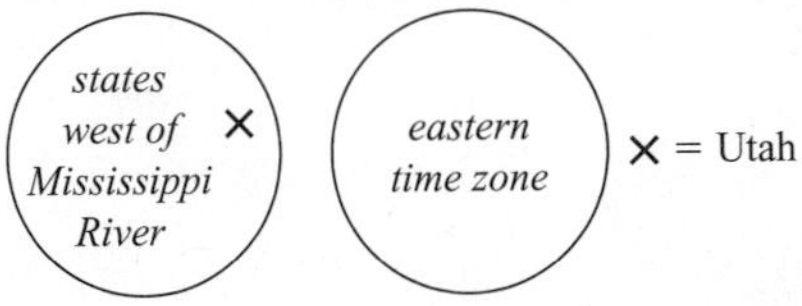

33. Not valid. The premises are true, but the argument is not sound.

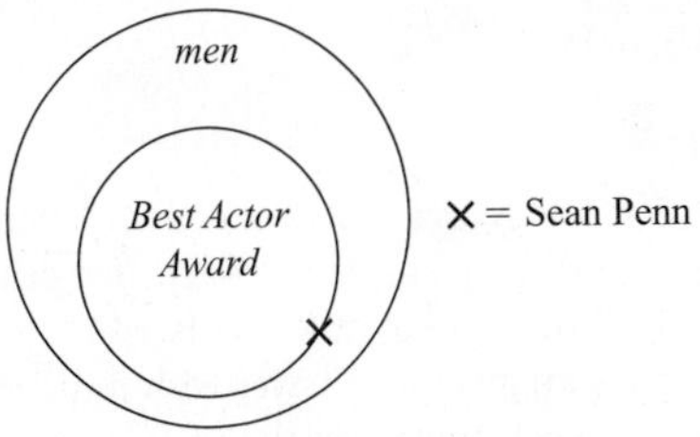

35. All opera singers are people who can whistle a Mozart tune; valid. The premises could be true, in which case the argument is sound.

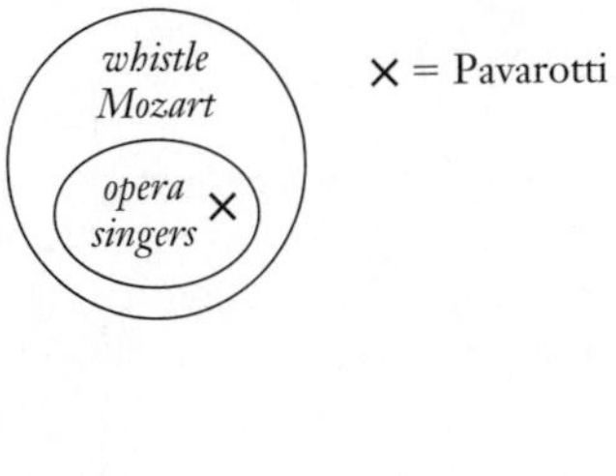

37. Affirming the hypothesis; valid. The premises are true, and the argument is sound.

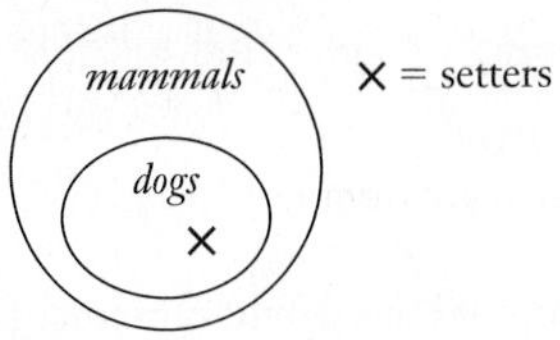

39. Denying the hypothesis; not valid. The argument is not sound.

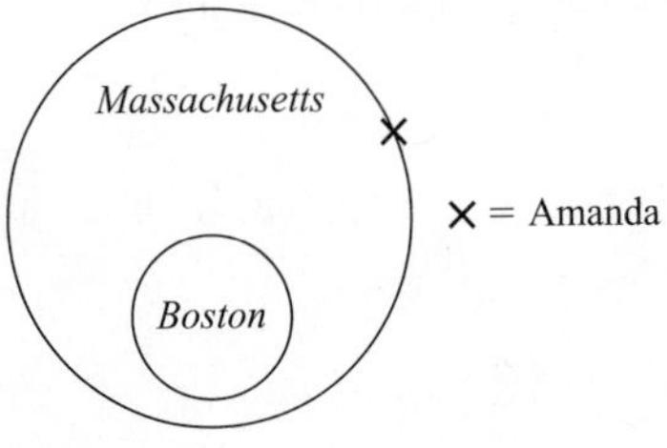

41. Denying the conclusion; valid. The premises are true, and the argument is sound.

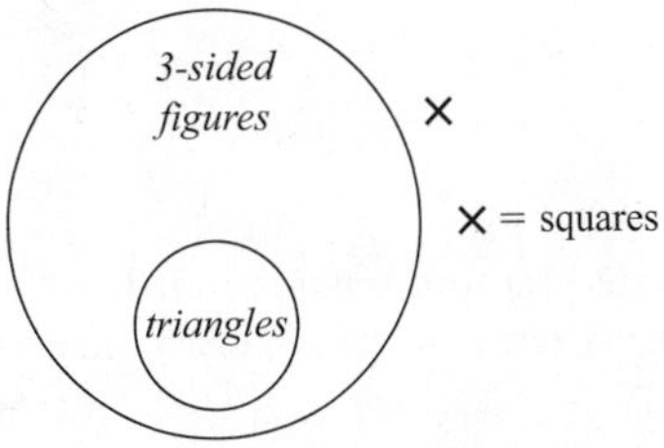

43. If a novel was written in the 19th century, then it was not written on a word processor. Denying the hypothesis; not valid. The argument is not sound.

45. Valid
47. If taxpayers have less disposable income, then the economy will slow down. If taxes are increased, then the economy will slow down. Valid.
49. True
51. Not true by counterexample
53. Example of valid and sound:
    Premise: All living mammals breathe.
    Premise: All monkeys are mammals.
    Conclusion: All living monkeys breathe.
55. Example of valid and not sound:
    Premise: All mammals fly. (false)
    Premise: All monkeys are mammals. (true)
    Conclusion: All monkeys fly. (false)
57. Example of not valid with true premises and conclusion:
    Premise: All mammals breathe. (true)
    Premise: All mammals have hair. (true)
    Conclusion: All hairy animals breathe. (true)
59. Affirming the conclusion (invalid):
    Premise: If I am in Phoenix, then I am in Arizona.
    Premise: I am in Arizona.
    Conclusion: I am in Phoenix.

61. Denying the conclusion (valid):
Premise: If I am in Phoenix, then I am in Arizona.
Premise: I am not in Arizona.
Conclusion: I am not in Phoenix.
63. a. Ford is punished by the market.
b. Toyota did not take market share from Ford.
c. No conclusion
65. a. Their vast remaining dollar holdings would plummet in value.
b. Chinese officials did not pull assets out of the U.S.
c. No conclusion

Unit 1E Quick Quiz

1. b 2. c 3. c 4. b 5. c 6. a 7. c 8. b 9. a 10. c

Unit 1E Exercises

5. Makes sense
7. Does not make sense
9. Makes sense
11. 4
13. Roosters don't lay eggs.
15. 5
17. 6
19. 1, 2, 3, 4
21. No
23. a. 12 b. 8 c. An eight-year wait is not required.
d. Three more consecutive terms are possible. The charter is not clear.
25. *Assumptions:* The interest rate remains the same. No withdrawals or additional deposits are made.
27. *Assumptions:* The Senator will keep her promise. There are no overriding reasons *not* to vote for the Senator.
29. The speaker may have a fundamental ideological opposition to paying taxes.
31. a. Must file b. Must file c. Needn't file d. Must file
33. a. Yes b. Yes c. No
35. a. You probably pay for service and insurance with either plan.
b. Yes; the total cost of the car at the end of the lease is $18,640.
c. You have years to decide if you want to buy it. You don't need to worry about selling the car. The dealer may offer special servicing prices with a lease.
37. Were there more than 350 people on each jet or both jets combined? And was there any damage or injuries?
39. Is $83 billion the gross domestic product or 6% of the gross domestic product?
41. a. They could be consistent because Alice does not specify the time period for her 253 cases.
b. They could be consistent if Alice obtained many convictions through plea agreements without going to trial.
43. a. The hire of a non-blood relative conforms with the law.
b. Is it legal to hire a former spouse? Is it legal to hire an adopted child?
45. The current policy costs $5035 for nine months. The upgrade costs $2475 for nine months.
47. If you plan to fly 10 times (or a multiple of 10 times), then Plan A ($3150) is better than Plan B ($3250).
49. The AFC has stronger teams or a streak of five games is not unexpected.
51. Sentencing by judges and juries became stricter.
53. If the population increases quickly enough, then the death *rate* can decrease even though the number of deaths increases.
55. Country Y has a high gun suicide rate.

CHAPTER 2

Unit 2A Quick Quiz

1. a 2. b 3. c 4. b 5. a 6. b 7. b 8. c 9. b 10. a

Unit 2A Exercises

7. Does not make sense
9. Does not make sense
11. Does not make sense
13. a. 3/8 b. 2/5 c. 2 d. 5/6 e. 1/6 f. 5/8 g. 3/8 h. 1
15. a. 7/2 b. 3/10 c. 1/20 d. 41/10 e. 43/20 f. 7/20 g. 49/50 h. 401/100
17. a. 0.25 b. 0.375 c. 0.667 d. 0.6 e. 6.5 f. 3.833 g. 2.06 h. 1.615
19. mi/hr
21. Dollars per square yard, $\$/yd^2$
23. yen/kg
25. gal/person
27. 288 in.
29. 1500 sec
31. 60 qt
33. 980 days
35. 26,280 hr
37. a. Area = 30,000 ft^2; volume = 1,050,000 ft^3
b. Area = 300 yd^2; volume = 90 yd^3
c. Area = 200 ft^2; volume = 300 ft^3
39. $1\ ft^2 = 144\ in.^2$; $144\ in.^2/1\ ft^2 = 1$; $1\ ft^2/144\ in.^2 = 1$
41. $1\ m^2 = 10{,}000\ cm^2$; $1\ m^2/10{,}000\ cm^2 = 1$; $10{,}000\ cm^2/1\ m^2 = 1$
43. 14.8 yd^3
45. 11.9 yd^3
47. 282.88 lb
49. $197.52
51. 1 peso
53. $6.42/gal
55. 540 mi/hr
57. 1.56 hr
59. $2300
61. 185 deaths/100,000 people
63. 5.7 births per minute
65. $25.89 67. 2920 hr
69. Wrong; the student's division gives an answer with units of pounds per dollar, but we seek an answer in dollars (or cents). Instead, multiply: $0.11 \cdot 7.70 = 0.85$, or 85 cents.
71. Wrong; the student's division gives an answer with units of pounds per dollar, but we seek an answer in dollars (or cents) per pound. Instead, divide dollars by pounds: 11/50 = 0.22, or 22 cents/pound, which is less than the 39 cents/pound for the smaller bag.
73. 62.5 gal; yes
75. a. 36.36 hr, 28.57 hr b. $152.63, $181.25
77. 0.007 km = 7 m
79. a. $309,375/game b. $6445/min c. $9668/min
d. $7583/hr

81. a. 700,000 pages b. 1400 books
83. a. Shower 2.33 ft^3; bath 22.5 ft^3 b. 96 min
c. Put the plug in the drain when you take a shower
85. About 15,603,840,000 ft^3; 13/1000 = 1.3%

Unit 2B Quick Quiz

1. c 2. c 3. a 4. a 5. c 6. c 7. b 8. c 9. a 10. b

Unit 2B Exercises

9. Does not make sense
11. Does not make sense
13. Makes sense
15. Does not make sense
17. Does not make sense
19. a. 10^{11} b. 10^2 c. 10^4 d. 10^{12}
21. a. 10^{10} b. 11 c. 100.1 d. 90
23. 82 in. 25. 62.3 lb; 997 oz av
27. 52.94 mi/hr
29. 6.75 cords
31. 1000
33. 1000
35. 10,000
37. 48.51 lb
39. 15.14 L
41. 88.51 km/hr
43. 40.27 mi/hr
45. 4916.12 cm^3
47. a. 7.2°C b. 68.0°F c. 5.0°F d. −22.0°F e. 21.1°C
49. a. −223.15°C b. −33.15°C c. 283.15 K
51. 697 watts
53. a. 3,240,000,000 joules b. 1210 watts c. 270 L = 71.33 gal
55. 0.74 gm/cm^3; it will float
57. 87 $people/mi^2$
59. NJ: 1173 $people/mi^2$; AK: 1 $person/mi^2$
61. a. 1.0 g/100 mL; lethal concentration
b. 0.25 g/100 mL; not safe to drive
63. $1.44/lb
65. $21.74
67. $0.24/oz
69. a. 93.2% b. 16.13 mi/hr; 16.29 mi/hr
c. 14.23 mi/hr; 14.55 mi/hr d. Yes; yes
71. a. About 40 m b. About 210 km^3 c. 7.6%
73. 9.1 g; 0.32 oz
75. 1.47 oz
77. $432
79. 750 kilowatt-hr; $90
81. 1080 million kilowatt-hr per month; 2.4 million kg of coal; 1,080,000 homes
83. 4.32 million joules per day; 50 watts
85. 1,752,000 kilowatt-hr in a year; 175 households
95. a. 20.1 km b. 0.000015 mi/hr c. 6.25 oz d. 2.47 acres
e. 0.15 $lb/in.^2$ f. 26.4 gal

Unit 2C Quick Quiz

1. c 2. a 3. b 4. b 5. b 6. a 7. c 8. c 9. b 10. b

Unit 2C Exercises

3. Does not make sense
5. Does not make sense
7. (cars, buses): (16, 0), (13,2), (10, 4), (7, 6), (4, 8), (1, 10)
9. a. Jordan b. Jordan c. Amari d. 10.53 m
13. 7.1 m
15. 41 million
17. (trucks, cars): (11, 1), (9, 4), (7, 7), (5, 10), (3, 13), (1, 16)
19. a. 0.5 hr b. 1 hr
c. Not true (more time is spent walking than running)
d. 8/3 mi/hr, 2.7 mi/hr
21. Reuben spoke on January 1, and he was born on December 31.
23. That man is my son.
25. $200 gain
27. Select one ball from the first barrel, two balls from the second barrel, and so on, up to ten balls from the tenth barrel
31. Start by dividing the coins into three groups of four coins.
33. Brown, gray, orange, pink, gold
35. The second (unkempt) barber, who must be cutting the well-groomed barber's hair
37. 11.25 s
39. The desk clerk has $25, the bellhop has $2, and the three guests have $1 each; so $30 is accounted for.

CHAPTER 3

Unit 3A Quick Quiz

1. b 2. b 3. c 4. c 5. c 6. c 7. a 8. c 9. c 10. b

Unit 3A Exercises

7. Makes sense
9. Makes sense
11. Does not make sense
13. Makes sense
15. Makes sense
17. 2/5 = 0.4 = 40%
19. 0.20 = 1/5 = 20%
21. 150% = 1.5 = 3/2
23. 4/9 = 0.444... = 44.44...%
25. 5/8 = 0.625 = 62.5%
27. 69% = 0.69 = 69/100
29. 7/5 = 1.4 = 140%
31. 4/3 = 1.333... = 133.33...%
33. 2; 1/2; *A* is 200% of *B*.
35. 3/8 = 0.375; 8/3 ≈ 2.67; *A* is 37.5% of *B*.
37. 3.21; 0.31; *A* is 321% of *B*.
39. 1.34; 0.744; *A* is 134% of *B*.
41. 1.14; 0.877; *A* is 114% of *B*.
43. $4/\pi \approx 1.27$; $\pi/4 \approx 0.785$; *A* is 127% of *B*.
45. 53.8%
47. 159%
49. 81.4%
51. Helen's salary increased more in absolute terms ($10,000 vs. $8000). Both salaries increased by 40%.
53. Absolute change = 59 million; percentage change = 23.7%
55. Absolute change = −806; percentage change = −36.2%
57. 20.9%
59. 33.3%
61. 19.2%
63. 122%
65. 82%

67. 0.6
69. 1.3
71. 0.5 percentage point; 21.7%
73. 11.6 percentage points; 17.3%
75. 33%; 40%
77. $817.76
79. 4463
81. $63.67
83. $2785
85. False; 11.5%
87. False; 1.92
89. Not possible
91. Possible
93. Possible
95. No, you cannot average averages.
97. True
99. False; some of the hotels with restaurants may also have pools.
101. $49.6 trillion
103. 19.7%
105. $516 million
107. a. 7.0% b. 508

Unit 3B Quick Quiz

1. a 2. c 3. c 4. c 5. c 6. c 7. b 8. b 9. c 10. a

Unit 3B Exercises

9. Makes sense
11. Makes sense
13. Does not make sense
15. a. 3000 = three thousand b. 6,000,000 = six million
 c. 340,000 = three hundred forty thousand
 d. 0.02 = two hundredths
 e. 0.00021 = twenty-one hundred-thousandths
 f. 0.00004 = four hundred-thousandths
17. a. 2.33×10^2 b. 1.26547×10^5 c. 1.1×10^{-1}
 d. 9.73623×10^3 e. 1.2458×10^2 f. 8.642×10^{-1}
19. a. 6×10^5 b. 1.2×10^{11} c. 3.2×10^3 d. 2×10^8
21. a. 10^{35} is 10^9, or 1 billion, times as large as 10^{26}.
 b. 10^{27} is 10^{10}, or 10 billion, times as large as 10^{17}.
 c. 1 billion is 10^3, or 1000, times as large as 1 million.
 d. 7 trillion is 10^9, or 1 billion, times as large as 7 thousand.
 e. 2×10^{-6} is 10^3, or 1000, times as large as 2×10^{-9}.
 f. 6.1×10^{29} is 10^2, or 100, times as large as 6.1×10^{27}.
23. 3.4×10^{11} bytes
25. $\$2.564 \times 10^{12}$
27. 10^{-6}m
29. a. 3×10^7; exact value is 3×10^7.
 b. 10^{10}; exact value is 9.69×10^9.
 c. 2×10^3; exact value is 1.9×10^3.
 d. 1×10^{11}; exact value is 1.023×10^{11}.
 e. 2×10^3; exact value is 2.011×10^3.
 f. 3×10^2; exact value is 2.79×10^2.
31. Answers will vary. One cup of coffee per day amounts to $30–$40 per month. One tank of gasoline per week amounts to $70–$80 per month.
33. If you study 6 hours per day for 30 weeks (two semesters), you spend about 1260 hours per year studying. If you sleep 7 hours per night every night, you spend about 2555 hours per year sleeping.
35. 86,400 beats (assuming one beat per second)
37. Approximately 90 gallons per year (assuming 2 pints per day)
39. 3500 miles (assuming you average 10 miles per day)
41. 24 candy bars
43. Uranium-235 releases 35,000 times as much energy.
45. About 7×10^{-7} L
47. About 1.8 million kg
49. 5,000,000 to 1
51. 50,000,000 to 1
53.

Planet	Model Diameter	Model Distance from Sun
Mercury	0.5 mm	6 m
Venus	1.2 mm	11 m
Earth	1.3 mm	15 m
Mars	0.7 mm	23 m
Jupiter	14.3 mm	78 m
Saturn	12.0 mm	143 m
Uranus	5.2 mm	287 m
Neptune	4.8 mm	450 m

55. a. 22.2 yd b. 0.008 in.
57. 4.6 deaths/min
59. 110 deaths/day
61. 9.7 crimes/sec; 1 crime per person
63. 2.1 pounds/person/month
65. a. About 10^{10} cells per cm^3 b. About 10^{13} cells per liter
 c. About 7×10^{14} cells per person
67. About 9000 gallons per month (assuming 100 million households)
69. a. About 1821 kg/cm^3 b. 7300 kg, or the mass of a tank
 c. 7×10^{11} kg/cm^3, more than the total mass of Mt. Everest
71. 1.5 mm; 1.8 mm; 1.3 mm; 1.7 mm; take your height in quarters.
81. a. 5.87×10^{12} miles b. 2,598,960 hands
 c. 4.4 metric tons d. 5.5 g/cm^3 e. 4.4×10^{17} sec

Unit 3C Quick Quiz

1. b 2. a 3. b 4. a 5. b 6. c 7. b 8. a 9. a 10. a

Unit 3C Exercises

7. Does not make sense
9. Does not make sense
11. Does not make sense
13. Makes sense
15. a. 3 b. 88 c. 0 d. 185 e. 1945 f. 3 g. 6
 h. 1500 i. −14
17. Four significant digits; precise to the nearest dollar
19. One significant digit; precise to the nearest 10 miles per hour
21. Six significant digits; precise to the nearest hundred-thousandth of a mile
23. Two significant digits; precise to the nearest thousand seconds
25. Seven significant digits; precise to the nearest ten-thousandth of a pound
27. Four significant digits; precise to the nearest tenth of a km/s
29. 1440
31. 6800
33. 1.83149×10^3
35. Random errors due to not counting some birds and double counting other birds

37. Systematic errors due to self-reporting (probably underestimating weight)
39. Random errors in measuring the weight of the cans
41. Random errors in reading the temperature and possibly systematic errors if the thermometer is not calibrated
43. (1) is a random error; (2) is a systematic error (most likely due to underreporting).
45. All altitude readings will be about 2780 feet too low; this is a systematic error.
47. Absolute error = −0.5 in., relative error = −0.7%
49. Absolute error = 2 mi/hr, relative error = 3.4%
51. Absolute error = 0.25 oz, relative error = 5.0%
53. Absolute error = 0.15 cm, relative error = 0.6%
55. Tape measure is more accurate; laser is more precise.
57. Digital scale is more precise and more accurate.
59. 12 lb
61. 160 mi/hr
63. 38 mi
65. $17 per person
67. Random or systematic errors could be present; not believable with the given precision.
69. Small random error could be present, but the figure is believable with the given precision.
71. Random or systematic errors could be present; not believable with the given precision.
73. Random or systematic errors could be present; not believable with the given precision.
75. a. Between 43 in. and 53 in.
    b. Between 17.20 in. and 53.03 in.

Unit 3D Quick Quiz

1. b 2. c 3. b 4. c 5. c 6. b 7. a 8. a 9. c 10. c

Unit 3D Exercises

5. Does not make sense
7. Makes sense
9. Does not make sense
11. 440.9
13. $32.59
15. 0.52 of the same tank
17. $75,677
19. 30.6%
21. $0.86
23. $3.44
25. $3.54
27. Palo Alto: $1.259 million; Sioux City: $162,000; Boston: $627,000
29. Spokane: $260,000; Denver: $290,000; Juneau: $333,000
31. Health care spending increased by 2700%, while the rate of inflation was 264%.
33. College costs increased by 69%, while the rate of inflation was 73%.
35. Home prices increased by 126%, while the rate of inflation was 65%.
37. $2.78
39. In 1996, actual dollars are 1996 dollars.
41. Yes, it is consistent ($6.27 either way).
43. 1968

Unit 3E Exercises (continued)

53. $261.93
55. $323.10
57. $A > B$

Unit 3E Quick Quiz

1. a 2. a 3. b 4. a 5. c 6. c 7. b 8. c 9. b 10. c

Unit 3E Exercises

5. Makes sense
7. Does not make sense
9. Does not make sense
11. a. Josh b. Josh c. Jude
13. a. New Jersey; Nebraska
    b. The percentage of nonwhites is significantly lower in Nebraska than in New Jersey.
15. a. Whites: 0.18%; nonwhites: 0.54%; total: 0.19%
    b. Whites: 0.16%; nonwhites: 0.34%; total: 0.23%
    c. The rate for both whites and nonwhites was higher in New York than in Richmond, yet the overall rate was higher in Richmond than in New York. The percentage of nonwhites was significantly lower in New York than in Richmond.
17. b. 8.3%, or about 8 in 100 c. 90%, or 9 in 10, which is the accuracy of the test d. 0.11%, or about 11 in 10,000
19. b. 90%
    c. 12%; in part b the comparison is to those who have the disease, and here the comparison is to all those who test positive.
    d. The chance of having the disease increases to (only) 12% given that the test was positive, compared to 1.5% (the incidence rate) without the test.
21. a. Spelman had a better record for home games (34.5% vs. 32.1%) and away games (75.0% vs. 73.7%) individually.
    b. Morehouse has the better overall average (62.5% vs. 48.9%).
    c. Teams are generally rated on their overall record.
23. b. 95% of those at risk for HIV test positive; 67.9% of those at risk who test positive have HIV.
    c. The chance of the patient having HIV is 67.9%, which is greater than the overall "at risk" incidence rate of 10%.
    d. 95% of those in the general population with HIV test positive; 5.4% of those in the general population who test positive have HIV.
    e. The chance of the patient having HIV is 5.4%, compared to the overall incidence rate of 0.3%.
25. Within each category, the percentage of women hired was greater than the percentage of men hired. Overall, the hiring rate was higher for men (55%) than for women (41.7%). Note that the number of blue-collar jobs was over five times greater than the number of white-collar jobs.
31. a. Absolute difference = $12,627;
    income $41,000 : savings 0.5% of income;
    income $530,000 : savings 2.4% of income
    b. Absolute difference = $12,234;
    income $41,000 : savings 2.9% of income;
    income $530,000 : savings 2.5% of income

CHAPTER 4

Unit 4A Quick Quiz

1. a 2. a 3. b 4. c 5. b 6. c 7. a 8. c 9. c 10. b

Unit 4A Exercises

7. Does not make sense
9. Makes sense
11. Does not make sense
13. 67%
15. 510%
17. 130%
19. 156%
21. $9.75
23. $57
25. $1000
27. $266.67
29. $70.42
31. −$133
33. $303
35. Below average
37. At average
39. Above average
41. Old car $20,333, new car $25,056
43. Buy $12,000, lease $10,000
45. In-state $12,400, out-of-state $11,900
47. You pay $1500 for college; you earn $1500 with the job.
49. About 62 months
51. a. With policy $2050, without policy $1375
b. With policy $1700, without policy $1650
c. With policy $1800, without policy $1700
53. a. $5675 b. $8220

Unit 4B Quick Quiz

1. b 2. a 3. c 4. a 5. c 6. b 7. c 8. a 9. a 10. c

Unit 4B Exercises

9. Does not make sense
11. Does not make sense
13. Makes sense
15. 8
17. 64
19. 4
21. 1/4
23. 9
25. 25
27. $x = 12$
29. $z = 16$
31. $p = 4$ 33. $z = 4$ 35. $x = 10$ 37. $a = -2$
39. $q = 40$ 41. $t = 80$ 43. $840 45. $3600
47.

End of Year	Suzanne's Annual Interest	Suzanne's Balance	Derek's Annual Interest	Derek's Balance
1	$75	$3075	$75	$3075
2	$75	$3150	$77	$3152
3	$75	$3225	$79	$3231
4	$75	$3300	$81	$3311
5	$75	$3375	$83	$3394

49. $14,802.44
51. $32,967.32
53. $7212.30
55. $12,207.94
57. $29,045.68
59. $4227.41
61. $75,472.89
63. 5.65%
65. 4.28%
67. $10,365.20; $11,912.46; $20,137.53; APY = 3.56%
69. $7322.20; $8766.26; $17,217.22; APY = 4.60%
71. $3185.51; $4049.58; $9960.35; APY = 6.18%
73. $16,920.98 75. $15,488.10 77. $65,859.56
79. $78,961.07
81. After 10 years, Chang has $705.30; after 30 years, he has $1403.40. After 10 years, Kio has $722.52; after 30 years, she has $1508.74. Kio has $17.22, or 2.4%, more than Chang after 10 years. Kio has $105.34, or 7.5%, more than Chang after 30 years.
83. 6.77%; 6.80%; 6.82%
85.

	Account 1		Account 2	
Year	Interest	Balance	Interest	Balance
0	–	$1000	–	$1000
1	$55	$1055	$57	$1057
2	$58	$1113	$59	$1116
3	$61	$1174	$63	$1179
4	$65	$1239	$67	$1246
5	$68	$1307	$70	$1317
6	$72	$1379	$74	$1391
7	$76	$1455	$79	$1470
8	$80	$1535	$83	$1553
9	$84	$1619	$87	$1640
10	$89	$1708	$93	$1733

Account 1 has increased in value by $708, or 70.8%.
Account 2 has increased in value by $733, or 73.3%.

87. a. Rosa: $3649.96, $6573.37; Julian: $3190.70, $6633.24
b. Rosa: 18%, 54%; Julian 22%, 62%
89. Plan A $27,765.29; Plan B $28,431.33
91. 14.3 years
93. 68.1 years
99. a. $161.05 b. $8,940,049.20
101. a. $5808.08 b. $3078.16 c. $6520.19
103. a. 24.5325 b. 1.0672 c. 4.0811%

Unit 4C Quick Quiz

1. a 2. c 3. c 4. b 5. a 6. a 7. c 8. a 9. b 10. c

Unit 4C Exercises

9. Makes sense
11. Does not make sense
13. Does not make sense
15. $x = \pm 5$
17. $x = 10$ or $x = -2$
19. $t = \pm 12$
21. $u = 2$
23. $1824.96
25. $15,272.62
27. $114,451.51; $36,000
29. $90,091.51; $64,800
31. $318.01
33. $384.19
35. Monthly deposit = $1659.18

37. 56.7%; 9.4%
39. 73.9%, 2.8%
41. −42.9%; −17.0%
43. 68.0%; 5.3%
45. Stocks $135,199; bonds $2359; cash $732
47. a. INTC b. $15.48 c. About $990 million d. 1.1% e. $56.04 f. $0.78 g. $4.37 billion
49. $2.80 per share; slightly overpriced
51. $9.02 per share; priced about right
55. 2.11%
57. 5.00%
59. $40.95
61. $70.87
63. a. 457.46 shares b. $5852.86 c. $7183.54
65. Yolanda: balance = $31,056.46; deposits = $24,000
Zach: balance = $30,186.94; deposits = $24,000
67. Juan: balance = $65,551.74; deposits = $48,000
Maria: balance = $67,472.11; deposits = $50,000
69. Balance of $15,848.11 is not enough.
71. Balance of $29,081.87 is not enough.
73. $2.20 per share or 37.9% per share
75. Total return = 439,900%; annual return = 18.3%; much higher than the average for stocks
77. a. $206,893.82 b. $199,635.11
c. Mitch deposits $10,000; Bill deposits $40,000.
87. a. $51,412.95 b. $95,102.64; less than double
c. $190,935.64; more than double
89. a. 1.293569 b. 4.932424 c. 14.27%

Unit 4D Quick Quiz

1. a 2. a 3. b 4. b 5. c 6. c 7. c 8. b 9. c 10. a

Unit 4D Exercises

7. Makes sense
9. Does not make sense
11. Makes sense
13. a. Starting principal = $80,000; APR = 7%; number of payments per year = 12; loan term = 20 years; payment amount = $620
b. Number of payments = 240; amount paid = $148,800
c. Principal 53.8%; interest 46.2%
15. a. $482.51 b. $115,804.40
c. Principal 43.2%; interest 56.8%
17. a. $1398.43 b. $503,434.80
c. Principal 39.7%; interest 60.3%
19. a. $2028.53 b. $365,134.40
c. Principal 54.8%, interest 45.2%
21. a. $332.14 b. $11,957.04
c. Principal 83.6%; interest 16.4%
23. a. $1433.48 b. $258,026.40
c. Principal 58.1%, interest 41.9%
25. Monthly payments = $1153.37

End of Month	Interest	Payment Toward Principal	New Principal
1	$1062.50	$90.87	$149,909.13
2	$1061.86	$91.51	$149,817.62
3	$1061.21	$92.16	$149,725.46

27. Monthly payments: $370.53; $290.15; $243.32. You can afford only option 3.
29. a. $458.40 b. $5500.80 c. 9.1%
31. a. $188.38 b. $6781.68 c. 26.3%
33.

Month	Payment	Expenses	Interest	New Balance
0				$1200.00
1	$200	$75	$18.00	$1093.00
2	$200	$75	$16.40	$984.40
3	$200	$75	$14.77	$874.17
4	$200	$75	$13.11	$762.28
5	$200	$75	$11.43	$648.71
6	$200	$75	$9.73	$533.44
7	$200	$75	$8.00	$416.44
8	$200	$75	$6.25	$297.69
9	$200	$75	$4.47	$177.16
10	$200	$75	$2.66	$54.82

A partial 11th payment will pay off the loan.

35.

Month	Payment	Expenses	Interest	Balance
0				$300.00
1	$300	$175	$4.50	$179.50
2	$150	$150	$2.69	$182.19
3	$400	$350	$2.73	$134.92
4	$500	$450	$2.02	$86.94
5	0	$100	$1.30	$188.24
6	$100	$100	$2.82	$191.06
7	$200	$150	$2.87	$143.93
8	$100	$80	$2.16	$126.09

37. Option 1: monthly payments = $1467.53; total payments = $528,310.80; Option 2: monthly payments = $1854.02; total payments = $333,723.60
39. Option 1: monthly payments = $405.24; total payments = $145,886.40; Option 2: monthly payments = $530.95; total payments = $95,571
41. Choice 1: monthly payments = $880.52; closing costs = $1200; Choice 2: monthly payments = $839.06; closing costs = $3600
43. Choice 1: monthly payments = $818.61; closing costs = $2400; Choice 2: monthly payments = $778.32; closing costs = $4800
45. a. $269.92 b. $380.03
c. Total payments for 20-year loan = $64,780.80; total payments for 10-year loan = $45,603.60
47. Savings of about $250 per month with the ARM; about $188 per month more with the ARM
49. $62,141; $77,676
51. a. $95.57; $130.17; $158.34 b. $67,444.20
c. $325.43; $78,103
53. a. $8718.46 every year, $716.43 every month, $330.43 every two weeks, $165.17 every week
b. $174,369.20; $171,943.20; $171,823.60; $171,776.80
65. a. $95.01 b. Payment decreases to $67.48
c. Payment decreases to $77.73

Unit 4E Quick Quiz

1. a 2. c 3. a 4. b 5. b 6. a 7. c 8. a 9. b 10. c

Unit 4E Exercises

11. Does not make sense
13. Makes sense
15. Makes sense
17. Makes sense
19. Gross income = $49,600; AGI = $46,100; taxable income = $37,650
21. Gross income = $93,650; AGI = $87,450; taxable income = $75,100
23. Itemize; your itemized deductions total $11,945, which is more than your standard deduction.
25. Gross income = $33,550; AGI = $33,050; taxable income = $23,700 (standard deduction)
27. Gross income and AGI = $35,900; taxable income = $19,250 (standard deduction)
29. $5038
31. $15,776
33. $16,178
35. $16,750
37. $500
39. $0
41. $280
43. Cheaper to own (home cost including savings through mortgage interest deduction = $1406, less than rent of $1600)
45. Maria's true cost = $6700; Steven's true cost = $8500
47. FICA tax = $2142; total tax = $4147; tax rate = 14.8%
49. FICA tax = $3427; total tax = $8290; tax rate = 18.0%
51. FICA tax = $3687; total tax = $9587; tax rate = 19.9%
53. Pierre: taxes = $33,038, tax rate = 27.5%; Katarina: taxes = $11,505, tax rate = 9.6%
55. Your take-home pay decreases by $340, rather than by $400.
57. Your take-home pay decreases by $600, rather than by $800.
59. Total tax at single rates = $8165 tax filing jointly = $8045; no marriage penalty
61. Total tax at single rates = $86,214; tax filing jointly = $93,750; marriage penalty

Unit 4F Quick Quiz

1. b 2. c 3. c 4. b 5. a 6. a 7. b 8. b 9. b 10. c

Unit 4F Exercises

9. Makes sense
11. Does not make sense
13. Makes sense
15. a. Surplus b. Reduces your surplus c. Yes
17. $81,250 per worker
19. a. $63,000 b. Outlays = $1,113,000; deficit = $63,000; debt = $836,000 c. $69,000 d. Outlays = $869,000; surplus = $231,000; debt = $605,000
21. Deficit would increase by about $21 billion; deficit would increase by about $18 billion.
23. $987 billion
25. $42 billion
27. $458 billion
29. $140 billion deficit
31. Cut government spending, borrow money, raise taxes
33. About 412,000 years
35. $14.36 trillion; $21.38 trillion
37. Outlays = $3614 billion; new deficit = $1244 billion
39. About $986 billion per year
41. About 1667 years

CHAPTER 5

Unit 5A Quick Quiz

1. a 2. c 3. a 4. b 5. c 6. a 7. c 8. c 9. b 10. b

Unit 5A Exercises

9. Does not make sense
11. Does not make sense
13. Makes sense
15. *Population*: all Americans; *sample*: 1001 Americans surveyed by telephone; *population parameters*: opinions of all Americans on Iran; *sample statistics*: opinions on Iran among those in the sample
17. *Population*: all Americans; *sample*: 998 Americans; *population parameters*: the percentage of Americans who believe there has been progress in finding a cure for cancer in the last 30 years; *sample statistics*: the percentage of the people in the sample (60%) who believe there has been progress in finding a cure for cancer in the last 30 years
19. *Population*: all American adults; *sample*: 1027 American adults; *population parameters*: the percentage of Americans who say there should be an investigation of the Bush administration; *sample statistics*: the percentage of the people in the sample who say there should be an investigation (62%)
21. *Step 1*: Population is all ninth-graders; goal is to determine the average number of hours per week they spend on cell phones. *Step 2*: Choose a representative sample. *Step 3*: Determine cell phone use (hours per week) of those in the sample and compute the average. *Step 4*: Infer average cell phone use for all ninth-graders. *Step 5*: Assess results and formulate conclusion.
23. *Step 1*: Population is American male college students; goal is to determine percentage of American male college students who play chess at least once a week. *Step 2*: Choose a representative sample. *Step 3*: Determine percentage of students in sample who play chess. *Step 4*: Infer percentage of chess players for population. *Step 5*: Assess results and formulate conclusion.
25. *Step 1*: Population is all batteries used in the specific model of laptop; goal is to determine average lifetime of the batteries. *Step 2*: Choose a representative sample. *Step 3*: Determine lifetime of batteries in the sample and compute the average. *Step 4*: Infer average lifetime for all batteries. *Step 5*: Assess results and formulate conclusion.
27. The third sample is most representative, because it is least likely to be biased. The other samples are biased toward certain subgroups within the population.
29. Stratified
31. Stratified
33. Simple random
35. Observational, case-control; cases are volunteers with a tendency to lie; controls are volunteers without such a tendency.
37. Observational, not case-control

39. Experiment; treatment group received ginkgo biloba extract; control group received placebo; double-blinding used.
41. Experiment
43. Observational
45. Experiment
47. 50.5% to 55.5%; yes
49. 43% to 49% (for the most recent data); yes
51. Good evidence
53. Good evidence
55. a. Population is all North American HIV patients who have undergone drug treatment; population parameters are survival rates and times at which treatment began.
 b. Sample is 17,517 asymptomatic North American patients with HIV; sample statistics are survival rates and times at which treatment began for those in sample.
 c. Observational
57. a. Population is all people over 60; population parameters are test scores for all elderly people, categorized by whether or not each individual was given a suggestion.
 b. Sample is 100 people in the 60–70 and 71–82 age categories; sample statistics are test scores categorized by whether or not each individual was given a suggestion.
 c. Experiment
59. a. Population is all adolescents in 36 states; population parameters are percentages of students in each state who became regular smokers.
 b. Sample is 16,000 adolescents in 36 states; sample statistics are percentages of students in the samples in each state who became regular smokers.
 c. Observational
73. The average of a large number of random numbers between 0 and 1 is near $\frac{1}{2}$.

Unit 5B Quick Quiz

1. c 2. b 3. a 4. b 5. b 6. a 7. c 8. c 9. b 10. b

Unit 5B Exercises

5. Does not make sense
7. Does not make sense
9. You should be suspicious. Do teachers' SAT scores predict their preparation? What variables were measured?
11. You should question the results of the study because of possible bias.
13. You should doubt the results of this study because call-in polls tend to be biased.
15. You should doubt the results of the study without knowing how happiness is defined and how it is measured.
17. You should doubt the results of this study because the sample is clearly biased; riders who do not use helmets should also be included.
19. You should doubt the results of the study; self-reporting is often not accurate.
21. You should doubt the claim (has inflation been taken into account?).
23. Without knowing the relationship between cell phone use and traffic fatalities, you should doubt the claim.
25. This claim is reliable.
27. Selection bias
29. Possible selection bias
31. Possible selection bias
33. Possible conflict of interest
37. How were respondents chosen? How was the question asked?
39. How large was the sample? How was the sample chosen?
41. How were respondents chosen? How was the question asked? Were respondents given the choice of potatoes or did they suggest potatoes without prompting?
43. 98% of all movies is different from 98% of top movie rentals.
45. It may be true, but the sample is very small and there could be bias in the study.

Unit 5C Quick Quiz

1. b 2. c 3. b 4. c 5. a 6. c 7. a 8. c 9. c 10. b

Unit 5C Exercises

7. Does not make sense
9. Does not make sense
11. Does not make sense
13. Does not make sense

15.

Grade	Freq.	Rel. Freq.	Cum. Freq.
A	2	0.10	2
B	5	0.25	7
C	8	0.40	15
D	3	0.15	18
F	2	0.10	20
Total	20	1.00	20

17. Qualitative
19. Qualitative
21. Qualitative
23. Quantitative

25.

Bin	Freq.	Rel. Freq.	Cum. Freq.
95–99	3	0.15	3
90–94	2	0.10	5
85–89	3	0.15	8
80–84	2	0.10	10
75–79	4	0.20	14
70–74	1	0.05	15
65–69	3	0.15	18
60–64	2	0.10	20
Total	20	1.00	20

27.

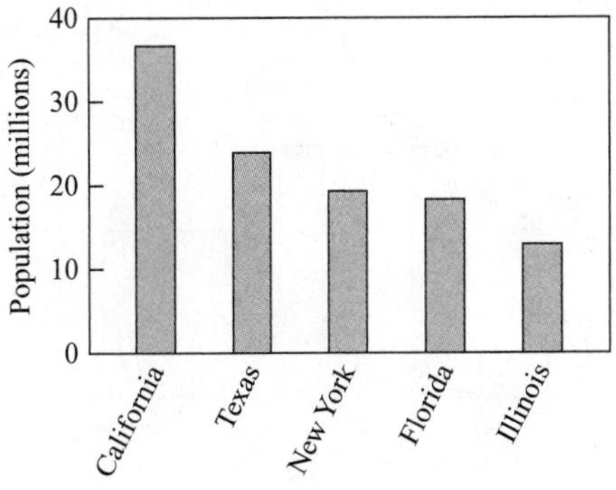

29.

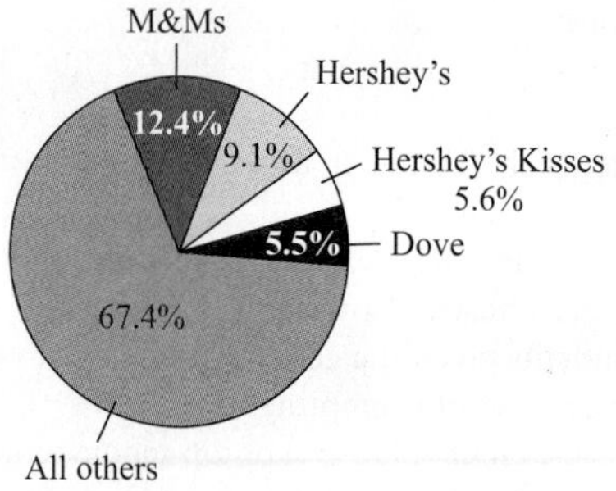

31.

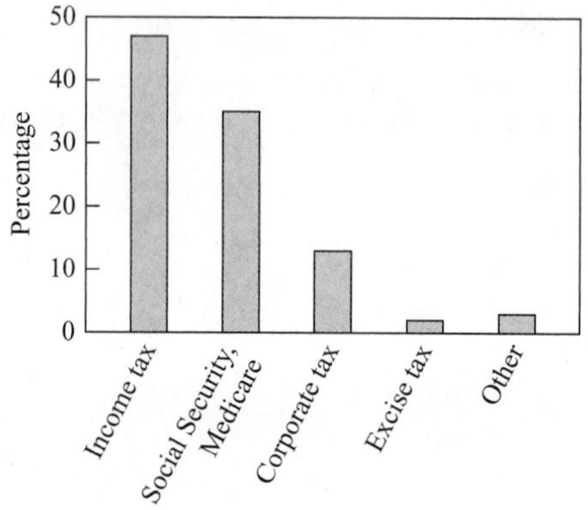

33.

20–29	1
30–39	8
40–49	9
50–59	4
60–69	2

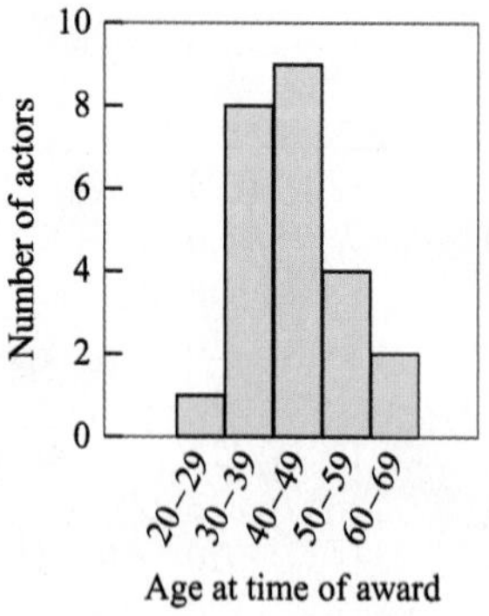

37. a. Ages are quantitative.

b.

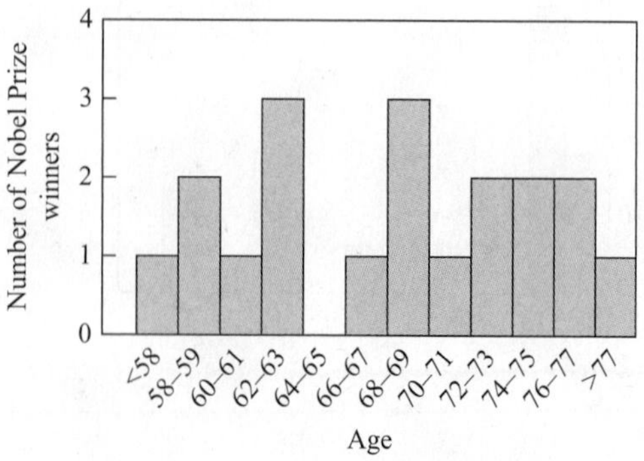

39. a. The data are quantitative.

b.

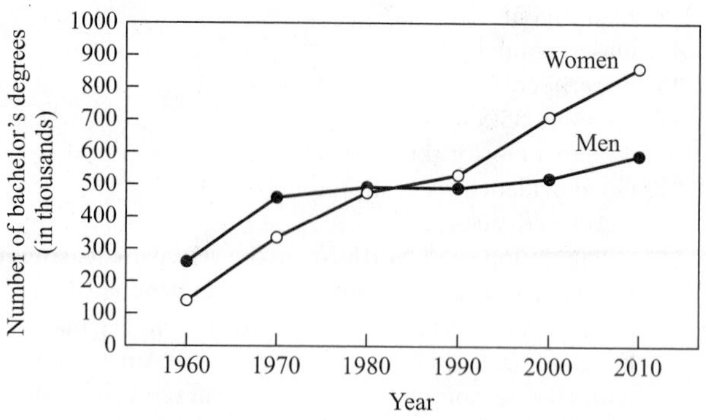

41. a. The data are quantitative.

b.

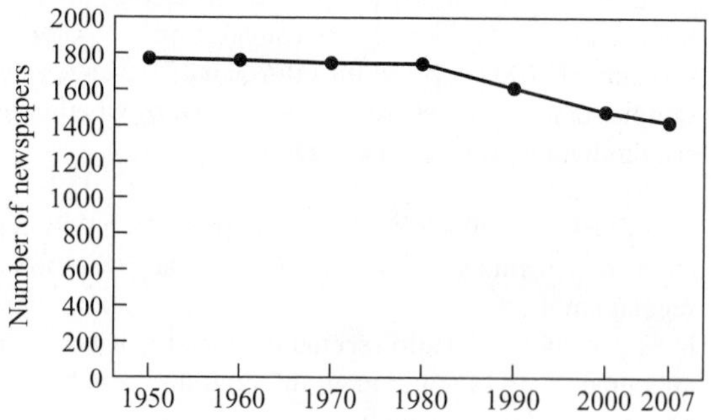

43. a. The religions are qualitative categories.

b.

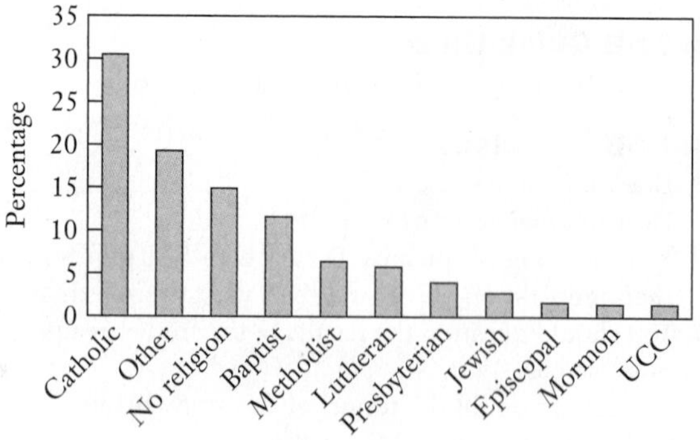

45. a. The years are quantitative categories.

b.

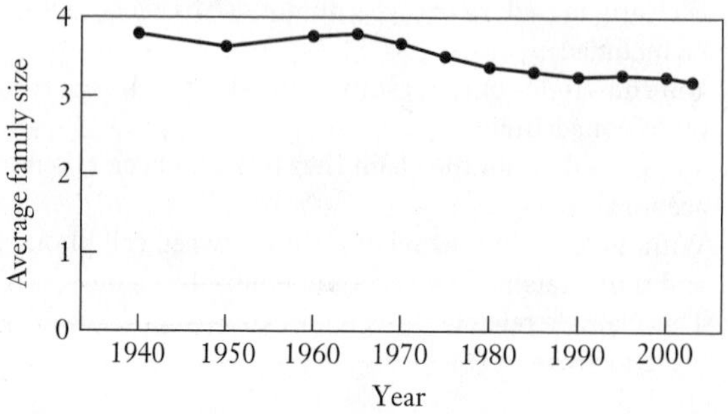

47. a.

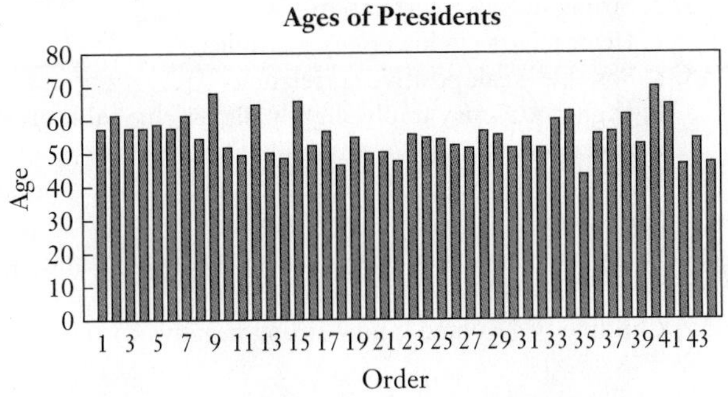

b. 1, 3, 4, 6, 8, 10, 11, 14, 18, 26 c. 1, 2, 7, 9, 40

57.

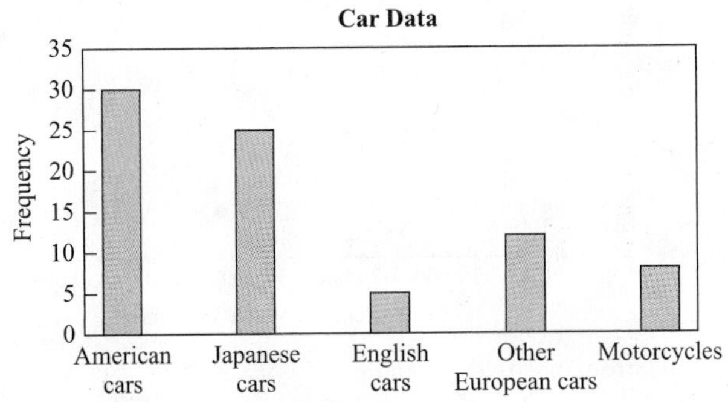

59.

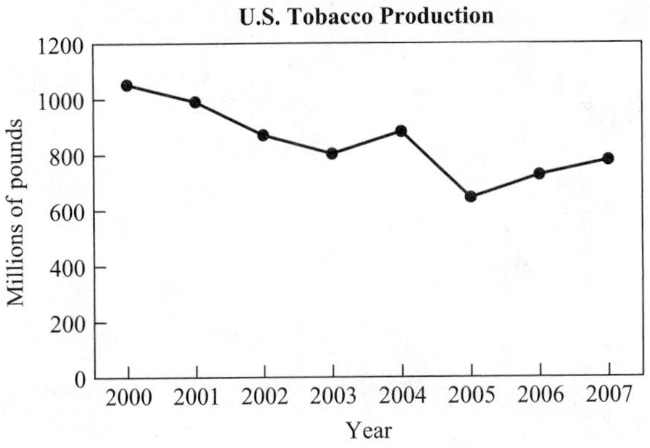

Unit 5D Quick Quiz

1. c 2. b 3. a 4. c 5. b 6. c 7. c 8. b 9. c 10. b

Unit 5D Exercises

9. Does not make sense
11. Makes sense
13. a. China, India, Russia b. China, India, Russia
15. a. Cancer increased; tuberculosis decreased; cardiovascular disease increased and then decreased, for an overall decrease; pneumonia decreased.
b. The death rate for cardiovascular disease reached a maximum of about 500 (deaths per 100,000) in 1950.
c. The death rate for cancer in 2000 was about 196 (deaths per 100,000).
d. If the lines of the graph were extended, cancer would overtake cardiovascular disease as the leading cause of death.
17. a. 1930: men, 75,000; women, 40,000; 2010: men, 590,000; women, 860,000
b. In 1980, more men than women earned degrees. In 2010, more women than men earned degrees.
c. During the 1960s
d. 1950: total degrees 450,000; 2010: total degrees 1,450,000
19. There are significant regional differences; probabilities tend to be much higher in the northern states.
21. a. 12%; 20% b. It decreases as a percentage of the population. c. It decreases. d. 2010
23. a. Qualitative. The meaning of zero is not clear, because the happiness scale is not explained in the display. b. No
c. Mostly European and North American countries
d. Mostly Central and South American countries
25. The area of the TV on the right is about 25 times greater than the area of the TV on the left. The volume of the TV on the right is about 125 times greater than the volume of the TV on the left.
27. The zero point is not shown on the vertical axis, so the disparity in earnings appears greater than it is.

29.

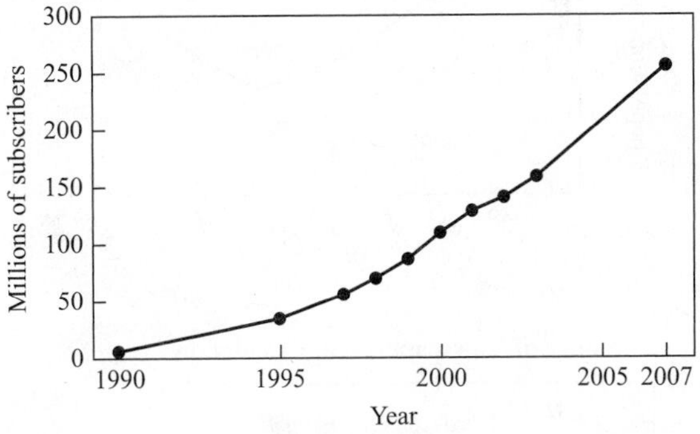

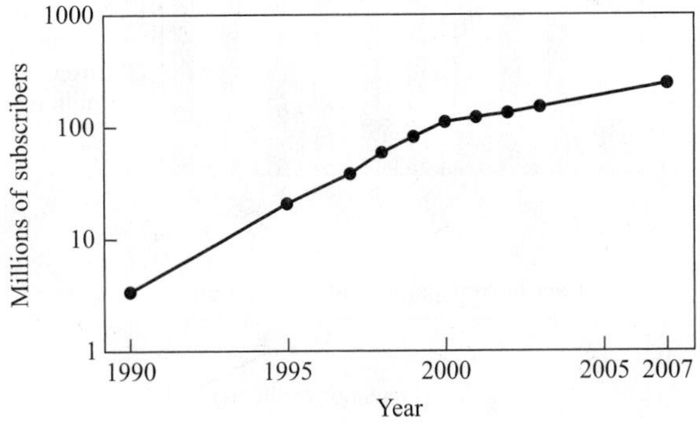

31. Most of the growth occurred after 1950.

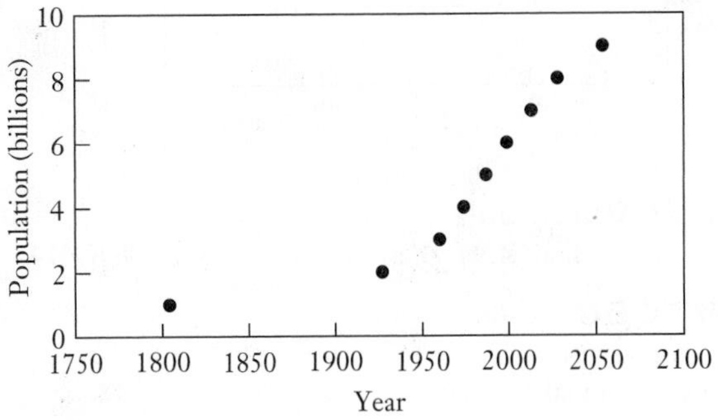

33. a. Change looks smaller.

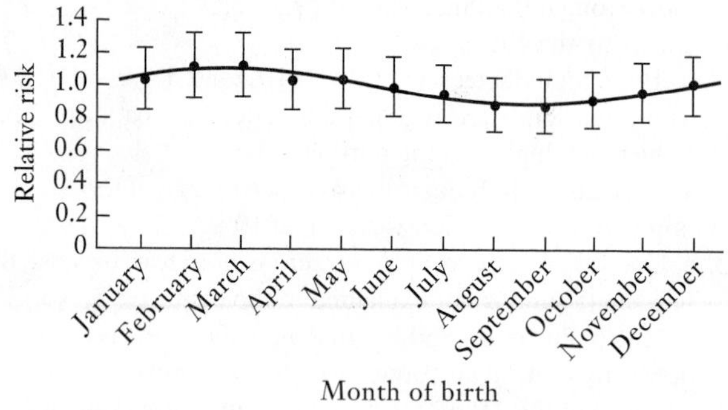

b. Claim is not justified.

35.

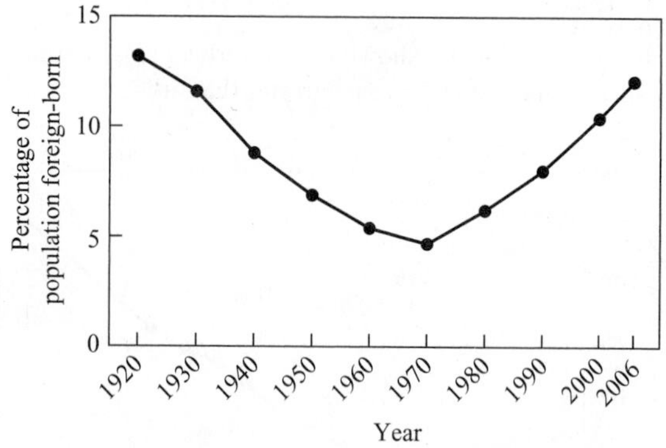

37.

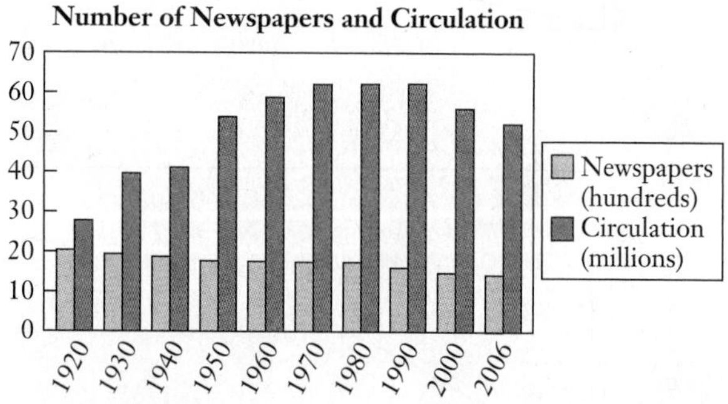

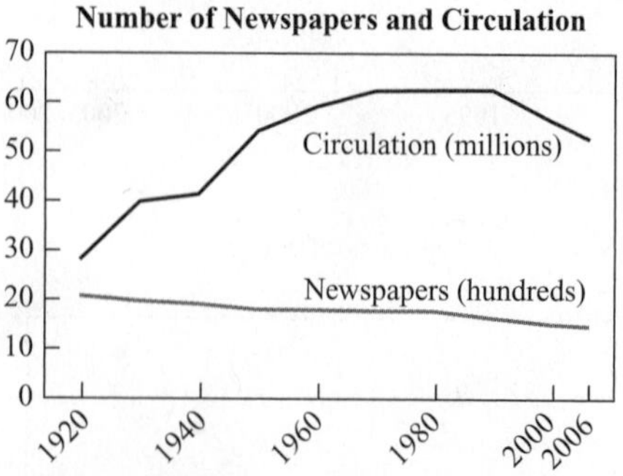

Unit 5E Quick Quiz

1. c 2. b 3. a 4. b 5. a 6. c 7. a 8. c 9. b 10. c

Unit 5E Exercises

7. Makes sense
9. Does not make sense
11. Makes sense
13. a. Strong negative correlation
    b. Heavier cars get lower city gas mileage.
15. a. Possible weak positive correlation
    b. Higher AGI may imply slightly higher charitable giving as a percentage of AGI.
17. Degrees of latitude, degrees of temperature; strong negative correlation
19. Years, hours; possible negative correlation over some ages
21. Year, square miles; positive correlation
23. Children per woman, years; strong negative correlation
25. a.

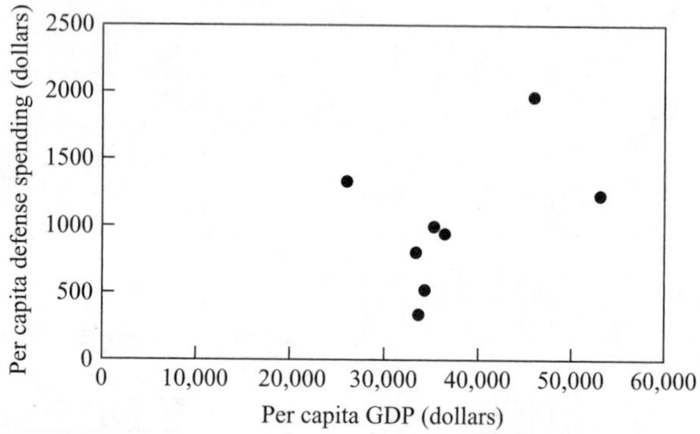

b. Strong positive correlation

27. a.

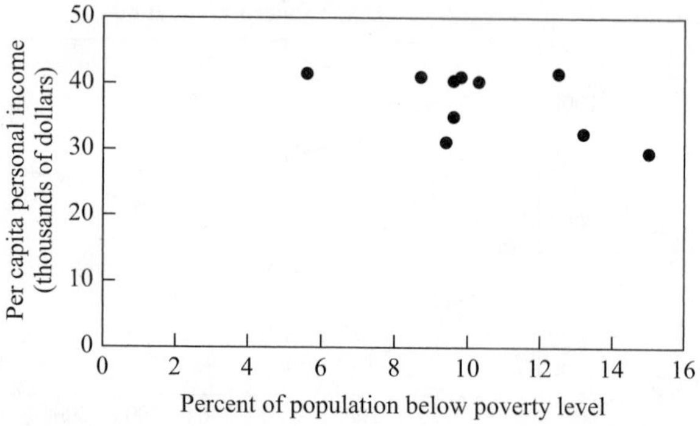

b. No correlation

29. a.

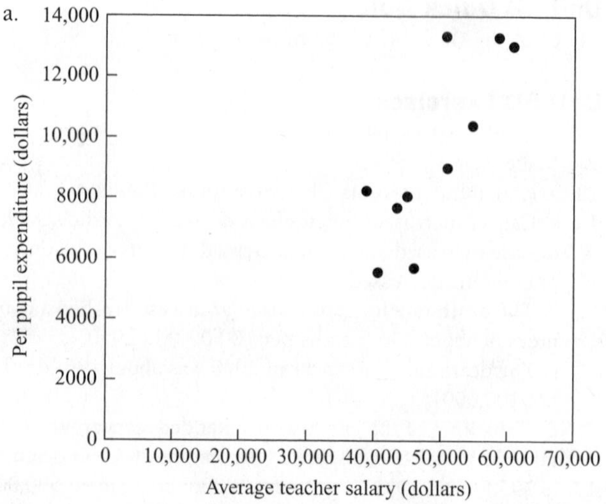

b. Strong positive correlation

31. There is a positive correlation between the crime rate and the number of taxi cabs; common underlying cause.
33. There is a negative correlation between gasoline prices and SUV sales; possible direct cause.
35. Gas mileage is positively correlated with tire pressure; direct cause.
37. Guideline 1; Guideline 2; Guideline 3. The observations suggest that perhaps your headaches are caused by bad air in the building in which you work (there is a "disease" called sick building syndrome).
39. People do not decide to become conductors until relatively late in life—say, 30 years of age or over. Having already survived this many years, a person has a longer-than-average life expectancy.
41. A plausible explanation is that many youth soccer leagues around the world use age divisions. Those children born earlier in a given year are slightly older than others born in the same year. Being slightly stronger and better developed, they survive and move on to more advanced leagues.

CHAPTER 6

Unit 6A Quick Quiz

1. b 2. b 3. c 4. a 5. c 6. c 7. a 8. a 9. b 10. b

Unit 6A Exercises

7. Makes sense
9. Make sense
11. Does not make sense
13. Mean 5.68; median 5.685; no mode
15. Mean 201.14; median 200; no mode
17. Mean 1.18; median 1.05; no mode
19. Mean = 0.81237 pound; median = 0.8161 pound; 0.7901 is an outlier; mean = 0.81608 pound; median = 0.8163 pound
21. Median
23. Median
25. Mean
27. a. One peak b. Right-skewed c. Large variation
29. a. Two peaks b. Symmetric c. Large variation
31. a. One peak b. Symmetric c. Moderate variation
33. a. One peak b. Symmetric c. Moderate variation
35. Distribution has two peaks (bimodal), is not symmetric, and has high variation.
37. Distribution has one peak, is symmetric, and has moderate variation.
39. a. Because the mean is greater than the median, the distribution is right-skewed.
 b. About 50% of the families earned less than $45,000.
 c. No

Unit 6B Quick Quiz

1. a 2. c 3. a 4. b 5. b 6. b 7. c 8. a 9. b 10. c

Unit 6B Exercises

7. Does not make sense
9. Makes sense
11. Makes sense
13. Mean = 7.2; median = 7.2
15. a. East Coast: mean = 135.00; median = 123.45; range = 117.8. West Coast: mean = 145.82; median = 150.30; range = 69.2
 b. East Coast: (98.2, 108.7, 123.45, 140.0, 216.0); West Coast: (113.2, 122.7, 150.3, 156.0, 182.4) Boxplot not shown.
 c. Standard deviation: East Coast, 42.86; West Coast, 25.06
 d. Range rule of thumb: East Coast, 29.45; West Coast, 17.30
17. a. No treatment: mean = 0.184; median = 0.16; range = 0.35. Treatment: mean = 1.334; median = 1.07; range = 2.11
 b. No treatment: (0.02, 0.085, 0.16, 0.295, 0.37); treatment: (0.27, 0.595, 1.07, 2.205, 2.38). Boxplot not shown.
 c. Standard deviation: no treatment, 0.127; treatment, 0.859
 d. Range rule of thumb: no treatment, 0.0875; treatment, 0.5275
19. a.

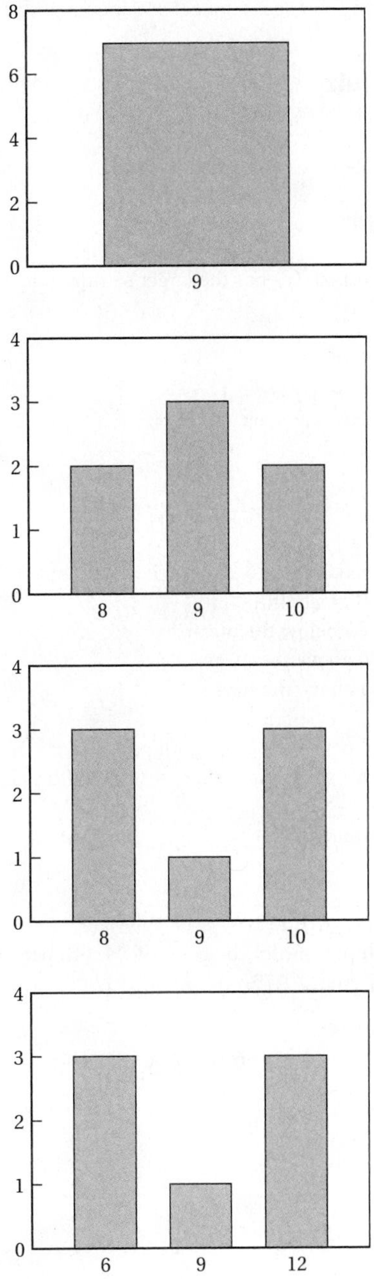

b.

	Set 1	Set 2	Set 3	Set 4
Low value	9	8	8	6
Lower quartile	9	8	8	6
Median	9	9	9	9
Upper quartile	9	10	10	12
High value	9	10	10	12

(Boxplot not shown.)

c. Standard deviations = 0.000, 0.816, 1.000, 3.000

21. The means are nearly equal, but the variation is significantly greater for the second shop than for the first. If you want a reliable delivery time, choose the first shop.
23. A lower standard deviation means more certainty in the return and less risk.
25. Batting averages are less varied today. Because the mean is unchanged, batting averages above 0.350 are (slightly) less common today.

Unit 6C Quick Quiz

1. b 2. a 3. a 4. c 5. a 6. c 7. a 8. c 9. c 10. b

Unit 6C Exercises

5. Makes sense
7. Does not make sense
9. Makes sense
11. (a) and (c) are normal; (c) has the larger standard deviation.
13. Not normal
15. Normal
17. Not normal
19. a. 50% b. 84% c. 97.5% d. 2.5% e. 97.5% f. 0.15% g. 84% h. 95%
21. 84%
23. 51; 2.5%
25. 0
27. −1.5
29. a. $z = 1$; 84.13 percentile b. $z = 0.5$; 69.15 percentile c. $z = -1.5$; 6.68 percentile
31. a. $z = -0.83$; 0.83 below the mean b. $z = 0.84$; 0.84 above the mean c. $z = 0.33$; 0.33 above the mean
33. 68% 35. 16%
37. a. $z = 0.96$; 83rd percentile b. 26th percentile c. $z = -0.84$; 20th percentile d. $z = 0.44$; 67th percentile
39. Not likely
41. Verbal 617, quantitative 780
43. 46%
45. 8%
47. Verbal 30%, quantitative 11%
53. a. $z = 0.85$; 80th percentile b. $z = -1.74$; 4th percentile c. About 1% d. About 1.7% e. About 33,000

Unit 6D Quick Quiz

1. c 2. b 3. a 4. c 5. b 6. c 7. c 8. a 9. c 10. b

Unit 6D Exercises

9. Makes sense
11. Does not make sense
13. Makes sense
15. Significant
17. Not significant
19. Significant
21. Significant at the 0.05 and 0.01 levels
23. Not significant at the 0.05 or 0.01 level
25. Margin of error = 0.03, or 3 percentage points; confidence interval is 29% to 35%.
27. Margin of error = 0.043, or 4.3 percentage points; confidence interval is 59.7% to 68.3%.
29. Margin of error = 0.03, or 3 percentage points; confidence interval is 45% to 51%.
31. Margin of error = 0.03, or 3 percentage points; confidence interval is 38% to 44%.
33. a. Null hypothesis percentage of high school graduates = 85%; alternative hypothesis: percentage of high school graduates > 85%
b. Rejecting the null hypothesis means there is evidence that the percentage of high school graduates exceeds 85%. Failing to reject the null hypothesis means there is insufficient evidence to conclude that the percentage of high school graduates exceeds 85%.
35. a. Null hypothesis: mean teacher salary = $47,750; alternative hypothesis: mean teacher salary > $47,750
b. Rejecting the null hypothesis means there is evidence that the mean teacher salary in the state exceeds $47,750. Failing to reject the null hypothesis means there is insufficient evidence to conclude that the mean teacher salary exceeds $47,750.
37. a. Null hypothesis: percentage of underrepresented students = 20%; alternative hypothesis: percentage of underrepresented students < 20%
b. Rejecting the null hypothesis means there is evidence that the percentage of underrepresented students is less than 20%. Failing to reject the null hypothesis means there is insufficient evidence to conclude that the percentage of underrepresented students is less than 20%.
39. Null hypothesis: mean annual mileage of cars in the fleet = 11,725 miles; alternative hypothesis: mean annual mileage of cars in the fleet > 11,725 miles. The result is significant at the 0.01 level and provides good evidence for rejecting the null hypothesis.
41. Null hypothesis: mean stay = 2.1 days; alternative hypothesis: mean stay > 2.1 days. The result is not significant at the 0.05 level, and there are no grounds for rejecting the null hypothesis.
43. Null hypothesis: mean income = $50,000; alternative hypothesis: mean income > $50,000. The result is significant at the 0.01 level and provides good evidence for rejecting the null hypothesis.
45. Margin of error = 0.009, or 0.9 percentage point; confidence interval is 64.1% to 65.9%.
47. The sample size must be four times as great.
49. The margin of error, 3 percentage points, is consistent with the sample size.

CHAPTER 7

Unit 7A Quick Quiz

1. b 2. b 3. a 4. c 5. c 6. b 7. c 8. b 9. a 10. a

Unit 7A Exercises

7. Makes sense
9. Makes sense

11. Does not make sense
13. 45 15. 90
17. 112 combinations
19. 693 systems
21. 1/13
23. 1/3
25. 3/13
27. 1/26
29. 1/5
31. 1/24
33. 1/2
35. 1/8
37. 1/10
39. 18/30 = 0.6
41. 0.72
43. 225/250 = 0.9
47. 5/6 = 0.83
49. 0.25
51. 5/6 = 0.83
53. 0.99
55.

Result	Probability
0 H	1/16
1 H	4/16
2 H	6/16
3 H	4/16
4 H	1/16

57. Odds for are 1 to 2; odds against are 2 to 1.
59. Odds for are 1 to 2; odds against are 2 to 1.
61. Gain of $15
63. a. 0.52 b. 0.10 c. 0.59 d. 0.21 e. 0.84
65. The coins appear to be unfair. There should be about 125 occurrences of 0 heads and 3 heads.
67. Odds for *A* are 99 to 1; odds for *B* are 24 to 1.

Unit 7B Quick Quiz

1. c 2. c 3. b 4. c 5. c 6. c 7. a 8. b 9. c 10. c

Unit 7B Exercises

5. Makes sense
7. Does not make sense
9. Does not make sense
11. 1/16
13. 1/216
15. 0.0002
17. 1/16 = 0.0625
19. 1/64 = 0.0156
21. 0.0001
23. 0.0031
25. 1/1728 = 0.0006
27. 1/13 = 0.0769
29. 4/13
31. 1/6 = 0.167
33. 1/2
35. 9/10 = 0.9
37. 3/4
39. 0.518
41. 0.421
43. 0.473
45. 0.738
47. 0.387
49. 0.832
51. a. 0.986 b. 0.619
53. a. Dependent b. 0.303 c. 0.309 d. Nearly equal
55. 0.506
57. a. 1/20 = 0.05 b. 0.0025 c. 0.401

Unit 7C Quick Quiz

1. b 2. c 3. c 4. c 5. b 6. a 7. c 8. c 9. c 10. c

Unit 7C Exercises

7. Makes sense
9. Does not make sense
11. Does not make sense
13. You shouldn't expect to get exactly 5000 heads. The proportion of heads should approach 0.5 as the number of tosses increases.
15. Expected value = −$0.25; outcome of one game cannot be predicted; over 100 games, you can expect to lose.
17. Expected value = −$0.25; outcome of one game cannot be predicted; over 100 games; you can expect to lose.
19. Expected value = $210, expected profit = $2.1 million
21. 15 minutes
23. a. 46% heads; lost $8 b. Lost $18
    c. You need 59 heads, which is possible but not likely.
    d. The probability of a head on any toss is always 0.5.
25. a. If you toss a head, the difference becomes 15; if you toss a tail, the difference becomes 17.
    b. On each toss, the difference in heads and tails is equally likely to increase or decrease. After 1000 tosses, the difference is equally likely to be greater than 16 or less than 16.
    c. Once you have fewer heads than tails, the deficit of heads is likely to remain.
27. *P*(10 heads in 10 tosses) = 1/1024; you should not be surprised.
29. a. −$0.014; house edge is $0.14. b. Lose $1.40
    c. Lose $7 d. $14,000
31. Expected value = −$0.53; loss over one year = $193
33. Expected value = −$0.79; loss over one year = $288
35. 1-pt kick: 0.96; 2-pt attempt: 0.98
37. 2.6 people

Unit 7D Quick Quiz

1. a 2. a 3. b 4. c 5. c 6. a 7. c 8. c 9. b 10. a

Unit 7D Exercises

5. Does not make sense
7. Does not make sense
9. 1.3 deaths per 100 million vehicle-miles
11. 18.0 deaths per 100,000 drivers
13. 0.016 death per 100,000 flight hours; 0.385 death per billion miles; 0.028 death per 100,000 departures; 0.15 accident per 100,000 flight hours; 3.59 accidents per billion miles; 0.259 accident per 100,000 departures
15. 0.00024; 2.1 times greater
17. 23.8 deaths per 100,000 people
19. 225 people
21. 162,000 deaths
23. 80 years
25. $50 million loss

27. a. 147 people b. 18 people
c. 2058 births per 100,000 people
d. 1050 births per 100,000 people
29. a. 4.35 million births b. 2.43 million deaths
c. 1.92 million people d. 1.6 million people; 46%
31. a. Approximately 0.032 b. Approximately 0.060
c. Approximately 0.064

Unit 7E Quick Quiz

1. b 2. c 3. c 4. b 5. b 6. c 7. c 8. b 9. c 10. c

Unit 7E Exercises

5. Makes sense
7. Makes sense
9. Makes sense
11. 720
13. 20
15. 3,326,400
17. 165
19. 56
21. 10,080
23. $10^9 = 1{,}000{,}000{,}000$
25. 7,893,600
27. 362,880
29. 38,760
31. 32
33. 67,600,000
35. 5,314,410,000
37. 64
39. About 479,001,600, assuming order matters
41. 0.0297; 0.167
43. a. 160 sundaes b. 8000 cones c. 6840 cones d. 1140 cones
45. 8 toppings; 9 toppings
47. 1/1,947,792
49. 1/649,740
51. 1/455 53. 0.000240
55. a. 0.025; 50 people b. 0.00065; 1.3 people
61. b. $n = 25$
63. 0.00144

CHAPTER 8

Unit 8A Quick Quiz

1. b 2. c 3. a 4. b 5. c 6. c 7. b 8. b 9. a 10. b

Unit 8A Exercises

5. Makes sense
7. Makes sense
9. Linear; 3800
11. Exponential; R$220
13. Exponential; $31.80
15. Linear; $110,000
17. 32,768 grains; 65,535 grains; about 9.36 pounds
19. 1.3×10^{12} tons
21. $41,943.04
23. About 37 days
25. 2^{50} bacteria; 1/1024 full
27. 2.6 meters; more than knee-deep
29. a. (Only 100-year intervals are shown here.)

Year	Population
2000	6.0×10^9
2100	2.4×10^{10}
2200	9.6×10^{10}
2300	3.8×10^{11}
2400	1.5×10^{12}
2500	6.1×10^{12}
2600	2.5×10^{13}
2700	9.8×10^{13}
2800	3.9×10^{14}
2900	1.6×10^{15}
3000	6.3×10^{15}

b. Between 2800 and 2850 c. About 2150

Unit 8B Quick Quiz

1. a 2. b 3. a 4. b 5. c 6. b 7. b 8. c 9. c 10. a

Unit 8B Exercises

9. Does not make sense
11. Does not make sense
13. True
15. False
17. False
19. False
21. True
23. a. 0.903 b. 3.301 c. −0.301
d. 1.806 e. −0.903 f. −0.699
25. $2^3 = 8$; $2^{21} = 2{,}097{,}152$
27. 34 years
29. 22,974 people; 52,780 people
31. 776 cells; 602,249 cells
33. 7.9 billion; 14.7 billion; 31.7 billion
35.

Month	Beginning-of-Month Population	End-of-Month Population
1	100	107
2	107	114
3	114	123
4	123	131
5	131	140
6	140	150
7	150	161
8	161	172
9	172	184
10	184	197
11	197	210
12	210	225
13	225	241
14	241	258
15	258	276

Doubling time is just over 10 months.
37. 17.5 years; 1.13
39. About 233 months; 1.036; 1.33
41. 0.25; 0.0625
43. About 0.40; 0.16
45. About 354,000 animals; about 88,000 animals
47. 0.26 kg; 0.067 kg

49. 10 years; 0.125
51. 8.75 years; about 190 elephants
53. Approximate: 5.8 years; exact: 6.12 years; price = $786.76
55. Approximate: 17.5 years; exact: 17.67 years; population = 324 million
63. a. 0.903090 b. 3.301030 c. −0.301030 d. 1.806180 e. −0.903090 f. −0.698970

Unit 8C Quick Quiz

1. c 2. b 3. b 4. b 5. c 6. a 7. c 8. a 9. a 10. c

Unit 8C Exercises

7. Makes sense
9. Does not make sense
11. Does not make sense
13. Doubling time ≈ 78 years; 2050 population ≈ 9.8 billion
15. Doubling time ≈ 44 years; 2050 population ≈ 13.0 billion
17. a. 1985 growth rate = 2.7 per 1000; 1995 growth rate = −2.1 per 1000; 2007 growth rate = −1.6 per 1000
 b. Trend: growth rate rapidly changed from positive to negative, but has rebounded slightly; next 20 years: negative growth rate means decreasing population.
19. a. 1985 growth rate = 0.5 per 1000; 1995 growth rate = 0.7 per 1000; 2007 growth rate = −0.1 per 1000
 b. Trend: growth rate increased for a time, but then fell to slightly negative growth; next 20 years: population will be stable or decline slightly.
21. 3.3%; 2.0%; 0.67%
23. 2059: 431 million; 2109: 610 million
25. 2059: 500 million; 2109: 821 million
27. Answers will vary with student's age. For a student who was 17 in 2009: population at age 50 = 10.1 billion; population at age 80 = 14.4 billion; population at age 100 = 18.2 billion
29. Base growth rate = 3.36%; current growth rate = 0.5%; prediction is much lower than actual growth rate.
31. Base growth rate = 2.625%; current growth rate = 1.4%; prediction is slightly higher than actual growth rate.
33. 2% growth rate: 122,000; 149,000; 328,000; 5% growth rate: 164,000; 269,000; 1,950,000

Unit 8D Quick Quiz

1. a 2. b 3. a 4. b 5. a 6. c 7. c 8. b 9. c 10. a

Unit 8D Exercises

5. Does not make sense
7. Does not make sense
9. 2.5×10^{10} joules
11. 7.9×10^{17} joules
13. The bomb releases 200 times as much energy.
15. 10^6 times as loud
17. 70 dB
19. 31,623 times as loud
21. 9 times as great at 1 meter as at 3 meters
23. 25 times as great at 10 meters as at 50 meters
25. Decreases by a factor of 10,000; more basic
27. 3.16×10^{-9} mole per liter
29. pH = 3; acid
31. 10,000 times
33. Minor event; few effects
35. Serious effects
37. Shout could not be heard
39. a. 40 dB b. 57 m c. 1.94 dB; factor of 640,000
41. a. 10^{-4} mole per liter b. 10^{-5} mole per liter; pH = 5
 c. 1.1×10^{-4} mole per liter; pH = 3.96
 d. The change in part b could be detected; the change in part c could not be detected.

CHAPTER 10

Unit 10C Quick Quiz

1. b 2. a 3. b 4. c 5. c 6. c 7. a 8. c 9. a 10. b

Unit 10C Exercises

9. Makes sense
11. Does not make sense
13. Makes sense
15. The dimension is 1 and the object is ordinary (non-fractal).
17. The dimension is 3 and the object is ordinary (non-fractal).
19. The dimension is 2.585 and the object is a fractal.
21. The dimension is 1 and the object is ordinary (non-fractal).
23. The dimension is 3 and the object is ordinary (non-fractal).
25. The dimension is 2.113 and the object is a fractal.
27. a. When the ruler size is reduced by a factor of $R = 4$, there are $N = 8$ times as many elements. b. 1.5
 c. The objects that lead to the quadric island all have the same area, because each time a piece of the boundary juts out (adding area) another piece juts in (removing the same amount of area). The length of the coastline of the island is infinite.
29. When the ruler is reduced by a factor of $R = 9$, there will be 4 elements found; fractal dimension = 0.631.
31. a. 1.301 b. 1.585 c. 2.585
33. The branching in many natural objects has the same pattern repeated on many different scales. This is the process by which self-similar fractals are generated. Euclidean geometry is not equipped to describe the repetition of patterns on many scales.

CHAPTER 11

Unit 11C Quick Quiz

1. c 2. c 3. c 4. b 5. b 6. a 7. a 8. b 9. b 10. b

Unit 11C Exercises

7. Does not make sense
9. Does not make sense
11. The longer segment should have a length of 3.71 inches, and the shorter segment should have a length of 2.29 inches.
13. Third and fifth rectangles
15. 9.40 m or 3.58 m
17. 1.07 cm or 0.41 cm

INDEX

E

F

G

H

I

M

Q

R

T

U

V

W

X

Y

Z

INDEX OF APPLICATIONS

Note: A = Activity, CS = Case Study, E = Example, IE = In-text Example, P = Problem, PM = Practical Matters, TE = Technology Exercise, UT = Using Technology, WP = Web Project, YW = In Your World

Arts and Entertainment

Biological and Health Sciences

Business and Economics

Education

Physical Sciences (Including Geography)

Social and Political Sciences

Sports